CW00672958

Flora of Hertfordshire

Trevor J. James

Hertfordshire Natural History Society
2009

Text and distribution maps copyright © the author and the Hertfordshire
Natural History Society 2009

Photographs copyright © Trevor James or, where indicated, Brian Sawford,
Chris James, Alan Reynolds, Paula Shipway, June Crew, Ian Denholm, the
late Enid Evans, and the Herts. & MIddx. Wildlife Trust

Line drawings copyright © Andrew Harris

Published in 2009 by the Hertfordshire Natural History Society
Registered Charity number 218418
24 Mandeville Rise, Welwyn Garden City, Hertfordshire, AL8 7JU
www.hnhs.org

With generous assistance from:
Botanical Society of the British Isles
The Environment Agency
Hertfordshire Biological Records Centre, Hertfordshire County Council
London Natural History Society
Lee Valley Regional Park Authority
LTD Design Consultants
Ecological Planning and Research consultants

With thanks for generous donations from:
Trevor James
Sylvia Kingsbury
Gerald Salisbury
Vernon Taylor
Shirley Watson
Bruce Bennett
A. P. Bernard
Bruce Bennett
June Crew
Michael Demidecki
John Foster
Ken Jackson's family
Anne Mariner's family
Bryan Sage
Paula Shipway
Steven Waters
And others who wish to remain anonymous.

Designed by LTD Design Consultants
54 Warwick Square, London SW1V 2AJ

Printed and bound in Great Britain by Crowes Complete Print
50 Hurricane Way, Norwich, NR6 6JB

British Library Cataloguing-in-publication Data
A catalogue record for this book is available from the British Library

ISBN: 978-0-9521685-8-4

For information about all HNHS publications visit our website at
www.hnhs.org

Contents

Yellow Bird's-nest Monotropa hypopitys *Oddy Hill, Tring, 2007.*

Foreword

I moved from Hertfordshire to Norfolk in 2002, after half a lifetime spent poking about on its commons and chalky slopes. I still go back, but absence changes and sharpens your perspective. I'm aware now – rather enviously – of how richly wooded Herts. is compared to south Norfolk; of how dried out it has become; of the continued disappearance, especially near towns, of the fascinating marginal patches where the best plants so often occur.

This kind of evidence abounds in this marvellous new *Flora*, which isn't just a log of the county's plants but a narrative about how they are changing. I share Trevor James's view that vegetation should be viewed not as a fixed entity, but as intrinsically dynamic: there would be gains and losses even if we humans weren't about, ransacking the landscape. In terms of overall tallies, the score for the 21st century Hertfordshire seems about even. About two dozen or so species extinct in the county since Dony's time, many more becoming scarce, but both figures exceeded by new species either recently discovered or recently moved in.

But these crude figures say little about the texture and subtlety of the changes. The special quality of all great local *Floras* – and this one will become a classic – is that they record the grain, the minute particulars of vegetation. It's at the level of the individual copse, the old green lane, the single clonal patch that Floras record plants. And this of course is the scale at which we experience and love them, whether as meticulous botanists or romantic flower hunters.

The place whose plants I got to know best was Harding's Wood near Tring, which I ran as a community wood for 20 years. I'm delighted that its remarkable flora has, so to speak, contributed to this volume. I've been back many times since it passed into the care of a village Trust, and seen changes which echo the complex shifts described in this book. The Wood Vetch which so miraculously appeared from buried seed when we cut out a new track, has moved into a dormant phase again (temporary I'm sure) now the ground has settled and the canopy closed. Twayblade has vanished probably for the same reason. Two locally scarce lily-family members, Wild Daffodil and Ramsons, have arrived in the wood entirely of their own accord – though it was probably the tyres of our truck which introduced garden varieties of Columbine and Meadow-rue to the main track. Far and away the biggest change though has been the rampant spread of the impeccably native Holly, perhaps as a result of milder winters.

County *Floras* are narratives of these intimate and significant changes. But they are also social documents, telling stories about our own enthusiasms and work. The immense list of contributors to this volume, unthinkable half a century ago, suggests something about our current cultural and ecological moods. Every single record is the story of an encounter between a person and a plant, a story of affection and respect. This is what makes this *Flora* both an historical document and a message of hope for the future.

Richard Mabey

Some extinct plants of Hertfordshire: Grass-of-Parnassus Parnassia palustris *(top left), Round-leaved Sundew* Drosera rotundifolia *(top right),*
Butterwort Pinguicula vulgaris *(mid left), Military Orchid* Orchis militaris *(centre), Mountain Everlasting* Antennaria dioica *(mid right),*
Moon Carrot Seseli libanotis *(bottom)*

Introduction

This *Flora* is an account of the flowering plants, conifers and ferns growing 'wild' in the County of Hertfordshire, England, based on an eighteen-year survey from 1987-2005, compared with a similar survey carried out between 1950-1967, together with a summary of earlier information and significant extra records up to the date of publication.

Hertfordshire, which is one of the smallest historic counties in England, largely occupies the northern slopes of the Thames basin, south-east of the Chalk ridge of the Chilterns, and north of the conurbation of London. In geographical terms it also straddles the boundary between East Anglia and the Chilterns proper, as well as the ancient border between the Danelaw and Wessex; while in climatic terms it occupies an intermediate position between the slightly moister and warmer-winter areas of the Chilterns to the west and the dry, relatively colder winter areas of East Anglia. Being near London, its natural flora has been strongly modified by mankind for centuries, and for much of its recorded history it has been both a food and fuel source for the capital, as well as a country retreat for its wealthier inhabitants, a source of its building materials, and traversed by a number of major arterial routes into and out of the city.

As perhaps never before in historical times, the 'natural' flora of Hertfordshire is at a turning point. This account attempts to record a picture of the County's plant life at a stage when the traditional, historic landscape of the County, inherited from its Medieval, Romano-British or even Bronze Age past was still predominantly the foundation of its environment, but which has been subject recently to intense levels of post second-world-war agricultural pressure and building development, and is also reaching the stage when urban life patterns and their attendant transport links have finally super-imposed themselves on the rural structure and way of life of country parishes, affecting the County's remotest corners.

Any study of this kind has to be carried out in the knowledge that it is only a snapshot along a continuum of change, just as its three predecessors have been. However, this account may be particularly significant because it also records the flora at the point when global climate change was finally being recognised as a major problem; when levels of especially nitrogen pollution of the environment and the atmosphere had become so obvious that major shifts in the character of plant communities were self-evident; and when most 'traditional' land management practices had finally succumbed to agri-business or urban-related leisure on the one hand and dereliction on the other. From this point, changes will continue, perhaps with the extensive removal of land from agricultural use, the implementation of large-scale schemes in the pursuit of 'nature conservation' or public access, and possibly even greater changes brought about through European Union common agricultural policy reforms, let alone major changes which seem likely from climate warming. Development pressures look set to increase even further, and transportation will probably continue to create demands for roads, railways, airports and the holes needed to find aggregate to make them. Large slices of central and eastern Hertfordshire, hitherto protected from these demands, currently look set to be transformed by wholesale change, while the countryside north of the County in Bedfordshire and Cambridgeshire is also succumbing to urban development, bringing pressures from the north as well as the south. It will be the task of the next 'Flora Survey', if there is one, to record the effect of these changes in due course.

Despite these pressures, though, I hope users of this book will recognise that, far from being the dull County that many botanists might consider it to be, Hertfordshire has much to offer. Its botanical inhabitants have certainly gained a lot of pleasure, as well as aching limbs, trudging the Hertfordshire landscape to find and re-find its many wild plants.

Acknowledgements

The contributors of records to the *Flora* are listed below. To all recorders I extend my very grateful thanks, because without their input, this *Flora* would not have been possible. Especially I would like to thank all those who valiantly adopted one or more tetrads, let alone those stalwarts that adopted whole 10km squares! Little did they know what they were letting themselves in for!

Organisations which have aided the work of the Survey in one way or another and in the production of the *Flora* include: the U.K. Biological Records Centre, Centre for Ecology and Hydrology: Monks Wood (now Wallingford) (formerly the Institute of Terrestrial Ecology), Bishop's Stortford Natural History Society, Botanical Society of the British Isles, Bucks. County Museum Service, Cheshunt Natural History Society, the former English Nature (formerly Nature Conservancy Council, now part of Natural England), Environment Agency (formerly National Rivers Authority), Hertfordshire and Barnet Countryside Management Service, Hertfordshire Biological Records Centre, the former Hertfordshire Environment Centre (Hertfordshire County Council Education Department), Hertfordshire and Middlesex Wildlife Trust, Hertfordshire Natural History Society, Lee Valley Regional Park Authority, Letchworth Natural History (formerly Letchworth Naturalists) Society, the former London Ecology Unit (now part of the Greater London Authority), London Natural History Society, National Trust, North Hertfordshire Museums Service, Rothamsted Research, St Albans Museum, University of Hertfordshire, Welwyn Natural History Society, and the Wildflower Society.

The personal assistance and encouragement of the late Dr John Dony to me in the years prior to the starting of the Flora Project were an immense help, and John and his late wife Chris survived long enough to see the Project under way. Likewise, in the initial few years, while the Project was under the auspices of North Hertfordshire Museums Service, my erstwhile colleague Brian Sawford helped me with setting the wheels in motion, and has since supplied me with both records and now especially with some of his superb photographs, including the one of the Pasque Flower that has been used for the cover. Other photographs have been provided in the past and recently by the late Enid Evans, Ian Denholm, Alan Reynolds, June Crew, the Herts. and Middx. Wildlife Trust, Paula Shipway and my wife, Chris. Other photographs were taken by myself at various times. The late Philip Kingsbury, long-term Secretary of the Hertfordshire Natural History Society, is owed much for having insisted that the project needed to be done, and for his support through the Society in the early days. Ann Boucher and Alan Whitaker gave me much assistance with specimens, especially when the Project was based at North Hertfordshire Museums in firstly Baldock, and then at Hitchin. The drawn illustrations were produced by Andrew Harris, our County lichen recorder, but also an artist of no mean talents, to whom I extend my very grateful thanks.

Various national experts in different areas have given me much assistance, acknowledged in the text, but notably Alan Newton and especially Alec Bull for *Rubus*, who also joined me in the field on numerous excursions to search for these plants, David McCosh for *Hieracium*, Tony Primavesi for *Rosa*, John Richards for *Taraxacum* and Jeanette Fryer for *Cotoneaster*. I would also like to thank Terri Tarpey of Essex, who was foolish enough to offer her services to carry out much of the initial computerisation into a *Recorder 3* database of the summarised dataset derived from the survey, a task paid for in part by the Hertfordshire Biological Records Centre. To Sally Rankin of Henley, I offer my special thanks for having 'sorted me out' a number of times with technical upgrades to this database and other problems. My colleague Chris Boon, BSBI Recorder for Bedfordshire, and forthcoming author of his own County flora, generously agreed to check over part of the text of the *Flora*; and Chris Preston of the U.K. Biological Records Centre I would especially like to thank for having carried out a similar job on the rest of the text, which has resulted in a much more accurate account. Linda Smith, Secretary of the Hertfordshire Natural History Society, and Jack Fearnside, also of the Society, but especially a very talented publications designer, have helped greatly in the production of the book itself.

Funding of the publication has been helped enormously by several very generous donations, principally:

Botanical Society of the British Isles
The Environment Agency
Hertfordshire Biological Records Centre, Hertfordshire County Council
London Natural History Society
Lee Valley Regional Park Authority

For a more complete list, see the imprint opposite the forword.

Finally, of course, I especially thank my wife, Chris, for having put up with 22 years or more of household chaos taken up with specimens and datasets; and my son, Edward, for having put up with such a terrible dad for the whole of his earlier life!

Contributors to the Hertfordshire Flora Project

The people listed below contributed records directly or indirectly to the Flora Project (sometimes without knowing it!), or in some cases subsequently up to the date of publication. Those who provided detailed site lists are marked: *; while those who 'adopted' one or more tetrads for survey are given in bold. Those whose names are followed by names or abbreviations of organisations with which they were associated at the time mainly (but by no means only) supplied records in an official capacity.

List of contributors:

David Acres (Herts. CC), Nigel Agar, Rose Ainsworth (HMWT), Ian D. Alexander (Herts. CC)*, G. Allen, Mark Allen (HMWT), Peter J. Alton, Janet Anders, E. (Liz) Anderson (Herts. BRC)*, John Archer, Julian Arikans, Miss Armstrong, Lorna Arnold, S. Austin, John B. Baker*, Martin Baker (HMWT)*, **Patricia**

Baker*, Pat Baker*, Jane Baldwin, E. Barclay, A. Barker, P. Barton, Richard M. Bateman, A. P. Bater (South Herts. ERC)*, Martin Beaton (Herts. CC), Chris Beech, Eoin Bell (Herts. CC), Mrs J. M. Benfield, David Bevan, C. R. Birkinshaw (NRA), William Bishop, Robin Blades, A. Blake, Nigel Blandford (Herts. CC), D. W. Bly, Garry Bolton, Chris R. Boon*, Les J. Borg, Shirley Bose (HMWT)*, **Ann M. Boucher***, Jenny Bowen (EN), J. Branscombe, Eddie Bredie, D. Bridges, A. Brown, P. Brown, S. Bryceland, J. Buchanan (NCC/EN), Alec L. Bull*, G. E. Bull, **Cyril W. Burton**, Rodney M. Burton*, Cliff Butterworth, A. Byfield, **Colin K. Campbell***, P. Carr, Peter Casselden, Mrs Chan, A. Clark, Jane Clark (HMWT), Philip J. Collins (South Herts. ERC)*, **Joan Colthup***, Alec Cooper*, Fiona Cooper, Carol Crafer, June Crew, R. Cripps, R. Crossley, Simon Cuming (Herts. Habitat Survey)*, David Curry, D. Curson, W. H. (Bill) Darling, Simon Davey (for EN)*, A. Davidson, F. H. Dawson, **Alan Dean***, J. Delharty (HMWT), Michael Demidecki, **Ian G. Denholm***, Mr De Vos, Robert Dimsdale, Marcus Dixon, Nick J. Donnithorne, John G. Dony, Mr Dowsett, Jack C. Doyle, P. Dyer, Robert Dyke, Janette Easton, John Edgington*, **Jim Egginton**, **Peter J. Ellison**, Enid M. Evans, **Grace Eve***, Colin M. Everett, M. Falvey, John L. Fielding*, J. Fisher, Richard S. R. Fitter, Angela Forster (Herts. CC), **Joan Foster***, Ronald Freeman, **Dendle French***, R. Frith, Diana Furley*, R. P. Gemmell, Andrew ('Ched') George, Tom W. Gladwin, John Godbey, John Godfrey, K. Golding, F. Barry Goldsmith*, David Gompertz, Graham Goodall, **Erica Goode**, E. (Liz) Goodyear, **Sonia Gorton***, G. Grant, Laura Gravestock, D. Green, **Diana Griffith**, Margaret Grocock, Mark Gurney*, Alan Guilford, Avis Hall (University of Hertfordshire), Fiona Hall (HMWT)*, **Kathy Hall***, Nick Hall (HMWT), Steven Halton, C. Gordon Hanson, Andy Hardstaff (Herts. CC), Brenda Harold*, Andrew T. Harris*, **Philip J. Harvey***, C. D. Hawkins, Stephen Hawkins*, Mrs J. Hayes, A. Heading, M. J. Healy, B. Hedley, **Stuart M. Hedley***, Clive Herbert, Martin J. Hicks (Herts. BRC)*, Tim Hill (Lee Valley Regional Park/HMWT), Margaret Holden, Peter C. Holland, Neale Holmes-Smith (HMWT)*, Dale Holt, K. Hooper, George Hounsome, Michael Humphreys (HMWT), Rosemary Humphreys (HMWT), Jonathan Iles, Dieter Iwan (Herts. CC), **J. Kenneth Jackson**, Chris M. James*, Joseph W. James, **Trevor J. James***, Neil C. Jarvis (Herts. CC), P. Jefferey, Ann Johnson, Ian G. Johnson, W. Johnson, Jenny Jones (Herts. BRC), E. J. Joscelyne, Jenifer Joseph, Rachel Keen (Herts. BRC/Herts. CC)*, J. Kelly, **Valerie Kempster***, **Peter J. Kerslake-Smith**, H. J. (John) Killick, **Philip J. Kingsbury***, Sylvia Kingsbury, Simon Knott, Sarah Lambert, Simon J. Leach (NCC/EN), David Leeming, Mrs J. Leftwich, **Olive Linford**, J. Lingley, G. Longman, J. H. Looney, A. John Lovell*, Frank Lucas (HMWT), **Richard Mabey***, Gillian Mahoney*, Andrew Marchant, **A. David Marshall**, Ian D. Marshall* (Herts. CC), Stephen Marshall, James Mason (Herts. CC), Howard W. Matthews, Elizabeth Maughan, Mr Maunder-Thompson, Roy Maycock, Robert McFadden, A. McGlynn, John Melling, C. Metherell, Peter Millman (Herts. CC), Edgar Milne-Redhead, B. Mist, Mrs Mitchell, Mrs Morgan, P. S. Moseley, John Moss (HMWT)*, S. Moss, Lucy Mottram (Herts. BRC)*, J. Owen Mountford (ITE/CEH), Mrs Muir, John Murray, Stephen Murray, Margaret Nash, Alan Newton, J. Nicholls, Barry Nicholson (Herts. CC)*, J. Norton, P. Nuttall (CEH), Peter Oakenfull, Steven Oakes-Monger, C. Orton, Alan R. Outen (Herts. BRC)*, Kate Page, R. A. Palmer, N. Parkes, Anita Parry (Herts. BRC)*, D. Parry, Kenneth Peak, Kevin Pearcey, Juliet Pennington, Franklyn R. Perring*, **Lyle E. Perrins**, Anthony Pigott, Sharon Pilkington, June R. Pitcher*, Dawn Pitts (HMWT), Jane Porter, M. Powell, Chris D. Preston (ITE/CEH), Revd. Anthony L. Primavesi*, Mr Rawlinson, Mrs Reiss, Alan P. Reynolds, **Tim C. G. Rich***, S. Richardson, J. S. Rider, Christine Rieser, D. Patrick Robinson (NCC)*, **Kerry Robinson***, Fred. W. Rockall, J. Rogers, S. Ronetz, J. Rowley, J. Russell, **Gerald Salisbury***, **Jill Saunders**, Mrs Saunders, Brian R. Sawford*, Mark Schofield, Lucy Scott (Herts. BRC), D. Scott-Miller, Keith Seaman, Christine Shepperson, Paula Shipway, Alan J. Showler, M. Simpson, **Graeme P. Smith***, **M. Joyce Smith**, R. E. N. Smith, Simon Smith (Herts. CC)*, T. Smith (EA), David W. Soden (NCC)*, **John F. Southey***, Paul G. Stapleton, Miss Sumner, Richard Tanner, Jim H. Terry, Vincent Thompson, Mrs Thornton, John Tomkins, Brad Tooze (HMWT)*, Ian Torrance, Barry Tranter (South Herts. ERC/Herts. BRC)*, Barry Trevis, M. Tucker, **Janine Tyler***, Raymond W. J. Uffen, A. Urquhart, **Anthony Vaughan***, Keith Wade, Angela M. Walker, (NRA/EA)*, Kevin Walker (CEH/BSBI), T. D. Walker, Diana Collingridge (née Wallace), S. Max Walters, **Peter D. Walton**, Geoffrey Ward, Stuart Warrington (University of Hertfordshire), **Charles Watson**, M. Watson, **Shirley Watson***, Pat M. Watt*, Terry C. E. Wells (ITE), Janet Welsh* (NCC), Graham J. White (HMWT)*, Alan Whitaker, M. White, Marianne J. Whittaker (Herts. BRC)*, **John P. Widgery**, Belinda Wiggs (Herts. BRC)*, P. Wilkinson, Neil Willcox (HMWT), Jean Williamson (HMWT), S. Willis (South Herts. ERC)*, D. Wingrave, Mrs Wise, Brian Wurzell, Gordon J. Wyatt (EN/NE)*, Marcus Yeo, Greg Yeoman, Carole Young (Herts. BRC).

My apologies are given to anyone or any organisation that has been omitted. All help was sincerely welcomed and much appreciated.

Gerald Salisbury at Wilstone Reservoir, 1990.

Chapter 1. The Hertfordshire Flora Survey, 1987-2005

Poplars Green Meadows, Tewin.

Background to the survey

This account principally summarises the results of an organised survey of the generally naturally occurring vascular plant flora of Hertfordshire, carried out between January 1987 and December 2001. The main body of records was compiled by the end of 1999. Miscellaneous general records received in 2000-2001 filled in some gaps. In addition, a specific effort was made between 1998 and 2003 to re-discover particularly scarce plants; while special attention to some critical genera was paid during 1999-2005, especially to the genus *Rubus*. Finally, all additional records from other field recording activities that were made available to the end of 2005 have been incorporated. Unless otherwise stated, therefore, and excepting brambles, the atlas maps show systematic survey records for 1987-2001 inclusive, while less common species and most critical groups give details up to and including 2005, with a few records of particular significance up to 2009. Records of most species are summarised as 'tetrad' maps (2 x 2km Ordnance Survey grid squares), although full details with detailed grid references and locality information of less common species are held on the underlying database maintained by the author. The text associated with each species account, however, summarises not only the present known occurrence in the County, but also tries to put this into context with historical information.

The Hertfordshire Flora Survey almost exactly parallels the time period covered by its predecessor carried out by Dr John Dony and his co-workers between about 1950 and 1967, which was published as *Flora of Hertfordshire* by Hitchin Museum in 1967. Between 1967 and the end of 1986, a moderate level of recording was maintained. Initially, until 1978, this was carried out under the guidance of Dr Dony, and subsequently by the present author and Brian Sawford until 1986, under the auspices of North Hertfordshire Museums Service's then Natural History Department. All the data compiled during these periods were compiled on a card index, whose objectives were to fill in 'gaps'

in the 1967 *Flora* and to give full details of records of all those species recorded in 1967 as occurring in 50 or fewer tetrads, as well as full details of less common alien species, casuals, or species new to the County. The original card index is now held by Hertfordshire Biological Records Centre, but a photocopy, together with some additional information received after 1990 is held by the author.

In 1987, the Botanical Society of the British Isles initiated its first 'Monitoring Scheme' across Britain and Ireland (Rich and Woodruff, 1990). This was designed to generate data for a fixed sample of one in every nine 10km grid squares across the countries, and for a fixed sample of three pre-determined tetrads within each of these 10km squares. The 10km squares involved in Hertfordshire were TL12, TL42 and TQ19, within which, following the standard 'DINTY' referencing system, tetrads A, J and W were recorded. Parts of all the 10km squares and some of the tetrads within each fell into neighbouring counties, necessitating cross-border collaboration. The method of recording was: detailed recording of all representative habitats within each tetrad, supplemented by extra recording of other habitats or known sites within each 10km square. The intention, therefore, was to compile detailed tetrad data for three out of 25 tetrads, and comprehensive general species lists for one in nine 10km squares.

The local effect of initiating this monitoring scheme was to bring together a team of interested people in the County. A need for a new account of the Hertfordshire flora had been evident for some time previously, and the work for the monitoring scheme acted as the catalyst for a re-survey of the entire County, just as it turned out to be a catalyst for the production of the *New atlas of the British and Irish flora* (Preston, *et al.*, 2002) nationally. The Hertfordshire Flora Survey got under way fully in 1988, following an inaugural meeting of interested parties at Hatfield in October 1987. It incorporated data collected for the monitoring scheme, but focused effort subsequently onto detailed tetrad (and site) recording across the entire County. The Survey was carried out under the auspices of North Hertfordshire Museums Service until 1990, when the Museum's biological recording function was transferred to the newly inaugurated Hertfordshire Biological Records Centre. However, from that date, only a minority of the work was undertaken through the Records Centre, most of it being overseen by the author in a voluntary capacity, working under the names jointly of the Hertfordshire Natural History Society and the Botanical Society of the British Isles. The database

The author working on flora specimens, Hertfordshire Biological Records Centre, Hitchin, 1992.

from the survey was initially compiled using *Recorder 3.3* software, and was transferred to *Recorder 2002*, subsequently upgraded to *Recorder 6*. The author holds the master copy of this database, while a copy of it will be deposited for use in the Hertfordshire Biological Records Centre, and with the Botanical Society of the British Isles. The archive of field survey record cards and correspondence will ultimately be deposited with North Hertfordshire Museums Service, along with the voucher specimens for critical species, new records, *etc.* The basic data will also be made available through the National Biodiversity Network's internet 'Gateway'.

Scope of the survey

The Hertfordshire Flora Survey 1987-2005 covers the whole of the Watsonian 'vice-county' VC20 Herts., defined under the so-called Watsonian system of botanical recording, which was based on the boundary of Hertfordshire in 1852 (now fixed as a 1:10,000 scale Ordnance Survey digital boundary by the National Biodiversity Network Trust). In addition, the survey also covers those areas of neighbouring vice-counties which form, or have until recently formed, the administrative County of Hertfordshire (Map 1). It therefore includes the parish of South Mimms (with Potters Bar), formerly in Middlesex, as well as the parishes of Kensworth and Caddington, now in administrative Bedfordshire, the parish of Holwell, formerly in Bedfordshire, and the parish of Barnet (with Totteridge), which is now in Greater London. In addition to the inclusion of whole parishes in this way, there are other areas where boundary changes have created a rather complex picture. Around Little Gaddesden, for example, the differences between the administrative and vice-county boundaries with VC24 Bucks. and VC30 Beds. have meant the inclusion of the whole of Hudnall Common and parts of Ashridge, *etc.* All these changes are shown on the map, and are essentially similar to those depicted in Dony (1967), following the local government boundary changes of 1964. However, there have also been boundary changes more recently. The most significant are: extensions to administrative Hertfordshire north of Royston (from VC29 Cambs.), up to and including both sides of the A505 Royston bypass; the addition of the formerly VC19 North Essex section of Hunsdon Mead and all of Thorley Flood Pound SSSI; the addition of Chorleywood West and areas near Bovingdon from VC24 Bucks.; and the extension of administrative Hertfordshire to include some important areas formerly in VC21 Middx., down to the M25 at Enfield and Hillingdon, including Fir and Pond Woods Nature Reserve. There are also numerous other minor changes along the Lea and Stort Valleys, following adoption of the Lee Navigation and Stort Navigation canals as the administrative boundary between Essex and Hertfordshire in the early 1990s, as well as other minor adjustments to the boundaries in west Hertfordshire with Buckinghamshire, especially around Bovingdon. The more extensive of these changes, up to 2003, have been included in the general Hertfordshire topography map, and all changes have been reflected in the tetrad distribution maps.

There is one apparently anomalous inclusion in the present account which needs to be justified. Dony (1967) included Hadley Common, Hadley Green and Hadley Wood in his account, which are part of VC21 Middx. The boundary in this area had been changed in 1965, resulting in the then recent loss of these areas from what had been administratively Hertfordshire from 1904. In order to compare the 1953-1966 survey as closely as possibly with the current survey, therefore, this small area of VC21 Middx. has been included in the present account as well.

As this survey includes all of what John Dony accounted for, as well as subsequent additions to administrative Hertfordshire, the geographical area which it covers is therefore somewhat larger than that included in 1967, to the extent that there are four extra part-tetrads covered in the present survey. Comparative statistics for the areas covered by the two surveys are:

1967 County area: 163,413 ha (403,803 acres); 1967 *Flora* area: *c.*170,373 ha (*c.*421,000 acres)

2009 County area: 164,306 ha (406,009 acres); 2009 *Flora* area: *c.*171,266 ha (*c.*423,207 acres)

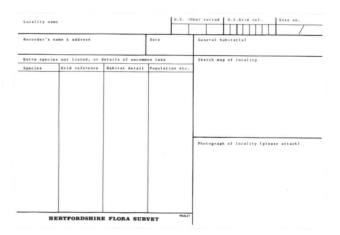

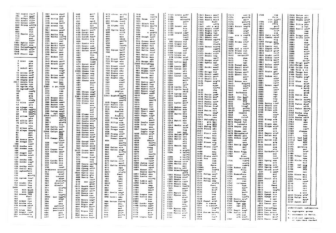

Figure 1. *Flora Survey record card front and back.*

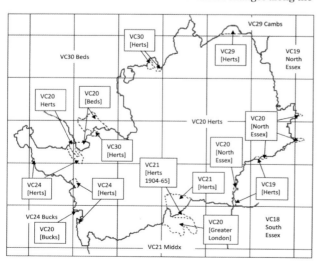

Map 1. *Administrative and Vice-county 20 Hertfordshire boundaries, illustrating the principal areas of overlap with adjoining areas.*

The 1987-2005 survey nominally covers all or parts of 508 2 x 2km squares (tetrads) in the following Ordnance Survey 10km squares:

SP: 81, 90, 91
TL: 00, 01, 02, 03, 10, 11, 12, 13, 20, 21, 22, 23, 24, 30, 31, 32, 33, 34, 41, 42, 43, 44, 51, 52
TQ: 09, 19, 29, 39

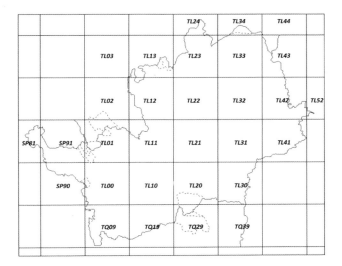

Map 2. *Distribution of Ordnance Survey 10km grid squares across Hertfordshire.*

Map 2. shows the distribution of 10km squares across the County, each of which is subdivided into 25 tetrads, referred to throughout this account in the format known as the 'DINTY' system, illustrated in Figure 2. References to tetrads in the text are given in the abbreviated form 09/A, B, C, *etc.*

E	J	P	U	Z	0
D	**I**	**N**	**T**	**Y**	8
C	H	M	S	X	6
B	G	L	R	W	4
A	F	K	Q	V	2
					0

0   2   4   6   8   0

Figure 2. *The standard 'DINTY' notation of tetrads in a 10km O. S. grid square.*
(Diagram supplied by the National Biodiversity Network Trust)

Of the 508 tetrads, records were received from 491. The 17 tetrads not covered by the survey were all marginal squares with only small areas of land actually within VC20 Herts., or in administrative Hertfordshire. The most botanically significant area omitted was a narrow strip of land at Ravensburgh Castle, Hexton, in tetrads 02/Z and 03/V, known to have remnants of chalk grassland.

This coverage compares with Dony (1967), where his survey nominally included 504 tetrads, of which 466 had at least some

records made in them. Again, all the 38 tetrads included in his survey that did not contribute any records were marginal ones. However, several botanically significant areas of the County were omitted in his survey. The results of the two surveys, therefore, while having been carried out in a similar time period across a similar nominal area, have a significant discrepancy in terms of actual recorded coverage, amounting to 25 partial tetrads, 4.9% of the present tetrad total, but probably about 2% of the total recording area.

The objective of the survey was to obtain as even and comprehensive a coverage of the habitats and their component species occurring within each tetrad as possible. With an area this size, even though Hertfordshire is small in comparison with many British counties, maintaining uniform coverage is difficult, depending on the spread of available skills, the effort contributed, and the allocation of that effort across seasons, as well as across the time period of the survey. As it was, we were fortunate that the most active field workers were very evenly distributed around the County. There was no precise measure kept of the relative effort put into each tetrad, although the general conclusion from records submitted was that, apart from tetrads where individuals actually lived, or a very few 'hot-spots' of interest, a relatively even effort was put in across much of the County. The survey instructions were that a minimum of three visits would be needed to each tetrad: in spring, summer and autumn, in order to achieve good coverage. Instructions were also given that all representative habitats within a tetrad should be examined if at all possible, based on an examination of the 1:25,000 Ordnance Survey map for the area, existing information and experience on the ground.

The survey was also designed to try and obtain information on sites and specific habitats considered to be locally important. In order to do this, surveyors were instructed to record all species present in an identifiable 'site', when it was found to contain one or more locally uncommon or rare species. These species (those reckoned from 1986 knowledge to occur in 50 or fewer tetrads in the County) were marked with an asterisk on the tick-list on the back of the specially designed Hertfordshire Flora Survey record cards (see Figure 1.). Identifying the boundaries of 'sites' can be problematic, and so instructions were given to regard the 'site' as an area of land with a uniform broad habitat type, or falling into a single 'management unit', such as a wood, a series of linked pastures, or a common. Whilst recording 'sites', care had also to be taken to ensure that data recorded only fell into the tetrad under consideration, because some 'sites' can straddle tetrad (or even 10km square) boundaries. Data on all field cards were requested to be either for specific survey dates, or, at the most, compilations within one year. Sketch maps of sites, with outline information on habitat and management, as well as a photograph of the site were also requested. The quality of the responses was somewhat variable, but in general a substantial amount of information was gathered in the process.

Data from site surveys not only therefore contributed to the Flora Survey, but also provided invaluable information which could be fed to conservation organisations in the County, through the Hertfordshire Biological Records Centre. An estimated 1700-2000 site survey record cards were completed during the Survey, as well as general tetrad survey cards for species not recorded at specific sites.

While the Flora Survey contributed to the site-related database of the Hertfordshire Biological Records Centre, there were also surveys being undertaken under its and other auspices which contributed to the *Flora*. These had been under way initially through the former 'South Hertfordshire Environmental Records Centre' at St Albans Museum (until 1989), some of whose surveys of sites from its 'Phase I' survey fell within the Flora Survey time-period. Later, the Herts. B.R.C. also jointly sponsored with the Hertfordshire and Middlesex Wildlife Trust a Hertfordshire Habitat Survey (1995-1997) (Cuming, 1997), as well as urban wildlife surveys for most of the major towns in the County. Botanical data from these surveys were available for the Flora Project, along with day-to-day routine site surveys carried out for development control and land-management responses within the Records Centre until 2001. Some survey data from other sources were also made available, notably from the Environment Agency's river corridor surveys, English Nature's site surveys, and some University of Hertfordshire student theses. Towards the end of the Flora Project, the Herts. B.R.C. and its partners, especially the Wildlife Trust, instituted an ongoing Wildlife Site monitoring programme, which involved re-survey or new survey of potential or recorded Wildlife Sites for conservation policies. Data from these surveys were also made available through to the end of the Project.

Measuring survey effort and evenness of cover

During the progress of the Flora Project, a particular source of unevenness which became apparent was the sequence of coverage of 10km squares. This was exacerbated by the period of severe droughts (especially winter droughts) that occurred from 1990 to about 1996/7. The first 10km squares covered, in 1987-1988, were those for the Monitoring Scheme: TL12, TL42, and most of TQ19. By the end of 1989, the survey had extended to parts of TL20, 23, 30, 33, and 41. Coverage proceeded especially quickly in east Hertfordshire, so that, by 1994, the whole of east and north-east Hertfordshire was covered. Similar levels of survey activity in west Hertfordshire occurred slightly later, achieving good coverage by 1996. However, even at this date, there were significant gaps in central Hertfordshire around St Albans and Harpenden, and in the south around Barnet. It was not until 1998 that almost complete coverage was achieved, leaving a few tetrads to be targeted in 1999/2000. The result of this progress was that species affected by drought, such as orchids, are likely to be especially under-recorded in central and western Hertfordshire. During this period, also, progressive loss or degradation of especially old grasslands and wetlands across the County was accelerating. Sites present and in reasonable condition in 1988 had often degraded or been lost by 1998. The effect of this on evenness of coverage is difficult to judge, but the maps will, in some cases, give a misleading impression of the occurrence of species across the County, either through imbalances caused by climatic factors, or because the rate of change of habitats through the survey period cannot be judged by examination of the maps alone. An attempt has been made to draw attention to problems like this in the text for particular species, where it is thought to be especially important.

In order to maintain some extra measure of the evenness of coverage of the survey, comparisons, tetrad by tetrad, were made with the number of species recorded for the same square in the 1953-1966 survey, based on the data given by Dony (1967) (map

56g). This can only be a very crude measure. Dr Dony himself (personal communication) estimated that his *Flora* had only achieved, on average, about 60% coverage, in terms of the number of species per tetrad. This was apparently an estimate he had come to through comparison of the number of species in tetrads known to be well recorded and those of similar mixes of habitats elsewhere. However, he never recorded any precise figures or working for how he had come to this estimate. Comparisons between his coverage and the current survey can, therefore, only be general. Nevertheless, the current survey has generally achieved much greater coverage than in 1953-66, sometimes to the extent of a 50% increase in the number of species recorded in a tetrad. The excess is least evident in the area south and east of Luton, and most evident in east Hertfordshire. This may be because the 1967 *Flora* is known to have had particularly thin coverage in the east of the County, while John Dony himself did much of the recording around Luton and Hitchin.

Finally, a measure of 'under-recordedness' was gained from considering the recorded presence or apparent absence of species considered likely to be present in every tetrad, where the relevant habitat might occur. Common grasses, common plants of specialised habitats like ponds, or weeds of disturbed ground were especially useful indicators of poor coverage, resulting in some specially targeted effort.

Some unevenness of coverage is still likely to be present, because it was not possible to re-visit all the areas which might have had this kind of problem. Some problems may therefore persist in parts of TQ19 around Watford, in TL02, TL10 and TL11. However, apart from marginal squares, only seven tetrads (1.4%) show significantly (<10) fewer species recorded than in the 1967 *Flora*. Of the rest, some 58 tetrads (11.4%) are reckoned to have more or less the same (+/-10) number of species as in 1967; while 440 tetrads (86.7%) show a significant (>10) increase in recorded species. The numbers of species recorded per tetrad, rounded down to the nearest 10, are shown in Map 3. The number of species recorded per tetrad will only be a rough guide to coverage, also, because it takes no account of change in habitats and the occurrence of species between the surveys. Some analysis of these changes is given in chapter 6.

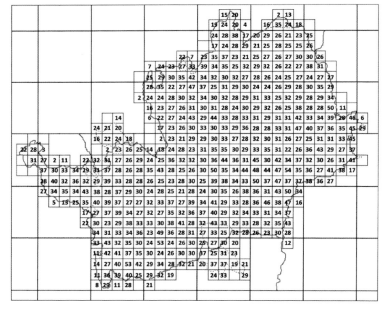

Map 3. *Number of species recorded per tetrad during the Flora Survey (for clarity the number shown is the number of species per tetrad rounded down to the nearest 10 and divided by 10; so the number 26 means 260 or more species were recorded in that tetrad).*

Chapter 2. A history of botanical recording in Hertfordshire

The beginnings of plant recording

The earliest known actual plant record in Hertfordshire is thought to be that of the Spindle *Euonymus europaeus*, which was noted to be 'in moste plentye' between Ware and Barkway by the side of the old road to Cambridge by the herbalist William Turner in 1548, and where it can still be found, if not so plentifully. However, there are even earlier references to plants, especially trees, which occur in Anglo-Saxon charters and other medieval documents or as part of place-names. John Dony gave a thorough account of the historical study of Hertfordshire's flora in his 1967 *Flora*, as did John Hopkinson in A. R. Pryor's *Flora of Hertfordshire* (1887), and so only a brief review is given here of what they have described, in order to set the scene, and to draw attention to some particular features.

The earliest scientific interest in the wild flora comes from the study of herbs for medicinal purposes. In time it became necessary not just to rely on folk herbalism, but also to search out plants in 'the wild'. Along with much other independent inquiry, scientific herbalism was therefore a product of the Renaissance, and so it is not surprising that the earliest field workers were generally fairly wealthy, medical men, usually from London, and that study started in the mid 16th century. Given Hertfordshire's location between the great seat of learning at Cambridge and London, it is also not surprising that it was an early focus of at least some passing interest. Another feature of Hertfordshire is that it has always been an area through which people have travelled to get to somewhere else more interesting! Early records, therefore, were, like the Spindle tree, often made from beside roads! In addition, it was not until the 16th century that changes in the way that communities lived allowed the opportunity for educated people to begin to look critically at the world they lived in and to document it. Unfortunately, this interest may have come too late, even then, for some of the County's formerly-existing 'wild' environment, such as the extensive common pasture woodlands which are known to have existed across most of south Hertfordshire in the Saxon period or earlier and into the late Norman era, and for the pre-Medieval swamps which occupied many of the river valleys in earlier times.

From the 16th century, Hertfordshire was always close enough to London for some of the people interested in plants to actually live here. William Coles, who lived near St Albans, was one herbalist who did so, and it is from him that we owe several early records, some of which give very special insights into the nature of the environment in the middle of the 17th century, such as his observation of the Royal Fern *Osmunda regalis* 'by a hedge side in a meadow on the left hand of the way that goes from St Albans to Windridge'. It is difficult to imagine the kind of swamp that such a plant would have lived in at this location now. It is even more difficult to picture the mire in which Bog Orchid *Hammarbya paludosa* was found 'between Hatfield and St Albans' in 1640, recorded by a contemporary of Coles, John Parkinson.

The late 17th and early 18th centuries saw the beginning of the scientific study of botany, centred on the work of John Ray, and a circle of colleagues arose around him, including several with Hertfordshire connections. At that time they tended to be gentlemen botanists who often had businesses in London, and who lived, or occupied fine houses at weekends, outside the city. One of the more important for his contributions locally was John Blackstone, who stayed with friends at Harefield, just in Middlesex, and compiled an account of the flora in the neighbourhood, published in 1737, followed by another more general account in 1740. His studies straddle the county boundary with Hertfordshire, and included a number of scarce plants in the area, some of which still survive, such as Meadow Rue *Thalictrum flavum* and Large Bitter-cress *Cardamine amara*, still its only genuine Hertfordshire locality, as well as Lesser Calamint *Clinopodium calamintha*, now restricted to one site in the same area.

The publication of Linnaeus' *Systema Naturae* in 1758 gave a great impetus to the study of botany, along with all of natural science. Hertfordshire shared directly in some of Linnaeus' interests, in that his assistant Per Kalm journeyed through the County on his way to America in 1748 on a collecting expedition, and in doing so made a number of observations in the County. There are a few plants recorded for the first time in Hertfordshire by him in his account of his travels, including Bracken *Pteridium aquilinum*! However, one of his most interesting observations was of the appearance of the County – mostly like a garden, but in the south-east having great expanses of 'barren heath' dotted with stunted trees, the last of the great wood pasture commons which, unfortunately, were scarcely botanised before they were destroyed shortly afterwards through Parliamentary inclosure.

The appearance of gentlemen and gentlewomen botanists in the mid-18th century continued into the early 19th century, and Hertfordshire had a number of these, who tended to be connected with each other in one way or another, politically, through marriage, religion, or through business. It was probably no coincidence that many of the gentlemen also had estates in the County, and were proud of their possessions. For example, we have important local studies around Welwyn in the period 1818-1824 carried out by William John Blake of Danesbury Park near Welwyn. As with many such botanists, they now created herbaria of pressed specimens, and made use of either the Linnean system of classification or the so-called 'natural' system devised later by John Sowerby and James Edward Smith to arrange them. Many of these collections survive, and give us very important insights into the nature of the flora from the period. In the case of Blake's collection, this is now in the Druce herbarium at Oxford. Another similar, and highly important collection is that of Frederica Sebright, daughter of the owner of the Beechwood Estate near Markyate, Sir John Sebright. This was eventually passed down through the family of her husband, Sir Augustus Wollaston Franks, and is now held at Luton Museum.

Another phenomenon of the period was the way in which the Society of Friends, the 'Quakers', became involved in the study of botany and taught it to others. A number of people from Quaker families took up the study: Alfred Ransom at Hitchin, and his later wife, Lucy Manser of Hertford, were two, the latter's herbarium now being at North Hertfordshire Museums Service in Hitchin. At Hitchin, also, a school was being run by a Quaker named Isaac Brown, and he became a tutor and mentor of a generation of young botanists, including the unrelated Henry Brown (whose herbarium is at the Natural History Museum in London), and Arthur Lister, brother of the famous Joseph. Unfortunately, Isaac Brown's important herbarium, which was bequeathed to the Hertfordshire Natural History Society, was later destroyed when it was in St Albans Museum.

The end of the 18th century and the early years of the 19th century began to see the publication of local, county floras or at least lists, often produced as aids to plant tourism for gentlemen travellers. Bedfordshire had an early proper *Flora* in that of Charles Abbott, published in 1798, but Hertfordshire remained without one for some time afterwards. However, the *Botanist's Guide* to plants across the country, produced by D. Turner and L. W. Dillwyn in 1805, was one of the better listings of plants which could be found in the County, and included a number of new records mainly made by Thomas Woodward and Joseph Woods. Other lists were made, and one was in volume 1 of Robert Clutterbuck's *History and Antiquities of the County of Hertford* (1815), containing a list of 'rare plants' found in the County, compiled by the famous naturalist Joseph Sabine of Tewin, mainly using existing sources. Another consists of a manuscript list of first flowering dates for plants seen by Joseph Ransom of Hitchin in 1814, although not all these are wild, and on some dates he was evidently in other parts of Britain. Such lists demonstrate an interesting phenomenon, probably unparalleled since – the recognition by the well-to-do that the wild flora of the landscape was an integral part of its interest, and that it was worth drawing attention to for its own sake.

Not only were natural sciences, including botany, now very much the interest of the educated classes, they were seen as a central part of the education of the young, and very much the province of the Christian gentleman and gentlewoman. It was therefore not surprising that, in Victorian Britain, ministers of religion became some of the most eminent botanists. They also seemed to have enough spare time to allow them to carry on the work! They would certainly have had the necessary Latin to understand the literature. Rather than being an idiosyncratic oddity, botany was a mainstream part of what it was to understand and teach about God's creation.

The making of the 'Flora Hertfordiensis' (1849)

By 1840, the scientific basis of botany had been established, and there was a growing body of people able to assist in studies. Landed gentlemen were often sympathetic to students of botany examining their land, and may well have taken part themselves. Improving transport links, with reasonable turnpike roads, freed from the plague of highwaymen (for which Hertfordshire had been notorious in the 18th century), allowed relatively rapid access by horse-back and carriage. Education and religious teaching were in the ascendant, and interest in the natural world encouraged by the new Romantic movement meant that more people were ready to devour information about the natural and historic 'antiquities' of their landscape.

It was against this background that the young curate William

W. H. Coleman manuscript introduction to his *Flora and a plant list from Mrs Morice, Ashwell.*
(in collection of North Herts. Museums)

Higgins Coleman, recently having taken up a classics teaching post at the Bluecoat School in Hertford, and his older botanical colleague, Richard Holden Webb, Rector of Essendon, announced their joint intention to produce a *Flora* of the County in a notice published in the local newspaper. It is remarkable that Coleman was only 23 at the time, but was already a highly competent botanist. There is no doubt that he was the inspiration behind the idea, and the creative element in the partnership. He in particular was behind the decision to approach the subject by dividing the County into 'natural' sub-divisions, using river catchments as the basis. This was a completely new innovation, and was the first attempt beyond merely listing plants to try to understand the distribution of the flora. Not only did their *Flora*, eventually published in 1849, break new ground in this way, but it also has a highly competent geological introduction, also written by Coleman. Considering that geology as a subject had only just ascended from the 'antediluvian' ideas of the past, this is also remarkable, even if his understanding of the subject in Hertfordshire was inevitably patchy. It is even more remarkable to consider that, when Webb and Coleman published the *Flora Hertfordiensis*, the only railway across Hertfordshire was the recently-opened one through Watford and Tring, and their evident excursions (particularly Coleman's) throughout the length and breadth of the County must have been made on horseback. They did have, however, a network of correspondents, which was no doubt increased by the publication of their announcement. Nevertheless, it is remarkable just how many competent botanists there were in the County at the time, willing and able to compile local lists. Manuscript copies of some of these are in the collections of North Hertfordshire Museums, while the original manuscript lists made by Coleman for the *Flora* are held at the Linnean Society and at Kew. His more productive correspondents included John Ansell of Hertford (whose herbarium is at Oxford), Isaac Brown of Hitchin, Alice Mary Barnard of Odsey (granddaughter of Sir James Edward Smith, founder of the Linnean Society), William Dawson of Hitchin (a pupil of Isaac Brown), Henry Fordham of Royston (whose herbarium is at Cambridge), Lucy Manser of Hertford (some of whose plants are at Hitchin), Dr John Coales at St Albans, and Miss Charlotte Henslow also of St Albans.

Although the *Flora Hertfordiensis* is a modest-looking volume, it was not only ground-breaking in its approach, but was also quite exhaustive. It is by no means unusual to return to a particular locality now, even at the extremes of the County, to find that a particular uncommon plant is still present at some obscure site. The precision with which much of the information is recorded is also astonishing, not to mention the rapidity of its collation. The *Flora* was actually completed and seen into print by Webb, because Coleman had himself left to take up another teaching post in Leicestershire by 1847. A first supplement, compiled by Webb, was produced in 1851, followed by a second supplement in 1859. Coleman continued his botanical career elsewhere, including work in Leicestershire, and on the taxonomy of brambles, dying at the early age of 47 in 1863, having established his reputation across Britain as one of the best botanists of his era.

Webb continued to botanise in Hertfordshire until his own death in 1880. This was just long enough for him to become a founder member of the Watford and District (later Hertfordshire) Natural History Society in 1875, and on his death his entire herbarium, along with much of Coleman's Hertfordshire material, as well as manuscripts and notes for the Flora, were bequeathed to the Society. These were held later at St Albans City Museum, but it appears that all this priceless material (except for printed books) was destroyed some time in the middle of the 20th century, owing to advice that it was suffering from 'infestation'!

Victorian botany and the work of A. R. Pryor

As always, it seems, after the publication of a county flora, there was a period when little new work was carried out in the County. Perhaps people felt that there was nothing new to add! In many ways this was a pity, because there were fundamental changes happening to the County during the period 1850–1880. First of all, there was the advent of the railways, along with all the disturbance of land, expanding road systems, new housing and industry that this spawned. These developments would have profoundly altered the natural vegetation in many areas. Another major change was the final inclosure by act of Parliament of most of the remaining old open field systems in the County, including large areas of ancient field strips and associated aftermath grazing on the Chalk in north Hertfordshire, as well as the loss of many of the remaining areas of extensive old commons, such as Wigginton Common, Ashwell Common, Hexton Common and so on. These losses of ancient, natural areas of vegetation, which would have been managed more or less uniformly for centuries, must have been great, but there was little or no record of their passing. Another insidious effect, which would not be formally publicised until the turn of the century, was the gradual lowering of natural water tables owing to water abstraction. The artesian waters in the Chalk under London had been tapped in the 1840s. So great was the head of water from the surrounding countryside that the fountains in Trafalgar Square rose 60 feet in the air without the aid of pumps! Needless to say, this steadily declined, and the effect in Hertfordshire (as elsewhere in the south-east of England) was a reduction in natural water tables, especially in river valley meadows, and in the flow of chalk springs. There are hints of the gradual losses in botanical records, but much of it also went undocumented.

In 1874, however, the 35-year-old Arthur Reginald Pryor offered to assist Webb in revising the *Flora Hertfordiensis*. Pryor, originally from Hatfield, later living at Baldock, was a man of private means, but of poor health. However, he was an excellent botanist, and his personal circumstances enabled him to launch more or less full-time into a study of the County's flora, including re-visiting known sites, discovering new localities, and doing much research for a period of 6 years. The volume of new work, however, soon made the project an entirely new *Flora*, which would have been a thorough review of both older and recent records, had not Pryor himself died shortly after Webb, in 1881. Nevertheless, he had managed to compile enough of the *Flora* to leave the basis for a publication, in twelve manuscript note-books, and thus it was that his posthumous *A Flora of Hertfordshire* was published jointly by Gurney and Jackson of London, and Stephen Austin of Hertford in 1887. This had been edited by none other than the Secretary of the Linnean Society of London, Benjamin Daydon Jackson, and with an introductory section on the County's geology, climate and landform by John Hopkinson, who was the Secretary of the Hertfordshire Natural History Society. However, neither of these were competent botanists, and the book was rendered less useful than it might have been because it was evidently not as thoroughly considered as Pryor would have done, had he managed to complete the work himself. Nevertheless, the text is full of detailed information on localities for species, which included both previously published information from Webb and Coleman and new material from Pryor and his contemporaries. The result is a *Flora* which is a compendium of detail, sometimes duplicated, difficult to use, but a mine of information for future botanists. It remained the standard Hertfordshire *Flora* for 80 years. Disastrously, however, his own herbarium and manuscripts, also bequeathed to the Hertfordshire Natural History Society, appear to have suffered the same fate as those of Webb, Coleman and Brown!

Hertfordshire botany after Pryor

Following the publication of the 1887 *Flora*, and without a single dominant figure in botanical study in the County, there followed a long period of relative inactivity, certainly in published studies. However, there continued to be good botanists in the County, especially a continued tradition of Quaker botanists around Hertford, and with their correspondents at Hitchin. The Graveson family of Hertford in particular was industrious. William Graveson (1862–1939), author of an interesting book *British wild flowers: their haunts and associations* (1917), was followed by his son, Arthur William, and they jointly compiled a substantial herbarium, especially concentrating on the burgeoning flora of

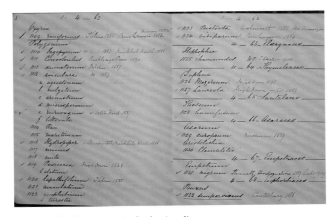

Joseph Pollard's manuscript herbarium list.
(in collection: North Herts. Museums)

Joseph Pollard, c.1900.

Thomas Bates Blow, aged 83.

Joseph Edward Little, c.1930.
(Photos by kind permission of North
Herts. Museums Service)

adventive weeds around the grain stores, maltings and refuse tips of Ware and Hertford. Having been moved with A. W. Graveson to Dorset when he retired from his family clothiers business at Hertford, the herbarium and accompanying photographic plates eventually returned to Hertfordshire, being donated to Hitchin Museum by Graveson before his death in the 1970s, and are now held in North Hertfordshire Museums Service. At Highdown, near Pirton, another Quaker, Joseph Pollard (1825-1909), continued the tradition of gentleman botanist, and corresponded with the Gravesons. He also compiled a substantial and important herbarium of local plants, which survives in the collections of North Hertfordshire Museums Service. Fortunately, this happens to contain at least some sheets from W. H. Coleman himself, and so at least something of Coleman's work survives in the County (other material being held especially at Bolton Museum).

Other botanists between 1880 and 1950 included Thomas Bates Blow (1853-1941) of Welwyn (a much travelled man, a specialist in stoneworts, and a pioneer of modern bee-keeping), H. C. Littlebury of Hitchin, Mrs Enid MacAlister-Hall and her brother Hugh Phillips, also of Hitchin (part of whose joint herbaria are in North Hertfordshire Museums Service and part at Edinburgh Botanic Garden), and especially Joseph Edward Little (1861-1935), who was formerly headmaster of Hitchin Grammar School. J. E. Little was the most prominent botanist of his day in the County, and contributed a substantial section on plants to *The Natural History of the Hitchin Region*, edited by Reginald Hine and published by the Hitchin and District Regional Survey Association in 1934. Unlike many of his contemporaries, he persisted in detailed field studies of plants, specialising in willows and poplars especially, but also taking a broader interest in the County's flora, compiling detailed records from his field diaries into four manuscript notebooks, which Dony considered could have made the basis of a new *Flora* of the County, had Little survived longer. His large herbarium is at

Cambridge Botanic Garden, and his notebooks are held in North Hertfordshire Museums Service. The local material from a small herbarium compiled by H. C. Littlebury is also in the Museums Service. Other herbarium material of the period also survives from the former collections of the Letchworth Natural History Society, incorporated with North Hertfordshire Museums, and including material from T. A. Dymes and A. G. Brunt, among others.

John Dony and the 'Flora of Hertfordshire' (1967)

The account given by John Dony in the introductory sections of his 1967 *Flora* concerning the origin and conduct of his survey is characteristically self-deprecating. Nevertheless, it bears stressing that there are not many botanists who can boast of having produced two complete '*Floras*' of different counties, as well as a supplementary atlas of one of them, and numerous other publications, both at a national and local level. John Dony was not a professional biologist, having acquired his doctorate in social history (the history of straw plait making and the straw hat industry around Luton). He was also a secondary school teacher by profession, and only followed botany in his 'spare' time, until he retired about 1960. In addition, he also undertook active senior administrative roles in both the Botanical Society of the British Isles and the Linnean Society of London. Helped by his equally botanically capable second wife, Chris (*née* Goodman), for much of the time, his full-time devotion to the survey after 1960 shows from its thoroughness, even though he himself did not think it was as good a coverage as he would have liked!

The survey for the 1967 *Flora* was started effectively about 1950 by George Evans, late curator of Hitchin Museum and the town Librarian, who was a friend of Katherine Little, J. E. Little's daughter. However, his botanical skills were insufficient for the task, and he was wise enough to engage the good offices of John Dony after the latter's *Flora of Bedfordshire* was published in 1953. John Dony started work in 1955, basing his operation at Hitchin Museum, where most of the principal surviving historical collections of plants and related manuscripts for the County were held. John continued the initial card index compiled by Evans, adding historical data from researches of various herbaria and manuscript sources, especially from J. E. Little's diaries. Katherine Little made some contributions, notably identifying some of the localities which her father had visited. The then Letchworth Naturalists Society was also engaged, with the active support of Doris Meyer, the long-serving secretary of the Society, and an able botanist and botanical illustrator. She and her naturalist brother, Harry, who were for so long a mainstay of natural history study in north Hertfordshire, carried out much of the work of survey in their area, along with Jean Bowden.

John Dony had a wide circle of contacts, and he was able to call on the expertise of some very able botanists of the day, such as E. B. Bangerter, J. E. Dandy, P. C. Hall, P. M. Benoit and R. M. Payne, to name but a few. The account of his survey given in the 1967 *Flora* gives a detailed picture of the help he received from across the County and beyond, which enabled him to carry out the kind of even coverage necessary for a 'tetrad' flora. However, we need to remember a few points in reviewing the place of his work in the history of botanical recording. The adoption of the Ordnance Survey grid system for recording in Britain by the Botanical Society of the British Isles in the early 1950s owed no small part to his influence at the time. It was therefore natural that he should develop this to use the newly-devised 'tetrad'

John G. Dony, 1966.
(Photo by permission of North Herts. Museums Service)

system of recording plant distribution at the local scale for his second county flora. He was, in fact, the deviser of the alphabetic 'DINTY' system of tetrad notation. While his *Flora of Bedfordshire* had been a more or less traditional flora, giving detailed listings of localities, as well as broader statements about habitat, the *Flora of Hertfordshire* was to break the mould (although it was just beaten into print by E. S. Edee's tetrad-based *Flora of Staffordshire*). For the first time, it was possible to see not only the detailed distribution of a species at a glance, but also to gain some idea of its scarcity or commonness. In order to get to this position required the systematic compilation of records in a way which had never previously been attempted. Field recorders had to be trained how to survey tetrads. They had to be motivated to approach the job methodically, and to persevere when more than a few tetrads were involved. The business of collating and working up the data into printable maps was also no small task. There were no computers. All the data were compiled onto single tetrad summary cards to start with, from multiple surveys, using different coloured pencils. From these, hand-made maps were constructed, species by species, at the end of the survey, followed by a second set of 'fine' maps, ready for the printer to use in plate making, over 600 in each set, the originals for which are held by North Hertfordshire Museums Service. In addition to this, Dony also had in mind the future interests of plant ecologists in the use of his *Flora*, for which he had already piloted in Bedfordshire the carrying out of detailed 'habitat studies'. He repeated this for Hertfordshire, producing 109 separate studies, each examined twice at different seasons, covering a circle of five yards in diameter at a fixed point in selected vegetation types across the County. This model has since been used by many others, and the Bedfordshire studies were repeated in 2006-7, in readiness for a projected new *Flora of Bedfordshire*. Added to this innovative work, was the inclusion of a series of hand-drawn maps, depicting geology, administrative boundaries, *etc.*, carried out by P. J. Ellison, and a set of high quality photographs of habitats, by various people, none of which had previously been possible in county floras. The result, while a slim volume, was a densely-packed, authoritative account of the County's plants which has stood the test of time.

Flora recording after 1967

Since the publication of Dony's *Flora*, botanical recording and the needs for information about plants have not stood still. Many of the field workers who had assisted Dony were still very active in the early 1970s and beyond, and contributed much information to the 'in-filling' which was carried out after 1967 (and some of whom also gave great assistance with the present Flora Project). Among these were the late Joan Foster of St Albans, Peter Ellison, formerly of Elstree, the late Dr Lyle Perrins of St Albans, the late John Fielding of Bishop's Stortford, the late John Lovell of Berkhamsted, the late Cyril Burton of Pirton, the late Frank

Bentley of Hitchin, John Killick, formerly of Cuffley, Jack Doyle of Hertford, and George Bloom (latterly more of a bryologist) who formerly lived at Knebworth. In this period, too, a number of other people also made major contributions, such as Prof. Richard Bateman, now at Kew, but who was then a research assistant at Rothamsted, and who began his interest in orchids through a detailed study of their distribution in Hertfordshire around 1980; Geoffrey Harper, who made a detailed study of Oxhey Woods, as well as looking at the distribution of the Wild Service *Sorbus torminalis* across the County; Janet Welsh, then of Weston, who found some unknown sites of importance in her local area, and who organised the Wildlife Trust's Meadow Survey in 1979; Michael Hooper and Roger Hawkins (mainly an entomologist), who jointly made useful contributions around Stevenage; Rachel Hemming, who contributed records from west Herts., and the late A. C. Jeffkins, who provided records from the Rickmansworth area. Others were later to take part in the present Flora Project itself, and are acknowledged elsewhere.

The needs for botanical information were increasing rapidly with the rise of 'conservation' in the late 1960s and early 1970s. A drawback of the concentration on 'tetrads' in Dony's *Flora* was that information about the sites in which plants occurred tended to be 'lost'. In many cases, these data were recorded on the card files underpinning the published book, but not always, so that potentially important sites quite often vanished before anyone had a chance to intervene to save them. The result was that recording in the later 1970s and 1980s tended to focus more and more on the 'site' rather than on overall distribution. A more detailed understanding of habitat and the way it was changing also became possible, backed up by the kind of insight generated from studying the detail of Dony's habitat studies.

By the mid-1970s plant recording had focused on the newly-established 'Natural History Department' of North Hertfordshire Museums Service. The Museums Service had been born from the bringing together of Hitchin and Letchworth Museums in 1974 through the effects of the 1972 Local Government Act, and the amalgamation of their two natural history collections in 1975 allowed the establishment of a unified Natural History Department. The result was an herbarium

Brian Sawford at Oughton Head, 1983.

second to none in the County, coupled with almost all the significant surviving historical manuscript resources, as well as a good library and study facilities. Brian Sawford, Keeper of Natural History from Letchworth, joined with myself, then Keeper of Natural History at Hitchin, and between other duties we focused to a large extent on botany, including active field work to re-find 'sites' examined by Dony's team, as well as any new ones they might have missed. At the same time, natural history work at St Albans Museum had revived, after a very long time without any active curation of its collections, but too late to save the irreplaceable herbaria of Coleman, Webb, Brown and Pryor. Habitat surveys were commenced, firstly under the aegis of the Hertfordshire and Middlesex Trust for Nature Conservation (latterly the Hertfordshire and Middlesex Wildlife Trust),

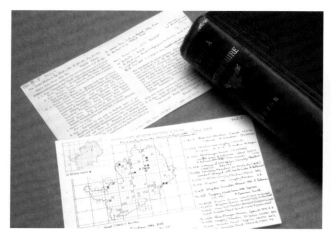

John Dony ms. index and Herts. Flora index cards 1970-1986, North Herts. Museums.

Ann Boucher at Rye Meads, 1994.

looking first at road verges, and then at green lanes, woodlands and meadows. Apart from the woodlands survey, these were somewhat piecemeal, but did generate large quantities of new records. Specimens from the woodland survey were checked and verified, and the herbarium at North Hertfordshire Museums Service became the focus of botanical work again. The activity and the availability of good quality resources encouraged new people to emerge as volunteers, adding to knowledge, such as of groups like alien plants, with the interest of people like Gordon Hanson of Ware and Ann Boucher of Hoddesdon.

The later 1980s saw the emergence of 'biological recording' as a defined activity. The setting up of the 'South Hertfordshire Environmental Records Centre' at St Albans Museum in 1984, under the guidance of Philip Collins, then Keeper of Natural History, and supported by government money through the Manpower Services Commission, enabled teams of surveyors to be employed to carry out a 'Phase 1 Habitat Survey' of southern Hertfordshire. These were led by Dr Barry Tranter of Hertford, who brought his meticulous approach to influence the recording effort. While the botanical quality of the results was variable, the coverage of especially more widespread species was greatly enhanced, and the cross-fertilisation with more traditional museum-based survey and research proved invaluable for both training and identification.

John Fielding (L. standing), Shirley Watson and Trevor James with others at Patmore Heath, 2008.

The progress of and the people behind the Flora Project, 1987-2005

It was against this picture of demand for information that the idea of a completely new *Flora* was born, in order to be able to put habitat and site surveys into proper perspective. From about 1984, the late Philip Kingsbury, Secretary of the Hertfordshire Natural History Society and a very able botanist, with his wife Sylvia, had mooted the idea of re-surveying the County's flora, pointing out, quite rightly, that Dony's survey was already becoming out-of-date. The advent of the BSBI's 'Monitoring Scheme' in 1987 was, therefore, the inevitable catalyst to setting up a 'Hertfordshire Flora Project'. A general meeting was held in the former Burleigh School at Hatfield in October of that year, and the 'Hertfordshire Flora Project' was born, with an initial group of over 70 people who had expressed an interest. Work was started under the auspices of the Natural History Department of North Hertfordshire Museums Service, then based at Baldock Town Hall, which produced the field recording cards and instruction sheets. The survey operation itself is described elsewhere in detail. However, the people involved must be highlighted. Without the stalwart help of many key field workers, the survey would not have been possible. In east Hertfordshire, backing up the early work of John Fielding, who had helped Dony in the 1960s and continued to supply records, we had the enthusiastic support of Shirley and the late Charles Watson, nursery garden owners from Bishop's Stortford; and it was their initial burst of activity which saw the rapid coverage of much of that part of the County, surveying nearly 50 tetrads in great detail. In south-east Hertfordshire, Ann Boucher, who had emerged in the 1980s as especially interested in alien plants, did an enormous amount of quiet work around Hoddesdon and Ware initially, moving across to Hertford, Welwyn Garden City and elsewhere later. To her eagle eye, we owe more than a little of the detail on adventive plants in Hertfordshire, together with the skills and knowledge of Gordon Hanson of Ware. They have also both contributed large numbers of specimens to the County herbarium, whilst maintaining their own highly important herbaria.

Around Hatfield, as well as elsewhere, David (A. D.) Marshall, then employed by the Electricity Board on maintaining overhead cables and sub-stations, used his access to the landscape as a means of gleaning important records, and supplying specimens, including early records of brambles, under the tutelage of national experts Alan Newton and Alec Bull. John Southey at Harpenden methodically surveyed much of his area before retiring out of

Gerald Salisbury at Aldbury Nowers, 2006.

the County, and especially focusing on identifying difficult roses, carefully named by Revd. A. Primavesi. John Southey's work was later supplemented by much detailed survey by Dr Ian Denholm of Rothamsted around the Harpenden area. Joan Colthup and especially Peter Ellison did large amounts of fieldwork around Rickmansworth, while at Bovingdon we were especially fortunate to have the steadfast support of Gerald Salisbury and his companion Jill Saunders. Gerald, formerly a farm stock husbandman by trade, also happens to be the nephew of the late Sir Edward Salisbury, former Director of Kew, father of plant ecology, and past Recorder for Plants in the Hertfordshire Natural History Society (before John Dony). Gerald and Jill managed to record much of west and south-west Hertfordshire between them, producing methodical site surveys as well as tetrad summaries, and re-finding many rare species.

Before her death in the early 1990s, Joan Foster, who had helped John Dony, also helped us with detailed work around St Albans, as well as with friends in the Hertfordshire Natural History Society: Janine Tyler and Joyce Smith, visiting other areas near Hitchin and Walkern. Down in the southern fringes of the County, Dr Lyle Perrins, very recently deceased, also resumed fieldwork with his wife Peggy in the areas around Radlett and Aldenham especially. After leaving his former home at Wigginton, Anthony Vaughan took up residence in north London, and carried out detailed and accurate surveys of much of the area around Barnet and Totteridge, initially for the former London Ecology Unit, but also supplied to the *Flora*. This work was augmented by the long-term knowledge and industry of the late Dr Diana Griffith of Totteridge, also a supplier of records to the London Ecology Unit and to Rodney Burton, for a very long time the Recorder of Botany of the London Natural History Society, whose recording area overlapped the County in the south, and with whom the survey communicated regularly. The late Ken (J. K.) Jackson, formerly of Pinner, meticulously recorded the flora around Bushey and parts of Watford,

Joyce Smith (L.) and Janine Tyler at Panshanger, 1991.

while other records around the town were contributed by Olive Linford. South of St Albans, Patricia Baker, long-term librarian for the Hertfordshire Natural History Society, was joined by her husband John in carrying out careful studies at Bricket Wood and elsewhere. David Marshall's work at Hatfield was augmented first by Colin Campbell, and later by Philip Harvey, while John Widgery (also a highly competent specialist in Orthoptera and Hemiptera, as well as an ornithologist) studied the flora of Potters Bar. In this area, too, we were fortunate in the early days of the survey coinciding with the BSBI Monitoring Survey, and having the help of Dr Tim Rich, the organiser of the BSBI's national Monitoring Scheme, who adopted tetrads around South Mimms service station on his travels up and down the country on the A1!

In north-west Hertfordshire, we were also extremely fortunate, early in the survey, to have the energetic support of Philip and Sylvia Kingsbury, who covered most of the Ashridge and Berkhamsted area, before Philip's sudden death in the early 1990s. This was also augmented even further west by Valerie Kempster of Leighton Buzzard, who valiantly took on the 'forgotten' land of the Long Marston area, which had been rather poorly covered in the 1960s. Richard Mabey was persuaded to take time off from his book-writing to undertake botanical surveys in a number of tetrads in his then home territory along the County's western fringes, and it is to him that we owe records of some important species, notably his amazing re-discovery of Wood Vetch *Vicia sylvatica* in a 19th century locality. Erica Goode also provided useful records from her home area at Kings Langley.

The Stevenage area and the country south of Hitchin was covered partly by myself, but also especially by Graeme Smith (in between studying the county's bryophytes), with contributions by Mark Gurney, Simon Smith, Jim Egginton, June Pitcher, Kerry Robinson and others. The vicar of St Paul's Walden in the early 1990s, Revd. Dendle French, added his bit in the area of his parish, in traditional naturalist-cleric style. At Hitchin, (as well as elsewhere across the County) we were supported by the determined efforts of especially Kathy Hall and Ann Robinson, as well as by Sonia Gorton. Cyril Burton, a well-known all-round naturalist at Pirton, who had also helped John Dony, took on his local tetrads early in the survey, before his death in the mid-1990s. Letchworth was recorded thoroughly by Alan Dean of the Letchworth Naturalists Society, who also regularly joined field meetings elsewhere; and Brian Sawford continued to supply records locally.

The Hertford area was largely recorded by Ann Boucher and myself, but with other recording by the late Grace Eve of Bengeo and Barry Tranter, and with some fieldwork by Dr Barry Goldsmith around his home at Hertford, in between university research. Jack Doyle continued to supply occasional records from around his home at Hertford and elsewhere, especially the Much Hadham area. Chris Boon, my counterpart vice-county Recorder for Bedfordshire, also helped, through joint field meetings to examine the shared flora of tetrads that fall both in administrative Hertfordshire and administrative Bedfordshire, but in either vice-county 30:Beds. or vice-county 20:Herts respectively. We therefore had a number of very interesting days around places like Dunstable Downs, the country around Caddington and Kensworth, and around Holwell and Ickleford, all of which we share.

The assistance given by colleagues in various organisations, but especially in Hertfordshire Biological Records Centre and the Hertfordshire and Middlesex Wildlife Trust, must also be especially recognised. Martin Hicks in the Herts. B.R.C. has

Ken Jackson (L.), Lyle Perrins and Graeme Smith (photographing) at Dane End, 1994.

Chris Boon at Wilbury Hill, 1996.

Patricia Baker (L.), Diana Furley, John Baker and others at Wilstone, 1990.

Alan Outen (L) and Martin Baker (Herts. & Middx. Wildlife Trust) at Bricket Wood Common, 1997.

Tim Rich, Lyle Perrins, Graeme Smith, Gordon Hanson (kneeling) et al. at Waterford, 1994.

Martin Hicks and Anita Parry (Herts B.R.C.) at Purwell, Hitchin, 1992.

Graeme Smith at Dane End, 1994.

Herts. Flora Group at Chipperfield Common, 1990.

provided especially detailed records of a wide range of special sites around the county, along with other detailed site records from Alan Outen, Anita Parry, Liz Anderson and temporary survey officers working in the Records Centre, especially Rachel Keen and Lucy Mottram. The various people involved in Wildlife Site monitoring under the direction of the Hertfordshire and Middlesex Wildlife Trust who have made significant contributions have included Fiona Hall, Brad Tooze, Graham White, Martin Baker, and members of the volunteer field teams, including Neale Holmes-Smith, Brenda Harold (the Botanical Society of the British Isles' specialist on *Potentilla*), John Moss, Alec Cooper, Paula Shipway and others.

Finally, my own field surveys, sometimes accompanied by my wife, Chris, largely covered north and north-east Hertfordshire (largely lacking other active botanists), as well as the area south-west of Hitchin, and other areas where gaps in coverage became evident. The programmes of the Hertfordshire Flora Group field meetings were also targeted at such areas. After the main tetrad survey was completed in 2001, work continued on scarce species, and I was especially helped in a belated field survey of brambles by Alec Bull, regional referee on the subject for the Botanical Society of the British Isles, which has enabled good partial coverage of this difficult group.

All the impetus of fieldwork for this Hertfordshire *Flora* also turned out to be fortuitous for the national BSBI Atlas fieldwork period, which eventually coincided almost exactly with the field period of the Hertfordshire survey. Thus nearly all the data provided for the Hertfordshire Flora Project were summarised at 10km scale in the national *Atlas* (Preston *et al.*, 2002), except for some of the post-2000 records of scarce species and some critical groups.

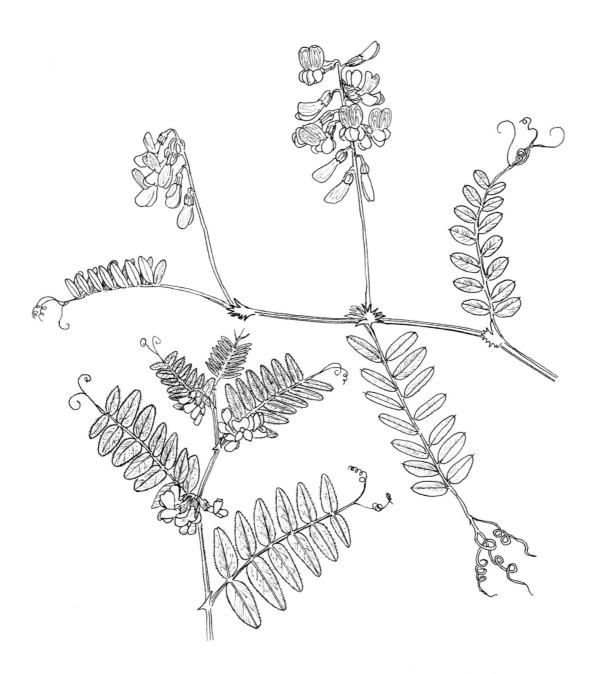

Woodland vetches – Wood Vetch Vicia sylvatica *(top), see page 230, Bush Vetch* Vicia sepium *(bottom), see page 231.*

Chapter 3. Hertfordshire's physical make-up – geography, topography, geology, hydrology, soils and climate

Nomansland Common.

As has been mentioned in the Introduction, Hertfordshire is a relatively small geographical area, forming part of the northern slopes of the London basin. As such, it has a lowland topography of relatively low hills, only moderate-sized river valleys, and a generally relatively dry, almost Continental, temperate climate. However, despite its size, it is remarkably varied, and this is down to both its geographical position, as well as to the complexity of its surface geology. This diversity has meant that it has quite varied natural plant communities, even though they may have suffered severely from especially recent land-use changes and other human impacts. An understanding of the County's physical characteristics is therefore essential if we are to understand the occurrence and distribution of its flora.

Hertfordshire's general environment

The County's overall geography is illustrated in Map 4. This demonstrates clearly that quite large areas of the County are dominated by fairly major urban centres, particularly around Stevenage, Watford, St Albans, Hemel Hempstead, Welwyn Garden City and Hatfield, Letchworth and Hitchin, Hertford itself, Bishop's Stortford, and the Lea Valley towns of Hoddesdon and Cheshunt. Major transport routes also cross the county, ranging from the Grand Union Canal, through the main railways from Euston, St Pancras and Kings Cross, as well as lesser commuter lines and the London Underground railway at Watford. Major roads include the M1, M10, M11, M25, A41(M), A1, A5, A6, A10, A41, A414, A505. Despite this, substantial areas of the County remain rural, particularly in north-east Hertfordshire, but also substantial areas in south-east Hertfordshire, protected by Green Belt legislation and the existence of the Hatfield Estate, as well as in west Hertfordshire, within the Chilterns Area of Outstanding Natural Beauty. Hertfordshire also has some modestly picturesque landscape, such as the Chilterns again, but also stretches of the Mimram Valley in central Hertfordshire, the

Chess Valley in the south-west, the mixed landscapes south-west of Hitchin, and the open landscapes of the East Anglian Heights in the far north. Much of the lower part of the Colne and Lea Valleys are protected as country parks, particularly the latter, established on extensive areas of flooded former gravel workings.

Hertfordshire's topography

Hertfordshire's landform is one of relatively low hills and dissected river valleys, typical of much of the northern Thames basin, and is depicted in Map 5.

The Chalk ridge of the Chiltern Hills and the East Anglian Heights, stretching from Wigginton and Tring in the west to Barley and Royston in the north-east, form a part of the northern rim of the Thames basin, with only small parts of the County falling north and north-west of this ridge. The highest point of the County is at Hastoe Hill, on the boundary with Buckinghamshire in the far west of the County, where the Chiltern ridge reaches just under 245 metres (803 feet). North and north-west of this ridge, the landscape tends to form a more or less well-defined scarp, overlooking the Midlands plain towards Aylesbury and the distant Greensand Ridge in Bedfordshire and Cambridgeshire. To the south and south-east, the land generally falls away towards the Thames, with a minimum elevation by the River Lea at Waltham Cross in south-east Hertfordshire of 16.8 metres (55 feet), and by the River Colne at West Hyde in south-west Hertfordshire of 39 metres (128 feet). However, the dip-slope of the Chiltern ridge does not fall away evenly across the County, owing to the existence of the remains of the proto-Thames river valley across the centre of the County (see below), which created a valley from Watford in the south-west, east-north-east through St Albans, Hatfield and Hertford to Sawbridgeworth in the east. This is best seen now in the Vale of St Albans. South of this lies the south-Hertfordshire plateau, between Oxhey in the south-west and Hertford Heath in the north-east, although at one time, before it was eroded by the Pleistocene ice sheet, the plateau would have extended further east towards Allens Green and High Wych. The current drainage systems of the Colne and Lea catchments occupy parts of the proto-Thames valley, as well as having created their own flood plains in the far south-west and south-east of the County through this ancient escarpment to reach the modern course of the Thames. Finally, a significant feature of the County is the Hitchin Gap in the Chiltern/East Anglian Heights ridge, where these two regions meet. This is a peri-glacial feature (explained below), but in landscape terms, it also forms the boundary between the Chilterns Natural Area (as recognised by Natural England), the East Anglian Plain and the London Basin Natural Areas. As such, it is also a boundary area in terms of the natural environment.

As for natural landscape features, Hertfordshire is blessed especially with ancient woodlands, compared with most of its neighbours, and indeed much of the south-east of England.

Map 4. *Administrative Hertfordshire's general geography: major settlements and transport links.*
(Courtesy: Hertfordshire County Council, © Crown Copyright all rights reserved. Licence numbers 100019606 and 100049441, 2009)

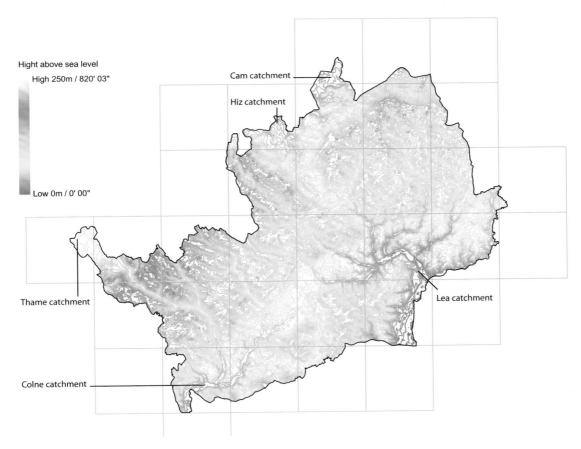

Hight above sea level

High 250m / 820' 03"

Low 0m / 0' 00"

Cam catchment

Hiz catchment

Thame catchment

Lea catchment

Colne catchment

Map 5. *Hertfordshire's general topography and river systems.* (Courtesy: Hertfordshire County Council,
© Crown Copyright, Licence numbers 100019606 and 100049441, 2009; © Intermap Technologies Inc. All rights reserved)

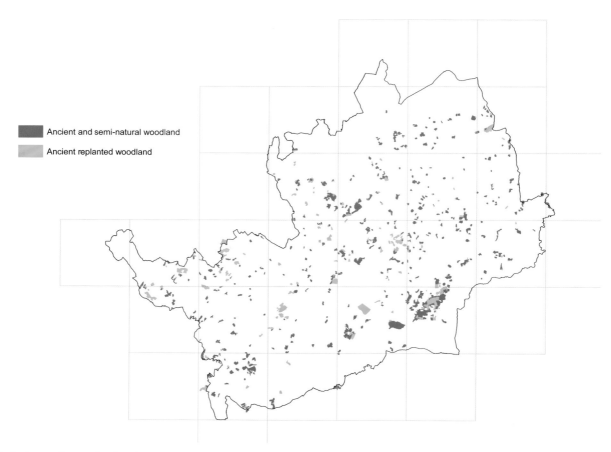

Ancient and semi-natural woodland

Ancient replanted woodland

Map 6. *Ancient semi-natural and re-planted ancient woodlands in administrative Hertfordshire (data courtesy of Natural England).*
(Courtesy: Hertfordshire County Council, © Crown Copyright all rights reserved. Licence numbers 100019606 and 100049441, 2009)

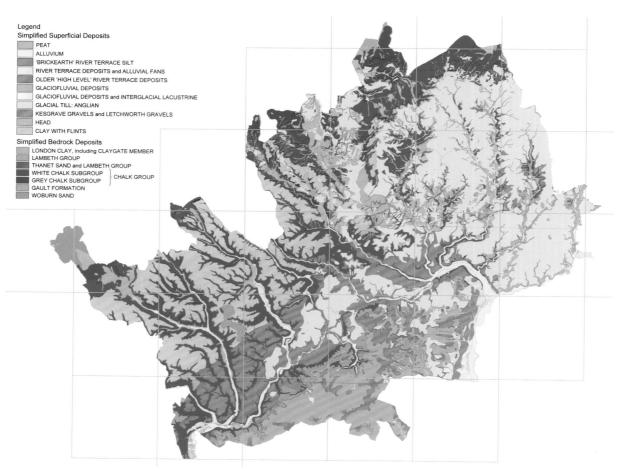

Legend
Simplified Superficial Deposits

PEAT
ALLUVIUM
'BRICKEARTH' RIVER TERRACE SILT
RIVER TERRACE DEPOSITS and ALLUVIAL FANS
OLDER 'HIGH LEVEL' RIVER TERRACE DEPOSITS
GLACIOFLUVIAL DEPOSITS
GLACIOFLUVIAL DEPOSITS and INTERGLACIAL LACUSTRINE
GLACIAL TILL: ANGLIAN
KESGRAVE GRAVELS and LETCHWORTH GRAVELS
HEAD
CLAY WITH FLINTS

Simplified Bedrock Deposits

LONDON CLAY, including CLAYGATE MEMBER
LAMBETH GROUP
THANET SAND and LAMBETH GROUP
WHITE CHALK SUBGROUP   } CHALK GROUP
GREY CHALK SUBGROUP
GAULT FORMATION
WOBURN SAND

Map 7. *The superficial geology of Hertfordshire.*
(Derived from 1:50,000 BGS geological digital data. British Geological Survey © NERC 2009. IPR/114-59C)

Although the principal blocks of these only make up some 8,963 ha of the County, nevertheless, as a whole, Hertfordshire has some important sites, as well as having a generally well-wooded environment, even in some of the new towns, such as Hemel Hempstead and Stevenage, where old woodland was deliberately encompassed within the new towns, rather than destroyed. The general distribution of ancient semi-natural woodlands, and planted woodlands on ancient sites is given in Map 6, courtesy of Hertfordshire County Council. Many of the County's larger woodlands are protected as public access areas, including the National Trust's Ashridge beech woods; the Woodland Trust managed Wormley and Hoddesdon Park Woods in the south-east, Harrocks Wood in the south-west, and Tring Park in the west; as well as local authority owned woodlands such as Northaw Great Wood, Broxbourne Wood, Sherrards Park Wood, Bishop's Wood at Rickmansworth, Whippendell Wood at Watford, and Oxhey Woods in the south. Hertfordshire is also famous for its historic commons (one of which, Berkhamsted, was the *causus belli* that led to the setting up of the Open Spaces Society), others including Aldbury and Northchurch Commons (part of the Ashridge complex), Nomansland Common, Gustard Wood Common, Therfield Heath (the County's main chalk grassland site), Chorleywood Common, Colney Heath, Harpenden Common and Patmore Heath. The County's wetlands include a number of at least regional significance, including Tring Reservoirs, Hilfield Park Reservoir, the Lea and Stort Valley area (especially Kings Meads, Hunsdon Mead, Amwell Quarry and Rye Meads), and some parts of the Colne and Gade valley wetlands around Watford and Rickmansworth. The County also has 43 designated Sites of Special Scientific Interest (although a number of these are geological sites, while some others are fairly small), and one National Nature Reserve, encompassing much of the remaining semi-natural parts of the Broxbourne/Wormley Woods complex in south-east Hertfordshire. The Hertfordshire and Middlesex Wildlife Trust also operate 41 nature reserves in the County (of which a number are also SSSIs).

An outline of the geology of the County

For the purposes of this *Flora*, an exposition of the County's physical make-up needs to focus on those aspects that directly or indirectly impact on the nature of its natural plant communities. Hertfordshire, along with neighbouring Counties, shares a geological position related to the landform of the London basin and the broader landscape of the South-East and East Anglia. In terms of the underlying 'solid' geology, two features especially stand out: the fact that most of the County is underlain by the Cretaceous Chalk formation, which 'dips' generally from the north-west to the south-east, so that the majority of the County's rivers drain south towards the Thames; and that large areas of the County have been affected over the last 400,000 years by a range of glacial, peri-glacial and alluvial processes and deposits that have strongly influenced the more recent development of its environment. Those wanting to find more detail about the County's geology are advised to examine the paper by John Catt (Catt, 1981), until a more detailed account of the County's geology is available. More technical detail can also be found in the British Geological Survey's 'British Regional Geology' series, particularly Sumbler (1996) and Hopson *et al.* (1996).

The basic geological make-up of south-eastern England is a series of sedimentary layers of marine origin overlying a Palaeozoic basement rock platform, which itself has been affected by Continental drift, so that it has been warped and folded to some extent, particularly as a result of the African and Eurasian tectonic plates colliding along the line of the Alps and Pyrenees. This has generally led to south-eastern England continuing to sink in relation to the north-west. The underlying warping of the bedrock and consequent fissuring and faulting in turn has influenced subsequent erosion patterns of more recent geological deposits, such as the Chalk.

The Chalk, which is upwards of 180m thick in places, overlies early-Cretaceous Gault Clay and Lower Greensand deposits. The latter does not really feature in Hertfordshire, except for the related Woburn Sands deposits now recognised around Long Marston, but Gault forms the surface geology around Holwell, as well as impinging on the landscape north of Ashwell. Chalk dips south-east as a syncline under the London Basin, re-appearing in the North Downs of Kent and Surrey, and is one of the most important aquifers in southern Britain. The upper layers were laid down in warm seas *c.*65 million years ago, after which a series of uplifts and marine transgressions of the landscape have occurred, forming higher level deposits of different kinds. In our area these have resulted in Palaeocene and Eocene deposits of gravels, sands and clays, especially the Reading Gravels that occur as an eroded, broken chain of outcrops trending south-west to north-east across the middle of the County, the result of marine estuary deposition in the Palaeocene; and the larger area of London Clay that occupies much of south and south-east Hertfordshire, with outliers in east Herts. Above the London Clay, of Eocene date, there are very small outcrops of marine Bagshot Sands around Bushey, which are an outlier of more extensive deposits in Berkshire and elsewhere in the London Basin, laid down after the Eocene seas shallowed, about 50 million years ago. Reading Gravels are free-draining, and produce acidic surface conditions, while London Clay is very poorly draining, and also tends to be acidic. All these ancient deposits have been subject to complex processes of erosion subsequent to their deposition, resulting in their occurrence as a sequence of layers that appear at the surface, with the youngest layers occurring generally furthest south-east, owing to the angle of slope of the underlying basement platform.

Overlying this sequence of mostly fairly straightforward ancient sedimentary deposits, we have a series of superficial deposits of more recent, different ages and origins that obscure a large part of the so-called solid geological formations, and which are often the most important soil-forming materials on which our local plant communities have developed. These superficial deposits, which are depicted in Map 7, supplied by courtesy of the British Geological Survey, consist of four principal kinds:

• *'Clay-with-Flints'*. This is a general term for related deposits derived from the eroded residue of both the upper layers of the Chalk and previously overlying deposits from the Reading Formation (part of the 'Lambeth Group' of deposits), which have been leached and eroded over millennia before and during the Pleistocene Ice Age. Geologically, these are complex materials, but essentially they are free-draining clayey deposits with abundant included flints and other stones from either the Chalk itself or from the Reading Gravels, *etc.* They form much of the surface geology of the dip-slope of the Chilterns, extending from Tring in the west across to Offley, and south towards Watford. Recent study has also shown that their remains underlie parts of the more recent Pleistocene 'till' (Boulder Clay) on the East Anglian Heights Chalk ridge in north-east Hertfordshire, where small outcrops often occur on valley sides, as a result of post-glacial erosion of the Boulder Clay. They tend to be moderately acidic and free-draining. Their depth varies considerably, dependent on the configuration of the underlying Chalk. In many places, this Chalk bedrock is highly convoluted, with deep solution hollows, called 'pipes', that are infilled with 'Clay-with-Flints' material.

• *Anglian Boulder Clay.* This consists of a fairly homogenous layer of glacial till overlying the Chalk and other deposits across much of north-east Hertfordshire, except where subsequent erosion has re-exposed Chalk or Clay-with-Flints, *etc.* The Anglian ice sheet, which advanced around 400,000 years ago, was the most southerly-extending ice sheet of the Pleistocene period, and reached to the southern borders of Hertfordshire around Enfield and beyond. It over-rode the Chalk ridge in the north-east of the County, and covered the plains to the north, eroding vast quantities of Chalk and other material in its progress. However, it apparently did not over-ride the Chalk in the west of our area, leaving the ancient Clay-with-Flints deposits of the Chilterns dip-slope to be further eroded by tundra conditions and recent fluvial activity. The Boulder Clay deposited when the ice sheet melted tends to be an un-differentiated clay rich in calcium carbonate, including abundant stones and even boulders from further north, such as fragments of millstone grit, Scandinavian rocks and so on, as well as fragments of Chalk. It is for the most part, therefore, both calcareous and poorly drained.

• *Peri-glacial gravels and sands.* As the Hertfordshire area was at the southern limit of the Anglian ice advance, the ice sheet would have produced vast quantities of melt-water at times, both along the leading edge of the ice, as well as from beneath, as with all glaciers and ice fields. This melt-water, particularly as the ice sheet eventually retreated, created a series of outwash channels, of which the most evident is that which created the

Hitchin Gap deposits at Vicar's Grove Pit, St Ippollitts, 1982.

'Hitchin Gap' in the Chiltern ridge. The channel here has eroded the entire depth of the Cretaceous Chalk, down into the Gault beneath, subsequently being filled with glacial gravels, sands and silts, which form a complex of deposits that trend from Hitchin almost to Hertford. Other, minor linked channels exist around Graveley and Letchworth. As they derive from calcareous material similar to Boulder Clay in origin, these deposits tend to be highly calcareous but also free-draining, contrasting with the older terrace gravels (Pebble Gravel, *etc.*) of the proto-Thames that occur in the south of the County.

• *'Proto-Thames' and river terrace gravels.* The Pleistocene ice advance not only deposited the Boulder Clay, it also had the effect of forcing an early precursor of the River Thames to alter

course from its original trend across central Hertfordshire, east into Essex and eventually joining the proto-Rhine in what is now the North Sea. The original river valley, which is a major feature across the centre of the County, best seen in the Vale of St Albans, had developed river gravel deposits and terraces over millennia before the Anglian ice advance, including the pre-Pleistocene Pebble Gravel, which consists of patchy deposits of sandy gravels of mainly ancient alluvial origin in the south of the County, with outliers near Berkhamsted and at Westland Green in the east. However, the proto-Thames also created an enormous glacial lake when the Anglian ice advance blocked its path. In time, the Thames itself broke through the more south-westerly Chalk ridge near Goring in Berkshire and altered course, but not before a large belt of alluvial sands and gravels was laid down across what is now central Hertfordshire. These gravels and sands vary greatly in form, and are of various dates, occurring from north of Watford in the south-west, through St Albans to Hertford and Ware, with outliers in various places in east Hertfordshire, often forming economically important sources of gravel for building purposes. Owing to the length of time over which they were deposited, and the variation of their sources, they vary in their acidity and permeability. A later consequence of this change of river drainage was also the eventual creation of the modern River Lea south from Hertford. This subsidiary source of the proto-Thames continued to flow south-east from the Chiltern ridge, and captured part of the proto-Thames valley around Hertford and Ware, north-east of which the Boulder Clay from the Anglian ice-sheet had been deposited. Probably fairly rapidly, the minor Chalk ridge at Amwell and Ware was breached by this river as it circumvented the Boulder Clay deposit, creating as it did so the steep river-valley slopes in the Hertford-Stapleford-Ware area, cutting down through both the Chalk and older river terrace gravels, and forming the lower Lea Valley.

Hertfordshire's hydrology and river drainage systems

Closely dependent on the County's geological history, its rivers and other hydrological features are also of great importance in understanding the County's vegetation. The County's principal river systems are also shown on Map 5 (page 15).

With the Chalk ridge of the Chilterns forming the backbone of the County, as well as forming the main subterranean aquifer and source of water for rivers and streams, most of Hertfordshire's rivers drain south or south-east towards the Thames. The principal catchment supports the Lea, which itself rises near Luton in Bedfordshire. As outlined above in the geological account, it was originally a tributary of the proto-Thames, and, subsequent to the diversion of that river in the Pleistocene period, it had captured a short section of the proto-Thames course around Hertford before turning south down what is now the lower Lea Valley at Ware. Around Hertford and Ware, down to Hoddesdon, it also acquires the flow of most of its major tributaries, making the Hertford-Hoddesdon section a principal area of natural wetlands in the County. The other major catchment is the Colne, which flows basically south-west towards the Thames, upstream of the Lea. Its catchment is largely from the Chilterns dip-slope, together with drainage from the river terrace gravels and other deposits in south-west Herts., although its headwaters are derived from the south Hertfordshire plateau, and also owe their origins to a captured section of the proto-Thames valley, albeit with a reversed direction of flow. The Lea and Colne catchments are separated from each other across a plateau of Thames terrace and glacial gravels in the vicinity of Hatfield and Coopers Green, an area that was the site of Hertfordshire's only natural mires, long since drained and more recently partly excavated for gravel.

The Chalk ridge of the Chilterns and East Anglian Heights in Hertfordshire also supports the headwaters of three other major rivers: the Thame in Buckinghamshire, the Ivel in Bedfordshire, and the Cam in Cambridgeshire. The Thame rises from the Chalk near Wilstone, while the latter two rivers flow north-east to join the Wash, and comprise the source of part of the water supply for the East Anglian fens, so that the foothills of the Chalk ridge around Hitchin, Baldock and Ashwell could be said to be the most south-westerly extent of the East Anglian fenland basin. The separation between the Lea and Ivel catchments occurs across the plateau between Knebworth and St Ippollitts, resulting in locally important wet areas around the woodlands near Knebworth. The upper reaches of the Thame in west Hertfordshire also comprise locally important ditch systems and wetlands associated with the canals and reservoirs around Tring.

It is important to remember that most (but not quite all) of the County's rivers were originally chalk streams, before modern pollution changed their chemical constitution to a greater or lesser degree, deriving their initial flows at least from chalk springs, and therefore having the characteristics of these kinds of river: high dissolved calcium content; relatively low plant nutrient content; and mostly stable flow levels, dependent on mainly winter rainfall re-charge of the Chalk aquifer.

A typical chalk stream, Oughton Head, 1974.

Chalk springs tend to occur where hard bands of the Chalk outcrop, especially the Totternhoe Stone and the Melbourn Rock, and are found especially associated with the rivers flowing from the Chilterns, but also with other rivers where the Chalk outcrops across the centre of the County, around Ware, Tewin, Welwyn and elsewhere. Re-charge of water in the Chalk aquifer is known to take up to six months or more, and so, often, rivers are higher in spring and mid-summer than they are in late autumn and early winter, regardless of the amount of rain. Flooding is rare in the upper reaches, but can occur in middle or lower reaches, where subsidiary inputs from surrounding clay uplands augment flows. River flood-plains are extensive, therefore, below Hertford in the Lea catchment, and below Watford in the Colne catchment. In times of very high winter rainfall over periods of time, water tables in the Chalk aquifer can rise substantially, and high level springs can re-appear in normally dry valleys, such as the 'lost' river at Kimpton, or the Bourne Gutter near Berkhamsted, as well

River Oughton, Oughton Head, Hitchin, 1985.

as creating ephemeral lakes, such as at Almshoe near Stevenage, or the vanishing lake above Whitwell in the upper Mimram Valley. The County's main chalk streams are (or were historically) the Lea, the Mimram, the Gade, the Chess and the Ver, with a range of other streams associated with them, notably the Bulbourne at Berkhamsted. As outlined above, a few chalk-spring-fed streams also flow north and west from the scarp slope of the Chilterns and the East Anglian Heights, such as the Thame; the Hiz (with its tributaries the Oughton, the Purwell and the Ippollitts Brook), as well as the Ivel, which all feed into the River Great Ouse in Bedfordshire; and the Rhee, which is a major source of the Cam, arising from springs at Ashwell.

Rivers that derive to a greater or lesser degree from surface run-off from the more impermeable clay uplands tend to have a different character. Those rising from the calcareous Boulder Clay of the north-east of the County are rather similar to chalk streams in water chemistry, and are often at least partly derived from similar spring sources, some of which actually rise from perched water tables in clay. However, they also receive much greater flows as run-off than rivers that flow through the Chilterns dip-slope, with its largely permeable superficial deposits. As a result, these east Hertfordshire rivers tend to have greater seasonal fluctuations in flows, and are more prone to flooding, carrying more sediment than their Chilterns counterparts, and forming more extensive flood-plains, often extremely important for their vegetation. Their catchments are also characterised often by having deeply incised bournes, often only flowing after heavy rain, forming steep-sided and wooded ravines. The main rivers in this category are the Beane, the Rib, the Quin, the Ash and the Stort. When the uplands from which streams arise are more acidic, such as the London Clay plateau, these streams, locally called brooks,

Northaw Great Wood, Cuffley Brook meanders, 1980.

often have at best neutral water chemistry, sometimes mildly acidic, such as the upper reaches of the Colne, and the Catherine Bourne in south Hertfordshire, as well as the various brooks in the south-east of the County associated with the Broxbourne Woods complex. Even in this area, however, some streams derive at least partly from somewhat calcareous deposits, and so there are no larger streams in Hertfordshire with oligotrophic characteristics or associated mires.

Spring systems have been mentioned as they relate to rivers, but it is worth mentioning that these tend to be of several different kinds in the County. The larger chalk springs, especially those associated with the Chalk scarp, often form deeply incised spring source hollows, sometimes called 'heads'. On the dip-slope, these are rarely as deeply incised, and the springs here may rise from multiple sources, often in the past utilised as watercress beds. The spring sources of the River Thame have been tapped as the major water source for the Grand Union Canal, through the creation of Wilstone Reservoir. Smaller seepages, both from the Chalk, and from the calcareous Boulder Clay, are often characterised by supporting small, but locally important and often unique plant communities associated with small areas of peat deposits. Very occasionally, these springs may be tufaceous in character, or even chalybeate, with high levels of dissolved minerals. Such springs occur mostly in east Herts., on the Boulder Clay, and are (or were) the sites of rare plant communities.

One particularly interesting characteristic feature of Hertfordshire is the occurrence of 'swallow-holes', and these can also have some importance for vegetation. Various streams, especially in the south of the County, arising either from surface run-off over clays, or sometimes from high level springs, flow onto permeable gravels or other deposits that overlie lower-level Chalk. When this happens, the stream often disappears into the Chalk aquifer, creating a series of hollows that sometimes become blocked, forcing the water to create another hollow nearby. These complexes of swallow-holes form locally significant features, including marshy pastures, such as one south of Bramfield. In some cases, there are other important ramifications. The Mimmshall Brook, arising from clay uplands in the south of the County, usually flows into swallow-holes at Water End near North Mymms. The water is non-calcareous here, but it actually reappears later from the Chalk at Chadwell Spring at Ware, forming a major source of the man-made New River, and formerly supplying natural fen habitat at King's Meads, although this fen was never as truly calcareous as similar fens in north Hertfordshire, owing to the less calcareous source of its water. However, if rainfall levels are high, the Mimmshall Brook

Kings Meads, Chadwell Spring, 1989.

overflows its swallow-holes, and supplies the normally almost dry upper reaches of the River Colne, flowing through Colney Heath, where historically it could cause major flooding.

Apart from flowing waters, the County also boasts a range of standing waters of different types. A glance at the Ordnance Survey map will demonstrate that the Boulder Clay of north-east Hertfordshire not only has vastly more watercourses than the Chilterns dip-slope, it also has vastly more ponds, especially on higher plateaux, and particularly on the highest watershed of the Chalk ridge. Although these are often at least heavily modified by mankind, there is every chance that some derive from naturally occurring hollows in the Boulder Clay, and may therefore be very ancient indeed. Many in ancient woodland, for example, show no signs of having been excavated. The south-east of the County also has a number of old ponds, but not as frequent, except on the highest plateau around the Broxbourne Woods complex. Some such ponds, where they are associated with acidic soils, can be almost oligotrophic in character, such as the pools on Hertford Heath and the outlying ponds on Patmore Heath, or around Shenley and Arkley. Apart from these more natural, possibly ancient ponds, there are almost no other naturally occurring standing water-bodies. However, mankind has produced a range of ponds and lakes of different sorts: moats and stew ponds for fish (with steep sides, usually lacking much marginal vegetation, the majority of which are associated with the calcareous Boulder Clay, where the main early settlements were), village ponds (often polluted over time with waterfowl and through road run-off), ornamental lakes (usually created through impoundment of small streams, resulting in sedimentation and rather eutrophic water quality), and most recently a range of flooded gravel pits of vastly different sizes. The latter now form a highly important series of habitats across the County, with variable water quality and chemical characteristics, depending on the nature of their water supply. A few, such as Frogmore Gravel Pit at Aston and Hollycross Lake at Amwell Quarry, derive their water directly from the Chalk aquifer, which can create an important aquatic habitat and associated fen. Others are excavated into alluvial flood-plains, and their water supplies can either be those of the water table itself in the underlying aquifer, or may be from adjacent rivers, which can cause problems of pollution through enrichment with run-off.

Hertfordshire's soils

No attempt is made here to give a detailed account of the County's soils, because it is not felt that this would help very much in understanding the occurrence of wild plants, as such. However, we do need to appreciate the broad kinds of soils that tend to be produced from different parent geological (or other) material. We also need to appreciate that, perhaps more than many Counties, Hertfordshire's soils have suffered from long-term human disturbance and degradation, to the extent that 'natural' soils are becoming something of a rarity, with the result that 'natural' plant communities are also becoming increasingly rare.

Soils are derived from the weathering of the surface layers of whatever material is at the top of a geological sequence at any one place, coupled with the incorporation in it of the decayed remains of plants (and animals). The precise nature of this weathering process and the nature of the resulting soil depend on the physical and chemical nature of the parent material, the angle and direction of slope, the local hydrology, and the overall climatic conditions (Davis *et al.*, 1992). Climate in our area has not (yet) been a major variable, as the whole of south-eastern England tends to have somewhat similar temperate conditions. There are, however, variations from the amount of water available, and the surface materials (as shown above) are also very variable, both in mineral content and permeability.

Chalk itself tends to produce a 'rendzina' soil, if it is not otherwise obscured by superficial deposits. In Hertfordshire, natural rendzina soils (which are characterised by being humus-rich, simple soils developed directly on the chalk parent material, and usually incorporating weathered fragments of chalk within them) are limited to areas where the Chalk outcrops directly, such as the steeper slopes of the Chilterns and East Anglian Heights scarps, or outcrops along valley sides. Given that many areas have been cultivated for millennia, undisturbed rendzina soils are rare and support important downland plant communities. Where chalk slopes have been eroded over long periods of time, lower areas become covered with slumped material, and develop what are called 'coombe' soils, somewhat like rendzinas, but with deeper profiles, and more inclusion of weathered chalk. The actual surface of rendzina soils can actually be mildly acidic or neutral, although calcareous conditions prevail at depth.

Rendzina soil section, Therfield Heath, 2008

Free-draining 'Clay-with-Flints' materials, or less acidic gravels and sands, will usually support forms of 'brown earth'. These are well-drained, usually slightly acidic soils with a pronounced layer of humus on the surface, when not disturbed, as well as lacking any strongly differentiated stratification. Because they are fertile and well-drained, most such soils tend to have been cultivated for a long time, although their acidity can cause problems, resulting in the need to lime them. Much of the Chilterns dip-slope is characterised by this kind of soil, as well as other areas in central Hertfordshire on free-draining substrates, giving the characteristic soils of Hertfordshire's Bluebell woodlands.

Where surface water-logging is present, as on many deeper clay soils, 'gleying' occurs, where ferrous iron salts in particular are not weathered, and remain in the soil profile. These kinds of soils can be rather infertile unless drained, and are characteristic of the London Clay and parts of the Boulder Clay, as well as poorly-drained soils over river alluvium that have not otherwise developed peat.

Strongly acidic conditions derived from acidic gravels and sands will usually produce strongly leached soils called 'podsols', especially if the area is free of trees, as on old commons. The resulting soils develop more or less strongly developed 'pans' of iron and aluminium salts at depth, while the surface layers may have few plant nutrients. Undecayed plant remains may also form

surface mats, especially under bracken cover. These conditions are typical of heathland, but similar soils can also occur under the more acidic grasslands. If woodland colonises such soils, root disturbance will eventually tend to break up the pan, allowing deeper minerals to be brought to the surface, when brown earths may eventually supervene, if conditions are not too acidic.

Peat development in our area is rare, partly for climatic reasons, although fen peat of various types has been developed over centuries in permanently wet, alluvial situations, or sometimes as a result of the formation of a 'peat dome' over the top of a spring source or seepage. After the end of the Atlantic period (*c.*5000 years ago), there is evidence of substantial peat deposits being formed in Hertfordshire's larger river valleys, resulting in extensive fen development, but following human clearance and drainage, these rapidly diminished.

Agricultural and other soil disturbance has the effect of breaking up any natural stratification of soils, and brings nutrients to the surface. If the disturbance is severe, such as the excavation of gravel pits, essentially the exposed mineral layers will begin to undergo weathering processes, and will produce 'skeletal soils' of different types, depending on the mineral content of the parent material and drainage. These are usually highly nutrient-poor, and can, as a result, develop locally important vegetation characteristic of such conditions. With agricultural soil disturbance, however, especially under modern conditions of fertiliser use, soils can become highly enriched with especially phosphate, as well as highly disturbed otherwise, resulting in impoverished plant communities of species dependent on high nutrient levels. Finally, artificial substrates, such as clinker waste, or special material such as pulverised fuel-ash (PFA) from power stations, will develop their own kinds of 'soils' over time. PFA waste tends to be poorly-draining, as well as extremely rich in mineral salts, especially boron, which restricts most plant growth, although some species can tolerate it, and eventually a characteristic vegetation can colonise as it is leached from surface levels. Developing humus layers appear, sharply demarcated from un-weathered PFA at depth.

The effects of geology and hydrology on Hertfordshire's plant communities

With the geological, soil and hydrological characteristics of the County outlined above, the surface topography of Hertfordshire, from the perspective of plant community development, consists of a number of strongly contrasting areas:

• The dry, calcareous Chalk ridge formed by the Chilterns and the East Anglian Heights, together with outcrops of Chalk further south, especially around Ware, Hertford, Tewin, and in the south-west at Rickmansworth, as well as along valley sides on the Chilterns dip-slope, *etc.* These areas are the home of chalk grasslands and calcareous Ash/Beech woodlands, but also vast areas of arable cultivation, especially in north Hertfordshire.

• The calcareous and poorly-drained Boulder Clay plateau of eastern Hertfordshire, extending about as far as Stevenage in the west, and the hills above Wormley in the south. Now largely heavily cultivated for arable, the main body of this area was historically often an area with semi-natural calcareous grasslands, as well as characteristic Ash/Maple/Hazel woodlands, where the soils are calcareous enough, or Dog's Mercury-dominated Hornbeam woodland elsewhere.

• The acidic, usually poorly-drained London Clay plateau of south

Hertfordshire, around Radlett and Borehamwood, *etc.*, overlain in various places by more free-draining Pebble Gravel, Bagshot Beds and other river terrace gravels of various ages. This area has historically always had extensive wet grasslands, with rather little woodland, often of English Elm, but also Hornbeam and Oak on less waterlogged sites.

- The freely-draining, moderately acidic Clay-with-Flints plateaux of the Chilterns dip-slope. Characteristic dry, mildly acidic grasslands have become rare, but woodlands dominated by Hornbeam or Wild Cherry and Beech are more widespread.
- The often acidic, usually, but not always, free-draining river terrace and alluvial gravels associated with the proto-Thames and its glacial lake in the Vale of St Albans and towards Hatfield. Acidic Oak/Hornbeam or Oak/Birch woodlands occur in this kind of environment, along with remnant heathlands and acidic grassland.
- The calcareous gravels and sands associated with the retreating Anglian ice sheet, especially in the Hitchin Gap complex, topped in places by wind-blown loess-like soils that were the product of glacial climatic conditions. No one kind of plant community dominates here, but the mix of soil types, often calcareous, can produce interesting mixed habitats, such as the grasslands around Ickleford, or the colonising gravels of old pits at Frogmore near Aston, Holwell and Wymondley.
- The wet, poorly-drained landscapes of the Woburn Sands complex and the Chalk Marl, as well as outwash glacial fan deposits, west of Tring. Here, old grasslands occur on especially the Woburn Sands deposits, while ditch communities with Common Reed and fenland species also occur. Black Poplars are a special feature near Tring. Similar landscapes on the small areas of Gault at Holwell and Ashwell have largely lost their native flora, although White Willows are conspicuous by stream sides.
- Finally, the alluvial flood-plains of the County's various main rivers, with wetlands developed over fluvial gravels, silts and sands of varying composition and alkalinity, and supported by high groundwater levels. Remnant Alder/Willow woodlands remain, along with Reed beds and various sedge fens, especially now associated with flooded gravel pits.

Within these broad areas, the detail of geological history, coupled with subsequent erosion patterns and human impacts means that, at any one site, soil types can be very varied indeed. For example, chalk arable weeds will often be limited to one corner of a field, where the parent Chalk comes to the surface, while other parts of the same field may have thin veneers of glacial sands, or the ploughed remains of fertile brown earths over Clay-with-Flints materials. It is this complexity that gives the County its very varied natural and semi-natural plant communities, but we also need to remember that it also contributes strongly to the occurrence even of 'weeds' of disturbed ground.

The climate of Hertfordshire and its effects on the flora

As mentioned above, Hertfordshire's climate is generally Sub-Atlantic temperate, but with a tendency to Continental conditions, especially in the east of the County. The influence of the Chilterns on rainfall is considerable. Map 8 (after Dony, 1967) shows the relative rainfall patterns across the County, with a substantially higher rainfall on the Chilterns than elsewhere, and a very much lower rainfall in the extreme north, north of the East Anglian

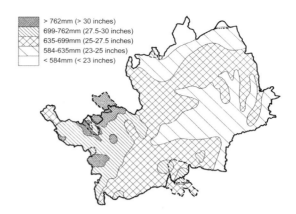

> 762mm (> 30 inches)
699-762mm (27.5-30 inches)
635-699mm (25-27.5 inches)
584-635mm (23-25 inches)
< 584mm (< 23 inches)

Map 8. *Average annual rainfall across Hertfordshire.*
(Adapted after the map by P. J. Ellison in Dony, 1967, by courtesy of North Hertfordshire District Council)

Heights, as well as to a lesser extent, the lower lying areas of the Lea Valley catchment. This results in a far greater availability of ground-water deriving from the Chilterns, as compared with the north and east, which affects river flows, as well as directly influencing the vegetation. For example, it should be noted that almost all the significant woodlands in Hertfordshire fall within areas with more than 635mm of rain a year. The difference between the rainfall in the Chilterns and the East Anglian Heights is also largely responsible for the demonstrable difference between the chalk grassland types in these two regions.

Data on precipitation (rain and snow) at Rothamsted, Harpenden, since 1988, the beginning of the Flora Survey, are shown in Figure 3. These data usefully derive from the median area of the County's rainfall, thus giving us an average picture of rainfall across the County as a whole. The total annual precipitation figures show that over that period the average (mean) precipitation was 738.9mm (29.1 inches), somewhat higher than the average rainfall indicated for the Harpenden area in the 1960s map. However, there were very significant peaks and troughs, which have affected the survey work for the flora, if not the flora itself. In 1990, for example, the mean precipitation was only 597.4mm (23.5 inches), while in 1996, at the height of the mid-1990s droughts, it fell to just 515.5mm (20.3 inches).

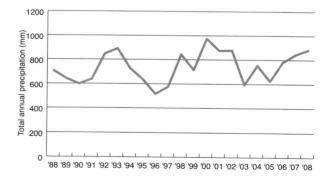

Figure 3. *Total annual precipitation at Rothamsted, 1988-2008.*
(Graph produced at Rothamsted Research, by courtesy of Dr I. G. Denholm)

More significant for the flora are the relative winter rainfall figures, shown in Figure 4.

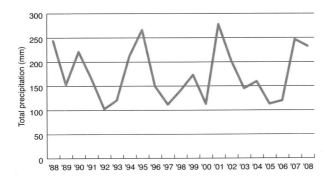

Figure 4. *Total January-March rainfall at Rothamsted, 1988-2008.*
(Graph produced at Rothamsted Research,
by courtesy of Dr I. G. Denholm)

The significance of these data are that they show the periods of winter drought that affected ground-water levels during the periods 1989-1993, and especially 1996-2000, as well as to a slightly less extent more recently. Fortunately, higher peaks in 1994-5 and 2001-2 intervened, reducing the long-term impact of these droughts, although there may be signs that some vulnerable species suffered as a result, particularly species that require damp early season conditions to come into flower.

Mid summer temperatures may also affect some species, and the mean July temperatures give some information on this, as shown in Figure 5.

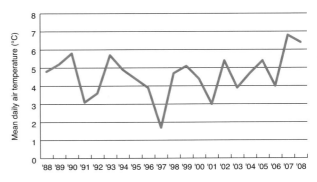

Figure 5. *Mean daily July air temperatures at Rothamsted, 1988-2008, showing trend.*
(Graph produced at Rothamsted Research,
by courtesy of Dr I. G. Denholm)

These figures show a steady general increase in summer temperatures quite well, although this is often obscured by yearly peaks and troughs, as well as the extremes of local daily variation. Different effects on plant growth are also experienced with combinations of winter drought and high summer temperatures, as was experienced in 2006, compared with wet winters and high summer temperatures, as was the case in 1994-5, the former being generally more damaging to native vegetation, although the precise timing of rainfall and the length of hot periods are often crucial. Over a longer time period, this trend in rising summer temperatures is even more marked, especially recently, and the future nature of the climate is increasingly uncertain, along with its potentially massive impact on the natural vegetation.

Fluellens – Sharp-leaved Fluellen Kickxia elatine *(left), Round-leaved Fluellen* Kickxia spuria *(right), see page 326.*

Chapter 4. Hertfordshire's natural landscape and its history

Water End Meadows, Great Gaddesden, spring pool.

It is not possible here to go into detail about the County's landscape history, a subject that, from the human historical perspective at least, has been covered very well by others (Munby, 1977; Williamson, 2000). However, it is necessary to try and set the scene for our understanding of the County's flora and vegetation, and so in this section we need to take a look at, firstly, some of our perceptions and possible misperceptions of what constitutes the 'natural' environment; secondly to focus on some key points of historical development that might give us a clearer picture of the natural occurrence of species in our landscape.

The basis of Hertfordshire's historical ecology

At one time, not so long ago, people's general idea of the landscape before the Bronze Age, at least, was that it was a mostly untamed wilderness of dense forest, except where large, marshy rivers drained the land, or where small scattered human communities had developed. By the mid-20th century, this view had changed to recognise that Neolithic man had had a large impact on the environment, and that cultivation and clearance had been a major part of this (*e.g.* Harley and Lewis (eds.), 1985). Williamson (2000) gives us a more up-to-date view of this in the Hertfordshire context and from the human point of view, and makes it clear that much of the natural vegetation had long since been essentially 'tamed' by Bronze Age times. Recent archaeological investigations, coupled with pollen analysis of ditch deposits have shown, for example, that the area we now know as the Broxbourne Woods was an extensively managed landscape that owes its basic pattern of boundary features (hedges, ditches) quite probably to Bronze Age land allocations, so that, even at the time of the Roman occupation, these boundaries were ancient. What we now think of as 'ancient woodland' in the area (Wormley Wood, *etc.*) had been parcelled up on an extensive scale and may well have been at least partly open land. A similar picture emerges with the very characteristic 'co-axial' field patterns of the Chilterns

dip-slope near Bovingdon and Great Gaddesden, which is not a modern enclosure landscape, but one that long pre-dates the Saxon conquest. Much of the basic structure of Hertfordshire's human-influenced landscape, therefore, is far older than many people have ever believed.

Whatever the early history of land occupation by humans, the question remains: what kind of landscape did they actually move into, what sort of vegetation did it support, and what were their impacts upon it? Also, what evidence is there for any of this, other than guesswork? The monumental compilation of information from prehistoric pollen deposits and other sources that was presented by Professor Sir Harry Godwin firstly in 1956 (revised 20 years later) (Godwin, 1975), has been used ever since as the basis for our ecological understanding of the British flora, paralleled by other similar studies across north-western Europe. Accounts in works like Pennington (1969) have depended heavily on these data, and the general conclusion has been that almost all of the British Isles was eventually re-colonised by forest following the final retreat of the Pleistocene late Weichselian ice sheet, about 12,000 years ago. The nature of this re-colonisation varied from area to area, and over time, with genera like oak *Quercus* spp. being supplanted by limes *Tilia* and eventually Beech *Fagus sylvatica* and Hornbeam *Carpinus betulus* before Britain was cut off from mainland Europe by rising sea-level. Elms *Ulmus* spp. colonised early, but suffered from a major decline around 5,000 years ago, possibly through human clearances. As humans appeared on the scene in numbers during the late Mesolithic, forest trees began to give way to plant communities of more open ground, with increased scrub species.

This straightforward interpretation of pollen rain diagrams and the remains of molluscs in buried soils under barrows, *etc.* remained the accepted view until 2000, when a seminal publication by F. W. M. Vera *Grazing ecology and forest history* (Vera, 2000) called some of it at least into question. His main thesis was that oaks do not regenerate under the shade of other trees. This, therefore contradicted their continued major presence in supposedly closed forests across western Europe throughout the late Mesolithic period, for which pollen analyses have provided apparently clear evidence. He therefore proposed that large grazing mammals, notably wild cattle (aurochs), as well as bison (in mainland Europe), red deer and boar, would have had a major influence not just on small clearings, but on the whole dynamic of forest ecology over long periods of time, resulting in a natural forest vegetation in which cyclic shifts between closed forest and open grasslands occurred, mediated by marginal shrub communities, within which pioneer forest trees, such as oaks, gained a foothold. The picture he paints is therefore of a park-like landscape, with extensive open spaces, as well as large 'groves' of closed forest, shifting slowly as forest succession occurred and eventually regressed over centuries in the face of grazing and browsing pressures. This remains a controversial thesis, but it has much to recommend it from an ecological perspective.

For our purposes, this revised view of 'natural' vegetation

is highly important, because it suggests that not only is closed forest vegetation 'natural', but so also are the mixed scrub and herb communities which now form patchwork vestiges around the modern-day remnants of woodland. 'Natural' grasslands and related habitats, therefore, do exist in our climatic zone , and these are not just the product of human interference with 'high forest'. Such a conclusion makes an enormous difference to the way we view plant communities and their origins, along with all the other native species of wildlife associated with open ground or the margins of forests.

The other major influences on natural vegetation patterns, of course, are those caused by geology and soils, as well as the physiographical processes that created land-forms and drainage patterns, as we have seen earlier. Coupled with climate shifts that enabled late Mesolithic hunters to expand populations, and also attracted Neolithic farming communities to move north-west through Europe, the natural vegetation would have firstly allowed human colonisation much more readily in the more open spaces. It would also have become more and more impacted by added clearances, as well as the establishment of permanent human occupation sites and their associated cultivation practices. These in turn would have been influenced by the productivity of soils, and the nature of the plant communities that grew on them. Well-drained, less fertile soils may have been originally more lightly wooded, but they may not have attracted early farming communities, or if they did, they would have been forced to move on as natural productivity declined and what we now know as heathland would have become more extensive.

Early human settlement and landscape history

The pattern of early settlement in Hertfordshire has gradually become more clear as archaeologists have carried out more survey and excavation. Williamson (2000) gives a good picture of this. While there is only scattered evidence for Neolithic communities in the County (c.4,000-3,500 BC), suggesting rather sparse populations, focused on lighter soils, more is known about the Bronze Age. In particular we know the distribution of Bronze Age round barrows and ring ditches (Williamson, *op. cit.*, p. 26), which, despite the existence of potentially early land-use patterns elsewhere, shows that there was a predominance of settled communities on the lighter soils of the Chalk in northern Hertfordshire, as well as along the sides of valleys where Chalk outcrops further south, especially in the Chilterns dip-slope region. The barrow monuments themselves, Williamson suggests, may have been on the margins of settled communities, as many are on watersheds, but the settled sites are likely to have been on lower slopes, above valley flood plains. This is also borne out by the fact that many of the County's middle course river flood plains were likely to have been occupied by extensive swamp areas at the time (2-3,000 BC), as evidenced by the existence of substantial deposits of alluvial peat along valley margins, above the present valley floor, at places like Stapleford, layers that were subsequently covered by hill-wash coombe deposits, presumably through erosion of cultivated slopes above.

The precise detail of settlement development across the County will probably never be known, but it is certain that, by Iron Age times, Hertfordshire was well-settled, with concentrations in certain areas. Before the Roman occupation, substantial, but apparently rather amorphous quasi-urban settlements had developed in a number of river valleys on more fertile, calcareous soils, from near Tring (Cow Roast) in the west, through St Albans (Verlamion – Verulamium), Wheathampstead, Welwyn and Ware, to Braughing and Baldock. There is also evidence of communities defining their territories more closely through the establishment of boundary banks like Grim's Ditch near Berkhamsted, and the construction of possibly defensive or ceremonial 'hill-forts' at strategic points, especially on (but not limited to) the open chalk downland areas along the Chilterns and East Anglian Heights ridge, such as at Hexton (Ravensburgh), near Letchworth (Wilbury Hill) and near Ashwell (Arbury Banks). Areas of heavy, clay soils appear to have remained thinly populated, and probably retained more extensive forests, such as on the London Clay, the Boulder Clay, and the more acidic areas of the Clay-with-Flints across the Chilterns dip-slope. This picture, in fact, is quite strongly supported by the modern distribution of ancient woodlands, except that later cultivation techniques allowed the otherwise very fertile Boulder Clay to become more heavily populated during late Saxon and Medieval times. It is also supported by the former distribution of extensive commons, which were very often on poor, acidic soils that would have derived from early clearances which had failed to support long-term populations of humans and their farming practices. These large commons were almost entirely across the south and west of the County, the very areas where human populations remained smallest as late as the Norman Conquest.

By the end of the Iron Age, therefore, when the Roman occupation began, the landscape was evidently well-partitioned and occupied by peasant farming communities. It still had extensive tracts of woodlands and 'waste', in the south and on the wetter plateau soils in the west and north-east, while chalk lands and free-draining ground along mid-course river valleys were quite heavily populated. It was not for nothing that the Belgic Catuvellauni tribe had its principal bases in our area, at places like Prae Wood and Braughing. As Williamson (*op. cit.*) has pointed out, the Roman occupation in Britain also seems to have built on pre-existing social structures, and therefore the landscape would have evolved rather than had a completely new pattern imposed upon it. For example, the sparse Roman finds in southern Hertfordshire strengthen the idea that this area remained more heavily wooded (perhaps also with extensive pasture), while the valley sides of the Chilterns dip-slope area were the setting for numerous villa holdings, no doubt creating a very similar patchwork of fields and woodlands to what we see today. Roman communication routes also built on previously existing links between the major Belgic settlements, themselves often following obvious routes along valley sides, while adding more, especially the two major military roads: Ermine Street and Watling Street, which are clearly seen to bisect previously-existing land holding boundaries in various places. He also points out that routes like the Icknield Way and Stane Street (leading from Braughing east towards Colchester) were 'tidied-up versions of much older trackways'. The former, at least, had been a major through-route associated with the sheltered dry lands beneath the Chilterns and East Anglian Heights scarp, but above the swampy lands of the lowland plain to the north, for millennia, presumably making use of a network of naturally occurring grazed lands on the Chalk, surrounding the obvious watering holes at various spring sources emanating from the Totternhoe Stone. This basic pattern of settlement and communication, therefore, is something that we can largely recognise today.

Just before the time of the collapse of the Roman Empire, what is now Hertfordshire was part of a well-organised market economy of farming, commerce and small-scale industry. The landscape was partitioned into land-holdings of various types, depending whether these were under villa control, or were British occupied lands held in common, the latter being more prevalent in the east (Williamson, *op. cit.*). There is evidence of substantial industry, including iron smelting on a fairly large scale around the Ashridge area, which would have used extensive quantities of fuel wood (pers. comm.: S. Bryant, Herts. County Archaeologist), as well as pottery making at various sites. Places like the Roman towns at Verulamium, Baldock and Braughing were major commercial centres, the first being one of the largest planned civic complexes north of the Alps in the Roman world. Although we may not have had quite the grand Roman villas found in places like the Cotswolds, Hertfordshire was an important area for the Roman economy in Britain.

This organised landscape suffered a serious blow by the collapse of Rome. Its economy almost ceased to function. Roman villas were abandoned wholesale, and the native population would have been forced to become entirely self-sufficient. There is extensive evidence of a retrenchment of occupation of poorer land, and it is very likely that extensive areas of secondary woodland developed on former open ground, especially in south-east Hertfordshire and on the clay uplands elsewhere. The Ashridge area, for example, is likely to have become more wooded around this time, as well as areas around Verulamium itself. Saxon invasion and subsequent re-distribution of land holdings would also have had substantial impacts, depending on the origin of incomers and their ways of running their affairs. Common field-strip practices became extensive in north-east Hertfordshire, for example. However, as Williamson suggests, there is substantial evidence for at least some significant continuity between pre-Saxon and later communities. Verulamium itself survived in some form well into the Saxon period, and there is evidence there of Christian continuity from the Roman period, eventually leading to the construction of St Albans nearby and the final abandonment of the Romano-British town. The Romano-British town at Braughing also survived for some time on its historic site overlooking Braughing Meads at Wickham Hill. Other early sites at Cheshunt, Welwyn and elsewhere also carried over into the Saxon landscape. However, as Williamson points out, actual evidence for the wholesale take-over of land by Saxon communities is lacking in our area, and it seems very likely that 'Saxon' tribes such as the Hicce around Hitchin, the Waeclingas at Verulamium and the Brahingas around Braughing were actually derived from British origins. This in itself would imply that their traditional land holding patterns would have remained essentially unchanged to a large extent, even if populations retrenched to better areas of land and large tracts elsewhere were abandoned. This contrasts with areas in Cambridgeshire to the north, where there is substantial evidence of early Saxon settlement. It also might be the reason that the fundamental landscape structure of much of Hertfordshire, with its very ancient field boundaries, sunken lanes, *etc.* contrasts so strongly with the former open-field structure of the landscapes further north.

During the majority of Saxon times, however, Hertfordshire did not exist as a separate political or civic entity. Instead, it was bisected by the boundary between the East Saxon and Mercian kingdoms, and later became a pivotal area in the conflict between Wessex and the Danelaw, with Hertford developing from twin fortified 'burhs' either side of the River Lea, built by the Saxons to control territory (Willamson, *op. cit.*). As Williamson points out (although the detail of who owned which area is disputed), Hertfordshire was 'frontier territory'. This may have given rise to a feature of Hertfordshire – the difference between its land holding patterns north-east of this division, as compared with the very different, more dispersed land holdings south-west of this line, corresponding to occupancy by different tribal groups, although the distribution of fertile and less fertile soils (as outlined above) will also have dictated human settlement patterns to some extent across this divide anyway.

At the time of the Norman Conquest, for the first time, we get a much firmer picture of Hertfordshire's landscape through the detail recorded in the Domesday Book. We find a pattern of a thinly-populated south and south-west of the County, compared with a quite densely populated north-east. This is especially evident through the number of swine that were able to be supported by different parishes, itself a measure of the extent of common pasture-woodlands and coppices. North-east Hertfordshire was a landscape of small woodlands interspersed with grasslands and cultivation; while south-west Hertfordshire was dominated in large part by extensive wooded commons on its generally more acidic soils. The far south, around Northaw, was almost uninhabited forest, deriving from a Saxon wood-pasture hunting enclosure apparently originally linked to the massive Enfield Chase hunting forest to the south ('Northaw' stemming from 'North-haga' (a hedged or pallisaded enclosure), as opposed to the 'South-haga' at Southall in Middlesex) (see the discussion of 'hagas' in Muir (2006), chapter 4).

Dury and Andrews map of Northaw, 1766.

Later development of the landscape in Medieval and more recent times is a process of extending and defining these landscapes. A major part of this process was the re-allocation of land following the Norman Conquest. Although native populations would have remained in their lands, large estates were created for the benefit of Norman overlords, such as the de Valoines and de Scales families. Probably the existence of extensive 'wastes' in various places also enabled the establishment of early deer parks (Rowe, 2009), themselves the focus of royal interests because of the proximity of the County to London. These estates, also, tend to have preserved such landscapes, as happened with the extensive Hatfield Estate and at places like Broxbournebury, Knebworth, Berkhamsted, Hertingfordbury and so on. The large land holdings of the Abbey of St Albans during the Middle Ages also tends to have preserved early landscapes, such as at Northaw and around St Albans itself.

Landscape history and the modern flora

The importance of this brief historical overview for understanding the flora is that it puts into perspective the reasons that some vestigial plant communities occur in some places and not in others. We find that we can understand why we have acidic wood-pasture communities around Ashridge because we know not only what its soils are like, but also that it has had a long history of extensive exploitation to fuel a Roman iron-smelting industry, and was subsequently used as extensive wood-pasture common land owing to its poor soils and impoverished state, later enabling it to become part of a major hunting preserve. We now understand more why large tracts of southern Hertfordshire, around Northaw, Cheshunt, North Mymms, Oxhey and Shenley have extensive areas of remaining ancient woodland, derived from wood-pasture forests on always thinly-populated, wet clay soils. In the north-east of the County, on the Boulder Clay, the remaining ancient woodlands, almost always carefully managed coppice-with-standards, often equate with land parcels of at least Saxon date, with probably almost unchanged boundaries, originally established to provide vital fuel and timber to large human populations. Old hedgerow systems, and the old pastures associated with them around places like Bovingdon and Wormley

Northaw Great Wood, Cuffley Camp pollard hornbeams, 1977, a part of the lost Northaw Common, enclosed 1806.

probably date back to Bronze Age or Iron Age times in part, so that their remaining ancient grasslands may well be just as old as the woods. Other areas owe their survival to their incorporation into other Medieval deer parks, or more recent estates, such as the 16th century parklands around the former mansion at Cassiobury, Watford, which have left us Whippendell Wood and the heathy ground that is now the adjacent golf course.

We also have some picture of our natural wetlands. We know that extensive swamp with broad peat beds, existed across most of the County's flood-plains into the Iron Age and probably well beyond. The River Lea was navigable from the sea by moderate-sized boats as far up as Hertford in the days of Saxon Britain, indicating that its natural flow was considerable. As it also formed a major political boundary, its valley was also likely to be pretty impassable for much of its lower reaches because of these swamps. Around the headwaters of the River Ivel at Baldock, we know that there were beavers as late as Roman times, adjacent to the Roman town itself, suggesting a substantial wetland around the spring sources here, which was probably a picture mirrored elsewhere at places like Oughton Head near Hitchin and the sources of the Thame around Tring.

All these factors come together to give us clues as to the survival of our flora over time. We can see that our semi-natural woodlands stem from two quite separate lines of probable continuity. Firstly, ancient woodlands in more intensively managed landscapes are likely to be derived from remnant 'groves' that were important for particular communities as a source of both timber and fuel. Elsewhere, our modern woodlands are more often than not derived from ancient wood-pasture commons, with quite impoverished soils, but with some continuity of tree cover that quite probably dates back to the Iron Age and beyond in many cases.

More importantly, we can begin to understand the much depleted remnants of our natural grasslands and wetlands, which have suffered from not having had proper recognition as the historic features that they are, with ecologically devastating consequences. Our forebears tended to conserve high quality grasslands with great care, especially where these were on good soil. They developed careful management practices designed to maintain soil fertility, based on hay-cropping and aftermath grazing. While this regulated management would have depleted natural herb communities, it did allow a good proportion of the natural flora to thrive, while encouraging others, such as perennial grasses. More natural 'grasslands' remained in our woods as a result of their ongoing management as coppices, or as wood-pastures, and their ride floras are probably the nearest we have to natural herbaceous vegetation in the County. Heath occurred on poor, acidic soils in much of southern Hertfordshire, and on the more acidic clays of the Chilterns dip-slope, as a result of both natural plant communities and the early depletion of soil fertility from human colonisation in the Neolithic era. This was also managed to maintain livestock, and as a source of kindling (Gorse was an important source of this for local communities until the early 20th century). In the north of the County, the Chalk uplands had continued to be managed by a combination of shifting cultivation and sheep grazing for centuries, with the result that a rich downland vegetation had developed, both the flora of chalk grassland, and as a characteristic chalk arable weed flora, the extent of open downland being gleaned from looking at Dury and Andrews map of Hertfordshire (1766), even if its detail is a little shaky. Meanwhile, our river valley swamplands were steadily drained over centuries by ditch construction, even if they were still extensive enough to figure clearly as late as in Bryant's map of Hertfordshire (1822). Hay meadow management developed in many flood-plains, after the swamps were drained, while a few sites are known to have had organised water-meadow systems put in place during the 18th century, which would probably have depleted their natural communities considerably. However, we also retained high quality flood-plain meadow and pasture in many places, and a few localities, such as part of Kings Meads by the Lea at Hertford and Croxley Common Moor in the Colne Valley near Rickmansworth, still show their natural land-forms of abandoned river-course meanders and gravel banks. Others, such as Hunsdon Mead in the Stort Valley, are known to have had more or less uniform management regimes of hay-cropping and grazing for centuries. Even our farmed landscapes had derived their natural plant communities from ancient introductions of crop-related hangers-on, often introduced in Neolithic times, depending on the soil characteristics as well as ongoing, year-by-year soil disturbance for their continued occurrence.

Hunsdon Mead, 1982, an ancient meadow in the Stort Valley.

During the last 200 years or so, however, our landscape has suffered, firstly, from having been exploited massively for the benefit of London and its communication routes (fuel-wood for the city, parks for the gentry, roads, canals, railways); secondly from the direct effects of urbanisation and the impact of intensive land-use (river and ground-water extraction, intensive agriculture and modern timber growing); and most recently from the final loss of traditional land management practices and its having been taken over by leisure activities in many areas. The result is that our natural vegetation has been relegated to remnant patches that have survived through various chances, by neglect, or as the direct effect of having been encompassed by conservation measures. Meanwhile, human impacts mount, with increasing demand for housing, more road building (requiring more gravel extraction), chemical pollution from highways, fertilisers, run-off into rivers and the like. Despite our belated realisation of the impact of these changes, it is in many ways too late to re-instate 'natural' plant communities, especially where soil disturbance has been severe, or where chemical pollution has taken its toll. In any case, our

long-term depletion of natural soil fertility over millennia had already resulted in large areas being relatively impoverished, so a 'natural' vegetation in these areas is something we cannot re-create.

However, natural regeneration of plants continues despite us. Ironically, some of our floristically most diverse habitats are now those derived from severe landscape disturbance, such as around gravel pits, or the wastelands left around derelict factories, disused railways and the like. The dumping of chemical wastes has also turned out fortuitously to be a boon for some species, such as the orchid colonists of power station fly-ash waste in the Lea Valley. The reason that so many of these sites are botanically rich is because, unlike so much of the farmed and urban landscape, they are on nutrient-poor soils. Likewise, some of our more important wetlands are now around the flooded remains of excavations, also low in dissolved nutrients, at least for a while.

Nevertheless, the remains of natural habitats remain across large parts of Hertfordshire. The fundamental land patterns of the County are often very ancient indeed, along with the hedges that survive on them, or the green lanes that thread through them. Spring sources in upland remnant pastures retain natural plant communities despite neglect; while our ancient coppice woodlands often retain important native plant communities, threatened though they may be by neglect of rides, the effects of dumped straw for pheasants, or over-grazing by deer that have no effective modern predators. Heathland remnants hang on round the golf courses constructed in ancient deer parks or on our neglected commons; and wood pasture remnants survive on others. Chalk grassland survives where roadside banks have to be cut for highways purposes, or where public open spaces have been created on old commons or in former parkland.

Knowing where our flora has come from is an important first step in conserving what remains for the future. Recognising the continuity of habitats from the past, and realising that even scraps of grassland might represent vestiges of some historic link with our natural vegetation is an important element in defending what is valuable, and using it as a resource for future conservation.

Deadman's Hill, Sandon, 1977, a surviving fragment of Sandon Heath.

More familiar helleborines – Violet Helleborine Epipactis purpurata *(left), Broad-leaved Helleborine* Epipactis helleborine *(right), see page 471.*

Chapter 5. Hertfordshire's wild plant habitats and their ecology

Pen Hills from Church Hill, Therfield Heath.

We all know what we mean by words like 'meadow', 'wood', 'marsh' or 'downland', but how do we define where a plant grows more precisely? What makes up the 'habitat' in which they actually live? William Graveson, in his fascinating but little-known book *British wild flowers: their haunts and associations* (Graveson, 1917) paints a series of superb vignettes of plant localities at different times of the year, around the British Isles, but focusing on at least some near his home at Hertford at the beginning of the 20th century. He does not name them, but a few are clearly identifiable. One is a common in May, and it actually describes the Roundings, at Hertford Heath:

'It was on one of those early May mornings that we took our way over the fields to a favourite common. Though near a main road along which motor cars and motor cycles race to and from London, it is far removed from the hurry and bustle of the modern world, and its old cottages have about them that air of peace and repose which is especially refreshing in days when the pace of life has been quickened to a rush. South and west are extensive woodlands, and though we know there are intervening pastures and fields, from some view-points the landscape looks one big tract of wood. Oaks are the predominant tree, and there are in these early May days subtle variations in foliage between the olive green of their opening leaves, and the fresher greenery of the trees that are in full leaf. A few Oaks are scattered about the common; and there are thickets of Blackthorn and Hawthorn, and clumps of bush and tree, with dark Hollies and grey Sallows, enlivened with blossoming Crab. The prettiest grouping formed a background to one of the large shallow ponds, where Water Crowfoot made a drift along one of the sides, and gave a snowy centre to its green water grasses, and where a dwarf Willow, and pink Lousewort adorned its edges. Here two Crabs gave life and colour to the background of Hollies and Thorns, one tree covered with fully-open white flowers, the other crowned with unopened buds flushed with pink, as exquisite in colour as anything in the Spring landscape. The great burst of blossom which was ushered in by the Blackthorn

bushes is now at the full... The bushes of Gorse are at their best, except that the fragrance is not so full as when the mid-day sun draws out their richest aroma. Tall clumps of Broom are there as well, and the lowly Genista bedecks the hillocks and more open spaces on the common. Two or three hours of sun have caused the white sheet of the morning frost spread over the ground to disappear, save where the trees and bushes keep his rays away, and the short grass and mosses sparkle in the sunlight before the moisture is all drawn up...

One of the features which impresses us as we stroll leisurely about the common, is the variety of plant life that has gathered around some of the thorn bushes and the hollies. For instance here is a dwarf shrub only some two feet high, yet over it Bramble and Honeysuckle are climbing, and there are a dozen plants that have found shelter beneath it and some of the larger thorns. Anemones are, alas, on the wane, but groups of a score or more retain their welcome starry flowers, and with them are mingled the drooping bells of the Hyacinth. Then there is Wood Sorrel with its exquisitely veined flowers, Stitchwort giving an even prettier setting to the Sloe bushes than their own blossom, Yellow Tormentil with Milkwort and Bedstraw to follow...

Whilst some plants protect themselves by weapons of defence others appear to escape through rendering themselves inconspicuous. There are half a dozen or so of these diminutive plants on the heath. Water Blinks is plentiful. We made its acquaintance at Easter on the south coast; and noted its sleepy look; here on the common it retains the same character. With it is Upright Moenchia, an annual about two inches high, with grass like leaves, and small white flowers open in the sunshine, but locked together in dull weather. Sandspurrey is also somewhat shy of displaying its small pinkish corolla. It has a prostrate habit and is often covered with a viscid down... Procumbent Pearl-wort belongs to the same family as the two previous species. It makes small tufts with very fine leaves, and green sepals with tiny corollas inside; frequently the latter are altogether absent.

The next plant, the Common Bird's-foot, is seen at a glance to be a member of the pea flower family. It has about half a dozen pairs of tiny leaflets on its four inch stem, and tiny creamy flowers touched with red. The seed case is curved, bearing some resemblance to a bird's foot, hence its name. The last of the diminutive plants is seen by the side of the pond, or in the shallow water. This is the Least Marsh-wort. It has small finely-divided leaves, and minute flowers, grouped five or six together in an umbel...

And now having looked at the lowly plants let us return to the shrubs and trees that are making such a bright display. Petty Whin, though it rises less than a foot high, makes a beautiful adornment to the small hillocks and to the banks of some ponds. It is armed with needles which, though more slender than gorse, are equally effective in affording it protection...'

Quite apart from the superb picture it paints of a past

Photo by J. Bowden, with permission from North Hertfordshire Museums Service)

Hertford Heath, Roundings, c.1965.

Hertfordshire landscape and the pleasure of being a part of it, as well as the mentions of several plants that sadly no longer occur at the Roundings (one, Upright Moenchia, apparently extinct in Hertfordshire altogether), this description is specially interesting for a number of reasons. Firstly, it indicates that, from this site, there were extensive views to the south and west, no longer the case because of scrub and tree growth, as succession to woodland across much of the common has progressed. Secondly, it shows that patchy scrub growth was a very obvious feature of the Heath even at the beginning of the last century. However, thirdly, it also shows that the habitat had extensive open areas with 'hillocks' (probably ant hills), where the vegetation was bare enough to support very low-growing plants, and even moss communities.

Hertford Heath, Roundings, 2002, from the same vantage point.

This was evidently a habitat of quite intensive grazing, despite the bushes (his description also elsewhere implies that many of these bushes were 'topiaried' by grazing, reducing them to small rounded clumps, and he mentions donkeys). We may be familiar with this sort of habitat – the patchwork mosaic of a classic grazing common in southern England, now almost a distant memory for most of us. It is a picture of something akin to the New Forest. But what is it from an ecological perspective? Woodland, various sorts of scrub, acidic grassland, heath?

Brian Sawford produced a thoughtful book on the subject of Hertfordshire's wild plant habitats from Graveson's kind of perspective 20 years ago (Sawford, 1989), based in part on the knowledge of the County's flora that Dony (1967) had provided, and partly on the recording effort subsequent to its publication, until 1987. It is a detailed account of the County's botanical landscape at that point in time, with a review of its potential, rather bleak future. This is not the place to repeat the kind of

account that he gave. Nevertheless, to understand and appreciate the relationships between plants, as well as to understand the natural basis of even our much changed landscape, we do need to reflect on what makes up plant communities, and how these relate to the Hertfordshire setting.

A principal issue is the extent to which we really understand the basis of our remaining natural and semi-natural plant communities or recognise them when we see them. While we can see the changes that are apparent from the kind of description William Graveson has given us, and also from the detailed account that Brian Sawford has presented, these approach the 'natural' landscape from the broader perspective. From a more 'scientific' point of view, there have been numerous accounts over the last 100 years, ranging from A. G. Tansley's *The British islands and their vegetation* (1939) through to the multiple volumes of the National Vegetation Classification (Rodwell, 1991-2000). Brian Sawford's account is one based on pragmatic landscape features: woodlands, grasslands, wetlands, arable fields and hedgerows, trackways and road verges, railways, urban habitats and 'waste' land. It is the kind of habitat breakdown that people like Graveson and most other people nowadays would be familiar with and to which we can relate. However, it is not one based on 'ecology', as such, more one based on human land use.

The problem is: we do not really have a very reliable base-line against which we can assess natural 'habitat'. We do not know precisely what 'natural' plant communities in our part of the world actually consisted of before human beings played havoc with them. We can make educated guesses, and we can glean some insight from things like pollen analysis of historic peat deposits and ancient soils, but we can never see what the lowland forests and the open grazed lands in between them were really like, or know in detail what species occurred where. As I have pointed out in the chapter on Hertfordshire's landscape history, even the basis upon which our ecological understanding of the landscape is founded as a whole has shifted recently, through Frans Vera's (2000) seminal work on the relationship between large herbivores and natural forests.

Another problem with the idea of plant 'habitat' is that it depends on the scale at which it is examined. Rodwell's vegetation classification essentially works at the scale of a fairly small land parcel, and was established from multiple 'quadrat' samples, which gave statistically deduced habitat categories. These in turn have been grouped in an overall classification that, while not dissimilar to the general one used by Sawford locally in that it separates woodland from grassland, *etc.*, nevertheless separates out 'grassland' from 'mire', 'aquatic' from 'swamp', 'woodland' from 'scrub' as clearly separable entities. There are also alternative approaches to some of these elsewhere. For example, George Peterken's well-known ancient woodland classification (Peterken, 1993) gives a very different approach to that used by Rodwell, and there are others. The differences lie in the way they approach the relationship of species to the structure (let alone the management history) of their overall habitat. Peterken focuses on the association of 'stand-types' of trees, which are then qualified by proportions and associated ground flora; while Rodwell uses the overall occurrence of all species, regardless of size, includes bryophytes in the analysis, and produces habitat classes based on statistical analysis of plant co-occurrences. While Peterken's stand-types tend to be more immediately approachable from the point of view of human perception of woodland forms, the NVC may be based on more subtle effects of soil type and plant ecology, although in some cases the result can be confusing when seemingly unrelated plant associations get lumped together.

From the point of view of a particular plant, its habitat is essentially governed by its complex requirements for soil type, water availability and quality, shade, support, and overall micro-climatic stability at the time of the year in which it has evolved to appear, as well as the availability of pollinators, the ability to develop effectively from seed and to successfully self-propagate over time. Its survival will depend on success or failure to germinate, competition with other neighbouring plants, drought, flood, ambient temperature, grazing or browsing, pest attack and disease. It will not, overtly, relate to a plant 'community' as such, but the 'community' will occur because a range of similar requirements will be met for its associated plants at any one locality. We may call this 'grassland' or 'woodland', because these similar conditions result in a vegetation structure to which we have given a label. As botanists, we may recognise different 'grassland' types, depending which system of habitat classification we are using, but we may instinctively recognise the more precise conditions and associations within which a particular plant is likely to grow, and this is what experienced botanists might be looking for when they are carrying out flora survey work.

The insight into the overall dynamics of our plant communities which Vera's (2000) analysis of forest ecology and its relationship with the animals that live in it has given us also forces us to think more of plant communities as dynamic entities, within which individual species occur. In some ways, this is not new, because we have long had some understanding of plant succession, following from the early work of people like Sir Edward Salisbury, whose studies of scrub colonisation, *etc.* were initially undertaken in our County (Salisbury, 1918). Studies like this were followed by people like A. S. Watt looking at various habitats, such as his pioneering studies of the detail of vegetation pattern shifts in chalk grassland over time. Vera's picture, though, shows us that not only are there localised shifts in plant communities, or even just that grassland passes through a phase of scrub growth to woodland, but that the whole natural (forest) landscape fluxes over time and that plant associations move around in response to these changes. Essentially, Rodwell's classification allows for this in some way, because it recognises that, for example, certain grassland areas will shift from one classification to another if other parameters, such as grazing or mowing, change. NVC are also mentioned.

Essentially, however, his classification is a means of 'pigeon-holing' a particular patch of habitat to make some sense of its occurrence. It cannot entirely satisfy our need to understand the dynamic environment in which individual plant species might occur. For this reason, standard classifications can only go so far in allowing us to understand the occurrence of particular plants at a particular place. The history of the locality, its management over time, its precise configuration and the impact of other external factors will all have a bearing. For this reason, the accounts of individual plant species in this *Flora* do not make reference to National Vegetation Classification communities.

Hertfordshire's plant habitat associations

Having qualified the value of identifying plant species with specific habitat 'associations', we do need, however, to give some view of which formations occur in our area, if only to take account of current thinking. Unfortunately, there are very few reliable data available based on quadrat studies gathered to identify NVC habitats in Hertfordshire, although there have been surveys carried out using the former Nature Conservancy Council's 'Phase 1' and 'Phase 2' habitat classification systems (*e.g.* Cuming, 1997), which give us some picture of the different broader habitats that survive in the County (see below). This is especially unfortunate, as Dony (1967) pioneered the NVC kind of approach in his series of 109 'Habitat Studies', and considered that the value of these would increase over time, because these habitats would change. Owing to pressures of time, these have not been re-visited systematically during the work for this *Flora*, and a review of his work needs to be undertaken. In the meantime, we can only guess at the relationship between his approach to habitats and those of Rodwell, and how the landscape that he documented compares with the results of the Hertfordshire Habitat Survey detailed by Cuming, or how it would now compare. However, such knowledge of the County's vegetation as we have does allow us to make some assessment of which NVC classes are known to occur locally.

The following is an annotated listing of the National Vegetation Classification community types which, from experience, are known to exist in Hertfordshire. A number of additional types of vegetation which do not so far appear to be accounted for in the

National Vegetation Classification habitats in Hertfordshire

In addition to the standard numbered formations derived from Rodwell (1991-2000) a number of additional vegetation types are listed at the end of each main section, where it is thought their existence needs to be highlighted, and it is not clear where they might fit in the NVC itself. Especially significant vegetation types, making up major parts of the County's 'semi-natural' or naturally occurring vegetation, are indicated with *.

Woodland [Table 1]

W1	Grey Willow *Salix cinerea*/Marsh Bedstraw *Galium palustre* woodland
	This is a fairly frequent scrub formation in semi-natural, ancient woodlands on wet, rather acidic soils in valley bottoms and by streams across southern Hertfordshire, especially around the Broxbourne Woods, such as at Danemead Nature Reserve (30/N).
W2	Grey Willow *Salix cinerea*/Downy Birch *Betula pubescens*/Common Reed *Phragmites australis* woodland.
	Very local in our area, but a feature of the wetlands around the headwaters of the River Hiz and its tributaries at Hitchin, such as Oughton Head Nature Reserve (13/Q). Here it is an outlier of the fen basin carr habitats in East Anglia. The Willow concerned is usually *Salix cinerea* ssp. *cinerea*.

W4	Downy Birch *Betula pubescens*/Purple Moor-grass *Molinia caerulea* woodland.
	A very local habitat type in Hertfordshire, only found as small patches on wet, acidic, heathy sites associated with woodlands, at places like Berrygrove Wood, Aldenham (19/J) and Bricket Wood Common (10/F).
W5	Alder *Alnus glutinosa*/Tussock Sedge *Carex paniculata* woodland.
	Another classic but rather local fen community, associated with river valley spring sources, such as at Willowmead Nature Reserve, Hertford (31/B), Oughton Head Nature Reserve (13/Q), and Folly Alder Swamp, St Ippollitts (12/Y).
W6*	Alder *Alnus glutinosa*/Common Nettle *Urtica dioica* woodland.
	This is frequent along some of Hertfordshire's river valleys, such as parts of the Chess Valley (09/E), and the Mimram around Poplar's Green and Panshanger (21/R, W). If the 'Stingless Nettle' *Urtica dioica* ssp. *galeopsifolia* is recognised as a more naturally occurring fen species/subspecies, then this kind of woodland can be separated into a natural formation on less calcareous peat, occurring mainly over gravels in the middle reaches of the Lea and the Colne valleys, and degraded calcareous fen types with Common Nettle elsewhere, where reduced water tables have caused degradation of W5 communities.
W8*	Ash *Fraxinus excelsior*/Field Maple *Acer campestre*/Dog's Mercury *Mercurialis perennis* woodland (including some Hornbeam *Carpinus betulus* stands).
	The basic Ash/Maple/Hazel woodland type of Peterken's classification fits here, found widely especially in north-east Hertfordshire on the Boulder Clay; *e.g.* Northey Wood (33/W, 43/B), Earl's Wood (33/X); and with its variants on drier, chalky soils, such as at Cross Leys Wood (43/C). It also includes some Hornbeam stand-types of Peterken's classification where these are on more calcareous soils with Dog's Mercury dominant, such as Benington High Wood (22/W).
W10*	Common Oak *Quercus robur*/Bracken *Pteridium aquilinum*/Bramble *Rubus fruticosus* woodland (including Hornbeam *Carpinus betulus*, etc.).
	This is the dominant woodland type across much of central and southern Hertfordshire on more acidic soils, where Hornbeam is a major constituent. The NVC does not distinguish between 'brambles', but in Hertfordshire, many Hornbeam sites are dominated by *Rubus rufescens*, while more acidic stands have other species, such as Rubus insectifolius. This is also, supposedly, where the County's main Bluebell woods are pigeon-holed.
W12*	Beech *Fagus sylvatica*/Dog's Mercury *Mercurialis perennis* woodland.
	This is the semi-natural Beech woodland of the Chilterns chalk ridge, such as at Stubbings Wood (91/A) and Aldbury Nowers (91/L).
W14*	Beech *Fagus sylvatica*/Bramble *Rubus fruticosus* woodland.
	Where the Chilterns Beech woods occur on more acidic Clay-with-Flints dip-slope soils, this becomes the major stand-type. The brambles present can include locally rare, but characteristic species, such as *Rubus pedemontanus*, as at High Scrubs (90/J). As with W10, Bluebell woods are frequent.
W15	Beech *Fagus sylvatica*/Wavy Hair-grass *Deschampsia flexuosa* woodland.
	Apparently a very rare woodland type in our area, this would appear to occur on more acidic, gravelly ground, such as in some stands of Beech on the Chilterns dip-slope near Wigginton (90/J), and in remaining natural parts of Bishop's Wood near Rickmansworth (09/Q).
W16	Oak *Quercus* spp./Birch *Betula* spp./Wavy Hair-grass *Deschampsia flexuosa* woodland.
	Very closely related to W15, this seems to be the natural stand type in a very few more acidic parts of woods on very poor gravels near Oxhey, and in the Northaw area, although it transitions into stands of W10 in most of these.

Scrub types [Table 2]

W21*	Hawthorn *Crataegus monogyna*/Ivy *Hedera helix* scrub (including calcareous variants with Wayfaring-tree *Viburnum lantana*, Dogwood *Swida sanguinea* and Wild Privet *Ligustrum vulgare*, etc.).
	This is an abundant natural seral community across much of the County. Many ordinary hedgerows are effectively this NVC class. The 'lumping' within it of calcareous communities including Wayfaring-tree, *etc.* is not very helpful, as these are clearly very different from the usual formation, which is common on moderately fertile neutral loams. The calcareous 'variants' are local in the County, with especially good examples around Hexton (12/E), where plantations have failed in the past.
W22*	Blackthorn *Prunus spinosa*/Bramble *Rubus fruticosus* scrub.
	This is the damp ground version of W21, and is common on Boulder Clay and London Clay especially, both as scrub and hedgerows. The bramble is often either *Rubus ulmifolius* or *Rubus hindii*.
W23	Gorse *Ulex europaeus*/Bramble *Rubus fruticosus* scrub.
	Formerly an abundant scrub community on places like Berkhamsted and Northchurch Commons, this has now become quite a local scrub community in the County through succession of sites to secondary Oak woodland. It is still a feature of places like Nomansland Common (11/R), and is found as scraps around most other areas of common land on acidic gravels in southern Hertfordshire, often indicating relict wood-pasture sites.

W24*	Bramble *Rubus fruticosus*/Yorkshire-fog *Holcus lanatus* under-scrub.
	Frequent around woodland glades and wood margins on the Clay-with-Flints dip-slope. It has a form that has Creeping Soft-grass *Holcus mollis* as the co-dominant on more acidic gravels, but this is not listed as a NVC community.
W25*	Bracken *Pteridium aquilinum*/Bramble Rubus *fruticosus* underscrub.
	This is also widespread on acidic soils associated with woodland glades and margins in southern and south-western Hertfordshire, extending as far north as Hitch Wood (12/W) and Wain Wood (12/S).

Other types:	Sycamore *Acer pseudoplatanus* woodland;
	English Elm *Ulmus procera* scrub;
	Sweet Chestnut *Castanea sativa* woodland;
	Hazel *Corylus avellana*/Silver Birch *Betula pendula* scrub.
	The first three of these are theoretically 'secondary' woodlands, especially if the idea that English Elm is a Roman introduction is upheld. Sycamore as a dominant woodland type is relatively uncommon, but can occur on both acidic soils (*e.g.* Northaw Great Wood (20/S)) and on calcareous soils (*e.g.:* Earl's Wood (33/X)). English Elm scrub is (or was) widespread in southern Hertfordshire on eutrophic soils around settlements, although affected in many areas by the death of the standing trees. It remains common around Aldenham, *etc.* Sweet Chestnut woodland (often occurring mixed with other stand types) occurs widely on acidic gravels in southern Hertfordshire. Hazel/Birch scrub may be a separable scrub type, which occurs rather rarely on chalk grassland areas, such as Telegraph Hill (12/E) and Therfield Heath (33/J).

Mires [Table 3]

The NVC separates these, to some extent rather unhelpfully, from other aquatic and wetland formations, on the basis of their being herbaceous and sub-shrub communities with permanently high water tables, often forming peat.

M13	Black Bog-rush *Schoenus nigricans*/Blunt-flowered Rush *Juncus subnodulosus* mire (+/- extinct).
	This was only properly known in Hertfordshire from the lost Barkway Moor site, where two of its characteristic plants: Black Bog-rush and Broad-leaved Cotton-grass *Eriophorum latifolium*, were known to occur. However, it does have affinities with a few spring-fed remnant mires in north-east Hertfordshire, notably Biggin Moor (33/R,W) and a mire adjacent to Blagrove Common (33/G), although some of its signature plants are missing. Other similar mire sites at Sandon Moor (33/G), Moor Hall Meadow (32/I) and perhaps Ridlins Mire (22/R) also have some affinity with this habitat.
M22	Blunt-flowered Rush *Juncus subnodulosus*/Marsh Thistle *Cirsium palustre* fen meadow.
	A rather rare, but characteristic plant community in permanently wet habitats associated with spring sources in pasture. It is scattered wherever chalk spring systems occur, but is specially characteristic of Oughton Head Common (13/Q), Purwell Meadow (22/E), Moor Hall Meadow (32/I) and similar wetlands elsewhere, many of which are highly species-rich.
M23*	Soft Rush *Juncus effusus*/Sharp-flowered Rush *Juncus acutiflorus*/Marsh Bedstraw *Galium palustre* rush pasture.
	More widespread than M22, this occurs in a number of places, especially around the Broxbourne Woods in south-east Hertfordshire and the Knebworth Woods area, such as Burleigh Meadow (22/G), and the northern end of Knebworth Park (22/F).
M24	Purple Moor-grass *Molinia caerulea*/Meadow Thistle *Cirsium dissectum* fen meadow.
	As with M13, this is only now found as impoverished forms in some localities where Purple Moor-grass survives, lacking at least Meadow Thistle, which is now extinct in the County. It was formerly a feature of Croxley Common Moor (09/X), and boggy sites in south-east Hertfordshire, including Hertford Heath (31/K), where stands of *Molinia* remain.
M27*	Meadowsweet *Filipendula ulmaria*/Wild Angelica *Angelica sylvestris* mire.
	This is a major feature of river valley wetlands, especially the Stort Valley and around Hitchin, but also in west Hertfordshire, wherever the water sources are calcareous. It can also occur as a ride flora in wet woodland, such as Marshland Wood (41/H).
M36	Lowland springs and streambanks of shaded situations.
	Rather an unsatisfactory NVC class, this includes spring-source vegetation with Opposite-leaved Golden-saxifrage *Chrysosplenium oppositifolium* and Wavy Bitter-cress *Cardamine flexuosa*, *etc.* in woodlands, rare in Hertfordshire, occurring mostly in the north-east of the County, such as at Hebing End, Benington (32/B) and Trenchern Hills, Little Munden (32/K). It could also include the characteristic stream-side vegetation in parts of Wormley Wood (30/C, I) and similar sites in the south-east of the County, although the former are more calcareous.

Other types:	Bulbous Rush *Juncus bulbosus*/Lesser Spearwort *Ranunculus flammula* flushes;
	Great Horsetail *Equisetum telmateia* mire;
	Hard Rush *Juncus inflexus*/Lesser Pond-sedge *Carex acutiformis* mire.
	The first of these is rare, but quite distinctive in more acidic wetlands around ponds and seepages in the south of the County, especially in the Broxbourne Woods area and parts of Northaw Great Wood (20/X). Great Horsetail mires are also a special feature of permanently wet seepages in woodlands in this part of the County (and a version of it occurs as a colonising vegetation on gravel pit silt beds where these are near woodlands). Mixed mires in flood-plain pastures and former hay meadows in many areas also support Hard Rush/Lesser Pond-sedge vegetation, which is a transitional wetland type between S7 (below) and the Hard Rush variant of M10 (below). It is widespread in places like Kings Meads, Panshanger, the Stort Valley meadows, and the Ver Valley near Sopwell, *etc.*

Heaths [Table 4]

As most of Hertfordshire's heathlands vanished during the 18th and early 19th centuries, it is difficult to know exactly what most of them were like when they were still grazed. The two vegetation types listed here are the last vestiges. The evidence for the former existence of any wet heath NVC community based on Cross-leaved Heath *Erica tetralix* in Hertfordshire is very slim.

H1	Heather *Calluna vulgaris*/Sheep's Fescue *Festuca ovina* heath.
	This is the most frequent lowland heath formation, and is evidently the main heathland habitat in Hertfordshire, especially on drier gravels and sands, in places like Berkhamsted Common (00/E), Chorleywood Common and Gustard Wood Common (11/X, S).
H2	Heather *Calluna vulgaris*/Dwarf Gorse *Ulex minor* heath.
	The only places where this was ever known to have occurred in Hertfordshire were Nomansland Common (11/R) and possibly Rowley Green (29/D), although quite how it really differs from H1 is unclear, except for the occurrence of Dwarf Gorse.

Grasslands [Table 5]

1. Neutral grasslands

MG1*	False Oat *Arrhenatherum elatius* grassland (including 'variants' of different herbaceous vegetation: calcareous Greater Knapweed *Centaurea scabiosa* grasslands; Rosebay Willowherb *Chamerion angustifolium* stands; Barren Brome *Anisantha sterilis*/Garlick Mustard *Alliaria petiolata* stands on disturbed ground; Common Nettle *Urtica dioica*/mixed umbellifer road verge communities; Mugwort *Artemisia vulgaris* ruderal grasslands; Great Willowherb *Epilobium hirsutum* damp grassland; a Meadowsweet *Filipendula ulmaria* variant; a calcareous Wild Parsnip *Pastinaca sativa* variant; the Common Knapweed *Centaurea nigra* variant; and a Burnet Saxifrage *Pimpinella saxifraga* variant).
	Normal False Oat grassland forms the basis of most rough calcareous grasslands across the County, on road verges, railway banks and the like. It is generally quite species-poor, and of low conservation value. Unfortunately, the NVC has 'lumped' a range of other grassland types with it, to the extent that it has become a rag-bag, including more species-rich, unimproved grasslands such as the Greater Knapweed or Burnet Saxifrage types found on old roadsides on the Chalk, and a form of Meadowsweet grassland characteristic of ancient hedgerows on the Boulder Clay, as well as ruderal vegetation dominated by Barren Brome or Mugwort, which are common vegetation types around disturbed sites, or by roads.
MG5*	Crested Dog's-tail *Cynosurus cristatus*/Common Knapweed *Centaurea nigra* grassland (another rag-bag, with variants: Meadow Vetchling *Lathyrus pratensis*; Lady's Bedstraw *Galium verum*; Heath-grass *Danthonia decumbens*/Upright Tormentil *Potentilla erecta*).
	The principal form is the characteristic unimproved grassland of old pastures across much of Hertfordshire, now sadly depleted. However, the NVC has again lumped various other grassland types with the normal form, and especially the more acidic Heath-grass habitat, which is rare in the County, found at very few sites, *e.g.* Brickendon Green (30/I).
MG6*	Rye-grass *Lolium perenne*/Crested Dog's-tail *Cynosurus cristatus* grassland (including variants: Meadow Foxtail *Alopecurus pratensis*; Marsh Foxtail *Alopecurus geniculatus*; and Tufted Hair-grass *Deschampsia cespitosa*).
	These are essentially semi-improved grasslands of only moderate conservation value, and occur widely in semi-derelict areas in former hay meadow/cattle-rearing landscape, especially in south Hertfordshire.
MG7*	Rye-grass *Lolium perenne* leys, *etc.*
	Scarcely worth including as a 'natural' vegetation type, these are essentially improved (often sown) grasslands, and occur widely on most soil types except the most acidic, calcareous or wet.
MG8	Crested Dog's-tail *Cynosurus cristatus*/Marsh Marigold *Caltha palustris* grassland.
	This is a rare alluvial flood-plain grassland in our area, now almost absent. It was once a feature of parts of the Beane Valley north of Hertford, and at places like Blackhorse Farm Meadow near Baldock (23/M). Remnants survive elsewhere, often derelict.

MG9*	Yorkshire-fog *Holcus lanatus*/Tufted Hair-grass *Deschampsia cespitosa* grasslands (with variants: Rough Meadow-grass *Poa trivialis*; and False Oat *Arrhenatherum elatius*).
	The basic Yorkshire-fog/Tufted Hair-grass type is fairly widely scattered across southern Hertfordshire on neutral to somewhat acidic clays and poorly-drained valley bottom sites, but is now often derelict where it occurs. It is essentially a semi-improved grassland type.
MG10*	Yorkshire-fog *Holcus lanatus*/Soft Rush *Juncus effusus* pasture (including variants: Hard Rush *Juncus inflexus*; and Yellow-flag *Iris pseudacorus*).
	It is also rather unfortunate that the NVC has lumped these wet grassland types together here, and separated them from related mire communities elsewhere in the classification. The nominal Yorkshire-fog/Soft Rush form is typical of many unimproved wet woodland rides and clearings across the south and centre of the County, and occasionally occurs in old pastures nearby. However, the Hard Rush form is typical of semi-improved wet grasslands on various soils (including colonising sites round old gravel pits), while the Yellow Flag variant is local, and found mostly in places where over-grazing by horses has occurred in old alluvial pasture, such as at Valley Farm, Sarratt (09/J). Thus species-poor semi-improved wet grasslands have been lumped in the classification with potentially important unimproved wet grasslands elsewhere.
MG13*	Creeping Bent *Agrostis stolonifera*/Marsh Foxtail *Alopecurus geniculatus* grassland.
	Essentially a semi-improved grassland on neutral to mildly calcareous damp soils, it is found fairly widely in Hertfordshire's river valleys.

Other types:	A more acidic grassland type similar to MG13 but with Velvet Bent *Agrostis canina* occurs in similar situations, usually less improved, on acidic clays in the south of the County, often in woodland rides and clearings, but does not appear to feature as a NVC class.

2. Calcareous grasslands

CG2	Sheep's Fescue *Festuca ovina*/Meadow Oat *Helictotrichon pratense* grassland (with several variants).
	This is the main type of chalk grassland in the County, on steeper grazed downland slopes especially, and in rabbit-grazed grassland round old chalk pits, although now increasingly uncommon.
CG3*	Upright Brome *Bromopsis erecta* grassland (with variants).
	This is the chalk grassland type typical of rather neglected ancient chalk grassland, and is frequent where grazing has ceased, such as large parts of Therfield Heath (33/J, 34/F, K).
CG5	Upright Brome *Bromopsis erecta*/Tor-grass *Brachypodium rupestre* grassland.
	Strictly speaking, this should involve Heath False-brome *Brachypodium pinnatum*, but the separation of two species here has caused problems of NVC habitat definition. Tor-grass occurs rarely in calcareous grassland in Hertfordshire *e.g.* part of Therfield Heath; while Heath False-brome is also rare, but forms a definite grassland type in damper, often semi-shaded locations on mildly acidic to mildly calcareous clays, *e.g.* Fir and Pond Woods meadow (20/Q). It is unclear if both of these fall within CG5.
CG6	Downy Oat *Helictotrichon pubescens* grassland.
	A rare grassland type now in Hertfordshire, occurring where unimproved calcareous hay meadow vegetation persists, such as around Letchworth Golf Course (23/A).
CG7*	Sheep's Fescue *Festuca ovina*/Mouse-ear Hawkweed *Pilosella officinalis*/Thyme *Thymus* spp. grassland (rather a rag-bag, with variants: Crested Hair-grass *Koeleria macrantha*; Wild Strawberry *Fragaria vesca*/Blue Fleabane *Erigeron acer*; Black Medick *Medicago lupulina*/Sorrel *Rumex acetosa*).
	As with other grassland types in the NVC, it is unfortunate that so many different types of grassland have been lumped together. The main form of CG7 is sometimes found on calcareous banks on gravelly as well as chalky sites, by roads and tracks, or around old mineral workings, although now rarely having all the signature species. The Crested Hair-grass variant is a rare ancient grassland type of similar places on thin, friable soils over Chalk, such as at Wilbury Hill (23/B) and mixed with other chalk grassland types on sites like Therfield Heath. Meanwhile the Wild Strawberry/Blue Fleabane variant appears to relate to often colonising vegetation associated with bare, calcareous gravels around old mineral sites, disturbed roadside banks and so on; and the Black Medick variant is the kind of grassland we might (rarely) find on heavily rabbit-grazed calcareous banks by arable fields on Boulder Clay. It is unclear how these really relate to each other, other than being on calcareous soils subject to disturbance, and sometimes with heavy grazing pressure.

U1*	Sheep's Fescue *Festuca ovina*/Common Bent *Agrostis capillaris*/Sheep's Sorrel *Rumex acetosella* grassland (a rag-bag, with variants: Common Stork's-bill *Erodium cicutarium* [and Shepherd's-cress *Teesdalia nudicaulis*]; Sweet Vernal-grass *Anthoxanthum odoratum*/Bird's-foot Trefoil *Lotus corniculatus*; Heath Bedstraw *Galium saxatile*/Upright Tormentil *Potentilla erecta*; and Common Cat's-ear *Hypochoeris radicata*).
	Again, this is an unsatisfactory rag-bag of different grassland types. The basic Sheep's Fescue/Common Bent grassland is uncommon in the County, usually now only on old commons, where it can form mosaics with H1 Heather/Sheep's Fescue heath. The Common Stork's-bill variant is an odd assemblage that may have been a feature of Colney Heath (21/C), where most of its constituents once occurred together (including Shepherd's-cress, now extinct in the County), although Common Stork's-bill in our area is more usually associated with colonising vegetation in somewhat calcareous gravel and sand pits. The Sweet Vernal-grass/Bird's-foot Trefoil variant occurs rather rarely now on Clay-with-Flints soils especially in west Herts., such as near Wigginton; while the Heath Bedstraw/Upright Tormentil variant is the main remnant acid grassland form in south Hertfordshire on London Clay and associated gravels. Finally, the Common Cat's-ear variant appears to be the rather degraded acidic grassland characteristic of over-mown churchyards and roadside banks on acidic soils generally, also increasingly uncommon, and often lacking Sheep's Fescue altogether.
U2	Wavy Hair-grass *Deschampsia flexuosa* grassland.
	A rare grassland type in Hertfordshire on its own (but rather uncertainly distinguished from woodland types where this grass can form extensive patches, such as in W15 and W16 stand types). It occurs sparsely on some acidic grass commons, such as at Patmore Heath (42/M) and remnants of Codicote Heath (21/E).
U20*	Bracken *Pteridium aquilinum*/Heath Bedstraw *Galium saxatile* community.
	In and around former wood-pasture woodlands in southern Hertfordshire, this can form extensive patches, mixed with W25 underscrub, which is scarcely differentiated from it.

Other types:	A lowland version of U5 Mat-grass *Nardus stricta*/Heath Bedstraw *Galium saxatile* grass heath.
	Brown Bent *Agrostis vinealis*/Sheep's Fescue *Festuca ovina* grassland.
	The former occurs most obviously now on Hadley Common (29/N), where it forms extensive patches, but also once occurred at Hertford Heath and other sites. The NVC does not account for a lowland form of Mat-grass heath. Brown Bent/Sheep's Fescue grassland is a very typical grassland type on more acidic, but freely-drained, gravelly sites over Clay-with-Flints in the Ashridge area (00/E, 91/Q, V) and elsewhere, mainly in west Hertfordshire. It is evidently related to some forms of the rag-bag U1 community.

Aquatic communities [Table 6]

The distinction between some of these communities leaves much to be desired, as many are based on single species occurrences, while some other fairly distinctive forms appear to have been relegated as 'variants'.

A1	Fat Duckweed *Lemna gibba* community.
	Supposed to be frequent in south-eastern England, the occurrence of Fat Duckweed is sparse in Hertfordshire, where it occurs mainly in the more calcareous, eutrophic waters of the east of the County. How this community really differs from A2 is unclear, other than having a different *Lemna* species present.
A2*	Common Duckweed *Lemna minor* community.
	A widespread and familiar plant community on more or less enriched standing waters in most places. The 'variant' dominated by the bryophyte *Riccia fluitans* occurs in more oligotrophic pools associated especially with the Broxbourne Woods.
A3	Greater Duckweed *Spirodela polyrhiza*/Frogbit *Hydrocharis morsus-ranae* community.
	This plant community, if it exists now at all in Hertfordshire, is a rare community in the lower sections of the Lea Valley, where Frogbit still occurs rarely around gravel pits. Greater Duckweed itself has a broader distribution, especially in ponds on rather more acidic soils.
A5*	Rigid Hornwort *Ceratophyllum demersum* community.
	This is a major submerged aquatic vegetation type in moderately eutrophic, less acidic and often somewhat shaded waters across much of the County.
A7	White Water-lily *Nymphaea alba* community.
	The NVC category for this includes a species-poor variant, often of planted origin, which is the characteristic form in standing waters in Hertfordshire. It scarcely merits a vegetation classification type, although a natural form might remain in some lower course river backwaters, where these are less eutrophic.

A8*	Yellow Water-lily *Nuphar lutea* community.
	The NVC describes this as both a standing and slow-moving water formation, but in Hertfordshire it is usually found in slow-flowing rivers in their lower courses, where water is eutrophic but not polluted, such as the old course of the River Lea by Amwell Quarry (31/R). It includes various pondweed *Potamogeton* species, where these remain, and a variant with frequent Common Water-starwort *Callitriche stagnalis* and Horned Pondweed *Zannichellia palustris* is also described.
A9*	Floating Pondweed *Potamogeton natans* community.
	This forms a frequent community in mesotrophic ponds across much of the County, with a variant containing Bulbous Rush *Juncus bulbosus* found in more acidic ponds in the Broxbourne Woods area, for example. A variant based on Canadian Pondweed *Elodea canadensis* seems to be only marginally different from A15 (below), and is frequent.
A10*	Amphibious Bistort *Persicaria amphibia* community.
	This is a frequent plant community around the margins of gravel pit and other lakes, and in ditches with standing water on less calcareous substrates, especially in southern Hertfordshire.
A11	Fennel Pondweed *Potamogeton pectinatus*/Spiked Water-milfoil *Myriophyllum spicatum* community.
	At one time a major feature of the Grand Union Canal system, and formerly also in some rivers, this is now limited to old gravel pits and reservoirs that retain high quality calcareous water supplies, such as Amwell Quarry Nature Reserve (31/R), although it tends to move towards the A15 community (but with *Elodea nuttallii*) as nutrient levels increase.
A12*	Fennel Pondweed *Potamogeton pectinatus* community.
	Essentially a species-poor version of A11, this is the remnant vegetation in heavily eutrophic and disturbed waterways, such as the Grand Union Canal and lower reaches of some rivers.
A14	Alternate Water-milfoil *Myriophyllum alterniflorum* community.
	Probably always very local in Hertfordshire, this occurs rarely in acidic pools on heaths, such as at Batchworth Heath (09/R).
A15*	Canadian Pondweed *Elodea canadensis* community.
	Essentially similar to the A9 community but often lacking Floating Pondweed, this is now common in smaller eutrophic ponds across the County, although its relative Nuttall's Pondweed *Elodea nuttallii* appears to replace it in larger water bodies.
A16*	Common Water-starwort *Callitriche stagnalis* community.
	Unfortunately rather a rag-bag of a plant community, because the NVC has lumped *C. obtusangula*, *C.brutia [= hamulata]* and *C. platycarpa* with *C. stagnalis*, and has also not distinguished between plant communities in flowing rivers and still water. For example *C. obtusangula* occurs in calcareous streams and *C. brutia* ssp. *hamulata* usually in more oligotrophic pools.
A17*	Stream Water-crowfoot *Ranunculus penicillatus* ssp. *pseudofluitans* community.
	A major feature of the upper courses of most of Hertfordshire's rivers, where the water supply is calcareous and relatively nutrient-poor over gravels.
A18	River Water-crowfoot *Ranunculus fluitans* community.
	It is not really known if the lower reaches of the Lea and Colne might still hold this community, as the species has only relatively recently been recognised in Hertfordshire's rivers, and there has not been any recent sampling.
A19	Common Water-crowfoot *Ranunculus aquatilis* community.
	This is mostly a rather local community associated with calcareous, unpolluted pools and ditches in grazing pastures on clay soils in our area.
A20	Pond Water-crowfoot *Ranunculus peltatus* community.
	Mostly limited to open ponds on less calcareous soils, this occurs scattered mainly across southern Hertfordshire, rarely in shallow rivers over gravel, such as the River Ver near Redbourn (11/A).
A24	Bulbous Rush *Juncus bulbosus* community.
	As an aquatic vegetation, this is rare in the County, in acidic pools in the south of the County, such as the pond in Berrygove Wood, Aldenham (19/J). The NVC lumps with it a 'variant' based on Bladderwort *Utricularia* species in general, which is not helpful, as different *Utricularia* species grow in different kinds of standing waters. All are rare in Hertfordshire.

Other types:	A distinctive vegetation type based on Unbranched Bur-reed *Sparganium emersum* is common in southern Hertfordshire rivers, occasionally associated with River Water-dropwort *Oenanthe fluviatilis*, but does not seem to relate to vegetation types in the NVC, unless as a variant of the A8 *Nuphar lutea* community. A Whorled Water-milfoil *Myriophyllum verticillatum* community (which could perhaps be linked with Fan-leaved Water-crowfoot *Ranunculus circinatus*) is rare, but occurs distinctively in some standing waters with highly calcareous spring sources, such as Wilstone Reservoir (91/B), or in bare gravel pits. The NVC also seems to relate rather poorly to the various communities of mixed broad-leaved pondweed *Potamogeton* species that used to be a major feature of some mid-course Hertfordshire rivers, such as the Stort, but which have suffered severe declines. In addition, various introduced aquatic plants occur widely, such as Curly Waterweed *Lagarosiphon major* and Water Fern *Azolla filiculoides*, but how much they can be classed as distinctive 'plant communities' is a moot point.

Swamps and tall-herb fens [Table 7]

As mentioned earlier, these are separated in the NVC from mire communities, into which they often grade. They also include water margin communities that relate to a greater or lesser extent to aquatic habitats.

S3	Tussock Sedge *Carex paniculata* sedge-swamp.
	This is a local, but distinctive vegetation type associated with calcareous spring sources or sometimes beside rivers where ground-water is upwelling. It is found at places with important fen habitats generally, such as Oughton Head Nature Reserve (13/Q), and Stanborough Reed-marsh (21/F) (forming a marginal vegetation around the Reed swamp).
S4*	Common Reed *Phragmites australis* swamp.
	A natural community in deep, calcareous water adjoining some larger rivers, and sometimes a sign of upwelling ground-water, but also the result of impeded drainage on flood plains elsewhere, such as at Stanborough Reedmarsh (21/F), Marsworth Reservoir (91/B) and Maple Lodge (09/G). It is also now being deliberately encouraged in old gravel pit sites. Natural stands tend to have a richer associated flora (but see community S25).
S5*	Reed Sweet-grass *Glyceria maxima* swamp.
	This forms a characteristic species-poor swamp vegetation in shallow, heavily eutrophic water, frequent in flood plains across the County, wherever grazing is reduced.
S6*	Greater Pond-sedge *Carex riparia* swamp.
	A frequent vegetation type alongside larger rivers where natural banks have been retained, as well as colonising the margins of some gravel pits, also sometimes forming stands in silted ponds.
S7*	Lesser Pond-sedge *Carex acutiformis* swamp.
	The most frequent kind of sedge swamp in the County, found in more or less calcareous conditions adjacent to both standing and flowing water, ofen forming a band of swamp vegetation in shallower water behind stands of *Carex riparia*.
S8	Common Club-rush *Schoenoplectus lacustris* swamp.
	A fairly frequent component of river vegetation, where it forms sometimes dense stands, but also occurring occasionally in swamps along the margins of lakes and reservoirs.
S10	Water Horsetail *Equisetum fluviatile* swamp.
	A rather local swamp type, occurring usually with other vegetation, in shallow, open water in pools, sometimes old flooded gravel pits.
S12*	Common Reed-mace *Typha latifolia* swamp.
	A common vegetation type floating on silted pools and in ditches, where the water is less calcareous and more eutrophic.
S13	Lesser Reed-mace *Typha angustifolia* swamp.
	A rather rare vegetation type, occurring as discrete stands by some less eutrophic water bodies, with calcareous water supplies, such as Wilstone Reservoir (91/B).
S14*	Branched Bur-reed *Sparganium erectum* swamp.
	A frequent vegetation type in deeper water of moderately eutrophic ponds, and on silted shoals in shallow rivers and streams.
S16	Arrowhead *Sagittaria sagittifolia* swamp.
	A local emergent swamp vegetation found on deep silts in shallow to moderately deep rivers where the current is slow. It could almost be classed as related to the aquatic A8 vegetation.
S18	False Fox-sedge *Carex otrubae* swamp.
	The extent to which this forms a separable, distinctive vegetation is doubtful. Stands matching its description in the NVC occur fairly frequently in ditches and very wet rides associated with old woodlands in a number of places but could equally be classed as a form of rush-pasture mire.
S19*	Common Spike-rush *Eleocharis palustris* swamp.
	A frequent and distinctive vegetation type along the margins of ponds and in ditches, often in grazed sites.

S20	Grey Club-rush *Schoenoplectus tabernaemontani* swamp.
	This has appeared as dominant stands colonising pools in back-filled gravel pit habitat at Moor Mill (10/L). It is usually a coastal vegetation type.
S22*	Flote-grass *Glyceria fluitans* water-margin vegetation.
	A distinctive vegetation around the margins of muddy ponds and in cart rut pools.
S23*	Other water-margin vegetation.
	A very unsatisfactory rag-bag of 'vegetation', essentially accounting for all the otherwise unlisted water margin species that do not feature in the named communities, such as Brooklime *Veronica beccabunga*, Water Mint *Mentha aquatica, etc.*
S25*	Common Reed *Phragmites australis*/Hemp Agrimony *Eupatorium cannabinum* tall herb fen.
	This is evidently constructed as a need to account for Common Reed habitats of calcareous fen in East Anglia, as distinct from Reed beds. The distinction is rather uncertain, except that many of the latter are species-poor, while natural Reed-fen is species-rich, in which Common Reed is not so dominant. In Hertfordshire, it occurs essentially where calcareous water supplies create the right environment in natural peatlands, such as the fen communities at Purwell (22/E) and Oughton Head (13/Q) near Hitchin, and some of the swamps in the upper Stort Valley (41/Y, Z).
S26*	Common Reed *Phragmites australis*/Common Nettle *Urtica dioica* fen.
	Essentially the open ground version of the Alder/Nettle woodland W6, this occurs widely in wetlands adjoining old flooded gravel pits and river margins, ditches, *etc.* in many alluvial flood-plain environments in the County, especially around the Colne Valley gravel pits, and parts of the Lee Valley Park gravel pits at Cheshunt and Wormley. As remarked in relation to the W6 stand type, if the 'Stingless Nettle' *Urtica dioica* ssp. *galeopsifolia* is regarded as a distinct taxon, this vegetation type might be regarded as a more genuine natural fen community in some areas, such as old wetlands at Panshanger (21/W) and around Amwell (31/R). The Great Willowherb *Epilobium hirsutum* variant is the most widespread form.
S28*	Reed Canary-grass *Phalaris arundinacea* swamp.
	This is a frequent swamp type along rivers, in ditches, and in neglected areas on wet ground elsewhere, usually in non-calcareous sites.

Other types:	A common vegetation type in neglected ditches and streams, as well as old cress beds, is that of dominant stands of Water-cress *Rorippa nasturtium-aquaticum*, sometimes mixed with another swamp species, Fool's Water-cress *Apium nodiflorum*. Narrow-fruited Water-cress *Rorippa microphylla* often replaces it in shallow streams and around seepages, but essentially also behaves as a dominant vegetation type in such places. None of these seem to be adequately accounted for in the NVC. Swamp stands of Great Horsetail *Equisetum telmateia* also exist, both in natural situations, and as a colonising vegetation type on gravel pit silt-beds. A rare, but characteristic water margin vegetation dominated by Red Goosefoot *Chenopodium rubrum*, alongside Marsh Cudweed *Gnaphalium uliginosum*, and with rare species such as Orange Foxtail *Alopecurus aequalis* and Shoreweed *Limosella aquatica* occurs at Wilstone Reservoir (91/B), and with similar, less species-rich variants rarely elsewhere on exposed mud (which may relate in part at least to communities listed below as OV29, OV31, *etc.*).

Salt-marsh communities [Table 8]

Unlikely though this may seem, the County now has at least one distinctive salt-marsh community associated with salted roads and motorway soakages. It perhaps ought to be included under 'Disturbed ground' habitats (below), but is distinctive enough to be worth highlighting.

SM23	Sea Spurrey *Spergularia maritima*/Reflexed Saltmarsh-grass *Puccinellia distans* community.
	This is now often dominant alongside main roads in the County, although such stands could also be attributed to SM27 Ephemeral salt-marsh vegetation with Sea Spurrey *S. maritima*.

Other types:	The NVC only mentions Danish Scurvy-grass *Cochlearia danica* in conjunction with SM27 vegetation types, although it can also dominate road verges as a result of road salting, often on its own.

Maritime cliff communities [Table 9]

As with salt-marsh communities, so Hertfordshire also now has one vegetation type typical of maritime cliffs, as a result of road salting.

MC10	Red Fescue *Festuca rubra*/plantain *Plantago* spp. maritime grassland.
	A sometimes dense, low vegetation dominated by Buck's-horn Plantain, alongside other salt-tolerant plants is characteristic of many roadsides, especially round towns, such as Stevenage. It is not completely comparable with natural maritime grasslands, in that it also may have Sea Spurrey *Spergularia maritima* and Danish Scurvy-grass *Cochlearia danica* associated with it in places. Sea Plantain *Plantago maritima* and Thrift *Armeria maritima* have been recorded in this vegetation type in the County.

Disturbed ground [Table 10]

Unfortunately the NVC inadequately deals with the very heterogeneous vegetation types that result from disturbed ground, while also including some of these under more 'natural' vegetation classes.

Communities OV1-OV18 are basically plant communities of arable fields or other cultivated soils. The extent to which some of the arable weed groupings are clear-cut, differentiated communities has to be questioned, while several other communities, such as the distinctive chalk arable weed flora involving Dwarf Spurge *Euphorbia exigua* and the chalk species of fumitory *Fumaria, etc.*, are missing altogether.

The rest of this group are mostly various weed communities of disturbed ground as such, although the level of disturbance is very varied, and a few probably ought to be included elsewhere in the classification altogether. I have separated out a group at the end that are specific to built structures.

Missing from this sequence are a whole suite of vegetation types of gravel pits, waste tips, railway track-sides and the like, some of which, such as the Buddleia *Buddleja davidii*/Goat Willow *Salix caprea*/Silver Birch *Betula pendula* vegetation, with variants, so abundant on rubble or track-beds, are extremely common, although their interpretation is often difficult.

1. Arable weeds

OV1	Field Pansy *Viola arvensis*/Slender Parsley-piert *Aphanes australis* community.
	Uncommon, on sandy, gravelly field margins.
OV3*	Common Poppy *Papaver rhoeas*/Field Pansy *Viola arvensis* community.
	Widespread.
OV7*	Common Field-speedwell *Veronica persica*/Grey Field-speedwell *Veronica polita* community.
	Widespread especially round root crops.
OV8*	Common Field-speedwell *Veronica persica*/Black-grass *Alopecurus myosuroides* community.
	Widespread.
OV9*	Scentless Mayweed *Tripleurospermum inodorum*/Chickweed *Stellaria media* community.
	Widespread on enriched soils.
OV10*	Annual Meadow-grass *Poa annua*/Groundsel *Senecio vulgaris* community.
	This is a common garden weed community, as well as in fields.
OV13*	Chickweed *Stellaria media*/Shepherd's-purse *Capsella bursa-pastoris* community.
	This is particularly a rag-bag, containing also Common Fumitory *Fumaria officinalis* communities.
OV14	Small Nettle *Urtica urens*/Henbit Dead-nettle *Lamium amplexicaule* community.
	A community of manured, gravelly areas of non-calcareous soils.
OV15*	Scarlet Pimpernel *Anagallis arvensis*/Common Field-speedwell *Veronica persica* community.
	A rag-bag community of arable crops. Includes communities with abundant Field Convolvulus *Convolvulus arvensis*, as well as the very localised Venus's-looking-glass *Legousia hybrida*/Small Toadflax *Chaenorhinum minus* and the Fluellen *Kickxia* spp. communities typical of chalk arable margins.
OV16	Red Poppy *Papaver rhoeas*/Night-flowering Catchfly *Silene noctiflora* community.
	The extent to which this now exists needs to be questioned, as *Silene noctiflora* no longer really occurs as an arable weed. However, the rest of the community does, although how it differs from OV3 as a result is doubtful.
OV18*	Knotweed *Polygonum aviculare*/Pineapple-weed *Matricaria discoidea* community.
	This is a community of disturbed ground and paths. The *Polygonum* involved may also be Equal-leaved Knotweed *P. arenastrum* in such places.

2. Ruderal weeds (including disturbed wetland habitats)

OV19*	Annual Meadow-grass *Poa annua*/Scentless Mayweed *Tripleurospermum inodorum* community.
	This is also a plant community of waste ground. It is common by tracks and roads.
OV20*	Annual Meadow-grass *Poa annua*/Procumbent Pearlwort *Sagina procumbens* community.
	The weeds of paving and garden paths.
OV21*	Annual Meadow-grass *Poa annua*/Great Plantain *Plantago major* community.
	A common plant community of trodden paths.
OV22*	Annual Meadow-grass *Poa annua*/Dandelion *Taraxacum officinale* agg. community.
	The classic ruderal community beside roads and disturbed margins of tracks.
OV23*	Rye-grass *Lolium perenne*/Cocksfoot *Dactylis glomerata* communities.
	This is a ragbag, including various secondary grasslands, very frequent on road verges, and which ought to have been included with the mesotrophic grasslands.

OV24*	Common Nettle *Urtica dioica*/Goosegrass *Galium aparine* community.
	Probably now one of the most abundant plant communities in the County, by roads, field margins, waste ground and so on. How the False Oat *Arrhenatherum elatius*/Bramble *Rubus fruticosus* variant differs from parts of MG1 is difficult to tell.
OV25*	Common Nettle *Urtica dioica*/Creeping Thistle *Cirsium arvense* community.
	An all-too-abundant vegetation type in weedy pastures and rough grasslands.
OV26*	Great Willowherb *Epilobium hirsutum* community.
	This is essentially the same as some forms of MG1 and S26, from which it is scarcely distinguishable, occurring by ditches and in disturbed wet areas.
OV27*	Rosebay Willowherb *Chamerion angustifolium* community.
	As with OV26, partly this is essentially the same habitat type as a variant of MG1, and occurs in disturbed places associated with scrub or on waste ground. Some of its supposed variants could relate to the missing Buddleia community mentioned above and other vegetation types in similar places.
OV28*	Creeping Bent *Agrostis stolonifera*/Creeping Buttercup *Ranunculus repens* community.
	This probably ought to be included with the 'swamp' vegetation types, as it has much in common with S23 at least, and its Water-pepper *Persicaria hydropiper* variant, found here on wet paths, is essentially the same as that which grows round ponds. The basic vegetation type is common in damp secondary grassland in seasonally flooded hollows.
OV29	Marsh Foxtail *Alopecurus geniculatus*/Marsh Yellow-cress *Rorippa palustris* community.
	Another water margin community that ought to be included under 'Swamps'. It is a frequent water margin vegetation on open, colonising silts and mud.
OV30	Trifid Bur-marigold *Bidens tripartita*/Amphibious Bistort *Persicaria amphibia* community.
	A frequent community around drying ponds. Should be listed under the 'Swamps', alongside S23.
OV31*	Marsh Yellow-cress *Rorippa palustris*/Marsh Cudweed *Gnaphalium uliginosum* community.
	Another wet mud community around ponds, essentially similar to S23 or OV29.
OV32*	Water Forget-me-not *Myosotis scorpioides*/Celery-leaved Buttercup *Ranunculus sceleratus* vegetation.
	A common pond and stream margin vegetation on moderately enriched sites. Again, this ought to be listed with other water margin vegetation types.
OV33*	Pale Persicaria *Persicaria lapathifolia*/Annual Meadow-grass *Poa annua* community.
	A plant community of disturbed ground and wet, muddy places by fields. Related to OV18 above.
OV35	Purslane *Lythrum portula*/Lesser Spearwort *Ranunculus flammula* community.
	This is typical of muddy patches in tracks in heathy woodland or in ditches in such areas.

Other types:	Some types, such as Buddleia/Goat Willow/Silver Birch scrub have been mentioned above. Others include the ubiquitous Elder *Sambucus nigra*/Common Nettle *Urtica dioica* scrub, Couch-grass *Elytrigia repens* vegetation by roads and fields; Ground-elder *Aegopodium podagraria* stands, *etc.*

3. Wall communities

These have been highlighted, because they form a discrete group of habitats usually with no natural counterparts in our area.

OV39	Maidenhair Spleenwort *Asplenium trichomanes*/Wall-rue *Asplenium ruta-muraria* community.
	With us, this is a fairly widespread community usually associated with old walls, especially by canals and rivers, very rarely on semi-natural features such as calcrete boulders in old pits. The NVC lists as a variant the Biting Stonecrop *Sedum acre*/Thyme-leaved Sandwort *Arenaria serpyllifolia* community that is more widespread in open, exposed sites, including bare ground by roads.
OV41	Pellitory-of-the-wall *Parietaria judaica* community.
	An increasing community associated with walls, often at their bases, in villages, churchyards, *etc.*
OV42*	Ivy-leaved Toadflax *Cymbalaria muralis* community.
	A frequent community of walls, but probably only one of several potential similar communities of introduced plants of rock crevices.

Other types:	There are a range of other plant communities typical of walls, such as a Spreading Meadow-grass *Poa humilis*/Flattened Meadow-grass *Poa compressa* community frequent on old brick walls especially; and an early-developing community with Whitlowgrass *Erophila verna*, Rue-leaved Saxifrage *Saxifraga tridactylites* and Thale-cress *Arabidopsis thaliana*, among others.

There have been a number of attempts at analysing the relative proportions of various vegetation types in the County, although no attempt has ever been made to define these to the kind of detail that the National Vegetation Classification has attempted. Smith *et al.* (1993) carried out a tetrad analysis of the County's major land-use types during the period of the Flora Survey, including the extent of various arable crops, based on an analysis of Ordnance Survey 1:25,000 maps. Their summary data are reproduced below (Tables 11-13).

	Area (hectares)	%	Tetrads	%
Derived from maps:				
Broad-leaved woodland	9,972	5.1	466	94.9
Coniferous woodland	863	0.4	136	27.7
Mixed woodland	6,310	3.2	346	70.5
Parkland	3,540	1.8	276	56.2
Golf courses	1,550	0.8	61	12.4
Mineral workings	574	0.3	36	7.3
Open water	1,022	0.5	125	25.5
Marsh	131	0.1	33	6.7
Built-up areas	32,385	16.5	485	98.8
Derived from MAFF census:				
Farmland	104,895	53.4	438	89.2
Other open country	35,157	17.9	339	69.0

Table 11. *Total area of each land-use category and number of tetrads in which these habitats are found for 491 tetrads of administrative Hertfordshire. The data were derived from measurements from 1:25. 000 Ordnance Survey maps using a grid of 100 points per square kilometre and 1988 MAFF census returns. (After Smith et al., 1993)*

	Length (kilometres)	Tetrads	%
Rivers	259.8	148	30.1
Streams	998	379	77.2

Table 12. *Total length of rivers and streams and number of tetrads in which these habitats are found, for the 491 tetrads of administrative Hertfordshire. The data were derived from measurements from 1:25. 000 Ordnance Survey maps using a grid of 100 circles per square kilometre, covering 32% of the square. Each segment of river or stream was taken to represent 127 metres of true length. (After Smith et al., 1993).*

	Total number	Tetrads	%
Ponds	3,086	434	88.4

Table 13. *Number of ponds and number of tetrads in which ponds were present, for the 491 tetrads of administrative Hertfordshire. Counted from 1:25,000 Ordnance Survey maps. (After Smith et al., 1993)*

This compares with data on the County's semi-natural habitats derived from more precise measurements carried out for the Hertfordshire Habitat Survey (Cuming, 1997), presented in Table 14. The habitat definitions used in this Survey were based on the Nature Conservancy Council 'Phase 1' habitat assessment, and

the broad habitat types recognised in Hertfordshire included a mixture of ecologically derived and land-use derived habitat types.

Habitat type	Extent (ha.)	% of total habitat
Woodland (including parkland)	14,938	9.26% of total County
Semi-natural broad-leaved woodland	8,994.4	60% all woodland
Planted broadleaved woodland	1,575.1	11% all woodland
Planted conifer woodland	1,346.1	9% all woodland
Planted mixed woodland	2,421.9	16% all woodland
Parkland (ancient and recent)	600	4% all woodland
Scrub	1,480.2	0.92% of total County
Grassland (all types)	34,292	21.26% of total County
Improved grassland	6,947.9	20% all grassland
Species-poor semi-improved grassland	9,223.1	27% all grassland
Amenity grassland	5,292.6	15% all grassland
Semi-improved grassland (all types)	11,548.9	33% all grassland
Semi-improved neutral grassland	10,795.5	93.5% all semi-improved grass
Semi-improved calcareous grassland	304.0	2.6% all semi-improved grass
Semi-improved acidic grassland	449.4	3.9% all semi-improved grass
Unimproved grassland (all types)	1,465.1	4.27% all grassland
Unimproved neutral grassland	946.7	64.6% all unimproved grass
Unimproved calcareous grassland	177.8	12.1% all unimproved grass
Unimproved acidic grassland	145.2	9.9% all unimproved grass
Heathland	21	0.013% of total County
Wetlands (except open water, marshy grassland)	113.8	0.07% of total County
Open water bodies	623.3	0.39% of total County
Artificial habitats (mineral workings, *etc.*)	613.2	0.38% of total County
All habitats (except arable and urban)	**53,722.2**	**33.31% of total County**
Total measured area of Survey (at 1997)	**161,280.72**	**98.7% current admin. Herts.**

Table 14. *Broad habitats in Hertfordshire at 1997. (adapted from the Hertfordshire Habitat Survey (Cuming, 1997)).*

In addition, Cuming gave the number of ponds less than 0.3ha in extent at 2,608; and the length of rivers and canals at 730.85 km.

There are inevitable discrepancies between the two sets of figures, depending on the way they were arrived at, but there are also some specifically interesting differences. For example, the area of parkland as estimated by Smith *et al.* is far greater than that measured by Cuming, which is difficult to account for. Smith *et al.* also give useful figures for the extent of mineral workings and golf courses, absent from Cuming's data, although both of these figures were no doubt rapidly superseded by the development of new pits or through the rapid expansion in golf course development that occurred during the 1990s. Another fairly major difference is the estimate of open water, which may depend on the threshold size of the water bodies concerned, although back-filling of gravel pits was still under way during the early 1990s, and swamp and wet woodland encroachment on others had also no doubt increased. The major omission from Smith *et al.* was the data on the remaining extent of semi-natural unimproved or semi-improved grasslands, and here the Habitat Survey demonstrated all too clearly that the County had lost much of this even by the 1990s, a loss that has continued, despite attempts to protect these by Wildlife Site designation.

Whichever source of information is used, however, it has to be stressed that, compared with the extent of 'natural' plant communities at the beginning of the 20th century, Hertfordshire is known to have lost upwards of 96% of all its semi-natural grasslands, while over 40% of its woodland has been replaced by artificial plantations, often on native woodland sites. Some

habitats, such as acid grassland and heath are now very restricted, particularly the latter, which only now remains as vestiges, although some attempt at expanding the habitat has more recently occurred, through creation of open spaces in former wood-pastures, and improved management of roughs on golf courses.

The important thing for plant communities, however, is that relatively undisturbed, ancient plant communities are, by definition, irreplaceable. No matter what 'habitat creation' schemes are carried out, or planning mitigation measures are put in place as 'replacements' for lost parcels of land, these will not replicate the kind of environment that William Graveson described. They will have their own ecology, almost despite what we try to do, but these will not be 'ancient'.

The principal threats, though, are not just development or even disturbance (there are high quality SSSI sites that are known to have been ploughed during the Second World War), but chemical pollution, nutrient over-enrichment, the catastrophic loss of livestock grazing throughout much of the County, and now, the potential effects of climate warming. Our native plant communities are inevitably affected by these factors, and the whole classification in the NVC may ultimately be called into question as plant relationships alter and plant communities shift unpredictably in the face of wholesale change.

Black Poplar Populus nigra *ssp.* betulifolia – *tree and leaf detail, showing spiral gall on petiole, see page 154.*

Chapter 6. The changing flora of Hertfordshire

Northaw Great Wood, old pollard.

Change is a fundamental characteristic of the natural world, so it is no real surprise that Hertfordshire's flora, along with everything else, is subject to it. While that may be so, we humans have a problem coming to terms with change, and understanding it. We worry whether it is a 'problem' or not.

In response to a comment about the changing flora, the late John Dony said in the mid 1980s that 'Hertfordshire's flora is becoming less and less 'natural' all the time'. This seemingly simple notion was actually an important insight. Yes, Hertfordshire's flora has always been 'changing', but now, perhaps, the changes are not as 'natural' as they once were, being more and more influenced by human activities and by factors introduced by mankind. Whether or not this is a problem comes down to whether 'natural' processes should be seen as preferable to changes wrought by humanity. As a life-long advocate of nature conservation, I tend to be in the former camp.

In 1997, I attempted to assess the 'changing flora' in an article that summarised the data gathered up to that point by the Hertfordshire Flora Survey (James, 1997), comparing these with a similar study carried out by John Dony (Dony, 1974) and an even earlier one by Sir Edward Salisbury (Salisbury, 1924). One thing stood out above all else when comparing these studies, and that was the changed perception of the 'natural' vegetation that each was based upon. Salisbury's classification of habitat types was essentially based upon the idea of 'waste' land as compared with cultivated or occupied land; that is, land that had a more or less 'natural' plant community, as opposed to land that had evidently been substantially modified by humans. So heaths, commons, and chalk grassland were all lumped together. Only wetlands (and to a lesser extent woodlands) were singled out as separate categories, and for wetlands, this was because Salisbury was very aware of human impacts upon them in the previous 100 years or so, with reduced water tables, canalisation of rivers and so on. Dony's analysis took more account of what we would now consider 'habitats' from an 'ecological' perspective, and he also drew attention to the large increase in alien species. In this most recent account, we might now witness the beginnings of another

shift – from seeing the landscape as a series of 'fixed' habitats, to a dynamic landscape where 'natural' processes of colonisation, competition and interaction of species are the rule. Such a view tends to emphasise the plastic nature of 'habitats', and to point up the factors that shift plant relationships. It also gives us potentially new and important insights into the probable nature of historic landscapes and therefore of the origins of our flora.

In addition to their overall view of the environment in which plants were recorded, both Dony and Salisbury gave assessments of what, in their times, were considered to be 'extinct', 'declining', or 'increasing' species associated with their categories of habitat. However, their assessments of these changes have since been found to be partly erroneous, illustrating all too well the difficulties of being too categorical about such things. Even my own statements, as recently as 1997, have in some cases been proved to be wrong, and this book, also, will no doubt be challenged by further recording activity. Certainly, records made in the last two years or so have re-found several 'extinct' species, and made further records of several others thought to be very rare, so we are not finished finding 'new' plants!

The following brief account, therefore, is an inevitably flawed attempt to assess the change over time in Hertfordshire's flora. It takes as a 'baseline' the data gathered by John Dony and his helpers in the 1950s and early 1960s. The recent Flora Project has now provided us with a comprehensive dataset with which to compare Dony's data. There are inevitable problems, stemming from the incompleteness of Dony's survey (he himself, in another comment he made to me, estimated an approximate 60% coverage, with especially thin coverage in east Hertfordshire); while the recent study has managed a greater degree of evenness, but still has evidently under-recorded areas, especially in the south and centre-west of the County. It is also important to remember, with this comparison, that even in the 1960s, Hertfordshire's plant communities had suffered from intensive change over many centuries, and particularly since the mid 19th century, as London's influence grew, land use change had accelerated (augmented by wartime ploughing and wholesale 'harvesting' of woodlands), water tables and river flows had declined owing to extraction, and chemical impacts on the land had increased. 'Natural', or even 'semi-natural' plant communities had therefore been much reduced by 1960, and this means that the baseline data gathered by Dony already reflected a much altered 'natural' state of affairs. However, his baseline data did stem from a period when climatic change was not so evident, and also from a period when nutrient enrichment was also not so obvious a factor in most habitats. These two elements, therefore, are potentially major factors that have driven more recent change, along with a range of other things, such as continued change in land-use patterns, major shifts in agricultural practice, disuse of 'traditional' land management regimes, the massive increase in mineral extraction on industrial scales, and the resulting neglect or mismanagement of much remaining semi-natural vegetation as its economic usefulness for society has disappeared. All too often, now, 'natural' plant communities are merely thought to form a kind of amenity backdrop to human activity, rather than being something we vitally depend on for living. As all wildlife tends to be species that survive despite our activities, living in the spaces we leave or create in our own environment, it is not surprising that a large number of especially native or 'archaeophyte' plant species are now 'relics' of both semi-natural vegetation, and of past land management practices.

Changing flora – the evidence

Dony (1967) recorded 1,376 species of plants, although he ignored brambles, elms and dandelions, and only skimmed the surface with hawkweeds, as well as only giving details of some 54 hybrids. The recent Flora Survey has accounted for 1,969 species, as well as 155 subspecies and 166 hybrids. It has included at least some attempt at recording the elms and dandelions, and has made a fairly concerted effort at recording brambles and hawkweeds.

Dony's insight, that alien species are increasing, is, however, strongly borne out. There are now 923 'neophyte' species recorded (some 47% of the total recorded flora), vastly more than Dony recorded, let alone those recorded by earlier botanists. However, strict comparison, even between his survey and ours for these species, is misleading, because we know that he disregarded quite a large number of species that were known 'in the wild' in his time, such as the Rhododendron thickets in various woods. This was down to botanical 'fashion' to some extent, because 'garden escapes' were often not really thought of as being 'wild' at all.

Although the baseline of species has altered considerably since Dony's survey, the area over which the studies were carried out has not altered so much. The current survey gathered data from 491 tetrads (out of a possible 508 complete or part tetrads), while Dony's survey recorded 466 tetrads (out of 504), the difference partly owing to changed County boundaries in some areas, while the rest is down to a more thorough coverage. The latter makes direct comparison of results problematic, and we need to bear this in mind in assessing statistics of change.

Extinction

The process of extinction is now a focus of attention, especially as changing climatic conditions threaten to undermine further the stability of ecosystems, and force species at the southern edge of their range to either move north, or become locally extinct. Details of the 83 'extinct' native or archaeophyte species on the Hertfordshire list are given in Table 15. It needs to be stressed, though, that this can only ever be an interim statement, based on the best possible knowledge at the time of writing. If the same table had been produced in 2007, at least two native species would have been included as not having been seen since the late 19th century and therefore likely to be extinct: Purple Small-reed *Calamagrostis canescens* and Creeping Forget-me-not *Myosotis secunda*. Both are now known in the County (even if they remain very rare, and one may now be an introduction!).

We can look at these losses from the perspective of habitats, which begins to give a bit of an insight into where changes have occurred, and therefore what might have been the major drivers of change. The table shows the list of 'extinct' species according to broad habitat category, and one thing immediately stands out: the over-riding importance of aquatic and wetland species in the list.

Wetlands/aquatic	Osmunda regalis (1657) (as native)	Pitularia globulifera (1838)	Ceratophyllum submersum (1956)	Stellaria palustris (1914)	Sagina nodosa (1957)	Anagallis tenella (1965)	Samolus valerandi (1984)	Parnassia palustris (1924)
Heath/acid grassland	Lycopodium clavatum (1981)	Moenchia erecta (1957)	Dianthus armeria? (1988)	Drosera rotundifolia (1914)	Salix aurita (1976) (as native)	Teesdalia nudicaulis (c.1940)	Erica tetralix? (1988)	Vaccinium myrtillus (c.1973)
Calcareous grassland	Hypericum montanum (1966?)	Seseli libanotis (1976)	Galium pumilum (1964)	Hypochaeris maculata? (1993) (as wild)	Antennaria dioica (1947)	Spiranthes spiralis (1980)	Herminium monorchis? (1987)	Orchis anthropophora (1957)
Neutral grassland	Oenanthe pimpinelloides (1962)	Centaurium pulchellum (c.1930)	Euphrasia arctica (1911)	Orobanche purpurea (1938)				
Woodland	Fallopia dumetorum (1875)	Gagea lutea (1954)						
Scrub/hedgerows	Rosa sherardii (1877 [1886?])	Cuscuta europaea (c.1880)	Cuscuta epithymum (1985)	Cynoglossum germanicum (c.1880)	Valerianella rimosa (1965)	Arnoseris minima (c.1875)	Filago lutescens (1919)	Filago gallica (1878)
Open gravel/sand	Arabis glabra (1976)	Anagallis minima (c.1931)	Trifolium scabrum (1980)	Ajuga chamaepitys (1964)				
Arable/cultivation	Adonis annua (1979)	Bupleurum rotundifolium (1941)	Misopates orontium (1966)	Melampyrum arvense (c.1840)				
Ruderal/wasteland	Chenopodium vulvaria (1966)	Chenopodium urbicum (1843)	Galium parisiense (1978)					

Potentilla palustris (c.1919)

Trifolium ornithopodioides (1846)

Orchis militaris (1902)

Lythrum hyssopifolium (1848) (as native)

Trifolium subterraneum (1913)

Neotinea ustulata? (1994)

Cicuta virosa (1929)

Radiola linoides (c.1840)

Himantoglossum hircinum (1931)

Mentha pulegium (c.1926) (as native)

Gentianella campestris (1875)

Littorella uniflora (1843)

Jasione montana (c.1914)

Pedicularis palustris (1955)

Eleocharis multicaulis (1843)

Pinguicula vulgaris (c.1870)

Platanthera bifolia (c.1849 [1883?])

Cirsium dissectum (1980)

Pulicaria vulgaris (1923)

Baldellia ranunculoides (1947)

Damasonium alisma (1928)

Potamogeton coloratus (1841)

Potamogeton alpinus (1971)

Potamogeton compressus (c.1944)

Potamogeton acutifolius (1846)

Eriophorum latifolium (1849)

Eleocharis acicularis (1975)

Schoenus nigricans (1843)

Wetlands/aquatic	Heath/acid grassland	Calcareous grassland	Neutral grassland	Woodland	Scrub/hedgerows	Open gravel/sand	Arable/cultivation	Ruderal/wasteland
Carex appropinquata (1885)								
Carex diandra (1843)								
Carex dioica (1878)								
Carex pulicaris (1958)								
Sparganium natans (c.1843)								
Hammarbya paludosa (c.1640)								
Total: 32 (39%)	Total: 15 (18%)	Total: 11 (12%)	Total: 4 (5%)	Total: 2 (2%)	Total: 4 (5%)	Total: 8 (10%)	Total: 4 (5%)	Total: 3 (4%)

Table 15. *Apparently extinct native or archaeophyte plant species in Hertfordshire, by broad habitat type, with last date of recording (83 species).*

The preponderance of wetland species under threat was something that Salisbury remarked upon in his assessment of change; while Dony's analysis tends to obscure the magnitude of this through having broken down 'wetland' plants into 'aquatic', 'riverside' and 'marshland', although the last of these still showed the largest number of species in any one habitat category. This also points up one other problem of this kind of assessment – the category into which species might be put. Salisbury, for example, included Stag's-horn Clubmoss *Lycopodium clavatum* and Lemon-scented Fern *Thelypteris limbosperma* in his wetland category, along with Cross-leaved Heath *Erica tetralix*. These have been split between heathland and woodland in the current scheme, although cases can be made out for either and emphasises again the plastic nature of plant communities, depending on the local context.

Another thing that stands out from these lists is that 'natural' plant communities associated with what Salisbury thought of as 'waste' or 'natural' land (heaths, commons and chalk grassland) taken together form the bulk of habitats where losses have occurred apart from the wetlands. This points up very strongly the overall loss of these more natural landscape (and land-use) types in our area compared with more remote parts of the country. As both Salisbury and Dony pointed out, only woodlands among 'natural' landscapes seem to have fared better to some extent. Other habitat categories are what Salisbury would have considered as very much 'cultivation' or 'other' habitats: most neutral grasslands (pastures, hay meadows), arable cultivation, open gravel and sand habitats and so on, as well as the more genuinely 'ruderal' – species of heavily disturbed, often enriched soils around habitation and roads. In many ways, some of these clearly overlap. For example, arable cultivation will include areas with open, gravelly ground, and so some species under this heading could have been included in the arable category instead.

Extinction has only been considered, here, for native and 'archaeophyte' species, because these are considered, by their nature, to be plants of our long-established 'natural' environment. Salisbury was less clear-cut about this, and a few of what we now think of as 'neophyte' species were included in his (and Dony's) assessments. It is not to say that all neophytes are increasing; far from it. Many neophyte species that were considered to be 'established' in the 19th century or later may have since disappeared altogether. Weeds of wool shoddy fields are an example. This, again, points up a problem of interpretation – when is a species regarded as part of our natural plant communities on a permanent basis, and might therefore become extinct? Lizard Orchid *Himantoglossum hircinum* is a case in point. It was only present briefly, but because it is regarded nationally as a plant of old chalk grassland, it has tended to be seen as 'natural', while it might have been classed as a casual incomer in our County.

Decreasing species

The direct comparison between Dony's survey data and ours has enabled us to have a more objective basis upon which to make judgements about change. As noted above, we do have to be careful in making these assessments, owing to the vagaries of the two surveys, and the level of coverage, in particular, of the 1967 survey, which has provided us with a baseline. Because of the issue of incomplete coverage in the 1960s, and the fact that the recent survey achieved at least a 20% increase in coverage across the County (based on the average number of species recorded per tetrad, as compared with the 1960s survey), the following assessments have tried to exclude species where the level of apparent change may not actually represent a real difference. Only species that have demonstrated at least a 20% difference either way between the two surveys have therefore been included.

Another problem is the size of any one sample. Some species in these analyses have shown large percentage shifts between the surveys, but part of this may be down to poor recording in the 1960s, as well as the effects of a colonising species that had only just gained a foothold at the time of the earlier survey. Reference has therefore been made in some analyses to the number of records upon which percentage changes have been based, so these issues can be more evident.

As explained in the Introduction to the Taxonomic accounts later in this book, the percentage changes have been arrived at from comparing the number of recorded tetrads for one survey against the number recorded from the other. The number of overall tetrads covered by each survey is slightly different (491 in the current survey, 466 in the earlier one), so the change is presented as a percentage change of relative tetrad occupancy between the two surveys. Table 16 shows the results of this analysis for native and archaeophyte species in terms of similar broad habitat categories to those used for extinct species above. As compared with the list of extinct species, this table shows us quite clearly that other habitat categories are now beginning to see serious declines, as well as wetlands, and that, although, for the moment, these have not so far seen extinctions to as great an extent, there are a wide number of native and long-established species in our area that are now seriously threatened. This applies especially to species of chalk grasslands, and what

remains of our heathland. But it also applies especially to plants of arable cultivation, most of which are actually archaeophytes, and therefore behave more or less like native species. However, 'natural' habitats are not alone in showing signs of losing species. Even our 'ruderal' environment has seven declining native/archaeophyte species, of which five are classed as 'threatened' to some extent.

Another feature of this analysis is the discrepancy between what might be considered 'threatened' at a national level, and what is shown to be declining locally. While, nationally, the threat to arable associated species has been picked up (64% of the declining species are classed as UK Red Data Book listed), only 21% of the calcareous grassland category are seen as nationally significant, whereas our figures show that 61% of the County's strongly declining species are neither recognised nationally as a conservation priority, nor, yet, at a local level. While neutral grassland and open gravel/sand habitats may not have so many species under threat, they do show a similar proportion so far unrecognised as a potential problem.

Which species are most affected? Table 17 gives a list of all the native and archaeophyte species that have decreased by at least 60% since Dony's survey. These might be classed as the most threatened (in fact the Herts Vulnerable category includes others that have decreased by between 50 and 60%, but which have been omitted here for reasons of space – see Appendix 1 for the complete list). However, the 'Herts Rare' category is actually based on the absolute number of localities from which a species is recorded (five or fewer), which may or may not have decreased as such. We therefore need to distinguish between threat from actual decline and rarity.

Habitat	Total decreasing	UKRDB (no.)	% total	Herts Rare/ Vulnerable + UKRDB (no.)	% total	Decreasing >20% (not UK or Herts Rare/ Vulnerable) (no.)	% total
Wetland/ aquatic	35	2	6%	18	51%	17	49%
Calcareous grass	33	7	21%	13	25%	20	61%
Arable/ cultivation	25	16	64%	18	72%	7	28%
Neutral grass/ road verges	13	2	15%	5	38%	8	62%
Heath/acid grass	19	4	21%	12	63%	7	37%
Woodland	11	4	36%	10	91%	1	9%
Open gravel/ sand	11	3	27%	5	45%	7	64%
Ruderal/ wasteland	7	2	29%	2	29%	5	71%
Scrub/ hedgerows	8	3	38%	5	63%	3	38%
All habitats	**162**	**43**	**27%**	**88**	**54%**	**74**	**46%**

Table 16. *Strongly decreasing (20%+ since 1967) native/archaeophyte plant species in Hertfordshire by habitat.*

Broad habitat	Species	English name	% decrease	No. of tetrads
Arable/cultivation	Ajuga chamaepitys**	Ground-pine	100%	0
	Galeopsis angustifolia**	Red Hemp-nettle	93%	2
	Silene noctiflora**	Night-flowering Catchfly	87%	8
	Ranunculus arvensis**	Corn Buttercup	85%	5
	Galeopsis speciosa**	Large-flowered Hemp-nettle	80%	1
	Torilis arvensis**	Spreading Hedge-parsley	79%	8
	Galium tricornutum**	Corn Cleavers	78%	1
	Scandix pecten-veneris**	Shepherd's-needle	71%	23
	Valerianella dentata**	Sharp-fruited Corn-salad	66%	12
	Spergula arvensis**	Corn Spurrey	61%	48
	Lithospermum arvense**	Field Gromwell	60%	36
Heath/acid grassland	Lycopodium clavatum*	Stag's-horn Clubmoss	100%	0
	Dianthus armeria**	Deptford Pink	100%	0
	Vaccinium myrtillus*	Bilberry	100%	0
	Salix aurita*	Eared Willow	87% (100%)	2 (0) (native)
	Polygala serpyllifolia*	Heath Milkwort	83%	2
	Pedicularis sylvatica*	Lousewort	70%	3
	Aira caryophyllea*	Silver Hair-grass	63%	13
Woodland	Gnaphalium sylvaticum**	Heath Cudweed	100%	0
	Gagea lutea*	Yellow Star-of-Bethlehem	100%	0
	Neottia nidus-avis**	Bird's-nest Orchid	81%	4
	Paris quadrifolia*	Herb Paris	69%	8
	Pyrola minor*	Common Wintergreen	67%	1
	Alchemilla xanthochlora*	A lady's-mantle	67%	1
	Bromopsis benekenii*	Lesser Hairy Brome	65%	4
Open gravel/sand	Moenchia erecta*	Upright Moenchia	100%	0
	Valerianella rimosa**	Broad-fruited Corn-salad	100%	0
	Scleranthus annuus**	Annual Knawel	90%	11
Calcareous grassland	Galium pumilum**	Slender Bedstraw	100%	0
	Seseli libanotis**	Moon-carrot	100%	0
	Spiranthes spiralis*	Autumn Lady's-tresses	100%	0
	Orchis anthropophora**	Man Orchid	100%	0
	Pulsatilla vulgaris**	Pasque Flower	67%	3 (1) (native)
	Astragalus danicus**	Purple Milk-vetch	66%	4?
	Clinopodium acinos**	Basil Thyme	65%	10
Neutral grassland/ verges	Oenanthe pimpinelloides*	Corky-fruited Water-dropwort	100	0
	Trifolium fragiferum*	Strawberry Clover	72%	11
	Alchemilla filicaulis*	Common Lady's mantle	68%	15
Ruderal/wasteland	[None]			
Wetland/aquatic	Ceratophyllum submersum*	Soft Hornwort	100%	0
	Sagina nodosa*	Knotted Pearlwort	100%	0
	Anagallis tenella*	Bog Pimpernel	100%	0

Broad habitat	Species	English name	% decrease	No. of tetrads
Wetland/aquatic (cont.)	*Samolus valerandi**	Brookweed	100%	0
	*Pedicularis palustris**	Marsh Lousewort	100%	0
	*Cirsium dissectum**	Meadow Thistle	100%	0
	*Potamogeton alpinus**	Red Pondweed	100%	0
	*Eleocharis acicularis**	Needle Spike-rush	100%	0
	*Oenanthe aquatica**	Fine-leaved Water-dropwort	69%	2
	*Potamogeton friesii***	Flat-stalked Pondweed	67%	2
Scrub/hedgerows	*Melampyrum cristatum***	Crested Cow-wheat	67%	1
	*Sedum telephium**	Orpine	68%	30

Table 17. *Native/archaeophyte plant species in Hertfordshire most strongly decreased (60% +) since 1967 by broad habitat. (**: UK Red Data listed; *: Herts Rare/Extinct or Vulnerable).*

While this table illustrates much the same points as above, that some groups are more recognised than others as under threat nationally, it also points up very strongly that other habitat categories are now showing severe signs of stress. Nationally the wetland category seems not to have attracted much attention, but this table alone shows that seven species have become extinct in the last 30 years locally. A number of woodland species are also now under direct threat for the first time; while our remaining heathland species are also strongly threatened, even species that are common enough on a national basis.

Increasing species

Given that Hertfordshire has apparently 'acquired' such a large number of plants over the last 150 years, we must have some things that are increasing, but which ones, and why? An analysis of the overall flora record between the two surveys gives us some interesting insights about the species that are actually increasing. However, one thing needs to be stressed in this analysis, and that is the absence in the lists of quite a few of the actually increasing non-native species because there is no baseline against which statistical increase can be calculated, even if the species was actually present in 1967. There are also a whole raft of species that have appeared on the scene since 1967 that also do not figure in this analysis for similar reasons.

Table 18 shows the species that have shown the greatest increase in occurrence between the two surveys, as a proportion according to their preferred habitat type, and also distinguishing between native/archaeophyte species and neophytes. The results show some interesting features. Top of the list comes the wetland habitat category! No less than 69 native or archaeophyte wetland species show strong signs of actually having **increased** in Hertfordshire since 1967. Counter-intuitive though this may appear, and oddly contrasting with the fact that so many native wetland species have also decreased or become extinct, this is a welcome finding. There is also the interesting number of 41 native/archaeophyte woodland species that are increasing, among which several fern species are prominent. Scrub and hedgerow plants also show signs of doing quite well, and even plants of open gravel and sand or neutral grassland (counter to expectations, for the latter at least). As we might expect, ruderal habitats figure prominently in the increasing species league, but it is worth pointing out that a large majority of these are actually native/archaeophyte species, not the expected invasive riff-raff.

Broad habitat	Natives/ archaeophytes	Neophytes	Total
Wetlands/ aquatic	69	6	75
Ruderal/ wasteland	29	19	48
Woodlands	41	1	42
Hedgerows/ scrub	22	17	39
Neutral grass/ verges	16	5	21
Open gravel/ sand	14	3	17
Arable/ cultivation	11	4	15
Calcareous grassland	8	0	8
Heath/acid grass	8	0	8
All habitats	218	55	273

Table 18. *Proportions of plant species increased strongly (20%+) in Hertfordshire since 1967, by habitat type.*

There is no doubt that non-native (neophyte) plants figure prominently in the lists of increasing species as well. Table 19 shows those non-native species that have increased the most since 1967 (although it omits a good number of species for which Dony gave no data). To give some idea of the baseline upon which this change has been measured, the actual current number of occupied tetrads is also given.

Species	Common name	% increased	No. of tetrads
Buddleja davidii	Buddleia	3,291	183
Cochlearia danica	Danish Scurvy-grass	3,233	97
Pentaglottis sempervirens	Blue Alkanet	3,118	174
Sedum rupestre	Rock Stonecrop	2,100	43
Symphytum orientale	White Comfrey	1,650	17

Species	Common name	% increased	No. of tetrads
Myosotis sylvatica (esc.)	Wood (Garden) Forget-me-not	1,113	143 (134)
Silybum marianum	Milk Thistle	1,100	12
Ranunculus lingua	Greater Spearwort	950	31
Sorbus intermedia (esc.)	Swedish Whitebeam	850	41 (19)
Avena sterilis	Winter Wild-oat	700	59
Cyperus longus	Galingale	675	15
Hesperis matronalis	Dame's Violet	650	81
Fallopia sachalinense	Sakhalin Knotweed	650	22
Mentha villosa	Apple Mint	583	20
Setaria pumila	Yellow Bristle-grass	575	13
Allium paradoxum	Few-flowered Garlic	550	19
Borago officinalis	Borage	545	35
Prunus cerasifera	Cherry Plum	523	159

Table 19. *Non-native plants most increased in Hertfordshire since 1967 (>500%).*

From this, it will be appreciated that the large percentage increases shown by some species are from a very small base, and the species concerned may not be widespread, such as White Comfrey *Symphytum orientale*, while others may be more pervasive, but show less percentage increase, partly because they already occurred widely by the 1960s, such as Cherry Plum *Prunus cerasifera*. A number of species stand out, however. The most evident are Buddleia *Buddleja davidii* and Green Alkanet *Pentaglottis sempervirens*, both of which are now very widespread, and, in the case of the former, potentially a menace in some places. Wood Forget-me-not *Myosotis sylvatica* presents us with a particular issue – the potential effects (if any) of a massive increase of the species as an introduction, while it is also a native plant in a very precisely defined area. In this case, the two entities may have enough genetic difference to remain separate, and there is no suggestion, yet, that the native form has been threatened at all by its look-alike escaped cousins.

There are two other features of this list that attract special attention. Firstly, the presence of Greater Spearwort *Ranunculus lingua* and Galingale *Cyperus longus* in the list highlights the steady accumulation of introduced wetland plants that may threaten native species. Very often these are the result of deliberate introduction, and the real problem may be in their obscuring of natural relationships between native plants and their environment, just as much as any potential direct threat to native plants or other wildlife. Secondly, Danish Scurvy-grass *Cochlearia danica* illustrates the effect of road salting. It is not the only such maritime species to be rapidly increasing, but most of the rest were not present in the 1960s at all, and therefore no statistic of increase has been generated. Again, the effects of this pollutant on roadside vegetation is a serious concern in some areas, where very old roadside vegetation (such as on narrow, ancient, chalky banks in the north of the County) has been seriously damaged by

its application, threatening scarce species.

So, from our survey results, what now are the most significant non-native plants in the County, and how might they have affected our environment? Table 20 gives a list of the most significant neophytes (along with a few UK native species that have been recently introduced in Hertfordshire).

Species/taxa	English name	No. of occupied tetrads	Increasing/ decreasing (+/-%)
Acer pseudoplatanus	Sycamore	470	-1
Veronica persica	Common Speedwell	463	-3
Matricaria discoidea	Pineapple-weed	462	-4
Aegopodium podagraria	Ground Elder	432	-9
Aesculus hippocastanum	Horse Chestnut	402	+?
Epilobium ciliatum	American Willowherb	325	+19
Armoracia rusticana	Horse Radish	324	+6
Calystegia silvatica	Great Bindweed	317	+85
Brassica napus	Rape	316	+?
Pinus sylvestris	Scots Pine	312	+?
Veronica filiformis	Slender Speedwell	298	+287
Conyza canadensis	Canadian Fleabane	257	+57
Populus canadensis	Hybrid Black Poplar	255	+?
Acer platanoides	Norway Maple	253	+?
Senecio squalidus	Oxford Ragwort	249	+12
Symphoricarpos albus	Snowberry	233	+?
Symphytum × uplandicum	Russian Comfrey	230	+112
Lolium multiflorum	Italian Rye-grass	223	- 44
Larix decidua	European Larch	223	+?
Lepidium draba	Hoary Cress	219	+45
Papaver somniferum	Opium Poppy	199	+371
Castanea sativa	Sweet Chestnut	196	+?
Fallopia japonica	Japanese Knotweed	193	+102
Picea abies	Norway Spruce	191	+?
Melilotus officinalis	Ribbed Melilot	184	+13

Species/taxa	English name	No. of occupied tetrads	Increasing/ decreasing (+/-%)
Buddleja davidii	Buddleia	183	+3291
Geranium pyrenaicum	Pyrenean Crane's-bill	179	+119
Pentaglottis sempervirens	Blue Alkanet	174	+3118
Melilotus altissimus	Tall Melilot	161	+18
Prunus cerasifera	Cherry Plum	159	+523
Prunus laurocerasus	Cherry Laurel	157	+?
Lunaria annua	Honesty	152	+?
Solidago canadensis	Canadian Golden-rod	151	+?
Veronica polita	Grey Field-speedwell	151	+28

Table 20. *Most significant neophyte or otherwise UK native plants introduced in Herts. (>150 tetrads).*
*: taxa mapped in Dony (1967).
?: taxa for which extent of increase/decline since 1967 is unknown.

An interesting feature of this list is that those with the greatest number of recorded tetrads are also likely to have reached the maximum extent of their spread, because they show no further signs of expanding, and may show some signs of decrease (although most of these decreases are not significant). A few that were already widespread have shown substantial increases since 1967, such as Large Bindweed *Calystegia silvatica* and Slender Speedwell *Veronica filiformis*. Towards the lower end of the list, with fewer current tetrads, two species stand out as rapidly expanding – Buddleia and Green Alkanet. Both of these look set to establish themselves widely across the County before they stabilise, although Buddleia may be limited by its habitat requirements to some extent. Cherry Plum also apparently shows substantial increase since the 1960s, but this may owe more to the effectiveness of recent recording than true spread, and demonstrates the need to be cautious about how we interpret such data. As for the species for which information in the 1960s is

lacking, there are clearly several species here that probably have experienced as significant increases as some of those mentioned above, but it is difficult to be certain. Field experience suggests, for example that Sweet Chestnut *Castanea sativa* has increased quite substantially in more acidic woodlands on gravels, while Norway Maple *Acer platanoides* shows every likelihood of achieving similar status to its cousin Sycamore *A. pseudoplatanus* in due course, especially on less calcareous soils. Other taxa, such as Hybrid Black-poplar *Populus canadensis*, are only where we have put them, and in fact are not naturally expanding at all. One species, Italian Rye-grass *Lolium multiflorum*, shows strong signs of actually decreasing from a substantial occupancy, probably owing to the reduction of its use as a fodder grass.

Factors driving change

Comparative statistics of changing flora are all very well, but what do they actually tell us about the causes, and what might be the longer term effects? The data collected from the recent survey has the potential for adding to other studies from elsewhere (*e.g.* Braithwaite *et al.,* 2006) to enlighten us about the drivers behind change of this kind. There are many mentions in the accounts of species that follow that suggest possible causes, such as nutrient enrichment of road verges and arable land, *etc.*, salt pollution from road salting, overgrowth of woodland rides or neglect of woodlands otherwise, and acidification of heathland or some woodlands from past acid rain. Many of these factors are well documented elsewhere, but showing precise effects of any one of them can be very difficult.

The data from changes recorded through this survey have been analysed, initially, to see whether the species concerned give us any clues from their known habitat and nutrient requirements. A range of 'attributes' of British species have been brought together and published by Hill *et al.* (2004), of which two: soil conductivity (related to pH) (R) and nitrogen requirements (N), expressed on numerical scales, are often thought to be specially indicative of habitat change. Table 21 presents the results of this initial analysis, applied to native and archaeophyte species reliably assessed to have increased or decreased by 20% or more since 1967.

Habitat category	No. spp decreased	% total	R (mean)	N (mean)	No spp. increased	% total	R (mean)	N (mean)
Wetland	35	34%	6.3	4.7	69	66%	6.3	5.5
Calcareous grassland	33	80%	7.2	2.7	8	20%	7.3	2.5
Acid grassland/heath	19	70%	3.8	2.3	8	30%	4.1	3.4
Neutral grassland	12	43%	6.5	3.8	16	57%	6.4	4.9
Woodland	11	21%	6.2	4.5	41	79%	5.9	5.3
Scrub/hedgerows	8	27%	6.3	4.3	22	73%	6.9	5.0
Open gravel/sand	12	46%	6.0	3.2	14	54%	6.6	4.3
Arable	25	69%	6.8	5.2	11	31%	7.2	5.5
Ruderal/waste	7	19%	6.6	7.0	29	81%	6.9	6.4
Walls	0	-	-	-	11	100%	5.9	2.6
All habitats	162	100	6.2	4.2	229	100	6.4	4.5

Table 21. Summary of analysis of relative conductivity (R) and nitrogen requirements (N) of known decreasing or increasing native/archaeophyte plants in Hertfordshire.

This analysis is evidently unsafe to base any great thesis upon, as the sample size of species in many categories is relatively low, and variations in the mean figures for both R and N are also rather small in some cases. However, there are some interesting features that emerge.

As might be expected, R is closely related to overall habitat type for those habitats defined by acidity/alkalinity (calcareous grassland and heath). For other habitat types, based on physical characteristics, or on levels of disturbance, this attribute is less governed by the nature of the environment, and may give us some interesting insights. The N attribute is generally reckoned to give more robust insights into the nutrient status at least of habitats, and therefore might provide us with confirmation of our suspicions about nutrient enrichment (Hill *et al.*, 2004).

We have seen, from analysis so far of the results of our survey, that wetlands have shown both marked losses and marked gains of native/archaeophyte species. Do these attributes shed any light on this conundrum? It is immediately evident that there appears to be no significant difference (indeed no difference at all) in the R attribute for either category of decreased or increased species. However, there is some evidence for an increase in N (4.7-5.5), which, although still showing that wetland plants are generally less demanding on nutrients than might be the case for other groups, gives evidence of an increase in the overall proportion of species preferring higher nitrogen levels, as would be expected from the impact of increases in river and other wetland nutrient statuses published elsewhere (*e.g.* Preston *et al.,* 2003). That levels are not yet reckoned to be seriously eutrophic in at least some of Hertfordshire's water bodies may be good news, however, and we can hope this remains the case with the efforts being made by the Environment Agency to limit run-off and pollution. However, other impacts on wetlands are not taken account of in this analysis, such as the impacts of prolonged droughts, which can increase nutrient levels in remaining water.

Wilstone Reservoir, dry, 1989, with a flora dominated by nutrient-loving Red Goosefoot Chenopodium rubrum.

There has been much discussion about the impact of nutrient enrichment on chalk grasslands, particularly from atmospheric deposition of nitrogen. However, from the small sample here, there is no evidence of either an increase or a decrease in either R or N attributes, showing that, if there are effects of atmospheric (or other nutrient) inputs, these do not appear to show up as an increase or decrease in soil conductivity in chalk grassland habitats, nor in higher levels of available nitrogen. This may come as something of a surprise, and may need better data to prove, but it might also suggest that there is more damage being done by wholesale neglect of downland and its invasion by coarse grasses

Aldbury Nowers, south banks 1989, showing severe scrub invasion.

Aldbury Nowers, south banks after scrub clearance, 2006, demonstrating patchy nature of resulting grassland.

and scrub, than by nutrient enrichment as such.

Heathland and acidic grassland have long been known to be in strong decline in the County (Cuming, 1997), but this is the first time any broad data on nutrient status, *etc.* have been brought forward locally to my knowledge. The results show a slight increase in the level of soil conductivity (implying raised pH levels in acidic soils), as well as some evidence for the effects of raised nitrogen levels (N: 2.3 for decreased species; 3.4 for those species increasing). Both figures remain on the low side, but species characteristic of very low fertility levels are specially adapted to acidic soil conditions, and very susceptible to raised nutrients and pH. This is very likely, therefore, to be an important factor in the decline of especially highly nutrient sensitive species, such as Stag's-horn Clubmoss and Mat-grass *Nardus stricta*, as we might expect.

Neutral grasslands, by their nature, tend to have species that are widely tolerant of a range of different habitat characteristics. The data, however, do give some evidence of differences. As might be expected, soil conductivity shows no signs of a difference between the decreasing or the increasing groups. However, again, requirement for nitrogen shows signs of an increase between the groups (N: 3.8 for decreasing species; 4.9 for increasing species). Unlike calcareous grassland, therefore, neutral grasslands are showing signs of nutrient enrichment. The difference may be to do with the capacity for loam and clay soils in particular to hold more available nitrogen than the often dry and free-draining chalk grasslands.

Changes in woodland have often been dismissed as not specially significant. The results of our admittedly small analysis, however, shows quite an interesting result: that there is actually some evidence of a reduction in soil conductivity (*i.e.* some soil acidification), as well as some evidence for nutrient enrichment (N: 4.5 for decreasing species; 5.3 for increasing species). These may well be significant results in understanding the combined effects of these two factors. Woodlands on more acidic soils in southern Hertfordshire have certainly shown some declines in species of less acidic conditions over the last 50 years or so (*e.g.* violets), while the increase of species of more nutrient rich environments, such as Nettle *Urtica dioica* and Cow Parsley *Anthriscus sylvestris* is also evident in others. The N attribute may also have something to do with the increase in species such as Pendulous Sedge *Carex pendula*, although increased deer browsing is also a likely factor, as well as the overall neglect of coppices and their shading out of herb communities generally, especially along rides or those characteristic of coppice coupes in the past. Other impacts on woodland have also included drought, especially on the Chalk, and wind-throw, especially from the storms of 1987 and 1990.

For species of scrub and hedgerows, there is also some evidence for change, but in this case the analysis shows a slight increase

Photo.: J. Bowden, with permission from North Hertfordshire Museums Service

Aldbury Nowers, old Beeches by Strawberry Wood, c.1965.

Aldbury Nowers Beech woodland, illustrating effects of drought and wind-throw on Beech woodlands.

in soil conductivity, implying an increasing pH in these habitats, as well as an increase in available nitrogen. These are effects we might attribute to the effects of increased eutrophication of hedgerows generally.

The results for open gravel and sand habitats, alongside those for heath and acid grassland, show that there is quite strong evidence for an increase in especially nutrient availability in such habitats (N: 3.2 for decreasing species; 4.3 for increasing ones), which supports the perception that many native species once characteristic of places like gravelly roadside banks have been supplanted by species of rank herbs. That this has not been offset

to any great extent by the advent of modern gravel pits shows that not all native plant species benefit from such massive disturbance to their natural habitats, even when their preference for disturbed, open ground might appear to be a dominant characteristic.

As for the arable habitat, where so many arable weeds have decreased massively, it is interesting to note that, while there is some evidence for an increase in soil conductivity, the evidence for the effects of increased nutrients is equivocal, based on the *Flora* data. This might suggest that suppression of plant populations through use of weed-killers and changes in cropping regimes might be having overall more impact on them than fertilisers, as such.

Finally, the most heavily human-impacted environments – ruderal habitats and the habitats associated with the built environment – also show some interesting features. One interesting finding of the Flora Survey was that there appear to be no native or archaeophyte species associated with walls and buildings that have decreased to any great extent; rather that such species have actually increased. This includes several fern species, as well as plants like Pellitory-of-the-wall *Parietaria judaica*, despite the local impact of wall repairs and overall 'tidying' of urban environments. Any comparative difference between increased or decreased groups, however, is not available. It is interesting, though, that the mean N requirement for wall species increasing was 2. 6, which indicates a very low overall level of nutrients for this habitat, despite any recent impact of atmospheric nitrogen deposition. As for species of ruderal environments, the results of this little analysis are also equivocal, with no real evidence for an increased nutrient level, although there is marginal evidence for an increase in pH levels in such places.

This analysis has only looked at two factors that might have been causing changes, and the data collected for the Flora could no doubt be examined in greater detail to provide further insights. One such study has recently been carried out for Bedfordshire (Walker, *et al.*, 2009), using as its baseline the 'habitat studies' that John Dony made in Bedfordshire in 1949, published in his *Flora of Bedfordshire* (Dony, 1953). It is unfortunate that we had no opportunity to carry out a detailed re-assessment of the similar series of habitat studies that he published in his *Flora of Hertfordshire*. However, comparison of some of the results in Walker *et al.* (2009) with the study outlined above shows several parallel conclusions, especially that nutrient enrichment is a major factor of change with especially acidic grasslands, as well as for neutral grasslands; while he also noted a lack of clear evidence for eutrophication or acidification in calcareous grasslands; and also noted some evidence for an increase in woodland soil acidification.

From the data gathered for this *Flora*, and evidence for change presented by others, it is obvious that major shifts have occurred over the last 40 years, but the reasons are not necessarily always clear cut, unless we can document the individual changes observable at multiple localities. Woodlands, for example, have demonstrated some effects of acidification, but in parallel with this we have seen large-scale re-planting of many areas of ancient woodland in the 1960s, followed by a long period of neglect, when not only the re-planted areas, but woodlands re-colonising after wartime felling became more and more overgrown, their rides becoming neglected and often almost entirely lost. This process may continue, or, if wood for fuel or other uses has an increased demand, we could see major shifts of woodland vegetation, perhaps even the re-appearance of supposedly extinct species.

Acidic grasslands associated with old pasture areas rapidly became uneconomic after the 1950s, and were often the first to suffer either from arable conversion, or to 'improvement', while those that remain now tend to rely on their amenity value, which itself is a shifting scene, depending on fashion, the availability of funding to maintain them and so on. Most semi-natural neutral pastures, once extensively used for both beef cattle rearing and dairy herds, have been extensively replaced by improved grasslands, unless they have become derelict or replaced by horse grazing, while hay meadows are almost non-existent. Old commons, which had already lost their economic use as grazing long before the 1960s, steadily became overgrown with scrub, unless they were kept open either for amenity purposes or for sports, especially golf, and again this continued use depends on fashion and finance. Chalk grassland has also suffered the same fate, but here its natural buffering against acidification has helped it, along with the fact that so many remaining sites have been maintained by conservation management. The massive increase in both dry and flooded gravel pits has already been mentioned as a major factor in the County, and one that has contributed to the increases in many species, although more specialised wetland plant communities, especially of rivers and spring-fed mires, have declined dramatically. Finally, we need to reflect on the parlous state of road verge flora in the County. At one time extensively used either as casual grazing by wandering livestock, or as a source of hay, these have been systematically degraded across the County through a combination of neglect, over-mowing in some cases, or mowing at the most deleterious time of year, and most recently from the impact of salting of roads in winter. Given that,

Fox Covert, Therfield, April 1988, after storm damage.

Fox Covert, Therfield, regeneration of chalk grassland after windthrow, 1992.

Sheethanger Common, old chalk pit, c.1965.

Sheethanger Common, 2005, demonstrating scrub encroachment and loss of important chalk grassland to golf course.

in arable areas, these are often the last vestiges of old grassland, this is unfortunate, to say the least.

Overall, the major shift has been away from plants characteristic of ancient habitats, maintained by centuries of stable management for one reason or another, towards a landscape of heavily disturbed habitats and the plants associated with them. This trend looks certain to continue, and the impact of climatic warming will only exacerbate the change, because it will tend to shift plant communities towards greater instability, as some species lose out, and others move in. Non-native species will be to the fore in this process, and the results of these changes are not entirely predictable. Future recording will need to be able to assess such changes as they occur.

Chapter 7. Alien plants in Hertfordshire

Given the County's proximity to London, the fact that it is crossed by all manner of communication routes, and that it is not that far from the south-east coastline, opposite the European mainland, it is not entirely surprising that it has got its fair share of introduced alien plants.

It is not always easy, though, to tell what is 'alien' and what is not. Mankind has been a feature of the natural environment in western Europe for a very long time, and 'natural' habitats have evolved alongside our activities during that time. We have brought species with us as we colonised, some deliberately, many not. Our physical effects on the environment, as with any animal species, includes some disturbance, which has often enabled these fellow-travellers to take hold. The advent of crop cultivation played a major part in the introduction of many species, especially arable weeds. Many of these arrived so long ago it is hard to identify them from the native vegetation, other than that they tend to occur in disturbed ground, and not to have any record in pollen profiles and other deposits of the late Pleistocene in Britain (Godwin, 1975). These early colonisers have been classed by Preston *et al.* (2002) as 'archaeophytes'.

From about the beginning of the 16th century, we began to have a much more noticeable effect on natural plant communities, partly because we began to keep records, but also because we started to organise our landscape more effectively. Trees began to be planted in large numbers, gardens expanded, trade came to connect with the wider world, roads were improved for the first time since the Romans left, major drainage and disturbance of large areas of wetland occurred, and so on. Plants that have arrived since 1500, therefore, have steadily increased in number (Clement and Foster, 1994; Ryves, Clement and Foster, 1996), so that the publication of any *Flora* these days needs to take account of a potentially enormous number of species, cultivars, hybrids and so on that were not at one time considered to be part of the 'wild' vegetation. Preston *et al.* (*op. cit.*) coined the term 'neophyte' for these plants, but this covers a multitude of sins, ranging from ephemeral occurrences of strange weeds that arrive with imported goods, through to species of trees that, once planted, have reproduced and 'taken off' in the natural environment.

As we often know so little about the arrival of archaeophytes, this brief account does not pay them any further attention, other than to say that they tend to behave much more like native parts of the flora, and are, in general, in decline, along with so many native species. This applies particularly to the arable weeds, although some buck the trend and do increase, given the chance. So, for example, seven long-established arable weed species have been found to be increasing, as compared with 21 that have significantly decreased.

For the neophytes, we can say much more. We have some 923 species (including a few fertile or aggressively invading hybrids) of neophyte recorded for all time as naturally occurring in the County, out of a total list of 1969 species, at the time of writing (around 47% of the total recorded flora). But, how many of these are really established? Also, do some sorts of introduced plants more readily establish themselves than others? By far the majority of these introduced species, though, are only ever ephemeral occurrences – they might turn up once or twice, maybe hang on at a location for a while, then disappear again. They may be interesting, but not really, perhaps, a problem for the native vegetation. However, some do become established, and increasingly some can cause concern.

Oxford Ragwort Senecio squalidus *Hitchin, 1990.*

Studying the alien flora

We are very fortunate in Hertfordshire that a small number of keen botanists have spent some considerable effort tracking many of these plants down, and trying to understand their occurrences. In the 19th century, A. R. Pryor made some records of alien weeds around railway sidings at Hatfield and other places, but it was not until A. W. Graveson and his father William began to study the increasingly varied alien weed flora associated with the grain depots and maltings by the Lee Navigation at Ware and Hertford around 1910-25 that we began to get a picture of just how many plants were involved. The Oxford-based G. C. Druce, accompanying Charlotte and Alice Trower from Stansteadbury, also added to records from this area; while Joseph Little picked up the existence of plants introduced with waste wool ('wool shoddy') used as a soil-conditioner on the fields in northern Hertfordshire; and Hugh Phillips collected some specimens from waste tips in various places. More recently, John Dony made some effort in the 1950s and 1960s to examine waste tips more systematically, at a time when every major settlement had its own rather poorly-managed dump. During our own survey and before, however, we have been specially fortunate to have Gordon Hanson at Ware, who has continued Graveson's work, but focusing on waste tips especially, as well as studying the species that arrive in different ways, ranging from wool shoddy, through bird-seed, to soya waste and sewage treatment works, including cultivating material at his home. He was joined in a lot of his excursions by Ann Boucher, who also examined garden centres and the urban wastelands associated with supermarkets, industrial car parking areas and building sites in various places. Most recently there has also been some work carried out studying the species enabled to expand through increased salting of roads, as well as colonisation processes in gravel pits and set-aside arable.

The sources and habitats of alien plants

Attempts have been made (Clement and Foster, *op. cit.*) to document how these species actually arrive, and the work locally of especially John Dony and Gordon Hanson has greatly added to our knowledge. In this account I need to stress that without their effort, we would know much less than we do about the alien flora and its impact locally, and I gladly acknowledge that this summary would not have been possible without them and others.

A brief analysis of the 923 neophyte species recorded from the County has been carried out, to try and assess the major sources from which they have derived, as well as to see if there are any differences in the way that different categories of introduced plant behave.

Known sources of alien plants in Britain as a whole, and Hertfordshire in particular, are bewilderingly varied, *e.g.*:

Docks and their cargoes (including ships' ballast).
Wool shoddy waste (from the cleaning and treatment of raw wool, often imported long distances in the past, from Australia, Argentina, *etc.*).
Grain processing and transport.
Spice importation and manufacture.
Oilseed cultivation and processing.
Road salt associates.
Medicinal herb cultivation.
Vegetable cultivation.
Garden and horticultural introductions.
Bird-seed spreading.
Game cover and feed sources.
Railways (including track ballast introductions).
'Wild-flower' mixes.
Pulverised fuel-ash introductions.
Timber planting.
Landscaping and ornamental planting.
Fodder and hay introductions.
Grass-seed contaminants.
Aquaculture and fish pond creation.
Compost processing.
Dune and bank stabilisation.
Bee-crop cultivation.
Vehicle movements.
'Night-soil' (human waste) importation or sewage sludge derivatives.

In practice, it is often not possible to separate out plants that have been introduced through one route and another. For example, grain contaminants are not easily separated from oilseed imports or species that have originated from dock cargo handling. Many wool-shoddy species, often those characteristic of fields where shoddy has been used regularly in the past, are also contaminants of grain, and in our area could be derived from either source, because wool shoddy manuring was only ever a localised practice

in Hertfordshire, mostly around Great Wymondley, Hitchin, Holwell and Newnham.

Two major sources over time of alien plant species in Hertfordshire, however, tend to stand out: grain processing and canal transportation of grain to and from Ware and Hertford (where the County's main grain stores and malting industries were); and horticultural importation or escapes (because Hertfordshire has long had fine gardens associated firstly with grand houses, latterly suburban gardens of the more wealthy middle-classes, as well as a thriving garden centre trade). A third source, urban waste tips and sewage processing works, could have been included in the analysis, but have not been listed separately, as most of the species involved actually derive from other sources, and merely happen to have been found at waste processing sites.

The following breakdown (inevitably full of potential misinterpretations, depending on our knowledge) shows the relative number of neophyte species deriving from different sources, as far as we can tell:

Source of introduction	No. of species/ established hybrids recorded in Herts.	No. (% total) of well-established species
Horticultural or garden escapes	325	55 (17%)
Grain/bird-seed or soya associates	208	7 (3%)
Ornamental tree/ shrub planting	90	15 (17%)
Food/fodder species	66	8 (12%)
Wool shoddy waste	47	0
Aquaculture/aquaria/ fish ponds	26	12 (46%)
Timber or fruit tree plantation	24	6 (25%)
Grass-seed contaminants	16	3 (19%)
Road salt associates	13	4 (31%)
Wild-flower seeding	6 (incl. alien subspecies)	0 (too soon to tell?)
Medicinal herb cultivation	5	3 (66%)
Oilseed species	5	1 (20%)
Arable crop contaminants	2	1 (50%)
Miscellaneous and uncertain sources (spice, ballast, fuel-ash associates, compost, timber associates, vehicle adherents, *etc.*)	90	16 (18%)
All sources	**923**	**131 (14%)**

Two things stand out from this table. Firstly, a relatively small proportion of all the escaped or introduced alien plants that occur in the County have ever really made much impact on the environment (although 131 well-established out of a total recorded flora of 1969 species is still a fair number – a little under

7%, and 14% of the recorded neophyte flora). Secondly, there are substantial differences between major categories of sources of introduced plants in the level of their eventual acclimatisation to our habitats. While the number of actual medicinal herbs that have ever really been recorded as escapes in the County is very low, the majority of these have become established, such as Greater Celandine *Chelidonium majus*. This is pretty insignificant, though, unlike the impact that aquaculture escapes seem to have on aquatic habitats. The 12 well-established aquatic escapes include such potential pests as New Zealand Pigmyweed *Crassula helmsii* and Parrot's-feathers *Myriophyllum aquaticum*. They also include both Canadian and Nuttall's Pondweeds *Elodea canadensis, E. nuttallii*, which seem to have replaced various native pondweed *Potamogeton* species in many of our freshwater habitats.

Himalayan Balsam Impatiens glandulifera *Braughing Meads, 1986.*

Monkeyflower Mimulus guttatus *R. Mimram, Tewin, 1982.*

Another category that is having a significant impact is the group of species that are encouraged (if not actually introduced) by road salting. Here we see that at least four of these often maritime plants (31% of all such species) have effectively supplanted native species along road margins in many places.

Conversely, there are some interesting reminders that some kinds of alien weeds do not necessarily result in future problems, even if, for a time, a particular plant appears to be 'well-established'. The wool-shoddy aliens are just such a case. While these may have become quite abundant for a while in the fields to which they were introduced, none appear to have become permanently established, now that the use of shoddy has ceased in our area. This may not be the case on sandy ground elsewhere, but certainly seems to be so on the Chalk in north Herts.

One major source that has tended to be ignored in the past is the scale of establishment of garden plants into the wild. Some are well-documented, such as Himalayan Balsam *Impatiens glandulifera* or Japanese Knotweed *Fallopia japonica*, but there are many others. A few of these have become substantial invaders

of semi-natural habitats, including the two mentioned. Others include the garden subspecies *argentatum* of the otherwise native Yellow Archangel *Lamiastrum galeobdolon*, Canadian Golden-rod *Solidago canadensis*, various Michaelmas-daisies, especially the hybrid *Aster × salignus*, and the Large Bindweed *Calystegia silvatica*. More often, though, they have merely taken advantage of our disturbance of habitats, as can be seen by the rapid spread of Himalayan Balsam along stretches of river that underwent massive dredging operations in the past, taking advantage of the exposed mud. One spectacular escape – Buddleia *Buddleja davidii* – has really, so far, only taken off in our heavily disturbed urban wastelands, and illustrates the way that bare, stony substrates, not a natural habitat in our County, are a prime target for such species, often native to mountainous or coastal environments, or to habitats where open ground is frequent, such as in the Mediterranean region.

Timber and ornamental tree or shrub species are also an interesting issue. We have recognised the massive invasive capability of Sycamore *Acer pseudoplatanus* for some time, and it certainly has become an established part of the woodland community, even in semi-natural woodlands, on many soil-types. Not so many people will have realised, yet, that its close relative Norway Maple *A. platanoides* is rapidly taking its place alongside Sycamore on more acidic soils; while, despite received wisdom to the contrary, Walnut *Juglans regia* shows signs of becoming a local menace on chalk grassland. It is also surprising that past botanists did not notice the rampant invasion of heathy sites by Rhododendron *Rhododendron ponticum* agg., now understood to be a virulent hybrid, the result of ill-thought-out genetic manipulation to produce a frost-hardy form of the plant for British gardens!

Few habitats, however, can have had the effect on them of invasive aliens as had the very man-made environment of the former sludge drying beds at Rye Meads Sewage Works. For a time in the 1980s and 1990s, this was an area with a strange vegetation totally dominated by alien plants, including Cape-gooseberry *Physalis peruviana*, various gourds and melons (*Cucumis, Cucurbita* and *Citrullus* species), Johnson-grass *Sorghum halepense* and Annual Sunflowers *Helianthus annuus*, to name but a few, alongside the ubiquitous Tomatoes *Lycopersicon esculentum*.

Rubbish-tip aliens were the subject of much study in the 1970s and 1980s, before modern rapid-capping methods became prevalent and access to the sites became difficult. Various goosefoot *Chenopodium* species owe their records to this work, and these sorts of plants have also been spread frequently through manuring of fields. Species of *Amaranthus* are spread similarly. Bird-seed aliens occurred regularly on these tips, but have also now tended to turn up frequently in gardens, where bird-tables are used. Given that few of these sites are actually botanically recorded, the occurrence of many plants, such as Yellow Bristle-grass *Setaria pumila* and Rough Cocklebur *Xanthium strumarium*, could be very much greater than the records so far suggest.

Alien plants and the future of our environment

It may well be that, until about 1900, invasive aliens (other than ignored species like Rhododendron) were not really a particular problem for the natural environment. We had been altering natural ecosystems for centuries, but we still had a landscape where natural grasslands, semi-natural woodlands (with or without some of the trees being planted), wetlands and even rough ground, were still essentially 'natural' in plant species composition. A study of Oughton Head Common at Hitchin that I carried out in the 1970s showed this (James, 1980a), where the plant community, from quite detailed records, showed very few 'alien' species before about 1930, but where many species not normally associated with natural wetlands, including a number of aliens, had become established by the 1970s as a result of mismanagement of the habitat and water sources, since when the process has continued, through further ground disturbance and introduction of path materials, for example.

Physical disturbance of our environment is one thing, often only a temporary effect, but chemical alteration, through misuse of fertilisers, the effect of broad-spectrum pesticides, over-manuring, road run-off or deposition of atmospheric nitrogen and other chemicals from internal combustion engines or power stations, *etc.* has probably had a major effect, although precise impacts are hard to dissociate from other factors. In a number of cases, the spread of some alien species seems to have been as a direct response to the opportunities that such chemical interference with the environment have offered. The advent of road-salt associated species is one obvious example, with species like Reflexed Saltmarsh-grass *Puccinellia distans*, Danish Scurvy-grass *Cochlearia danica* and Sea Spurrey *Spergularia marina* all occurring along road verges, often to the exclusion of native plants. Other examples, however, include otherwise native species, such as Hemlock *Conium maculatum* or Prickly Lettuce *Lactuca serriola*, which have recently massively expanded as an apparent response to nitrogen enrichment along roadsides. As nutrient enrichment continues to mount, these kinds of effects will increase, and allow other changes.

The real potential impact of some alien plants, however, has probably not yet been felt. This may be the case with many species of warmer, southern climates, such as Great Brome *Anisantha diandra*, which is quite likely to increase if summer temperatures rise substantially. Climatic warming is therefore likely to be a releasing factor on the occurrence of some currently infrequent alien weeds. Hoary Mustard *Hirschfeldia incana* is one that has recently expanded through the County along roadsides, while Guernsey Fleabane *Conyza sumatrensis* is another, the latter capable of colonising open areas in semi-natural woodland as well.

One area where there is genuine cause for concern, though, is the recent trend in 'conservation' to feel that looking after the natural environment must include adding species to what is there

A505 with Danish Scurvy-grass Cochlearia danica *Kelshall, 1992.*

naturally. Sometimes this is deliberate, such as the sowing of road verge seed-mixes that include pretty flowers. Unfortunately, all too often, the plants are in the wrong place, even if they are supposed to be 'native' species. A more disastrous problem is the misguided introduction of alien forms of otherwise native plants into these so-called environmental enhancement schemes. Quite often, this is because the seed-suppliers, or sometimes those planning the work, have a limited idea of what 'native' means. As a result, we get south-eastern subspecies of Kidney-vetch *Anthyllis vulneraria* or southern subspecies of an otherwise rare plant like Yellow Chamomile *Anthemis tinctoria* in places where native grassland plants could arrive perfectly well on their own, with much more positive long-term conservation benefit.

Ivel Springs, Baldock, sown wildflower meadow, 2009, this time with truly native seed.

A more insidious problem still has recently become more evident, although similar problems have probably existed for at least 200 years. This is the introduction into the wider environment of non-native trees and shrubs. In the past, these were usually brought in either to ornamental parklands, or to forestry plantations, and the unnatural origin of these was usually (but not always) pretty evident. Since about 1980, however, we have seen an explosion of 'landscaping' and 'amenity planting'. This has not just involved the tidying up and 'prettifying' of our townscapes, with extensive *Cotoneaster* beds, for example, but also has involved extensive planting of replacement hedgerows in the open countryside, and, more recently, the introduction of native look-alike species into even our nature reserves and other wild sites, a problem highlighted recently by Peter Sell of Cambridge Botanic Garden (Sell, 2007). Native shrubs like Dogwood, Wayfaring-tree, Guelder Rose, and even ancient woodland indicator species like Field Maple and Hazel are being planted out in the landscape, not with the real locally-native form, but with similar looking species or subspecies, often from south-eastern Europe or Asia. The real problem is that, all too often these can hybridise with our native plants and effectively infiltrate our natural plant communities, with what long-term effect we cannot tell. All we do know is that some native tree species, such as the Common Oak *Quercus robur*, have had the impact of plantation of look-alike forms for a long time, and we might ask, has this affected their reproduction in some areas? Certainly the oaks in some woods, such as parts of Northaw Great Wood, for example, look nothing like true *Q. robur*, and natural regeneration in these areas is often minimal.

In general, though, many scare stories about alien plants tend not to reflect reality. Even species that are reckoned to be 'virulent weeds' may not eventually turn out to be a major issue. Water Fern *Azolla filiculoides*, for example, is capable of totally covering a pond, but is also quite likely to just disappear again. If Walnut does take off in some open woodlands (as opposed to prime chalk grassland), is that necessarily a problem, given that native trees like Beech are likely to suffer and retrench as a result of changing climate? Do Sycamore trees in a native wood really badly affect other species? Are the conifers self-seeding in some woods presenting any real threat to the native Hornbeam, any more than past forestry has done?

One thing is certain, though, disturbance of genuinely natural plant communities is going to continue. Every new development involving soil-disturbance in a piece of genuinely ancient habitat, involves the likelihood of an alien species gaining a foothold. Climate warming, with its effects on these natural plant communities adversely affecting the balanced ecosystems that they represent, will allow more plants from especially southern Europe or similar climates elsewhere to increase in the gaps created in such environments by the loss of native species. Climate warming also affects the nature of colonisation processes

Hollyhock Alcea rosea *with Pot Marigolds* Calendula officinalis *self sown at Ashwell, 2004.*

when we do disturb soils. Whereas only 20 years go, we could predict with some certainty what might develop in a particular situation, on particular soil-types, as a result of major disturbance (*e.g.* road-works or gravel extraction), this is becoming less so as alien species are given an advantage that they previously did not have.

The importance of continued recording and study of alien plants, therefore, must not be underestimated. As the processes of colonisation by species continue, we need to record the arrival of species in new localities, and to register their impacts, if any. This perhaps requires more active recording of such plants than the more usual native species of semi-natural habitats, because they are in the process of moving in to our existing environment. Looking out for interesting aliens, too, is a challenge for identification and a spur to look in unlikely places. We never know what might be found.

Chapter 8. A gallery of Hertfordshire plant sites and habitats

The following photographs illustrate some of the major plant localities and their habitats in Hertfordshire, mostly taken during the period of the Hertfordshire Flora Survey. Some were taken earlier, and have been included either because I feel they reflect the nature of the sites concerned during the survey, or, in a few instances, illustrate the habitat before significant changes that have now taken place at these sites. There are also some more general views that demonstrate some other aspects of the County's habitats, partly for the benefit of those who do not know the County well, or at all.

These photographs will gain in value over time, because they show what it was we were surveying in the 1980s, 1990s and 2000s. I hope they also demonstrate that Hertfordshire still has a diverse and attractive natural environment, in places, if we make an effort to find it. Long may it remain so.

Chiltern Hills and valleys

Telegraph Hill and Icknield Way, Lilley, 1975.

Telegraph Hill, Lilley, 1987.

Tring Park, lower slopes, 1980.

Hexton Chalk Pit, 1987.

Berkhamsted Common, Beech avenue, 1983.

Icknield Way, Lilley, 1989.

Redbournbury Meadows, 1988.

Gade Valley Meadows, spring pool, 1995.

Wilstone Reservoir, inlet marsh, 1989.

Roughdown Common, old chalk pit, 2005.

Chorleywood Common, 1990.

Pitstone Quarry 2, Herts-Bucks, 2006.

Gaddesden Hoo Meadows, 1992.

Frogmore Meadows, Sarratt (West), 2007.

Colne Valley

Colney Heath, Furze Field, 1991.

Near Bricket Wood, old pastures, 1997.

Moor Mill Pit, Park Street, back-fill pools, 1991.

Croxley Common Moor, 2006.

East Anglian Heights chalk lands

Clothall Common Fields, 1983.

Pen Hills, Therfield Heath, 1986.

Kelshall, Coombe Road view, 1999.

Therfield Heath, east end, 1992.

Weston Hills, Gibbet Hill, 2009.

Lea Valley

Old R. Lea, Amwell, 1984.

Cheshunt Gravel Pits, Seventy Acre Pit, 1989.

Hollycross Lake, Amwell Quarry, 1988.

Chadwell Banks, Kings Meads, 1989.

Rye Meads Meadows, 1993.

By Codicote Heath, acid grassland, 1978.

Norton Green, Knebworth, 1986.

Hitch Wood, Langley, 1978.

Frogmore Pit, Aston, 1987.

Watery Grove, Knebworth, 1980.

Hitch Spring, Langley, 1988.

Poplars Green Meadows, Tewin, 1982.

Panshanger, by old house site, 1989.

Photo:: Brian Sawford

Graffridge Wood, Knebworth, 1997.

Burleigh Meadow, Knebworth, 1998.

Nomansland Common, 2005.

North Herts wetlands

Purwell Meadow, Hitchin, 1983.

Blackhorse Meadow, Baldock, 1987.

Folly Alder Swamp, St Ippollitts, 1989.

Oughton Head Common, Hitchin, 2000.

Norton Common, Letchworth, marsh, 2009.

North-east plateaux and river valleys

Patmore Heath, swamp by pond, 1982.

Bury Mead, Ardeley, aerial view, April 1985.

Moor Hall Meadow, Ardeley, with Brian Sawford, 1985.

Patmore Heath, aerial view, April 1985.

Bury Mead, Ardeley, 1998.

Great Hormead Park Wood, 1987.

Moor Green, Ardeley, 1996.

Cross Leys Wood, Barley, 1993.

Blagrove Common, Sandon, 1998.

Photo.: Brian Sawford

Sawbridgeworth Marsh, 1995.

Nuthampstead, conservation headland, 2001.

South Herts. plateaux

Berrygrove Wood, Aldenham, pond, 2001.

Potwells, North Mymms, 1996.

Claypits Meadow, Bayford, 1976.

Northaw Great Wood, Middle Way, 1995.

Hatfield Home Park, 1988.

Ermine Street, Broxbourne Woods, 1991.

Foulwells Spring and pond, Brickendon, 1994.

H.M. Queen Mother opening Aldbury Nowers Nature Reserve, June 1991.

Chapter 9. Results of the Flora Survey: taxonomic accounts and plant distributions

The following accounts comprise the results of the Hertfordshire Flora Survey for individual species, subspecies and hybrids, together with summary details of all other taxa recorded in the wild in Hertfordshire since the 16th century. The species accounts are given in taxonomic order, following the currently accepted Order and Family sequence, proposed by Cronquist (1981), as amended by Stace (1997). Taxonomic Orders and Sub-Orders are indicated, including a general group name in English to identify which groups of plants these cover. Within each of these, the taxonomic Family (and some Sub-family, Tribe and Section) names are given, with English group names in brackets, under which the Genera are in taxonomic sequence. Individual species then follow, with detailed accounts; followed by notes on recorded subspecies, varieties and hybrids. Some Families and Genera are also given brief general accounts where there is a need to indicate specific issues about recording, or to show how identifications have been approached.

Presentation of information in the taxonomic accounts

Each species account follows a standard format:

Taxonomic name and authority
Map number (where relevant)
Common (English) name(s)
Conservation status: national or local
Ecological status: national/local
First documented record in Hertfordshire
Tetrad occurrence in Hertfordshire from the Flora Survey/
 proportion of total area surveyed
Statement of change since the 1967 Flora/percentage change
General account of occurrence in Hertfordshire: habitat,
 distribution characteristics, results of current survey, issues
 concerning conservation and interpretation of data
Tetrad statistics for Dony (1967 survey); and from combined
 records: 1950-1986

Taxonomy

The taxonomic name and authority follow the recommended forms adopted by Stace (1997), except that, for orchids, recommended taxonomy proposed by Bateman (2001) have been used; while some extra taxa and nomenclatural changes proposed by Sell and Murrell (1996, 2006, 2009) have also been adopted; and, where Stace does not deal with a particular alien species, the taxonomy recommended by Clement and Foster (1994), or Ryves, Clement and Foster (1996) have been adopted The taxonomy of the critical groups *Rubus*, *Hieracium* and *Taraxacum* follows that recommended by the respective BSBI authorities: A. Newton/A. Randall, D. J. McCosh/P. D. Sell, and A. J. Richards/A. Dudman.

Common names

These are generally those adopted in Stace (1997), although a few more familiar or especially current local names have been given as alternatives.

Species maps

Most regularly occurring species and a few hybrids have been provided with a tetrad (2 x 2km) distribution map showing all records for the main survey period (1987-2005). Species with fewer than nine records have generally not been supplied with a map, as all records are detailed in the text. Distribution maps have a sequential number, referred to at the head of each species account. The map base adopted is the combined vice-county and administrative boundary map of Hertfordshire, as provided by Dr Alan Morton, author of the DMAP mapping package used for the production of the individual maps. These are overlain by the O.S. 10km grid to aid identification of the tetrad represented by any one record.

In addition to the map of recent records, less frequent species, or species that have had a significant change in distribution from the 1960s demonstrated, are provided with a vignette map taken from Dony (1967), to aid interpretation of the text.

Conservation status

National conservation statuses are taken from Cheffings and Farrell (2007). The statuses of 'Herts Rare' and 'Herts Vulnerable' are derived from the results of the current survey for native or archaeophyte species which appear to occur, for 'Herts Rare' species, in five or fewer localities (sites), or with a recorded decrease of 50% or more for 'Herts Vulnerable' species, where these are not otherwise designated as nationally rare or scarce. These together are taken to form the basis of a Red List of the County's higher plants (Appendix 1), and form the basis for a forthcoming *Hertfordshire Rare Plant Register*.

Ecological status

Ecological status is given as one of: 'native' (i.e. apparently having arrived in Britain naturally after the retreat of the last glaciation) or 'introduced'. The latter are also classed as 'archaeophyte' (having arrived in Britain through human agency before 1500);'neophyte' (considered to have arrived and become established through human agency after 1500); and 'casual' (where occurrence is sporadic and populations are not considered to be established). These statuses follow those adopted by Preston *et al.* (2002). Occasionally a species with a given status of 'native', 'archaeophyte' or 'neophyte' nationally may be a casual introduction locally, and this is stated. A few 'planted' species, particularly trees, are also included in the accounts, where these form an evident feature of the wider environment. Species planted in gardens and in ornamental or urban settings were not included in the survey.

First records

In general, these follow information provided in Dony (1967), except where subsequent research has suggested earlier occurrences. No systematic attempt has been made to independently verify these. Quite frequently, first records may be uncertain for various reasons, explained in the text. Where possible, some indication of the approximate first date is given, but in some cases, owing to confusion over taxonomy, etc., this may not have been possible, in which case a later date for the first properly documented record is substituted.

Tetrad occurrence in Hertfordshire

The total numbers of records for each species are derived from the author's Recorder database, and sum records shown in the tetrad maps. The proportion of tetrads that is given in which the species has been recorded during the survey is the rounded-up percentage of the **recorded tetrads in the Flora Survey** (491), not a percentage of the total number of tetrads that entirely or partly fall in administrative or vice-county Hertfordshire (508).

Statement of change since 1967

The statement of change is derived initially from a direct comparison of the recorded occurrences between the 1960s survey and the current survey. No attempt has been made to derive the kind of complex 'change indicators' that were used in Preston *et al.* (2002) or Braithwaite *et al.* (2006).

The number of recorded tetrads for a species in the current survey, expressed as a percentage of the total number of recorded tetrads (491) has been compared with the number of tetrads for the species from Dony's survey, expressed as a percentage of the recorded tetrads in his survey (466). These two percentages were then divided one into the other, and the result expressed as a **relative percentage change**, which is the figure given in brackets. The percentage change is therefore an expression of the overall extent of change relative to the original recorded occurrence. However, for species with a small sample of occurrences in both surveys, large percentage changes will only reflect a relatively small change in the number of actual tetrad records, and this needs to be borne in mind when interpreting any one change statistic. Factors that may also severely affect the change statistic will include the relative effectiveness of either survey, and especially whether a species was examined in a systematic way in the 1960s survey. For these reasons, the statement of change may, or may not reflect the percentage change quoted, and any discrepancies are reviewed in the species account. Finally, it should be borne in mind that the relative percentage change has been calculated strictly on the records given in Dony (1967) (except where errors in his account have been identified), and not on any subsequent understanding of the species at that time, as may be reflected in the totals of records for the period 1950-1986, which are given after the species accounts (see below).

General species accounts

Trying to account in any useful way for all the species, subspecies and hybrids of wild plants occurring even in a small County like Hertfordshire is quite a tall order, without creating a massive and unusable tome! The result has to be a compromise between facts, space and readability. As a result, an attempt has been made to standardise the approach to species accounts where possible, in addition to giving certain bits of information in abbreviated form, as described above.

For most species, general information is given first for the preferred habitats identified for each species in the context of Hertfordshire. No attempt was made to define standard vegetation (NVC) types for these, as it was felt that broader habitat characteristics, or sometimes more specific features, were of more importance for readers to gain an understanding of where the plants occur.

A brief statement is then given on the observed distribution in Hertfordshire, and on any likely reasons for this, such as soil or geological characteristics, etc. Factors influencing the recorded change in occurrence since Dony's or other surveys are then given, followed by notes on conservation issues.

In the case of less common species, where more detail may be required, or occurrences are very few (eight or less), the general statement on habitat occurrence is followed by an iteration of individual records in a standard format: locality, abbreviated tetrad reference in brackets, using the 'DINTY' notation (see Chapter 1 above) followed by the original recorder(s) in italics, the year of record, expert referees (where relevant), and the location of any voucher specimen (with standard abbreviation of herbaria, as devised by the Botanical Society of the British Isles and detailed in the section: 'Archives and biological collections sourced', at the end of this book). Records made by myself are given by initials: T.J. only. Most other observers' names are given in full, except where more than one record by an individual is given in a particular species account.

Occasionally, where I think a species is particularly interesting, I have sometimes expanded a little on historical or other characteristics, in the hope people will find this interesting and useful as well. All opinions expressed are my own, and so are any errors!

Tetrad statistics

At the end of most species accounts, statistics are given, in brackets, of the number of tetrad records for the species given by John Dony in his *Flora*; followed by a similar statistic for the total number of records available for a species made between 1950 (the assumed start of Dony's survey) and the end of 1986, including the records in Dony (1967). The reason for giving the latter statistic is that, in most cases, there were substantial numbers of extra records compiled after the end of the 1960s survey, and in some cases other records from Dony's survey period, not known to him, were subsequently received. As these data were not derived from a systematic survey, and as the date span over which the records were made is much greater than the present survey, it was not thought to be useful to make any direct comparison between these data and the recent assessment. However, enough recording was often carried out for many species to show evidence of increase or decrease between 1967 and 1987, and the text for the relevant species has picked this up.

Abbreviations and technical terms used in the text

(Latin 'tags' used as a shorthand way of expressing detail are shown in italics)

Acidic: of soils or ground-water, with pH 6 or lower.

Acidophile: of plants that prefer acidic soil conditions.

Adventive: a non-native plant species that can take advantage of disturbed habitats to become established.

Agg.: 'aggregate' (a group of species or other taxa treated together).

Alluvium/alluvial: (of) soils developed on superficial geological horizons deposited by post-glacial river activity.

Ancient woodland: apparently natural woodland considered to have been in existence since at least 1600 (Peterken, 1993).

Apomictic: plants that regenerate by direct production of fruits without sexual reproduction. The individual plants are therefore clones.

Archaeophyte: plants considered to have been introduced by human agency before 1500 (Preston *et al.*, 2002).

Base-rich: soils or water supplies with high available calcium/magnesium (compare with 'base-poor').

Bourne: a seasonal or periodic river or stream. Often 'winter-bournes', streams derived from springs, only flowing in winter.

B.S.B.I.: Botanical Society of the British Isles.

c.: *circa* – 'about', 'approximately'.

Calcareous: soils or ground-water with pH 8 or more.

Calcifuge: of plants that tend to avoid calcareous soils.

Calciphile: of plants that prefer calcareous soil conditions.

Carr: wet woodland developed on fen peat.

Casual: plants which are introduced through human agency but which do not generally become established in the wild for any length of time (five years or more) (Preston *et al.*, 2002).

Cf.: *'confer'* – 'compare with'(similar to).

Cleistogamous: plants with flowers that do not (sometimes) open fully.

Clone: a plant of identical genetic make-up to another, produced either by apomictic reproduction, or through vegetative spread.

Coll.: 'collected by'/'in the collection of'.

Colonist: of plants that can take advantage of disruptions in habitats to establish populations, often temporarily.

Comm.: *'communicavit'*: 'communicated' (by).

Conf.: 'confirmed by' (of plant identifications).

Coppice: trees cut for fuel wood, etc. at or just above ground level on a repeated basis over time. The normal method of managing smaller woods (often called 'springs') across most of the County for centuries (compare with 'wood-pasture').

Cultivar: a plant derived from artificial selection and propagation by plant breeders.

Det.: 'determined'; 'identified by...'.

e.g.: *exempli gratia* – 'for example'.

Endemic: species confined as natives to a limited geographical area. In this book: the U.K. or British Isles.

Epiphyte: a plant that grows on the surface of another plant, especially on trees.

et al.: *'et alii'* – 'and others'.

etc.: *'et cetera'* – 'and other things', 'and so on'.

Eutrophic: nutrient rich or polluted with excess plant nutrients, especially nitrogen or phosphorus.

f.: *'filius'*; 'son' 'junior' (used as part of a species authority in relation to a named taxonomist).

Family: a group of genera regarded by taxonomists as sharing an evolutionary origin.

Flush: (plant communities developed on) a spring source or seepage.

Fly-ash: ash derived from the burning of coal at power stations (see: PFA).

Genus (plural: genera): a group of species considered by taxonomists to be derived from a single evolutionary parentage.

Halophyte: a plant that favours or is specially able to tolerate salt-enriched habitats.

Hb.: Herbarium (with standard abbreviation of the relevant institution – see list under 'Archives and biological research collections sourced for information on the Hertfordshire flora' at the back of the book).

Hort.: (plants) of horticultural origin.

ibid.: *'ibidem'* – 'the same as previously' (in relation to publications cited).

i.e.: *'id est'* – 'that is (to say...)'.

Indicator species: plant species used as 'indicators' of high quality plant habitat, on account of their restricted habitat requirements.

Km.: kilometre.

Loam: soil with relatively uniform mixes of silt, sand and clay, and with a relatively high humus content.

Maiden-stem: of a tree that has been allowed to grow naturally to full height without pollarding or coppicing.

Mesotrophic: with a moderate plant nutrient status.

Ms(s): manuscript(s) (with the name of the compiler and/or institution where housed (see list of sources at the end of this book)

Native: of plants thought to have arrived naturally in Britain after the end of the Pleistocene glaciation, c.10,000 years ago or subsequently.

Neophyte: plants thought to have been introduced through human agency since 1500 and which have become established in the wild (Preston *et al.*, 2002).

Neutral: of soils, etc., with pH between 6 and 8.

Nominate: of a subspecies that has been designated as the typical form of a species.

Op. cit.: *'opus(ero) citatum(e)'* – 'the work(s) quoted' (in relation to literature sources cited earlier in the text).

Order/Sub-order: higher taxonomic rankings, bringing together related families of genera and species.

Parasite: of plants that obtain their nutrients through direct association with the tissues of another plant.

Pers. comm.: 'personal communication' (from...).

PFA: pulverised fuel ash (fly-ash), a waste product of burning coal for electricity generation. It is highly calcareous and supports a specialised flora (Shaw, 1994).

pH: standard measure of soil or fluid acidity/alkalinity.

Podsol: acidic, leached soil developed over gravels or sands, showing a more or less well-marked iron-rich horizon or 'pan' at depth. A characteristic soil of dry heath.

Pollard: a tree lopped for fuel wood, etc. at head height or above on a periodic basis , to avoid grazing of regrowth by animals, a management system often used historically on common land or in parks.

Poor-fen: plant communities developed on peat with base-poor water supplies.

Rendzina: thin, organic-rich soil with no sub-horizons developed directly over Chalk or limestones. The characteristic soil of chalk downland (or some limestone pastures elsewhere).

Rich-fen: plant communities developed on peat with base-rich water supplies.

Ruderal: heavily disturbed, often eutrophic habitats associated with human habitation, highways and other disturbed land.

Saprophyte: plants that obtain their nutrients from the decaying remains of other plants.

Segregate: a species or other taxon identified and separated from a close relation by taxonomists.

Semi-natural: of plant communities which have been derived from natural plant associations but which have been substantially reduced in species-richness by human activity.

***Sensu lato/s. l.*:** of species, etc. 'in the broad sense' (compare with 'aggregate').

***Sensu stricto/s. str.*:** of species, etc. 'in the strict sense', i.e. as precisely described by the taxonomist who named the species.

Shoddy/wool-shoddy: waste wool combings from the production of yarn or cloth, formerly widely used as a soil conditioner and manure.

Sp./ssp.: 'species' or 'subspecies'. 'Sp.' is sometimes used to denote 'precise species uncertain'.

S.S.S.I.: Site of Special Scientific Interest, designated under the Wildlife and Countryside Act, 1981.

Stand-type: of an area of woodland with a defined association of tree species (Peterken, 1993).

Stool: the periodically re-cut stump of a coppiced tree, often of great age.

Subspecies: a taxonomically named race of a species, sometimes occupying a specific geographical area or habitat type.

Superficial deposits: surface geological horizons, in Hertfordshire often derived from Pleistocene glaciation or recent river activity (alluvium).

Taxon/taxa: defined biological entity(ies) at whatever level of classification.

'Teste': 'On the authority of...'

Tetrad: four Ordnance Survey 1km grid squares taken together to form a square for recording or sampling purposes. From the Greek: '*tetra*', 'four'.

U.K.: the United Kingdom of Great Britain and Northern Ireland.

VC: 'vice-county' – standard boundary of a recording 'county' defined by H. C. Watson in the 19th century to stabilise recording areas in Britain. The boundaries of these vice-counties are now set as a standard by the National Biodiversity Network Trust. Each vice-county is numbered and named: 20: Herts.; 21: Middx.; 24: Bucks.; 29: Cambs.; and 30: Beds. Vice-county numbers followed by a name in brackets [ ] denotes a section of a vice-county that is or has been in a different administrative County.

Var.: 'variety' – a taxonomically named form of a species, not regarded as significant enough to deserve subspecific rank.

Wood-pasture: open woodland used (usually historically) for grazing livestock. Often a management system used on ancient commons (compare with 'pollard').

In addition, the following have been used:

SP, TL, TQ: for the standard 100km squares of the Ordnance Survey grid that cover Hertfordshire. (see the introductory text above for a description of 'tetrad' references and the use of letters A-Z (omitting 'O') to denote these).

N., S., E., W.: for the points of the compass.

23/U, *etc.*: abbreviated references to denote the tetrad in which a record was made, omitting the 100km reference letters (see Chapter 2).

Wild Daffodil Narcissus pseudonarcissus *ssp.* pseudonarcissus, *see page 466.*

Chapter 10. Taxonomic account of the Hertfordshire Flora

LYCOPODIOPSIDA
(Clubmosses)

Lycopodiaceae (Clubmosses)

Genus: *Lycopodium*

Lycopodium clavatum L.   Herts Rare
Stag's-horn Clubmoss
Native.
First record: 1837.
Rare/extinct?

A plant of dry heath. There are 19th century records from the lost Wigginton Common and from Broxbourne Wood. It was noted as 'well-established' at a gravel pit S. of St. Albans in 1963 (Dony, 1967), the exact location not recorded. It was then recorded in relict heath habitat at Mardley Heath (21/P), 1973 *M. Hooper/J. Tomkins*, (Dony, 1975) (Hb. HTN), but became extinct there by 1982, over-shaded by young oaks. It was also reported by J. Saunders at Birchin Grove, Pepperstock (01/Y) in 1907, (Saunders, 1911) (specimen in Hb. LTN), but this was actually in Herts. It may yet re-appear in the County.

Stag's-horn Clubmoss Lycopodium clavatum *at Mardley Heath, 1978.*

Selaginellaceae (Lesser Clubmosses)

Genus: *Selaginella*

Selaginella kraussiana (Kunze) A. Braun
Krauss's Clubmoss
Introduced: neophyte.
First record: 1970.

This greenhouse weed was found as a casual at Ashridge, 1970 *J. G. Dony/J. Wilson* (Dony, 1971).

EQUISETOPSIDA
(Horsetails)

Equisetaceae (Horsetails)

Genus: *Equisetum*

Equisetum fluviatile L.
Water Horsetail
Native.
First record: 1838.
Tetrad occurrence: 29 (6%).
Decreased (-25%).

This is a plant usually of standing or slowly flowing water, sometimes in swamps. It is a good indicator of better quality aquatic habitat but is also capable of colonising new sites. It may be affected by high nutrient levels or pollutants.
(37 tetrads: Dony, 1967; 53 tetrads: 1950-1986)

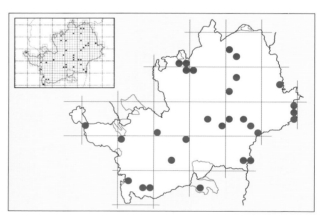

Map 1. *Equisetum fluviatile.*

Equisetum × litorale Kuhl ex Rupr.
(*E. fluviatile × E. arvense*)
Shore Horsetail
Native.
First record: 1987.

This scarce hybrid was found by the Lee Navigation, Cheshunt Gravel Pits (30/R), June 1987, *D. Bevan* (*comm.*: H. W. Matthews).

Equisetum arvense L.
Field Horsetail
Native.
First record: 1838.
Tetrad occurrence: 355 (72%).
Stable (-1%).

This is a frequent weed of waste places, cultivated or disturbed

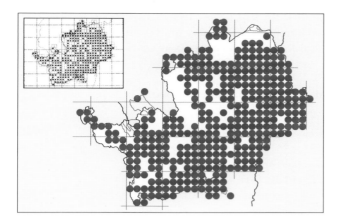

Map 2. *Equisetum arvense.*

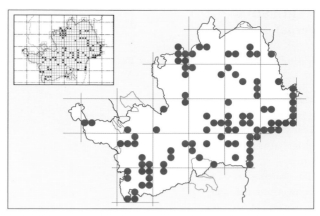

Map 3. *Equisetum palustre.*

ground across the county, only avoiding the driest soils, especially the Chalk.
(341 tetrads: Dony, 1967; 356 tetrads: 1950-1986)

Equisetum × rothmaleri C. Page
(*E. arvense × E. palustre*)
Native.
First record: 1987.
Very rare.

A U.K. endemic hybrid of damp, often disturbed ground. It was found on mud by a gravel pit at Stanstead Abbots (31/R) (= Amwell Quarry?), 1987 *B. Wurzell/D. Bevan* (Burton, 1988).

Equisetum sylvaticum L.   Herts Rare
Wood Horsetail
Native.
First record: 1838.
Tetrad occurrence: 3 (<1%).
Decreasing?

An attractive but rare plant of flushed ground on acidic soils, often under shade. It survives in quantity in a flushed meadow W. of Bayford Wood (30/E) *T. J./G. Salisbury*, 2002, where it was first recorded in 1919 (Hb. Graveson, HTN). It is apparently extinct at nearby Bells Wood (30/D), where it was last seen in 1989 *T. J./A. Pigott*, possibly affected by polluted water from the adjoining field. It was recorded in 1975 from Pope's Pondholes (20/N) *H. J. Killick*, where it is reported to survive. It was also recorded in Dony (1967) from hedgerows by Watling Street, Elstree; and in the 19th century from 'Hitchin Common' (= Oughton Head Common). The latter record is without supporting evidence, and the habitat is unlikely. There is also a record from a railway bank at Hitchin but the specimen in the Phillips Herbarium at HTN is wrongly identified.

Equisetum palustre L.
Marsh Horsetail
Native.
First record: *c.*1820.
Tetrad occurrence: 97 (20%).
Stable or slightly increased? (+5%).

A plant of of permanently damp, moderately base-rich soils in marshes, unimproved meadows and by ditches, sometimes also in disturbed, damp ground. Although the occurrence by tetrad does not show a significant increase or decrease, 19th century

records suggest rather more sites than have been recorded recently. Some sites are becoming shaded out or degraded as wet meadows are replaced by gravel pits, scrub and so on.
(87 tetrads: Dony, 1967; 104 tetrads: 1950-1986)

Equisetum telmateia Ehrh.
Great Horsetail
Native
First record: 1838.
Tetrad occurrence: 46 (9%).
Increasing? (+68%).

A plant of flushed ground on base-rich clays, sometimes in open woodland, but more often in fen or on waste ground. Apparently increasing, having colonised new waste ground habitats, especially in south Herts., although there are signs that the species has been lost from some historic sites on natural flushes.
(26 tetrads: Dony, 1967; 44 tetrads: 1950-1986)

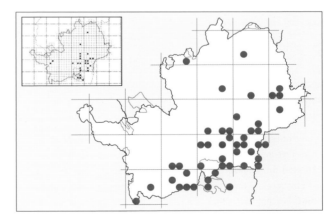

Map 4. *Equisetum telmateia.*

Great Horsetail Equisetum telmateia *at Cheshunt Gravel Pits, 1989.*

PTEROPSIDA
(Ferns)

Ophioglossaceae (Adder's-tongue Ferns)

Genus: *Ophioglossum*

Ophioglossum vulgatum L.
Adder's-tongue
Native.
First record: 1737.
Tetrad occurrence: 33 (7%).
Decreasing (-32%).

A plant of unimproved base-rich or mildly acidic grasslands, sometimes in open woodland. Lost from many damp pastures in river valleys, but capable of re-appearing in quantity, as at King's Meads (31/L) in 1994, where it appeared in hundreds following a period of intensive grazing.
(46 tetrads: Dony, 1967; 61 tetrads: 1950-1986)

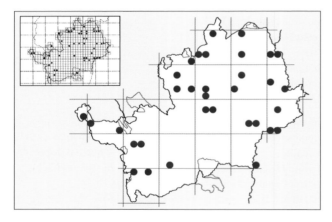

Map 5. *Ophioglossum vulgatum.*

[Genus: *Botrychium*]

[*Botrychium lunaria* (L.) Sw.
Moonwort
Native.

A plant of base-rich grasslands. There is a record from High Down, Pirton in 1882 (Babington, 1897), but Dony (1967) dismissed this as unlikely, unsupported by other evidence. In fact the habitat could have been suitable, but the record must remain doubtful owing to the lack of a specimen.]

Osmundaceae (Royal Fern family)

Genus: *Osmunda*

Osmunda regalis L.   Herts Extinct (as native)
Royal Fern
Introduced [formerly native].
First record: 1657.

At one time native of acidic poor-fen, now planted or escape from cultivation. Recorded from a meadow between St Albans and Windridge in 1657 by W.Coles (Dony, 1967). It was an apparent introduction at Crouch Green, Knebworth (22/A), in 1978

T. J./B. R. Sawford, where it remained in 1988, *M. J. Hicks*. It was also reported from Hadley Wood (VC21 [Herts: 1904-1965]), c.1950 *J. Sparling* (omitted by Dony, 1967).

Adiantaceae (Maidenhair Ferns)

Genus: *Adiantum*

Adiantum capillus-veneris L.
Maidenhair Fern
Introduced [native in the U.K.].
First record: 1925.

Recorded as established on a wall at Haileybury (31/K), 1988 *A. M. Boucher* during the survey. Dony (1967) reported it from a wall by the Lee Navigation at Ware, but omitted an earlier record from Ashridge, 1925, by R. Sworder. It is possible that either or both these latter records actually refer to the following species.

Adiantum raddianum C. Presl.
Introduced: neophyte.
First record: 1996?

Established on a wall at South Road Nurseries, Bishop's Stortford (42/V), 1996. *S. Watson*. (Hb. HTN).

Pteridaceae (Ribbon Ferns)

Genus: *Pteris*

Pteris cretica L.
Ribbon Fern
Introduced: neophyte.
First record: 1989.

Established on a wall at Bishop's Stortford (42/V), 1989 *S. Watson*. No ferns had been cultivated at the site for 50 years.

Pteris vittata L.
Introduced: neophyte
First record: 1980.

Established in derelict greenhouses at Westfield Road, Hertford (31/G), 1980-1993 *C. G. Hanson*.

Marsiliaceae (Pillworts)

Genus: *Pilularia*

Pilularia globulifera L.   UK Near Threatened
Pillwort   Herts Extinct
Native.
First (only) record: 1838.

This inconspicuous plant of open margins of acidic pools was found near Northaw Place (20/R) by W. H. Coleman. This was at the entrance to the former Northaw Common, a site lost after 1806. There were no further records.

Polypodiaceae (Polypodies)

Genus: *Polypodium*

Polypodium vulgare L.
Polypody
Native.
First record: 1819.
Tetrad occurrence: 22 (for the agg.) (5%).
Rare but increasing (+22%).

This is usually an epiphyte of walls, sometimes on trees, and rarely on shady banks. There were records from 22 scattered tetrads for either *P. vulgare* s. str. or unidentified records of the aggregate during the survey (13 for the segregate). This compares with 17 records for Polypody *sensu lato* in Dony (1967) (20 tetrads 1950-1986), indicating a moderate increase.

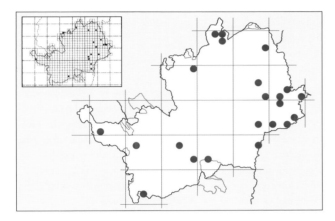

Map 6. *Polypodium vulgare.*

Polypodium × mantoniae Roth. and U.Schneider
(*P. vulgare × P. interjectum*)
Native.
First record: 1965.

Only so far reported from Aldenham Park (Dony, 1967).

Polypodium interjectum Shivas
Intermediate Polypody
Native epiphyte of trees, walls, *etc.*
First record: 1835.
Tetrad occurrence: 9 (2%).
Rare, but may be increasing (+38%).

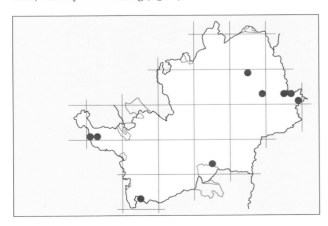

Map 7. *Polypodium interjectum.*

Dony (1967) recorded this from six localities, together with the first record, identified from a specimen. The identity of polypody species had been doubtful until this time, and so the species may have been under-recorded. The current survey found it mostly in the east of the County and around Tring.

Dennstaedtiaceae (Brackens)

Genus: *Pteridium*

Pteridium aquilinum (L.) Kuhn
Bracken
Native.
First record: 1748.
Tetrad occurrence: 354 (72%).
Stable (-3%).

Abundant in acidic woodland habitats, especially former wood pasture sites, and also on acidic soils elsewhere. The distribution of Bracken remains much as it was in 1967, generally avoiding Boulder Clay and Chalk. There is no real evidence of decline. In fact it may have increased its hold on woodland glade habitats, and especially on some remnant acidic grassland in a few areas, despite attempts to control it.
(348 tetrads: Dony, 1967; 358 tetrads: 1950-1986)

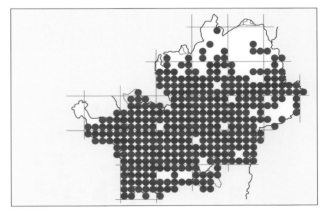

Map 8. *Pteridium aquilinum.*

Thelypteridaceae (Marsh Fern and allies)

Genus: *Oreopteris*

Oreopteris limbosperma (Bellardi ex All.) Bech.   Herts Rare
Lemon-scented Fern
Native.
First record: 1838.
Very rare.

A plant of damp, shaded places by streams on acidic soils in woods and former wood-pastures. Before the survey, it was last recorded in Bishop's Wood (09/R), 1980 *A. C. Jeffkins* (James, 1982); and also from the High Scrubs area (90/J) in 1973 *E. Byrne* (*comm.*: B.R.C.: CEH Monks Wood). A record for Wormley Wood quoted by G. Matthews in a report to the Woodland Trust (1982) probably refers to the 1955 record (Dony, 1967). Formerly (19th century), it was also in several localities in S.E. and W. Herts. During the survey itself it was not re-found, but a single young plant was re-discovered in Bishop's Wood (09/Q), 2008 *H. Matthews.*

Genus: [*Phegopteris*]

[*Phegopteris connectilis* (Michaux) Watt
Beech Fern

A record of *Phegopteris connectilis* in Pryor (1887) (as
P. calcarea) has been discounted as an error for *Gymnocarpium
robertianum* – see below.]

Aspleniaceae (Spleenworts)

Genus: *Phyllitis*

Phyllitis scolopendrium (L.) Newman
Hart's-tongue
Native.
First record: 1597.
Tetrad occurrence: 102 (20%).
Slowly increasing (+37%).

Relatively uncommon, in shaded banks, walls and sometimes
by watercourses, although perhaps formerly under-recorded.
As it needs damp conditions it is not surprising that this is most
frequent in the Chilterns, where it occurs on shady lane banks, but
it is also quite widespread in E. Herts. It is quite often a feature of
brickwork by rivers, and also the banks of the Grand Union Canal.
(71 tetrads: Dony, 1967; 90 tetrads: 1950-1986)

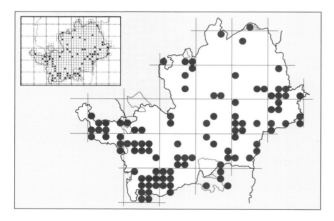

Map 9. *Phyllitis scolopendrium.*

Genus: *Asplenium*

Asplenium adiantum-nigrum L.
Black Spleenwort
Native.
First record: 1834 (Leighton: in Hb. Warwick Museum).
Tetrad occurrence: 27 (6%).
Stable, or slightly increasing (+15%).

Uncommon on old walls, especially near water, formerly
sometimes on lane banks but sometimes overlooked, and
occasionally lost through pointing of walls. It is scattered across
the county except in the driest areas, such as on the Chalk. The
map also shows its frequent occurrence by the Grand Union Canal.
It was probably lost from lane banks because of traffic pollution.
(22 tetrads: Dony, 1967; 29 tetrads: 1950-1986)

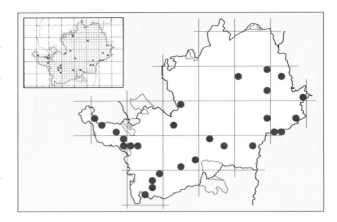

Map 10. *Asplenium adiantum-nigrum.*

Asplenium trichomanes L.
Maidenhair Spleenwort
Native.
First record: 1657.
Tetrad occurrence: 27 (6%).
Increasing (+59%).

An uncommon species of old walls, and formerly old lane banks.
Records from the current survey show a slight concentration in
the W., S. and central-E. Hertfordshire, but comparison with the
distribution shown by Dony shows rather little overlap, suggesting
either that it is under-recorded, or that it is an opportunistic
species which moves around readily. However, the kind of old
walls it likes are relatively rare, and liable to being 'tidied up'.
(16 tetrads: Dony, 1967; 21 tetrads: 1950-1986)

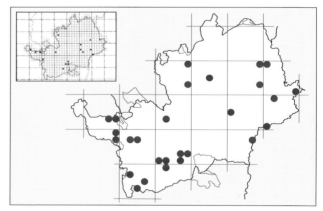

Map 11. *Asplenium trichomanes.*

Hertfordshire plants all appear to be ssp. *quadrivalens*
D. E. Meyer.

Asplenium ruta-muraria L.
Wall Rue
Native.
First record: 1843.
Tetrad occurrence: 71 (15%).
Increasing (+47%).

Also a plant almost restricted in our area to old walls, especially
near water. It shows significant signs of consolidating its presence,
especially in W. Herts. It occurs widely on railway bridges, in
churchyards and by canals. Dony also noted its increase from the
19th century, when it was described as rare.
(46 tetrads: Dony, 1967; 58 tetrads: 1950-1986)

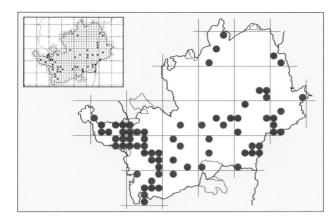

Map 12. *Asplenium ruta-muraria.*

Genus: *Ceterach*

Ceterach officinarum Willd.
Rusty-back
Native.
First record: 1787.
Tetrad occurrence: 10 (2%).
Stable, or slightly increased (+18%).

Rare, usually on old walls. There is perhaps some evidence of it having increased slightly in W. Herts., in damper conditions, but there does seem to have been a decrease in the drier E., perhaps owing to the droughts of the 1990s. Often long-persistent in favoured places, such as the wall of Standon Churchyard (32/W); also subject to the same tidying up of its habitat as other wall ferns, lichens and bryophytes.
(8 tetrads: Dony, 1967; 12 tetrads: 1950-1986)

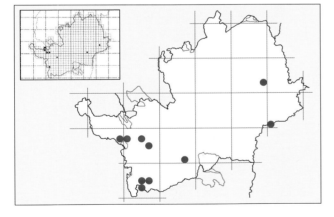

Map 13. *Ceterach officinarum.*

Woodsiaceae (Lady Fern and allies)

Genus: *Athyrium*

Athyrium filix-femina (L.) Roth
Lady Fern
Native.
First record: 1838.
Tetrad occurrence: 68 (14%).
Probably increasing (+89%).

This species of damp, shaded woodlands on mildly acidic or slightly calcareous soils is apparently especially susceptible to winter and early spring droughts, and therefore the current survey may have under-recorded it in the early 1990s. It occurs widely, especially in ancient woodlands in the W. and centre of the county, but will also appear in old secondary woodland in the right conditions. Dony (1967) may have under-recorded it also, because of droughts in the late 1950s, but there does seem to be good evidence for its real increase, because it appeared in many more tetrads in the damper period of the 1980s.
(34 tetrads: Dony, 1967; 93 tetrads: 1950-1986)

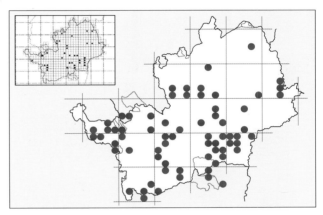

Map 14. *Athyrium filix-femina.*

Genus: *Gymnocarpium*

Gymnocarpium dryopteris (L.) Newman
Oak Fern
Introduced? [native in the U.K.].
First record: 1916.

Dismissed as doubtfully recorded by Dony (1967), but subsequently recorded on a railway bridge at Radlett (19/U), 1968 *D. J. Hinson* (Hb. HTN). The first record from Broxbourne in 1916 by J. W. Higgins was likely to be a similar occurrence.

Gymnocarpium robertianum (Hoffm.) Newman
Limestone Fern
Introduced [native in the U.K.].
First (only) record: *c.*1880.

The record of *Phegopteris calcarea* quoted in Pryor (1887) from Broxbournebury by R. T. Andrews should be referred here. The species was omitted from Dony (1967).

Shield Ferns to compare – Hard Shield-fern Polystichum aculeatum *(left) and Soft Shield-fern* Polystichum setiferum *(right), see opposite.*

Genus: *Cystopteris*

Cystopteris fragilis (L.) Bernh.
Brittle Bladder-fern
Introduced [native in the U.K.].
First record: 1882.

Not recorded during the current survey. Both the 1882 occurrence at Berrygrove Wood and the 1963 record from Barkway were casuals (Dony, 1967).

Dryopteridaceae (Buckler Ferns)

Genus: *Polystichum*

Polystichum setiferum (Forskål) Moore ex Woy.
Soft Shield-fern
Native.
First record: 1838.
Tetrad occurrence: 47 (9%).
Increasing markedly (+600%).

An uncommon plant of damp, shaded banks and wooded stream-sides, usually on acidic soils, although it seems to have increased enormously since 1970. Dony (1967) only found it at three localities. Nineteenth century records are hard to interpret because of confusion over identity between this and Hard Shield Fern. The current survey has found it scattered across most of S., W., central and E. Hertfordshire, but especially in the Broxbourne Woods area, where it is a regular, if local component of the flora in incised wooded stream gullies. In a few localities it may have been an escape.
(3 tetrads: Dony, 1967; 13 tetrads: 1950-1986)

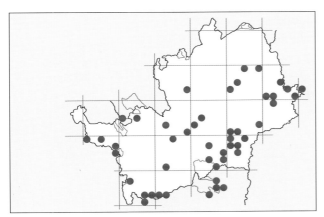

Map 15. *Polystichum setiferum.*

Polystichum aculeatum (L.) Roth
Hard Shield-fern
Native.
First record: *c.*1820.
Tetrad occurrence: 19 (4%).
Rare, but increasing (+255%).

Dony regarded this as rare, if slightly more widespread than Soft Shield-fern. It is a plant of ancient shaded road and stream banks on more or less calcareous soils, occasionally occurring as an escape. It has been a special feature of the shaded, eroded banks of several bournes in E. Herts. for some time, notably Nimney

Hard Shield-fern Polystichum aculeatum *Old Bourne, High Cross, 1987.*

Bourne (41/D) and the Bourne at High Cross (31/P). Dony gave a couple of records also from W. Herts. The current survey has shown that it has either been overlooked or has increased substantially. Its occurrence in the bourne gullies of E. Herts. is confirmed, but more significantly it has appeared in a number of old hedge banks around Flamstead and elsewhere in west Herts., including near one of Dony's sites at Ballingdon Bottom (01/H). A couple of records in south Herts. may be escapes.
(5 tetrads: Dony, 1967; 11 tetrads: 1950-1986)

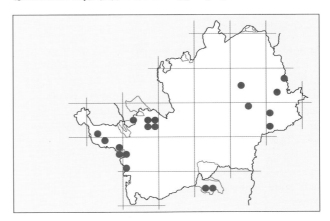

Map 16. *Polystichum aculeatum.*

Genus: *Cyrtomium*

Cyrtomium falcatum (L. *f.*) C. Presl
House Holly-fern
Introduced: neophyte.
First record: 1994.
Very rare casual.

Recorded from a drainage sump at Bishop's Stortford (42/V), 1994, *S. Watson*, in company with *Phyllitis scolopendrium* and *Asplenium trichomanes*. It re-appeared here in 2000 (Hb. HTN).

Genus: *Dryopteris*

Dryopteris filix-mas (L.) Schott
Male-fern
Native.
First record: 1833.
Tetrad occurrence: 380 (77%).
Stable (+4%).

A common plant of woodland, mature scrub and hedge banks,

rarely as an escape on walls, across the county in wooded situations, but becoming scarce on the drier calcareous soils, although more tolerant of calcareous conditions than most other species of local fern. The distribution has remained almost the same as shown by Dony.

(348 tetrads: Dony, 1967; 360 tetrads: 1950-1986)

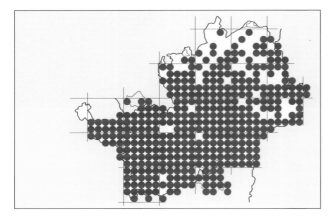

Map 17. *Dryopteris filix-mas.*

Dryopteris × *complexa* Fraser-Jenkins
(*D. filix-mas* × *D. affinis*)
Native.
First record: 1988.

This hybrid fern probably occurs quite widely, but only two records have been confirmed during the survey: Harding's Wood (90/P), 1988, *R. Mabey*; and Walk Wood (12/V), 1988, *T. J.*, (Hb. HTN). Two 'nothosubspecies' probably occur in the area: *D.* × *complexa* itself (with *D. affinis* ssp. *affinis* as the parent), and *D.* × *critica* Fraser-Jenkins (with *D. affinis* ssp. *borreri* as the parent). The Walk Wood specimen is the former.

Dryopteris affinis (Lowe) Fraser-Jenkins
Scaly Male-fern (aggregate)
Native.
First record: 1860 (for both ssp. *affinis* and ssp. *borreri*).
Tetrad occurrence: 69 (for the agg.) (14%).
Stable or perhaps increasing.

Regarded now by many as several different species, these were recorded during the survey under the aggregate name. As such, they are plants of especially ancient woodland on acidic or moderately acidic soils. They are widespread across W., central, and S. Herts., becoming rare in the E. and generally absent on the

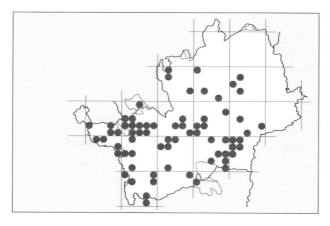

Map 18. *Dryopteris affinis.*

Boulder Clay and Chalk. They are most abundant on the damper Clay-with-Flints soils of the Chilterns dip-slope woodlands, but also in the Broxbourne Woods complex. Dony (1967) severely under-recorded them, owing to identification problems, giving only eight tetrads. Between 1970 and 1986 the then recognised 'species' was found in a further 21 tetrads, outlining much the same distribution as is now recorded. The current survey recorded the aggregate in 69 tetrads. However, 10 (35%) of the pre-1987 tetrad records were not re-recorded during the survey. Attempts were made to distinguish recognised subspecies, with 46 records made during the survey:

D. affinis ssp. *borreri* (Newman) Fraser-Jenkins
Borrer's Male-fern

Mentioned alongside *affinis* in Pryor (1887), this appears to be the principal subspecies (or species) (31 tetrads), and also appears to tolerate less acidic conditions. Dony's records may or may not have been of this.

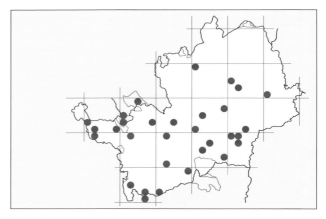

Map 18a. *D. affinis* ssp. *borreri.*

D. affinis ssp. *affinis*
Scaly Male-fern *s. str.*

Still widespread, but less common than *borreri* (22 tetrads), despite being more conspicuous. It occurs usually on more acidic soils.

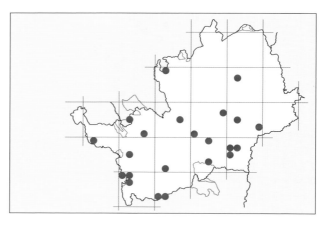

Map 18b. *D. affinis* ssp. *affinis.*

D. affinis ssp. *cambrensis* Fraser-Jenkins
Western Scaly Male-fern

Two specimens have been identified as this subspecies: from Oak Hill Park Wood (29/S) (VC20 [Greater London]), 1998,

T. J./G. P. Smith, (Hb. HTN); Mason's Plantation, Studham (01/C) (VC20 [Beds.]), 1999, *T. J./C. R. Boon/G. Salisbury* (Hb. HTN).

Dryopteris carthusiana (Villars) H. P. Fuchs
Narrow Buckler-fern
Native.
First record: 1843.
Tetrad occurrence: 73 (15%).
Probably increasing (+204%).

A plant of acidic woodland or former wood-pastures, rarely on damp heath or in poor-fen. The evidence for the increase in this species is equivocal, owing to identification difficulties in the past. It occurs quite frequently in heathy areas in the Broxbourne Woods complex, and at Ashridge, but also in acidic woodlands elsewhere, even mildly acidic woodlands in N. E. Herts. on Clay-with-Flints outliers. It is a feature of Alder fen at Oughton Head (13/Q), and is also characteristic of wet heath at Patmore Heath (42/M).
(23 tetrads: Dony, 1967; 41 tetrads: 1950-1986)

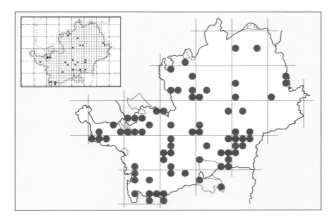

Map 19. *Dryopteris carthusiana.*

Dryopteris × deweveri (J. Jansen) Wachter
(*D. carthusiana × D. dilatata*)
Native.
First record: J. Godfree, *c.*1979.

Probably widespread, but the confirmed records are from Patmore Heath (42/M), *c.*1979, *J. Godfree* and again 1987-8, *J. L. Fielding*; Harpenden Common (11/G), 1990, *J. F. Southey*; Chalkleys Wood (12/W), 2003 *T. J.*; and Berrygrove Wood (19/J), 2001 *T. J.*

Dryopteris dilatata (Hoffm.) A. Gray
Broad Buckler-fern
Native.
First record: *c.*1820.
Tetrad occurrence: 313 (64%).
Increased markedly (+68%).

Frequent and common in woodlands, mature scrub, poor-fen and hedgerows, usually on acidic soils across most of the county, only avoiding the Chalk, urban centres and major river flood-plains. It becomes less frequent in woodlands on the Boulder Clay. The reasons for its increase are uncertain, but it does prefer nutrient-rich conditions, and may be responding to eutrophication, or it could have responded to increased shade in derelict woodland.
(177 tetrads: Dony, 1967; 240 tetrads: 1950-1986)

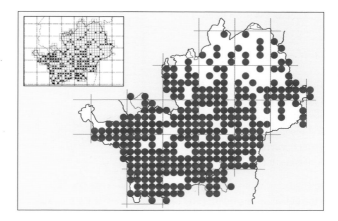

Map 20. *Dryopteris dilatata.*

Blechnaceae (Hard Ferns)

Genus: *Blechnum*

Blechnum spicant (L.) Roth
Hard Fern
Native.
First record: 1787.
Tetrad occurrence: 8 (2%).
Rare, but possibly increasing (+167%).

A plant of acidic woodlands and former wood-pastures; more frequent in the 19th century, this had become rare by the early 20th century, and remains rare now. It occurs sporadically, especially where former wood-pasture sites have survived as woodland. Current records are from: High Scrubs (90/J), 1987, *R. Mabey*; 1993, *T. J.*; Roundhill Wood (90/J), 1993, *M. J. Hicks*; Hare's Garden Wood (90/J), 2002, *T. J.*; Bricket Wood Common (10/F), 1998, *S. M. Hedley*; Sherrards Park Wood (21/G), 1988, *G. P. Smith*; Claypits Wood (30/I), 1999, *H. Matthews*; Cowheath Wood (30/I), 2006 *T. J.*; Highfield Wood (30/P), 2003, *T. J.*; Bishop's Wood (09/Q), 1989, *I. D. Marshall*; 1990, *H. Matthews*. Other sites from which records were made between 1967 and 1986 included: woodland at Lilley Hoo (12/I), 1967, *F. Bentley*; and Oxhey Woods (19/A), 1966-1979, *A. C. Jeffkins*.
(3 tetrads: Dony, 1967; 6 tetrads: 1950-1986)

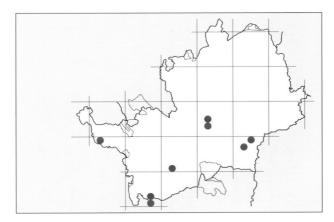

Map 21. *Blechnum spicant.*

Azollaceae (Water Ferns)

Genus: *Azolla*

Azolla filiculoides Lam.
Water Fern
Introduced: neophyte.
First record: 1915.
Tetrad occurrence: 35 (7%).
Increasing, but only relatively slowly (+373%).

This has now appeared in quantity in a number of sites, especially in the eutrophic gravel pits and canals of the lower Colne and Lea valleys, where it can sometimes carpet the water surface with red. It continues to appear erratically, however, just as Dony reported. (7 tetrads: Dony, 1967; 21 tetrads: 1950-1986)

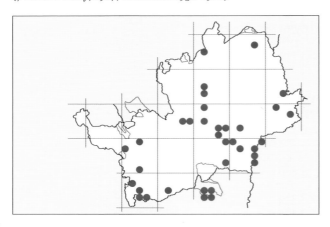

Map 22. *Azolla filiculoides.*

Water Fern Azolla filiculoides *Cheshunt Gravel Pits, 1989.*

PINOPSIDA (Conifers)

Pinaceae (Pines, Spruces and allies)

Genus: *Abies*

Abies alba Miller
European Silver Fir
Introduced: neophyte.
First record: 1978.
Tetrad occurrence: 8 (2%).

First recorded by B. R. Sawford at Roundabouts Plantation (12/L) in 1978, but probably only as planted. Recorded during the survey from eight tetrads, with self-sown trees recorded especially on the Reading Gravels in the Bramfield Woods complex: Park Wood (21/X), Brickground Wood (21/T), and Bright's Hill (21/Y), as well as possibly at Hare's Garden Wood, Tring (90/J).

Abies grandis (Douglas ex D. Don) Lindley
Giant Fir
Planted only.
First record: this survey.

Recorded as mature planted trees at Brickground Wood (21/T), 2000, *T. J.* There were no signs of regeneration.

Genus: *Pseudotsuga*

Pseudotsuga menziesii (Mirbel) Franco
Douglas Fir
Introduced: neophyte.
First record: *c.*1965.
Tetrad occurrence: 18 (4%).

Noted first as already mature planted trees in Broombarns Wood (20/X), *c.*1965, *T. J.*, since felled. Now known from 18 tetrads, in some of which at least it is regenerating, especially on acidic gravels, *e.g.* at Brickground Wood (21/T). Probably under-recorded.

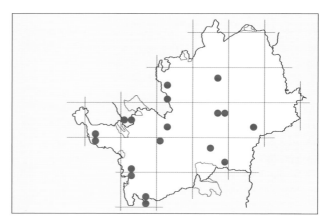

Map 23. *Pseudotsuga menziesii.*

Tsuga heterophylla (Raf.) Sarg.
Western Hemlock-spruce
Introduced: neophyte.
First record: 1988.
Tetrad occurrence: 16 (3%).

First recorded as mature trees at Rossway (90/T), 1988, *P. J. Kingsbury*. Recorded during the survey from 16 tetrads, in some of which it was noted as regenerating, but no doubt under-recorded. The frequency of naturalised trees is unclear.

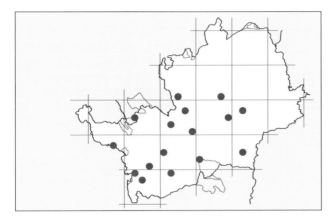

Map 24. *Tsuga heterophylla.*

Genus: *Picea*

Picea abies (L.) Karsten
Norway Spruce
Introduced: neophyte.
First record: *c.*1960.
Tetrad occurrence: 191 (39%).

Mentioned by Dony (1967) as a planted tree only. Noted from 23 tetrads between 1970 and 1986, almost solely as planted trees intermixed with other conifers or sometimes hardwoods, such as beech. The current survey recorded it very widely, with its most frequent occurrence on mildly acidic, free-draining gravels and Clay-with-Flints soils. Regeneration was recorded, but not widely, although accurate data are not available.

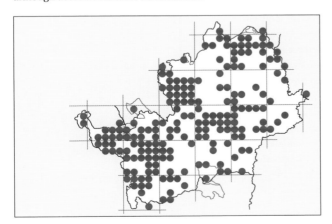

Map 25. *Picea abies.*

Picea sitchensis (Bong.) Carrière
Sitka Spruce
Planted only.
First record: 1994.

Recorded from tetrads 00/A, 00/P, 12/E and 42/J in small plantings. Under-recorded, but likely to be rare, owing to its poor adaptation to southern woodlands. No evidence of regeneration.

Genus: *Larix*

Larix decidua Miller
European Larch
Introduced: neophyte.
First record: 1957.
Tetrad occurrence: 223 (45%).

Mentioned as a planted tree in Dony (1967). Recorded from 34 tetrads between 1970 and 1986, and first noted as self-seeding at Oddy Hill, Wigginton (91/F), on chalk, in 1982 by J. Welsh. During the present survey, it was recorded from about half the County, although some of these records may have been mis-identifications. Fairly widely noted as self-seeding, especially on free-draining gravels.

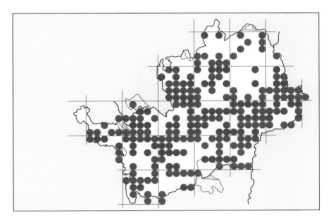

Map 26. *Larix decidua.*

Larix × *marschlinsii* Coaz (*L. decidua* × *L. kaempferi*)
Hybrid Larch
Introduced: neophyte.
First record: *c.*1987.
Tetrad occurrence: 55 (11%).

Widely planted, but probably also of natural occurrence in some sites where the parents have been planted together.

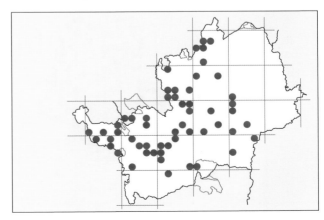

Map 27. *Larix* × *marschlinsii.*

Larix kaempferi (Lindley) Carrière
Japanese Larch
Introduced: neophyte.
First record: *c*.1987.
Tetrad occurrence: 38 (8%).

Fairly widely planted, especially in west Herts., but less so than the hybrid, and more recently than many of the European Larch. Evidence for self-sown trees is doubtful, owing to mis-identification of the hybrid.

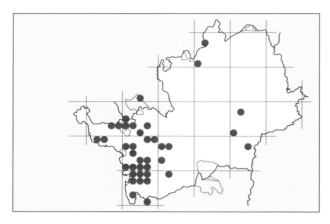

Map 28. *Larix kaempferi.*

Genus: *Cedrus*

Cedrus libani A. Rich.
Cedar of Lebanon
Planted only.
Only found in parks and ornamental settings, such as Evergreen Wood, Panshanger (21/W).

Genus: *Pinus*

Pinus sylvestris L.
Scots Pine
Introduced: [native in the U.K.].
First record: *c*.1840.
Tetrad occurrence: 312 (64%).

Coleman (1849) remarked on its regeneration at some sites, but it was omitted entirely by Pryor (1887) and recorded by Dony (1967) only as a planted tree. Some of these have been present for a long time, as there are folk tales of some being planted as 'markers' for Jacobite hiding places. The species has also been used as a nurse

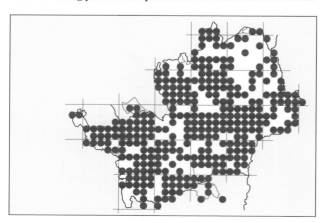

Map 29. *Pinus sylvestris.*

tree, especially for Oak, from the 19th century onwards. It was recorded from 36 tetrads between 1970 and 1986, but the recent recording showed that it is widely self-sown, particularly on acidic gravels, on former heaths and in wood-pasture woodlands. It was recorded during the current survey on almost every soil type, including Chalk, only becoming rare on the Boulder Clay and the wetter parts of the London Clay.

Pinus nigra Arnold
Austrian Pine/Corsican Pine
Introduced: neophyte.
First record: *c*.1965.
Tetrad occurrence: 104 (21%).

Dony mentions the Corsican Pine as being planted. The current survey showed that the broad species is widespread as a planted tree. No attempt was made to determine the separate distribution of the subspecies, although both occur. The predominant planted tree appears to be Corsican Pine, ssp. *laricio* Maire, although only three actual records of the subspecies were received. Natural regeneration is widespread, especially on more calcareous soils.

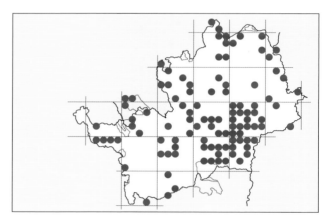

Map 30. *Pinus nigra.*

Taxodiaceae (Redwoods)

Genus: *Sequoia*

Sequoia sempervirens (D. Don) Endl.
Coastal Redwood
Planted only.
First record: this survey.
Occurs in parks, but also in woodland at Bayfordbury (former pinetum).

Genus: *Sequoiadendron*

Sequoiadendron giganteum (Lindl.) Buchholz
Wellingtonia
Planted only.
First record: this survey.

Often found in ornamental woodlands as a result of 19th century planting, sometimes away from obvious parkland, *e.g.* Home Wood, Cuffley (20/X).

Genus: *Taxodium*

Taxodium distichum (L.) Rich.
Swamp Cypress
Planted only.
First record: this survey.

Recorded at Bayfordbury (31/A), and by a derelict lake at Sacombe (31/P) during this survey. Also present in some formal park settings, *e.g.* Brocket Park (21/B).

Cupressaceae (Cypresses and Junipers)

Genus: *Chamaecyparis*

Chamaecyparis lawsoniana (A. Murray) Parl.
Lawson's Cypress
Introduced: neophyte
First record: 1988.
Tetrad occurrence: 20 (4%).

Widely used in plantations as a windbreak or sometimes as a nurse. Self-seeding freely in some sites, such as Bramfield Woods (21/Y), and Broxbourne Wood (30/I).

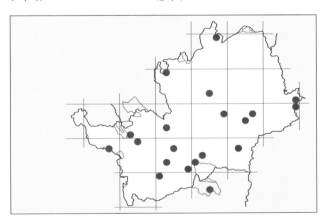

Map 31. *Chamaecyparis lawsoniana.*

Hybrid Genus: ✕*Cupressocyparis*

✕*Cupressocyparis leylandii* (A. B. Jack and Dallim.) Dallim.
(*Cupressus macrocarpa* × *Chamaecyparis nootkatensis*)
Leyland Cypress
Planted.
First record: this survey.

Recorded from a few plantations, *e.g.* Birchley Wood (01/K), but possibly in error for Lawson's Cypress. Most usually planted round houses, *etc.*

Genus: *Thuja*

Thuja plicata Donn ex D. Don
Western Red Cedar
Introduced: neophyte.
First record: 1988.
Tetrad occurrence: 40 (8%).

Widely used as a shelter tree in plantations, occasionally as a

nurse or for game cover. Self-seeds freely, especially on acidic soils, *e.g.* Bramfield Woods (21/Y), Broxbourne Wood (30/I).

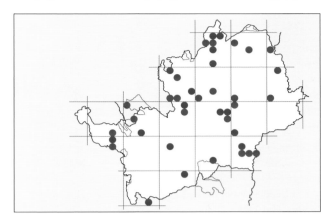

Map 32. *Thuja plicata.*

Genus: *Juniperus*

Juniperus communis L.   Herts Rare
Juniper
Native.
First record: *c*.1730.
Tetrad occurrence: 8 (2%).
Rare and decreasing.

Found as a native plant on both heaths and chalk grassland. Dony (1967) recorded it from eight tetrads, and the current survey found it in a similar number, although not all the same. Dony made the plant the subject of a special study, and population maps were drawn up for the main sites (Dony mss., North Herts. Museums). He noted that it had vanished long ago from Therfield Heath (33/J and P; 34/F and K) and from Ravensburgh Castle (02/Z; 12/E), but made no mention of the other sites from which it was recorded in Pryor (1887), such as Batchworth Heath and Garrett Wood at Rickmansworth. Why it was lost from Therfield Heath is not known, as it remains open, but Ravensburgh was planted with trees in the early 20th century. It is now doing well again at Gustard Wood Common (11/S and T), where the golf club is aware of its importance and has opened up areas from encroaching scrub. At Roughdown Common (00/M) it is still regenerating well, and it has also been found sparingly on Sheethanger Common (00/H). The chalky banks below the Monument at Aldbury (91/R) are steadily losing ground to scrub, and it was last recorded from there in 1994. Similarly, it was last reported from Chipperfield Common (00/K) as two old bushes near a pond in 1988, while it had disappeared at Commonwood Common soon after Dony's survey. There are, however two other sites. It was found, as columnar bushes amongst young thorn scrub, growing on the slopes above Kensworth Quarry (01/J) (VC20 [Beds.]) in 1996 *T. J.* where it could conceivably be natural; and a single bush, of doubtful origin, was found growing in the central reservation of the A505 at Slip End (23/Y) in 1999, *T. J.*

Taxaceae (Yews)

Genus: *Taxus*

Taxus baccata L.
Yew
Native?
First record: *c*.1960.
Tetrad occurrence: 290 (59%).
Increasing?

Despite the fact that the first botanical mention of the Yew in Hertfordshire was by Dony (1967), it has obviously been a well-known tree in the County for a very long time. There are some ancient trees in churchyards, such as at Abbots Langley and Little Munden, and folklore associations with these are widespread. There are also occasionally very old trees with no apparent association with churches or even old houses, such as one very old spreading specimen at Home Wood, Cuffley (20/W), which presumably grew on the lost Northaw Common (enclosed in 1806). The current survey also proved that the tree is by far from uncommon in the wild, very often as relatively young saplings, evidently self-sown in woodlands and hedgerows. It was found to be widespread across the County, but with some evidence of a greater concentration on the Clay-with-Flints soils of the Chilterns dip-slope, and on the acidic gravels of S. E. Herts. It is relatively uncommon on the Boulder Clay.

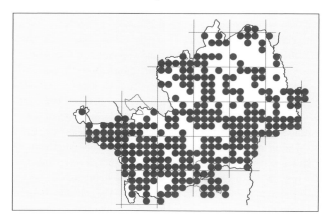

Map 33. *Taxus baccata.*

Birthwort Aristolochia clematitis *Walkern, 1979.*

MAGNOLIOPSIDA
(Flowering Plants)

Magnoliidae (Dicotyledons)

Lauraceae (Bay family)

Genus: *Laurus*

Laurus nobilis L.
Laurel
Planted.
First record: 1991.

Apparently rarely planted in 'wild' situations, as game cover or for ornament. Recorded from Darlands (29/L); Messina Plantation, Kings Walden (12/H); and Woodside, Hatfield (20/N). It could be confused with Cherry Laurel.

Aristolochiaceae (Birthworts)

Genus: *Asarum*

Asarum europaeum L.
Asarabacca
Introduced: neophyte.
First record: *c*.1840.

Found near Cheverells Green as an escape in the 19th century, and also reported from woodland at Weston Park (22/U) in 1969 *P. D. Walton.*

Genus: *Aristolochia*

Aristolochia clematitis L.
Birthwort
Introduced: neophyte.
First record: *c*.1840.

Known at Harmer Green in the 19th century, but more recently reported growing well by the roadside at Totts Lane, Walkern (22/Y) in 1978 M. Peacock, where it still thrives. It was also a feature of derelict grounds at Bayfordbury (31/A), 1994, 1996 *A. M. Boucher; C. G. Hanson.*

Nymphaeaceae (Water Lilies)

Genus: *Nymphaea*

Nymphaea alba L.
White Water Lily
Native (often introduced).
First record: 1653.
Tetrad occurrence: 60 (12%).

This was dismissed as then only planted by Dony (1967), although he acknowledged it had been native in the lower Lea and Colne rivers at one time. The current survey found it to be widespread as an evidently introduced species, but also frequent in the gravel pits of the larger river valleys. It was found in 60 tetrads overall, but there were six records from the rivers Lea, Colne, Gade and the Lee Navigation, suggesting that it may have remained as a native in at least some of these, and may have colonised some of the gravel pit lakes naturally, although in others it is known to have been planted.

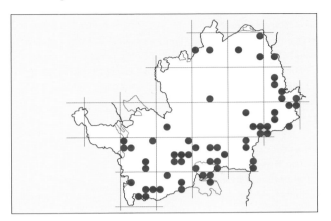

Map 34. *Nymphaea alba.*

Genus: *Nuphar*

Nuphar lutea (L.) Smith
Yellow Water Lily *or* **Brandy-bottle**
Native.
First record: 1737.
Tetrad occurrence: 68 (14%).
Possibly increased (+27%).

Found in larger rivers, sometimes in gravel pit lakes and ponds, where it is occasionally also planted. Possibly increasing somewhat because of introductions, especially in lakes.
(51 tetrads: Dony, 1967; 58 tetrads: 1950-1986)

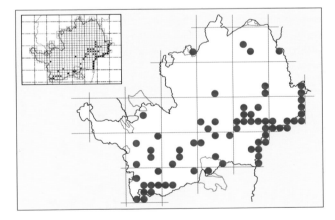

Map 35. *Nuphar lutea.*

Ceratophyllaceae (Hornworts)

Genus: *Ceratophyllum*

Ceratophyllum demersum L.
Rigid Hornwort
Native.
First record: 1838.
Tetrad occurrence: 51 (10%).
Apparently increased (+93%).

This is found in ponds, canals and slow-flowing streams or rivers, as well as ditches, and has colonised new gravel pits, not showing much sign of sensitivity to eutrophication.
(25 tetrads: Dony, 1967; 44 tetrads: 1950-1986)

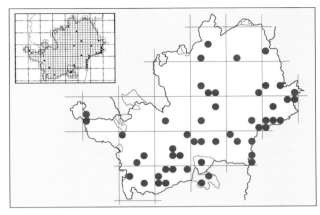

Map 36. *Ceratophyllum demersum.*

Ceratophyllum submersum L.   Herts Rare
Soft Hornwort
Native [in Herts.?].
Only record: 1956.
Extinct?

A mainly coastal species of eutrophic, brackish ponds and ditches. Formerly at Totteridge Long Pond (29/H), but there are no current records.

Ranunculaceae (Buttercups and allies)

Genus: *Caltha*

Caltha palustris L.
Marsh Marigold *or* **Kingcup, Mayblobs**
Native.
First record: 1821.
Tetrad occurrence: 122 (25%).
Increased (decreased as native) (+64%).

Almost certainly decreasing in its truly natural habitats, especially in wet river-valley pastures and mires, such as the former damp meadows along the Beane Valley around Waterford, where it was once a splendid feature, visible from the railway. However, it is

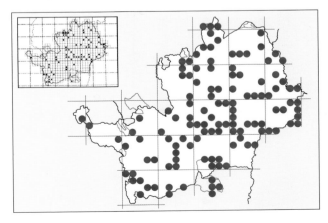

Map 37. *Caltha palustris.*

increasingly planted by ponds, and its natural occurrence is hard to interpret.

(71 tetrads: Dony, 1967; 104 tetrads: 1950-1986)

Genus: *Helleborus*

Helleborus foetidus L.
Stinking Hellebore
Introduced [native in the U.K.].
First record: 1836.
Tetrad occurrence: 14 (3%).
Increasing (+123%).

There are no real signs that this has ever been genuinely native in Herts., and all the current records are thought to be escapes, although the Tingley Wood site (13/F) first recorded by Joseph Pollard in the 19th century (Dony, 1967) is very long-standing, last recorded with a single plant at the beginning of the current survey by *C. W. Burton*, although still quite likely to be there. Some colonies have shown a marked increase since 2001, particularly on road banks at Radwell (23/I), where it is now locally abundant.

(6 tetrads: Dony, 1967; 8 tetrads: 1950-1986)

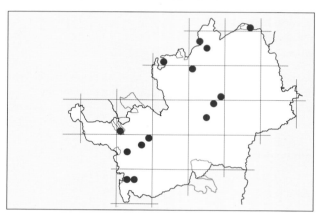

Map 38. *Helleborus foetidus*

Helleborus viridis L.
Green Hellebore
Probably native.
First record: *c.*1730.
Tetrad occurrence: 10 (2%).
Stable? (+5%).

This is an interesting plant in the Hertfordshire flora, because it has been known as a garden plant for 500 years, and some

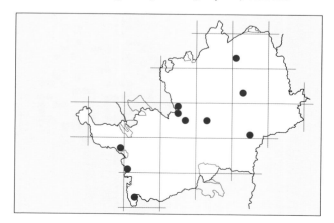

Map 39. *Helleborus viridis*.

records are evidently from long-standing introductions. However, its occurrence in other sites suggests it is also native, at least in the Chilterns, and especially in free-draining loamy woods over Chalk between Harpenden and Welwyn, where it has been known historically from a wide range of copses over a long period of time (Pryor, 1887, Dony, 1967 and Dony mss.). However, the current survey only recorded it in ten scattered tetrads across the County. This is almost certainly an under-estimate, because several of its previous sites, such as Box Wood near Stevenage, and Harmergreen Wood, where it was recorded in the 1970s and 1980s, may have been overlooked. Our plant is subspecies *occidentalis* (Reuter) Schiffner.

(9 tetrads: Dony, 1967; 18 tetrads 1950-1986)

Helleborus orientalis Lam.
Lenten Rose
Introduced: neophyte.
First record: this survey.

Discovered as an escape at High Scrubs, Tring, (90/J) in 1998 *R. Mabey.*

Genus: *Eranthis*

Eranthis hyemalis (L.) Salisb.
Winter Aconite
Introduced: neophyte.
First record: 1843.
Tetrad occurrence: 24 (5%).

Only noted from three or four localities by Dony (1967), but actually recorded from the 19th century until Dony's time from at least 13 sites, usually as the result of long-standing introductions. It does not appear to spread much naturally, but there are some signs that it is increasing in occurrence. The current survey showed that it is widespread in ornamental woodlands, *etc.* across the more calcareous parts of the County, especially on damp ground. It remains a special feature of the copse at Roxford, Hertingfordbury (31/A), and at Panshanger (21/W), where it has remained for over 100 years.

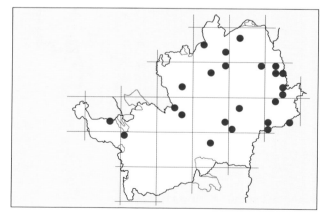

Map 40. *Eranthis hyemalis*.

Genus: *Nigella*

Nigella damascena L.
Love-in-a-Mist
Introduced: neophyte.
First record: 1917.
Tetrad occurrence: 9 (2%).

Dony (1967) only recorded this as a rare casual of old rubbish tips, but it now occurs occasionally on disturbed ground around settlements and occasionally in the countryside as well, *e.g.* King's Meads (31/L), 2000, and Lawns Wood (41/H), 1990 *T. J.*

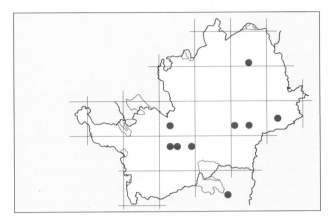

Map 41. *Nigella damascena.*

Genus: *Aconitum*

Aconitum napellus L.
Monk's-hood
Introduced: neophyte.
First record: *c.*1840.

A rare garden escape, as it has always been., but with evidence that it persists for a long time. Recorded during the current survey from Priory Park, Hitchin (12/Z), 1996 *B. Hedley*; site of garden, Graveley (22/J), 1995 *K. Hall/A. Johnson*; and Smaley Wood (43/G), 2007 *J. Moss*. Interestingly enough, the Hitchin Priory site was the first recorded in the County by Isaac Brown in *c.*1840 (Webb and Coleman, 1849).

Genus: *Delphinium*

Delphinium × *cultorum* Voss
Delphinium
Introduced: casual.
First (only) record: 1986.

This was found as an escape on Ware tip (31/M), 1986 *C. G. Hanson*.

Genus: *Consolida*

Consolida ajacis (L.) Schur
Larkspur
Introduced: neophyte.
First record: 1840.
Tetrad occurrence: 15 (3%).

Not effectually considered by Dony (1967), this has much decreased as a weed of cultivated land, compared to its occurrence in the 19th century (Pryor, 1887), but is regular as a casual of waste ground and tips. It is still found in two distinct habitats: as a rare weed of arable land and broken ground on the Chalk in north Hertfordshire, and as a casual on waste ground, especially on gravels, in the south of the County. It persists as an arable weed especially at Whiteley Hill, Barley (33/U), 1991, *etc. T. J.*; but has also been found on disturbed chalk at Weston Hills (23/L), 1988 *T. J.*; Barkway (33/Y), 1993 *A. M. Boucher*; and at Grange Farm, Kelshall (33/I), 1992 *T. J.*
(13 tetrads: 1970-1986)

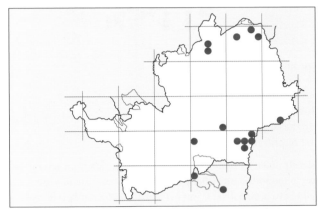

Map 42. *Consolida ajacis.*

[*Consolida orientalis* (J. Gay) Schroedinger
Eastern Larkspur

Three tetrad records given under this name within VC20, with doubt, in Burton (1983) almost certainly refer to *C. ajacis*, and are included in the account above].

[*Consolida regalis* Gray
Forking Larkspur

Recorded from Weston Hills (20/L), 1977, by B. R. Sawford, but possibly in error for *C. ajacis*, especially as the latter is known to occur there.]

Genus: *Anemone*

Anemone nemorosa L.
Wood Anemone
Native.
First record: 1814.
Tetrad occurrence: 198 (40%).
Stable? (+14%).

Found in ancient semi-natural woodlands on damper clay or loam soils, occasionally under bracken on commons, rarely in old neutral/acidic grassland. The distribution recorded during the survey demonstrates a very similar one to that recorded by Dony (1967), except that the better present coverage in some areas gives a misleading impression of increase. It is especially a plant of winter-damp mildly acidic soils in woods, such as in hollows by streams, but can survive in the open after the removal of woodland for a long time, especially where it can take advantage of its early flowering and compete with taller vegetation in later summer. Its occurrence in ancient grassland is interesting, where its flowers are often tinted pink, such as at Northaw Place (20/R) and an old pasture by Sacombe Park (31/I).
(165 tetrads: Dony, 1967; 193 tetrads: 1950-1986)

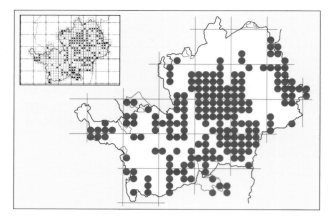

Map 43. *Anemone nemorosa.*

Anemone apennina L.
Blue Anemone
Introduced: neophyte.
First record: 1805.

Scarcely noted by Dony, but with detailed records from several sites in the 19th century floras, when there was some thought it could have been native. It was evidently a feature of Berrygrove Wood at Aldenham (19/J) for over 30 years in the mid 19th century. Recorded from the current survey at Holcroft Springs (11/N), 1999 *T. J.*; and grassland at Rothamsted (11/G), 1989 *I. G. Denholm.*

Anemone ranunculoides L.
Yellow Anemone
Introduced: neophyte
First record: *c.*1760.

The first record was a vague one given by Hudson in his *'Flora Anglica'* in 1762 (Pryor, 1887). Dony only mentions the plant, but

there were a number of 19th century records. Last recorded as a garden relict in 1967 at Little Gaddesden (SP91?), *C. F. Cowan.*

Anemone blanda Schott and Kotschy
Balkan Anemone
Introduced: neophyte.
First record: this survey.

Recorded as an escape at Butts Close, Hitchin (12/Z), 1996 *S. Gorton*, but possibly deliberately introduced. A record from TL11 given in Preston *et al.* (2002) may be an error for *A. apennina.*

Genus: *Pulsatilla*

Pulsatilla vulgaris Miller   UK Vulnerable
Pasque Flower
Native.
First record: 1815.
Very rare (-67%).

A highly habitat-specific plant of old, species-rich chalk grassland on S. and S.W. facing slopes. Now limited as a native plant in Hertfordshire to one site: Therfield Heath (33/J), where it is thankfully now abundant on Church Hill, but also occurs sparingly on Pen Hills. In good flowering years, it can number 60,000 or more plants, which probably ranks as one of the largest (if not the largest) populations in the country, although it was regarded as rare here in the 19th century (Pryor, 1887). The colony unfortunately occasionally suffers from illegal seed-harvesting. However, it appears to have increased markedly following the re-introduction of conservation grazing by sheep in the 1990s, and at least some of this increase must be from germinated seed, although it has been thought to be a poorly germinating species. It was formerly also at Arbury Banks, Ashwell (23/U) (last recorded in the 19th century); Ravensburgh Castle, Hexton (12/E) (last

Pasque Flower Pulsatilla vulgaris *Therfield Heath, 2007.*

seen in Herts. in 1904, and then lost to tree-planting, but still present over the County boundary in Beds.); by Tingley Wood (13/F) (last recorded 1951); and at Aldbury Nowers (91/L), where it was last seen about 1970 by A. Vaughan, later succumbing to scrub invasion, and not re-appearing after conservation action returned the site to grassland in the 1990s. It has also appeared as introduced specimens (of the rather leggier, hairy garden form) on the banks of the A505 at Offley (12/I), 1992 *T. J.*, and at Martin's Way chalk banks, Stevenage (22/N), 1995, *J. Pitcher*. An historical name for the plant in Hertfordshire was 'Dane's-blood', because it was only reckoned to grow where the blood of Danes was spilt in their fight with the Saxons.

Genus: *Clematis*

Clematis vitalba L.
Traveller's-joy *or* Old Man's Beard
Native.
First record: 1548.
Tetrad occurrence: 394 (80%).
Stable (-4%).

Old Man's Beard is a rather rampant plant of scrub, wood borders, *etc.*, especially on more calcareous ground. Regarded by foresters as a menace in young plantations, it is an attractive feature of roadsides and hedges across much of the County on most soils, except the London Clay and acidic gravels. Its distribution is almost exactly the same now as recorded in 1967.
(388 tetrads: Dony, 1967; 407 tetrads 1950-1986)

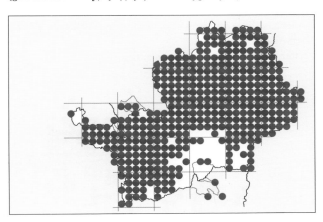

Map 44. *Clematis vitalba.*

Clematis tangutica (agg.)
Orange-peel Clematis
Introduced: casual.
First record: *c.*1900.

Noted as established 'in a field called "Ruinous", later a gravel pit, at Hoddesdon', *c.*1900, in the memoirs of J. G. Barclay (Dony, ms. index). There is no other record.

Genus: *Ranunculus*

Ranunculus acris L.
Meadow Buttercup
Native.
First record: 1814.
Tetrad occurrence: 425 (87%).
Decreasing (-11%).

Characteristic of neutral to mildly acidic, semi-natural grasslands. This was regarded as being abundant in meadows and pastures by Dony (1967), but it is only patchily so now, although at a national scale it is still thought to be 'stable' (Preston *et al.*, 2002). Despite the fact that it can survive severe mismanagement of its habitat, it has been shown to be a moderately good indicator of long-established grasslands (Cuming, 1997). As such, its apparent loss (or at the very least extreme rarity) in several tetrads, especially in north-eastern Hertfordshire, shows the rapid demise of this habitat since the 1960s.
(452 tetrads: Dony, 1967; 447 tetrads: 1950-1986)

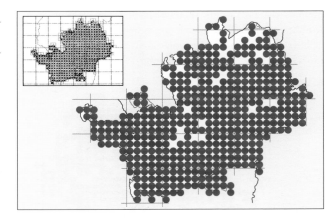

Map 45. *Ranunculus acris.*

Ranunculus repens L.
Creeping Buttercup
Native.
First record: 1814.
Tetrad occurrence: 481 (98%).
Stable (-1%).

A plant of especially damp grasslands and disturbed ground. Ubiquitous across the County, and a feature especially of disturbed and secondary grasslands, although possibly somewhat less abundant than it might have been in the 1960s, owing to the effects of grassland 'improvement'. Although not recorded from all tetrads in the County, the missing records were only for marginal tetrads not covered effectively.
(463 tetrads: Dony, 1967 and 1950-1986)

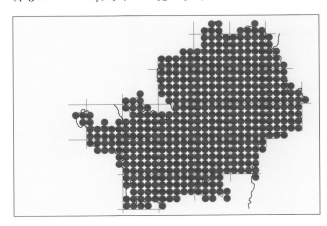

Map 46. *Ranunculus repens.*

Ranunculus bulbosus L.

Bulbous Buttercup

Native.

First record: 1814.

Tetrad occurrence: 374 (76%).

Decreasing (-20%).

Mainly a plant of dry, especially calcareous grasslands. Although at the national level this may be thought of as stable, it is showing strong signs of decline locally in Hertfordshire, even taking into account the fact that it can be overlooked if surveys are not carried out early in the year. It is quite a good indicator of old, unimproved grassland, and therefore its loss from many areas might be expected. Quite often it is only hanging on in remnant patches of road verge in more arable areas.

(446 tetrads: Dony, 1967 and 1950-1986)

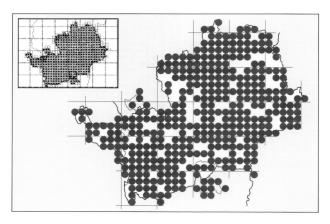

Map 47. *Ranunculus bulbosus.*

Ranunculus sardous Crantz

Hairy Buttercup

Introduced? [Native in the U.K.].

First record: 1841.

Extinct?

Last recorded at Croxley Common Moor (09/S, X) in 1965 *L. M. P. Small* (Burton, 1983). Mostly a coastal plant, this was also at one time a feature of the Hertford Heath area, but was last recorded there *c.*1908. Otherwise it has only ever been a casual.

Ranunculus parviflorus L.   Herts Rare

Small-flowered Buttercup

Native.

First record: 1805.

This was formerly a local plant of bare sandy or gravelly ground around Hertford and Bramfield, with occasional outliers towards Hitchin and elsewhere. Dony only recorded it as a casual. It was recorded during the current survey in gardens at Sawbridgeworth (41/X), 1989, *S. Watson* (Hb. HTN); Ware (31/S), 1991, *C. G. Hanson*; and The Node, Codicote (21/E), 2006 *T. J.*

Ranunculus arvensis L.   UK Critically Endangered

Corn Buttercup

Introduced: archaeophyte.

First record: 1750.

Tetrad occurrence: 9 (2%).

Strongly decreased (-85%).

A long-established arable weed of especially calcareous clay

soils, this had decreased, but was still quite widespread, by the 1960s. It is almost absent from such habitats now. The current survey recorded it in eight scattered tetrads, most of the recent ones being plants introduced in seed-mixes: Hertford, 'set-aside' field (31/F), 1991, *A. M. Boucher*; near Bridge Farm (32/C), 1988, *K. Robinson*; near Stortford Park (42/Q), 1989, *S. Watson*; Rothamsted, 'Broadbalk' (11/G), 1989, *I. G. Denholm*, 2007 *T. J.*, where it is locally frequent in untreated strips; Potterells (20/H), 1989, *C. Campbell*; Kings Langley, by A41 (00/R), 1991, *G. Salisbury/J. Saunders*; Borehamwood, Merryfield School (19/Y) (introduced), 1997, *S. Smith*; Bushey, Little Reddings School (19/H) (introduced), 1997 *S. Smith*; and a single plant, probably from disturbed seed, in newly sown grass near Moor Hall (32/I), 2009 *G. Salisbury/G. Smith et al.*

(56 tetrads: Dony, 1967; 64 tetrads 1950-1986)

Ranunculus auricomus L. (aggregate).

Goldilocks Buttercup

Native.

First record: 1814.

Tetrad occurrence: 194 (39%).

Stable (+8%).

A plant of old woodlands, scrub and hedge-banks on especially the more calcareous clay soils, Goldilocks shows an almost exactly similar distribution to that given in Dony (1967). However, it can often be patchy and sparse in occurrence, and tends therefore to be under-recorded, especially if it has been missed in the Spring. It is also a complex plant taxonomically because it is apomictic, and is known to have a large number of isolated clones. Some colonies have been seen with complete flowers, but usually it has deformed or absent petals.

(170 tetrads: Dony, 1967; 207 tetrads: 1950-1986)

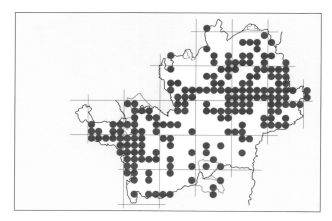

Map 48. *Ranunculus auricomus.*

Ranunculus sceleratus L.

Celery-leaved Buttercup

Native.

First record: 1814.

Tetrad occurrence: 241 (49%).

Apparently increasing (+32%).

Even taking into account better coverage by this survey, the increase in records for this species might indicate an increase in its occurrence, for reasons which are unclear. It is widespread wherever there are conditions of drying mud around water bodies, and is often especially abundant around gravel pits.

(174 tetrads: Dony, 1967; 209 tetrads: 1950-1986)

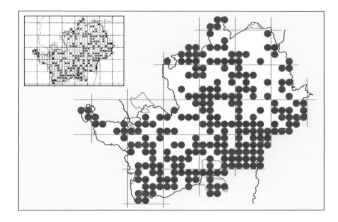

Map 49. *Ranunculus sceleratus.*

Ranunculus lingua L.
Greater Spearwort
Introduced [native in the U.K.].
First record: *c.*1840.
Tetrad occurrence: 31 (6%).
Increased substantially (950%)

The supposed native status of this plant in Herts. is extremely
doubtful. It was regarded as such at a pond near The Thrift,
Stanstead Abbots, in the early 19th century (Pryor, 1887).
However, it was already known as an introduction in Middlesex
by 1780 (Kent, 1975), and so it seems quite likely that this too
was an introduction. It has increased greatly since Dony (1967)
recorded it from only two sites (with another omitted from his
account). By 1986 it had been found at 10 localities, mostly ponds
near settlements or gravel pits. The current survey found it in no
less than 31 tetrads, where it had often been planted along with a
range of other exotic aquatic plants!

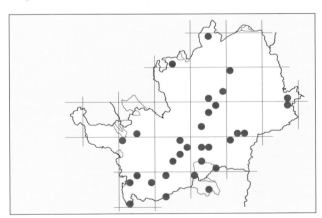

Map 50. *Ranunculus lingua.*

Ranunculus flammula L.
Lesser Spearwort
Native.
First record: 1749.
Tetrad occurrence: 71 (15%).
Probably stable (+21%).

Lesser Spearwort is a plant of moderately acidic flushes, wet
woodland rides and the sides of old ponds on acidic soils, rarely
in semi-natural fen on peat soils. It is quite frequent in suitable
places throughout southern Hertfordshire, especially in former
wood-pasture habitats, and in a belt of acidic woodlands across

central Hertfordshire up to the Knebworth area. Elsewhere, it
turns up rarely in peaty fen at places like Folly Alder Swamp
(12/Y); and Blagrove Common (33/G). Its apparent increase may
be due to better recording.
(56 tetrads: Dony, 1967; 75 tetrads: 1950-1986)

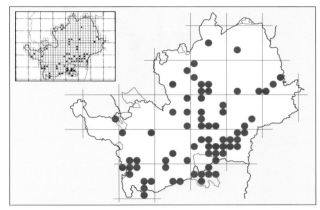

Map 51. *Ranunculus flammula.*

Ranunculus ficaria L.
Lesser Celandine
Native.
First record: 1814.
Tetrad occurrence: 445 (91%).
Possibly decreasing (-7%).

The species as an aggregate occurs in old grassland, damp
woodland, silted ditches and stream-sides throughout the County.
It remains generally common, and locally abundant, but there is
some evidence of a decrease, particularly in the more arable areas,
and on the drier, chalky soils of north Herts. It is also likely to
have vanished from many of the semi-natural grasslands across
especially the north-east of the County, although remaining in
nearby ditches.
(456 tetrads: Dony, 1967 and from 1950-1986)

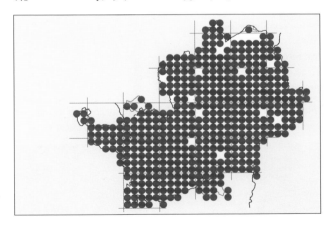

Map 52. *Ranunculus ficaria.*

Records made of the segregate sub-species were inconsistent,
but, along with ssp. *ficaria*, ssp. *bulbilifer* Lambinon (Map 52a)
is widespread, recorded from 179 tetrads, but with no apparent
habitat preference as compared with the nominate form.

There are also records of two alien subspecies:

R. ficaria ssp. *ficariiformis* (F. W. Schultz) Rouy and Foucaud.

Found in quantity by a stream by Potters Bar Golf Course (20/K)

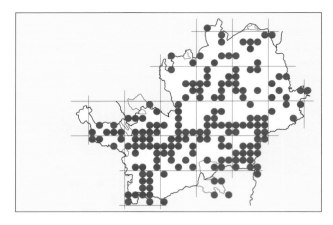

Map 52a. *Ranunculus ficaria* ssp. *bulbilifer.*

(VC21 [Herts.]), 1995, *A. M. Boucher* (Hb. Boucher) (Hb. HTN) (Burton, 1996). It has also been found naturalised in a hedgerow at Widbury Hill, Ware (31/S) since the 1980s, and was still there in 2000 *C. G. Hanson* (det. E. J. Clement) (Hb. HTN).

R. ficaria ssp. *chrysocephalus* P. D. Sell.

This was also found between Little Widbury and Widbury Gardens, Ware, at the base of a hedge (31/S), 1994, *C. G. Hanson* (det. P. D. Sell) (Hb. Hanson); and *A. M. Boucher* (Hb. Boucher, Hb. HTN).

Water crowfoots (sub-genus *Batrachium*) are a notoriously difficult group, the taxonomy of which continues to be debated. The present account is based on the species definitions used by Stace (1997), but more recent studies especially of the riverine species in southern England, suggests that real 'species' are in fact often not present in populations, which may be formed of hybrid swarms whose parents are uncertain. The following accounts, therefore, need to be treated with caution, especially for taxa occurring in flowing waters.

Ranunculus hederaceus L.
Ivy-leaved Crowfoot
Native.
First record: 1820.
Tetrad occurrence: 7 (1%).
Rare, stable? (+56%).

A plant of old pastures, *etc.* with damp, muddy ground, usually on moderately acidic soils. Probably recently stable, but rare, as

Ivy-leaved Crowfoot Ranunculus hederaceus *Goldingtons, Hertford Heath, 1999.*

it has always been, although in the 19th century recorded more widely. Dony (1967) recorded this from only four sites, while another four were recorded between 1970 and 1986. One of these was, interestingly, in 1976, at a small field pond in Essendon Glebe Meadow (20/U), *T. J.*, where it had been recorded about 1840 by Coleman, but not since. The current survey found it (or re-found it) in seven localities: by Much Wood, Hertford Heath (31/K), 1999 *T. J./G. P. Smith*; Patmore Heath (42/M), 1988, 1994, *J. L. Fielding, S. Watson*; Broadwater Farm Meadow, Knebworth (22/K), 1988, *T. J./B. R. Sawford* (a site later destroyed to make way for a drainage sump for the nearby Glaxo site); Wildhill Meadow (20/T), 1993, *T. J.*; pond at Woodside (20/N), 1993 *T. J.*; Arkley Meadows (29/H), 1992 *A. Vaughan*; Harrison's Moor, Boxmoor (00/N), 1989, 1994, 2008 *M. J. Hicks/G. Salisbury*. It may no longer be at some of these. A record from Bricket Wood Common (10/F), 2004 (*comm.*: J. Edgington) needs confirmation.

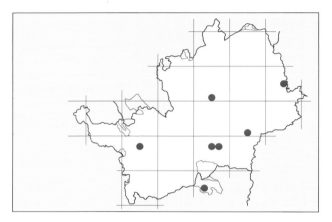

Map 53. *Ranunculus hederaceus.*

Ranunculus trichophyllus Chaix
Thread-leaved Water-crowfoot
Native.
First record: 1874.
Tetrad occurrence: 70 (14%).
Apparently increasing (+147%).

The distribution of this plant of open muddy margins of drying ponds, *etc.* remains much as it was in 1967, with a preponderance of occurrences by ponds on Boulder Clay in N. E. Herts. It can be sporadic in appearance, but there does seem to be evidence of a genuine increase.
(27 tetrads: Dony, 1967; 37 tetrads: 1950-1986)

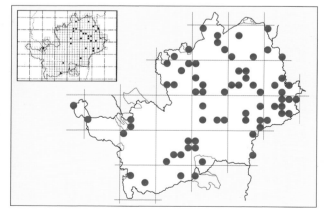

Map 54. *Ranunculus trichophyllus.*

Ranunculus × lutzii A. Félix (*R. trichophyllus* × *R. aquatilis*)
Native.

Only given as an unlocalised record by C. D. K. Cook in Stace (1975), for which details no longer seem to be available.

Ranunculus aquatilis L.
Common Water-crowfoot
Native.
First record: 1814 (for the aggregate), 1875.
Tetrad occurrence: 21 (4%).

This is one of the water crowfoots of ponds and shallow flood areas, mainly on more calcareous substrates. Although it is generally reckoned to be the commonest species of the group, the confusion over identification has meant that there is little information to go on to judge whether it is stable or not. The current survey confirmed it in considerably fewer sites than for *R. peltatus*, concentrated largely on the Boulder Clay.

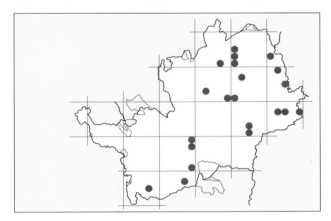

Map 55. *Ranunculus aquatilis.*

Ranunculus peltatus Schrank
Pond Water-crowfoot
Native.
First record: 1869.
Tetrad occurrence: 35 (7%).

Mainly a species of ponds, but also sometimes in slow-moving streams over gravel, usually on less calcareous substrates. It appears to be a feature of ponds around the Broxbourne Woods area, where its large flowers are conspicuous, especially after ponds have been cleared out. The survey found it in more tetrads than its supposedly commoner relative *R. aquatilis*, but there are

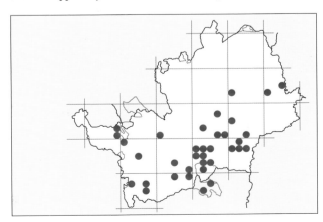

Map 56. *Ranunculus peltatus.*

no historic records from Dony (1967) with which to compare.

Ranunculus penicillatus (Dumort.) Bab.
Stream Water-crowfoot
Native.
First record: 1875.
Tetrad occurrence: 75 (15%).

This seems to be the usual 'species' in our area of shallower rivers and streams, especially with calcareous waters. Where a subspecies has been identified, this has been ssp. *pseudofluitans* (Syme) S. Webster. It is found throughout the river systems of the county, on both chalk and gravel substrates, but not on deep silt. Its variability, the likelihood of some if not all populations being hybrid in origin, and the fact that it often does not flower, has made identification difficult. The current survey recorded it with more or less certainty from 74 tetrads, but it is probably under-recorded in the R. Ver, partly owing to low flows in the early 1990s (although *R. peltatus* has also been recorded here, on less calcareous gravels), and was missed in some sections of the Colne and Lea. There were insufficient records in the 1960s survey with which to compare its present occurrence.

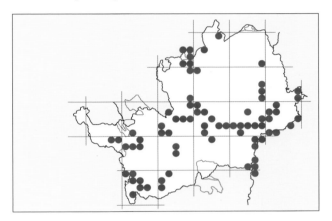

Map 57. *Ranunculus penicillatus.*

Var. *vertumnus* Cook is found in the R. Oughton at Oughton Head, Hitchin (13/Q), 1988 *T. J.*, where it has been known for over 100 years, but it has not been re-recorded from Water End, Great Gaddesden, where Dony (1967) reported it.

Ranunculus fluitans Lam.   Herts Rare?
River Water-crowfoot
Native.
First record: 1984.

Although a number of claims for this species in Herts. have been made previously, these were never substantiated by satisfactory specimens. River sampling in the mid-1980s showed that it was apparently present in the lower reaches of the River Colne (09/K, L, S), 1984, *N. T. Holmes*; and in the Small Lea (30/R), 1985 *A. M. Boucher*. It was re-recorded from the latter early in the current survey: 1988 *R. M. Burton*, but not since.

Ranunculus circinatus Sibth.
Fan-leaved Water-crowfoot
Native.
First record: 1841.
Tetrad occurrence: 7 (1%).
Decreased (-36%).

Characteristic of clean, deep, often standing waters, this has always been relatively uncommon, but is now much rarer than it was in the 19th century, when it was a feature of river pools and marsh dykes as well as the kinds of sites it now inhabits: recently-created gravel pits and the like. It appears that water quality is a major limiting factor in its occurrence, but it is capable of rapid colonisation and occasionally becomes abundant in new water bodies. It has recently been recorded from only eight localities: Wilstone Reservoir (91/B), 1996, 2009 *T. J.*; Smallford Pit (10/Y), 1992 *T. J.*; gravel pit at East End Green (21/V), 2007 *T. J.*; Metropolitan Police Pit, Cheshunt (30/R), 1988, 1989 *G. J. White, T. J.*; North Metropolitan Pit, Cheshunt (30/R), 1990 *A. M. Boucher/T. J.*; Cheshunt Lake (30/R), 1990, 1994 *A. M. B./T. J./ G. P. Smith*; Gilston Park Lake (41/L), 1990 *S. Watson*; Bury Lake, Rickmansworth (09/L), 1990 *P. J. Ellison*. It was recorded also from Amwell Quarry (31/R) in 1986; from Broad Colney Lake (10/R) in 1976 and the River Ash at Watersplace (31/X) in 1979. The latter was the last record from its natural river habitat in the County. It has also apparently disappeared from the canals around Wilstone and Tring, where it was formerly abundant.
(10 tetrads: Dony, 1967; 14 tetrads: 1950-1986)

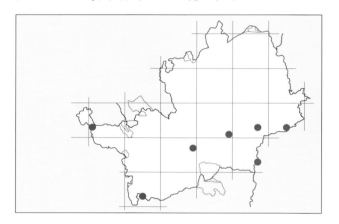

Map 58. *Ranunculus circinatus.*

Genus: *Adonis*

Adonis annua L.   UK Endangered
Pheasant's-eye
Introduced: archaeophyte.
First record: *c.*1860?
Extinct?

There is an unlocalised and anonymous record from TL21 in the B.S.B.I.'s Vascular Plant Database (Preston *et al.*, 2002), for the period 1987-1999. Otherwise, it was last recorded in Herts. in 1979 from a cornfield at Barley (43/E) *B. L. Sage*; and from Ridge Churchyard (20/A), *R. Rafferty*, both as casuals. It appears never to have been an established weed of arable in Herts.

Genus: Myosurus

Myosurus minimus L.   UK Vulnerable
Mousetail
Native?
First record: 1805.
Tetrad occurrence: 6 (1%).
Stable? (+33%).

This is an unpredictable species, and may be more widespread than current records suggest. It appears in muddy, arable

Mousetail Myosurus minimus *North Mymms, 1986.*

margins, trackways, *etc.* after winter rain, and can disappear for many decades before re-appearing. Its current records are from six localities only: Alswick Hall (32/Z), 1992 *S. Watson*; near Trenchern Hills (32/K), 1994 *S. W., T. J./G. P. Smith*; near Queer Wood, Little Hadham (42/G), 1988 *G. P. S.*; near Tewin (21/S), 1995 *A. Guilford*; Thickney Wood, Codicote (21/J), 1988 *P. D. Walton*; and at Waterend (21/B), 2003 *P. Carr*. Between 1970 and 1986, it was also recorded from a further two tetrads, including a site at North Mymms (20/G) in 1986 *T. J./G. P. S.*, from where it had been recorded in *c.*1800 by Joseph Sabine, but not since. None of these localities corresponds with any of Dony's (1967) four records.

Genus: *Aquilegia*

Aquilegia vulgaris L.
Columbine
Formerly native (and introduced).
First record: 1815.
Tetrad occurrence: 42 (9%).

Much increased recently, but as a garden escape. It was recorded widely in the survey, but in none of these localities can it be considered a native plant. In the 19th century, however, it was apparently a native of a number of woodlands, mostly on the Clay-with-Flints, from Sherrards Park Wood and Bramfield Woods in the east to Stubbings Wood in the west (Pryor, 1887).

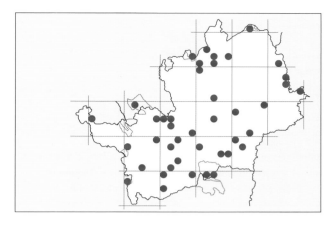

Map 59. *Aquilegia vulgaris.*

Genus: *Thalictrum*

Thalictrum flavum L.
Common Meadow-rue
Native.
First record: 1737.
Tetrad occurrence: 11 (2%).
Decreasing? (-8%).

This is a plant of tall fen vegetation and old wet meadows, mainly by the rivers Lea, Colne and Stort. Although it appears to be stable in terms of the number of sites it has recently been recorded in, the habitat it prefers has declined substantially in both extent and quality since the 19th century, and continues to do so. Several of the sites it was known from by Dony have been lost. It was once a frequent feature of river margins, as well as in fen woodlands. Although it survives at several recent gravel pit sites, its need for long-established peaty soils makes it vulnerable, and it is often scarce at any one locality.
(11 tetrads: Dony, 1967; 14 tetrads 1950-1986)

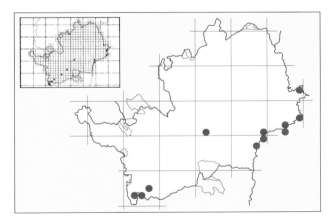

Map 60. *Thalictrum flavum.*

Thalictrum minus L.   Herts Rare
Lesser Meadow-rue
Native (and introduced).
First record: 1849.
Tetrad occurrence: (6) 4 (<1%).
Rare but stable.

This is a conspicuous feature of the east end of Therfield Heath (33/P, 34/F, K), but there is no current record from the part of the site in tetrad 33/J (*cf.* Dony, 1967). It seems never

Lesser Meadow-rue Thalictrum minus *Therfield Heath, 2008.*

to have extended west of the Coombe Road (Pryor, 1887). However, it remains on a vulnerably narrow chalk grassland bank by Deadman's Hill, Sandon (23/Y), where it was found by B. R. Sawford in 1974 (Sawford, 1974), a re-discovery of a site, formerly on Sandon Heath, originally found by H. G. Fordham in the 1840s. It remained here, as a few poor-looking plants, in 2008 *T. J.* It has also been recorded as a presumed garden escape from near Corneybury (33/K), 1992 *T. J.*; and from Harpenden Common (11/G), 1989 *I. G. Denholm.*

Berberidaceae (Barberries)

Genus: *Berberis*

Berberis vulgaris L.
Barberry
Native?
First record: *c.*1730.
Tetrad occurrence: 13 (3%).
Increasing? (+100%).

Although only recorded from six localities by Dony, the current survey shows it to be widespread, if rare, occurring usually as isolated bushes in old hedges, mostly in east Herts., on more calcareous soils. It was apparently once more common, and was planted as hedging, but later eradicated in the 19th century, because it is a winter host of the wheat rust *Puccinia graminis*.

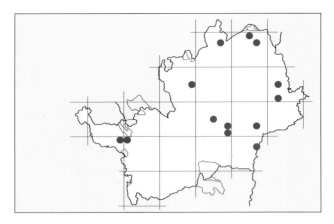

Map 61. *Berberis vulgaris.*

Barberry Berberis vulgaris *Mitchell Hill, Ashwell, 1988.*

Berberis aggregata C. K. Schneid.
Clustered Barberry
Introduced: neophyte.
First record: 1998.

Found as an escape in a hedge near Tewin (21/S), 1998
A. Guilford. It could be more widespread.

Berberis gagnepainii C. K. Schneid.
Gagnepain's Barberry
Introduced: neophyte.
First record: 1993.

The only record of this in the wild is from beside the R. Lea,
Ware Lock (31/M), 1993 *B. Wurzell* (*comm.*: B.R.C., CEH Monks
Wood). It is frequently grown in gardens, and could be found in
damper ground elsewhere.

Berberis darwinii Hook.
Darwin's Barberry
Introduced: neophyte.
First record: 1988.

Recorded from scrub near Radlett (19/U), 1988, *L. E. Perrins*;
and on the edge of Hoo Wood, Great Gaddesden (01/G), 1990
J. F. Southey. It may also be more widespread.

Genus: *Mahonia*

Mahonia aquifolium (Pursh) Nutt.
Oregon-grape
Introduced: neophyte.
First record: 1922.
Tetrad occurrence: 119 (24%).
Increasing (+98%).

Found in scrub and secondary woodland, often on calcareous
soils. It is often difficult to distinguish between deliberately
introduced plants of this and wild spread, because of its use for
game cover. It has, however, apparently greatly increased since
Dony's survey.
(57 tetrads: Dony, 1967; 86 tetrads: 1950-1986)

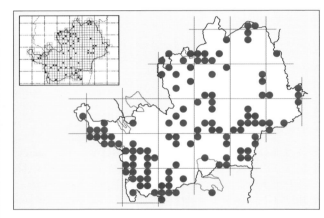

Map 62. *Mahonia aquifolium.*

Mahonia × decumbens Stace (*M. aquifolium × M. repens*).
Newmarket Oregon-grape
Introduced: neophyte.
First record: 1996.
This was first found at Fox Covert near Wilbury Hill (13/W)
(VC30[Herts.]), 1996 *T. J./C. R. Boon* (Hb. HTN); and
subsequently in a roadside copse near St Albans (10/P), 1998
T. J./F. Hall. It may well be more widespread, along with other
Mahonia taxa.

Papaveraceae (Poppies and allies)

Genus: *Papaver*

Papaver pseudoorientale (Fedde) Medw.
Oriental Poppy
Introduced: neophyte.
First record: 2000.

Not formally recorded in the wild until 2000, when plants were
noted near Watton-at-Stone (31/E), Baldock (23/M) and by the
New River at King's Meads (31/L) *T. J.* Further records were
made from Chorleywood Common (09/I) and Bedwell Pit (20/Z),
2004 *T. J.*; from Box Lane, Hemel Hempstead (00/H), 2005 *T. J.*;
and at Ashwell (23/U), 2006 *T. J.* It is quite likely to have been
widespread for some time, but assumed to be planted. It can also
be confused with *P. somniferum* in its vegetative state.

Papaver atlanticum (Ball) Cosson
Atlas Poppy
Introduced: neophyte.
First record: *c*.1950.
Tetrad occurrence: 11 (2%).

Although this was reported (in error as *Papaver lateritium*) from Bishop's Stortford by D. McClintock (Dony mss.), it was not included in Dony's Flora. It was then found on a road bank at Hertford (31/G), 1978 *A. M. Boucher* (Hb. HTN), where it persisted for some time, despite mowing. It is now apparently quite widespread, appearing to prefer sparse grassy ground on calcareous gravels. Recorded from 11 scattered tetrads, with a cluster around Hertford and Ware.

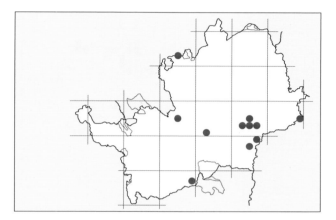

Map 63. *Papaver atlanticum.*

Papaver somniferum L.
Opium Poppy
Introduced: neophyte.
First record: 1840.
Tetrad occurrence: 199 (41%).
Increasing (+371%).

Although this was first recorded as long ago as 1840, it only appears to have increased massively relatively recently. It now occurs widely as a weed of disturbed ground and waste places, perhaps showing a preference for more calcareous soils. In a few sites it has been a persistent weed for a very long time, such as the field below Benington High Wood (22/W), its first recorded site. It may occasionally be confused with *P. pseudoorientale*.
(40 tetrads: Dony, 1967; 68 tetrads: 1950-1986)

The usual subspecies is apparently *somniferum*, but ssp.

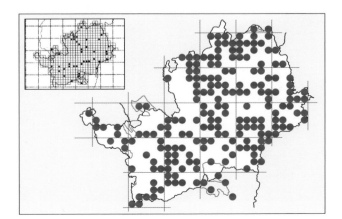

Map 64. *Papaver somniferum.*

setigerum (DC.) Arcang. has been recorded from Bayfordbury (31/A), 1996 *A. M. Boucher/C. G. Hanson*; and from the field by Benington High Wood (22/W), 2005 *T. J.* It may be more widespread.

Papaver rhoeas L.
Common Poppy
Introduced: archaeophyte.
First record: 1814.
Tetrad occurrence: 425 (87%).
Decreasing (-9%).

While the familiar red poppy is still a common plant, and capable of re-appearing spectacularly when cultivation fails, it is becoming scarce in some areas, especially on the acidic clays in south Herts., and is even un-recorded from some intensively arable tetrads in the east. White and pink-flowered forms have been noted.
(444 tetrads: Dony 1967; 445 tetrads: 1950-1986)

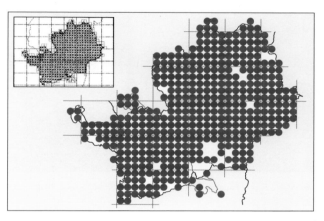

Map 65. *Papaver rhoeas.*

Papaver dubium L. ssp. *dubium*
Long-headed Poppy
Introduced: archaeophyte.
First record: 1838.
Tetrad occurrence: 141 (29%).
Stable (+1%).

The map shows the distribution of ssp. *dubium* only, as this was also mapped separately by Dony. The plant occurs widely, but is usually found on dry, gravelly or sandy substrates, sometimes on Chalk, but usually where it is mixed with superficial deposits, and possibly more often on disturbed ground and tipped material than in arable. Despite received wisdom, it does not appear to be

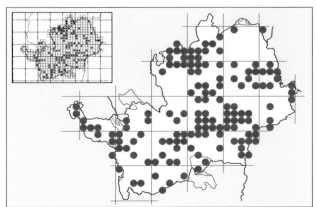

Map 66. *Papaver dubium* ssp. *dubium.*

any less common now than formerly, and given its propensity for disappearing and re-appearing, the trends are not significant. (132 tetrads: Dony, 1967; 169 tetrads: 1950-1986)

Babington's Poppy Papaver dubium *ssp.* lecoquii *Bassus Green, Walkern, 1996.*

Papaver dubium ssp. *lecoquii* (Lamotte) Syme
Babington's Poppy
Introduced: archaeophyte.
First record: 1874.
Tetrad occurrence: 120 (24%).
Possibly increasing (+34%).

This was treated as a species by Dony, and is mapped separately here. It has a very distinctive distribution, being very much a plant of the arable on Boulder Clay, where it is the earliest poppy to flower, and, although it is affected badly by weed-killers, it is also still capable of re-appearing in quantity. Owing to likely under-recording in the 1967 survey, it is possible it has not actually increased, at least as much as the records might indicate.
(85 tetrads: Dony, 1967; 99 tetrads: 1950-1986)

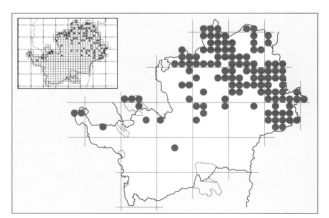

Map 67. *Papaver dubium* ssp. *lecoquii.*

Papaver hybridum L.
Rough Poppy
Introduced: archaeophyte.
First record: 1840.
Tetrad occurrence: 18 (4%).
Increased or stable? (+32%).

This was always apparently quite a rare species, and there is no evidence of a decrease, either recently or in the past, owing to its ability to reappear from buried seed. In fact, it may have actually increased slightly. It is almost entirely a plant of bare ground in arable fields on chalky soils, where its beautiful cerise-pink flowers with blue anthers are especially attractive, mixed with other poppies.
(13 tetrads: Dony, 1967; 20 tetrads: 1950-1986)

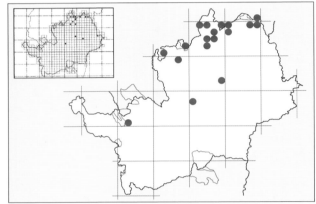

Map 68. *Papaver hybridum.*

Rough Poppy Papaver hybridum *Therfield, 1981.*

Papaver argemone L. UK Vulnerable
Prickly Poppy
Introduced: archaeophyte.
First record: *c.*1820.
Tetrad occurrence: 33 (7%).
Decreased (-46%).

This appears to be the only poppy to be genuinely decreasing in occurrence at the tetrad level, although it is still more frequent than *P. hybridum*. It is a plant of nutrient-poor, light, gravelly or chalky soils, and occurs both as an arable weed and as a plant of bare, disturbed ground. Its distribution remains much the same as in 1967, but it has not been recorded from many of its former sites. (58 tetrads: Dony, 1967; 71 tetrads: 1950-1986)

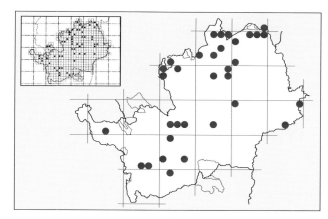

Map 69. *Papaver argemone.*

Genus: *Meconopsis*

Meconopsis cambrica (L.) Viguier
Welsh Poppy
Introduced [native in the U.K.].
First record: 1950.
Tetrad occurrence: 12 (2%).

A more or less ephemeral colonist of shady waysides and hedgebanks near houses, or rarely on waste land. Erroneously reported as a first record in James (1982), it was actually first found at Bishop's Stortford in 1950 *D. McClintock* (Dony mss.), but omitted from Dony (1967). Rarely persistent for long at any one site, probably because the climate is too dry.

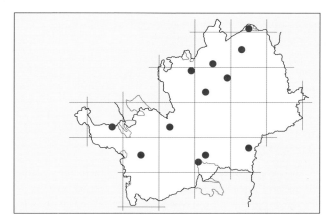

Map 70. *Meconopsis cambrica.*

Genus: *Glaucium*

Glaucium corniculatum (L.) Rudolph
Red Horned-poppy
Introduced: neophyte.
First record: 1916.

First found at Ware, 1916 by Mrs Knowling and J. W. Higgens (*Rep. Bot. Exch. Club*: 470 (1917)), and subsequently at Hitchin, Hertford, and Cole Green. Last record: 1923.

Genus: *Roemeria*

Roemeria hybrida (L.) DC.
Violet Horned-poppy
Introduced: neophyte.
First record: 1912 (VC21 [Herts.]), 1915.

Only ever a casual, at Potters Bar, Ware, Royston and Hoddesdon. Last record: 1926.

Genus: *Chelidonium*

Chelidonium majus L.
Greater Celandine
Introduced: archaeophyte.
First record: 1814.
Tetrad occurrence: 176 (36%).
Stable or slightly decreased (-5%).

This was at one time thought to be native, but it is now considered to be an early introduction as a medicinal plant. Its yellow juice is still used against warts in some places. The plant is rarely found away from settlements, where it tends to grow in shady hedgebanks.
(177 tetrads: Dony, 1967; 203 tetrads: 1950-1986)

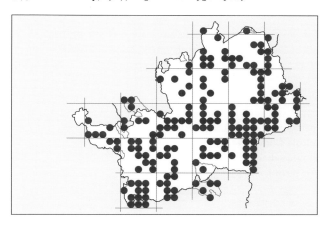

Map 71. *Chelidonium majus.*

Genus: *Eschscholzia*

Eschscholzia californica Cham.
Californian Poppy
Introduced: neophyte.
First record: 1924.
Tetrad occurrence: 9 (2%).

Probably increasing slowly on bare ground, roadsides, *etc.* After its first report at Ware by A. W. Graveson, it was recorded from a few sites, but only mentioned by Dony (1967). During this survey it has been recorded in nine scattered tetrads, with concentrations around Hitchin, Hertford and Ware.

Fumariaceae (Fumitories and allies)

Genus: *Corydalis*

Corydalis cava (L.) Schweigger and Koerte
Hollow-root
Introduced: neophyte.
First record: *c.*1885.

There appears to be some confusion over records of garden-escape *Corydalis* species. *Corydalis bulbosa* DC. was recorded by Pryor (1887) from a number of places (first record: *c.*1885), with established colonies at Baldock and Totteridge. These were repeated by Dony (1967). *C. bulbosa* records have been referred by authors to *C. solida* (L.) Clairv., although the attribution may be doubtful. A record of the latter was made at Loudwater (09/N), 1979 *J. G. Dony/J. Colthup*, reported in Burton (1980), and again, but equivocally, in Burton (1983). The recent survey has found the colony at Totteridge (29/L) still to be present (1992, *D. Griffith*), but referable to *C. cava*. An established colony in wooded ground near Wallington Church (23/W), 1997 *T. J.*, is also *C. cava*, although originally recorded in 1981 as *Corydalis ochroleuca* Koch = *Pseudofumaria alba* (Mill.) Lidén (see below). Another small colony at Jubilee Plantation, Walkern (22/X), 1992 *T. J.*, is also *C. cava* (Hb. HTN). Owing to this confusion, until specimens of *C. solida* can be confirmed, it must remain in some doubt as a Hertfordshire plant.

Corydalis cheilanthifolia Hemsl.
Fern-leaved Corydalis
Introduced: casual.
First record: 2008.

This garden plant was found as an escape, well-established by a path at Gorst Close, Letchworth (23/B), 2008 *C. Cheffings* (Hb. HTN).

Genus: *Pseudofumaria*

Pseudofumaria lutea (L.) Borkh.
Yellow Corydalis
Introduced: neophyte.
First record: *c.*1820.

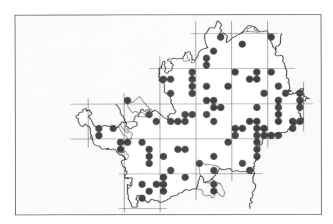

Map 72. *Pseudofumaria lutea.*

Tetrad occurrence: 92 (19%).
Increased (+149%).

Frequently escapes from gardens onto old walls across the County, and is sometimes found on dumped soil, disturbed ground, *etc.* (35 tetrads: Dony, 1967; 52 tetrads: 1950-1986)

[*Pseudofumaria alba* (Miller) Lidén

Pale Corydalis was recorded in error in James (1982). The colony at Wallington is referable to *Corydalis cava* (see above).]

Genus: *Ceratocapnos*

Ceratocapnos claviculata (L.) Lidén
Climbing Corydalis
Introduced [native in the U.K.].
First record: 1965.

There is an unlocalised record, apparently unsupported by further information, from Commonwood (00/K), 1965, in the London N.H.S. plant database (Burton, 1983). The only other record is as a casual from imported compost, at Bishop's Stortford (42/Q), 1992 *J. L. Fielding*.

Genus: *Fumaria*

[*Fumaria capreolata* L.
White Ramping-fumitory

There is a mention of this as occurring at Hexton in Whiteman (1936), but this was likely to be an error.]

Fumaria bastardii Boreau
Tall Ramping-fumitory
Introduced? [native in the U.K.].
First (only) record: 1931.

There is one enigmatic record of this plant at Hitchin (12/Z), 1931 *J. E. Little* (Hb. CGE) (Dony, 1967).

Fumaria muralis Sonder ex Koch
Common Ramping-fumitory
Introduced [native in the U.K.].
First record: 1855.

Only ever a casual in Herts., one plant of ssp. *boraei* (Jordan) Pugsley was recorded during the survey: Ware Churchyard wall (31/M), 1995 *A. M. Boucher* (Hb. HTN).

Fumaria officinalis L.
Common Fumitory
Introduced: archaeophyte.
First record: 1814.
Tetrad occurrence: 308 (63%).
Stable? (-2%).

This species appears to have a similar distribution to that recorded by Dony, and has not decreased significantly at the tetrad level, although its populations can now be very small at any one locality. It occurs mainly as an arable weed, especially on drier, more calcareous soils, and has always been uncommon in south Herts. (298 tetrads: Dony, 1967; 328 tetrads: 1950-1986)

Most plants seem to be ssp. *officinalis*, but ssp. *wirtgenii* (Koch)

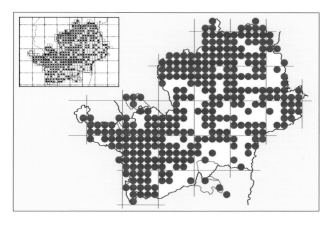

Map 73. *Fumaria officinalis.*

Arcang. has been recorded a number of times, although not enough records are available for a useful map.

Fumaria officinalis × *F. densiflora*

This rare hybrid is reported from Herts., without further details, in Stace (1975). This is apparently a record from Dunstable (02/A), 1972 *P. M. Benoit* (*Watsonia*, 16: 163-17), which was assigned to Beds., but is probably from VC20 [Beds.].

Fumaria densiflora DC.
Dense-flowered Fumitory
Introduced: archaeophyte.
First record: 1841.
Tetrad occurrence: 21 (4%).
Stable or increasing? (+43%).

This has always been a local, if not rare species in Herts., mainly on chalky arable soils in the north, occasionally as a casual. The distribution shown by the current map, however, differs from Dony's in that the plant appears more frequent in the Baldock-Royston area, and to have decreased west of Hitchin. This might be a function of the seasons when recording was carried out in the different areas.
(14 tetrads: Dony, 1967; 17 tetrads: 1950-1986)

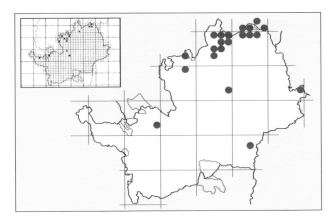

Map 74. *Fumaria densiflora.*

Fumaria parviflora Lam.   UK Vulnerable
Fine-leaved Fumitory
Introduced: archaeophyte.
First record: 1842.
Tetrad occurrence: 7 (1%).
Stable? (+56%).

This has always been a rare plant of the Chalk in Herts., even in the 19th century, but has not been recorded west of Baldock for many years. Dony only lists four localities, but the apparent increase is almost certainly due to increased recording effort. It is vulnerable to weed-killers, but can appear suddenly from buried seed. The current survey recorded it in seven localities: arable by Bogmoor Road, Barkway (33/Y), 1991, 1998 *T. J.*, *F. Hall*; arable near Chishill Road, Barley (43/E), 1997 *S. Watson*; Royston allotments (34/K) (VC29 [Herts.]), 1998 *T. J.*; arable near Hinxworth (24/F), 1996 *T. J.*; rough ground by Partridge Hill, Ashwell (23/U), 1988, 1989 *T. J.*; Baldock allotments (23/M), 1987 *T. J.*; and arable at Deadman's Hill, Sandon (23/Y), 2008 *T. J.*
(4 tetrads: Dony, 1967; 7 tetrads: 1950-1986)

Fumaria vaillantii Lois.   UK Vulnerable
Few-flowered Fumitory
Introduced: archaeophyte.
First record: 1843.
Tetrad occurrence: 15 (3%).
Stable? (+29%).

As with the previous species, this plant of the north Herts. Chalk ridge or chalk outcrops elsewhere has always been a scarce arable weed in the County, and it too has become rare in the west since the 19th century. However, although the current survey recorded it from slightly more tetrads than Dony (1967), evidence for any recent change is marginal.
(11 tetrads: Dony, 1967; 15 tetrads: 1950-1986)

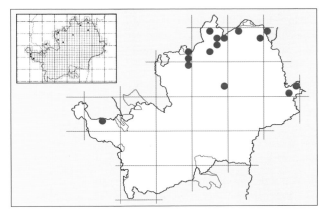

Map 75. *Fumaria vaillantii.*

Platanaceae (Planes)

Genus: *Platanus*

Platanus × *hispanica* Mill. ex Münchh.
(*P. occidentalis* × *P. orientalis*)
London Plane
Planted, rarely self-seeding.
First record: 1998 (as self-sown).

Mature planted trees occur in a number of localities, *e.g.* Cassiobury (09/Y), although detailed records were not made. The only hints of regeneration were from a solitary tree by the railway at Osidge (29/W), 1998 *T. J./G. P. Smith* and a sapling, without a mature tree nearby, in scrub at Berkhamsted Common (00/E), 2004 *T. J.*

Ulmaceae (Elms)

Genus: *Ulmus*

The demise of most mature elms in the County, following the outbreak of the severe form of Dutch elm disease in the early 1970s, has meant that identifying these enigmatic trees has become even more difficult than it previously was. For many people now, the sight of a fine English Elm by a field is a thing of the past, and their loss, especially to some landscapes in southern Hertfordshire, is to be lamented. As outlined by Dony (1967), the number of different treatments given to this difficult group has varied according to the fashions of the time, and no previous survey has ever been fully attempted. However, recent taxonomic treatments seem to suggest that, despite a multitude of clones that could be called different 'species', there are three basic elm taxa in the County, together with at least one hybrid, which is widespread. Apart from recent doubts placed on the status of '*Ulmus plotii*' again, the treatment given here follows the taxonomy outlined in Stace (1997), which largely mirrors the work of Dr R. Melville in the 1950s, and differs strongly from the attempt to separate forms of especially *U. minor* which R. H. Richens outlined in his 'Studies on *Ulmus* III: the village elms of Hertfordshire' (Forestry, 32, (1959)). No attempt has been made in this survey to separate the clones of *Ulmus minor*, nor to distinguish between resulting different forms of the hybrids between *Ulmus glabra* and *Ulmus minor*. Recording of taxa across the County may also be uneven, depending on the attention paid, and the difficulty of dealing with suckering hedgerow saplings. The following maps, therefore, need to be treated with caution, but are the first attempt to apply systematic recording of the group across the County. Collections of representative material from Hertfordshire will be deposited in Hb. HTN.

Ulmus glabra Hudson
Wych Elm
Native.
First record: 1838.
Tetrad occurrence: 205 (42%).

The map of this species needs interpretation with care, as it is quite likely that a number of hybrid *U. glabra* × *U. minor* have crept in, particularly in the extreme east. It is a widespread component of semi-natural woodland, especially with beech, or with ash/maple on more calcareous soils, and also occurs widely in ancient hedgerows, especially along the Chilterns dip-slope, and

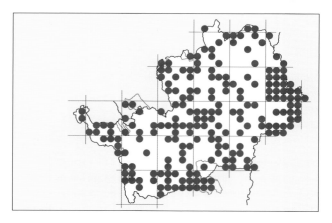

Map 76. *Ulmus glabra.*

across central Hertfordshire. It eventually succumbed to Dutch elm disease in the late 1970s, but young trees survive in many areas, self-seeding well. No useful comparisons can be made with previous attempts to record the species.

Ulmus × *vegeta* (Loudon) Ley (*U. glabra* × *U. minor*)
Native.
First record uncertain.
Tetrad occurrence: 177 (36%).

Once again, the map given needs to be interpreted with care, and may not be entirely reliable. The 'Huntingdon Elm' is recorded as a planted tree in the County, and is supposed to differ from the apparently natural hybrid, which is frequent, especially in east Herts. in stream-side woodlands and hedges (and which may have been mis-recorded in places as *U. glabra*, in TL42 especially). In contrast, in west Herts., there is a chance that *U. glabra* may have been mis-identified as the hybrid in places, giving an impression of greater frequency than it really has in the Chilterns. Occasionally, however, the hybrid appears to have been planted for coppice.

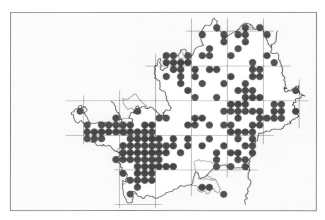

Map 77. *Ulmus* × *vegeta.*

[*Ulmus* × *hollandica* Mill. (*U. glabra* × *minor* × *plotii*).
Dutch Elm
Introduced?

Only four records of this were determined during the survey: Dane End (32/G), 1989 *H. Armstrong* (Hb. CGE); Totteridge (29/H), 1997 *A. Vaughan*; Weepings Wood at Bayford (30/E), 1995 *A. D. Marshall* (Hb. HTN); and Hatfield Home Park (20/P), 1995 *A. D. Marshall* (Hb. HTN). However, owing to the doubts now placed on the validity of *Ulmus plotii* as a separate species, it is probably not reliably distinguishable from *U.* × *vegeta.*]

[*Ulmus* × *elegantissima* Horw. (*U. glabra* × *U. plotii*).

This hybrid is reported from Herts. in Stace (1975), but without further details. Given the doubts over the status of *Ulmus plotii*, this also must be somewhat suspect as a separate taxon.]

Ulmus procera Salisbury
English Elm
Introduced?
First record: 1838.
Tetrad occurrence: 341 (70%).

Although treated by some as a cloned variety of *U. minor*, and reputed to have been introduced to Britain from Italy by the

Romans for training vines (Gil *et al.*, 2004), this was always a distinctive tree, until its disastrous destruction by Dutch elm disease. It is now mostly a major shrub component of hedgerows, but not in old woodlands, especially across southern and central Hertfordshire, in river valleys and on the London Clay, as well as around settlements elsewhere. Only in east Hertfordshire does it become scarce, where its place is largely taken by *U. minor*. It was formerly widely planted, both for hedging and for cattle browse, and its timber was a major resource for building. A few large trees have survived, such as those at Gobions (20/L). The map is likely to be a good reflection of its true occurrence, owing to the relative ease of identification using mature leaves on side shoots.

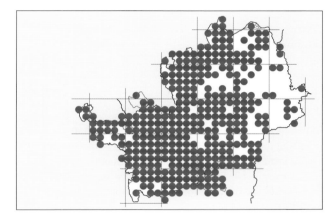

Map 78. *Ulmus procera.*

Field Elm Ulmus minor, *Offley Great Elm, by Minsbury Hill, 1986.*

Ulmus minor Miller
Small-leaved Elm
Native.
First record: 1838.
Tetrad occurrence: 308 (63%).

The distribution of this tree tends to be a mirror image of the distribution of *U. procera*. The two overlap extensively across central Hertfordshire, but *U. minor* in the broad sense is the dominant tree in the east, on the Boulder Clay, where it occurs in both hedgerows and as stands suckering into ancient woodland. The two species are reputed to hybridise (Stace, 1997), and rough-leaved '*Ulmus minor*' could conceivably be these. The species has been severely affected by Dutch elm disease, but there are a number of fine mature trees remaining at the time of writing. It is, however, a variable 'species', and some specialists regard it as a broad name including several taxa. There does appear to be some difference between forms in northern Hertfordshire on the Chalk and those throughout east Hertfordshire. The former is distinctive, with broader, shorter and highly asymmetric leaves (described by Dr Melville as a separate species: *U. coritana*). However, no attempt was made during the survey to maintain a distinction between this and what was formerly called *U. carpinifolia* Gled., the usual form in east Herts. One of the finest trees of the species in the County, the Offley Great Elm, which grew near Minsbury Hill (12/N), was lost in the storm of October 1987, although suckers remain.

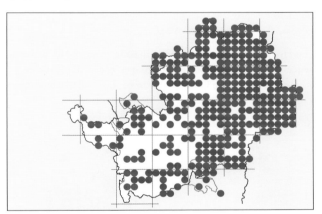

Map 79. *Ulmus minor.*

[*Ulmus* × *viminalis* Lodd. ex Loudon)? (*U. minor* × *U. plotii*)

This reputed hybrid is reported from Hertfordshire in Stace (1975), without further details, and is listed in Stace *et al.* (2003). As *U. plotii* itself is now considered not to be reliably identifiable, this taxon must also be doubtful.]

[*Ulmus plotii* Druce
Plot's Elm
Reputed native, nationally scarce.
First record: 1847.

Although this is regarded in Stace (1997) as an accepted species, and is included in Preston *et al.* (2002), recent cytological studies (Coleman, Hollingsworth and Hollingsworth, 2000) have shown convincingly that it cannot be reliably separated from *Ulmus minor*. For this reason it is not included in the Herts. flora, even though there are a number of older records for it, the first being from Morgan's Walk, Hertford (31/F), 1847 by J. Andrews, and identified by Druce (*Rep. Bot. Exch. Club*: 147 (1920)). There were a number of subsequent records, although the species itself is not listed for Hertfordshire in Stace (2003), and there was only one specimen matching its description found during the recent survey.]

Cannabaceae (Hop family)

Genus: *Cannabis*

Cannabis sativa L.
Hemp
Introduced: neophyte.
First record: *c.*1880.
Tetrad occurrence: 8 (2%).

There were eight casual records of this plant across the County, probably deriving from bird-seed, or, more recently, as a result of cultivation of the non-narcotic form for its fibre. At Rye Meads Sewage Works (31/V) it was, until recently, a regular component of the alien flora on sludge tips.

Genus: *Humulus*

Humulus lupulus L.
Hop
Native and introduced.
First record: 1750.
Tetrad occurrence: 251 (51%).
Stable or slightly increased (+6%).

Found frequently across the County in hedgerows and by streams, particularly in river valleys and on damper, clay soils elsewhere. Its natural distribution has probably been obscured to some extent by escapes from cultivation for the brewing industry.
(225 tetrads: Dony, 1967; 264 tetrads: 1950-1986)

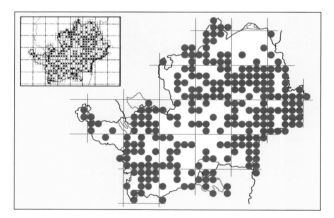

Map 80. *Humulus lupulus.*

Moraceae (Mulberry family)

Genus: *Ficus*

Ficus carica L.
Fig
Introduced: neophyte.
First record: 1924.
Tetrad occurrence: 6 (1%).

Recorded, often as long-established trees, at six localities during the survey: Digswell, by viaduct (21/M), 1993 *A. M. Boucher*; Rye Meads Sewage Works, self-established trees in works (31/V), 1995, etc. *A. M. Boucher/C. G. Hanson/T. J.*; Ware, by maltings (31/S), 1993 *A. M. B.*; Rickmansworth, on wall (09/S), 1996, *J. Colthup*; Watford, by railway (19/D), 1992 *P. J. Ellison*; Totteridge, Ellern Mede stables (29/H), 1996 *D. Griffith*.

Urticaceae (Nettle family)

Genus: *Urtica*

Urtica dioica L.
Common Nettle
Native.
First record: 1748.
Tetrad occurrence: 485 (99%).
Probably greatly increased (-1%).

Ubiquitous in nutrient-enriched and disturbed habitats throughout the County, although un-recorded from a few marginal tetrads. At the tetrad level, there is no significant change from Dony's survey, but its frequency has massively increased in the general landscape since the 1960s as pollution from nitrogen especially has taken hold.
(466 tetrads: Dony, 1967 and from 1950-1986)

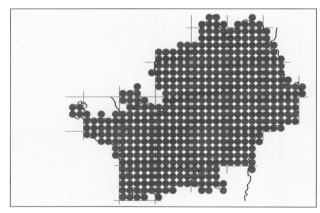

Map 81. *Urtica dioica.*

Plants identical in appearance to the so-called 'stingless nettle', long-known from Wicken Fen in Cambs., and referred to *Urtica galeopsifolia* Wierzb. ex Opiz by Geltman (1992), have been found in several old wet woodland and riparian fen sites across the County: by Amwell walkway, in fen woodland near R. Lea

'Stingless Nettle' Urtica *'galeopsifolia' Lemsford Springs, 2005.*

(31/R), 1997 *T. J.* (Hb. HTN); Brocket Park, wet woodland by R. Lea (21/B), 1997 *T. J.* (Hb. HTN); Panshanger, fen by Broadwater (21/W), 1997 *T. J.* (Hb. HTN); Stockers Lake, near R. Colne (09/L), 2002 *T. J.*; Lemsford Springs (21/F, G), 2005 *T. J.*; by the R. Lea at Willowmead N. R., Hertford (31/B), 2006 *T. J.*; by Croxley Common Moor (09/S), 2006; and at Waterford Marsh (31/C), 2006 *T. J.* At all these sites, it was found to be quite distinct from common nettle, flowering later. Stace (1997) does not accept the identification of the Wicken Fen plants. More work needs to be done to assess just how widespread this plant is in the County and what its status is. If it is a relict of old fen, as suggested by Geltman, it might be an important indicator of continuity for such habitats.

Urtica urens L.
Small Nettle
Introduced: archaeophyte.
First record: 1820.
Tetrad occurrence: 136 (28%).
Decreasing (-35%).

This is a plant of arable land, allotments and so on, especially where manure is used. Probably because of the decline in the use of farmyard manure, it is also decreasing, although its distribution is similar to that shown in Dony (1967).
(199 tetrads: Dony, 1967; 219 tetrads: 1950-1986)

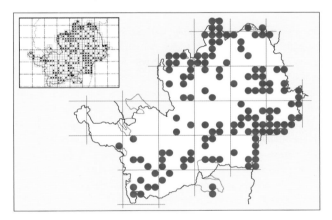

Map 82. *Urtica urens.*

Genus: *Parietaria*

Parietaria judaica L.
Pellitory-of-the-wall
Native.
First record: 1820.
Tetrad occurrence: 46 (9%).
Increasing (+68%).

Although reckoned to be native, this is a plant usually associated with old buildings, especially churches, where it grows around the bases of sun-baked walls. It can also grow in hedge-banks, and appears to be increasing in both abundance and distribution, occurring more frequently as a garden weed. Past taxonomic confusion with *P. officinalis* L. may have resulted in the latter now being overlooked in the County, as it has been shown to occur in Britain, especially in shady, wooded habitats, and should be looked for. The distribution of Pellitory is concentrated in the east of the County, and it appears to be spreading from favoured centres around Ware, Hertford and Hitchin.
(26 tetrads: Dony, 1967; 34 tetrads: 1950-1986)

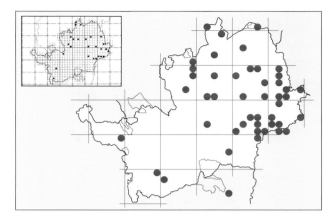

Map 83. *Parietaria judaica.*

Genus: *Soleirolia*

Soleirolia soleirolii (Req.) Dandy
Mind-your-own-business
Introduced: neophyte.
First record: *c.*1960.
Tetrad occurrence: 22 (5%).

Dony (1967) merely mentions this as an escape from cultivation around houses, and kept no detailed records. It is now well-established in many localities in and around settlements, often in damp lawns, or by paths. Being inconspicuous, it may well be under-recorded. The survey found it widely, with a concentration around Hertford.

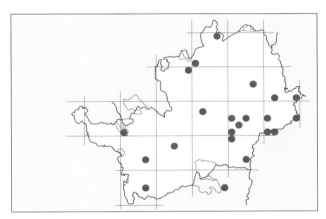

Map 84. *Soleirolia soleirolii.*

Juglandaceae (Walnut family)

Genus: *Juglans*

Juglans regia L.
Walnut
Introduced: neophyte.
First record: *c.*1920 (as self-sown).
Tetrad occurrence: 52 (11%).
Increasing.

J. E. Little recorded this *c.*1920 from Therfield Heath, and from sites near Hitchin on the Chalk. Dony (1967) dismisses it for the most part as a planted tree. It is now widespread and increasing steadily as a self-sown tree in the north of the County, including

Therfield Heath (33/P, 34/K), where it is potentially a menace on old chalk grassland. Some records from central Herts. may be of old planted trees.

(9 tetrads: 1950-1986)

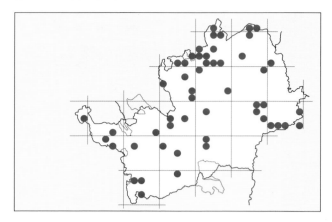

Map 85. *Juglans regia.*

Juglans nigra L.
Black Walnut
Planted.

Noted as recently planted trees in Claggbottom Plantation, Kimpton (11/Y), 1994 *T. J./A. R. Outen.* It may be more widespread.

Fagaceae (Beech family)

Genus: *Fagus*

Fagus sylvatica L.
Beech
Native (and introduced).
First record: 1690.
Tetrad occurrence: 406 (83%).
Increasing (+32%).

The increase in the occurrence of Beech, despite its proneness to drought, may be explained by its use in new plantations. The distribution map from the present survey certainly does not show the clear preponderance of the species in the woodlands in the west that was apparent in 1967. It is native as a major component tree in the Chiltern woodlands, south to Watford, and east as

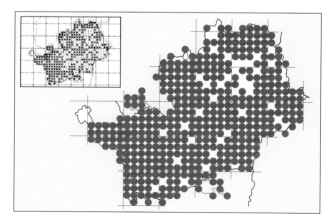

Map 86. *Fagus sylvatica.*

It also appears to be native in Oak/Hornbeam woodlands on acidic gravels in the south of the County, where it has been until recently increasing steadily at the expense of oak. In east Herts., it has always apparently been a planted tree (except at a few old woodland sites on Chalk perhaps), and has often succumbed to drought or wind-throw in old plantations.

(293 tetrads: Dony, 1967; 328 tetrads: 1950-1986)

Genus: *Nothofagus*

[*Nothofagus fusca* (Hook. *f.*) Oerst
Red Beech
Planted.

This was reported from Prae Wood (10/D) in 2000, but needs confirmation. Other species of southern beech may have been used elsewhere to replace native Beech in woodlands damaged by gales, and could regenerate.]

Genus: *Castanea*

Castanea sativa Miller
Sweet Chestnut
Introduced: archaeophyte.
First record: 1728.
Tetrad occurrence: 196 (40%).
Increasing.

This was only thought of as a planted tree by Dony (1967), although he did give records widely across Hertfordshire in his ms. index. It was scarcely noted by Pryor, and yet the earliest record (of old trees) was at least as long ago as 1728, when some were felled at Ashridge. It is now thought to have been introduced to Britain as long ago as Roman times. Very large old trees exist at Digswell Park (21/H), and at Chipperfield Common (00/K), among other places, and old coppice stools occur at Ashridge and Northaw Great Wood. The tree was found during the survey wherever there were extensive woods across central, southern and western Hertfordshire, only becoming scarce on the Boulder Clay and the Chalk. Its natural regeneration, though, is more limited, and it is only becoming frequent in places where the soils are dry and gravelly, such as at Ashridge and Northaw.

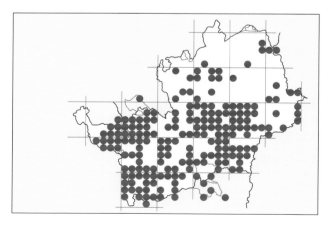

Map 87. *Castanea sativa.*

Quercus cerris L.
Turkey Oak
Introduced: neophyte.
First record: 1917.
Tetrad occurrence: 134 (27%).
Increasing.

J. E. Little first recorded this in 1917 from a number of sites, but it was no doubt planted in woodlands during the 19th century, when it was thought it might make a useful timber tree. Dony (1967) scarcely mentions it, but does note natural regeneration, and gives some records in his ms. index, although not consistently enough for comparison with the present survey. It is now widespread across the County, both as a planted tree and especially as naturally regenerated young trees in woodland and scrub. It is able to grow on Chalk, and has been found self-sown in scrub on chalk grassland at Telegraph Hill (12/E). Its associated gall-wasp *Andricus quercus-calicis* (the 'Knopper-gall Wasp'), which affects the acorns of Pedunculate Oak as its alternate host, may be more of a threat to the natural environment than the tree itself.
(45 tetrads: Dony mss. and to 1986)

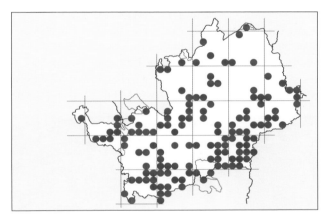

Map 88. *Quercus cerris.*

Quercus ilex L.
Holm Oak
Introduced: neophyte.
First record: 1978 (as self-sown).
Tetrad occurrence: 22 (5%).
Increasing.

A record made by the I.T.E. railway survey in 1978 at Bricket

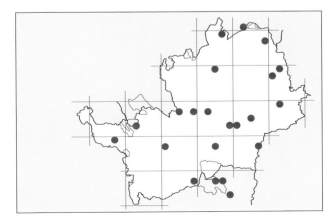

Map 89. *Quercus ilex.*

Wood (10/F) may have been self-sown. It was also noted at Prior's Wood (11/Y), 1979 *T. J.* Dony only knew it as a planted tree. The current survey found self-sown seedlings or young trees in nine tetrads of the 22 in which the tree was reported, sometimes without an immediately apparent source, such as at Therfield Heath (34/F), 1993; Holcroft Springs (11/N), 1999; and by the Dollis Brook, Osidge (29/W), 1998 (VC20 [Greater London]) *T. J.*

Quercus petraea (Matt.) Liebl.
Sessile Oak
Native (and introduced).
First record: 1843.
Tetrad occurrence: 49 (10%).
Probably stable (+213%).

Webb and Coleman, Pryor and Dony all concur that this tree only occurs on the higher, heathy ground in the County. Its current distribution bears this out, but the apparent increase from Dony's survey may be unreliable, because it was found to be much more widespread than he recorded in the period between 1970 and 1986. It forms the dominant oak in Wormley Wood and a few other adjacent woods, as well as in Sherrards Park Wood, and also formerly in Symondshyde Great Wood. However, Salisbury (*Trans. Herts. N.H.S.*, 14 (1912)) pointed out the occurrence of the hybrid with *Q. robur*, and Dony (1967) suggested that the true species might scarcely occur in the County. While the present survey has shown that *Q. petraea* in a 'typical' form does occur, there is a strong suspicion that most, if not all of the mature trees were actually planted for timber during the late 18th and early 19th centuries. Certainly, the form of the tree which occurs in Herts. tends to be rather different from native stands in western and northern Britain, suggesting maybe that it was brought in from Europe. Many of the woods where it occurs were or are part of the Hatfield Estate, and it is quite likely that they would have been carrying out concerted forestry at this period. Another reason to suspect this is the case is that there are apparently very few ancient Sessile Oaks in the County, although ancient Pedunculate Oaks are common. Also, while the latter was recorded from early times, Sessile Oak was only first noted by botanists well into the 19th century, by which time it had become obvious. However, it does occur where it may not have been planted, and one historic pollard of the hybrid is known from Hitch Wood Shrubs (12/W), which suggests its early occurrence in the area, so the jury must remain out on the subject.
(15 tetrads: Dony, 1967; 50 tetrads 1950-1986)

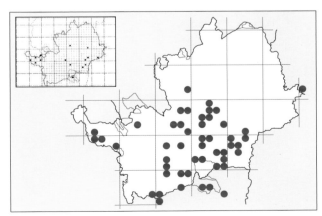

Map 90. *Quercus petraea.*

Quercus × rosacea Bechst. (*Q. petraea × Q. robur*)
Native.
First record: *c.*1912.
Tetrad occurrence: 35 (7%).

First noted by E. J. Salisbury at Symondshyde Great Wood (11/V) (Salisbury, 1912), hybrid oak was found to be present almost everywhere that *Q. petraea* was recorded, often as young saplings This included woods where *Q. petraea* is the dominant timber tree. Introgression between the two oaks is apparently occurring in these areas. A few records were made where *Q. petraea* is now apparently absent. As mentioned above, one old pollard of the hybrid has been noted beside Hitch Wood (12/W), 2009 *T. J.*, which supports the idea that *Q. petraea* itself is native in the area.

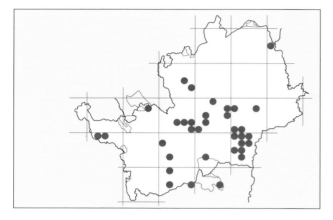

Map 91. *Quercus × rosacea.*

Quercus robur L.
Pedunculate Oak
Native.
First (botanical) record: 1733.
Tetrad occurrence: 456 (93%).
Stable (no change).

This occurs throughout the County, except on the Chalk ridge in the north-east as far west as Baldock (one meaning of the name of which is supposed to be 'bald oak', perhaps suggesting the town never had any!). It forms the dominant timber tree in most old coppices and ancient hedgerows, and is a major constituent of old secondary woods on former commons. Its most important occurrences, however, are as ancient pollard (and a few maiden stem) trees in former wood-pasture commons and mediaeval parks. Famous, historic trees survive, such as the Elephant Oak in Hatfield Home Park, and the Panshanger Oak (reputed to be Britain's largest maiden oak), although the Queen Elizabeth Oak at Hatfield Home Park succumbed in the 1950s, and Goff's Oak about the same time. Some historically recorded trees were also massive, such as the lost Dog Kennel Oak on the former Northaw Common, which was reckoned to have a girth of 14 yards in 1766! However, there are many fine, ancient, less well-known trees elsewhere, some with names, such as the Frame Oak, also from the former Northaw Common at Cuffley, which may be the massive tree that survives near Thornton's Farm; and numerous ancient but unnamed trees at Brocket Park, Sacombe Park, Ashridge, Broxbournebury, Stagenhoe Park, Kings Walden Park, Ardeleybury and elsewhere. A survey in the 1990s at Panshanger found that the Park held over 500 ancient trees, a large number of

Pedunculate Oak Quercus robur, *The Elephant Oak, Hatfield Home Park, 2009.*

century at least. Northaw Great Wood, for example, has a distinctive form of the species as 100 year old specimens and younger growth, with very cut leaves, present in quantity in the southern half of the wood, which is known to have been planted after 1811. Recent amenity and forestry planting has no doubt supplemented these introduced stocks elsewhere.
(432 tetrads: Dony, 1967; 437 tetrads 1950-1986)

Quercus palustris Muench.
Pin Oak
Planted.
First record: 1999.

This has been identified as the planted oak at Much Wood, Hertford Heath (31/K), 1999 *T. J./G. P. Smith.* (det. A. Cooper/ T. J., 2008). It was also recorded as a planted tree from the 'nature reserve' at Buncefield oil depot, Hemel Hempstead (00/Z), 1992, where its survival is now unlikely, following the destruction of the depot in the much-reported explosion! It may occur elsewhere.

Quercus rubra L.
Red Oak
Introduced: neophyte.
First record: *c.*1970.
Tetrad occurrence: 25 (5%).

This has been planted on a fairly extensive scale in a number of ancient woodlands since the Second World War, where it can become established, mainly by suckering and regeneration from cut stools. It is particularly a feature now of woods around Bramfield (21/T, X, Y). Recorded quite widely during the survey, although one or two may be misidentifications of *Q. palustris*.

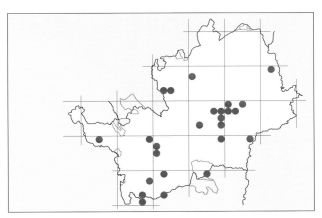

Map 93. *Quercus rubra.*

Quercus velutina Lam.
Black Oak
Planted.

One old specimen tree of this was found at Well Wood, Northaw (20/R), 1981 *T. J.*, but has not been re-examined since.

Pedunculate Oak Quercus robur, *The Panshanger Oak, 1995.*

which were oaks. The oldest tree in the Park (not the Panshanger Oak itself) was estimated to be about 1000 years old (recently surrounded by gravel excavations and now dead), and since, similar dates have been assigned to large pollards in Hatfield Park. Such trees, and the remnants of wood-pasture in which they occur, are the nearest thing the County has to natural woodland, and often support rare insects and fungi. In a few places, there is some evidence to suggest that introduced (possibly European) Pedunculate Oak stock was planted into woodlands in the 19th

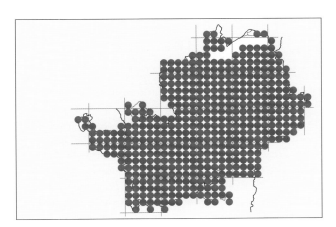

Map 92. *Quercus robur.*

Betulaceae (Birch family)

Genus: *Betula*

Betula pendula Roth
Silver Birch
Native (and introduced).
First record: 1676.
Tetrad occurrence: 393 (80%).
Apparently increasing (+91%).

How much this is actually increasing, or is better recorded is difficult to say, but it is now found throughout the County, except for the dampest parts of the Boulder Clay plateau, the Woburn Sands plain at Long Marston, and some parts of the Chalk. Even here, it can become abundant, such as in scrub by Therfield Heath (33/J). It is sometimes a feature of roadside and amenity planting elsewhere, from which seedlings may have spread, although the true identity of some of these might be suspect, because similar non-native species or varieties may also have been planted, such as the North American *B. populifolia* (**Grey Birch**). It is, of course, a major component of some ancient woodland types, notably the oak/birch woodland found *e.g.* at Oxhey Woods (19/B), Northaw Great Wood (20/S, X), and Bencroft Wood (30/I). It is also a pioneer in gaps in other woodland stand-types.
(195 tetrads: Dony, 1967; 237 tetrads 1950-1986)

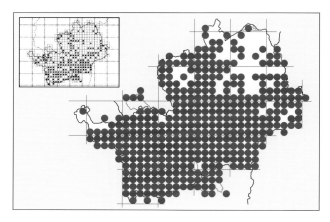

Map 94. *Betula pendula.*

Betula × *aurata* Borkh. (*B. pendula* × *B. pubescens*)
Native.
First record: 1967.
Tetrad occurrence: 17 (4%).

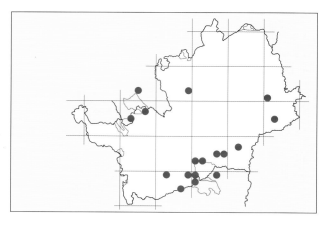

Map 95. *Betula* × *aurata.*

First noted at Hertford Heath (31/K), 1967 *M. Kennedy*. The current records from 17 tetrads no doubt severely under-estimate its occurrence. In some sites where the two birch species occur, it is now probably the dominant tree. At Rowley Green (29/D) (VC20 [Greater London]), a close inspection in 2008 failed to find any other birch.

Betula pubescens Ehrh.
Downy Birch
Native.
First record: 1851.
Tetrad occurrence: 155 (32%).
Increasing? (+66%).
Native of damp, acid woods and heaths and of peat fen by rivers. It was only recognised as a separate species relatively late. Where the two species meet, hybrid swarms occur, and it is likely that the true Downy Birch may have been much over-recorded in a number of areas.
(89 tetrads: Dony, 1967; 128 tetrads: 1950-1986)

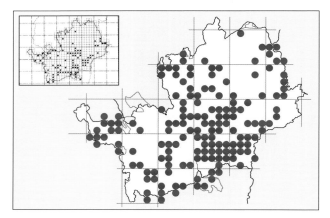

Map 96. *Betula pubescens.*

Genus: *Alnus*

Alnus viridis (Chaix) DC.
Green Alder
Planted.

A few stunted trees of this species, mixed with a line of old *A. glutinosa*, were found near Colney Heath (20/C), 1991 *T. J.* (Hb. HTN), presumably a misguided planting.

Alnus glutinosa (L.) Gaertner
Alder
Native (and introduced).
First record: 1733.
Tetrad occurrence: 225 (46%).
Increasing? (+72%).

The principal colonies of Alder in the County occur in some fen woodlands (a few of which may have been planted in the 19th century for the hat-block industry), such as at Oughton Head (12/U, 13/Q), Purwell (22/E) and Folly Alder Swamp, St Ippollitts (12/Y) around Hitchin; and beside rivers in the Colne and Lea systems, *e.g.* Stanborough (21/F), Panshanger (21/W), Bayfordbury (31/A) and Stockers Lake (09/L). It also occurs naturally, if rarely, as stands around seepages in some ancient woodlands, and frequently as remnant linear stands along river banks. However, its natural distribution is increasingly obscured by incongruous plantings on unnatural sites in new plantations, and by some roads, because it grows readily on poor soils. Some of these are also likely not to be native forms, or could be hybrids with other species. The cultivated variety *laciniata* Willd. has recently been recorded from a few localities, all originally planted, *e.g.* Oughton Head (13/Q), Woodhall Park (31/E), and Nyn Pond, Northaw (20/R).

(124 tetrads: Dony, 1967; 156 tetrads: 1950-1986)

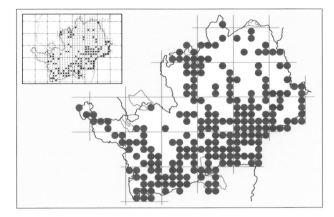

Map 97. *Alnus glutinosa.*

Alnus incana (L.) Moench
Grey Alder
Introduced: neophyte.
First record: 1923.
Tetrad occurrence: 16 (3%).

Rare, but increasing, as a planted tree, and regenerating at some sites. It is often planted alongside *A. glutinosa* and could hybridise.

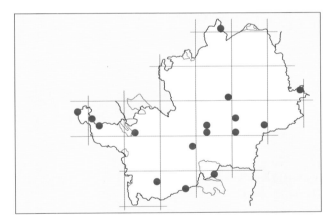

Map 98. *Alnus incana.*

Alnus cordata (Lois.) Duby
Italian Alder
Introduced: planted.
First record: 1988.
Tetrad occurrence: 16 (3%).

Recorded from an increasing number of sites, especially amenity plantings round gravel pits, or by roads. Thankfully, it does not seem to reproduce from seed.

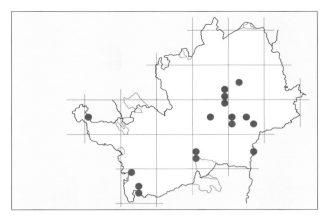

Map 99. *Alnus cordata.*

Genus: *Carpinus*

Carpinus betulus L.
Hornbeam
Native.
First record: 1733.
Tetrad occurrence: 405 (83%).
Stable or slightly increasing (+14%).

The Hornbeam probably reaches its northernmost extent as a native tree in south-eastern England along the Chiltern dip-slope. Hertfordshire has one of its strongholds, in the coppice-with-standards woods on mildly acidic clays and gravels in the centre and south-east of the County. It is also a major component in this area of former wood-pasture, where it was formerly managed as pollard trees for fuel. Some stands of these survive, although the largest areas formerly used for charcoal in Broxbourne Woods were mostly felled in the 1960s to make way for conifers. Important, historic stands now survive especially at Northaw Great Wood (Cuffley Camp) (20/X) (known to be over 250 years old), Hook Wood, Northaw (20/Q), Harmergreen Wood (21/N), Broxbourne Common (30/N), Blackfan Wood (30/D), Emmanuel Pollards (30/I), and Mardley Heath (21/P), among other sites, but odd pollards are frequent along green lanes and on old commons, *etc.* elsewhere. A large ornamental stand of pollards,

Hornbeam Carpinus betulus *Cuffley Camp, old pollards, March 1977.*

of more recent origin, occurs in Knebworth Park (22/A, F), and is still actively managed. Hornbeam becomes scarce in the Chiltern Beech woods, and again in the north-east, in the area dominated by Field Maple and Ash. On the Chalk, it is also almost absent, except as planted trees. It is capable of colonising old grassland, which enables it to spread in some areas, and it is frequently used in new amenity plantations.

(340 tetrads: Dony, 1967; 361 tetrads: 1950-1986)

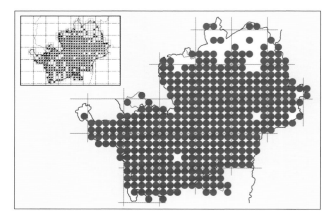

Map 100. *Carpinus betulus.*

Genus: *Corylus*

Corylus avellana L.
Hazel
Native.
First record: 1733.
Tetrad occurrence: 465 (95%).
Stable (-1%).

Hazel is more or less ubiquitous. However, as a major constituent of semi-natural woodlands, it is most frequent in the north-east, forming coppice-with-standards stand-types with Ash and Field Maple on Boulder Clay. In the west, it occasionally predominates with Oak and Ash where Beech is absent, and occurs as coppice with Oak on acidic clays in the south, in the virtual absence of Hornbeam *e.g.* Berrygrove Wood (19/J) and Combe Wood (10/V). It can be a good colonist of calcareous grasslands, and forms an interesting scrub with other species, such as at Ravensburgh Castle and Hoo Bit, Hexton (12/E).

(445 tetrads: Dony, 1967; 454 tetrads: 1950-1986)

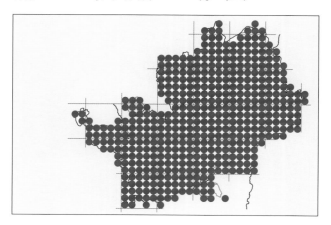

Map 101. *Corylus avellana.*

Phytolaccaceae (Pokeweed family)

Genus: *Phytolacca*

Phytolacca acinosa Roxb.
Indian Pokeweed
Introduced: neophyte.
First record: *c.*1960.

No locations are given by Dony for this plant (formerly confused with *P. americana* L. and possibly other species). It was recorded during the survey from Ware (31/M), 1996/7 *A. M. Boucher/ C. G. Hanson* and as a long-persistent weed at Baldock (23/L, M), 2000, *etc. T. J.* It has also been recorded from Hunsdon Churchyard (41/B), 1984 *C. G. H.*

Phytolacca polyandra Batalin
Chinese Pokeweed

This was reported in 1985 from Widford Churchyard (41/C) *C. G. Hanson* (det. E. J. Clement) (Hb. CGH). Its distinction from *P. acinosa* may be dubious (Stace, 1997).

Nyctaginaceae

Genus: *Mirabilis*

Mirabilis jalapa L.
Marvel-of-Peru
Introduced: casual.
First record: *c.*1975.

This native of South America was first found as a casual at Offley *c.*1975 (finder not recorded) (det. T. J.); and was found again as a casual during the survey at Broxbourne (30/S), 1999 *J. Crew* (det. E. J. Clement).

Aizoaceae (Dewplant family)

Genus: *Aptenia*

Aptenia cordifolia (L. *f.*) Schwantes
Heart-leaf Ice-plant
Introduced: neophyte.
First (only) record: 1970.

Recorded from a rubbish tip at Hitchin (13/V), 1970 *M. Webster* (Preston and Sell, 1989).

Genus: *Tetragonia*

Tetragonia tetragonioides (Pallas) Kuntze
New Zealand Spinach
Introduced: neophyte.

First recorded from a rubbish tip at Broxbourne (30/T), 1968 *comm.: J. G. Dony* (Hb. HTN) (Dony, 1971), and subsequently from tips at Hitchin (13/V), 1974 *C. G. Hanson*; and Waterford (31/C), 1979 *C. G. H.* (Hb. HTN).

Chenopodiaceae (Goosefoots)

Genus: *Chenopodium*

[*Chenopodium pumilio* R. Br.
Clammy Goosefoot
Introduced: neophyte.

Appears spontaneously, having been introduced to a garden at Ware (31/S), *e.g.* 1995 *C. G. Hanson* (Hb. HTN), but not so far found elsewhere.]

Chenopodium hircinum Schrader
Foetid Goosefoot
Introduced: neophyte.
First record: 1964.

Not seen since Dony's record at Park Street dump (10/L) (Dony, 1967).

Chenopodium berlandieri Moq.
Pitseed Goosefoot
Introduced: neophyte.
First (only) record: 1923.

There have been no records since it occurred at Ware (Dony, 1967).

Chenopodium strictum Roth
Striped Goosefoot
Introduced: neophyte.
First record: 1970.

This was first found at High Leigh tip (30/P), 1970 *C. G. Hanson*. It was later seen at Rickmansworth tip (09/L), with soya aliens, 1976 *J. G. Dony*; and Rye Meads Sewage Works (31/V), 1980 *C. G. H.* During the current survey, it was found again at Rye Meads in 1990, 1994 and 1995 *A. M. Boucher/C. G. H.* (Hb. HTN); and on a dung heap at Cole Green (21/Q), 1987 *A. M. B./C. G. H.* As it is similar to some forms of *C. album* it could be overlooked elsewhere.

Chenopodium suecicum Murr
Swedish Goosefoot
Introduced: neophyte.
First record: 2006.

This *C. album* look-alike was found at Church End, Little Hadham (42/L), 2006 *T. J.* (Hb. HTN). It may also occur elsewhere on tips.

Chenopodium probstii Aellen
Probst's Goosefoot
Introduced: neophyte.
First record: 1956.
Tetrad occurrence: 6.

Another species similar to *C. album*, found on nutrient enriched tips. Seen during the survey at Rye Meads Sewage Works (31/V), 1992, 1994 and 1995 *C. G. Hanson* (Hb. HTN); Ware tip (31/M), 1987 *C. G. H.*; Welwyn Garden City (21/G), 1991 *A. M. Boucher*; Dunsley Orchard, Tring (91/F), 2001 *M. J. Hicks* (det. *T. J.*) (Hb. HTN); on a dung heap at Chapmore End (31/I), 2006 *T. J.* (Hb. HTN); and on disturbed banks by the A505, Baldock (23/L), 2007 *T. J.* (Hb. HTN).

Chenopodium desiccatum A. Nelson
(*C. pratericola* Rydb.)
Slimleaf Goosefoot
Introduced: neophyte.
First record: 1912.

There were three early records from tips (Dony, 1967), and it was apparently last recorded in 1929 at a locality in TQ29 *J. E. Lousley* (det. *J. P. M. Brennan*) (record *comm.*: B.R.C.: CEH Monks Wood).

Chenopodium giganteum D. Don
Tree Spinach
Introduced: neophyte.
First record: 1994.

This impressive plant was first recorded at Rye Meads Sewage Works (31/V), 1994 *C. G. Hanson/A. M. Boucher*; and has subsequently established itself from introduced seed in a garden at Ware (31/S) *C. G. H.* (Hb. HTN).

Chenopodium capitatum (L.) Asch.
Strawberry Blite
Introduced: neophyte.
First record: 1956.

Recorded as established at Rabley Heath by Dony (1967), but only seen recently as a casual at Graveley (22/J), 1994 *K. Hall*.

Chenopodium bonus-henricus L.   UK Vulnerable
Good King Henry
Introduced: archaeophyte.
First recorded: 1814.

Tetrad occurrence: 21 (4%).
Decreasing (-26%).

Formerly cultivated for its edible leaves, it is now a casual weed of waste places near habitation. The map may include one or two mis-identifications of the robust form of *Atriplex prostrata*.
(27 tetrads: Dony, 1967; 37 tetrads: 1950-1986)

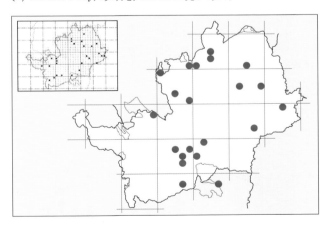

Map 102. *Chenopodium bonus-henricus.*

Chenopodium glaucum L.   UK Vulnerable
Oak-leaved Goosefoot
Introduced: archaeophyte.
First record: 1830.
Tetrad occurrence: 3 (<1%).
Stable? (+20%).

Reckoned by Dony to be a casual, but it occurs, often with long intervals, in certain areas. However, it has decreased since the early 20th century. Recorded after Dony's *Flora* (1967) at Park Street (10/L), Rye House (30/Z), and Ware (31/M). During the current survey it was also found at Hailey Farm (31/Q), 1989, 1991 *A. M. Boucher* (Hb. HTN); at Sawbridgeworth (41/S), 1989 *S. Watson* (det. T. J.) (Hb. HTN); on a dung heap at Chapmore End (31/I), 2006 *T. J.* (Hb. HTN); and also from a dung heap adjoining Woodhall Park (31/I), 2008 *T. J.* (Hb. HTN). Most of these are in areas from which earlier records were made.

Chenopodium rubrum L.
Red Goosefoot
Native.
First record: 1840.
Tetrad occurrence: 193 (39%).
Probably stable or slightly increased (+10%).

A frequent plant of refuse tips and manure heaps, but also in more natural settings around the drying margins of eutrophic ponds. It formed a carpet across the bed of Wilstone Reservoir when it almost dried up in the mid-1990s. It has decreased in urban areas, but otherwise has much the same distribution as it had in 1967. (167 tetrads: Dony, 1967; 184 tetrads: 1950-1986)

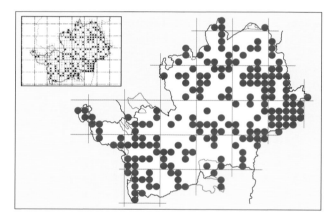

Map 103. *Chenopodium rubrum.*

Chenopodium polyspermum L.
Many-seeded Goosefoot
Introduced: archaeophyte.
First record: 1843.
Tetrad occurrence: 165 (34%).
Slightly decreased (-4%).

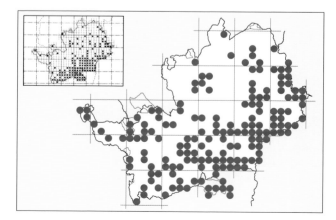

Map 104. *Chenopodium polyspermum.*

Considered to be introduced, but it can be found in disturbed semi-natural habitats, as well as a weed of cultivation. It occurs mainly on less calcareous soils in the south of the County, and has decreased especially in this core area, because of urban development and the reduction in vegetable cultivation in gardens, while being more widely recorded elsewhere. (165 tetrads: Dony, 1967; 182 tetrads: 1950-1986)

Chenopodium vulvaria L.   UK Endangered
Stinking Goosefoot
Introduced: archaeophyte.
First record: 1843.

Formerly occasional in waste ground, this is now nationally a rare plant, the last record in the wild in Herts. being Dony's from Park Street dump (10/L), 1966 (Dony, 1967). It has appeared spontaneously from introduced seed in a garden at Ware (31/S), 1993 *C. G. Hanson* (Hb. HTN).

Chenopodium hybridum L.
Maple-leaved Goosefoot *or* **Sowbane**
Introduced: archaeophyte.
First record: 1822.
Tetrad occurrence: 8 (1%).
Stable? (+20%).

This plant of disturbed, humus-rich soils has always been a feature of the Hertford and Hoddesdon areas, where it remains. Recorded from five localities by Dony (1967) and during the current survey from: spoil by Aldenham Reservoir (19/S), 1988 *T. J.*; Hoddesdon (30/N, U), 1989 *A. M. Boucher*; Broxbourne (30/T), 1989 *A. M. B.*; Hertford (31/G), 1989 *A. M. B.*, and 2001 *T. J.*; Hunsdon (41/B), 1989 *S. Watson*; Little Hadham (42/L), 1989 *S. W.*; and Hinxworth (23/J), 1995 *T. J.* (Hb. HTN).

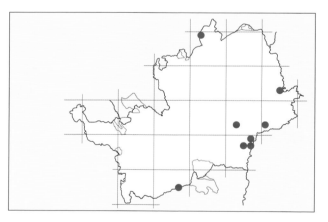

Map 105. *Chenopodium hybridum.*

Chenopodium urbicum L.   UK Critically Endangered
Upright Goosefoot   Herts Extinct
Introduced: archaeophyte.
Only records: 1843.

Not confirmed in the wild since 1843, but appears spontaneously in a garden at Ware (31/S) from imported seed *C. G. Hanson*.

Chenopodium murale L.   UK Vulnerable
Nettle-leaved Goosefoot
Introduced: archaeophyte.
First record: 1841.
Tetrad occurrence: 4 (<1%).
Stable? (+33%).

Usually a rare casual of tips and waste ground, this was found
at Rye Meads Sewage Works (31/V), 1989 *A. M. Boucher/
C. G. Hanson* (Hb. HTN); Bishop's Stortford (42/V), 1996
J. L. Fielding; Watford (19/D), 1994 *J. K. Jackson* (Hb. HTN);
and, unusually, with *C. album* by a field at Dowdells Wood (21/C),
1994 *T. J.* (Hb. HTN).

Chenopodium ficifolium Smith
Fig-leaved Goosefoot
Introduced: archaeophyte.
First record: 1851.
Tetrad occurrence: 153 (31%).
Increased (+75%).

This weed of arable and waste ground was considered to be only
occasional by Dony, but is now quite frequent in some areas,
although with a patchy distribution, suggesting that it may be
under-recorded.
(83 tetrads: Dony, 1967; 112 tetrads: 1950-1986)

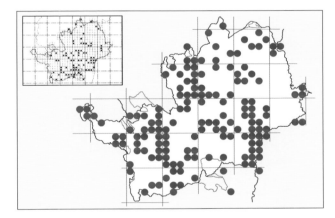

Map 106. *Chenopodium ficifolium.*

Chenopodium opulifolium Schrad. ex Koch and Ziz
Grey Goosefoot
Introduced: neophyte.
First record: 1913.

A rare casual, recorded during the survey from Rye Meads Sewage
Works (31/V), 1994 *A. M. Boucher*; and Ware (31/S), 1996
C. G. Hanson (det. E. J. Clement) (Hb. HTN).

Chenopodium album L.
Fat-hen
Native.
First record: 1814.
Tetrad occurrence: 415 (85%).
Decreasing (-13%).

This familiar weed of cultivated ground, tips, dung heaps, *etc.*,
once used as a food-of-last-resort by country folk, was considered
'abundant' by Dony (1967). It is still frequent in most areas, but
is often very limited in quantity, because of modern agricultural
practices. It has become so scarce in some more arable, as well as

urban areas that it is now showing a decrease at the tetrad level.
This has affected farmland birds, because its seeds formed one of
the main autumn foods for many species.
(454 tetrads: Dony, 1967; 453 tetrads: 1950-1986)

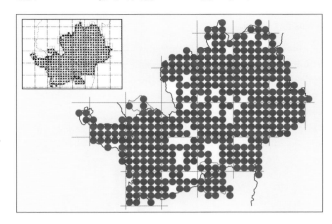

Map 107. *Chenopodium album.*

Genus: *Bassia*

Bassia scoparia (L.) A. J. Scott
Summer-cypress
Introduced: neophyte.
First record: 1964.
Increasing?

A rare casual of waste tips. It was recorded since 1967 at Park
Street (10/L), 1970, and at Ware (31/N), 1972 *C. G. Hanson*.
During the survey it was reported from Rye Meads Sewage Works
(31/V), 1994, 1995 *A. M. Boucher/C. G. H.* (Hb. HTN). It may
begin to appear by roads, and should be watched for.

Genus: *Spinacea*

Spinacea oleracea L.
Spinach
Introduced: neophyte.
First record: 1987.

A casual of cultivation, on waste tips at Ware (31/M), 1987;
Waterford (31/C), 1987; and Rye Meads Sewage Works (31/V),
1991-1996 *C. G. Hanson*.

Genus: *Atriplex*

Atriplex hortensis L.
Garden Orache
Introduced: neophyte.
First record: *c.*1880.
Tetrad occurrence: 8 (2%).
Increasing (+300%).

A casual of garden origin, usually in its purple form, found on
waste ground, in shrubberies and the like, recorded from eight
tetrads, mostly in the south and east of the County.

Atriplex prostrata Boucher ex DC.

Spear-leaved Orache

Native.

First record: 1838.

Tetrad occurrence: 397 (81%).

Increasing (+61%).

Dony found this to be especially a feature of the London Clay in south Herts., but since then, it has become an abundant weed beside over- salted roads throughout the County, to the detriment of native flora, as well as becoming increasingly common in field margins.

(234 tetrads: Dony, 1967; 250 tetrads: 1950-1986)

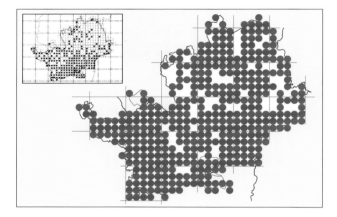

Map 108. *Atriplex prostrata.*

Atriplex littoralis L.

Grass-leaved Orache

Introduced [native of salt-marshes in U.K.].

First record: 1927.

Tetrad occurrence: 6 (1%).

Increasing.

This was first found on waste ground at Hitchin (12/Z), 1927 (Hb. Phillips, HTN), but omitted by Dony (1967). More recently it was found by a road in Harpenden (11/C), 1989, *J. F. Southey* (det. T. J.) (Hb. HTN); and has since appeared at a number of roadside sites where salting no doubt helps its spread: Odsey, A505 (23/Y), 1992; Radwell, A1 (23/J), 1997; Bygrave, A505 (23/S), 1997 *T. J.* (Hb. HTN); Holwell, A600 (13/R), 1999 *P. G. Stapleton*; and Bishop's Stortford bypass (42/W), 2004 *S. Watson*. It may well be under-recorded.

Atriplex patula L.

Common Orache

Native.

First record: 1838.

Tetrad occurrence: 404 (82%).

Stable or slightly increasing (+3%).

This is an abundant plant of waste places, especially by salted roads, and also as a cornfield weed across most of the County, but strangely absent from a few areas, including from some where Dony recorded it.

(373 tetrads: Dony, 1967; 382 tetrads: 1950-1986)

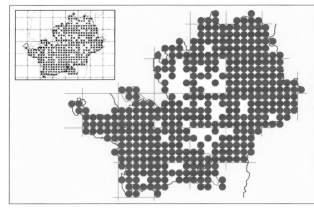

Map 109. *Atriplex patula.*

[*Atriplex suberecta* Verd.

Australian Orache

Only known as a spontaneous weed from introduced seed in a garden at Ware (31/S) *C. G. Hanson*].

[*Atriplex tatarica* L.

A record by Druce, 1915 (Dony, 1967), may be an error for *A. oblongifolia* Waldst. and Kit, and needs confirmation.]

Atriplex spongiosa F. Muell.

Pop Saltbush

Introduced: casual.

First (only) record: 1921.

Recorded once, from Ware *A. W. Graveson* (Dony, 1967).

Genus: *Beta*

Beta vulgaris L.

Beet

Introduced: neophyte.

First record: 1956.

Tetrad occurrence: 32 (7%).

The more usual crops ssp. *cicla* (L.) Arcang. (**Foliage Beet**) and ssp. *vulgaris* (**Root Beet**) are occasionally found as escapes in their various forms, including Chard and Spinach Beet. All introduced subspecies are mapped together.

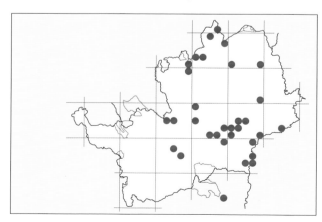

Map 110. *Beta vulgaris.*

The U.K. native ssp. *maritima* (L.) Arcang. (**Sea Beet**) was found by the road at Hertford Heath (31/K), 1999 *T. J./G. P. Smith* (Hb. HTN), no doubt encouraged by salting.

Genus: *Axyris*

Axyris amaranthoides L.
Russian Pigweed
Introduced: casual.
First record: 1926.

Recorded at Ware, 1926 and Hitchin, 1927 (Dony, 1967), but with no recent records.

Genus: *Salsola*

Salsola kali L. ssp. *ruthenica* (Iljin) Soó
Spineless Saltwort
Introduced: casual.
First (only) record: 1966.

Not recorded since Dony found it at Park Street (10/L) (Dony, 1967) (and repeated in Burton, 1983).

Amaranthaceae (Pigweed family)

Genus *Amaranthus*

Amaranthus caudatus L.
Love-lies-bleeding
Introduced: casual.
First record: 1956.

First recorded by Dony at Blackbridge tip, Wheathampstead (11/X), 1956 (Dony, 1967 and ms. index). Subsequently on other tips: High Leigh (30/U), 1970; Pye Corner (41/L), 1970; and Ware (31/M), 1977 *C. G. Hanson*. There were no records during the current survey.

Amaranthus quitensis Kunth
Mucronate Amaranth
Introduced: neophyte.
First record: 1958.

Found since 1970 at Ware tip (31/M), 1975; Blackbridge tip, Wheathampstead (11/X), 1976; Cock Lane tip, Hoddesdon (30/U), 1982; and at Rye Meads Sewage Works (31/V), 1975 and 1984 *C. G. Hanson*. During the recent survey, the only site was Rye Meads, where it occurred in 1990, 1992 and 1994 *A. M. Boucher/C. G. Hanson*.

Amaranthus blitoides S. Watson
Prostrate Pigweed
Introduced: casual.
First recorded: 1955.

The first record was from Bushey, 1955 *J. G. Dony* (det. J. P. M. Brenan), omitted in Dony, 1967. Recorded as a wool alien from Newnham (23/N), 1973 *C. G. Hanson* (det. E. J. Clement), but no further wild records. Occurs as a bird-seed introduction in a garden at Ware (31/S) *C. G. H.*

Amaranthus capensis Thell. (*A. dinteri* auct.)
Cape Pigweed
Introduced: casual.
First (only) record: 1973.

This was recorded as a wool alien from Newnham (23/N) *C. G. Hanson* (det. E. J. Clement) (Hb. HTN) (Dony, 1975).

Amaranthus standleyanus Parodi ex Covas
Indehiscent Pigweed
Introduced: casual.
First (only) record: 1973.

Recorded only as a wool alien at Newnham (23/N) *C. G. H.* (Dony, 1975).

Amaranthus thunbergii Moq.
Thunberg's Pigweed
Introduced: casual.
First (only) record: 1964.

The only record was from Hitchin (13/V), 1964 (Dony, 1967).

Amaranthus retroflexus L.
Common Amaranth
Introduced: neophyte.
First record: 1846.
Tetrad occurrence: 12 (2%).
Increasing slowly?

Recorded as a casual in two locations by Dony (1967), but earlier records were quite frequent, especially around Hertford and Ware. During the current survey, it was found as a casual, and also as a field weed, occasionally perhaps sown for game, in 12 scattered localities.

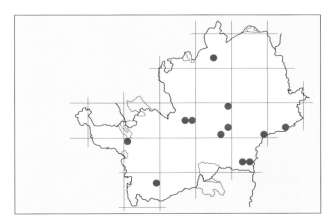

Map 111. *Amaranthus retroflexus.*

Amaranthus × ozanonii (Thell.) C. Schust. and M. Goldschm. (*A. retroflexus × A. hybridus*)

Found at Ware tip (31/M), 1984 *C. G. Hanson* (det. E. J. Clement) (*comm.*: B.R.C.: CEH Monks Wood).

Amaranthus hybridus L.
Green Amaranth
Introduced: neophyte.
First record: 1928.
Tetrad occurrence: 5 (1%).

First recorded by J. E. Little from Great Wymondley as a wool alien, 1928 (Hb. BM), but the record was omitted from Dony (1967). It was found at a number of sites from 1967 to 1986, and from five sites during the current survey: Rye Meads Sewage Works (31/V), regularly from 1989 to 1994 *A. M. Boucher/ C. G. Hanson* (Hb. HTN); Puckeridge (32/W), 1991 *S. Watson* (det. T. J.) (Hb. HTN); Little Hadham (42/K), 1993 *S. W.* (det. T. J.) (Hb. HTN); near Cole Green (21/Q), 1987 *A. M. B./C. G. H.*; and from introduced seed in a garden at Ware (31/S) *C. G. H.*

Amaranthus cruentus L.
Purple Amaranth
Introduced: neophyte.
First record: 1967.

First found on a dung heap at Latchford (32/V), 1967 *C. G. Hanson* (det. J. P. M. Brenan) (Hb. CGH), and later at Ware tip (31/M), 1977 *C. G. Hanson* (the latter mistakenly reported as the first record in James, 1985). Recorded during this survey from a dung heap near Cole Green (21/Q), 1987 *C. G. H.* (det. E. J. Clement); and from Rye Meads Sewage Works (31/V), 1992 *A. M. Boucher* (det. C. G. H.) (Hb. Boucher).

Amaranthus bouchonii Thell.
Indehiscent Amaranth
Introduced: neophyte.
First record: 1970.

Recorded first from Moor Mill tip (10/L), 1970; and from near Cole Green (21/Q), 1978 *C. G. Hanson* (det. E. J. Clement), where it was re-found in 1987 *C. G. H.*

Amaranthus deflexus L.
Perennial Pigweed
Introduced: neophyte.
First (only) record: 1989.

Found as a weed at Welwyn Garden City (21/K), 1989 *A. D. Marshall* (det. T. J.) (Hb. HTN).

Amaranthus albus L.
White Pigweed
Introduced: neophyte.
First record: 1959.

Found several times since its first record (Dony, 1967). During the current survey, it was found at Hoddesdon (30/U), 1989, 1993 *A. M. Boucher* (Hb. Boucher); Rye Meads Sewage Works (31/V), 1989 *A. M. B./C. G. Hanson* (Hb. HTN); and regularly as a 'serious weed' from bird-seed mixtures at Ware (31/S) *C. G. H.*

Amaranthus blitum L. (*A. lividus* L.)
Guernsey Pigweed
Introduced: neophyte.
First record: 1919.

First found by A. W. Graveson at Hertford (31/G), 1919 (Hb. Graveson, HTN) (Dony, 1967). There is also an early specimen from Welwyn, 1932, in the Phillips herbarium at North Herts. Museums (HTN). During the current survey it was recorded from Rye Meads Sewage Works (31/V), 1989, 1996 *A. M. Boucher/C. G. Hanson/ T. J.* (Hb. HTN); and from derelict greenhouses at Bayfordbury (31/A), 1997, 1999 *C. G. H.* It is also a persistent weed at Ware (31/S), from introduced seed *C. G. H.*

Amaranthus viridis L.
Spiny Amaranth
Introduced: casual.
First (only) record: 1959.

Its only reliable record remains that from Bulls Mill tip (31/C) (Dony, 1967).

Amaranthus muricatus (Moq.) Hieron.
Rough-fruited Amaranth
Introduced: casual.
First (only) record: 1969.

Its only record is from Park Street tip (10/L) *J. G. Dony* (Hb. K; Hb. HTN) (Dony, 1970) (and Burton, 1983).

Portulacaceae (Purslanes)

Genus: *Portulaca*

Portulaca oleracea L.
Common Purslane
Introduced: casual.
First record: 1969.

First recorded on Park Street tip (10/L) *J. G. Dony* (Hb. HTN). Its only record during the survey was from Rye Meads Sewage Works (31/V), 1989 *C. G. Hanson/A. M. Boucher*.

Genus: *Claytonia*

Claytonia perfoliata Donn ex Willd.
Spring Beauty
Introduced: neophyte.
First confirmed record: 1902.
Tetrad occurrence: 21 (4%).
Increased after Dony's survey, but may have decreased again more recently (+153%).

The distribution of this strange-looking plant remains scattered, with a tendency for it to occur on light gravelly soils, often where grass-seeding has been carried out.
(8 tetrads: Dony, 1967; 26 tetrads: 1950-1986)

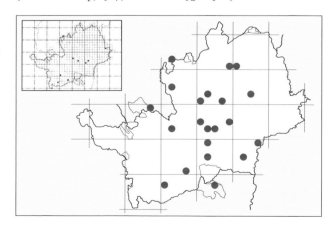

Map 112. *Claytonia perfoliata.*

Claytonia sibirica L.
Pink Purslane
Introduced: neophyte.
First record: 1921.
Tetrad occurrence: 7 (1%).
Increasing slowly.

This was mistakenly first recorded as found at Norton Common in 1931 by R. Morse in Dony (1967), the real date being 1921. It was also found at Welwyn Garden City in 1949 by P. Vernon, but the record was omitted by Dony. It has since increased steadily, but is not common. Between 1967 and 1986 it was re-found at Welwyn Garden City, and also turned up at Hertford (31/G); near Totteridge (29/H, M); at Frithsden (00/E); and near Stevenage (22/L). The recent survey found it at Totteridge again (29/M), 1989 *A. Vaughan*; Northchurch Common (90/Z, 91/Q), 1988, 1995 *P. Kingsbury, G. Salisbury*; Tewin (21/T), 1992 *T. J.*; Brookmans Park (20/M), 1993 *A. D. Marshall*; Harpenden Common (11/G), 2001 *L. Mottram/E. Anderson*; and at Frithsden again, near Berkhamsted Common (00/E), 2004 *T. J./ G. Salisbury*. It usually forms scattered patches amongst mature, shady scrub, often in semi-natural woodland.

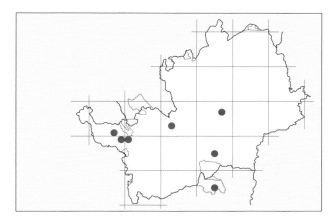

Map 113. *Claytonia sibirica.*

Genus: *Montia*

Montia fontana L.
Blinks
Native.
First record: 1838.
Tetrad occurrence: 15 (3%).
Probably stable (+139%).

This has always been regarded as a rare plant of short, damp, acidic grassland, and disturbed muddy areas on boggy soils, but is in reality probably overlooked, owing to its small size, the sporadic nature of its occurrence and its proneness to drought. It occurs mainly in over-grazed pastures or heavily-mown lawns on the acidic soils of southern Hertfordshire, or where there are outliers of acidic gravels elsewhere. It is taxonomically diverse, and there are at least two subspecies in Herts., although not all of the records made were allocated to either. Most specimens sub-specifically determined have been ssp. *chondrosperma* (Fenzl) Walters, which has been found at Hoddesdon (30/U), 1991 *A. M. Boucher*; near Plashes Wood (31/V), 1994 *S. Watson*; by Peplins Wood (20/M), 1989 *A. D. Marshall*; Croxley Common Moor (09/X), 1991 *P. J. Ellison* and at Potters Bar (20/K), 1996 *S. Hawkins*. Subspecies *amporitana* Sennen has only been found

during the survey at Parkway, Welwyn Garden City (21/G), 1994 *A. D. Marshall* (Hb. HTN).
(Overall species: 6 tetrads: Dony, 1967; 18 tetrads: 1950-1986)

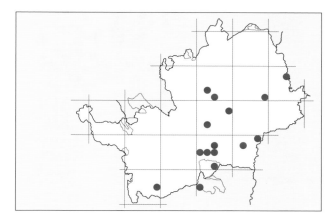

Map 114. *Montia fontana.*

Caryophyllaceae (Pink family)

Genus: *Arenaria*

Arenaria serpyllifolia L.
Thyme-leaved Sandwort
Native.
First record: 1820.
Tetrad occurrence: 222 (for the broad species) (45%).
Decreasing (-24%).

This is a plant of bare, dry, and usually nutrient-poor ground, and also of old walls, where it can be abundant, although prone to destruction by 'tidying'. It occurs on both calcareous and mildly acidic substrates, on Chalk, Boulder Clay and on gravels or sand.

There are two subspecies recorded: the nominate form (Map 115a), and ssp. *leptoclados* (Reichb.) Nyman (Map 115b), which Dony (1967) recognised as a separate species. In fact their distributions are broadly similar, and they are often difficult to separate, although ssp. *leptoclados* tends to be less common, occurring on drier, gravelly soils and walls in the north and east more than the nominate form. If Dony's records for the two taxa are aggregated, there is evidence of a significant decrease, possibly because of enrichment of habitats and loss of bare ground, re-pointing or removal of old walls.
(278 tetrads: Dony, 1967; 294 tetrads: 1950-1986)

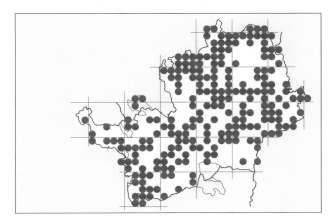

Map 115. *Arenaria serpyllifolia.*

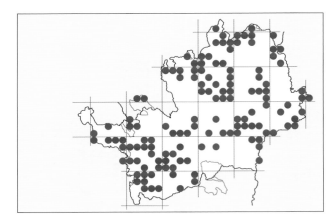

Map 115a. *Arenaria serpyllifolia* ssp. *serpyllifolia*.

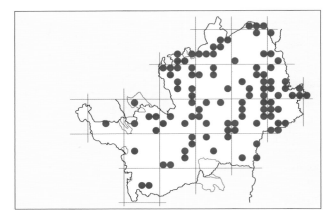

Map 115b. *Arenaria serpyllifolia* ssp. *leptoclados*.

Genus: *Moehringia*

Moehringia trinervia (L.) Clairv.
Three-nerved Sandwort
Native.
First record: 1690.
Tetrad occurrence: 330 (67%).
Stable or slightly increasing (+12%).

This is a plant of semi-natural woodland, and is frequent across the County wherever there is any ancient woodland remaining, only becoming rare on the Chalk, the more arable areas of the Boulder Clay, where woodland is sparse on the Clay-with-Flints, or in the Vale of Aylesbury.
(280 tetrads: Dony, 1967; 299 tetrads: 1950-1986)

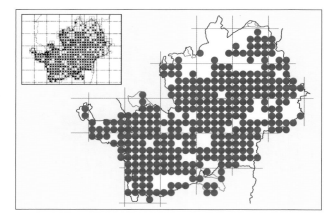

Map 116. *Moehringia trinervia*.

Genus: *Minuartia*

Minuartia hybrida (Villars) Schischkin   UK Endangered
Fine-leaved Sandwort
Native.
First record: 1838.
Tetrad occurrence: 3 (<1%).
Recently stable? (+200%).

This was once a scarce, but regular plant of bare chalky and sandy soils, in arable field margins, and on bare ground by tracks in the 19th and earlier in the 20th centuries. By the time Dony was reporting in 1967, it had become rare. He only knew it from the railway sidings at Hitchin. It was still present in abundance on the remaining areas here (12/Z), 1998 *A. R. Outen*, but is threatened with development. Although Dony did not know it, it has remained a frequent feature of the un-fertilised plots at Broadbalk, Rothamsted (11/G), and was recorded regularly during the survey period *I. G. Denholm*. It was also found nearby at Harpenden Common (11/G), 2001 *L. Mottram/E. Anderson* (Hb. HTN); and on a wall by the canal at Charlotte's Vale, Cassiobury (09/Z), 1999 *G. Salisbury* (Hb. HTN).

Genus: *Stellaria*

Stellaria media (L.) Villars
Common Chickweed
Native.
First record: 1733.
Tetrad occurrence: 473 (96%).
Stable (-2%).

An ubiquitous plant of enriched soils in usually open habitats throughout the County. It is probably less abundant now than formerly in arable fields, but is common in most other suitable habitats. Only unrecorded from a few marginal tetrads.
(459 tetrads: Dony, 1967 and from 1950-1986)

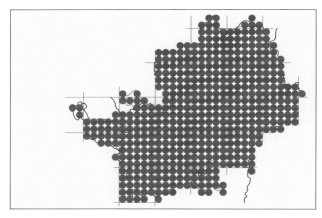

Map 117. *Stellaria media*.

Stellaria pallida (Dumort) Crépin
Lesser Chickweed
Native.
First record: 1991.
Tetrad occurrence: 28 (6%).

First confirmed from mossy concrete in semi-shade on the former airfield at Scales Park, Nuthampstead (43/B), 1991 *T. J.* (Hb. HTN). However, there is an undated record of 'Stellaria apetala' by F. A. Robinson from 'Tewin' in Dony's card index, which may have been this species, but it was never confirmed. It has probably always been in the County, but owing to its similarity to impoverished forms of its common relative, has been overlooked. However, the survey found it sporadically, mainly in the south and around the towns in north Herts. It may, therefore, have genuinely increased in occurrence. Its habitat is usually rather bare, poor ground, with mown grass or even just mosses on mildly acidic or highly enriched soils, often under trees. As it flowers in spring and then disappears, it may have been missed in many areas.

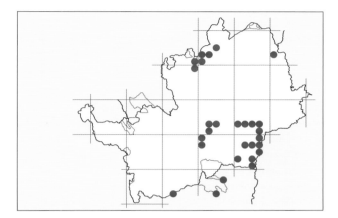

Map 118. *Stellaria pallid*a.

Stellaria neglecta Weihe　　　　　　　　　　Herts Rare
Greater Chickweed
Native.
First record: 1915.
Tetrad occurrence: 3 (<1%).
Rare, as it has always been.

This enigmatic plant may be overlooked as the frequent robust form of *Stellaria media* in damp places, but it does appear to be both genuinely rare, and also unpredictable. It is a plant of rich, lush vegetation near water. Dony (1967) reported two old records, from Bramfield and Hertford, but he had also received an unconfirmed record from Welwyn by E. G. Kellett. It was found at Buttway, Ashwell (24/Q), 1979 *T. J.* (Hb. HTN), but not thereafter. It had also been reported to the Herts. and Middx. Wildlife Trust at Stanborough (21/F) in 1973, without further details. The recent survey confirmed the Stanborough Reed Marsh (21/F) record, 1994 *A. M. Boucher* (Hb. HTN); and it has also been found at Stanstead Abbots Gravel Pit (31/V), 1996 *S. Cuming*; and at Woodside, Hatfield (20/M), 1998 *T. J.* (Hb. HTN).

Stellaria holostea L.
Greater Stitchwort
Native.
First record: 1814.
Tetrad occurrence: 395 (81%).
Stable (no measured change).

This is a frequent plant especially of hedgerows and wood borders, but less so in woodlands themselves. It is especially abundant on the Clay-with-Flints in west Herts., where it forms a characteristic spring community with Bluebells, Bracken and Blackthorn. Only on the Chalk or in heavily urban areas does it become rare or absent.
(376 tetrads: Dony, 1967; 383 tetrads: 1950-1986)

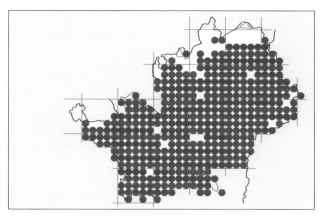

Map 119. *Stellaria holostea.*

Stellaria palustris Retz.　　　　　　　　　UK Vulnerable
Marsh Stitchwort　　　　　　　　　　　　Herts Extinct
Native.
First record: 1839.

This beautiful plant of swamp on mildly acidic peat was a special feature of the lost Hoddesdon Marsh, and also from sites at Broxbourne, Amwell and King's Meads, in the Lea Valley. It was last seen at Hoddesdon Marsh in 1914.

Stellaria graminea L.
Lesser Stitchwort
Native.
First record: 1814.
Tetrad occurrence: 336 (68%).
Probably stable in overall distribution (+5%).

This is a plant of old, semi-natural grasslands on neutral to mildly acidic, free-draining soils. As such, it is much less abundant in general than it was in 1967. Its tetrad distribution remains much as it was then, although better recording has found it to be present, rarely, in more places on the Boulder Clay in east Herts. It is fairly susceptible to over-fertilisation and weed-killing, but is one of the last old grassland indicator plant species to go in derelict pasture.
(304 tetrads: Dony, 1967; 316 tetrads: 1950-1986)

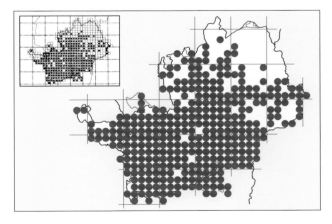

Map 120. *Stellaria graminea.*

Stellaria uliginosa Murray
Bog Stitchwort
Native.
First record: 1820.
Tetrad occurrence: 133 (27%).
Apparently increasing (+49%).

Whether it is better recording or a genuine increase, this plant has certainly been found in more areas than recorded by Dony. It is especially more widespread around Stevenage and in east Herts. than was previously thought, but its distribution otherwise closely mirrors the occurrence of historic commons and ancient woodland blocks. It is a plant of more or less permanently wet or damp, often shaded habitats, in woodland rides, by streams, in damp grasslands and mires, usually on neutral to moderately acidic soils.
(85 tetrads: Dony, 1967; 116 tetrads: 1950-1986)

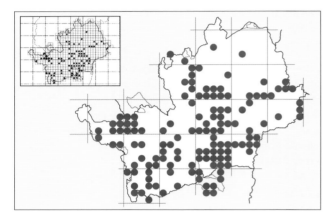

Map 121. *Stellaria uliginosa.*

Genus: *Cerastium*

Cerastium arvense L.   Herts Vulnerable
Field Mouse-ear
Native.
First record: 1814.
Tetrad occurrence: 10 (2%).
Decreasing (-51%).

This is a local plant of old, dry, calcareous rough grassland, where it can form spectacular patches in early summer. At one time it was also a cornfield weed, but not now. It becomes inconspicuous after flowering, and can then pass undetected, but it is also erratic in its appearance, and the fact that several of the current records

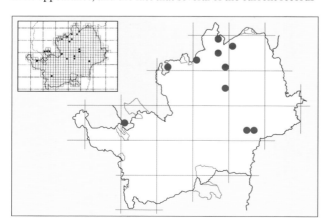

Map 122. *Cerastium arvense.*

are in places where it was not seen by Dony, nor between 1970 and 1986, suggests that it may be decreasing less than it would appear. However, its favoured habitat of calcareous roadsides has been badly affected by salt and eutrophication, so some losses are very likely.
(19 tetrads: Dony, 1967; 30 tetrads: 1950-1986)

Cerastium tomentosum L.
Snow-in-summer
Introduced: neophyte.
First record: 1946.
Tetrad occurrence: 32 (7%).
Increasing?

Dony only noted two records in his card index, but may have known about others, although his account in the *Flora* was brief. It is now a regular plant of the very field banks and roadsides, especially on the Chalk, where its native cousin *C. arvense* formerly grew. It seems to tolerate more eutrophic conditions, and even road salt, as it can occur adjacent to the tarmac on major roads. The fact that the two species hybridise and produce fertile seed suggests that some colonies were actually of the hybrid, although this requires confirmation.
(11 tetrads: 1970-1986)

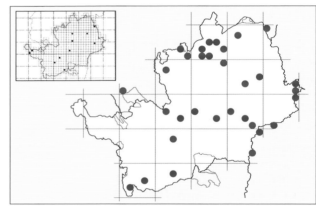

Map 123. *Cerastium tomentosum.*

Cerastium fontanum Baumg.
Common Mouse-ear
Native.
First record: 1748.
Tetrad occurrence: 474 (97%).
Probably stable (-1 %).

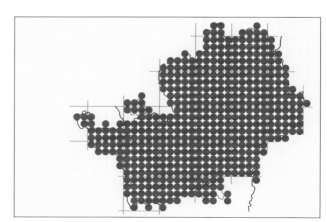

Map 124. *Cerastium fontanum.*

This is a plant of semi-improved as well as old grassland, and also occurs in ruderal and waste ground habitats. No attempt has been made to distinguish subspecies, although Dony allotted Herts. records to ssp. *vulgare* (*triviale* (Spenn.) Jalas).
(453 tetrads: Dony, 1967; 456 tetrads: 1950-1986)

Cerastium glomeratum Thuill.
Sticky Mouse-ear
Native.
First record: 1814.
Tetrad occurrence: 366 (75%).
Increasing (+52%).

As this species occurs in often disturbed and ruderal habitats, as well as mown grass, or on waste ground, it is quite likely to be increasing. However, it is easily overlooked, because it disappears early in the season, and so some of the increase may be down to more thorough recording in some areas.
(229 tetrads: Dony, 1967; 250 tetrads: 1950-1986)

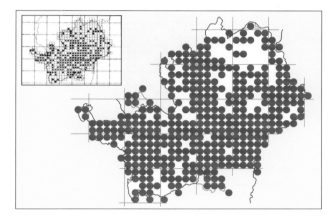

Map 125. *Cerastium glomeratum.*

Cerastium diffusum Pers.
Sea Mouse-ear
Introduced [native in the U.K.].
First record: 1953.
Tetrad occurrence: 5 (<1%).
Decreased (-83%).

This was a plant of railway ballast during and after the Second World War, but had already decreased by 1967, although Dony still recorded it widely. It now appears to be rare, but is also likely to be overlooked. Some recent records have suggested it is to be found by salted roads, even in towns. Seen during the survey at Stevenage (22/G, L), 2001 *M. Gurney*; industrial estate, Letchworth (23/G), 2001 *P. Stapleton*; by station, Letchworth (23/B), 2003 *T. J.*; and at the site of Rye House Power Station (30/Z), 2005 *S. Pilkington*.
(27 tetrads: Dony, 1967; 29 tetrads: 1950-1986)

Cerastium pumilum Curtis [UK Near Threatened]
Dwarf Mouse-ear Herts Extinct?
Introduced [native in the U.K.].
First record: 1953.
Apparently extinct.

This mainly limestone species was at one time a feature of the old ballast on the disused Hitchin-Bedford railway, but as most of this once attractive old railway has either been eradicated, re-profiled or infilled with refuse by the local authorities, it has not been seen

Dwarf Mouse-ear Cerastium pumilum *Ickleford 1977.*

since. The last record was at Ickleford (13/W), 1978 *B. Wurzell*.

Cerastium semidecandrum L.
Little Mouse-ear
Native.
First record: 1838.
Tetrad occurrence: 12 (2%).
Stable or increased? (+85%).

Although it would appear from the records that there has been an increase, this may well be down to plants having been spotted during more diligent recording. It is a very inconspicuous, short-lived, Spring-flowering species of dry, sandy ground, sometimes also on wall tops. Apparently rare, although quite likely to be under-recorded. For example, it may well occur widely in gravel pits, especially around Hertford, where it has always had its stronghold on the Lea gravels.
(6 tetrads: Dony, 1967; 9 tetrads: 1950-1986)

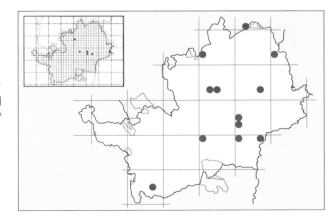

Map 126. *Cerastium semidecandrum.*

Genus: *Moenchia*

Moenchia erecta (L.) P. Gaertner, Meyer and Scherb. Herts Extinct
Upright Chickweed
Native.
First record: 1838.

This plant of dry, bare gravelly ground on heaths was last seen by Dony at Gustard Wood Common in 1957 (Dony, 1967). There are old records from 21 tetrads across central Hertfordshire, on the Lea gravels. It may have been a casualty not only of scrub-growth on heaths, but also of habitat enrichment.

Genus: *Myosoton*

Myosoton aquaticum (L.) Moench
Water Chickweed
Native.
First record: 1819.
Tetrad occurrence: 105 (21%).
Probably slightly increased (+31%).

This is a plant which is found wherever there is rough herbage or tall fen by water, especially rivers. The evidence for its increase is slender, because it may have been under-recorded in the past, especially in the east, although there may be a case for it having increased in places where rank vegetation has spread, such as old gravel pits.
(76 tetrads: Dony, 1967; 97 tetrads: 1950-1986)

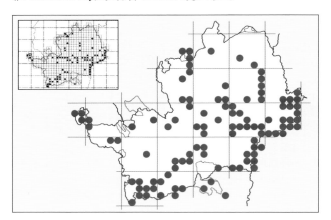

Map 127. *Myosoton aquaticum.*

Genus: *Sagina*

Sagina nodosa (L.) Fenzi   Herts Extinct?
Knotted Pearlwort
Native.
First record: 1746.

Known to former botanists from a number of bare, wet, often gravelly pastures, such as at Waterford, Hoddesdon Marsh, Colney Heath, Croxley Common Moor, Water End Meadows at Gaddesden and Oughton Head Common, this was last seen in a bare patch at Blagrove Common (33/G) in 1957 by J. G. Dony. It does not tolerate competition from tall vegetation following the loss of grazing, or through increased habitat enrichment, both major problems with old damp grasslands.

Sagina procumbens L.
Procumbent Pearlwort
Native.
First record: 1820.
Tetrad occurrence: 366 (75%).
Stable, or slightly increased (+5%).

This is characteristic of the cracks between paving stones on paths, and round the entrance to driveways, but is more natural on bare ground in poor, often damp grassland, lawns or heaths. It only becomes uncommon in the more arable clay farmland or on the Chalk.
(331 tetrads: Dony, 1967; 349 tetrads: 1950-1986)

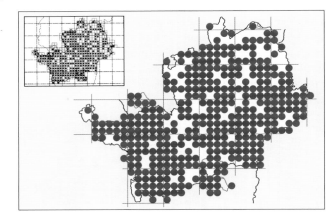

Map 128. *Sagina procumbens.*

Sagina apetala Ard.
Annual Pearlwort
Native.
First record: 1838.
Tetrad occurrence: 227 (46%).
Increased (+96%).

Specially characteristic of open gravelly ground, or old walls, this is also found in similar bare ground to its relative, and often with it. There does appear to be evidence of its having increased quite substantially, although the reasons are not clear. It is also usually regarded as comprising two subspecies, which were recorded as such for the Flora Survey.
(110 tetrads: Dony, 1967; 133 tetrads: 1950-1986)

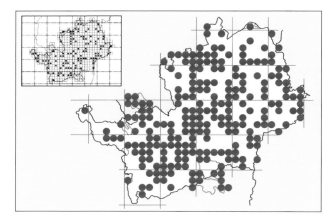

Map 129. *Sagina apetala.*

Subspecies *apetala* is apparently more usual in bare grassland; while ssp. *erecta* F. Herm. is the usual form on wall-tops, where its spreading sepals are evident. The latter is more than twice as common as the former, but they have similar, widespread distributions.

Genus: *Scleranthus*

Scleranthus annuus L.   UK Endangered
Annual Knawel
Native.
First record: *c.*1820.
Tetrad occurrence: 11 (2%).
Decreased markedly (-90%).

Now a rare plant of gravelly, arable fields, and, even more rarely, of bare gravelly ground in unimproved pastures, probably its natural habitat. However, there is some evidence that it is under-recorded, because some of the tetrads with current records had none recorded in 1967. It is very susceptible to fertiliser enrichment of its arable habitat, and eutrophication elsewhere. Interestingly, it was recently found to be quite frequent on natural gravelly banks in ancient grassland at King's Meads (31/L). (98 tetrads: Dony, 1967; 102 tetrads: 1950-1986)

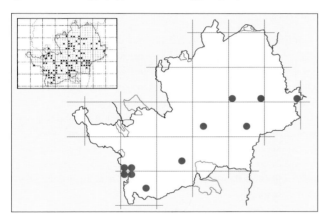

Map 130. *Scleranthus annuus.*

Genus: *Corrigiola*

Corrigiola litoralis L.   [UK Critically Endangered]
Strapwort
Introduced [native in the U.K.].
First record: 1958.

This rare native plant of muddy shingle, was found to be abundant at Oakleigh Park railway sidings (29/S) (VC20 [Greater London]) in 1958, and was still there in 1966 (Dony, 1967). Whether it survives we do not know, as access is now difficult.

Genus: *Herniaria*

Herniaria glabra L.
Smooth Rupturewort
Introduced: casual [native in the U.K.].
First record: 1904.

Only recorded in Herts. at Ware Park between 1904 and 1909 *A. W. Graveson* (Dony, 1967).

Genus: *Polycarpon*

Polycarpon tetraphyllum (L.) L.
Four-leaved Allseed
Introduced [native in the U.K.].
First record: 1927.

This was found at Hitchin by J. E. Little (Dony, 1967), and was also reported from the Oakleigh Park area as a garden weed (29/W) in 1968 *P. E. G. Irvine*, but not confirmed.

Genus: *Spergula*

Spergula arvensis L.   UK Vulnerable
Corn Spurrey
Native.
First record: *c.*1820.
Tetrad occurrence: 48 (10%).
Decreased substantially (-61%).

The distribution of this plant of open, gravelly arable fields, and occasionally in disturbed ground around gravel pits, is substantially the same as shown by Dony (1967), but its occurrence is much more sporadic. Nowhere does it form large colonies.
(116 tetrads: Dony, 1967; 135 tetrads: 1950-1986)

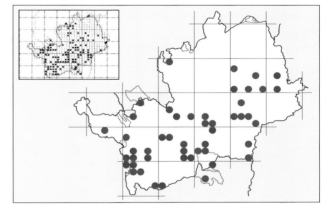

Map 131. *Spergula arvensis.*

Genus: *Spergularia*

Spergularia marina (L.) Griseb.
Lesser Sea-spurrey
Introduced [native in the U.K.].
First record: *c.*1880.
Tetrad occurrence: 27 (6%).
Increasing.

This plant of salt marshes was a feature of Ware Park brickfields, first recorded by Pryor (Pryor, 1887; Dony, 1967), and persisting there for over 40 years. It was then found by A. M. Boucher by the B197 at Welwyn, adjoining the A1(M) (21/G) in 1991 (Hb. HTN). It has since become a locally abundant plant by major roads and junctions, especially around the M1/M25 area, encouraged by road salting. No doubt the map is already well out-of-date.

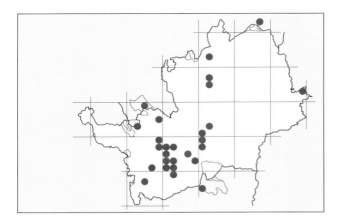

Map 132. *Spergularia marina.*

Spergularia rubra (L.) J. S. Presl and C. Presl
Sand Spurrey
Native.
First record: 1839.
Tetrad occurrence: 22 (5%).
Decreasing (-27%).

A plant of bare, periodically disturbed, nutrient poor soils on gravel and sands, this species is frequent in limited areas on the Lea and Colne gravels, but rare elsewhere. It was also once a frequent plant in recently-cut coppice on gravelly soils. Its distribution remains much as it was in 1967, but its occurrences are fewer.
(29 tetrads: Dony, 1967; 39 tetrads: 1950-1986)

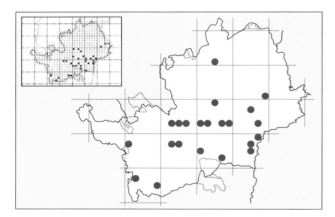

Map 133. *Spergularia rubra.*

Genus: *Lychnis*

Lychnis coronaria (L.) Murray
Rose Campion
Introduced: neophyte.
First record: 1985.
Tetrad occurrence: 17 (4%).

First noticed as an escape at Hoddesdon (30/U) *A. M. Boucher* (James, 1989), this has become much more frequent recently, with some evidence of persistence in places like old gravel pits.

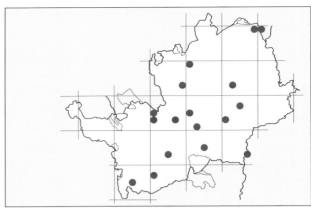

Map 134. *Lychnis coronaria.*

Lychnis flos-cuculi L.
Ragged Robin
Native.
First record: 1814.
Tetrad occurrence: 129 (26%).
Stable? (+3%).

It is difficult to interpret the occurrence of this charismatic species, because Dony's survey almost certainly under-recorded it, despite its conspicuousness in flower. Its current distribution appears to be much more widespread in especially northern and eastern Hertfordshire, but its natural habitats have been greatly diminished in many areas, particularly old unimproved damp pastures. It can survive considerable shade in damp woodland rides, and occasionally appears as a colonist in new wetlands. A few records could conceivably be introductions, as it can feature in seed-mixes for damp habitats. White-flowered forms have been noted occasionally.
(119 tetrads: Dony, 1967; 146 tetrads: 1950-1986)

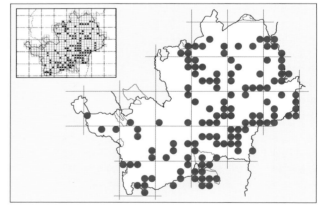

Map 135. *Lychnis flos-cuculi.*

Lychnis viscaria L.
Sticky Catchfly
Introduced [native in the U.K.].
First record: *c.*1870.

This was a feature of a rough, gravelly paddock at Easneye *c.*1870-1874 *C. Buxton* (Pryor, 1887), a record omitted by Dony (1967). It was also found as an escape near Radlett *c.*1890 (Dony *op. cit.*).

Lychnis chalcedonica L.
Maltese-cross
Introduced: casual.

First recorded as an escape at Welwyn, 1933 *H. Phillips* (Hb. HTN). There is also a record from tetrad 10/X in Burton (1983) without further details.

Genus: *Agrostemma*

Agrostemma githago L.   UK Pending Red List
Corncockle
Introduced: archaeophyte.
First record: 1750.
Tetrad occurrence: 12 (3%).
Rare and sporadic.

Although Dony (1967) mourned its demise, the recent survey has recorded a number of occurrences that do not appear to be from introduced seed: near Tingley Plantation, on disturbed chalk by a new fence (13/F), 1988 *R. Crossley*; on a disturbed bank by old railway sidings, Walsworth (12/Z), 1999 *T. J.*; old sidings near Croxley Green (09/S) 1998 (per London NHS); near Ivel Springs, Baldock (23/M) on disturbed soils of an archaeological dig, 1998 *B. R. Sawford*. Long-buried seed seems a possibility from most of these. The records from railway sidings are interesting, as the seed may have been from former grain depots. Other records are more likely to be introductions.

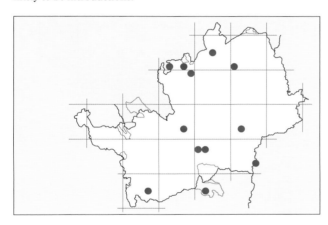

Map 136. *Agrostemma githago.*

Genus: *Silene*

Silene pendula L.
Nodding Catchfly
Introduced: casual.
First (only) record: 1919.

Only recorded once, as a garden escape, at Hertford, 1919 (Dony, 1967).

Silene nutans L.   [UK Near Threatened]
Nottingham Catchfly
Introduced: casual [native in the U.K.].
First record: 1820.

This was first found as an established escape at St Albans, *c.*1840 *J. Coales* (Pryor, 1887); and subsequently on the railway bank at Harpenden, 1888 *J. Saunders* (Hb. LTN) (Dony, 1967). There are no recent records.

Silene vulgaris Garcke
Bladder Campion
Native.
First record: 1750.
Tetrad occurrence: 351 (72%).
Decreasing (-17%).

This attractive plant of rough, grassy places on dry, relatively nutrient-poor, often calcareous soils shows distinct signs of retreat from more marginal habitats, especially in intensively arable and also in heavily urban landscapes. It was always rare on the acidic clays of south Hertfordshire, but is now becoming scarce in other areas.
(402 tetrads: Dony, 1967; 406 tetrads: 1950-1986)

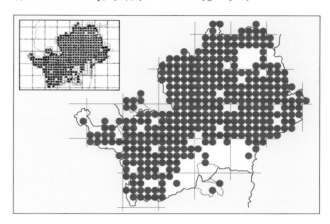

Map 137. *Silene vulgaris.*

Silene armeria L.
Sweet-William Catchfly
Introduced: casual.
First record: 1841.

Recorded first as an escape on walls at Hatfield in the 19th century (Pryor, 1887), there have been no proper records since it was found at Welwyn in 1931 (Dony, 1967), although it was included on a list of plants received by Dony from Bayfordbury (Dony, ms. index).

Silene noctiflora L.   UK Vulnerable
Night-flowering Catchfly
Introduced: archaeophyte.
First record: 1805.
Tetrad occurrence: 8 (2%).
Severely reduced by 1970s, now rare (-87%).

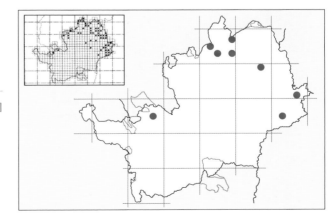

Map 138. *Silene noctiflora.*

Formerly a characteristic arable weed of especially the Boulder Clay in north-east Herts., this species is now reduced to more or less casual occurrences in waste places, and rarely in the edges of arable fields. The only records during the survey were: arable near Maplecroft Wood (41/H), 1996 *T. J.*; garden, Bishop's Stortford (42/Q), 1997 *S. Watson*; Radwell (23/H), 1991 *A. Dean*; ride, Spital Wood (23/W), 1998 *T. J.*; arable, Deadman's Hill, Sandon (23/Y), 1999 *T. J.*; waste ground, Welbury Farm, Clothall (23/L), 1996 *T. J.*; roadside, Markyate (01/S), 1995 *J. P. Widgery*; and disturbed ground, Buntingford (32/U), 1991 *S. Watson*. Only ten other records were made between 1970-1986.

(59 tetrads: Dony, 1967; 62 tetrads: 1950-1986)

Silene latifolia Poiret
White Campion
Introduced: archaeophyte.
First record: 1838.
Tetrad occurrence: 427 (87%).
Stable (-4%).

This is a plant of waysides and waste ground rather than semi-natural habitat, but is curiously absent from some areas, including some heavily urban areas where it might have been thought to occur. As Dony found, it becomes quite scarce on the damp, acidic London Clay.

(421 tetrads: Dony, 1967; 427 tetrads: 1950-1986)

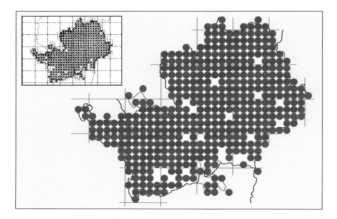

Map 139. *Silene latifolia.*

Silene × *hampeana* Meusel and K. Werner
(*S. latifolia* × *S. dioica*)
First record: 1917.
Tetrad occurrence: 86 (18%).

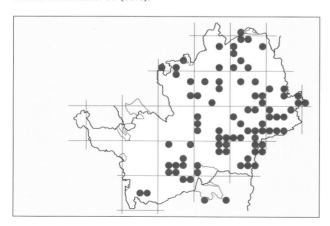

Map 140. *Silene* × *hampeana.*

First actually recorded by J. E. Little, but overlooked as pale forms of *S. dioica* in the 19th century. It is frequent wherever the two parent species co-exist, such as disturbed hedgebanks, or gravel pits by woods. Its distribution mirrors that of Red Campion.

Silene dioica (L.) Clairv.
Red Campion
Native.
First record: 1814.
Tetrad occurrence: 318 (65%).
Apparently increasing (+64%).

Dony (1967) professed to be puzzled by the distribution of this plant, which remains more or less the same, although it appears to have increased, perhaps as the habitats in which it grows have become more shady. It is, in fact, a characteristic plant of shady woodlands, old hedgerows and stream-sides on damp, neutral loam soils over clay or gravel, and is therefore rare on the free-draining Clay-with-Flints, and on the drier areas of the Chalk. It is rare in north and north-west Herts., but does occur occasionally where damp clays are less strongly calcareous, and rarely on damper Chalk soils.

(184 tetrads: Dony, 1967; 221 tetrads: 1950-1986)

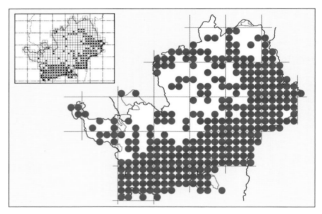

Map 141. *Silene dioica.*

Silene gallica L.   [UK Endangered]
Small-flowered Catchfly
Introduced: archaeophyte [casual in Herts.].
First record: 1862.

This occurred occasionally in barren, gravelly fields around Hertford and other towns in the 19th century, and was last recorded in the grounds of Bishop's Stortford College, 1941 (Dony, 1967). There is a specimen from between Pegsdon and Hexton (TL13), 1881 *Miss Mercer* in Hb. LTN.

Silene conica L.   [UK Vulnerable]
Sand Catchfly
Introduced: casual [native in the U.K.].
First record: 1910.

This was reported in error in Pryor (1887) (Dony, 1967), but was recorded from both Ware and Hoddesdon, 1910 *H. F. Hayllar* (Salisbury, 1916) (records overlooked by Dony), and recently as a casual at Bishop's Stortford (42/V), 1994 *S. Watson* (Hb. HTN).

Silene cordifolia All.
Introduced: casual.
First (only) record: 1931.

Only recorded from Welwyn (TL21) *H. Phillips* (Dony, 1967).

Silene muscipula L.
Introduced: casual.
First record: 1924.

Last recorded at Welwyn (TL21), 1931 *H. Phillips* (Dony, 1967).

Silene dichotoma Ehrh.
Introduced: casual.
First record: 1870.

Occasionally in the past a significant weed of waste ground and sown clover (Salisbury, 1916), this was last recorded at Ware, 1925 *C. G. Trower* and *G. C. Druce* (Dony, 1967).

Silene conoidea L.
Introduced: casual.
First record: 1910.

Recorded at Hoddesdon, 1910 *H. F. Hayllar*; and then at Hertford, 1913 *A. W. Graveson* (Hb. HTN) (Dony, ms. index) (omitted in Dony, 1967). Subsequently found at Ware, 1914-1916 *H. F. Hayllar*, but not recorded since.

[*Silene diversifolia* Otth in DC

A record of *Silene rubella* L. from Ware, 1919 *G. C. Druce* (Dony, 1967), may refer to this species, but needs confirmation.]

Genus: *Saponaria*

Saponaria officinalis L.
Soapwort
Introduced: archaeophyte.
First record: 1843.
Tetrad occurrence: 36 (7%).
More or less stable (-5%).

The current survey found this in exactly the same number of tetrads as Dony did, but often in different places! It tends to occur as a colonist of waste ground and roadsides for a number of years, only to disappear again. The double-flowered form is less frequent than the single-flowered one.
(36 tetrads: Dony, 1967; 47 tetrads: 1950-1986)

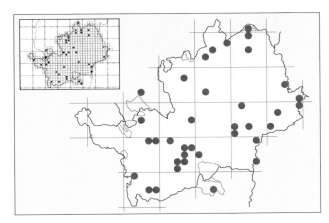

Map 142. *Saponaria officinalis.*

Saponaria calabrica Guss.
Calabrian Soapwort
Introduced: casual.
First record: 1933.

Only recorded from Welwyn, 1933 *H. Phillips* (Hb. HTN) (Dony, 1967 – where the date is given in error as 1923).

Saponaria ocymoides L.
Rock Soapwort
Introduced: casual.
First (only) record: 1914.

The only record was from Knebworth (TL22) (Dony, 1967).

Genus: *Vaccaria*

Vaccaria hispanica (Miller) Rauschert
Cowherb
Introduced: neophyte.
First record: 1841.

This has occurred, usually as a casual, on waste tips, and on disturbed ground, often from bird-seed, but has not been found in the County since it was reported from Blackbridge tip (11/X) and Bulls Mill tip (31/D), 1971 *C. G. Hanson*, although it could have been overlooked (Burton, 1983).

Genus: *Petrorhagia*

Petrorhagia saxifraga (L.) Link
Tunicflower
Introduced: neophyte.
First record: 1965.

Reported as an established plant at Much Hadham Churchyard (41/J), 1965 *J. Mason*, where it appears to have survived until the late-1970s (*Wildflower Mag.*, 382 (1978)). A specimen collected there in 1977 by John Dony is in Hb. LTN.

Genus: *Gypsophila*

Gypsophila elegans M. Bieb.
Annual Baby's Breath
Introduced: casual.
First record: 1931.

Recorded from Letchworth and Welwyn, 1931 *H. Phillips* (Hb. HTN) (Dony, 1967, which omits the Letchworth record).

Genus: *Dianthus*

Dianthus carthusianorum L.
Carthusian Pink
Introduced: casual.
First (only) record: 1914.

Only recorded once: from New Farm, St Albans (Dony, 1967 and *Trans. Herts. N.H.S.*, vol. 16 (1918), p. 14).

Dianthus deltoides L.   UK Near Threatened
Maiden Pink
Native and introduced.
First record: 1846.

As a native plant, this was once a feature of drier, gravelly hummocks which formerly occurred in the Lea Valley meadows on the site of what is now Amwell Quarry (31/R), from where it was last recorded about 1880, probably because the pasture was later levelled and drained. It was also at Easneye, nearby; and was recorded once from Totteridge Green (where it may have been an escape). It turned up at Bishop's Stortford Golf Course (52/A) in 1942 and at Wilbury Hill (23/B) in 1948 (Dony, 1967). Subsequently it was found at Smallford Pit (10/Y), 1973-4 *P. Brown* (Hb. HTN), and was a feature of shallow gravel pits south of the road across Mardley Heath (21/P), 1978-9 *M. Hooper*. In 1984-5, it was also found by Ware tip (31/M) *C. G. Hanson*. During the present survey, it re-appeared at Smallford Pit, on the old railway (10/Y), 1989 *B. Tranter*; on the walls of Hadham Lordship (41/J), 1991 *S. Watson* (where it had been present for years); a track by the railway at Woolmer Green (21/N), 1994 *T. J./T. C. G. Rich/G. Salisbury*; and as introduced plants on a roadside chalk bank at Slip End (23/Y), 1999 *T. J.*

Dianthus barbatus L.
Sweet William
Introduced: neophyte.
First record: 1917.

A rare escape from gardens, but sometimes long-persisting, on damp gravelly, or even sometimes peaty ground. Found during the recent survey at Oughton Head Common (13/Q), 1991, 1996 *T. J.* (where it has been known since 1975); Frogmore Pit, Aston (22/Q), 1989, 2000 *T. J./B. R. Sawford*; Nicky Line, Harpenden (11/C), 1991 *J. F. Southey*; old railway, Widford (41/D), 1991 *S. Watson*; and disused allotments, Bishop's Stortford (42/W), 1996 *A. R. Outen*.

Dianthus armeria L.   UK Endangered
Deptford Pink
Native.
First record: *c*.1683.
Extinct?

This was last recorded from the old railway line at Harpenden (11/M) on 25th July 1988 *M. Banthorpe*. The plants in question were cut down by a 'conservation' group shortly afterwards! This site was the last of a considerable number of former sites on gravelly banks and the edges of copses on the Lea gravels and elsewhere across central Hertfordshire. We can but hope that someone might re-find this now nationally rare plant.

Polygonaceae (Knotweeds)

Genus: *Persicaria*

Persicaria wallichii Greuter and Burdet
Himalayan Knotweed
Introduced: neophyte.
First record: 1927.

A colonist of waste places and disturbed ground, this was recorded by Dony (1967) from two localities, and was subsequently found at Cole Green tip (21/Q), 1973 *C. G. Hanson*; and at Hertford (31/B), 1979 *C. G. H.* During the present survey it was found at Aldenham (19/J), 1987 *A. D. Marshall*; Rothamsted (11/G), 1989 *I. G. Denholm*; and Watford (19/D), 1992 *P. J. Ellison*.

Persicaria bistorta (L.) Samp.
Bistort
Native and introduced.
First record: 1657.
Tetrad occurrence: 14 (3%).
Stable? (+4%).

At one time this was a frequent plant, forming extensive patches in damp pastures throughout the County. It was reckoned to be rare by the 1960s, and may still be decreasing as a native plant, although it also occurs as an escape. It was recorded during the survey in 14 tetrads, but only 11 of these were probably native sites.
(13 tetrads: Dony, 1967; 20 tetrads: 1950-1986)

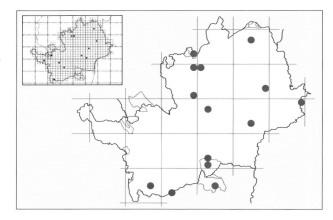

Map 143. *Persicaria bistorta.*

Common Bistort Persicaria bistorta *Purwell Meadow, 1995.*

Photo: Brian Sawford

Persicaria amplexicaulis (D. Don) Ronse Decr.
Red Bistort
Introduced: neophyte.
First record: *c*.1970.

Reported first as a garden escape from East Barnet (29/S), *c*.1970 *E. B. Bangerter* (*comm.*: J. G. Dony) (Burton, 1983). It was found during the survey established at north Hemel Hempstead (01/Q), 1996 *C. G. Hanson* (Hb. HTN).

Persicaria amphibia (L.) Gray
Amphibious Bistort
Native.
First record: 1750.
Tetrad occurrence: 124 (25%).
Stable or slightly increased (+16%).

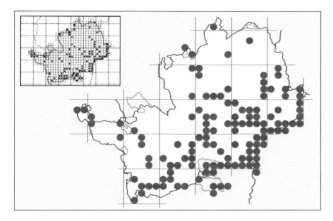

Map 144. *Persicaria amphibia.*

A frequent plant of winter-wet pastures, damp disturbed ground, and also as a floating aquatic in less calcareous waters. It occurs mainly in the river valleys, but also in neutral to moderately acidic damp pastures on the London Clay and similar soils elsewhere.
(102 tetrads: Dony, 1967; 121 tetrads: 1950-1986)

Persicaria capitata (Buch. -Ham. ex D. Don) H. Gross
Pink Knotweed
Introduced: neophyte.
First record: 1995.
Tetrad occurrence: 5 (1%).

Although supposed not to survive in Britain, this has increasingly appeared as persistent escapes from cultivation, sometimes near the window boxes from which it originated! First found at Hertford (31/G) and Watton-at-Stone (31/E), 1995 *A. M. Boucher* (Hb. HTN); it has subsequently been found at Great Amwell (31/R), 1996 *A. M. B.*; St Albans (10/N), 1999 *S. Hawkins* (det. *T. J.*) (Hb. HTN); and Ashwell (23/U), 2000 *T. J.*

Persicaria maculosa Gray
Redshank
Native.
First record: 1819.
Tetrad occurrence: 394 (80%).
Stable (no significant change).

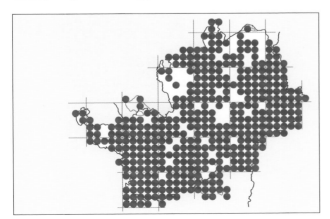

Map 145. *Persicaria maculosa.*

A plant of damp arable, disturbed or seasonally flooded ground, this appears to have changed little in occurrence since 1967, but may be less abundant in some areas.
(373 tetrads: Dony, 1967; 389 tetrads: 1950-1986)

Persicaria lapathifolia (L.) Gray
Pale Persicaria
Native.
First record: 1819.
Tetrad occurrence: 227 (46%).
Probably stable (-3%).

This is similar in its ecology to *P. persicaria*, but slightly more frequent on calcareous ground, and less frequent overall. In terms of its general occurrence, it has remained more or less stable, but its actual distribution appears to have changed somewhat. It is now more frequent on the Boulder Clay, and less common on the London Clay than it was in 1967, perhaps associated with raised nitrogen levels.
(222 tetrads: Dony, 1967; 246 tetrads: 1950-1986)

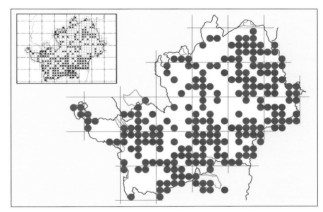

Map 146. *Persicaria lapathifolia.*

Persicaria hydropiper (L.) Spach
Water-pepper
Native.
First record: c.1820.
Tetrad occurrence: 163 (33%).
Stable (-3%).

A plant of seasonally wet mud on more or less acidic soils, in woodland rides, muddy margins of pools, gravel pits, rivers and streams. It remains especially frequent on the acidic London Clay, and on the damper Clay-with-Flints soils, *etc.* However, the

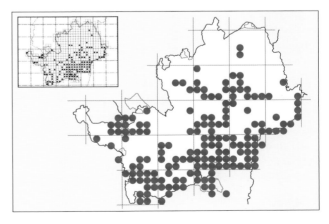

Map 147. *Persicaria hydropiper.*

distribution map shows less of a concentration in the south-east of the County and more records elsewhere. Whether this is a real change or not is difficult to determine.
(159 tetrads: Dony, 1967; 174 tetrads: 1950-1986)

[*Persicaria mitis* (Schrank) Opiz ex Assenov   UK Vulnerable
Tasteless Water-pepper

Dony (1967) noted that plants from Broxbourne Wood in 1916 were mis-identified as this. Burton (1983) also reports 'two stunted plants at Rye Meads (31/V) in 1980'. However, no confirmation of this record was provided, and it must remain in doubt.]

Persicaria minor (Hudson) Opiz   UK Vulnerable
Small Water-pepper
Native.
First record: 1842.
Very rare.

This is a plant of grazed, permanently wet ground on heathy soils, which was once found on a number of sites in central and southern Hertfordshire. Until recently, it had not been found since John Dony discovered it at Boxmoor (00/N) in 1964 (Dony, 1967), but it has now appeared by a small, recently excavated pond on Berkhamsted Common (00/E), 2004 *T. J.* (Hb. HTN). It could remain undetected elsewhere.

Genus: *Fagopyrum*

Fagopyrum esculentum Moench
Buckwheat
Introduced: neophyte.
First record: *c.*1840.
Tetrad occurrence: 15 (3%).

Mostly occurring as a relict of cultivation, or as a result of deliberate spreading as pheasant food. Never persisting for long, and recorded from scattered tetrads across the County.

Fagopyrum tataricum (L.) Gaertner
Green Buckwheat
Introduced: casual.
First (only) record: 1924.

Only recorded once: at Cole Green (TL21) (Dony, 1967).

Genus: *Polygonum*

Polygonum patulum M. Bieb.
Red Knotgrass
Introduced: casual.
First record: 1918.

Only recorded at Ware in 1918 *J. W. Higgens*; and again in 1926 *G. C. Druce* (Dony, ms. index; only the first given in Dony, 1967).

Polygonum arenarium Waldst. and Kit.
Lesser Red Knotgrass
Introduced: casual.
First (only) record: 1915.

Again, only recorded once: Ware (Dony, 1967).

Polygonum arenastrum Boreau
Equal-leaved Knotgrass
Introduced: archaeophyte.
First record: *c.*1880.
Tetrad occurrence: 280 (57%).
Change uncertain.

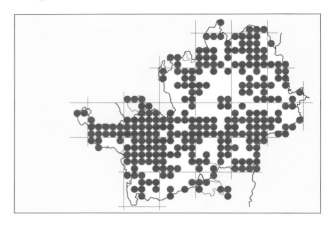

Map 148. *Polygonum arenastrum.*

First recognised as a separate taxon in Herts. by Pryor (Pryor, 1887). Dony gave a map for it, but it was probably very under-recorded. Even now, it is probably under-recorded in some areas. It occurs on muddy tracks and pavements, rather than in cultivated fields.
(34 tetrads: Dony, 1967; 41 tetrads: 1950-1986)

Polygonum aviculare L.
Knotgrass
Native.
First record: 1838.
Tetrad occurrence: 459 (for the segregate and undifferentiated records) (94%).
Probably stable, or slightly decreasing (-6%).

The strict species was recorded from 327 tetrads, mainly in arable fields and other cultivated ground, as well as in waste places. The map shows the distribution of the segregate as well as unattributed records of the aggregate (but not records of *P. arenastrum* and *P. rurivagum*), because records for the strict species are somewhat patchy, especially in east Herts.
(464 tetrads for the agg.: Dony, 1967 and from 1950-1986)

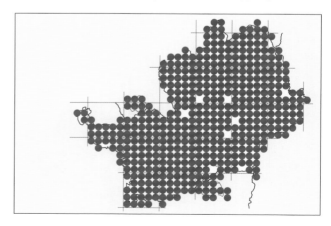

Map 149. *Polygonum aviculare.*

Polygonum rurivagum Jordan ex Boreau
Cornfield Knotgrass
Native.
First record: *c.*1880.
Tetrad occurrence: 6 (1%).
Rare, but under-recorded.

Pryor recognised this as a separate taxon, but Dony only mentions it. It remains under-recorded, although apparently scarce, usually in cornfields, but sometimes on tracks and waste ground in and around villages. There were records to 1963 from Elstree, Sandon, Hertford and Much Hadham subsequent to Pryor's published records. It was identified at Ashwell (23/U), 1983 *T. J.* (Hb. HTN); and during the present survey, it was found in seven locations in six tetrads: Little Wymondley (two localities) (22/D), 1988, 1990 *K. Robinson* (Hb. HTN); near Ashwell (23/P), 1992 *T. J.* (Hb. HTN); Thorley (41/Z), 1996 *S. Watson* (Hb. HTN); Deadman's Hill, Sandon (23/Y), 1999 *T. J.* (Hb. HTN); Bromley (42/A), 2003 *T. J.* (Hb. HTN); and near Shilley Green (12/W), 2004 *T. J.* (Hb. HTN).

Genus: *Fallopia*

Fallopia japonica (Houtt.) Ronse Decraene
Japanese Knotweed
Introduced: neophyte
First recorded: 1912.
Tetrad occurrence: 193 (39%).
Increasing (+102%).

This noxious weed, originally considered a fine addition to gardens when it was first introduced, has spread considerably since Dony's survey. It especially infests disturbed ground and waste places across southern and central Hertfordshire, although in a few tetrads where it had been found earlier, it was not re-recorded.
(91 tetrads: Dony, 1967; 130 tetrads: 1950-1986)

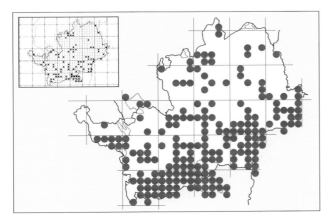

Map 150. *Fallopia japonica.*

Fallopia × *bohemica* (Chrtek and Chrtková) J. Bailey
Introduced: neophyte.
First recorded: 1985.
Tetrad occurrence: 7 (1%).

This extremely robust, fertile hybrid was only recognised clearly by botanists in the 1980s, and was first identified from Cheshunt Gravel Pits (30/R), 1985 *B. Wurzell* (Burton, 1986). It was subsequently recorded from the same locality in 1988 by *D. Bevan/A. M. Boucher* where it persists vigorously; and

also from Salisbury Hall (10/W), 1988 *A. D. Marshall* (Hb. HTN); near Berkhamsted (90/T), 1988 *P. and S. Kingsbury*. It has also been found near Northwood (19/B), 1994 *J. Leftwich*; Pouchen End, Berkhamsted (00/I) and Potten End (00/J), 1994 *G. Salisbury/J. Saunders* (Hb. HTN); Stanborough Park (21/F), 1999 *T. J.*; and by Croxley Common Moor (09/S), 2006 *T. J.* It may well occur elsewhere.

Fallopia sachalinensis (F. Schmidt ex Maxim.) Ronse Decraene
Giant Knotweed
Introduced: neophyte.
First recorded: 1960.
Tetrad occurrence: 22 (5%).
Increasing slowly (+650%).

First identified by the canal at Berkhamsted by Dony (Dony, 1967), this has slowly established itself, especially in disturbed ground in the Lea and Colne valleys, where it hybridises with Japanese Knotweed.
(3 tetrads: Dony, 1967; 10 tetrads: 1960-1986)

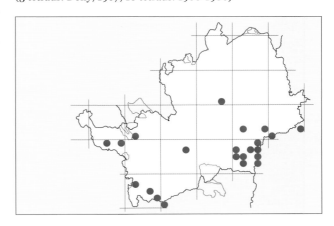

Map 151. *Fallopia sachalinensis.*

Fallopia baldschuanica (Regel) Holub
Russian Vine
Introduced: neophyte.
First record: 1944 (VC21 [Herts.]).
Tetrad occurrence: 14 (3%).
Possibly increasing.

Recorded as more or less established in scrub or roadside hedges from scattered tetrads during the survey, but sometimes difficult to tell from deliberately introduced plants.

Fallopia convolvulus (L.) À. Löve
Black Bindweed
Introduced: archaeophyte.
First record: 1822.
Tetrad occurrence: 382 (78%).
Decreasing (-20%).

Formerly an ubiquitous arable weed throughout the County, this has decreased sharply especially in the south, where arable has been abandoned, and in urban areas.
(454 tetrads: Dony, 1967 and from 1950-1986)

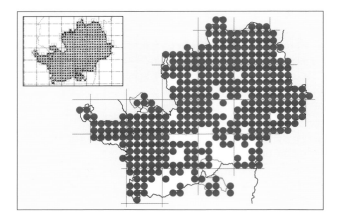

Map 152. *Fallopia convolvulus.*

Fallopia dumetorum (L.) Holub   UK Vulnerable
Copse Bindweed   Herts Extinct
Native.
First record: 1838.

This was never common in the County, found in old hedgerows and by coppices on the gravels around Hertford and Welwyn, but has not been seen since 1875 (Dony, 1967).

Genus: *Rheum*

Rheum palmatum L.
Ornamental Rhubarb
Introduced: casual.
First (only) record: 1992.

The only record is of a casual plant by the River Lea, Ware (31/M), 1992 *R. Tanner* (conf. T. J.).

Rheum × *hybridum* Murray (*R. rhaponticum* × *R. palmatum*)
Rhubarb
Introduced: neophyte.
First record: 1971.
Tetrad occurrence: 6 (1%).

Disregarded by Dony and earlier botanists, and only first recorded as an escape at Hitchin tip (13/V), 1971 *C. G. Hanson*. It has subsequently turned up occasionally on waste ground, where it can persist for some time.

Genus: *Rumex*

Rumex dentatus L.
Aegean Dock
Introduced: casual.
First record: 1922.
Only recorded twice, the last record being Bulls Mill tip (31/C), 1958 (Dony, 1967).

Rumex obovatus Danser
Obovate-leaved Dock
Introduced: casual.
First record: 1932.

A grain contaminant, recorded twice in Herts., last at St Margarets (TL31), 1933 *A. W. Graveson* (Dony, 1967).

Rumex bucephalophorus L.
Horned Dock
Introduced: casual.
First (only) record: 1917.

There are no records since it was found at Ware (Dony, 1967).

Rumex acetosella L.
Sheep's Sorrel
Native.
First record: 1814.
Tetrad occurrence: 280 (57%).
Decreasing (-15%).

The 15% decrease in overall occurrence at tetrad level, sad that this is, masks a massive decrease of this characteristic plant of heathy pastures in many areas, owing to the loss of semi-natural acidic grassland. Its overall distribution remains much the same, although it was evidently under-recorded in east Herts. in the 1960s, where it is now known to exist. The main losses have been in south Herts. It occasionally occurs as an introduced weed in gardens, from garden centres.
(312 tetrads: Dony, 1967; 316 tetrads: 1950-1986)

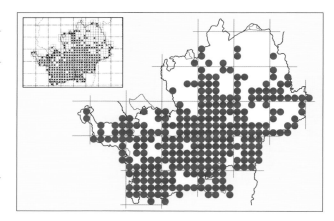

Map 153. *Rumex acetosella.*

Rumex scutatus L.
French Sorrel
Introduced: casual.
First (only) record: 1858.

Only recorded once in Herts., at Hitchin in 1858 (Dony, 1967).

Rumex acetosa L.
Common Sorrel
Native.
First record: 1748.
Tetrad occurrence: 432 (88%).
Decreasing (-8%).

This is one of a suite of plants characteristic of more-or-less unimproved, mostly neutral to mildly acidic grassland, although it is able to tolerate some agricultural fertiliser, and persists in derelict grassland. It has also decreased, but to a lesser extent than *R. acetosella*, most noticeably on the Chalk and chalky Boulder Clay, where it was never quite so abundant.
(446 tetrads: Dony, 1967; 447 tetrads: 1950-1986)

The usual subspecies is ssp. *acetosa*, but the alien ssp. *ambiguus* (Gren.) À Löve was found in filled gravel workings near Cheshunt station (30/R), 1990 *A. M. Boucher* (det. E. J. Clement) (Hb.

HTN), the second British record.

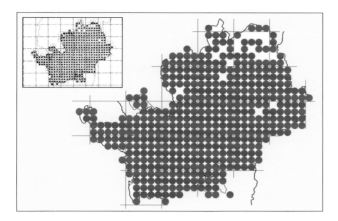

Map 154. *Rumex acetosa.*

Rumex salicifolius Weinm.
Willow-leaved Dock
Introduced: casual.
First record: 1920.

This was recorded (as *R. triangulivalvis* (Danser) Rech.) a few times around Hertford and Ware, lastly in 1928 (Dony, 1967).

Rumex hydrolapathum Hudson
Water Dock
Native.
First record: 1838.
Tetrad occurrence: 77 (16%).
Stable or slightly increased (+8%).

This is a fine plant, mostly of the margins of rivers and larger streams, and especially the Grand Union Canal, but occasionally also by gravel pits and in very wet swamps. Its distribution remains much the same as it was in the previous survey, although it may have increased slightly in some areas, possibly through provision of more large water bodies since the 1960s.
(71 tetrads: Dony, 1967; 81 tetrads: 1950-1986)

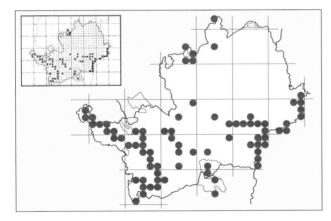

Map 155. *Rumex hydrolapathum.*

Rumex cristatus DC.
Greek Dock
Introduced: neophyte.
First record: 1995.
Tetrad occurrence: 5 (1%).

This was found to occur on waste ground in several places in the

Lea Valley in 1995 by Ann Boucher. Records from the survey were: Waltham Cross (39/U), 'hundreds' 1995 *A. M. B.* (det. G. D. Kitchener) (Hb. HTN); Waltham Cross (30/Q), 1995 *A. M. B.*; Turnford (2 sites) (30/S), 1995 *A. M. B.*; Cheshunt: Pindar Road (30/R), 1996 *T. J.* (Hb. HTN); Ware: garden weed, from introduced seed (31/S), 1999 *C. G. Hanson.*

Rumex × dimidiatus Hausskn. (*R. cristatus × R. crispus*)

The only record is the plant found near Cheshunt station (30/R), 1990 *A. M. Boucher* (det. G. D. Kitchener) (Hb. HTN), before *R. cristatus* itself was found there.

Rumex patientia L.
Patience Dock
Introduced: neophyte.
First record: 1910.

This was first found at Hertford brick fields in 1910 *A. W. Graveson* (Hb. HTN); and subsequently near Hitchin gas works (23/A), 1921-2 *J. E. Little* (Dony, 1967, and ms. index). It may well re-appear, as it is a feature around London.

Rumex crispus L.
Curled Dock
Native.
First record: 1833.
Tetrad occurrence: 458 (93%).
Stable or marginally decreased (-5%).

A common plant of roadsides, rough grassland, and waste places, most often on somewhat calcareous ground. It is sometimes hard to find in southern Hertfordshire.
(458 tetrads: Dony, 1967 and from 1950-1986)

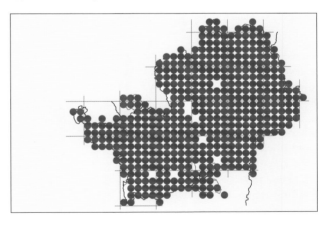

Map 156. *Rumex crispus.*

Rumex × sagorskii Hausskn. (*R. crispus × R. sanguineus*)

There is a record from VC20 Herts. without data in Stace (1975). It was also found, with the parent species, south of Dunstable (02/A) (VC20 [Beds.]), 1999 *T. J./G. P. Smith* (Hb. HTN). It may well be more widespread.

Rumex × pratensis Mert. and Koch (*R. crispus × R. obtusifolius*)
Meadow Dock
First record: *c.*1840.
Tetrad occurrence: 14 (3%).

When this was thought to be a separate species, in the 19th century, it was recorded widely (as both *R. pratensis* and *R. acutus*) (Pryor,

1887). It was not seriously recorded by Dony, and the current survey found it in only 14 tetrads, with a slight predominance in south Herts., although it is probably in many other places.

Rumex conglomeratus Murray
Clustered Dock
Native.
First record: 1838.
Tetrad occurrence: 251 (51%).
Decreasing (-25%).

This is a plant of seasonally damp grassland, edges of ponds and grazed areas by streams. Its apparently quite severe decrease in some areas seems to be quite recent, and may owe much to the demise of stock-rearing across the County. It has decreased especially strongly in the south and south-west.
(317 tetrads: Dony, 1967; 342 tetrads: 1950-1986)

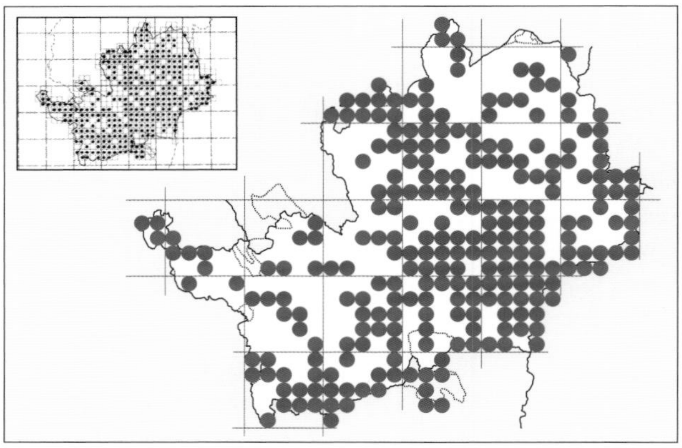

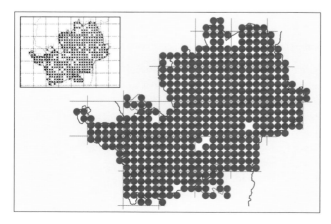

Map 157. *Rumex conglomeratus.*

Rumex × abortivus Ruhmer (*R. conglomeratus × R. obtusifolius*)
Native.

First recorded at Dobbs Weir (30/Z) in 1973, with *R. obtusifolius* var. *transiens* as one parent (Burton, 1983). It was found nearby during the survey at Broxbourne (30/T), 1988 *D. Bevan* (Burton, 1989).

Rumex sanguineus L.
Wood Dock
Native.
First record: 1839.
Tetrad occurrence: 457 (93%).
Apparently increasing (+28%).

Map 158. *Rumex sanguineus.*

This plant of shaded habitats on fertile soils appears to have become even more frequent than it was formerly, possibly owing to habitat enrichment.
(340 tetrads: Dony, 1967; 354 tetrads: 1950-1986)

Rumex × dufftii Hausskn. (*R. sanguineus × R. obtusifolius*)
Native.
First record: 1966.

Rare, but probably overlooked. Recorded during this survey at Panshanger (21/W), 1997 *T. J.*; at Broadlands, Harpenden (11/I), 1999 *T. J.*; and in Bull's Wood, Tring Park (91/F), 2007 *T. J.* (Hb. HTN).

Rumex pulcher L.
Fiddle Dock
Native.
First record: 1843.
Tetrad occurrence: 11 (2%).
Probably stable (+16%).

This is a sporadic plant of often old, dry, moderately calcareous grassland which is occasionally disturbed, sometimes also in waste ground. It has never been particularly common, but may be overlooked in short grass when not flowering. In the 19th century, it was identified as a feature of churchyards, but it is more frequent elsewhere now.
(9 tetrads: Dony, 1967; 15 tetrads: 1950-1986)

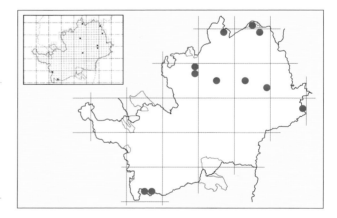

Map 159. *Rumex pulcher.*

Rumex × ogulinensis Borbás (*R. pulcher × R. obtusifolius*)
Native.
First record: 1924.

Rare. This has only been found once during the survey: Windmill Hill, Hitchin (12/Z), 1998 *T. J.* (Hb. HTN), with both parents.

Rumex obtusifolius L.
Broad-leaved Dock
Native.
First record: 1838.
Tetrad occurrence: 479 (98%).
Stable (+4%).

Although there is a slight increase in the number of tetrads recorded, there is no real evidence that this plant of rough grassland and waste places has become more abundant.
(461 tetrads: Dony, 1967 and from 1950-1986)

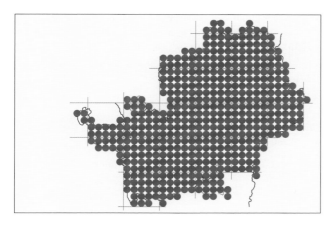

Map 160. *Rumex obtusifolius.*

Two alien varieties are also recorded: var. *microcarpus* Dierb. (Dony, 1967); and var. *transiens* (Simonk.) Kubát, at Dobbs Weir (30/Z), 1973 (Burton, 1983). Both are probably under-recorded.

Rumex × *steinii* A. Becker (*R. obtusifolius* × *R. palustris*)
Native.

The only record is from near Broxbourne (30/Y), 1973 (Burton, 1983).

Rumex × *callianthemus* Danser (*R. obtusifolius* × *R. maritimus*)
Native.
First documented record: 1996.
Rare.

There is an undated and unlocalised record from VC20 by Lousley and Williams, quoted in Stace (1975). Otherwise, the only record is from Old Parkbury (10/R), 1996 *A. D. Marshall* (Hb. Marshall).

Rumex palustris Smith
Marsh Dock
Native.
First record: 1840.
Tetrad occurrence: 8 (2%).
Stable or possibly increased (+46%).

This has always been a rare plant of long-standing wet habitats, by ponds, *etc.*, on neutral or rather acidic soils in southern Hertfordshire. It is particularly a feature of King's Meads (31/L), Rye Meads (31/V) and Amwell Quarry (31/R), but also occurs at marshes around Cuffley and Northaw (20/V, 30/A), and at Waterend, Wheathampstead, by the River Lea (11/X).
(5 tetrads: Dony, 1967; 8 tetrads: 1950-1986)

Map 161. *Rumex palustris.*

Rumex maritimus L.
Golden Dock
Native.
First record: 1899.
Tetrad occurrence: 10 (2%).
Rare and erratic, slowly increased (+122%).

Dony considered this to have derived from introduced plants, but there is no real evidence that this is the case and it may merely have been overlooked earlier. It is a plant of bare mud by ponds and rivers, and has benefited from the rash of gravel pits across southern Hertfordshire, where it colonises new mud for a period, before vanishing again. It also turns up by old ponds in times of drought, probably moved around by birds, and occasionally occurs on waste tips. It may decline somewhat again, as gravel pit sites become vegetated, without new ones being created.
(4 tetrads: Dony, 1967; 12 tetrads: 1950-1986)

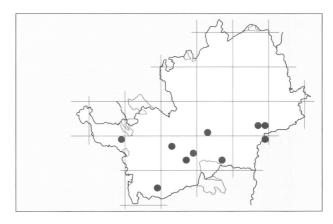

Map 162. *Rumex maritimus.*

Golden Dock Rumex maritimus *Amwell Quarry, 1987.*

Plumbaginaceae (Thrift family)

Genus: *Armeria*

Armeria maritima (Miller) Willd.
Thrift
Introduced [native in the U.K.].
First (only) record: 1990.

This appeared as a roadside weed for a short time by the B653 near Wheathampstead (11/W), 1990 *A. D. Marshall* (Hb. HTN), no doubt because of road salting.

Paeoniaceae (Paeony family)

Genus: *Paeonia*

Paeonia officinalis L.
Garden Paeony
Introduced: casual.
First record: 1989.

This appeared for a while as an escape at Frogmore Pit, Aston (22/V), 1989, *etc. T. J.*

Clusiaceae (St John's-worts)

Genus: *Hypericum*

Hypericum calycinum L.
Rose-of-Sharon
Introduced: neophyte.
First record: 1857.
Tetrad occurrence: 9 (2%).
Possibly increasing (+350%).

Occasionally surviving as an outcast from cultivation, and probably self-seeding in some places. For example, it has been known from one place or another around Hertingfordbury (31/A) for over 100 years.
(2 tetrads: Dony, 1967; 3 tetrads: 1950-1986)

Hypericum androsaemum L.
Tutsan
Native and introduced.
First record: 1730.
Tetrad occurrence: 25 (5%).
Decreased since 1880s, now increasing again?

Rare as a native, but occasional as a bird-sown escape from gardens. This was occasional in woods on moderately acidic loamy soils over gravels and Clay-with-Flints across central, southern and western Hertfordshire in the 19th century, but by the 1960s had become rare. Dony (1967) expressed doubt about most records, and thought it was extinct as a native. After 1970, it was found in a number of its old woodland haunts, such as Northaw Great Wood (20/S), Harmergreen Wood (21/N), Wormley Wood (30/I) and Hoo Wood, Gaddesden (01/G). During the current

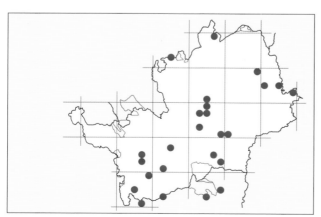

Map 163. *Hypericum androsaemum.*

survey, it was found again in Sherrards Park Wood (21/G), Harmergreen Wood (21/N), Coldharbour Wood (20/S), Home Wood at Cuffley (20/W), Bishop's Wood, Rickmansworth (09/R), and Solomon's Wood (09/M). Elsewhere it was certainly or likely to be an escape.
(12 tetrads: 1950-1986)

Hypericum × *inodorum* Miller (*H. androsaemum* × *H. hircinum*)
Introduced: casual.

Only record: Hitchin (12/Z), *c.*1880 (Dony, 1967).

Hypericum perforatum L.
Perforate St John's-wort
Native.
First record: 1822.
Tetrad occurrence: 431 (88%).
Probably increasing slightly (+7%).

This is a plant of rough grassland, scrub, waste ground and woodland rides, usually on moderately calcareous soils. Although it does not tolerate high nutrient levels, it has probably benefited from recently disturbed gravel pits and new roads across the county. It is only scarce on the more barren parts of the Boulder Clay in north-east Herts., and in some areas on the acidic soils of south Herts.
(384 tetrads: Dony, 1967; 402 tetrads: 1950-1986)

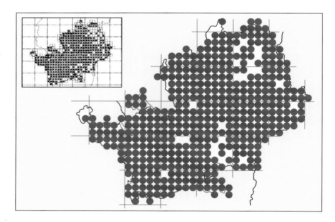

Map 164. *Hypericum perforatum.*

Hypericum × *desetangsii* Lamotte
(*H. perforatum* × *H. maculatum*)
Native.
First record: 1983.

Only first noticed at Lemsford Springs (21/G), 1983 *T. J.* (Hb. HTN), where it occurred with *H. perforatum*, and survives, 2005. It has since been found on waste ground by Pryor's Wood (22/T), 1996 *K. Hall/G. P. Smith*; Harpenden (11/H), 1992, 1993 *J. Southey* (Hb. HTN); Kentish Lane (20/S), 1998 *T. J.*; Trenchern Hills (32/K), 1993 *S. Watson*; 'Totteridge Common' [*sic.*] (29/L?), 1995 *D. Griffith* (Burton, 1996); and Rush Green Airfield (22/C), 2006 *J. Williamson/J. Moss* (det. T. J.) (Hb. HTN. Some of these are away from known sites for *H. maculatum*.

Hypericum maculatum Crantz
Imperforate St John's-wort
Native.
First record: 1805.
Tetrad occurrence: 26 (5%).
Stable (+2%).

This is an interesting and rather uncommon species. Two subspecies are recorded in the County, the native one being ssp. *obtusiusculum* (Tourlet) Hayek, shown here on the map. It occurs mainly in slightly damp unimproved rough grassland over gravel or clay. Most of its sites are concentrated in the south of the County, particularly around North Mymms and Hatfield, but it also occurs at scattered sites elsewhere, particularly on the Clay-with-Flints. The outlier on the bank of an ancient track on the Chalk near Barley (33/Z) is also apparently on a small area of Clay-with-Flints.
(24 tetrads: Dony, 1967; 32 tetrads: 1950-1986)

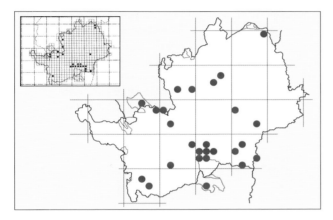

Map 165. *Hypericum maculatum.*

Subspecies *maculatum* occurs only at Hoo Wood, Great Gaddesden (01/G), where it was re-found in 1990 by A. D. Marshall (det. T. J.) (Hb. HTN), having first been identified in 1962 (Dony, 1967). This is mainly a northern plant, and may have been introduced here with imported timber trees.

Hypericum tetrapterum Fries.
Square-stalked St John's-wort
Native.
First recorded: 1820.
Tetrad occurrence: 167 (34%).
Stable or slightly increased (+9%).

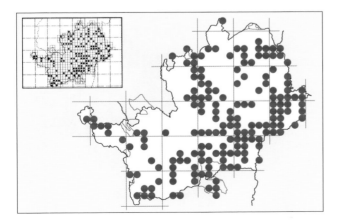

Map 166. *Hypericum tetrapterum.*

This is a plant of marshy places, woodland rides and so on, usually on clay soils. It is widely-distributed across the County, but most frequent on the Boulder Clay, London Clay and similar soils. It can colonise new wetlands around gravel pits, and survives in rank habitat for long periods.
(145 tetrads: Dony, 1967; 169 tetrads: 1950-1986)

Hypericum humifusum L.
Trailing St John's-wort
Native.
First record: c.1820.
Tetrad occurrence: 48 (10%).
Probably stable or slightly increased (+20%).

Found mainly on more acidic soils on scrubby commons, and in open woods, this plant is quite widespread, but not common, in suitable sites across most of south and central Hertfordshire. It occasionally turns up in secondary habitat, such as the scrub over old fly-ash tips at Cheshunt Gravel Pits (30/R).
(38 tetrads: Dony, 1967; 50 tetrads: 1950-1986)

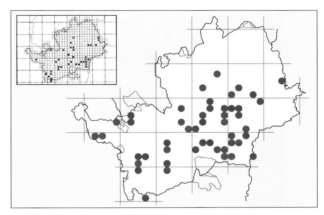

Map 167. *Hypericum humifusum.*

Hypericum pulchrum L.
Slender St John's-wort
Native.
First record: 1787.
Tetrad occurrence: 61 (12%).
Stable? (+3%).

Found in clearings in woodland, and on scrubby commons, on more acidic, but free-draining soils across south-eastern, western and central Hertfordshire. The fact that it was recorded more

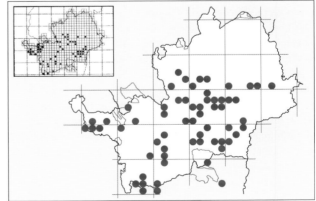

Map 168. *Hypericum pulchrum.*

widely between the 1960s and the present survey suggests it may have decreased somewhat since Dony (1967) carried out his survey, which itself may have under-recorded it.
(56 tetrads: Dony, 1967; 76 tetrads: 1950-1986)

Hypericum hirsutum L.
Hairy St John's-wort
Native.
First record: 1814.
Tetrad occurrence: 227 (46%).
Stable (+1%).

This is a plant of damp calcareous clays, especially on the Boulder Clay, where it occurs widely in rough grassland, scrub, road verges and woodland rides. Its distribution remains almost exactly the same as it was in the 1960s, except that it is better recorded in the south-west.
(213 tetrads: Dony, 1967; 228 tetrads: 1950-1986)

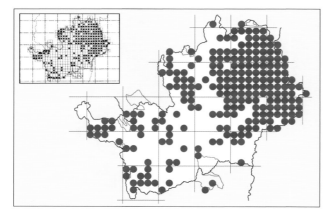

Map 169. *Hypericum hirsutum.*

Hypericum montanum L.   UK Near Threatened
Pale St John's-wort
Native.
First record: 1858.
Extinct in Herts.?

This is a plant of chalk or limestone grassland and scrub. Dony was doubtful about its status in Herts. It was first identified in a field at Pirton Cross (12/U) (a rather unlikely-looking habitat), 1858, by Robert Bentley, but the record was questioned by Pryor (Pryor, 1887). It was later found in a hedgebank near Hudnall (TL01), 1915, by E. J. Salisbury (photo in Hb. BM) (Salisbury, 1917); and subsequently at Aldbury (SP91), 1923 by A. W. Graveson (a record omitted by Dony). F. M. Day then recorded it at 'Chorley Green' (Chorleywood Common?) (TQ09), in 1944 (another record omitted by Dony), and finally there was a record from Little Berkhamsted (20/Z), 1966, *M. Kennedy* (det. J. Lousley), which was queried by Burton (Burton, 1983). These scant records might be regarded as errors, but for the fact that it is a plant of the Chilterns to the south-west. The Hertfordshire records (except for the Little Berkhamsted occurrence) are all on the Chalk in the Chilterns Natural Area, and therefore it is quite probable that they represent rare outliers of a native population. The plant needs to be looked for elsewhere.

Tiliaceae (Limes)

Genus: *Tilia*

Tilia platyphyllos Scop.
Large-leaved Lime
Native? (or introduced) [native in the U.K.].
First record: *c.*1840.
Tetrad occurrence: 43 (9%).

The status of this species in Herts. is uncertain. Coleman recorded old trees on the west side of Wormley Wood and in nearby hedges (Webb and Coleman, 1849). Dony noted that A. W. Graveson had also recorded these in 1919, but considered them to be planted. The current survey recorded it from no less than 43 tetrads, mostly as planted trees. However, there were several sites where the origin was not obviously from plantings, such as Walk Wood, St Paul's Walden (old coppice) (12/W); Whippendell Wood (09/U); Balls Wood (31/K) (old coppice); and The Nuckett (00/R). Very old, presumably planted trees were found at Botanybay Plantation, Offley (12/N) (with old beeches and a natural woodland flora); and a self-sown sapling was found (source unknown) at Chesham Road, near Berkhamsted (90/P), 1997 *G. Salisbury.* Some old coppice stools present on the west side of Wormley Wood (30/C) are apparently hybrids, but there are also old trees of the species still there as well, apparently planted, along the boundary of the wood. However, as apparently native trees occur at Barton, Beds., not far away in the Chilterns, it is just possible that a few of the other sites in north Herts. might be native also.

Tilia × *europaea* L. (*T. platyphyllos* × *T. cordata*)
Common Lime
Introduced (or native?) [native in the U.K.].
First record: 1660 (as planted tree).
Tetrad occurrence: 318 (65%).

Dony (1967) dismisses this as always planted, as did Webb and Coleman (1849). It is certainly very frequently planted across the County, and forms fine avenues at places like Marden Hill, St Paul's Waldenbury, Hatfield Park and Moor Place at Much Hadham, often festooned with Mistletoe. However, there are occasionally old coppice stools in unlikely places, particularly those by Wormley Wood (30/C), referred to above, and some superb old trees in Pudler's Wood, Sandridge (11/K, Q), alongside very old coppiced Hornbeam, which might just be the result of

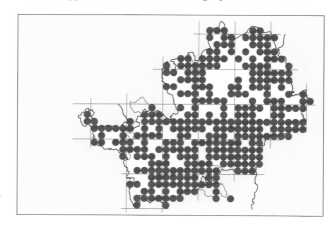

Map 170. *Tilia* × *europaea.*

natural hybrids. Unfortunately not enough attention was paid to these elsewhere to distinguish them.

Tilia cordata L.
Small-leaved Lime
Introduced [native in the U.K.].
First record: *c.*1960 (as planted).
Tetrad occurrence: 30 (6%).

Probably always now originally planted, rarely self-sown. This was a rare planted tree when Dony first noted it, mainly in towns, although there are some old ornamental plantings elswhere, such as by Therfield Heath (33/J). More recently it has become a favourite in the so-called amenity plantings around road works, which may have been the source of the self-sown sapling at Oddy Hill (91/F), 1988 *T. J.* The fact that it is a major component of ancient woodland in Essex, and appears to have been present in Epping Forest in historic times, suggests that it may once also have occurred in Herts. in natural habitat. This may explain the origin of some of the hybrid lime coppice stools which occur in such places, especially if the other parent occurred naturally in the Chilterns.

Malvaceae (Mallow family)

Genus: *Malope*

Malope trifida Cav.
Mallow-wort
Introduced: casual.
First record: 1969.

This was recorded as a casual at Park Street dump (10/L), 1969 *J. G. Dony* (Dony, 1970; Burton, 1983).

Genus: *Sida*

Sida spinosa L.
Prickly Mallow
Introduced: casual.
First record: 1976.

This was recorded from tips at Rickmansworth (09/L, M) in 1976, from soya bean waste *J. G.* and *C. M. Dony* (Dony, 1977) (Hb. HTN; Hb. LTN). It was also found on sludge dumps at Rye Meads Sewage Works (31/V), 1995 *A. M. Boucher/C. G. Hanson* (Hb. HTN).

Genus: *Hibiscus*

Hibiscus trionum L.
Bladder Ketmia
Introduced: casual.
First record: 1920.

This is a casual from bird-seed or formerly wool-waste origins, and was first recorded at Hitchin (12/Z) (Dony, 1967). It turns up occasionally on tips and in gardens. During the survey it was found on a dung heap near Cole Green (21/Q), 1987 *A. M. Boucher/C. G. Hanson* (Hb. HTN); and at Garston (19/E), 1989 *O. Linford.*

Genus: *Malva*

Malva moschata L.
Musk-mallow
Native.
First record: 1597.
Tetrad occurrence: 246 (50%).
Probably increased (+20%).

This may have increased since Dony's survey, as a result of seeding or escapes from cultivation. As a wild plant it occurs widely, but thinly, on grassy rough ground, woodland rides, road verges and sometimes by arable fields, mostly on calcareous gravels or the free-draining Clay-with-Flints soils of the Chilterns dip-slope. It is rare on damp clay, and on the Chalk itself.
(195 tetrads: Dony, 1967; 234 tetrads: 1950-1986)

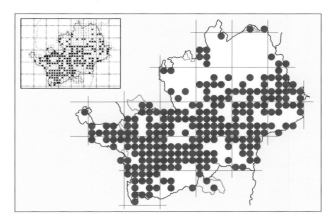

Map 171. *Malva moschata.*

Malva alcea L.
Greater Musk-mallow
Introduced: casual or neophyte.
First record: 2005.

This was found on the roadside of the A414 near Mill Green (21/K), 2005 *T. J.* (Hb. HTN); and subsequently in a derelict field by Croxley Hall Wood (09/S), 2006 *T. J.* (Hb. HTN). It is probably elsewhere, as it can be mistaken for the native species.

Malva sylvestris L.
Common Mallow
Introduced: archaeophyte.
First record: 1814.

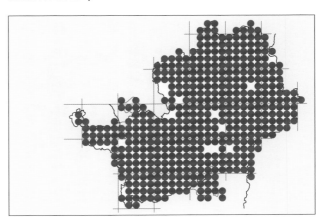

Map 172. *Malva sylvestris.*

Tetrad occurrence: 444 (90%).
Increased (+14%).

Now regarded as an ancient introduction, this is a plant of moderately eutrophic waste ground, and has responded to nitrogen enrichment in field margins and roadsides, now being almost ubiquitous, although still sparse in a few areas.
(370 tetrads: Dony, 1967; 385 tetrads: 1950-1967).

Subspecies *mauritiana* (L.) Thellung., with purple flowers, sometimes grown in gardens, has been recorded at Rye Meads (31/V), 1996 *A. M. Boucher/C. G. Hanson* and occasionally by roads elsewhere.

Malva parviflora L.
Least Mallow
Introduced: casual.
First record: 1878.

A rare casual of waste heaps. It has occurred occasionally across the County, but was only found once during the survey: Wadesmill (31/N), 1989 *A. M. Boucher* (Hb. HTN).

Malva × *oxyloba* Boiss. (*M. parviflora* × *M. neglecta*)

This rare hybrid was recorded at Welwyn (TL21), 1932, *H. Phillips* (det. Schinz) (*Rep. Bot. Exch. Club*: 21 (1932)) (Hb. HTN).

Malva pusilla Smith
Small Mallow
Introduced: casual.
First record: 1876.

Never a common plant, this occurs occasionally on bare ground and waste sites. It has occurred sporadically across the County, but especially in the Hoddesdon-Ware area. During the survey it was found only at Rye Meads (31/V), 1989 *A. M. Boucher/C. G. Hanson.*

Malva neglecta Wallr.
Dwarf Mallow
Introduced: archaeophyte.
First record: c.1820.
Tetrad occurrence: 151 (31%).
Probably decreasing (-9%).

Formerly thought to be native, but now considered an ancient introduction, this occurs widely on road verges and waste ground.

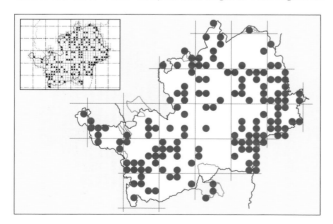

Map 173. *Malva neglecta.*

It appears to have strongholds, but has disappeared from some areas.
(158 tetrads: Dony, 1967; 178 tetrads: 1950-1986)

Malva verticillata L.
Chinese Mallow
Introduced: casual.
First (only) record: 1989.

This was found growing in long grass by the disused railway, the 'Nicky Line', Harpenden (11/C), 1989 *J. F. Southey* (Hb. HTN).

Genus: *Lavatera*

Lavatera arborea L.
Tree-mallow
Introduced: casual.
First record: 1987.

Reported from the 'Rickmansworth area', 1987 *P. J. Ellison* (Burton, 1988), presumably the site at West Hyde (09/F), where it remained in 1990 *P. J. E.* It was subsequently found as an escape at Standon (32/W), 1991 *S. Watson*, and at Letchworth Gate (23/F), 1992 *K. Hall.*

Lavatera cretica L.
Smaller Tree-mallow
Introduced: casual.
First record: 1916.

There have been no further records after its first occurrence at Ware (Dony, 1967), although it is increasing nationally in the south, and could re-appear.

Lavatera thuringiaca L. (= *L. olbia* auct.)
Garden Tree-mallow
Introduced: casual.
First record: 1986.

This first appeared as an escape at Hertford Heath (31/K), 1986 *C. G. Hanson* (Hb. HTN). The only subsequent records are from rough ground by factories at Dunstable (02/L) (VC20 [Beds.]), 1995 *C. R. Boon/T. J.*; and from a roadside near Mobb's Hole, Ashwell (24/R), 2007 *T. J.*

Genus: *Althaea*

Althaea officinalis L.
Marsh-mallow
Introduced [native in the U.K.].
First (only) record: 1993.

This native of marshes usually near the sea was found on waste ground by Fanhams Hall Road, Ware (31/S), 1993 *A. M. Boucher* (Hb. HTN). Its source is unknown.

Althaea hirsuta L.
Rough Marsh-mallow
Introduced: casual.
First record: 1871.

A rare casual, last seen at Grove Mill Pit, Hitchin (13/V), 1968 *H. Bowry.*

Genus: *Alcea*

Alcea rosea L.
Hollyhock
Introduced: neophyte.
First record: *c*.1975.
Tetrad occurrence: 17 (4%).

It seems strange that this was not noted as occurring naturally until Burton (1983) reported three unlocalised records (10/X, Y; 30/U). It appeared at Oaklands Gravel Pit (10/Z), 1984 *T. J.*, but by 1986 it was becoming frequent as a tolerated weed at Ashwell (23/U) *T. J.*, from where it has spread slowly into surrounding countryside. It has also appeared elsewhere round villages.

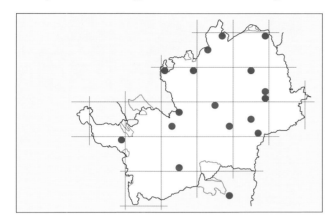

Map 174. *Alcea rosea.*

Genus: *Sidalcea*

Sidalcea malviflora agg.
Greek Mallow
Introduced: casual.
First (only) record: 1988.

Two plants reported as '*S. oregana*' were found on tipped soil by the old A414 at Great Amwell (31/Q), 1988 *A. M. Boucher* (Hb. Boucher).

Genus: *Abutilon*

Abutilon theophrasti Medikus
Velvetleaf
Introduced: casual.
First record: 1949.
Tetrad occurrence: 7 (1%).

This has occurred quite frequently on waste tips. It was found in eight tetrads between 1967 and 1986; and during the survey at: Waterford tip (31/C), 1987 *C. G. Hanson*; Wilstone (91/B), 1989 *C. Mead*; Pole Hole tip (41/L), 1989 *S. Watson*; Hadham Towers pit (41/I), 1989 *S. W.*; Plashes Farm, flax field (32/V), 1992 *S. W.*; Wadesmill (31/N), 1989 *A. M. Boucher*; and Rye Meads (31/V), 1995 *C. G. Hanson*.

Genus: *Anoda*

Anoda cristata (L.) Schlecht.
Introduced: casual.
First (only) record: 1958.

This was recorded from Bushey, 1958 (Dony, 1967).

Droseraceae (Sundews)

Genus: *Drosera*

Drosera rotundifolia L.   Herts Extinct
Round-leaved Sundew
Native.
First record: *c*.1840.

Always rare in Herts., this was a feature of bogs at Bell Bar, Hatfield Woodside, Kentish Lane, Hertford Heath and Bushey Heath in the 19th century, last recorded near Barber's Lodge Farm (20/S) in 1914 (Pryor, 1887; Dony, 1967).

Cistaceae (Rock-rose family)

Genus: *Helianthemum*

Helianthemum nummularium (L.) Miller   Herts Vulnerable
Common Rock-rose
Native.
First record: 1746.
Tetrad occurrence: 50 (10%).
Decreasing sharply (-50%).

Characteristic of good quality chalk grassland, sometimes on calcareous gravels and rarely in short turf on heaths where Chalk is close to the surface, as at Nomansland Common (11/R), 1984, 1989 *T. J.*; 2005 *J. P. Widgery*. It is one of a suite of species which is rapidly disappearing from the ordinary countryside, able to hang on in rank grass for a time, but eventually succumbing. Many of the records in Dony (1967) were probably for remnant sites, such as old chalk pits or road verges, but most of these have now gone. It now mostly remains on surviving high quality sites, but its records are also a good indicator of where high quality natural calcareous grassland used to be.
(95 tetrads: Dony, 1967; 108 tetrads: 1950-1986)

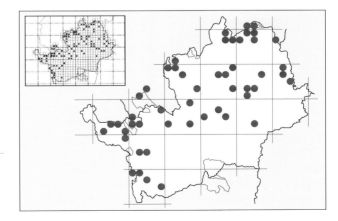

Map 175. *Helianthemum nummularium.*

Violaceae (Violets)

Genus: *Viola*

Viola odorata L.
Sweet Violet
Native.
First record: 1814.
Tetrad occurrence: 325 (66%) (for the broad species).
Increasing (+27%).

This is a puzzling plant. Usually regarded as native, it comes in several different forms: the two most widespread being plain blue-violet (var. *odorata*), and another being white with a violet spur (var. *dumetorum* (Jordan) Rouy and Fouc.), both of which occur widely in the open countryside. However, there are also dull pinkish-purple forms, and forms with pale lilac and whitish streaked flowers, some with forward-pointing and/or bearded lateral petals, which suggest it is a complex of different taxa. The survey did not attempt to separate these. Overall, it occurs mainly on the damper, more calcareous Boulder Clay, but also in sheltered places on more calcareous soils elsewhere. It does not usually occur in ancient woods or grassland, but is a plant of roadsides, hedges and scrub, suggesting that they may be derived from long-standing garden escapes.
(243 tetrads: Dony, 1967; 261 tetrads: 1950-1986)

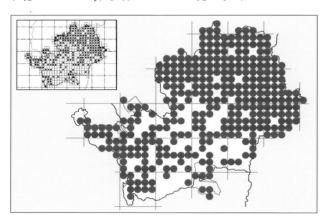

Map 176. *Viola odorata.*

Variety *praecox* Gregory, which has reddish-purple flowers on long peduncles, and narrower, brighter green summer leaves, flowering very early in spring, occurs quite widely around settlements, and is almost certainly a relatively recent escape. It appears to be increasing, but there are not enough records to be certain. It is also characteristically rather rank smelling!

Viola × *scabra* F. Braun (*V. odorata* × *V. hirta*)
Native.
First record: c.1880.

Although Dony (1967) had not seen it in Herts., this could occur wherever the parents meet. It has been recorded recently at Ashwell Quarry (23/P), 2000 *T. J.*; Tring Park (91/F), 2000 *T. J.* and Chorleywood Dell (09/I), 2003 *B. Harold*, where it was also found by D. Bevan in 1981. Which forms of *V. odorata* might have been involved in the hybrid are mostly unrecorded, although the Ashwell Quarry record derived from the normal violet-coloured var. *odorata*.

Viola hirta L.
Hairy Violet
Native.
First record: 1805.
Tetrad occurrence: 201 (41%).
Probably stable (+7%).

A plant of short, open calcareous turf, sometimes in scrub or hedgebanks, and able to colonise new sites quite readily. Although recorded in more tetrads than in 1967, this may reflect better recording.
(178 tetrads: Dony, 1967; 206 tetrads: 1950-1986)

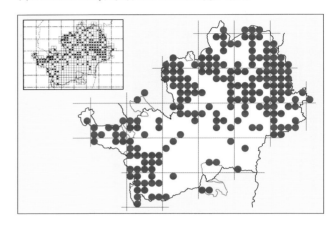

Map 177. *Viola hirta.*

Ssp. *calcarea* (Bab.) E. F. Warburg has been recorded in the past (Dony, 1967), but is a doubtful taxon (Stace, 1997).

Viola riviniana Reichb.
Common Dog-violet
Native.
First record: 1874 (as the segregate).
Tetrad occurrence: 281 (57%).
Apparently decreasing (-12%).

Confusion seems to have reigned over this plant in the past. It was lumped with *Viola canina* by Webb and Coleman, and may have been somewhat over-recorded for *V. reichenbachiana* or hybrids by Dony. However, it may actually be decreasing in its native woodland sites, where it prefers less calcareous soils, owing to shading, or the spread of acidophile plants like Bracken.
(303 tetrads: Dony, 1967; 325 tetrads: 1950-1986)

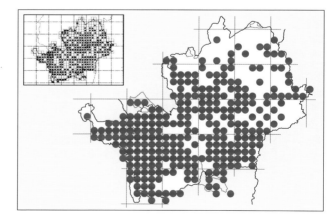

Map 178. *Viola riviniana.*

Viola × *bavarica* Schrank (*V. riviniana* × *V. reichenbachiana*)
Native.
First record: 1995.

First noted at Bishop's Wood, Tring (91/F), 1995 *T. J./
G. Salisbury*, this has now been identified in seven tetrads across
the County on more calcareous woodland soils. It is probably
common.

Viola × *intersita* G. Beck (*V. riviniana* × *V. canina*)
Native.

This was recorded from Codicote High Heath (21/E), 1932
H. Phillips (*Rept. Bot. Exch. Club*, 91, 1932). An unlocalised record
for VC20 in Stace (1975) may be the same. However, it is quite
likely that many of our former sites for *V. canina* on former wood-
pasture commons came to have only this hybrid, and it may be
under-recorded.

Viola reichenbachiana Jordan ex Boreau
Early Dog-violet
Native.
First record: 1874 (for the segregate).
Tetrad occurrence: 297 (61%).
Possibly increasing (+124%).

This is the common woodland violet on more calcareous soils
across the County, but also occasionally appears in wooded
gardens as well. It was almost certainly badly under-recorded in
Dony (1967), but also may have been genuinely increasing.
(126 tetrads: Dony, 1967; 175 tetrads: 1950-1986)

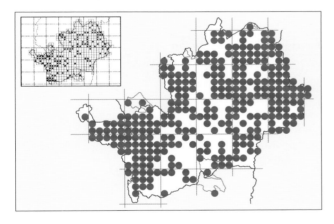

Map 179. *Viola reichenbachiana.*

Viola canina L.   UK Near Threatened
Heath Dog-violet
Native.
First record: 1874 (for the segregate).
Tetrad occurrence: 7 (1%).
Rare and decreasing (-26%).

From having been quite widespread in the early 20th century, this
is now apparently one of the County's rarer native plants, growing
in short acid grassland on heaths and in heathy woodland rides.
It was found in only seven localities during the survey: Patmore
Heath (42/M), 1986, non-flowering thereafter *J. L. Fielding*;
Broxbourne Wood (30/I), 1989 *T. J.*; rough acid grassland,
Chisel Shelf, Panshanger (21/W), 1994 *T. J.*; road verge, Bentley
Heath (29/P), 1998 *T. J./G. P. Smith*; ride, Bramfield Woods
(21/Y), 2000 *T. J.* (Hb. HTN); ride, Brickground Wood (21/T),

2000 *T. J.*; and path, Bricket Wood Common (10/F), 1999 *T. J./
G. Salisbury/G. P. Smith*. It also appeared at Burleigh Meadow,
Knebworth (22/G), 1974 *R. Hawkins*; Knebworth Park (22/F),
1983 *T. J.*; and near Peplins Wood (20/M), 1984 *T. J./B. R.
Sawford*. Although it was recorded in 12 tetrads between 1950-
1986 overall, few of these were areas where it has appeared
recently, so it may yet be under-recorded, although many of the
sites where it was recorded before 1987 were searched in vain
during the survey.
(9 tetrads: Dony, 1967; 12 tetrads: 1950-1986)

Viola palustris L.   Herts Rare
Marsh Violet
Native.
First record: 1994.

This must rank as one of the outstanding records of the
Hertfordshire Flora Survey. A few non-flowering plants were
found in damp ground near the main pond on Patmore Heath
(42/M) in 1994 *J. L. Fielding* (Hb. HTN), where its survival is
uncertain, as it has not been re-found recently. As this is a well-
studied site, this is a most extraordinary find. The plant is rare
throughout most of eastern England.

Marsh Violet Viola palustris *(leaves) Patmore Heath, 1994.*

Viola cornuta L.
Horned Pansy
Introduced: casual.
First record: 1988.

The current survey found this at four locations, all in east Herts.:
Hunsdon (41/G), 1988; Hadham Towers (41/I), 1991; Great
Hormead (43/A), 1991; Westmill: by A10 (32/T), 1992; and
Sacombe (31/J), 1998 *S. Watson*. All of these were ascribed to the
cultivated form 'Prince Henry'. It may well occur elsewhere.

Viola × *wittrockiana* Gams ex Kappert
(*V. lutea* × *V. tricolor* × *V. altaica*?)
Garden Pansy
Introduced: casual/neophyte.
First record: 1986.
Tetrad occurrence: 29 (6%).

Only when standard floras began to note that the garden pansy
back-crosses to form hybrid swarms was this taxon first recorded
at Ware tip (31/M), 1986 by C. G. Hanson. The recent survey
found similar plants, in different forms, in no less than 29 tetrads.
These long-standing hybrids, of disputed origin, which can look all

too like *Viola tricolor*, probably account for most, if not all of the so-called 'Wild Pansy' records from the past as well. Strict hybrids between *Viola arvensis* and *V. tricolor* (= *Viola × contempta* Jord.) reported in the past might also be included with these, but have not been clearly supported by specimens. A complex hybrid of *V. arvensis*, *V. tricolor* and *V. × wittrockiana* is also supposed to have been found in Herts. in 1931 (Stace, 1975), but it is hard to think how this could have been identified.

Viola tricolor L.   UK Near Threatened
Wild Pansy
Native.
First record: 1841?

The status of the true Wild Pansy in Hertfordshire is very unclear. Coleman recorded it as 'common', but his records actually refer also to *V. arvensis*. The account in Pryor (1887) goes into great detail with *V. arvensis*, including various supposed varieties, and separates the species from *V. tricolor*, for which a number of stations are recorded. There were also a number of subsequent localities for it, from Tring to Royston and south to Cheshunt. Specimens supposed to be this are included in the Graveson herbarium, from Hertford, and it was still being recorded by various people into the 1960s. Dony (1967) shows that he was unhappy with many of these records, but did not dismiss them. He merely says that he only found it once: at Bury Plantation (23/S), a site since lost. Examination of his specimen (Hb. HTN) shows that it is a hybrid. No other records are actually supported by an adequate specimen, and therefore it was thought that the true Wild Pansy may never have occurred in the County. However, one plant of a yellow-flowered variant was found on disturbed soil at Levens Green (32/L), 2003 *T. J.* (Hb. HTN), which might also have been from an introduction in such a place. It may also have been recorded at Thorley (41/Z), 2004 *J. L. Fielding*, but needs confirmation. If it does actually have a genuine claim to be a native plant, it is one of our rarest species.

Viola × contempta (Jord.) (*V. tricolor × V. arvensis*)
Native.
First authentic record: 2004.

Quite a number of plants of what seem genuinely to be this hybrid were found in a bean field near Thorley (41/Z), 2004 *J. L. Fielding* (conf. T. J.) (Hb. HTN). Plants which may have been true *Viola tricolor* were also found nearby in 2003, but not confirmed (see above). It is possible that it may be overlooked elsewhere.

Viola arvensis Murray
Field Pansy *or* **Heart's-ease**
Introduced: archaeophyte.
First record: 1838.
Tetrad occurrence: 387 (79%).
Stable (-2%).

Despite the confusion with garden pansies, outlined above, and the effects of agricultural pesticides, this remains a frequent weed of field margins and waste ground across the County, only becoming scarce on damp clays. It comes in both a pale yellow form and in forms with more or less violet on the lateral petals, which may account for some of the older *V. tricolor* records mentioned above.
(376 tetrads: Dony, 1967; 388 tetrads: 1950-1986)

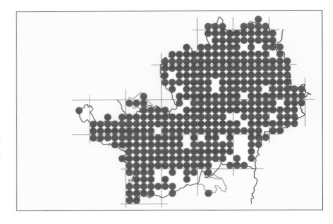

Map 180. *Viola arvensis*.

Passifloraceae (Passion-flowers)

Genus: Passiflora

Passiflora caerulea L.
Passion-flower
Introduced: casual.
First record: 1995.

One plant was found on sludge dumps at Rye Meads Sewage Works (31/V), 1995 *C. G. Hanson*; and non-flowering plants were found growing in pavement cracks in Rickmansworth (09/R), 2003 *P. J. Ellison* and at Ashwell (23/U), 2008 *T. J.*

Cucurbitaceae (Pumpkin family)

Genus: Cucumis

Cucumis melo L.
Melon
Introduced: casual.
First record: 1959.

During the 1960s-1970s, this and other Cucurbitaceae became frequent on tips, but modern methods of waste management have restricted these occurrences. The current survey found it frequently at Rye Meads Sewage Works on sludge dumps (31/V) *A. M. Boucher/G. Hanson*, but only twice elsewhere: Ware tip (31/M), 1987 *C. G. Hanson*; and Pole Hole tip (41/L), 1989 *S. Watson*.

Cucumis sativus L.
Cucumber
Introduced: casual.
First record: *c.*1960.

Never as frequent as Melon on waste tips, this was recorded from seven sites between 1970 and 1983, being last noted at Rye Meads Sewage Works (31/V), 1983 *C. G. Hanson*.

Genus: *Citrullus*

Citrullus lanatus (Thunb.) Matsum and Nakai
Water Melon
Introduced: casual.
First record: 1934.

As with its relatives, this became frequent on tips between 1960 and 1980, but has since decreased. It was found on nine sites between 1970 and 1986, but during the survey was only found at Rye Meads Sewage Works (31/V), where it was frequent until 1997 *A. M. Boucher/C. G. Hanson*.

Genus: *Cucurbita*

Cucurbita pepo L.
Marrow
First record: *c.*1960.

Frequent on tips across the County, having been recorded between 1970 and 1986 at 12 localities, but only from three localities during the survey: Ware tip (31/M), 1991 *C. G. Hanson*; Waterford tip (31/C), 1992 *C. G. Hanson*; and frequently at Rye Meads Sewage Works (31/V), with the last record in 1997 *A. M. Boucher/ C. G. Hanson*.

Plants recorded as *Cucurbita maxima* Duchesne ex Lam. **Pumpkin** from Rye Meads, 1984-1995, *A. M. B./C. G. H.* are probably botanically identical with *C. pepo* (*comm.*: E. J. Clement).

Genus: *Bryonia*

Bryonia dioica Jacq.
White Bryony
Native.
First record: *c.*1820.
Tetrad occurrence: 436 (89%).
Probably stable (+4%).

This sole native representative of the family remains widespread and common in scrub and hedgerows across the County, only becoming scarce on the damp, acidic London Clay. The apparent increase is almost certainly down to more thorough recording. (399 tetrads: Dony, 1967; 411 tetrads: 1950-1986)

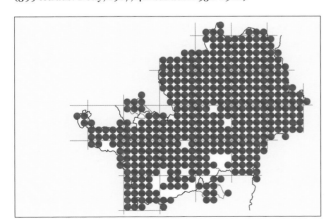

Map 181. *Bryonia dioica.*

Genus: *Ecballium*

Ecballium elaterium (L.) A. Rich.
Squirting Cucumber
Introduced: casual.
First record: 1921.

Having first been found as a casual in 1921, from medicinal herb cultivation at Hitchin (12/Z), a plant appeared spontaneously in a garden at Common Rise, Hitchin (12/Z) (on the site of the medicinal plant field) in 1984 *E. Butterfield* (det. T. J.) (Hb. HTN), illustrating remarkably how long-persistent seeds of some species can be! It has also appeared in the grounds of Bayfordbury (31/A), 1983 *C. G. Hanson* (Hb. HTN), where it was also formerly cultivated.

Genus: *Sicyos*

Sicyos angulatus L.
Bur Cucumber
Introduced: casual.
First (only) record: 1991.

This was found on a tip at Puckeridge (32/W), 1991 *S. Watson* (det. E. J. Clement) (Hb. HTN).

Salicaceae (Willow family)

Genus: *Populus*

The poplars, of north Herts. especially, were the subject of some extensive investigation by J. E. Little of Hitchin in the early part of the 20th century (Little, 1916), but his views on species, varieties and hybrids may no longer be tenable in some cases.

Populus alba L.
White Poplar
Introduced: neophyte.
First record: 1750.
Tetrad occurrence: 90 (18%).
Increasing as an introduced tree (+274%).

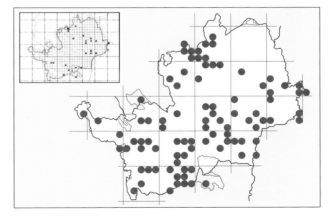

Map 182. *Populus alba.*

There is very little evidence of this species spreading by seed naturally. It has long been planted in parks for ornament, but more recently has featured as screen planting around developments, or as part of amenity plantings. It frequently

spreads by suckering.
(23 tetrads: Dony, 1967; 48 tetrads: 1950-1986)

Populus × *canescens* (Aiton) Smith (*P. alba* × *P. tremula*).
Grey Poplar
Introduced: planted/neophyte.
First record: 1849.
Tetrad occurrence: 107 (22%).
Increased? (+154%).

Previous recorders may have overlooked or ignored this, because
its apparent increase seems unlikely, even as a planted tree. It was
formerly regarded as a separate species, and can be mistaken for
Aspen or White Poplar in some cases. It was evidently a favourite
ornamental tree, especially in parklands in south Herts., and in
hedgerows on Chalk Marl and Woburn Sands. It suckers freely.
(40 tetrads: Dony, 1967; 52 tetrads: 1950-1986)

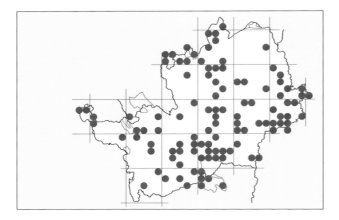

Map 183. *Populus* × *canescens*.

Populus tremula L.
Aspen
Native.
First record: 1750.
Tetrad occurrence: 214 (44%).
Apparently increasing (+42%).

Aspen is a characteristic tree forming cloned thickets or stands
in damp woodlands on more or less acidic clays, mainly in the
south and centre of the County. It is possible that it is genuinely
increasing in its natural wet woodland habitats, as well as
colonising new sites around gravel pits. It was regarded by
woodmen as a 'weed' in woodlands, but it is an important

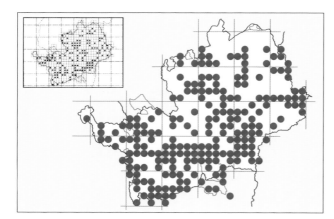

Map 184. *Populus tremula*.

colonising species on damp ground, and is valuable for a number
of scarce insects.
(143 tetrads: Dony, 1967; 169 tetrads: 1950-1986)

Populus nigra L.
Black Poplar
Native.
First record: 1676.
Tetrad occurrence: 23 (5%).

Dony (1967) gave the impression that this was no longer a
genuinely wild tree in Hertfordshire, although he did draw
attention to it having formerly been a feature of the lower Lea
Valley. Research into the status and occurrence of trees across the
County has shown that it remains a rare native tree, but its natural
distribution is obscured by planting. In west Herts., it has been
shown to be the dominant hedgerow tree around Long Marston,
Wilstone, *etc.* (81/T, X, Y; 91/B, C, G), where many trees appear
to have been planted in the early 19th century, forming part of a
large-scale planting which extends across the Vale of Aylesbury
into Bucks. However, it also seems to occur in the area naturally,
especially by the upper reaches of the River Thame (81/T, X,
Y; 91/B), where trees of the native subspecies *betulifolia* Pursh
(Dippel) occur (infested by their characteristic petiole spiral-gall).
In the Lea Valley tributaries, ssp. *betulifolia* still occurs as old
trees by the R. Ash at Wareside (31/X) and Widford (41/D), where

Black Poplar Populus nigra *Mardocks, Wareside, 1988.*

a large female tree was found in 2008; and by the Stort at Bishop's
Stortford (42/V) and Sawbridgeworth (41/X). Old trees are also
recorded at Hoddesdon (30/Z), and as an apparently planted
stand at Bengeo Hall (31/G). In south Herts. the native subspecies
has been found at Elstree (19/S) by the Tykes Water, while it has
also been found to occur rarely at Bourne End (00/C). At Hitchin,
J. E. Little recorded several trees, assumed to be planted, although
the group of trees which is still by the River Hiz at Ickleford
(13/V) looks very natural. Another old tree near Great Wymondley
(22/E), which was recorded by Little as having been felled in 1916,
survives as a triple-stemmed coppice stool by the road. It is likely
to have been planted, as is the old tree by Tingley Wood (13/K).
More recently, trees have been planted in the Lee Valley Park at
Waltham Cross (30/Q), and near Amwell Quarry (31/R), as well as
near Tring (90/P) and Bourne End (00/D), from reputedly native
sources. As the tree's natural habitats of eroding river banks and
shingle or mud bars are habitats no longer really found in our
area, owing to river engineering and low river flows, this may be
the only way this fine tree can survive, and especially as most of

the old trees appear to be male. The species was recorded from 23 tetrads during the survey (but as recently planted in several of these). Older records are insufficient and not reliable enough for comparison, although many old trees around Hertford are known to have been lost since 1900.

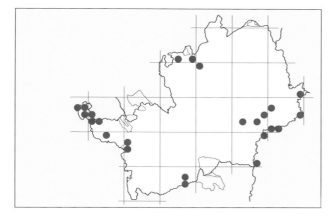

Map 185. *Populus nigra* ssp. *betulifolia*.

Planted trees of the fastigiate variety '*italica*' (Lombardy Poplar) and the similar hybrid with *P.* × *canadensis*: '*plantierensis*' have also been recorded across the County, the former having been popular 19th and early 20th century ornamental features.

Populus × *canadensis* Moench (*P. nigra* × *P. deltoides*)
Hybrid Black Poplar
Introduced: planted.
First record: 1916.
Tetrad occurrence: 255 (52%).

Dony (1967) stated that this was planted across the County, but gave little more information. A map is given to show just how much it has become a very commonly planted tree, but there is no suggestion that these have become naturalised. The main hybrid appears to be var. *serotina*, or one of its related cultivars, but there appear to be occasional occurrences of var. *marilandica*, which can look more like the true Black Poplar, and therefore can cause problems with identification. Some of these, like the fine tree by the Ash Brook near Purwell (22/E), are superb features of the landscape in their own right. Other cultivars also probably occur, but have not been studied in any detail. Early records of *Populus deltoides* itself would need confirmation.
(50 tetrads: Dony, 1967; 57 tetrads: 1950-1986)

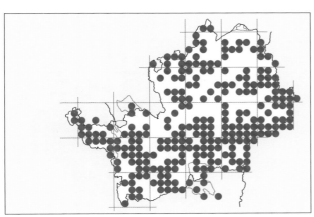

Map 186. *Populus* × *canadensis*.

Populus trichocarpa Torrey and A. Gray ex Hook
Western Balsam-poplar
Introduced: mostly planted.
First record: *c.*1950?
Tetrad occurrence: 11 (2%).

This was first recognised by botanists in the County at West Hyde (TQ09/F?) with an undated specimen by G. Matthews (Hb. BM), (Dony, mss. index). Since then, there were no records until the current survey, when it has been found to be fairly widespread, especially near rivers, usually obviously planted. However, a mature tree at Westmill Gravel Pit, Ware (31/I), 2006 *T. J.* appeared to have developed naturally.

Populus × *jackii* Sarg. (*P. deltoides* × *P. balsamifera*)
Balm-of-Gilead
Introduced: neophyte.
First record: *c.*1920.
Tetrad occurrence: 23 (5%).

There is uncertainty over the records for this, especially in the past, owing to taxonomic confusion. The first record of a 'balsam poplar' in Dony's ms. index dates to the early 1920s, from The Node, Codicote *J. E. Little*, recorded under the name '*Populus tacamahacca*'. There were also early records of '*P. gileadensis*' and '*P. candicans*'. The usual planted balsam-poplar is a hybrid, which often develops suckering stands on wood margins and in hedgerows. However, it is likely that some records may refer to the true **Eastern Balsam-poplar** *P. balsamifera* L., or the cultivated hybrid '**Balsam Spire**' *P. trichocarpa* × *P. balsamifera*, which have narrower crowns. Balm-of-Gilead was recorded in 23 tetrads during the survey, usually under the name *Populus candicans*, most of which probably refer to the hybrid. They may be more widespread.

Genus: *Salix*

Early studies on willows in north Herts. were also carried out by J. E. Little (1922), but not followed up with more widespread studies. His ms. notebooks contain much information and detailed observations of specimens, and Hb. CGE holds many of his specimens. With the current survey, much help has been given with the identification of voucher specimens for this difficult genus by R. D. Meikle. Many of the hybrid taxa are still probably under-recorded, and the heavily disturbed wetlands around gravel pits offer great opportunities for more to emerge.

Salix pentandra L.
Bay-leaved Willow
Introduced [native in the U.K.].
First record: 1843.
Tetrad occurrence: 8 (2%).
Increased? (+166%).

This has always been a rather rare shrub or small tree in Herts., apparently always originally introduced. It can persist for long periods, as at West Mill, Ickleford (13/Q), where it was first recorded by J. E. Little in 1920. Dony recorded it from four tetrads, but one of his records, for Tednambury Lock, appears to be an error for *S. triandra*. After Dony's *Flora* there were also records from near Stevenage (22/G) and near Purwell (22/E) *F. Bentley*; and from Woodhall, Hatfield (21/F), 1986 *T. J.* It was then recorded during the current survey from: West Mill, Ickleford

(13/Q) 1991, *etc. T. J.*; by the R. Beane, Hertford (31/G), 1990 *M. J. Hicks* (det. *T. J.*); near Briggens (41/A), 1989 *S. Watson* (Hb. HTN); Mill Green (21/F), 1996 *A. D. Marshall*; old railway, Bushy Leys, Welwyn Garden City (21/L), 1996 *T. J.*; Smallford Pit (10/Y), 1992 *T. J.*; by the River Red, Redbourn Common (11/A), 1988 *T. J.*; and from Bovingdon Brickworks (00/B), 1998 *T. J.* (Hb. HTN).
(4(3?) tetrads: Dony, 1967; 6 tetrads: 1950-1986)

Salix × ehrhartiana Smith (*S. pentandra × S. alba*)
Ehrhart's Willow
Introduced: planted.
First documented record: 1998.

There is a reference to this hybrid being in Herts. included in Stace (1975). Planted trees were found at Eastwick (41/F), 1998 *S. Watson*.

Salix lucida Muhl.
Shining Willow
Introduced: planted, possibly seeding.
First record: 1994.

Several mature trees and apparent seedlings of this rarely introduced North American species were found at Silvermead, Broxbourne (30/T), 1994 *A. M. Boucher* and initially mis-identified as *S. pentandra* or a hybrid. A specimen collected in 1995 *T. J.* has now been identified by R. D. Meikle (Hb. HTN).

Salix fragilis L.
Crack Willow
Introduced: archaeophyte (or native?)
First record: 1838.
Tetrad occurrence: 312 (64%).
Increasing (+29%).

The native status of this species has been questioned (Preston *et al.*, 2002), but it does appear to be quite natural in riparian woodland. It is a frequent tree, often pollarded and sometimes planted, but also naturally occurring by the main rivers and streams in the County. It has also become a dominant tree with other willows round old gravel pits, and forms a characteristic regenerating swamp when allowed to collapse into the water margins of these. However, the increase in records has partly come from areas away from obvious rivers, where it has been found to be quite widespread by ditches, sometimes in new plantings, and therefore some of the apparent increase is down to better recording. The species is usually represented by var.

fragilis, but var. *furcata* Ser. ex Gaudin is recorded from a few localities, *e.g.* Ashwell Springs (23/U), 1994 *S. M. Walters* (conf. P. D. Sell) (Hb. HTN); and var. *decipiens* (Hoffm.)W. D. J. Koch was found at Long Marston (81/Y), 2000 *T. J.* (Hb. HTN) and at Stanborough (21/F), 1999 *T. J.* (Hb. HTN).
(230 tetrads: Dony, 1967; 266 tetrads: 1950-1986)

Salix × rubens Schrank (*S. fragilis × S. alba*)
Hybrid Crack-willow
Introduced or native?
First record: 1924.

Although Dony (1967) lists this, and notes that it was first recorded by J. E. Little, there seems to be some confusion between it and the so-called Cricket-bat Willow *S. alba* var. *caerulea*. *Salix × rubens* occurs naturally, especially in disturbed sites around gravel pits where the parents come together, and is probably widespread. Burton (1983) gives four unlocalised tetrad records for our area. However, it was only positively recorded in eight localities during our survey: Waterford Gravel Pit (31/C), 1995 *A. M. Boucher* (det. R. D. Meikle) (Hb. HTN); Stanstead Abbots Gravel Pits and Rye Meads (31/V), 1996 *T. J.* (where most of the willows appeared to be this); Amwell Quarry (31/R), 1997 *T. J.* (where it is frequent); Ivel Springs (23/M), 1996 *T. J.*; Birklands, St Albans (10/S), 1997 *T. J.*; and Brunswick Park (29/W), 1998 *T. J.* Nothovar. '*basfordiana*', derived from the hybrid with *Salix alba* ssp. *vitellina*, was recorded from King George's Fields, Barnet (29/M), 1989, *A. W. Vaughan* (det. R. D. Meikle), probably planted; and from Ivel Springs, Baldock (23/M), 2008 *T. J.*, where old trees of this form had been overlooked for some time.

Salix alba L.
White Willow
Introduced or native?
First record: 1838.
Tetrad occurrence: 245 (50%).
Increased (+37%).

As with Crack Willow, this has been questioned as a native. It has also benefited from the creation of gravel pits. However, it appears to be a natural part of semi-natural riparian fen, especially in more calcareous conditions, and is often the dominant tree by streams flowing from the Chalk in the north of the County, for example. It is also very widespread by streams on the Boulder Clay.
(170 tetrads: Dony, 1967; 191 tetrads: 1950-1986)

Var. *vitellina* (L.) Stokes **Golden Willow** occurs quite widely, often as planted shrubs or small trees in amenity plantings near

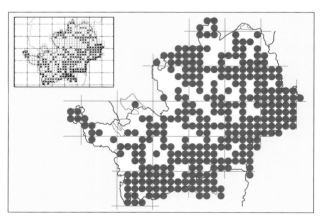

Map 187. *Salix fragilis.*

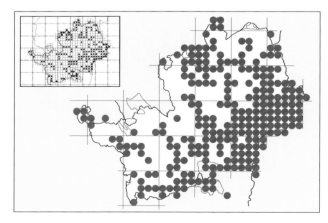

Map 188. *Salix alba.*

rivers, but sometimes apparently self-sown, *e.g.* Pitstone Quarry (91/M), 1995 *T. J.*; Moor Mill pit (10/L), 1994 *T. J.*; by R. Stort, Redericks (41/R), 1991 *T. J.* Var. *caerulea* (Smith) Dumort **Cricket-bat Willow** is frequently planted as a timber crop in river valleys, but does not appear to occur naturally.

Salix × *sepulchralis* Simonkai (*S. alba* × *S. babylonica*)
Weeping Willow
Introduced: usually planted.
First record: 1988.
Tetrad occurrence: 10 (2%).

This appears to have been first recorded (as nothovar. *chrysocoma* (Dode) Meikle) at Walsworth (13/V), 1988 *T. J.*, but has probably been present elsewhere for a long time previously and ignored. It is frequently planted, and does not normally show signs of regenerating naturally, although it was identified as young, apparently self-sown trees at Frogmore Pit, Aston (22/V), 1991 *T. J.* (det. R. D. Meikle) (Hb. HTN). The survey only produced ten records, but it is much more frequent than this would suggest.

Salix triandra L.
Almond Willow
Native?
First record: 1838.
Tetrad occurrence: 19 (4%).
Increased or stable? (+39%).

This is now apparently rather rare in the County, even if it was recorded more frequently during the survey than in the 1960s. It was regarded as quite frequent in the 19th century (Pryor, 1887). It might be overlooked, because several tetrads where it was found in the 1980s had no record in the current survey. It occurs near water, on river banks and in wet fen woodland, occasionally in damp ground elsewhere. However, its status in the County seems questionable, as many sites are or were former planted osier beds, and it is known to have been used for basket making. Young bushes also seem to be rare.
(13 tetrads: Dony, 1967; 23 tetrads: 1950-1986)

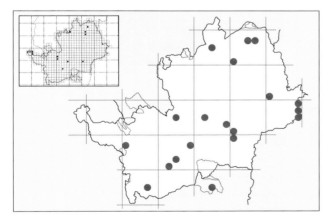

Map 189. *Salix triandra.*

Salix × *mollissima* Hoffm. ex Elwert (*S. triandra* × *S. viminalis*)
Native?
First (only) record: 1922.

This hybrid was recorded from Purwell (22/E?), 1922 *J. E. Little* (*Rep. Bot. Exch. Club*: 405 (1923)). The record was overlooked by Dony (1967), but included in his ms. index.

Salix purpurea L.
Purple Willow
Native.
First record: 1839.
Tetrad occurrence: 23 (5%).
Decreasing (-30%).

A species of calcareous fen peat, where it occurs by streams and in open scrub or hedgerows, rarely by field ditches where spring water is flowing. It was apparently also formerly used as an osier in some areas. As fen sites have deteriorated, it becomes shaded out, and there is evidence of its gradual loss across the County. (31 tetrads: Dony, 1967; 35 tetrads: 1950-1986)

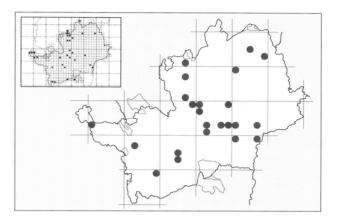

Map 190. *Salix purpurea.*

Salix × *rubra* Hudson (*S. purpurea* × *S. viminalis*)
Green-leaved Willow
Probably introduced.
First (only) record: 1924.

There is one record of this: from Purwell, Hitchin, 1924 (Dony, 1967). It was probably planted.

Salix × *forbyana* Smith (*S. purpurea* × *S. viminalis* × *S. cinerea*)
Fine Osier
Introduced.
First record: c.1960.

Recorded in Dony (1967) from Kimpton Mill (11/Z), and also listed for VC20 in Stace (1975).

[*Salix daphnoides* Vill.
European Violet-willow

A record given in James (1990b) from Amwell Quarry was an error. The species may be planted elsewhere, but is not so far confirmed from the County, although there is a record by A. W. Graveson from beside the Dunmow Road, east of Bishop's Stortford, 1921, that may have been in Herts. (Dony, ms. index).]

Salix viminalis L.
Osier
Introduced: archaeophyte.
First record: 1838.
Tetrad occurrence: 164 (33%).
Increasing (+64%).

Formerly cultivated for basket making and hedging, this is now more often planted as an ornamental in amenity plantings, but is also frequently self-sown by gravel pits, rivers, *etc.*, where it

hybridises freely with several other willow species.
(95 tetrads: Dony, 1967; 121 tetrads: 1950-1986)

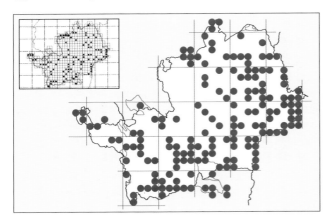

Map 191. *Salix viminalis.*

Salix × sericans Tausch ex A. Kerner (*S. viminalis × S. caprea*)
Broad-leaved Osier
Native and introduced.
First record: 1956.
Tetrad occurrence: 44 (9%).

This readily-identifiable hybrid is now known to be widespread across the County wherever the two parents meet, especially in disturbed areas round old gravel pits, but also in wet woodland elsewhere. It is occasionally planted for ornament.

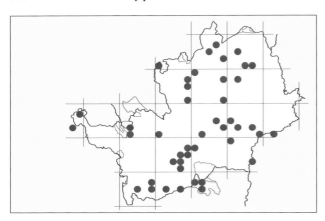

Map 192. *Salix × sericans.*

Salix × calodendron Wimmer
(*S. viminalis × S. caprea × S. cinerea*)
Holme Willow
Introduced.
First record: *c.*1920.

There have been no further records of this triple hybrid since J. E. Little found it at St Ippollitts and Ickleford (Dony, 1967).

Salix × holosericea Willd. (*S. viminalis × S. cinerea*)
Silky-leaved Osier
Native or introduced?
Tetrad occurrence: 10 (2%).
First record: *c.*1840.

This hybrid willow occurs in wet scrub, by rivers and streams. Dony (1967) mentions that it was recorded by Coleman and Pryor, and by J. E. Little, but was evidently not familiar with it. The current survey found it in ten tetrads, mostly in southern Herts.,

but it is probably overlooked elsewhere.

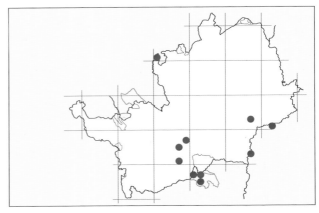

Map 193. *Salix × holosericea.*

Salix caprea L.
Goat Willow
Native.
First record: 1750.
Tetrad occurrence: 431 (88%).
Increasing (+31%).

As a native this is a species of semi-natural woodland and old wooded hedgerows on damp soils, but it has also spread into disturbed sites, along with other willows, where it hybridises freely. There is evidence of considerable increase in the last 30 years as a result.
(313 tetrads: Dony, 1967; 360 tetrads: 1950-1986)

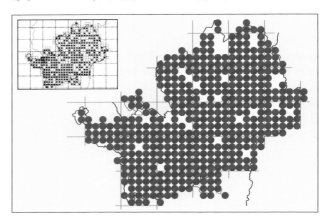

Map 194. *Salix caprea.*

Salix × capreola J. Kerner ex Anderson (*S. caprea × S. aurita*)
Native.
First record: 1923.

There have been no records of this hybrid since J. E. Little found it at Hitchin and Langley (Dony, 1967).

Salix × reichardtii A. Kerner (*S. caprea × S. cinerea*)
Native.
First record: 1990.
Tetrad occurrence: 33 (67%).

Although this was not formally recorded until 1990 at Hitchin (13/V) *T. J.*, it has probably been widespread for a long time, although disturbance to semi-natural habitats has no doubt added to its frequency.

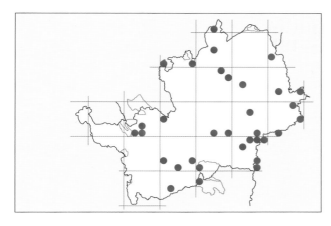

Map 195. *Salix × reichardtii.*

Salix cinerea L.
Grey Willow
Native.
First record: 1843.
Tetrad occurrence: 346 (71%).
Increased (+34%).

Native by ponds, streams and in marshy hollows in old pastures, but also readily colonising newly-created wetlands, and hybridising with other willows.
(246 tetrads: Dony, 1967; 283 tetrads: 1950-1986)

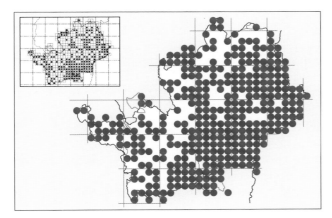

Map 196. *Salix cinerea.*

There are two distinct subspecies in the County:

The nominate subspecies *cinerea* is a rather local shrub of fen peat, and ditches, *etc.* on more calcareous soils, occurring mostly

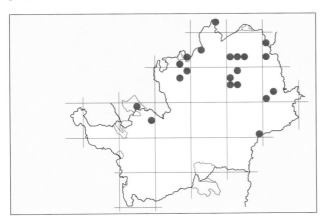

Map 197. *Salix cinerea* ssp. *cinerea.*

---

in north-eastern Hertfordshire (Map 197), where it is probably under-recorded. It was confirmed from 20 tetrads in the survey period.

Subspecies *oleifolia* Macreight (Map 198) is found widely on a range of soils, but is most frequent on the less calcareous clays and river valley gravels in the south of the County, although the two subspecies overlap. Recorded from 250 tetrads, although many of the records where no subspecies was determined will be this as well.

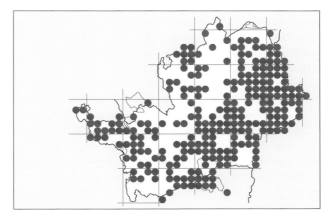

Map 198. *Salix cinerea* ssp. *oleifolia.*

Salix × multinervis Döll (*S. cinerea × S. aurita*)
Native.
First record: 1924.

Dony (1967) found this a couple of times: at Bricket Wood and Aldenham, in areas formerly with heath communities, and J. E. Little found it as far north as Hitchin. It was re-found at Bricket Wood Common (10/F), 2003-7 *J. Edgington.* During the survey specimens that appeared to have its characteristics were also found in a number of other places, but most of these were thought by R. D. Meikle to be extreme forms of *S. cinerea* ssp. *oleifolia.* Two records, from Patmore Heath (42/M), 1995 *T. J.*; and Oaklands Gravel Pit (10/Z), 1995 *T. J.* may also be errors. Its real status in the County is obscure, even where *S. aurita* was once recorded.

Salix aurita L.   Herts Rare
Eared Willow
Native.
First record: 1839.
Decreased (-87%), extinct as a native species?

Dony (1967) recorded this from no less than seven tetrads in heathy areas of south-east and central Herts. Repeated attempts to find it in its former localities around Broxbourne Woods and Bricket Wood, *etc.*, have failed, although possible hybrids with *S. cinerea* are occasionally recorded, but remain mostly unconfirmed. However, a single bush of what appears to be the species was found by the R. Colne near Stockers Lake (09/L), 2002 *G. Salisbury/J. Saunders* (Hb. HTN), a most unlikely locality for a species of heathland, and probably introduced; while a certainly planted specimen was found by the old R. Stort at Hunsdon Mead (41/A), 2006 *T. J.* It may yet be re-discovered in one of its former native sites, but it was really a species of historic wood-pasture commons, and succumbed following their disuse as grazing.

Salix repens L.

Creeping Willow

Native.

First record: 1838.

Very rare.

Tetrad occurrence: 3 (<1%).

Never common in Herts., this has only ever been recorded from wet heaths in a few places, such as Bricket Wood Common, Croxley Common Moor, Batchworth Heath, Hatfield Park and Northaw. It was found in very small quantity in a clearing by the main ride at Hawkshead Wood (20/B) in 1984 *T. J.* (Hb. HTN). During the current survey it was re-recorded on a regular basis at the well-known site on the Roundings, Hertford Heath (31/K), where it has been well-tended, but is very vulnerable to scrub encroachment and to accidental fires, as well as possibly to hybridisation with *S. cinerea*. Surveys carried out of S.S.S.Is in the county also revealed very small, vulnerable patches at Well Wood, Northaw (20/R), 2004; and at Redwell Wood (20/B), 2005 *G. J. Wyatt*, both known to have formerly been wood pasture sites, and the latter very close to the site at Hawkshead Wood.

(2 tetrads: Dony, 1967; 3 tetrads: 1950-1986)

Salix elaeagnos Scop.

Olive Willow

Introduced: neophyte.

First record: 1992.

This was found growing as an escape from the side of the Lee Navigation at Great Amwell (31/R), 1992 *A. M. Boucher* (Hb. HTN), and has also been recorded rarely as a planted shrub elsewhere.

Brassicaceae (Cabbage family)

Genus: *Sisymbrium*

Sisymbrium irio L.

London Rocket

Introduced: casual.

First record: 1849.

A rare casual of waste ground, formerly a casual weed of arable. The only record since 1929 (Dony, 1967) was of a single plant on the roadside at Wallington (23/W), 1996 *T. J.* (Hb. HTN).

Sisymbrium loeselii L.

False London Rocket

Introduced: neophyte.

First record: 1912.

At one time frequent on waste tips, now scarce. It was last seen at Blackbridge tip (11/X), 1970; Bulls Mill tip (31/D), 1970; Moor Mill tip (10/L), 1976; and Waterford tip (31/C), 1982 *C. G. Hanson*. During the current survey, it was found in abundance on former tipped ground by the railway at Woolmer Green, 1994 *T. J./T. C. G. Rich/G. P. Smith* (Hb. HTN); and on earth banks at Hertford (31/L), 1993 *A. M. Boucher* (Hb. Boucher).

Sisymbrium altissimum L.

Tall Rocket

Introduced: neophyte.

First record: 1909.

Tetrad occurrence: 18 (4%).

Decreasing (-59%).

This apparently became quite a widespread weed of waste places, railway yards, *etc.* after the First World War, but has decreased substantially, especially since 1980. It remains fairly frequent in the lower Lea Valley, and around St Albans, but is almost absent elsewhere.

(42 tetrads: Dony, 1967; 54 tetrads: 1950-1986)

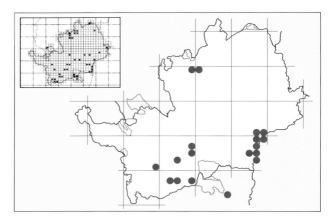

Map 199. *Sisymbrium altissimum.*

Sisymbrium orientale L.

Eastern Rocket

Introduced: neophyte.

First record: 1912.

Tetrad occurrence: 38 (8%).

Decreasing (-33%).

Having become a frequent weed of waste places by the 1960s (Dony, 1967), this plant has since decreased again, although it is still fairly frequent in urban areas.

(54 tetrads: Dony, 1967; 68 tetrads: 1950-1986)

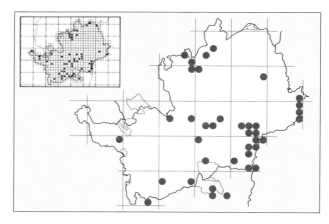

Map 200. *Sisymbrium orientale.*

Sisymbrium erysimoides Desf.

French Rocket

Introduced: casual.

First (only) record: 1956.

Its only record remains as a wool alien at Wymondley sidings

(22/D), 1956 *J. G. Dony* (given in error as 1959 in Dony, 1967) (Dony, ms. index).

Sisymbrium officinale (L.) Scop.
Hedge Mustard
Introduced: archaeophyte.
First record: 1814.
Tetrad occurrence: 464 (95%).
Possibly increased (+4%).

A frequent, rather scruffy weed of nutrient-rich, bare ground, waste places, *etc*. It is found almost ubiquitously across the County.
(423 tetrads: Dony, 1967; 426 tetrads: 1950-1986)

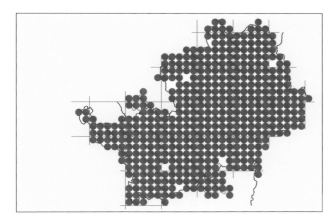

Map 201. *Sisymbrium officinale.*

Genus: *Descurainia*

Descurainia sophia (L.) Webb ex Prantl
Flixweed
Introduced: archaeophyte.
First record: 1838.
Tetrad occurrence: 13 (3%).
Possibly increased (+107%).

This is usually a casual species of waste places, but can occur as a colonist of arable fields on light chalky or sandy soils, as it does in East Anglia, where it is an ancient part of the flora. It has, for example, appeared occasionally at Therfield Heath (34/K), a habitat akin to those in Breckland. Elsewhere, it turns up occasionally on waste ground.
(6 tetrads: Dony, 1967; 11 tetrads: 1950-1986)

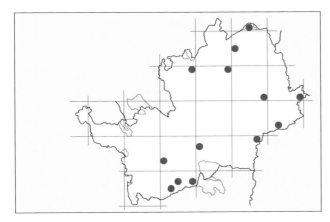

Map 202. *Descurainia sophia.*

Descurainia brachycarpa (Richardson) O. E. Schulz
Tansy-mustard
Introduced: casual.
First (only) record: 1924.

There have been no records since this was found at Ware (Dony, 1967).

Genus: *Alliaria*

Alliaria petiolata (M. Bieb.) Cav. and Grande
Garlic Mustard *or* **Jack-by-the-hedge**
Native.
First record: 1750.
Tetrad occurrence: 471 (96%).
Probably stable (-2 %).

A very frequent plant of roadside hedges and margins of woodland on moderately rich soil, only avoiding the most acid or very damp conditions. Although it is recorded from more tetrads than in 1967, there is no evidence of an increase.
(457 tetrads: Dony, 1967; 458 tetrads: 1950-1986)

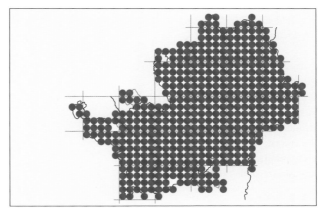

Map 203. *Alliaria petiolata.*

Genus: *Arabidopsis*

Arabidopsis thaliana (L.) Heynh.
Thale Cress
Native.
First record: 1838.
Tetrad occurrence: 237 (48%).
Possibly increasing (+29%).

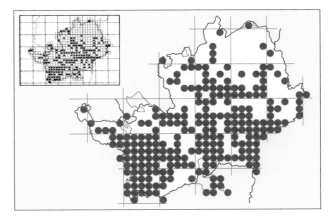

Map 204. *Arabidopsis thaliana.*

A frequent annual of walls, gardens, bare sandy ground and waste places, but easily overlooked, especially after it has dropped seed. Some of the apparent increase may be down to increased recording effort rather than to a real increase in occurrence.
(175 tetrads: Dony, 1967; 203 tetrads: 1950-1986)

Genus: *Myagrum*

Myagrum perfoliatum L.
Mitre Cress
Introduced: casual.
First (only) record: 1912.

Only recorded once, at Hertford (TL31) (Dony, 1967).

Genus: *Isatis*

Isatis tinctoria L.
Woad
Introduced: casual.
First record: 1996.

Six plants appeared in grassland at Bayfordbury (31/A), 1996 *A. M. Boucher/C. G. Hanson*, perhaps as the result of deliberate introduction.

Genus: *Bunias*

Bunias orientalis L.
Warty-cabbage
Introduced: neophyte.
First record: 1877.
Tetrad occurrence: 26 (5%).
Increasing steadily (+253%).

Having been a casual of waste ground and chalk pits, *etc.* for 100 years, this has begun to establish itself as quite a frequent weed of waste places, sometimes by arable fields, persisting in some sites for long periods. It is particularly frequent around Welwyn Garden City, Ware and Baldock, in the last of which it has remained round the station for 136 years, despite frequent attempts to exterminate it (and all other weeds!).
(7 tetrads: Dony, 1967; 13 tetrads: 1950-1986)

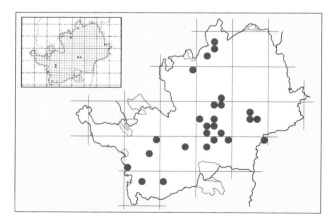

Map 205. *Bunias orientalis.*

Genus: *Erysimum*

Erysimum repandum L.
Spreading Treacle-mustard
Introduced: casual.
First record: 1845.

Only recorded from Hertford, 1845 and Ware, 1914 (Dony, 1967).

Erysimum jugicola Jordan (= *E. helveticum* (Jacq.) DC.)
Introduced: casual.
First (only) record: 1993.

About ten plants of this alpine garden plant appeared with other casuals on an earth bank by King's Meads (31/L), 1993 *A. M. Boucher* (Hb. Boucher) (Burton, 1994).

Erysimum cheiranthoides L.
Treacle-mustard
Introduced: archaeophyte.
First record: 1820.
Tetrad occurrence: 57 (12%).
Decreased (-47%).

Formerly quite widespread as an arable weed, especially in south Herts., Treacle-mustard is now scarce in this habitat, owing to the effects of herbicides, although it can sometimes develop in field margins later in the season. It otherwise appears as a casual in waste places.
(102 tetrads: Dony, 1967; 117 tetrads: 1950-1986)

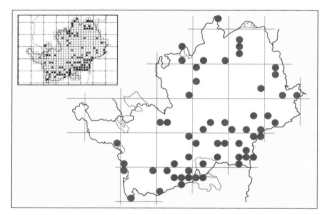

Map 206. *Erysimum cheiranthoides.*

Erysimum × marshallii (Henfr.) Bois.
(*E. decumbens* × *E. perofskianum*)
Siberian Wallflower
Introduced: casual.
First (only) record: 1970.

This was recorded as an escape on Moor Mill tip (10/L), 1970 *C. G. Hanson* (as *E. allionii*).

Erysimum cheiri (L.) Crantz
Wallflower
Introduced: neophyte.
First record: 1838.
Tetrad occurrence: 13 (3%).

An occasionally established plant of walls and bare ground, but more usually a garden throw-out. The well-established colony on Hertford Castle walls (31/G) has been known for 160 years at least. Dony (1967) did not really account for the species.

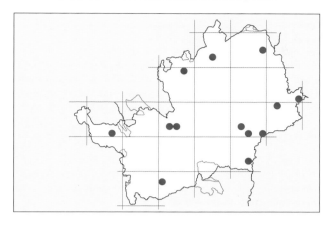

Map 207. *Erysimum cheiri.*

Genus: *Hesperis*

Hesperis matronalis L.
Dame's-violet
Introduced: neophyte.
First record: 1856.
Tetrad occurrence: 81 (17%).
Increased (+650%).
Dony did not have enough records to bother with a map, although he did know of it from ten localities from 1950-1966 (Dony, ms. index). It now occurs widely as a more-or-less established escape in many places, such as roadsides, waste land, tips and so on.
(10 tetrads: Dony mss.; 33 tetrads: 1950-1986)

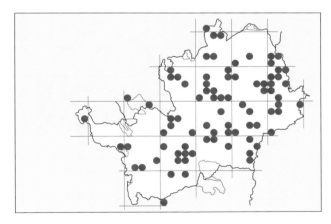

Map 208. *Hesperis matronalis.*

Genus: *Malcolmia*

Malcolmia maritima (L.) W. T. Aiton
Virginia Stock
Introduced: casual.
First record: 1922.

Occasional in the past on tips, but apparently not so now. The last record was from Blackbridge tip (11/X), 1971 *C. G. Hanson.*

Malcolmia africana (L.) R. Br.
African Stock
Introduced: casual.
First record: 1907.

There have been no further records since it was found at Ware, 1916 (Dony, 1967).

[*Malcolmia ramosissima* (Desf.) Thell.

A record of this in Dony (1967) was in error. The specimen (Hb. HTN) was re-determined as *M. maritima* by T. C. G. Rich, 1991.]

Genus: *Barbarea*

Barbarea vulgaris R. Br.
Common Winter-cress
Native.
First record: 1814.
Tetrad occurrence: 355 (72%).
Apparently increasing (+21%).

A frequent species of wet ditches and damp disturbed ground, mainly on clay soils, but not often in long-established wetlands. It is quite rare on the drier Clay-with-Flints and the Chalk.
(279 tetrads: Dony, 1967; 311 tetrads: 1950-1986)

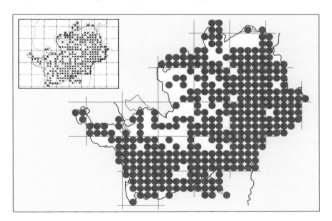

Map 209. *Barbarea vulgaris.*

Barbarea intermedia Boreau
Medium-flowered Winter-cress
Introduced: neophyte.
First record: 1919.
Tetrad occurrence: 17 (4%).
Increasing slowly (+288%).

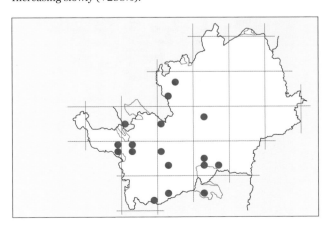

Map 210. *Barbarea intermedia.*

An occasional patch-forming plant colonising bare, grassy road-banks and waste ground. Dony (1967) gave three recent records, and there was one extra pre-1967 record which he omitted. Between 1967 and 1986 it was only noted from 5 extra tetrads, but the recent survey found it to be fairly widespread, but only in W. and S. Herts.

Barbarea verna (Miller) Asch.
American Winter-cress
Introduced: casual.
First record: 1849.

Despite having been recorded for over 150 years, this is only ever a casual of disturbed ground. It was recorded three times during the survey: from beside a maize field at Kings Langley (00/R), 1992 *G. Salisbury*; Stevenage station car park (22/G), 1998 *G. P. Smith*; and on a road verge at South Oxhey (19/B), 2003 *J. Lingley* (*comm.*: R. M. Burton)

Genus: Rorippa

Rorippa nasturtium-aquaticum (L.) Hayek
Water-cress
Native.
First record: 1819.
Tetrad occurrence: 224 (46%).
Stable?

This is the main species in larger streams and rivers, but also occurs in ditches elsewhere. It prefers calcareous water supplies, but can tolerate relatively eutrophic water better than most emergent water plants. It was formerly cultivated 'to the great prejudice of the rarer aquatics' (Pryor, 1887), but not as frequently as the hybrid. It was much under-recorded in Dony (1967), particularly in the Stort catchment, where it is frequent. The map given is for the broad taxon, thus including occurrences not specified to species, but excluding records specifically for *R. microphylla*. The strict species was recorded from 125 tetrads, representing an 8% increase on Dony's records, assuming this is what he mapped.
(110 tetrads: Dony, 1967; 135 tetrads: 1950-1986)

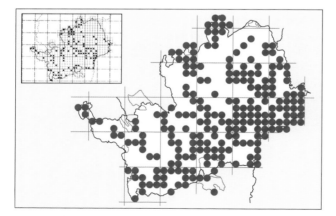

Map 211. *Rorippa nasturtium-aquaticum.*

Rorippa × *sterilis* Airy Shaw
(*R. nasturtium-aquaticum* × *R. microphylla*)
Hybrid Water-cress
Native.
First record: *c*.1960.

Dony (1967) notes this as 'frequent', but with no records listed. He also only notes four records in his ms. index. It was apparently the main form of water-cress grown commercially in Herts., but few water-cress beds now remain in production. It was only recorded three times during the survey: 12/V, 31/G and 11/M, but is certainly likely to be more frequent than these would suggest.

Rorippa microphylla (Boenn.) N. Hylander ex A. Löve and D. Löve
Narrow-fruited Water-cress
Native.
First record (as the segregate): 1899.
Tetrad occurrence: 71 (15%).
Probably decreasing (-12%).

This is the main species in natural seepages, ponds and shallow streams, especially on clay soils, although it can also occur by larger watercourses. It was not formally separated from its more robust cousin until the 1950s. Even now, it has probably been under-recorded in west Herts., but otherwise shows a similar distribution to that found by Dony (1967), although the old wet pastures where it would once have occurred are steadily disappearing. There is an early record from Totteridge (TQ29), 1899 (Hb. BM) (*comm.*: Kent and Lousley, 1951) , which Dony (1967) overlooked.
(77 tetrads: Dony, 1967; 92 tetrads: 1950-1986)

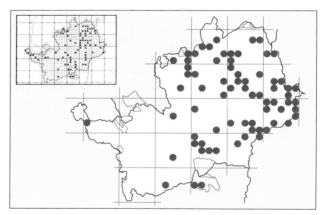

Map 212. *Rorippa microphylla.*

Rorippa palustris (L.) Besser
Marsh Yellow-cress
Native.
First record: 1839.
Tetrad occurrence: 99 (20%).
Probably decreasing (-21%).

This is always a rather inconspicuous plant of muddy patches in marshy ground and drying pond margins, mainly on less calcareous soils in southern Hertfordshire. However, the kind of old-fashioned wet pasture where it was formerly frequent is now becoming rare, and it often only persists as the odd plant on waste ground.
(119 tetrads: Dony, 1967; 139 tetrads: 1950-1986)

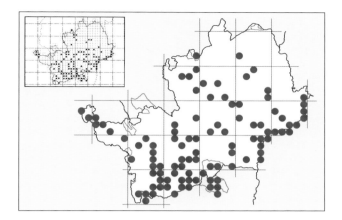

Map 213. *Rorippa palustris.*

Rorippa sylvestris (L.) Besser
Creeping Yellow-cress
Native.
First record: 1843.
Tetrad occurrence: 88 (18%).
Increased (+39%).

A native plant of bare, damp places, by streams and rivers, but also occurring increasingly as a weed of disturbed ground. It remains rare in northern Herts., but appears to have become much more frequent from Stevenage southwards.
(60 tetrads: Dony, 1967; 79 tetrads: 1950-1986)

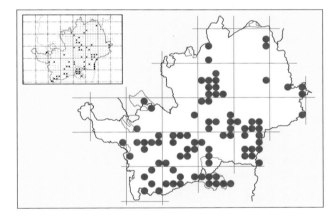

Map 214. *Rorippa sylvestris.*

Rorippa × anceps (Wahlenb.) Rchb. (*R. amphibia × R. sylvestris*)
Hybrid Yellow-cress
Native.
First record: *c.*1840?

Webb and Coleman (1849) give two records for '*Nasturtium anceps*': Ludwick Hyde (TL21) and Cheshunt (TL30), which probably refer to this hybrid. There is also a record from Rothamsted (11/G), post-1950 (*comm.*: Biological Records Centre, CEH Monks Wood).

Rorippa amphibia (L.) Besser
Great Yellow-cress
Native.
First record: 1840.
Tetrad occurrence: 26 (5%).
Possibly increased (+36%).

Always rather scarce, this plant occurs unpredictably by rivers and

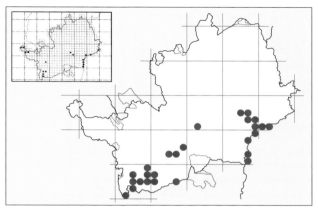

Map 215. *Rorippa amphibia.*

streams in the lower reaches of the Colne and Lea catchments especially. It is apparently extinct around Tring, where Dony recorded it. However, the recent survey shows that it may have consolidated its presence along the Colne especially, possibly owing to the creation of gravel pits, as it can compete immediately by the water margin against tall vegetation.
(18 tetrads: Dony, 1967; 27 tetrads: 1950-1986)

Rorippa austriaca (Crantz) Besser
Austrian Yellow-cress
Introduced: neophyte.
First record: 1984.

First found at a gravel pit by Rye Meads (31/V), 1984 *T. J.* (Hb. HTN) (James, 1989), where it did not persist. It later appeared at Turnford Gravel Pits (30/R), 1987 *D. Bevan* (Burton, 1988); where it was then recorded, and from nearby Cheshunt Gravel Pits, until at least 1994 *G. P. Smith*.

Genus: *Armoracia*

Armoracia rusticana P. Gaertner, Meyer and Scherb.
Horse-radish
Introduced: neophyte.
First record: 1843.
Tetrad occurrence: 324 (66%).
Possibly increasing (+6%).

A persistent and dominant weed, sometimes, of waste places, roadsides and badly managed horse pastures, having escaped from cultivation. It is only absent from the more open, arable landscapes.
(290 tetrads: Dony, 1967; 315 tetrads: 1950-1986)

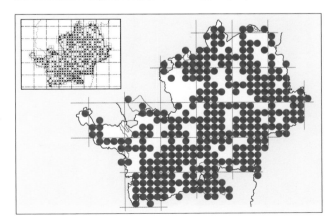

Map 216. *Armoracia rusticana.*

Cardamine bulbifera (L.) Crantz
Coralroot
Native.
First record: 1843.
Tetrad occurrence: 12 (2%).
Stable? (+41%).

As Dony (1967) said, this is one of the most intriguing and charismatic plants in the Hertfordshire flora. It is mostly found in slightly damp woodlands at the foot of the Chiltern dip-slope west of Watford. Until boundary changes brought a site formerly in Bucks. at Bovingdon into our area, it had only ever been found in 10km square TQ09, where it can be locally abundant. However, recently, a record has come to light of it having been found at Bricket Wood (Building Research Establishment grounds) (10/F), 1966 *P. J. Ellison* (Showler and Rich, 1993). It can survive the destruction of woodland and its replacement by large gardens, as at Loudwater, where it is sometimes a garden weed! Nationally, it has a similar strange distribution elsewhere, occurring otherwise almost exclusively in damp Wealden woodlands south of the Thames, although it does sometimes escape from cultivation. Our County therefore has a particular responsibility for this plant in the U.K. Dony's survey missed it in several places where it had been known to occur for more than a hundred years, and therefore it is probably not actually increasing.
(8 tetrads: Dony, 1967; 11 tetrads: 1950-1986)

Coralroot Cardamine bulbifera *Harrocks Wood, 1997.*

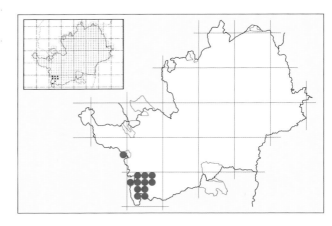

Map 217. *Cardamine bulbifera.*

Cardamine amara L.   Herts Rare
Large Bitter-cress
Native.
First record: 1737.

Very rare in Hertfordshire, and apparently only found as a true native in a swampy area over acidic gravels beside a back-stream of the River Colne at Stockers Lake (09/L), where it has been known on and off for 200 years, despite the excavation of the gravel pit nearby. It was last firmly recorded here in 1996 *P. J. Ellison*. It also used to occur further south towards Troy Mill (Pryor, 1887), and might still do so. In 1992, a small number of plants was discovered in a damp patch in Totteridge Churchyard (29/M) *D. Griffith* (det. T. C. G. Rich), a most unlikely locality. How they got there is an open question. It was also recorded in Dony (1967) from Pirton, but there is no specimen to substantiate this record, and it was probably an error.

Cardamine pratensis L.
Lady's Smock *or* **Cuckoo-flower**, **Milkmaids**
Native.
First record: 1653.
Tetrad occurrence: 294 (60%).
Apparently increased substantially (+55%).

Counter-intuitively, this attractive plant of damp pastures, streamsides, gravel pits and woodland rides appears to have increased quite markedly since 1967, although some of this may be down to better recording, especially of a species which disappears after mid-summer. Nevertheless, it is difficult to account for the much greater density of records, especially in east Herts. It is also

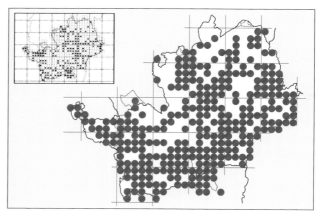

Map 218. *Cardamine pratensis.*

taxonomically obscure, with different 'species' described from Europe, depending on the plant's chromosome number. We may therefore have more than one taxon in the County, although no attempt has been made to examine these.
(180 tetrads: Dony, 1967; 225 tetrads: 1950-1986)

Cardamine impatiens L.   UK Near Threatened
Narrow-leaved Bitter-cress
Native.
First record: 1929.

This was first formally published as a Hertfordshire species following its discovery in damp woodland by the River Chess at Sarratt (09/J) in 1978 *T. Bell* (Hb. HTN) (James, 1982). However, a reference to its having occurred at Dudswell, Berkhamsted (90/U) in 1929 *R. I. Sworder* (Dony, ms. index) has come to light, although Dony had queried it. As the plant occurs quite widely as a native south-west of Herts., there seems no reason to doubt these occurrences as being anything other than genuinely native. It was re-found during the survey at Valley Farm, Sarratt (09/J) in 1989 *G. Salisbury/J. Saunders*, but is evidently rare in the area, and has not been re-found recently. It is nationally scarce, occurring most frequently in wooded streamsides in the Welsh borders.

Cardamine flexuosa With.
Wavy Bitter-cress
Native.
First record: 1843.
Tetrad occurrence: 217 (44%).
Increased markedly (+146%).

This is a plant of damp, shaded ground on moderately acidic clay or loam soils, by streams, or in damp woodlands, occasionally a weed elsewhere. It has always been a feature of woodlands in southern Hertfordshire, but its apparently marked increase, and its spread northwards into damp woodland and streamsides in northern Hertfordshire may reflect the effects of eutrophication.
(84 tetrads: Dony, 1967; 107 tetrads: 1950-1986)

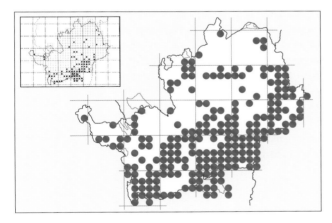

Map 219. *Cardamine flexuosa.*

Cardamine hirsuta L.
Hairy Bitter-cress
Native.
First record: 1838.
Tetrad occurrence: 385 (78%).
Greatly increased (+179%).

Now an abundant weed of most gardens and waste places throughout the County, this was a rare plant in the early 19th

Century (Webb and Coleman, 1849), but had become 'occasional' by the time of Dony's survey.
(131 tetrads: Dony, 1967; 181 tetrads: 1950-1986)

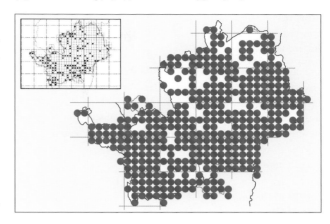

Map 220. *Cardamine hirsuta.*

Genus: *Arabis*

Arabis glabra (L.) Bernh.   UK Endangered
Tower Mustard
Native.
First record: 1820.
Extinct in Herts. in the wild?

This is a plant of nutrient-poor, gravelly grassland or disturbed ground, and was formerly fairly widespread between Hertford and Welwyn, north to Stevenage, and in a few places in south-west Herts. It was last seen wild at Hertford Heath (31/K) in 1979 *J. R. Geary*, and at old gravel pits at Waterford (31/C) and Cole Green (21/Q) in 1976 *C. G. Hanson*. Its loss is almost certainly due to eutrophication of roadsides and agricultural 'improvement' of grasslands. It grows in some abundance at allotments by King's Meads, Hertford (31/L), where it was originally introduced from the Waterford colony *J. C. Doyle*.

Arabis caucasica Willd. ex Schldl.
Garden Arabis
Introduced: casual.
First record: 1913.

A garden escape, recorded during the survey from near Hertford (31/B), 1991 *A. M. Boucher*; and Standon (32/W), 1991 *S. Watson*.

Arabis hirsuta (L.) Scop.   Herts Rare
Hairy Rock-cress
Native? (or introduced).
First record: 1967.

This native plant of limestone grassland and rocky ground was noticed on railway banks on Chalk at Bygrave (23/S) in 1967 *R. M. Burton* (Dony, 1969) (Hb. HTN). Dony's ms. index gives two earlier records by W. F. Hayllar from Ettridge Farm (30/I), 1908; and a gravel pit at Hoddesdon (30/Z), 1914. As neither of these is supported by a specimen, they must remain in doubt, especially as neither site is on calcareous soils. The plant still occurs at Bygrave, being last seen there in 1997 *T. J.* (Hb. HTN). It may have been introduced with ballast in the past.

Aubrieta deltoidea (L.) DC.
Aubretia
Introduced: neophyte.
First record: 1990.

First noticed as an escape at Chorleywood (09/I), 1990 *T. J.*
However, the colony on the walls at Hertford Castle (31/G), first
noted by *A. M. Boucher* in 1991, and still flourishing in 1996 *T. J.*,
has probably been there much longer. It is probably quite frequent
elsewhere as an escape but has been disregarded by botanists.

Genus: *Lunaria*

Lunaria annua L.
Honesty
Introduced: neophyte.
First record: *c.*1880.
Tetrad occurrence: 152 (31%).
Increased.

Dony only casually mentions this as a 'garden relic', and his ms.
index only gives four records, but it is now quite frequent as an
apparently established plant of shady hedgerows throughout
the County, especially in the south, although it does not spread
vigorously.

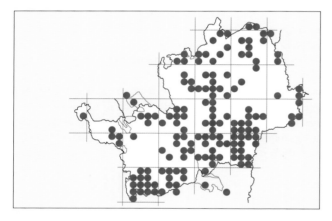

Map 221. *Lunaria annua.*

Genus: *Alyssum*

Alyssum alyssoides (L.) L.
Small Alison
Introduced: neophyte.
First record: 1839.

In the 19th century this was an occasional weed of cultivated land
and disturbed ground. Two recent records: from tetrads 30/T, and
10/L (*comm.*: B.R.C., CEH Monks Wood) (Preston *et al.*, 2002)
actually refer to *A. saxatile*.

Alyssum saxatile L.
Golden Alison
Introduced: casual.
First record: 1970.

Originally mis-identified as *A. alyssoides*, this garden escape was
first found at Moor Mill tip (10/L), 1970 *C. G. Hanson*. It also

subsequently appeared at Ware UDC tip (31/M), and at Cock Lane
tip, Hoddesdon (30/T), 1982 *C. G. H.*; and was found during the
survey on dumped chalk at Chorleywood Common (09/I), 1990
T. J.

Genus: *Berteroa*

Berteroa incana (L.) DC.
Hoary Alison
Introduced: casual.
First record: 1871.

This was a feature of gravelly places around Ware and Hoddesdon
in the late 19th century, and was also found at Knebworth,
Rickmansworth, Hemel Hempstead and Letchworth (Dony, ms.
index). Burton (1983) gives an un-dated, post-1970 record from
Smallford (10/Y), but it has not been seen since.

Genus: *Lobularia*

Lobularia maritima (L.) Desv.
Sweet Alison
Introduced: casual.
First record: 1912.
Tetrad occurrence: 8 (2%).

First noted at Welwyn, 1912 (Dony, ms. index), this became quite
frequent on tips (Dony, 1967), but is more often noted now as
an escape from gardens, growing in pavement cracks and bare
ground. The recent survey noted it in eight scattered tetrads, but it
is probably much more widespread.

Genus: *Draba*

Draba muralis L.
Wall Whitlowgrass
Introduced [native in the U.K.].
First record: 1925.

This is a native plant on limestone rocks in Britain, but in Herts.
it only turns up occasionally on old walls and such like. It was a
feature of walls at Loudwater (09/N) for some time (Dony, 1967;
Burton, 1983), but has only recently been confirmed from Ayot St
Peter Churchyard (21/C), 2003 *T. J.* (Hb. HTN).

Genus: *Erophila*

Erophila majuscula Jordan   Herts Rare
Hairy Whitlowgrass
Native?
First record: 1913.

As this was not recognised as a separate species in the U.K.
until 1987, earlier records are only those based on herbarium
specimens. However, it does appear to be rare in Herts., occurring
in disturbed areas. There is a specimen in Hb. CGE, collected by
J. E. Little from Codicote High Heath (21/E), 1913 (det.: T. C. G.
Rich). During the recent survey it was recorded at Startop's End
Reservoir, Tring (91/G), 2001 *T. J.* (Hb. HTN); and as a pavement
weed at Letchworth Station (23/B), 2003 *T. J.* (Hb. HTN).

Erophila verna (L.) DC.

Common Whitlowgrass

Native.

First record (as the aggregate): 1748 (1989 for current species concept).

Tetrad occurrence: 94 (for the agg.) (19%).

Probably stable, or slightly increased (+36%).

This is a fairly frequent plant of gravelly ground and old walls, especially around Hertford, Ware and Hoddesdon, and up to Hitchin, following the Hitchin Gap gravels. However, it can be overlooked, owing to its early flowering, and so an apparent increase may not be real. *Erophila spathulata* Ling, which was recorded by Dony (1967), is now not recognised as a separate species. The map shows the occurrence of the species in the broad sense, but excludes records of the other two segregates. It may therefore be slightly over-recorded at the expense of these, although the distribution of the species in its strict sense is similar to that shown. There were 50 tetrad records for *E. verna s. str.* during the survey.

(65 tetrads for the aggregate: Dony, 1967; 85 tetrads for the aggregate: 1950-1986)

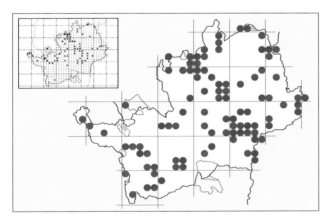

Map 222. *Erophila verna.*

Erophila glabrescens Jordan

Glabrous Whitlowgrass

Native.

First record: 1989.

Tetrad occurrence: 12 (2%).

This appears to be mainly a plant of less calcareous sandy or gravelly ground, as almost all the records so far have come from the south of the County. It was first found on a gravelly path at

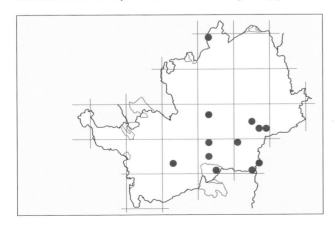

Map 223. *Erophila glabrescens.*

North Mymms Churchyard (20/H), 1989 *A. D. Marshall* (Hb. HTN), and has subsequently been found sparsely on gravelly ground elsewhere. Its only record from north Herts. was from a gravelly track at Hinxworth, where it may have been introduced with aggregate.

Genus: *Cochlearia*

Cochlearia danica L.

Danish Scurvygrass

Introduced [native in the U.K.].

First record: 1945.

Tetrad occurrence: 98 (20%).

Massively increased (+3233%).

Dony (1967) knew this from railway ballast, where he thought that it had spread during war-time. It was also found in this habitat at Kings Langley (00/R) in 1979 during the I.T.E. survey of railways. In 1991, it was found by the A414 at London Colney (10/S) by A. D. Marshall (Hb. HTN). Subsequently it expanded its range rapidly along the A1/A414 corridors, and later along the A10 and A505, although it was some time before it appeared to become a feature of the M25 and M1, probably owing to retention of previous different salting regimes. It is now all too common along most major roads, encouraged by the excessive use of common salt in winter, instead of the previously employed calcium chloride. It is also now by many minor roads as well, where it and other halophytic plants are steadily replacing the natural roadside flora. It also occurs in road drainage sumps at Stevenage and other places., with other halophytes, and is continuing to increase, spreading farther from the roads as salt levels in surrounding vegetation increase.

(3 tetrads: Dony, 1967; 4 tetrads: 1950-1986)

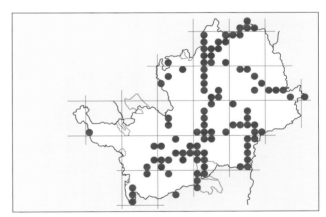

Map 224. *Cochlearia danica.*

Genus: *Camelina*

Camelina microcarpa Andrz. ex DC.

Lesser Gold-of-pleasure

Introduced: casual.

First record: 1871.

A casual of waste ground, last recorded at Ware, 1912 by A. W. Graveson (Dony, 1967).

Camelina sativa (L.) Crantz
Gold-of-pleasure
Introduced: casual.
First record: 1839.

Formerly a frequent casual plant from imported seed, now rare. In the 1970s and early 1980s it was found on a number of waste tips, but was only recorded during the survey from waste ground at Letchworth (23/G), 1998 *A. R. Outen*.

Camelina alyssum (Miller) Thell.
Introduced: casual.
First (only) record: 1931.

The only record is from a tip at Welwyn *H. Phillips* (Dony, 1967).

Genus: *Neslia*

Neslia paniculata (L.) Desv.
Ball Mustard
Introduced: casual.
First record: 1875.

Not seen since it was found at Hitchin, 1927 (Dony, 1967).

Genus: *Capsella*

Capsella bursa-pastoris (L.) Medikus
Shepherd's-purse
Introduced: archaeophyte.
First record: 1750.
Tetrad occurrence: 470 (96%).
Stable (-3%).
Very variable, with many described forms. It is found throughout the County on nutrient-rich, disturbed ground, only becoming rare on poor, acidic soils. Missed in a few tetrads.
(460 tetrads: Dony, 1967 and between 1950-1986)

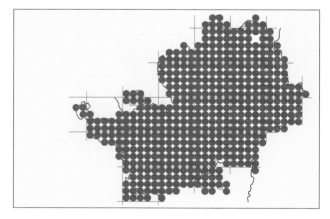

Map 225. *Capsella bursa-pastoris.*

Capsella × *gracilis* Gren. (*C. bursa-pastoris* × *C. rubella*)

This was found with the parents at Boxmoor (00/M, N), 1976 *J. G. Dony* (det. A. O. Chater) (Dony, 1977) (Hb. LTN).

Capsella rubella Reuter
Pink Shepherd's-purse
Introduced: casual.
First (only) record: 1976.

The only record is from Boxmoor (00/M, N), 1976 *J. G. Dony*,

source unknown (det. A. O. Chater) (Hb. HTN; Hb. LTN) (Dony, 1977).

Genus: *Teesdalia*

Teesdalia nudicaulis (L.) R. Br.   UK Near Threatened
Shepherd's Cress   Herts Extinct
Native.
First record: 1859.

This was only ever recorded from the south side of Colney Heath (20/C), where it was last seen *c.*1940 by E. J. Salisbury. An undated specimen in Hb. BM from 'near Hitchin' *A. J. Crosfield* (*comm.*: B.R.C., CEH Monks Wood) must be regarded with suspicion, given its habitat requirements.

Genus: *Thlaspi*

Thlaspi arvense L.
Field Penny-cress
Introduced: archaeophyte.
First record: 1814.
Tetrad occurrence: 130 (27%).
Decreased (-9%).

Formerly a frequent arable weed on damp, less calcareous clay soils, this now occurs more often as a casual in waste places. Its distribution remains much as it was in Dony's survey, being especially frequent in S.W. Herts., but it was then somewhat under-recorded.
(136 tetrads: Dony, 1967; 173 tetrads: 1950-1986)

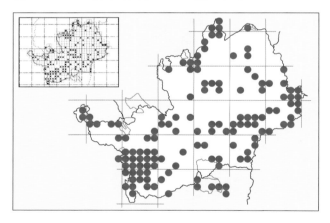

Map 226. *Thlaspi arvense.*

Genus: *Iberis*

Iberis amara L.   UK Vulnerable
Wild Candytuft
Native.
First record: 1835.
Tetrad occurrence: 5 (1%).
Decreased before 1967, possibly still decreasing (-9%).

A rare native plant of disturbed soils on Chalk, this has always been scarce in the County, but was much more widespread in the 19th century than it is now. It has not been seen in the Tring area since 1955, and around Pirton it is now very scarce (although still frequent on Pegsdon Hills in Bedfordshire nearby). It was found during the survey at Therfield Heath (33/J, 34/F), 1989, 1992, 1993, *etc. T. J.*, where it occurs sporadically by rabbit burrows

Wild Candytuft Iberis amara *Therfield Heath, 2009.*

and in disturbed places, especially at Church Hill and beside the Therfield Road; by Tingley Wood (13/F), 1988 *C. W. Burton* (but not since); on banks by Prior's Wood, Kimpton (11/Y), 1996 *T. J.* (in very small quantity) (a long-recorded site); and on chalky roadside banks at Redbourn (11/B), 1994 *T. J.* (where it was probably introduced with chalk grassland seeding when the bypass was constructed).
(5 tetrads: Dony, 1967; 6 tetrads: 1950-1986)

Iberis umbellata L.
Garden Candytuft
Introduced: casual.
First record: 1970.

An occasional garden escape, first noted at Moor Mill tip (10/L), 1970 *C. G. Hanson*. It has subsequently been found at various waste tips, and occurs rarely as a casual elsewhere. It was found once during the survey: Water End, North Mymms (20/H), 1989 *A. D. Marshall.*

Genus: *Lepidium*

Lepidium sativum I L.
Garden Cress
Introduced: casual.
First record: 1871.

A rare casual from cultivation, or from bird seed, recorded four times during the survey: Bushey (19/H), 1989 *J. K. Jackson*; Hitchin (13/V), 1990 *A. R. Outen*; Stevenage (22/G), 1994 *G. P. Smith*; and Ware (31/M), 1998 *C. G. Hanson.*

Lepidium campestre (L.) R. Br.
Field Pepperwort
Introduced: archaeophyte.
First record: 1652.
Tetrad occurrence: 13 (3%).
Stable? (+13%).

A scarce weed of bare, gravelly places by fields and on waste ground, usually on less calcareous soils. This was quite frequent in the 19th century, but had decreased by 1967. Its widespread distribution remains much the same as it was then, but none of its colonies are large, and they tend to come and go.
(11 tetrads: Dony, 1967 and ms. index; 16 tetrads: 1950-1986)

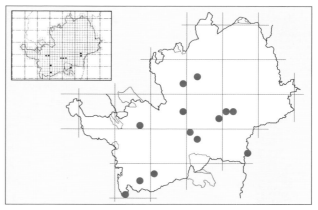

Map 227. *Lepidium campestre.*

Lepidium heterophyllum Benth.
Smith's Pepperwort
Native [introduced in Herts.?]
First record: 1957.
Tetrad occurrence: 8 (2%).
Rare, but possibly increasing (+78%).

This is a native plant of bare, gravelly ground on acidic soils, in pastures, as well as a weed of waste places. It was first found in Hertfordshire next to Croxley Common Moor in 1957 (Dony, 1967), and it persists on the Moor itself (09/X), 1999, growing on anthills, *G. Salisbury*, as well as on nearby waste ground (09/S, X), 2006 *T. J./G. S.* (Hb. HTN). It was also found during the current survey by Brunswick Park (29/W) (VC20 [Greater London]), 1988 *A. W. Vaughan*; on a road verge at Hoddesdon (30/U), 1989, 1992 *A. M. Boucher*; roadside, Bushey Park (19/I), 1989 *J. K. Jackson*; roadside, Broxbourne (30/T), 1996 *A. M. Boucher*; and at old gravel pits, Old Parkbury (10/L,R), 1996 *A. D. Marshall*. It was also found on heathy ground by a covered reservoir at Sherrards Park Wood (21/G), 1981 *S. Gorton.*
(4 tetrads: Dony, 1967; 7 tetrads: 1950-1986)

Lepidium virginicum L. (incl. *L. densiflorum* Schrad. and *L. neglectum* Thell.)
Least Pepperwort
Introduced: casual.
First record: 1922.

Only rarely recorded after it was first found at Ware, 1922 *A. W. Graveson* (Hb. HTN); and at Hitchin, 1922, *J. E. Little* (Hb. BM) (the latter record reported as *L. neglectum* in Dony, 1967). The record of *L. densiflorum* from Royston, 1934 *H. Phillips* (Hb. HTN) also refers here. There have been no recent records.

Lepidium bonariense L.
Argentine Pepperwort
Introduced: casual.
First (only) record: 1924.

This was found at Hitchin gas works (13/V), 1924, *J. E. Little* (Hb. CGE). It was originally itdentified as *L. neglectum* (= L. *virginicum*), but was re-determined by P. D. Sell, 1962. It was omitted from Dony (1967).

Lepidium ruderale L.
Narrow-leaved Pepperwort
Introduced: archaeophyte.
First record: 1872.
Tetrad occurrence: 25 (5%).
Apparently decreasing (-26%).

This rather scruffy weed became quite frequent in waste places on acidic, gravelly soils across southern Herts. during the 1960s and 1970s, and, although it occurs fairly frequently in waste ground and as a roadside weed in some areas, it now appears to have decreased again. (32 tetrads: Dony, 1967; 35 tetrads: 1950-1986)

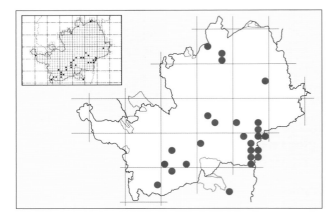

Map 228. *Lepidium ruderale.*

Lepidium graminifolium L.
Tall Pepperwort
Introduced: casual.
First record: 1962.

Only ever seen twice in the County: at Pye Corner tip (41/L), 1962 *L. Lloyd-Evans* (Dony, 1967) (Hb. HTN); and at Moor Mill tip (10/L), 1970 *C. G. Hanson.*

Lepidium perfoliatum L.
Perfoliate Pepperwort
Introduced: casual.
First record: 1912.

Although Dony (1967) only gave one record: Ware, 1915 *H. F. Hayllar,* he conflated this with another record from Ware, 1912 by *A. W. Graveson* (Hb. HTN). Graveson also recorded it from Mead Lane, Hertford (31/G), 1919 (Dony, ms. index). A record of '*Thlaspi perfoliatum*' from somewhere near Hitchin, 1814, given by Joseph Ransom in his diary, cannot be accepted without further evidence. There have been no other records.

Lepidium latifolium L.
Dittander
Introduced [native in the U.K.].
First record: 1929.
Tetrad occurrence: 27 (6%).
Increased (+129%).

As a native, this is a plant of the margins of coastal marshes, but it has also been cultivated as a pot-herb for centuries. Quite how the plant arrived by the A505 at Baldock (23/M), we do not know, but this was its first recorded locality, and it remains abundant there. Dony (1967) also notes its widespread occurrence by the canal and gravel pits around Rickmansworth, where it also still occurs. It has spread into other gravel pit sites, and along some roads, notably

the A505 at Royston, and parts of the M25, no doubt encouraged by road salt.
(11 tetrads: Dony, 1967 and ms. index; 15 tetrads: 1950-1986)

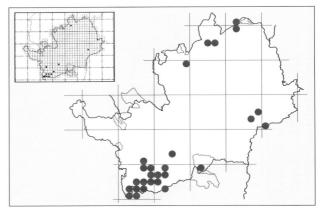

Map 229. *Lepidium latifolium.*

Lepidium draba L.
Hoary Cress
Introduced: neophyte.
First record: 1873.
Tetrad occurrence: 219 (45%).
Increased (+45%).

Having first been introduced to Herts. near Pirton, this has become a conspicuous plant of roadside verges and waste places, mainly on calcareous soils. While still remaining abundant on the Chalk in north Hertfordshire, it has consolidated its range elsewhere in the County since 1967.
(143 tetrads: Dony, 1967; 175 tetrads: 1950-1986)

The usual plant is subspecies *draba,* but the rarer ssp. *chalepense* (L.) Thell. was discovered on waste ground at Mead Lane, Hertford (31/G), 1988 *A. M. Boucher* (det. T. C. G. Rich) (Hb. HTN), where it remained in 1989 *T. J.* (Burton, 1989, 1991).

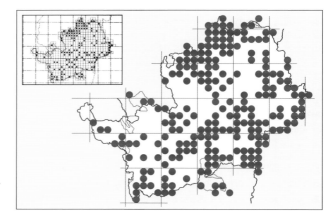

Map 230. *Lepidium draba.*

Genus: *Coronopus*

Coronopus squamatus (Forsskål) Asch.
Swine-cress
Introduced: archaeophyte.
First record: 1838.
Tetrad occurrence: 385 (78%).
Increased (+21%).

This is a weed of bare, muddy places, very often in farm tracks or gateways, and is relatively tolerant of weed-killers. It was 'not uncommon' in the 19th century (Pryor, 1887), but had increased by the 1960s. It has continued to consolidate its position, especially in the south-west of the County, where it was previously thinly spread.

(301 tetrads: Dony, 1967; 324 tetrads: 1950-1986)

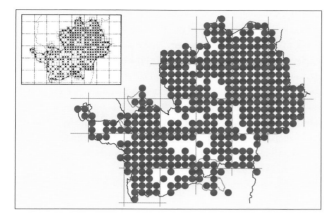

Map 231. *Coronopus squamatus.*

Coronopus didymus (L.) Smith
Lesser Swine-cress
Introduced: neophyte.
First record: 1843.
Tetrad occurrence: 122 (25%).
Markedly increased (+204%).

This evil-smelling weed of nutrient-rich, bare ground, which arrived from South America in the ballast on ships, is now found across the County, although it remains most frequent on the less calcareous soils in the south.

(38 tetrads: Dony, 1967; 67 tetrads: 1950-1986)

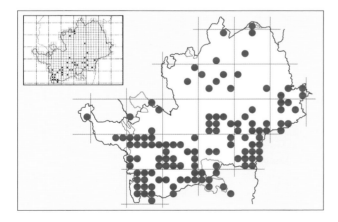

Map 232. *Coronopus didymus.*

Genus: *Conringia*

Conringia orientalis (L.) Dumort.
Hare's-ear Mustard
Introduced: casual.
First record: 1841.

This persisted in the Hertford and Ware area until 1916, but became a rare casual everywhere by 1929 (Dony, 1967). It has appeared once since: at High Leigh tip, Hoddesdon (30/U), 1970 *C. G. Hanson/J. G. Dony* (Hb. LTN).

Genus: *Moricandia*

Moricandia arvensis (L.) DC.
Violet Cabbage
Introduced: casual.
First (only) record: 1916.

Only recorded from Ware (TL31) *H. F. Hayllar* (Dony, 1967).

Genus: *Diplotaxis*

Diplotaxis tenuifolia (L.) DC.
Perennial Wall-rocket
Introduced: archaeophyte.
First record: 1657.
Tetrad occurrence: 29 (6%).
Probably slightly increasing (+31%).

The 'common wild rocket' was apparently abundant on the walls of St Albans Abbey when Coles described it in 1657, and it persisted here until at least the 1920s (Dony, ms. index), although there is no recent record. It is, however, persistent by railways and by gravel pits, where it occurs scattered across southern Hertfordshire. As its seeds are now being sold as 'wild rocket' for salads (pers. comm.: C. A. Stace), it may well increase.

(21 tetrads: Dony, 1967; 29 tetrads: 1950-1986)

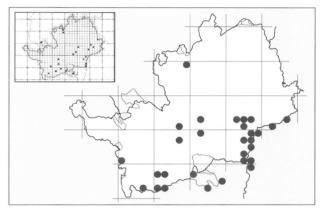

Map 233. *Diplotaxis tenuifolia.*

Diplotaxis erucoides (L.) DC.
White Wall-rocket
Introduced: casual.
First (only) record: 1916.

Only ever found once: at Ware *A. W. Graveson* (Hb. HTN) (Dony, 1967).

Diplotaxis muralis (L.) DC.
Annual Wall-rocket
Introduced: neophyte.
First record: 1874.
Tetrad occurrence: 24 (5%).
Decreased sharply (-71%).

Despite the comments by Preston *et al.* (2002) that this attractive plant is 'continuing to spread into rural areas', it has shown a marked decrease in Hertfordshire since 1967. It still occurs, sparsely, along the Chalk ridge in north Herts., but is very scarce now in the south, except around Watford and Rickmansworth.

(78 tetrads: Dony, 1967; 84 tetrads: 1950-1986)

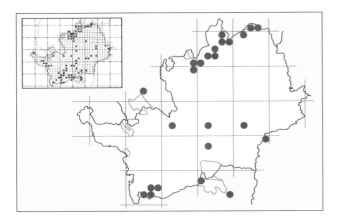

Map 234. *Diplotaxis muralis.*

Genus: *Brassica*

Brassica oleracea L.
Cabbage
Introduced: casual.
First documented record: 1989.

Escapes from cultivation must have been known for a long time, but there are few actual records on file. It was recorded during the survey from Pole Hole tip (41/L), 1989 *S. Watson*; and from Rye Meads Sewage Works (31/V), 1995 *C. G. Hanson.*

Brassica napus L.
Rape
Introduced: neophyte.
First record: *c.*1841.
Tetrad occurrence: 316 (64%).
Increased markedly.

This was ignored by Dony (1967), but has been an escape from cultivation for a long time, having first been recorded by Coleman (Webb and Coleman, 1849; Pryor, 1887). Almost all the recent records refer to escapes of subspecies *oleifera* (DC.) Metzger **Oil-seed Rape**, which has increased enormously since the 1970s, but ssp *rapifera* Metzger **Swede**, may also occur, and possibly other subspecies. The recent survey found it as a casual or established escape in 316 tetrads, making it by far the commonest escaped crucifer in the County.

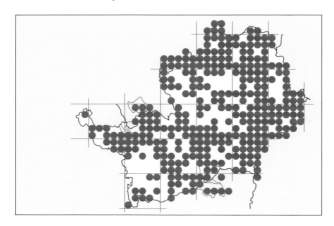

Map 235. *Brassica napus.*

Brassica rapa L.
Wild Turnip *or* **Bargeman's Cabbage**
Introduced: archaeophyte.
First record: 1814.
Tetrad occurrence: 25 (5%).
Probably slightly increased (+38%).

The usual wild plant is ssp. *campestris* (L.) A. R. Clapham, a long-established introduction to Britain, and is represented by the records on the map given here. It is a plant of rough herbage by rivers and ditches, now apparently entirely by rivers in the Lea catchment, where it can be mistaken for escaped oil-seed rape. It used to occur in the Colne catchment as well, and may have been overlooked here. The hybrid with *B. napus* has not been formally recorded from the County, but may be frequent in the Lea Valley. Some records given in Burton (1983) are doubtful, and therefore it is not possible to be sure how many extra records there might have been since Dony's *Flora*.
(17 tetrads: Dony, 1967; 33 tetrads: 1950-1986)

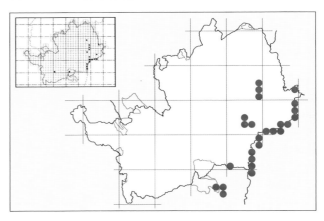

Map 236. *Brassica rapa.*

Subspecies *oleifera* (DC.) Metzger **Turnip-rape** was recorded as an escape at Ware tip (31/M), 1984 *C. G. Hanson* (det. E. J. Clement) (*comm.*: B.R.C., CEH Monks Wood). It may also have been overlooked elsewhere.

Ssp. *rapa*, **Cultivated Turnip**, was also recorded at Ware tip (31/M), 1977 *C. G. H.* (det. E. J. Clement), and no doubt has occurred elsewhere.

Brassica tournefortii Gouan
Pale Cabbage
Introduced: casual.
First (only) record: 1965.

This has not been reported since its sole record in the County from Hitchin (Dony, 1967).

Brassica juncea (L.) Czernj.
Chinese Mustard
Introduced: neophyte.
First record: 1911.

There have been a number of records of this, mostly on tips, but also as a casual in waste places, since Dony's *Flora*, but during the recent survey it was only found at Bushey (19/H), 1989, *J. K. Jackson*; at Rye Meads Sewage Works (31/V), 1995, 1996 *C. G. Hanson et al.* (Hb. HTN); and in a roadside pool polluted with sewage at Beaumont (30/H), 2004 *T. J.*

Brassica nigra (L.) Koch
Black Mustard
Probably introduced [native in the U.K.].
First record: *c.*1820.
Tetrad occurrence: 13 (3%).
Possibly decreasing (-21%).

In Hertfordshire, this is a plant of waste places and tips, and only rarely occurs by rivers, its more natural home. It may also occasionally be mistaken for Hoary Mustard *Hirschfeldia incana*, which it somewhat resembles.
(16 tetrads: Dony, 1967; 20 tetrads: 1950-1986)

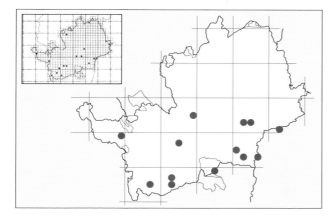

Map 237. *Brassica nigra.*

Genus: *Sinapis*

Sinapis arvensis L.
Charlock
Introduced: archaeophyte.
First record: 1744.
Tetrad occurrence: 407 (83%).
Decreased (-13%).

The tetrad distribution does not show a major change, but experience in the field shows that this plant has all but disappeared from most arable landscapes, having at one time been the bane of cereal growers. It prefers heavier soils, but is found throughout the County. Its most obvious losses, however, appear to be in the south, where it should be commonest. Its ability to reappear from long-buried seed accounts for many records.
(444 tetrads: Dony, 1967; 447 tetrads: 1950-1986)

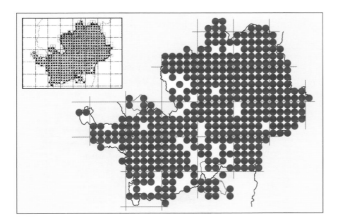

Map 238. *Sinapis arvensis.*

Sinapis alba L.
White Mustard
Introduced: archaeophyte.
First record: *c.*1820.
Tetrad occurrence: 196 (40%).
Slightly decreased (-12%).

This is a weed of disturbed ground on more calcareous soils, becoming the main yellow crucifer as a weed on the Chalk. It is still cultivated for its seed, and therefore escapes continue to occur; and it is also occasionally sown as a game mix. Evidence for a decrease is therefore slight, because it has appeared more frequently in some areas (*e.g.* TL31), although this may also be a result of better recording.
(211 tetrads: Dony, 1967; 222 tetrads: 1950-1986)

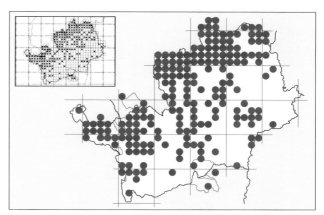

Map 239. *Sinapis alba.*

Genus: *Eruca*

Eruca vesicaria (L.) Cav.
Garden Rocket
Introduced: casual.
First record: 1873.

Our plant is subspecies *sativa* (Miller) Thell. With the new fashion for rocket in salads, it is not surprising that this has reappeared as a casual after a very long absence: by the disused canal, Little Tring (91/B), 1995 *G. Salisbury/J. Saunders.*

Genus: *Erucastrum*

Erucastrum gallicum (Willd.) O. E. Schulz
Hairy Rocket
Introduced: casual.
First record: 1920.

Having only ever previously been recorded once, at Ware (Dony, 1967), this appeared three times during the survey: as a pavement weed, Station Road, Cuffley (30/B), 1987 *A. M. Boucher*, where it still occurred in 1989 *A. D. Marshall* (Hb. HTN); and then at Theobalds Grove, Waltham Cross (30/K), 1990 *A. M. B.*

[*Erucastrum nasturtiifolium* (Poiret) O. E. Schulz

A plant initially identified as this occurred as a casual at Ashwell (23/U), 1979 *T. J.* (James, 1982), possibly from bird-seed, but the specimen was lost before it could be confirmed. The species should therefore not be included in the Hertfordshire flora.]

Genus: *Hirschfeldia*

Hirschfeldia incana (L.) Lagr. -Fossat
Hoary Mustard
Introduced: neophyte.
First record: c.1880.
Tetrad occurrence: 60 (12%).
Increasing.

From having only been recorded three times in the County (Pryor, 1887; Dony, 1967 and ms. index), this has spread steadily across the County from south to north since 1970, when it was found at Moor Mill tip (10/L) *C. G. Hanson*. It colonised much of the lower Lea Valley by 1986, and progressed later to Welwyn Garden City. It now occurs frequently by roads and on waste ground across much of the County, just as it does in its Mediterranean homeland, and it is still spreading.

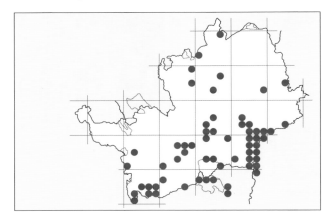

Map 240. *Hirschfeldia incana.*

Genus: *Carrichtera*

Carrichtera annua (L.) DC.
Cress Rocket
Introduced: casual.
First record: 1916.

Not seen since it was first found at Ware (Dony, 1967).

Genus: *Erucaria*

Erucaria hispanica (L.) Druce
Introduced: casual.
First record: 1871.

There were several records of this wool alien, under different names, in the 19th century, but none since the undated record by H. Bowry from Hitchin (Dony, 1967).

Genus: *Rapistrum*

Rapistrum rugosum (L.) Bergeret
Bastard Cabbage
Introduced: neophyte.
First record: 1874.
Tetrad occurrence: 7 (1%).
Probably stable.

Dony (1967) describes this as a rare casual, but notes that it had increased as a bird seed alien, although he did not keep

records. It may no longer be increasing, but it is still found quite widely, often persisting in suitable places, especially on gravelly soils. It was recorded seven times during the survey: Kings Langley (00/Q), 1990 *P. J. Ellison*; Bushey (19/I), 1990 *J. K. Jackson*; by Blackbridge tip (11/X), 1991 *T. J.* (where it has been known for a long time).; Numbers Farm (00/W), 1993 *G. Salisbury/J. Saunders*; Sawbridgeworth (41/Y), 1994 *S. Watson*; Ickleford Lower Green (13/W), 1996 *C. R. Boon/T. J.*; and from disturbed banks by the A505, Baldock (23/L), 2007 *T. J.* The plant in Britain is ssp. *linnaeanum* (Cosson) Rouy and Fouc.

Rapistrum perenne (L.) All.
Steppe Cabbage
Introduced: casual.
First record: 1910.

Possibly not recorded since it was seen at Cole Green in 1924 (not 1922 as given in Dony, 1967) (Dony, ms. index), although the latter also gives a record from Colney Heath Gravel Pit, 1958 by Dony, omitted from his *Flora*.

Genus: *Crambe*

Crambe maritima L.
Sea-kale
Introduced [native in the U.K.].
First (only) record: 1914.

This was apparently established for a short time on the face of the chalk pit by Hitchin Station (12/Z), 1914 *J. E. Little* (Dony, 1967, and ms. index). How it got there can only be guessed at!

Genus: *Raphanus*

Raphanus raphanistrum L.
Wild Radish
Introduced: archaeophyte.
First record: 1750.
Tetrad occurrence: 225 (46%).
Decreased substantially (-40%).

Formerly a considerable pest of arable fields, this is now only occasional throughout its range, occurring regularly in both its pale yellow and white forms. While the distribution remains much the same as it was in 1967, it is only reasonably regular on the drier Clay-with-Flints soils in west Herts. Our plant is ssp. *raphanistrum*.
(358 tetrads: Dony, 1967; 370 tetrads: 1950-1986)

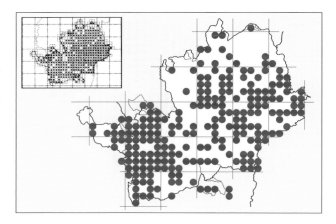

Map 241. *Raphanus raphanistrum.*

Raphanus sativus L.
Garden Radish
Introduced: casual.
First record: *c.*1880.
Tetrad occurrence: 7 (1%).

This only appears as a casual of waste ground, and was recorded in seven scattered tetrads during the survey.

Resedaceae (Mignonette family)

Genus: *Reseda*

Reseda luteola L.
Weld
Introduced: archaeophyte.
First record: 1819.
Tetrad occurrence: 241 (49%).
Increased substantially (+102%).

A characteristic plant of bare, often gravelly soils, on disturbed ground, in gravel pits or on urban wasteland, although it can tolerate a reasonable level of nutrient-enrichment. It has become more widespread as traditional landscapes and habitats have been increasingly disturbed during the last century, and it has moved especially into more rural areas, as well as having increased especially on the Chalk and Boulder Clay, where it was formerly scarce.
(113 tetrads: Dony, 1967; 152 tetrads: 1950-1986)

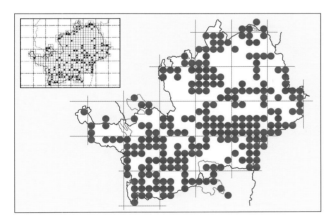

Map 242. *Reseda luteola.*

Reseda alba L.
White Mignonette
Introduced: casual.
First record: 1932.

This was first recorded at a gravel pit at Letchworth (TL23) *H. Phillips* (Hb. Phillips, HTN) (Dony, 1967). More recently a single plant was found by the roadside near Ashwell (23/Z), 1978 *T. J.* (James, 1982). During the recent survey it also appeared on abandoned allotments at Hatfield Park (20/J), 1996 *A. D. Marshall.*

Reseda lutea L.
Wild Mignonette
Native.
First record: 1814.
Tetrad occurrence: 175 (36%).
Probably stable (+4%).

This is a native plant of bare, disturbed places on chalky soils, and also occurs occasionally on calcareous gravels or waste ground elsewhere. It is especially characteristic on chalk grassland where rabbits have created scrapes, and it also grows by chalky arable fields where nutrient levels are not too high. Its distribution remains similar to what it was in 1967, although there is some evidence of an increase on the Boulder Clay and in south Herts.
(160 tetrads: Dony, 1967; 179 tetrads: 1950-1986)

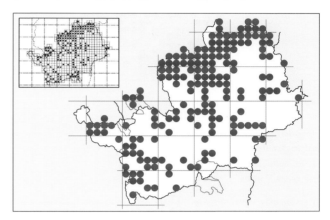

Map 243. *Reseda lutea.*

Reseda odorata L.
Garden Mignonette
Introduced: casual.
First record: *c.*1880.

There have been no records since the 19th century of this garden escape (Pryor, 1887), although it is just possible that some records of Wild Mignonette are actually errors for this.

Ericaceae (Heather family)

Genus: *Rhododendron*

Rhododendron ponticum (*s. l.*)
Rhododendron
Introduced: neophyte.
First record: *c.*1950 (in the wild).
Tetrad occurrence: 117 (24%).
Increasing or stable.

The precise identity of plants hitherto known as *R. ponticum* L. has recently been reviewed, and this has found them to be a complex hybrid of horticultural origin. Quite unaccountably, Dony (1967) totally ignored the plant, even though it had already been introduced widely by the end of the 19th century, and was probably regenerating in some places by the early 20th century at least. Its first apparent mention was as an escape around Bayfordbury, *c.*1950 (Dony, ms. index). It was recorded reasonably systematically during the 1980s, with the result that, by 1986, it had been recorded in 89 tetrads across the south of the County especially. It is now recorded from 117 tetrads as an established plant of woodlands and scrub, often in former parklands, or in the ornamental woodlands of former Victorian estates, where it can come to dominate large areas, almost to the exclusion of everything else. It is especially common on acidic gravels and clays, and only becomes rare on the Chalk or Boulder Clay.

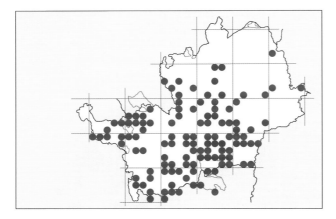

Map 244. *Rhododendron ponticum (s. l.).*

Rhododendron luteum Sweet
Yellow Azalea
Introduced: casual?
First record: 1993.

This was discovered, apparently established, in woodland by Mardley Heath (21/P), 1993 by *C. G. Hanson* (det. E. J. Clement). It could occur elsewhere, and could potentially develop in a similar fashion to *R. ponticum*.

Genus: *Arbutus*

Arbutus unedo L.
Strawberry Tree
Introduced: casual.
First record: *c.*1980.

This was reported as a self-sown plant from near Waltham Cross (30/Q) in Burton (1983).

Genus: *Calluna*

Calluna vulgaris (L.) Hull
Heather
Native.
First record: 1748.
Tetrad occurrence: 40 (8%).
Decreased slightly (-9%).

The former occurrence of large tracts of heathland across southern and western Hertfordshire can scarcely be credited in today's landscape, but when this plant was first noted by Per Kalm, Linnaeus' botanical collector, on his journey on horseback across Hertfordshire in 1748, the landscape had plenty of this habitat, possibly as much as 10,000 acres, in such places as the contiguous Northaw, North Mymms, and Cheshunt Commons (which ran into the landscape of Enfield Chase in Middlesex to the south), and the expanses of Tring, Wigginton, Aldbury, Berkhamsted and Northchurch Commons in west Herts., to name but a few. Not all this was heather, but it was certainly a prominent part of the vegetation. In medieval times and earlier it must have been even

more widespread, because in many so-called ancient woodlands in south Hertfordshire it appears from buried seed in new clearings, such as at Bencroft Wood, or in Sherrards Park Wood, the latter known to have been much its present shape by as early as 1590, but obviously at least partly former wood-pasture. Many of these wood-pastures had either been destroyed or converted to high forest or coppice woodland by the end of the 18th century or shortly after. On some commons it remained until pasturing of livestock went out of fashion by the early 20th century. It remains in patches on commons, where golf courses have often allowed it to remain, and sometimes appears in clearings in woodlands elsewhere. The longevity of its seed is extraordinary. Buried seed regenerated in the drought year of 1976 at Cuffley on a long-established lawn, constructed from an enclosed pasture in 1936 that was known to have been in existence since about 1800, but formerly part of the waste of Northaw Common. More recently, attempts have been made to rejuvenate some of this former heathland. The plant has made something of a come-back in such places, albeit partly from introduced seed, such as at Mardley Heath and Symondshyde Great Wood, while much effort has been put into encouraging its regeneration at some of its historic sites, notably Chorleywood and Berkhamsted Commons. The current survey found it mostly as scraps and vestiges, but with reasonable patches at Berkhamsted, Nomansland, Chorleywood, and Gustard Wood Commons, and on the unique floodplain pasture of Croxley Common Moor. The map given here therefore can almost be seen as the ghost of the former extent of Hertfordshire's wood-pasture landscape.

(42 tetrads: Dony, 1967; 53 tetrads: 1950-1986)

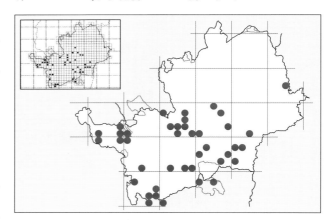

Map 245. *Calluna vulgaris.*

Genus: *Erica*

Erica tetralix L.   Herts Extinct?
Cross-leaved Heath
Native.
First record: 1843.

This was recorded as a rare plant even in the early 19th century at a few damp heathland sites, such as Batchworth Common, Leggatts at Northaw, Berkhamsted and Wigginton Commons and Bushey Heath, but it had become extremely rare by the early 20th century, being seen at Colney Heath ('Furze Field') until 1927, and at Bricket Wood in 1939. Dony thought that a plant at Moor Park (09/W) in 1966 may have been planted (although this is next to Batchworth Heath), but its occurrence more recently at Patmore Heath (42/M) appears to have been a native occurrence, although it was last seen here in 1988 *J. Godfree*, before the droughts of the 1990s. It may well have once been more frequent, but by the early 19th century, many commons had either already been lost or become over-grazed, and so it may have missed being seen in its historic sites.

Erica cinerea L.   Herts Rare
Bell Heather
Native.
First record: 1819.
Very rare.

This was also very rare in the early 19th century, being only known to Webb and Coleman from Prae Wood at St Albans, from the lost Wigginton Common (Webb and Coleman, 1849); and from Caddington Common, Markyate (01/N), 1819 *F. Sebright* (Hb. LTN), presumably the same site that it was found 'near Market-Street', *c.*1843 *Miss C. Crouch* (Hb. LTN). It was discovered in small quantity at Bricket Wood Common (10/F) in 1939 (Dony, 1967), where it has survived, despite the massive spread of birch scrub over the remains of the heath here until recently. Despite attempts to open up the heath, it is still threatened by extinction from massive growth of Bracken and birch saplings. Quite why it was always so rare is a mystery, although it does tend to prefer lighter sandy soils, which are limited in Herts.

Bell Heather Erica cinerea *Bricket Wood Common 1988.*

Erica vagans L.
Cornish Heath
Introduced [native in the U.K.].

The appearance of this at Bencroft Wood (30/I), 1981 *C. M. James* and at Patmore Heath (42/M), about the same time *J. Godfree*, was as a result of possibly deliberate introduction from gardens. Incredibly, it survived at both sites, being still recorded at Bencroft Wood in 1999 and at Patmore Heath in 1995 *T. J.* (Hb. HTN), where it is reported still to be present, 2008 *J. L. Fielding.*

Genus: *Vaccinium*

Vaccinium myrtillus L.   Herts Extinct?
Bilberry
Native.
First record: *c.*1850?

Both Pryor and Dony give 1861 as the first record, but there was a mention of it at 'Eastborough' in Coleman's ms. additions to his *Flora* (Pryor, 1887), which was presumably Eastbury Wood (09/W) (adjoining Oxhey Woods), its other former site. It was also

found at Chipperfield Common (00/K) in 1935 (Dony, 1967), last being seen there in about 1973 *J. Saunders*. It was probably more widespread as a component of scrub on wood-pasture commons in earlier times, as it was formerly quite widespread in heathy woods in Middlesex, including South Mimms, now in administrative Hertfordshire (Kent, 1975).

Pyrolaceae (Wintergreens)

Genus: *Pyrola*

Pyrola minor L.   Herts Rare
Common Wintergreen
Native.
First record: 1783.
Extinct?

This plant of shady, often somewhat damp woodland on calcareous soils was last seen in 1989, when B. Tranter found upwards of 150 plants round a Beech tree in Stubbings Wood, Tring (91/A). Since then, these woods have suffered severely from windthrow, and despite repeated attempts, the plant has not been found again. It was also formerly in woods at Ayot and Sherrards Park Wood (Dony, 1967), and in the 19th century, was recorded from Beechwood near Markyate, at Aldbury Nowers, and from near Northchurch Common (Pryor, 1887). It may yet re-appear in one of these sites.

[A record of *P. rotundifolia* L. (**Round-leaved Wintergreen**) from Redheath, Watford given in Pryor (1887) must be an error, as was a record of *P. media* Sw. (**Intermediate Wintergreen**) by Pamplin in H. C. Watson's '*New Botanist's Guide*' (1835). The latter at least was almost certainly *P. minor.*]

Monotropaceae (Yellow Bird's-nests)

Genus: *Monotropa*

Monotropa hypopitys L.   UK Endangered
Yellow Bird's-nest
Native.
First record: 1696.
Tetrad occurrence: 4 (<1%).
Rare, and sporadic (-47%).

This is a plant of shade in Beech woodland, and sometimes under pines. It was evidently quite widespread in west Herts. in the 19th century (Pryor, 1887), but had decreased by the time Dony surveyed the County (Dony, 1967), although he found it sparsely along the Chilterns to Royston (Fox Covert/Fordham's Wood). Subsequently it was found at Sherrards Park Wood (21/G), 1978 *R. M. Bateman*; on a roadside at Martin Hill, Tring (90/J), 1980 *R. M. B.*; and on Aldbury Common (91/Q), 1982 *R. M. B.* During the present survey, it was eventually found in very small numbers at Whitelands Wood, Chorleywood (09/D) (VC24 [Herts.]), 1994 *A. R. Outen*; and then recently at Stubbings Wood (90/J), 2003 *J. P. Widgery*; Tring Park (91/F), 2007 *G. Salisbury*; Oddy Hill (91/F), 2007 *T. J.* and Ashridge (91/R), 2007 *R. Keen*, after some wet winters.

(7 tetrads: Dony, 1967; 10 tetrads: 1950-1986)

The main subspecies in the County was thought by Dony (1967) to be ssp. *hypophegea* (Wallr.) Holmboe. The only recent record identified to subspecies (*hypophegea*) was that from Oddy Hill. Subspecies *hypopitys* was recorded by Dony from Aldbury Nowers (91/L), and a specimen in Hb. HTN from Offley Holes (12/T), 1920 *R. Morse* has been determined as *hypophegea*.

Primulaceae (Primrose family)

Genus: *Primula*

Primula vulgaris Hudson
Primrose
Native.
First record: 1748.
Tetrad occurrence: 255 (52%).
Increasing (+46%).

It seems counter-intuitive that this plant has increased significantly since the 1960s, because it does not seem to be in anywhere near the numbers that were met with in Hertfordshire's coppices in the 1930s, as evidenced by old photographs. Some of the increase may be escapes from churchyards and gardens, but surely not all. It is still mainly found in damper, calcareous woods on the Boulder Clay, and in Chilterns dip-slope woodlands on Clay-with-Flints, sometimes in wooded hedgerows, but becoming rare on more acidic soils in south Hertfordshire (although even here quite widely), and on the Chalk itself.
(166 tetrads: Dony, 1967; 201 tetrads: 1950-1986)

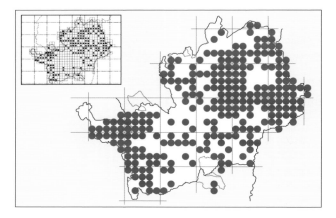

Map 246. *Primula vulgaris*

Primula × digenea A. Kerner (*P. vulgaris × P. elatior*)
Native.
First record: *c.*1959.

Until recently, this hybrid had only been recorded at Great Hormead Park Wood (42/E), with the parents (Dony, 1967), where it was noted again in 1979 and 1984, *T. J./B. R. Sawford*. During the current survey, it was noted here in 1988, *S. Watson* and independently by *G. P. Smith*, who reported that it was abundant and variable. With the discovery of an isolated population of Oxlip in the Bovingdon-Berkhamsted area in the 1980s (see below), it is not surprising that it has now also been recorded from west Herts.: at Heathen Grove (90/X) (VC24 [Herts.]), 1998, *R. Mabey*; Long Wood, near Bovingdon (00/D), 1994 *G. Salisbury/J. Saunders*; copse near Mounts Hill, Bovingdon (90/X) (VC24 [Herts.]), 1990, *R. Mabey*.

Primula × polyantha Miller (*P. vulgaris × P. veris*).
False Oxlip
Native.
First record: 1838 (Pryor, 1887) (as *P. vulgaris* var. *caulescens*).
Tetrad occurrence: 26 (5%).

Dony briefly mentions that it is commonest on the Boulder Clay, which is still the case, but the map shows that it is widespread, if sporadic, elsewhere, much as it was in the 19th century. It occurs usually in woodlands or scrub near old grassland, where the parents are close together, or in old plantations on former grassland.

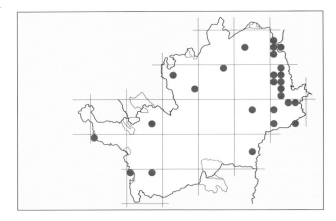

Map 247. *Primula × polyantha.*

Primula 'Wanda' (*P. vulgaris × P. juliae* Krecz.)
Garden Primula
Introduced: casual.
First documented record: 1987.

This garden hybrid with red flowers has been noted a few times as an escape from churchyards, (*e.g.* Stocking Pelham 42/J), 1987 *T. J.*), but there are few detailed records from the current survey.

Primula elatior (L.) Hill   UK Near Threatened
Oxlip
Native.
First record: *c.*1959.
Tetrad occurrence: 5 (1%).

Dony (1967) gives a very brief account of this enigmatic plant, but he did produce a much more detailed account in a separate paper (Dony, 1961). The plant's occurrence in Britain was studied in great detail by Doris and Harry Meyer of Letchworth (Meyer, D. and H., 1951), who later discovered its first colony in Hertfordshire at Great Hormead Park (42/E). Other Ash/Maple/Hazel woodlands in north-east Herts. were also proposed as possible sites, such as Beeches Wood (43/K), but there has never been a fully satisfactory record from any of these. In 1977, some 40 plants were discovered flowering in a copse near The Larches, south of Berkhamsted (90/Y), *J. Robertson*, although other plants were known to R. Mabey from woodlands nearby, then in Bucks. It was then also reported from Long Wood, Berkhamsted (00/D), in Herts., 1983, *R. M.* In 1992, boundary changes brought the Buckinghamshire sites into administrative Hertfordshire. The current survey has therefore recorded it from Great Hormead Park Wood (42/E), 1987, 1999 *T. J. et al.*; an ancient parish boundary hedgerow east of Great Hormead Park Wood (42/J), 1987, *T. J.*; Heathen Grove (90/X) (VC24 [Herts.]), 1990, 1998 *R. M.*; Long Wood, Berkhamsted (00/D), 1989 *R. M.* and 1994

AH 08

Primula taxa to compare: Oxlip Primula elatior *(centre and top right), with Cowslip* Primula veris *(far left),* Primrose Primula vulgaris *(centre left), and the hybrid False Oxlip* Primula × polyantha *between them, see opposite and page 182.'*

Photo: Brian Sawford

Oxlip Primula elatior *Great Hormead Park, 1984.*

G. *Salisbury/J. Saunders*; copse near Mount Hill, Bovingdon (90/X) (VC24 [Herts.]), 1990 *R. M.*; and Bovingdon Great Wood (00/C) (VC24 [Herts.]), 1990 *R. M.* The sites in west Herts./ Bucks. are outliers of a plant which is otherwise very tightly confined in Britain to an area on Boulder Clay stretching from the Herts./Beds./Cambs. borders to Suffolk, where it tends to replace the Primrose in damp woodlands. However, recent attempts to re-find some of the Berkhamsted colonies have not been successful, and its survival here is in doubt.

Primula veris L.
Cowslip *or* **Paigles**
Native.
First record: 1653.
Tetrad occurrence: 286 (58%).
Stable or increasing? (+20%).

This native plant of calcareous grassland is also very much a survivor. It can often be one of the first plants to reappear after scrub removal on downland, and can tolerate quite a lot of habitat disturbance, but not eutrophication. Its apparent increase since 1967 may be more a function of better recording in some areas than a real increase, although it has appeared more in southern Herts., where it is scarce on the more acidic soils.
(226 tetrads: Dony, 1967; 281 tetrads: 1950-1986)

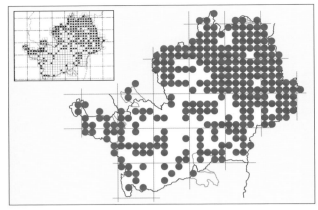

Map 248. *Primula veris.*

Genus: *Hottonia*

Hottonia palustris L.
Water-violet
Native.
First record: 1814.
Tetrad occurrence: 13 (3%).
Apparently increasing (+108%).

This beautiful and sometimes unpredictable native of drains on grazing marshes and sometimes old ponds, has never been abundant, although considered to be 'not uncommon' in the 19th century. However, in some sites, especially ponds, it was regarded with suspicion as a likely introduction. Interestingly enough, it has often thrived in some of these, such as Crabtree Pond on Hertford Heath (31/K), where it has been known for 150 years; the so-called 'Decoy Pond' at Watery Grove (22/G), first noticed in 1957 (although recently not seen); and at Halfway-oak Pond, Milwards Park (20/N), first recorded in 1960. At King's Meads, Hertford (31/L, M), it is a long-standing feature of the

Photo: Alan Reynolds

Water Violet Hottonia palustris *Kings Meads, 2009.*

old course of the River Lea, the Manifold Ditch, where it has responded magnificently to conservation efforts, spreading into other ditches; but its arrival at Amwell Quarry (31/R), 1985, 1989, *T. J./G. J. White* was at a new site, although not reported recently. It is thought to have been planted at a pond on the tetrad boundary at Rolls and Blackthorn Woods (21/Q, R); but is quite likely to be native at other sites, such as the River Colne at Watford (19/C), 1996 *S. Cuming*, because it was known from this area in the 19th century.

(6 tetrads: Dony, 1967, 11 tetrads: 1950-1986)

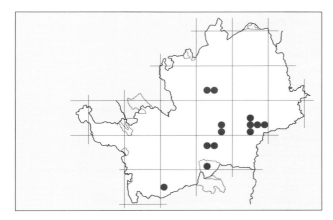

Map 249. *Hottonia palustris.*

Genus: *Cyclamen*

Cyclamen hederifolium Aiton
Sowbread
Introduced: neophyte.
First record: 1959.

J. Gardiner's record from Smaley Wood (43/G), 1959 (given in error as 43/L in Dony, 1967) was actually the first, because the earlier record he refers to in Pryor (1887) was actually of *C. repandum*. Sowbread has also been recorded more recently as an escape on a pathside near Great Amwell (31/R), 1984 *M. J. Barrett*; from Sherrards Park Wood (21/G), 1992 *A. M. Boucher*, 2007 *T. J.*; a roadside at Hertford (31/G), 2008 *T. J. et. al.*, and the banks of the old railway at Cole Green (21/V), 2008 *W. Bishop/T. J.*

Cyclamen repandum Sibth. and Sm.
Spring Sowbread
Introduced: casual.
First (only) record: *c.*1880.
The record of this as an apparent escape at Totteridge in Pryor (1887) remains the only one.

Genus: *Lysimachia*

Lysimachia nemorum L.
Yellow Pimpernel
Native.
First record: 1814.
Tetrad occurrence: 104 (21%).
Stable (+5%).

This is an especially characteristic plant of ancient woodland on the more acidic, clay soils, where it can tolerate a fair amount of shade, and is a good indicator of woodland continuity. There is

no real evidence for an increase as this is owing more to better recording in some areas as compared with the 1960s survey, and, if anything its abundance has decreased somewhat owing to the neglect of woodland rides.

(94 tetrads: Dony, 1967; 113 tetrads: 1950-1986)

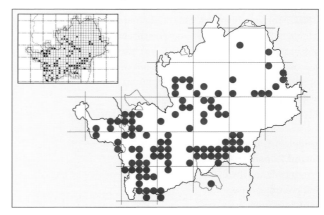

Map 250. *Lysimachia nemorum.*

Lysimachia nummularia L.
Creeping Jenny
Native and introduced.
First record: 1814.
Tetrad occurrence: 170 (35%).
Decreasing (-19%).

As a native plant, this is most frequent in waterlogged areas of old grazing pastures on more calcareous clay soils, or in open, wet woodland rides, where it can occur almost alongside Yellow Pimpernel. However, it is quite often likely to occur from escaped plants from gardens in places like road verges, as many colonies are clonal, not setting good seed. It is showing clear signs of decrease, both from its native sites, owing to the degradation of old, wet grasslands and woodland rides, and from roadside sites, owing to eutrophication and salt-pollution.

(198 tetrads: Dony, 1967; 212 tetrads: 1950-1986)

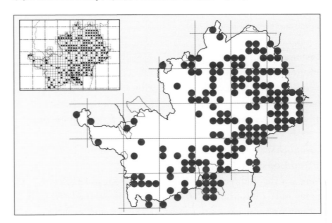

Map 251. *Lysimachia nummularia.*

Lysimachia vulgaris L.   Herts Rare
Yellow Loosestrife
Native.
First record: 1650.
Tetrad occurrence: 3 (<1%).
Very rare and decreasing (-33%).

This was always uncommon in the County, mainly found on the

more acidic gravels of the lower Colne valley, but has decreased almost to the point of extinction. It has only recently been found in three locations in two tetrads, two of which at least are introductions: clearing in Bishop's Wood, Rickmansworth (09/Q), 1987 *I. D. Marshall* (one of Dony's native sites, not seen since); moat pond at Batlers Green Farm (19/P), 1982, 1988 *D. Graham, P. Baker* (originally introduced); and pond at Edgegrove School, Aldenham (19/P), 1993 *J. K. Jackson* (probably planted). Since 1967, it was also seen at Stockers Lake (09/L), 1983 *J. Welsh*; at Cassiobury Park (09/Y), 1973 *K. Preston-Mafham*; and at Kings Langley Lake (00/R), 1971 *B. Ing*, at none of which has it recently been recorded.

(4 tetrads: Dony, 1967; 8 tetrads: 1950-1986)

Lysimachia punctata L.
Dotted Loosestrife
Introduced: neophyte.
First record: *c.*1960?
Tetrad occurrence: 45 (9%).
Increasing (+283%).

Usually a plant of rough herbage on dry, moderately acidic or neutral soils, this turns up occasionally as a persistent escape from gardens, but is rarely established in any one site for very long.
(11 tetrads: Dony, 1967; 21 tetrads: 1950-1986)

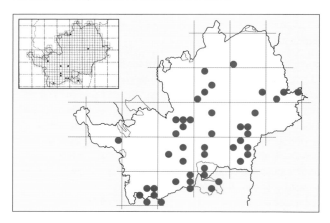

Map 252. *Lysimachia punctata.*

[*Lysimachia ciliata* L.
Fringed Loosestrife
Records of this were published by Burton (1983), but he was doubtful about them, and therefore they cannot be accepted without further evidence, as they probably refer to *L. punctata*.]

[*Lysimachia thyrsiflora* L.
Tufted Loosestrife
There is a very old record by John Ray from Kings Langley, quoted in H. Clutterbuck's '*History of Hertfordshire*' (1815), but without further evidence this must also be rejected, especially as *L. vulgaris* was recorded from here in the past.]

Genus: *Anagallis*

Anagallis tenella (L.) L.   Herts Extinct
Bog Pimpernel
Native.
First record: 1835.

If we need to see just how Hertfordshire's wetlands have been degraded, this is one of the plants to give us the evidence. It was a feature of permanently wet, grazed boggy pastures and fens at Hitchin (Oughton Head and Walsworth Commons); Hatfield (Bell Bar, Grub's Lane bog; Barber's Lodge bog); Wilstone (Rushy Meadow); and Hoddesdon (Hoddesdon Marsh) (Pryor, 1887). Its last record is that given in Dony (1967): Rushy Meadow, by Wilstone Reservoir (91/B), 1965, when it was re-discovered by P. M. Benoit. This locality, a 'Site of Special Scientific Interest', is now, nevertheless, a degraded, overgrown swamp.

Anagallis arvensis L.
Scarlet Pimpernel
Native.
First record: 1814.
Tetrad occurrence: 390 (79%).
Decreasing (-15%).

This once familiar and charismatic weed of arable fields, waste ground and disturbed patches in semi-natural grasslands is now often limited to a few scraps around field margins. Its 15% decrease at the tetrad level masks a much greater loss in overall frequency, although it can still be fairly numerous, especially on drier, gravelly ground.
(438 tetrads: Dony, 1967; 443 tetrads: 1950-1986)

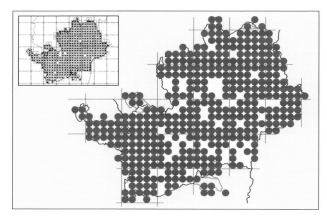

Map 253. *Anagallis arvensis.*

The main plant in the County is the familiar red form of ssp. *arvensis*. The blue variety '*caerulea*' of the nominate subspecies

Blue Pimpernel Anagallis arvensis *ssp.* foemina *Little Hadham, 1979.*

is rare, but does occur here and there, such as around Lilley. It needs to be distinguished from ssp. *foemina* (Mill.) Schinz and Thell., **Blue Pimpernel** itself, an introduced archaeophyte, which was disputed as a Hertfordshire plant by earlier botanists (Dony, 1967), but which has now been confirmed by old specimens from Offley Holes (12/T), 1843 *J. W. Curtis* (det. G. A. Matthews) (Hb. BM) and (det. F. M. Perring) (Hb. CGE); from Royston, 1909 *Mrs Burden* (det. F. M. Perring) (Hb. CGE); and from Welwyn, 1931 [H. Phillips?] (Hb. E) (*comm.*: B.R.C., CEH Monks Wood). It was also found more recently at Digswell (21/M), 1971 *J. M. Mullin* (*comm.*: B.R.C., CEH Monks Wood); and at Little Hadham (42/G), 1979 *J. Welsh* (conf. T. J./B. R. Sawford) (Hb. HTN). During the recent survey, it was again found at Little Hadham (42/L), 1988 *S. Watson* (det. T. J.) (Hb. HTN); and by Roe Wood, Sandon (33/C), 1996 *T. J.* (Hb. HTN).

Anagallis minima (L.) E. H. Krause   UK Near Threatened
Chaffweed   Herts Extinct
Native.
First record: 1843.

This is another casualty of the dereliction of Hertfordshire's heaths, as it is a speciality of bare, disturbed sandy ground. It was a rare plant by Webb and Coleman's time at Moor Park and Colney Heath. It was also found later in Broxbourne Woods (TL30), and was last seen there in about 1931 by A. W. Graveson (Dony, 1967).

Genus: *Samolus*

Samolus valerandi L.   Herts Rare
Brookweed
Native.
First record: 1843.
Extinct?

This plant of flushes and ditch-sides on Chalk Marl and similar soils was always rare in Herts., and was thought to be extinct since the 1950s at its last former stronghold, Oughton Head Common (Dony, 1967). However, it made a brief re-appearance in a cleared stream by the roadside at Mobbs Hole, Ashwell (24/R) in 1982-4

Photo: Brian Sawford

Brookweed Samolus valerandi *Mobbs Hole, Ashwell, 1982.*

T. J. (Hb. HTN), after which it succumbed again to overgrowth of the ditch. This was at one time adjacent to the other site known to Coleman: Ashwell Common, which was destroyed about 1860 by Parliamentary inclosure!

Hydrangeaceae (Hydrangea family)

Genus: *Philadelphus*

Philadelphus coronarius L.
Mock-orange
Introduced: neophyte.
First record: 1979.

The first record of this appears to have been by M. V. Marsden at West Hyde (09/F), 1979 (Burton, 1980), where it was noted as apparently self-sown on the causeway between the gravel pits. A record from Ware in 1982 (James, 1985) was subsequently re-identified as the hybrid *P. × virginalis*. During the survey, however, there were records from eight widely scattered sites in seven tetrads, sometimes as relicts from former planting, but occasionally self-sown in waste ground, such as at the Russells Yard site, Hitchin, (12/Z), 1998 *T. J.*; and Cheshunt Gravel Pits (30/R), 1994 *A. M. Boucher.*

Philadelphus × virginalis Rehder
(*P. coronarius?* × *P. microphyllus* × *P. pubescens*)
Hairy Mock-orange
Introduced: neophyte.
First record: 1982.

This sterile hybrid occurs occasionally as a throw-out, and one or two of the records for *P. coronarius* itself may be misidentifications of this, because it is now commoner in gardens than the species. First eventually identified from material collected at Ware (31/M), 1982 *A. M. Boucher* (Hb. AMB). During the survey it was also identified at Shilley Green (22/B), 1996 *A. D. Marshall*; Temple Wood, Welwyn (21/H), 1993 *T. J.*; by R. Lea, Mill Green (21/F), 1996 *A. D. M.*

Grossulariaceae (Currants)

Genus: *Ribes*

Ribes rubrum L.
Red Currant
Native or introduced.
First record: 1838.
Tetrad occurrence: 249 (51%).
Increased markedly (+129%).

Red Currant is the most common species of the family, found in woods and thickets across the County, but most abundantly in the Chilterns. In the 19th century, it was quite local, usually by streams, but can now be found in almost any type of woodland, although most frequently in damp, secondary woods. Many occcurrences are no doubt bird-sown, but it may be native in some sites.
(103 tetrads: Dony, 1967; 139 tetrads: 1950-1986)

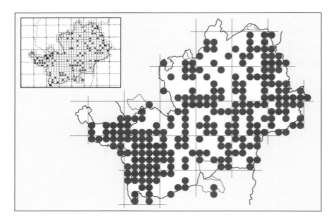

Map 254. *Ribes rubrum.*

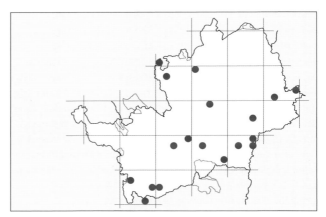

Map 256. *Ribes sanguineum.*

Ribes nigrum L.
Black Currant
Introduced (or native?).
First record: 1838.
Tetrad occurrence: 68 (14%).
Increasing (+156%).

The opinion nationally is that this is a long-standing introduction, but its occurrence in calcareous fen, and damp seepages in ancient woodlands in several places suggests that it may actually be native in such sites, as Dony (1967) suggested. It was recorded widely during the survey, some at long-standing sites, but others are evidently of bird-sown origin.
(25 tetrads: Dony, 1967; 41 tetrads: 1950-1986)

Ribes uva-crispa L.
Gooseberry
Introduced: neophyte.
First record: 1838.
Tetrad occurrence: 202 (41%).
Increased markedly (+159%).

This occurs widely on usually fairly dry, calcareous loam soils in woodland, scrub, and hedgerows across the County, but especially in the Chilterns, and on the drier, southern part of the Boulder Clay.
(74 tetrads: Dony, 1967; 100 tetrads: 1950-1986)

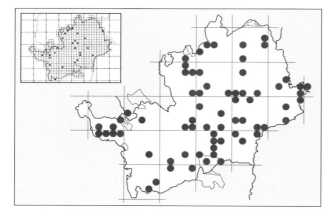

Map 255. *Ribes nigrum.*

Ribes sanguineum L.
Flowering Currant
Introduced: neophyte.
First record: 1957.
Tetrad occurrence: 18 (4%).
Increasing.

Dony (1967) dismissed this as only a relict of old gardens and gave no records, but the first was actually from Hay Wood, near Hemel Hempstead (00/H), 1957 *C. J. Leach*, where it may have been self-sown from the gardens of Westbrook Hay. It certainly now turns up quite frequently in waste places, or by old railways, *etc.*
(3 tetrads: 1950-1986)

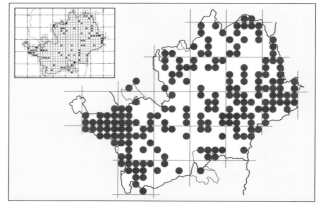

Map 257. *Ribes uva-crispa.*

Crassulaceae (Stonecrops)

Genus: *Crassula*

Crassula tillaea L.
Mossy Stonecrop
Introduced? [native in the U.K.].
First record: *c.*1945.

The only record of this in Hertfordshire remains the one made of it from the drying margin of Marsworth Reservoir, Tring (91/B), about 1945 by Sir Edward Salisbury (Dony, 1969). It was probably introduced by birds, and did not persist.

Crassula helmsii (Kirk) Cockayne
New Zealand Pigmyweed
Introduced: neophyte.
First record: 1976.
Tetrad occurrence: 21 (4%).
Increasing.

This invasive aquarium plant was first found in a pond at Hadley Green (29/N) (VC21 [Herts.: 1904-1965]), 1976 *A. M. Boucher* (Dony, 1977). It was later found in the pond on Batchworth Heath (09/R), 1979 *A. R. Jeffkins*; and at a pool by Hoddesdon Power Station (30/Z), 1982 *A. M. B./T. J.* (Hb. HTN). It was not abundant at the beginning of the Flora Survey, but by the end of the survey had been found widely spread across the County, although not as dominant in many of these sites as it is in some parts of the country.

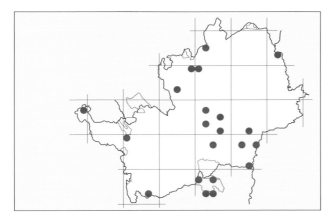

Map 258. *Crassula helmsii.*

Genus: *Sempervivum*

Sempervivum tectorum L.
House-leek
Introduced: neophyte.
First record: 1838.
Tetrad occurrence: 10 (2%).
Probably decreasing.

This plant tends not to be recorded effectively, because it is so often regarded as only planted when it occurs on old tile or thatched roofs. The result is that there are few properly documented records, although the suggestion is that its habitats are declining. One of our surveyors, Shirley Watson, made a point of recording the species, and it was therefore recorded widely in east Hertfordshire. One other long-standing site is known at Langley near Hitchin. It would be good to know if it does persist naturally, and if so, how frequent it really is.

Genus: *Sedum*

Sedum spectabile Boreau
Butterfly Stonecrop
Introduced: casual.
First (only) record: 1995.

The only record in the wild in Herts. is from tipped earth on a roadside at Symondshyde (11/V), 1995 *A. M. Boucher/G. P. Smith*. It may well have been overlooked elsewhere.

Sedum telephium L.   Herts Vulnerable
Orpine
Native.
First record: *c*.1730.
Tetrad occurrence: 30 (6%).
Decreasing quite sharply (-65%).

Orpine was at one time a frequent plant of gravelly loam soils supporting rough vegetation in woodland rides and wood margins, roadsides, and railway banks across central and southern Hertfordshire. It has decreased with the loss or eutrophication of this kind of rough, marginal habitat everywhere.
(81 tetrads: Dony, 1967; 91 tetrads: 1950-1986)

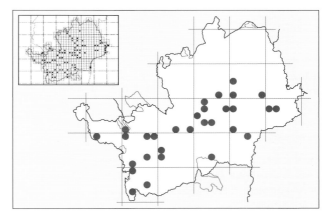

Map 259. *Sedum telephium.*

Although 19th century botanists recognised different forms, most plants have not been identified recently to the currently recognised subspecies, although ssp. *fabaria* (Koch) Kirschl. has been recorded in a number of localities previously, and was identified at Cole Green Way (31/A), 1993 *A. M. Boucher* during the survey. It may be the common form.

Sedum spurium M. Bieb.
Caucasian Stonecrop
Introduced: neophyte.
First record: 1979.

This was first noted as an escape at Kings Langley (00/S), 1979 *E. Goode* (James, 1985). It was found three times during the survey: old course of A414, Great Amwell (31/Q), 1988 *A. M. Boucher*; Welwyn Garden City (21/G), 1990 *C. G. Hanson*; and on an old wall at Wood End, Ardeley (32/H), 1998 *S. Watson*. It may well be established elsewhere.

Sedum rupestre L.
Reflexed Stonecrop
Introduced: neophyte.
First record: *c*.1840.
Tetrad occurrence: 43 (9%).
Increased (+2100%).

The apparent spread of this plant may be due partly to a lack of recording earlier, because it was noted quite widely in the 19th century on old walls, such as those of Hertford Castle (31/G), from where it has, however, not been recorded recently.
(2 tetrads: Dony, 1967; 6 tetrads: 1950-1986)

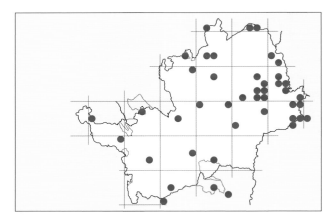

Map 260. *Sedum rupestre.*

Sedum acre L.
Biting Stonecrop
Native (sometimes escaped).
First record: 1824.
Tetrad occurrence 183 (+37%).
Increased (+102%).

Found across the County on old walls, roofs, edges of roads, gravel pits and waste ground, wherever lack of competition allows it to thrive. It is a frequent garden plant as well, and some records no doubt derive from escapees. It has evidently increased substantially since 1967, owing to urban expansion, new roads and gravel pit creation. It seems to be somewhat tolerant of salt by roads, and has become abundant by some, such as the A505 near Royston.
(86 tetrads: Dony 1967; 107 tetrads: 1950-1986)

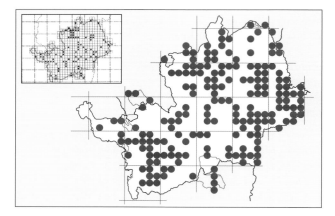

Map 261. *Sedum acre.*

Sedum album L.
White Stonecrop
Introduced: neophyte.
First record: 1839.
Tetrad occurrence: 81 (17%).
Increased.

Whether this species has genuinely expanded as dramatically as it appears to have done, or whether people previously ignored or misidentified it, it is difficult to say. It is now a frequent plant of bare, stony ground around towns and villages, old railways, and in churchyards (where it has been a favourite plant for decorating graves, and from which it readily spreads) throughout the County, but especially in east Herts. It may, however, have been under-

recorded when not in flower elsewhere, and could then also be misidentified for other species.
(1 tetrad: Dony, 1967; 9 tetrads: 1950-1986)

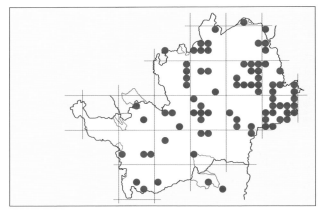

Map 262. *Sedum album.*

Sedum dasyphyllum L.
Thick-leaved Stonecrop
Introduced: neophyte.
First record: 1840.

This was apparently fairly widespread, if rare, in the 19th century on old walls, but had not been recorded since (Dony, 1967), until it was found on a wall at Much Hadham (41/J), 1979 *K. E. Bull.* During the recent survey it was found by a path at Colney Heath Farm (20/C), 1992 *S. M. Hedley.* It may be overlooked as *S. album* elsewhere.

Sedum hispanicum L.
Spanish Stonecrop
Introduced: neophyte.
First record: 1989.

Not recorded before the current survey, a large patch was discovered by the road at Shingle Hall, High Wych (41/T), 1989 *S. Watson.* It was then also found as an escape at Buntingford (32/U), 1992 *S. W.*

Saxifragaceae (Saxifrages)

Genus: *Saxifraga*

Saxifraga cymbalaria L.
Celandine Saxifrage
Introduced: casual.
First record: 1962.

Not recorded during the current survey, but found during the 1970s as an escape at Berkhamsted (90/Y), *Mrs Harris* (*comm.*: Herts. N.H.S.).

Saxifraga × urbium D. A. Webb (*S. umbrosa × S. spathularis*)
London Pride
Introduced: casual.
First record: *c.*1980?

Three isolated tetrad records in the County are indicated in Burton (1983), but there have been no other records.

Saxifraga granulata L.
Meadow Saxifrage
Native.
First record: 1737.
Tetrad occurrence: 34 (7%).
Stable? (+11%).

The distribution of this attractive native plant of unimproved calcareous, gravelly grassland remains much the same as it was in 1967, with concentrations of sites around Hertford, and between Stevenage and Hitchin. There may be some indication that it has disappeared from some sites, while being better recorded elsewhere.
(29 tetrads: Dony, 1967; 42 tetrads: 1950-1986)

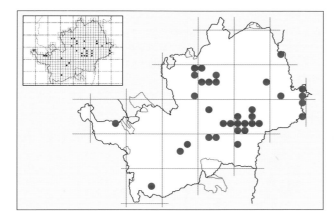

Map 263. *Saxifraga granulata.*

Saxifraga tridactylites L.
Rue-leaved Saxifrage
Native.
First record: 1814.
Tetrad occurrence: 12 (2%).
Apparently increased or stable (+85%).

Dony (1967) thought that this had become rare, but the evidence is that it is sparsely, yet regularly scattered across the County, growing on old walls and roofs, and sometimes on stony ground. There is also good evidence that it persists at favoured localities, because some of its present sites are the same as those known to earlier botanists. The main threat to it appears to be the 'tidying up' of old walls and re-roofing of old buildings, but it can go unnoticed for long periods, and is very drought-resistant, the whole plant turning bright red in very impoverished situations.
(6 tetrads: Dony, 1967; 13 tetrads: 1950-1986)

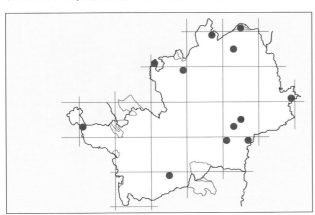

Map 264. *Saxifraga tridactylites.*

Genus: *Tellima*

Tellima grandiflora (Pursh) Douglas ex Lindley
Fringe-cups
Introduced: neophyte.
First record: 1992.
First found at Woodcock Hill, Berkhamsted (90/T), 1992 *M. J. Hicks* (det. T. J.) (Hb. HTN). It was subsequently found by Symondshyde Great Wood (11/V), 1995 *A. M. Boucher/T. J.* (Hb. HTN); and at Darlands (29/L), 2002 *R. M. Burton.*

Genus: *Chrysosplenium*

Chrysosplenium oppositifolium L.
Opposite-leaved Golden-saxifrage
Native.
First record: 1838.
Tetrad occurrence: 15 (3%).
Possibly decreasing (-3%).

This is local, and an inconspicuous plant when not in flower, found on wet mud by wooded streams, and around shaded spring sources. Although the overall distribution is much the same as recorded by Dony (1967), it was not re-found at a few sites, possibly owing to the effects of drought during the 1990s.
(15 tetrads: Dony, 1967; 19 tetrads: 1950-1986)

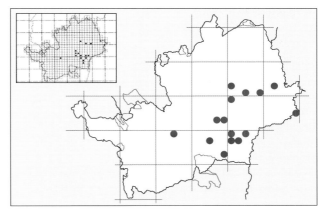

Map 265. *Chrysosplenium oppositifolium.*

Genus: *Parnassia*

Parnassia palustris L.   Herts Extinct
Grass-of-Parnassus
Native.
First record: 1737.

The loss of this beautiful plant of flushed mires is one of the greatest losses from the Hertfordshire flora, but parallels several other species of the same kind of habitat. Its demise was due to a combination of reduced ground-water levels during the 19th and early 20th centuries, and the dereliction and destruction of grazing marsh. It was last seen by Charles Oldham at Rushy Meadow, by Wilstone Reservoir (91/B) in August 1924 (but with 'a great deal... in flower' there at the time) (postcard to E. J. Salisbury), so it probably lasted a little longer.

Rosaceae (Rose family)

Sorbaria sorbifolia (L.) A. Braun
Sorbaria
Introduced: neophyte.

This ornamental shrub from Asia was noted growing by the track-bed of the railway south of Hatfield Station (20/J), 2004, *T. J.*, having spread from nearby planted shrubberies.

Genus: *Spiraea*

Spiraea salicifolia L.
Bridewort
Introduced: neophyte.
First record: *c*.1877.

This garden shrub only occurs as a relic of old gardens or as a garden throw-out. It was first found at St Albans (Pryor, 1887), and it was found at Knebworth Park Lake (22/F), *c*.1950 *E. G. Kellett* (Dony, ms index). During the survey, it was found at Carpenders Park Cemetery (19/G), 1988 and at Aldenham (19/T), 1991 *J. K. Jackson*.

Spiraea × rosalba Dippel (*S. salicifolius × S. alba*)
Intermediate Bridewort
Introduced: neophyte, casual.
First record: 1999.

A solitary old bush was found, presumably originally planted, at Peartree Wood, Bricket Wood (10/F), 1999 *T. J.*

Spiraea × billardii Hérincq (*S. alba × S. douglasii*)
Billard's Bridewort
Introduced: neophyte.
First record: 1991.
This was established near the car park in Northaw Great Wood, evidently from nearby gardens (20/X), 1991 *T. J.* (Hb. HTN).

Spiraea douglasii Hooker
Steeple-bush
Introduced: neophyte.
First record: 1989.

This was first confirmed by a pond at Albury (42/M), 1989 *S. Watson*; but was also later found at Smallford Pit (10/Y), 1992 *T. J.*; and independently by a pond at Edgegrove School, Aldenham (19/P), 1993 *T. J., J. K. Jackson*.

Genus: *Aruncus*

Aruncus dioicus (Walter) Fernald
Buck's-beard
Introduced: casual.
First (only) record: 1991.

This was found, apparently self-sown, at Hertford Castle grounds (31/G) *A. M. Boucher*.

Genus: *Filipendula*

Filipendula vulgaris Moench
Dropwort
Native.
First record: 1748.
Tetrad occurrence: 18 (4%).
Stable or decreased? (no recorded change).

Although currently recorded from a similar number of tetrads as in 1967, there is evidence that this plant of chalk downland and dry calcareous grassland has retreated to its favoured sites on chalk scarps, especially at Therfield Heath, the hills around Hexton, and at Blows Down (VC20 [Beds.]). It was once fairly widespread in calcareous meadows on the Boulder Clay, but its last such sites are at Weston Church Meadow and Recreation Ground (23/Q) and a rough grassy paddock at Gresley Way, Stevenage (22/R). It has, however, appeared on the margin of Waterford Gravel Pit (31/C), 1997 *G. P. Smith*.
(17 tetrads: Dony, 1967; 22 tetrads: 1950-1986)

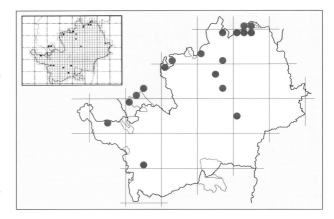

Map 266. *Filipendula vulgaris*.

Filipendula ulmaria (L.) Maxim.
Meadowsweet
Native.
First record: 1750.
Tetrad occurrence: 276 (56%).
Slightly decreased (-8%).

A frequent and attractive plant of more calcareous wetland sites, streamsides, ditches, wet woodland rides, *etc*. There is some evidence that it has decreased in some areas, notably marginal

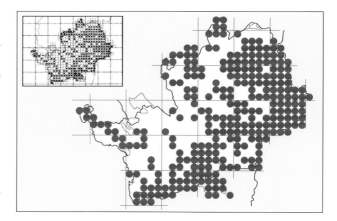

Map 267. *Filipendula ulmaria*.

habitats in arable farmland or where old pastures have been lost. It has always been absent from acidic clays in south Hertfordshire, and from the Chalk itself.

(284 tetrads: Dony, 1967; 298 tetrads: 1950-1986)

Genus: *Kerria*

Kerria japonica (L.) DC.
Kerria
Introduced: casual.
First (only) record: 1989.

One bush was found, possibly introduced, in scrub by Carpenders Park Cemetery (19/G) *J. K. Jackson*.

Genus: *Rubus*

Apart from the easily identified Raspberry, and the somewhat less easily identified Dewberry, the account of the genus *Rubus* in Dony (1967) does not attempt to cover this difficult group. This therefore represents the first modern attempt to cover the brambles reasonably systematically. Pryor (1887) included a summary account of records from Hertfordshire, some made by W. H. Coleman, and later ones by C. C. Babington and others. W. C. R. Watson also made a number of visits to Herts., and his records for the south of the County were incorporated in Kent and Lousley's '*Handlist of the plants of the London area*' (1952). Unfortunately, Watson's views on the identification of brambles have proved problematic, which has rendered many earlier records unacceptable, although some of both his and earlier ones can be used as a starting point for modern study. No systematic attempt, however, has been made to re-examine all the Hertfordshire specimens in various herbaria, although some from Coleman in Bolton Museum have been re-examined by D. P. Earl, and are accounted for here, along with others at Cambridge, communicated by R. J. Pankhurst.

This account owes a great debt especially to Alec Bull of Norfolk, who helped with numerous field visits from 1998-2005, and contributed most to identifying specimens. Alan Newton, the national referee for the genus, has also given much help, and thanks is due to them both for their encouragement. A. D. Marshall also contributed many records earlier in the survey, especially from the Hatfield area, and many of his records, also, were validated by Alec Bull or Alan Newton.

Hertfordshire's geographical position, coupled with its mix of geology and soils, has resulted in it being particularly rich in species for its size. Study of the U.K.'s brambles over the last 30 years has shown that there tend to be discrete communities of species in specific areas of the country (called 'florulas' by those involved in their study). Hertfordshire lies at the junction between at least four of these: the East Anglian, Chiltern, Thames Valley and Midlands florulas. In addition, there is some evidence that a number of species have arrived owing to the activities of forestry plantation. Within Hertfordshire, there are also distinct groups of species to some extent on the major soil types: the Boulder Clay and the north-east Chalk (rather species-poor), the river valley gravels of central Hertfordshire, the Clay-with-Flints of the Chilterns, and the acidic London Clay in south Herts. The greatest diversity comes where soil-types meet: Mardley Heath (on a mixture of mid-Herts. gravels and Chilterns clays) and Whippendell Wood (where the Thames Valley gravels meet the Chilterns dip-slope clays), for example. Finally, Hertfordshire

is fortunate to have extensive areas of historic commons (and woodlands derived from others), which have allowed a rich diversity to survive into the modern landscape.

The bramble flora has now had reasonable coverage across much of the County, field visits since 1999 having been concentrated especially in the southern and western areas, where the diversity is greatest. However, there are, no doubt, more micro-species to discover, and much is still to be learned about the occurrence of these difficult plants, many of which have precise habitat requirements, and demonstrate fascinating distributions. Voucher specimens of many of the records given here are to be deposited in the herbarium at North Herts. Museums, and Alec Bull holds duplicates for the more important records. Quite a few gatherings of specimens remain unidentified, and there is one readily identifiable micro-species that has yet to be formally described. Others may also be named in the future.

The '*Rubus fruticosus*' aggregate, covering mostly the sub-genus *Rubus* itself, was recorded during the recent survey from 482 tetrads (98%).

Sub-genus *Anoplobatus*

Rubus odoratus L.
Purple-flowered Raspberry
Introduced: neophyte.
First record: 1987.

This was found under trees in Bayfordbury Pinetum (31/A), 1987, 1989, 1994, 1995 *A. M. Boucher/C. G. Hanson* (Hb. HTN), no doubt introduced with some of the trees from North America.

Rubus × fraseri Rehder (*R. odoratus × R. parviflorus*)

Specimens were collected from Bayfordbury Pinetum (31/A), 1987, 1989 *C. G. Hanson* (later det. E. J. Clement) (Hb. Hanson).

Rubus parviflorus Nutt.
Thimbleberry
Introduced: neophyte.
First record: 1980.
This was recorded from Ayot (21/H), 1980 *C. G. Hanson* (det. E. J. Clement), and also from Bayfordbury Pinetum (31/A), 1987, 1989, 1994, 1995; no doubt introduced with imported trees *A. M. Boucher/C. G. Hanson* (Hb. HTN).

Sub-genus: *Dalibardastrum*

Rubus tricolor Focke
Chinese Bramble
Introduced: neophyte.

The only record is as an escape at Bayfordbury (31/A), 1980 *C. G. Hanson*.

Sub-genus: *Idaeobatus*

Rubus idaeus L.
Raspberry
Native (and introduced).
First record: 1787.
Tetrad occurrence: 309 (63%).
Increasing (+47%).

The native habitat of wild Raspberry is light woodland on moderately acidic, gravelly soils. Even accounting for the increased coverage since Dony's *Flora*, it has evidently increased substantially, particularly as a bird-sown escape in ruderal habitats. It has also appeared more frequently on the Chalk, where it would not naturally be found, possibly as a result of surface eutrophication, and on damper clays, perhaps encouraged here by recent droughts.
(229 tetrads: Dony, 1967; 263 tetrads: 1950-1986)

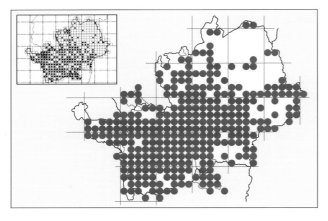

Map 268. *Rubus idaeus.*

Rubus × *paxii* Focke (*R. idaeus* × *R. phoenicolasius*)

This appeared with the parents on old allotments at Hatfield (20/D), 1996 *A. D. Marshall* (Hb. Marshall) (*comm.*: R. M. Burton).

Rubus phoenicolasius Maxim.
Japanese Wineberry
Introduced: neophyte.
First record: 1999.

Found at old allotments, Hatfield (20/D), 1996 *A. D. Marshall*, and in chalk scrub at Weston Hills (23/L), 1999 *K. Robinson* (det. T. J.) (Hb. HTN).

Rubus cockburnianus Hemsley
White-stemmed Bramble
Introduced: neophyte.
First record: 1995.

This was found as an escape, established by a wall at Ware (31/M), 1995, 1996 *A. M. Boucher/C. G. Hanson* (Hb. HTN).

Sub-genus: *Idaeobatus* × *Rubus*

Rubus loganobaccus L. Bailey (derived from *R. idaeus* × *R. vitifolius*)
Loganberry
Introduced: neophyte.
First record: 1990.

This is well-established at Ashwell Quarry (23/P), 1990, *etc. T. J.* (det. A. L. Bull), where it is a potential pest, and has also been reported as an escape at Brookmans Park (20/M), 1995 *A. D. Marshall*. No doubt it is more widespread.

Rubus idaeus can also hybridise naturally with sexually reproducing species of sub-genus *Rubus* and these could be confused with this taxon.

Sub-genus *Rubus*

Section: *Rubus*

Sub-section: *Rubus*

Rubus canadensis L.
Introduced: neophyte.
First record: 1993.

This thornless North American bramble was noted as an escape at Berkhamsted Golf Course (00/E), 1993 and subsequently by Potters Bar Golf Course (20/L) (VC21 [Herts.]), 1995 *A. D. Marshall*.

Rubus nessensis W. Hall   Herts Rare
Native.
First record: *c.*1914.

A plant of heath margins. There is an old record from TL31 in Edees and Newton (1988), presumably the one reported from Easneye (31/W) by Trower and Druce (*Rep. Bot. Exch. Club*: 263 (1915)). In 1987, *c.*5-10 bushes were found in a new conifer plantation at Aldenham (19/J) *A. D. Marshall*, presumably introduced. There are no other records.

Rubus plicatus Weihe and Nees   Herts Extinct
Native.
First record: 1841.

A collection of this plant of heaths on sandy soils was made by Coleman at Easneye (31/W), 1841 (det. D. P. Earl, 2000) (Hb. BON). This is the only confirmed locality, although Coleman (Webb and Coleman, 1849, 1851) thought he had also recorded it at the lost Tring Heath (90/P).

Rubus scissus W. C. R. Watson   Herts Extinct
Native.
First record: 1841.

A patch-forming bramble of peaty places on heaths, this was found by Coleman at Tring Heath (90/J), 1841; and subsequently at Easneye Wood (31/W), 1844 (Hb. BON) (det. D. P. Earl, 1997). There have been no recent records.

Rubus vigorosus P. J. Mueller and Wirtgen   Herts Rare
Native.
First record: 1993.

A plant of heaths. Remarkably, considering the history of plantation and excavation the site has had, this was found at Mardley Heath (21/P), 1993 *A. D. Marshall* (det. A. L. Bull and A. Newton) (Hb. Marshall), and remains the only confirmed record, although plants named 'R. affinis' were recorded by C. C. Babington at Milwards Park and may refer to this.

Sub-section: *Hiemales*

Series: *Sylvatici*

Rubus calvatus Lees ex Bloxam   Herts Rare
Native (U.K. endemic).
First record: 2004.

This scarce bramble of wood borders and heaths was found at Oxhey Woods (19/B), 2004 *A. L. Bull/T. J.* (det. A. Newton) (Hb. HTN); and again the same year at St John's Wood (32/C) *A. L. B./T. J.* (det. A. L. B.) (Hb. HTN).

[*Rubus crespignyanus* W. C. R. Watson

There is a specimen named this from Bricket Wood (10/G) collected by W. H. Mills in 1955, in Hb. CGE (*comm.*: R. J. Pankhurst). This is almost certainly an error, as the species has not been recorded outside Kent (*comm.*: A. Newton).]

Rubus errabundus W. C. R. Watson   Herts Rare
Native.
First record: 1998.

This is mostly a north-western plant of wood borders and heaths, and was first found in Herts. at Wain Wood (12/S, X), 1998 *A. L. Bull/A. Newton/T. J.* (det. A. N) (Hb. HTN).

Rubus laciniatus Willd.
Cut-leaved Bramble
Introduced: neophyte.
First record: *c*.1960?
Tetrad occurrence: 19 (4%).

Dony (1967) mentions this as an escape, with no further details. It was recorded during the survey as an occasional escape in scrub, mostly on more acidic soils, but it is difficult to know how long any one plant survives.

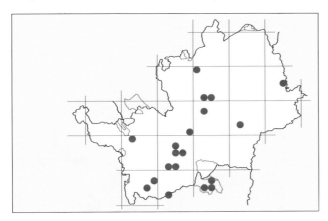

Map 269. *Rubus laciniatus.*

Rubus leptothyrsos G. Braun   Herts Rare
Native.
First record: 2004.

Mainly a northern bramble of wood borders and heaths, this was found at Oxhey Woods (19/B), 2004 *A. L. Bull/T. J.* (det. A. L. B.) (Hb. HTN).

Rubus lindleianus Lees
Native.
First record: 1840.
Tetrad occurrence: 23 (5%).

This is a conspicuous hedgerow bramble with white flowers. The first record is provided by a specimen collected by W. H. Coleman from 'Panshanger Park' (21/W?), 1840 (Hb. BON). It was also recorded by Babington near Hertford in 1875 (Pryor, 1887). The current survey recorded it mainly on the Lea and Colne gravels.

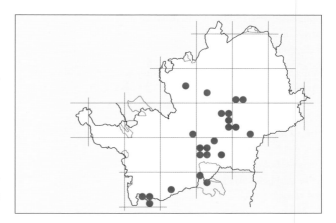

Map 270. *Rubus lindleianus.*

Rubus macrophyllus Weihe and Nees
Native.
First record: 1869.
Tetrad occurrence: 9 (2%).

This is a large-leaved, pink-flowered bramble of woodlands, scrub and heathland margins on acidic soils. Babington recorded it from Welwyn, and Webb made a few subsequent records (Pryor, 1887), which may be correct. There was a specimen in Watson's herbarium from Mardley Heath (*teste* J. G. Dony, ms. index), and B. A. Miles collected another from Bricket Wood, near the 'Black Boy' inn (10/G), 1964 (Hb. CGE) (*comm.*: R. J. Pankhurst). The current survey found it in nine tetrads: at Mardley Heath (21/P), 1993 *A. D. Marshall*; Sherrards Park Wood (21/G), 1993 *A. L. Bull/A. D. Marshall/A. Newton*; beside Graffridge Wood (22/A), 1998 *A. L. B/A. N./T. J.*; Plashes Wood (32/Q, V), 2000 *A. L. B.*, 2007 *T. J.* (Hb. HTN); Berkhamsted Common (00/E), 2001; Bricket Wood Common (10/F), 2001; Nomansland Common (11/R), 2002 *A. L. B/T. J.* (det. A. L. B.); and Box Wood, Walkern (22/T), 2006 *T. J.* (det. A. L. B.) (Hb. HTN).

Rubus poliodes W. C. R. Watson   Herts Extinct
Native (U.K. endemic).
First record: 1849.

This is almost restricted to heathland margins and wood borders on gravelly soils in East Anglia. There is one old record from Essendon (TL20), 1849 *A. Bloxam* (conf. C. C. Babington) (Hb. CGE) (*comm.*: A. Newton).

Rubus pyramidalis Kaltenb.   Herts Rare
Native.
First record: before 1988.

A species of wood margins and heaths. There are old records for SP90 [Herts.?] and TL21 in Edees and Newton (1988). The current survey only recorded it from Mardley Heath (21/P), 1993 *A. D. Marshall*; and Highfield Wood (30/P), 1999 *A. L. Bull/T. J.* (det. A. L. B.) (Hb. HTN).

Rubus robiae (W. C. R. Watson) Newton   Herts Rare
Native (U.K. endemic).
First record: *c*.1850.

This is mostly a bramble of the north-west, where it is frequent in the Pennine foothills. It was first recorded from TL21 by C. C. Babington in *c*.1850 (*comm.*: A. Newton). There is also a specimen from TL22 collected by W. H. Mills in 1954 (Hb. CGE).

Rubus sciocharis (Sudre) W. C. R. Watson   Herts Rare
Native.
First record: 2002.

Mainly a local, western bramble, the only record from the County is from Nomansland Common (11/R), 2002 *A. L. B./T. J.* (det. A. L. B.) (Hb. HTN).

Series: *Rhamnifolii*

Rubus acclivitatum W. C. R. Watson   Herts Rare
Native (U.K. endemic).
First record: 1953.

This is mainly restricted to the south-east of Wales, occurring on wood borders. A specimen collected by C. Avery from Berkhamsted Common, 1953 was in Watson's herbarium (Dony, ms. index) (Hb. NMW). There is a recent (post-1988) record from SP90, presumably the same locality, in Newton and Randall (2004), but no other record has been made during the survey.

Rubus amplificatus Lees in Steele
Native (U.K. endemic).
First record: *c.*1950?
Tetrad occurrence: 4 (<1%).

A bramble of hedgerows and wood borders. This was apparently first recorded with any certainty by W. C. R. Watson from Northaw Great Wood (TL20), *c.*1950 (Hb. Watson, teste Dony, ms. index). Local but widespread, but currently under-recorded: other pre-1987 records for TL01, 21, 23 and TQ29 are published in Edees and Newton (1988). The current survey recorded it from Highfield Wood (30/P), 1999 (Hb. HTN); by Prae Wood (10/I), 2001 (Hb. HTN); Hertford Heath (31/K), 2002; and Upper Stonyhills Wood (31/I), 2003 *A. L. Bull/T. J.* (all det. A. L. B.).

Rubus cardiophyllus Lef and P. J. Mueller
Native.
First record: 1838? (Pryor, 1887: attributed to *R. rhamnifolius* Weihe and Nees).
Tetrad occurrence: 12 (2%).

A bramble of wood-borders and hedgerows on more acidic soils, the present survey found this to be fairly widespread, but local, across southern Hertfordshire, which would be supported by most of the records quoted by Pryor, many of which were made by Coleman.

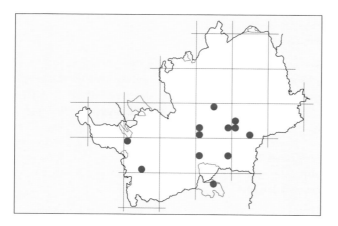

Map 271. *Rubus cardiophyllus.*

Rubus cissburiensis W. C. Barton and Riddelsd.   Herts Rare
Native (U.K. endemic).
First record: 2001.
Tetrad occurrence: 4 (<1%).

A scrambling plant of hedgerows and scrub. This is a species mainly found south of London (with another population around Liverpool). It was discovered at Saffron Green (29/I), 2001 *T. J.* (det. A. L. Bull) (Hb. HTN), and subsequently at Hadley Common (29/N), and at nearby Fir and Pond Woods Nature Reserve (20/Q), 2005 *T. J./A. L. B.* (Hb. HTN). It has also appeared, probably on introduced soil, at Purwell (22/E), 2005 *T. J.* (det. A. Newton) (Hb. HTN).

Rubus nemoralis Mueller   Herts Extinct?
Native.
First record: before 1988.

There is an undated field record by E. S. Edees from TL21 in Edees and Newton (1988) (and *comm.*: A. Newton). This is the only record. The species is widespread in some parts of Britain around heathland margins.

Rubus polyanthemus Lindeb.
Native.
First record: 1849.
Tetrad occurrence: 39 (8%).

This bramble is particularly frequent in damp scrub, woodland glades*, etc.* It was first collected by W. H. Coleman from 'Broxbourne Wood' (30/I?), 1849 (Hb. BON). It was also recorded by Watson (in: Kent and Lousley, 1952). The current survey found it to be particularly frequent on the damp London Clay in south-east Hertfordshire.

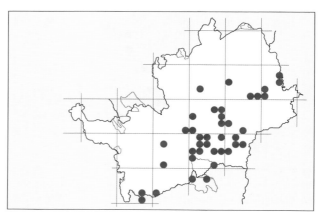

Map 272. *Rubus polyanthemus.*

Rubus rhombifolius Weihe ex Boenn.   Herts Rare
Native.
First record: 1913?

A species of heath and woodland margins, this was first reported by Trower and Druce (*Rep. Bot. Exch. Club*: 386 (1913)) from Broxbourne Woods (TL30), and by Watson, *c.*1950 from Bricket Wood Common (10/F) (in: Kent and Lousley, 1952). It has been found during the current survey only at one locality: Colney Heath (10/X, 20/C), 2001 *A. L. B./T. J.* (det. A. L. B.) (conf. A. Newton) (Hb. HTN).

Rubus subinermoides Druce
Native (U.K. endemic).
First record: 1849.
Tetrad occurrence: 54 (11%).

There is a specimen from Milwards Park (TL20/I?) collected by
W. H. Coleman in 1849 (det. D. P. Earl) (Hb. BON). Edees and
Newton (1988) show this from at least eight 10km squares in
southern Hertfordshire, but some earlier records may have been
confused with *R. macrophyllus*. The current survey found it to
be common in woodlands and hedgerows, especially on the drier
clays and gravels of south-west Herts. and the Chilterns dip-slope.

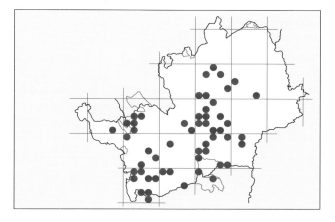

Map 273. *Rubus subinermoides.*

Series: *Sprengeliani*

Rubus sprengelii Weihe
Native.
First record: 1849.
Tetrad occurrence: 9 (2%).

A low-growing and dainty pink-flowered bramble of heathy
ground and woods on gravel. This was found by Coleman at
Milwards Park, 1849 (det. W. M. Rogers) (Hb. BON), and by
Babington at Hatfield (Pryor, 1887). Edees and Newton (1988)
give 10km records from TL20, 21 and 31. The current survey has
found it especially associated with old wood-pasture habitats in
the Hatfield, Northaw and Bramfield areas, and in the area around
Ashridge and Berkhamsted Common.

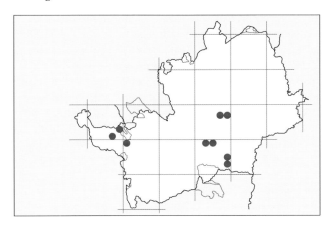

Map 274. *Rubus sprengelii.*

Series: *Discolores*

Rubus armeniacus Focke (= *R. procerus* Mueller ex Boulay)
Himalayan Giant
Introduced: neophyte.
First record: 1955?
Tetrad occurrence: 126 (26%).
Increasing dramatically.

Dony (1967) notes this as an escape, and his ms. index includes
a record from Wormley, 1955, but it may have occurred earlier.
The current survey has found it to be widespread and increasing
in waste places, roadsides, and disturbed ground. Despite being
widely noted, it remains under-recorded, especially in west Herts.

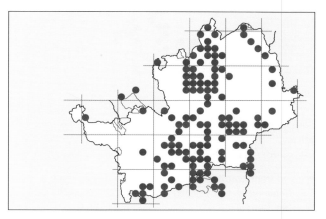

Map 275. *Rubus armeniacus.*

Rubus armipotens W. C. Barton ex Newton
Native (U.K. endemic).
First record: *c.*1950?
Tetrad occurrence: 8 (2%).

A plant of heaths and wood margins, especially between London
and Hampshire. There is a record from Oxhey Woods (19/B) in
Kent and Lousley (1952), given by Watson as *R. pseudo-bifrons*
(Sudre) Bouv., which may refer to this species. During the present
survey, it was found at Panshanger (31/B), 2002; Dancers Hill and
Dyrham Park (29/J), 2003; at Packhorse Lane, Borehamwood
(29/E), 2003 *A. L. B./T. J.* (det. A. L. B.) (Hb. HTN); Birch
Green (21/V), 2005 *T. J.*; Evergreen Wood, Panshanger (21/W),
2005 *T. J.*; Wynnel's Grove and Messop's Grove (43/C), 2005
A. L. B/T. J. (possibly introduced); Hadley Common (29/N) (VC21
[Herts., 1904-1965]), 2005 *A. L. B./T. J.*; and by Waterford Gravel
Pit (31/C), 2006 *T. J.*

Rubus ulmifolius Schott
Common Blackberry
Native.
First record: 1849 (1748?).
Tetrad occurrence: 209 (43%).

A common plant of hedgerows and wood margins throughout
much of the County, except on the more acidic gravels and clays.
Per Kalm refers to the common hedgerow bramble in his account
of Hertfordshire in 1748, most likely this species. Otherwise it
was first recorded by Coleman. It can be readily identified, even
in winter, by its neat, white-backed leaves and dark purple stems,
and when in bloom, especially by its cerise-pink flowers. It is
the only wholly sexually-reproducing bramble in the U.K., and

produces some of the most abundant blackberry crops, quite late into autumn. Dony (1967) noted it as common, and regretted not mapping it. Despite attempts to identify it as often as possible, it remains under-recorded, especially in west and extreme east Herts.

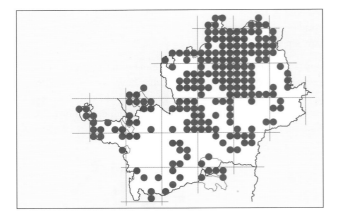

Map 276. *Rubus ulmifolius.*

Rubus ulmifolius × *R. vestitus*
Native.
First record: 1844.

Recorded from near Bricket Wood Common (10/F), 1844 *W. H. Coleman* (det. D. P. Earl) (Hb. BON). It is probably quite widespread where the two species meet, and has been recorded during the present survey from 18 widely-scattered tetrads across the centre of the County.

Rubus ulmifolius × *R. caesius*
Native.
First record: 2003.

Also probably fairly common in north Herts., this was first identified from Therfield Heath (33/P), 2003 *T. J.* (conf. A. L. Bull) and subsequently from seven other tetrads in this general area, where both plants are widespread.

Many other unidentified hybrid brambles are likely to have *R. ulmifolius* as one of the parents.

Series: *Vestiti*

Rubus adscitus Genev.
Native.
First record: 1950.
Tetrad occurrence: 7 (1%).

This occurs in open woodland and hedgerows, and is mostly confined to south-western Britain. It was first reported from Whippendell Wood in 1950 by W. H. Mills (W. C. R. Watson, in Kent and Lousley, 1952); and there is a specimen from there collected by B. A. Miles, 1964 in Hb. CGE. The current survey confirmed it at Whippendell Wood (09/T), 1990, *A. D. Marshall*, and from the same area, including Harrocks Wood (09/T, Y), 1999 *A. L. B./T. J.* (Hb. HTN). It has also been found at Graffridge Wood (22/A), 1993 *A. L. B/A. Newton/A. D. M.*; Highfield Wood (30/P), 1999 *A. L. B./T. J.*; Plashes Wood (32/Q, V), 2000 *A. L. B.*; and by Mutchetts Wood (10/F), 2001 *A. L. B./T. J.* (all det. A. L. B.).

Rubus boraeanus Genev.   Herts Rare
Native.
First record: 1955.

This conspicuous pink-flowered bramble occurs in hedgebanks and woodland margins, especially in Norfolk. It was first found near the 'Black Boy' inn at Garston (10/G), 1955 by W. H. Mills (Hb. CGE); and during the current survey not far away by the M1 at Mutchetts Wood (10/F), 2001 *A. L. B./T. J.* (det. A. L. B.) (Hb. HTN).

Rubus criniger (E. F. Linton) Rogers
Native (U.K. endemic).
First record: *c.*1950.
Tetrad occurrence: 12 (2%).

A greyish-green bramble of hedgebanks and wood borders on lighter, more acidic soils. This was first noted at Whippendell Wood and Hertford Heath by Watson (in Kent and Lousley, 1952); and was recorded from four 10km squares in Edees and Newton (1988). During the current survey it has been recorded particularly in the Broxbourne Woods and Bramfield areas.

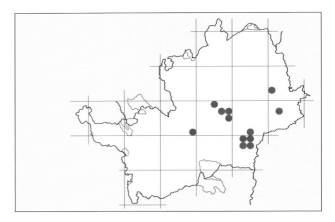

Map 277. *Rubus criniger.*

Rubus leucostachys Schleicher ex Sm.
Native (U.K. endemic).
First record: before 1988.
Tetrad occurrence: 6 (1%).

A bramble of wood borders and hedgerows on moderately acidic soils, especially the Clay-with-Flints, mainly occurring south of the Thames. There are records of '*R. leucostachys*' in Pryor (1887), who thought it was common, and in Webb and Coleman (1849), but their application of the name was probably erroneous, at least in part. Edees and Newton (1988) give a 10km record from TL01; and the current survey has recorded it from Cuffley (30/B), 1990 *A. Newton*; Pig's Green (42/A), 2002 *A. L. B./T. J.* (det. A. L. B.) (Hb. HTN); the Great Gaddesden area (01/G), 2003; Hudnall Common (01/B), 2003; Cheverells Green (01/M), 2003 *A. L. B./ T. J.* (det. A. L. B.) (Hb. HTN); and S. of Sarratt (09/P), 2007 *T. J.*

Rubus surrejanus W. C. Barton and Riddelsd.
Native (U.K. endemic).
First record: 2001.
Tetrad occurrence: 5 (1%).

A conspicuous bramble of hedgerows and wood margins, which may be spreading. Its main home is south of the Thames, but it has recently appeared also in Cambs. It can be locally dominant.

First found at Bricket Wood Common (10/F), 2001 *T. J.* (det. *A. Newton*) (Hb. HTN), it has since appeared by Upper Stonyhills Wood (31/I), 2003 *A. L. B./T. J.*; Hoo Wood, Great Gaddesden (01/G), 2003; Squitmore Spring, Ardeley (32/D), 2004; and beside the old Newmarket Road at Burloes, Royston (34/Q), 2004 *A. L. B./T. J.* (det. *A. L. B.*) (Hb. HTN).

Rubus vestitus Weihe
Native.
First record: 1843.
Tetrad occurrence: 147 (30%).

A common bramble of woodlands, hedgerows and scrub on a range of soils, including the Chalk, only becoming scarce on very acidic gravels. Although this is a readily-recognisable species, it was not properly identified in Herts. until the mid 20th century. Early specimens collected by Coleman, including the first from near Bramfield (21/X), 1843 (Hb. BON), have been examined by D. P. Earl. Edees and Newton (1988) record it from most 10km squares, and the present survey has found it to be very widespread, especially where hedgerows and woods are of ancient origin, although it remains under-recorded especially in west Herts. It occasionally appears with pink flowers.

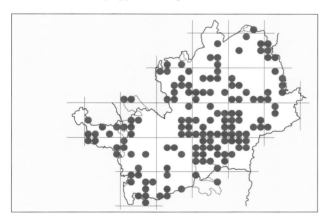

Map 278. *Rubus vestitus.*

Series: *Mucronati*

Rubus wirralensis Newton   Herts Rare
Native (U.K. endemic).
First record: 1993.

The only record remains that from Mardley Heath (21/P), 1993 *A. D. Marshall* (det. *A. Newton*) (Hb. HTN). It may have come in with planted trees on the former Heath in the 19th century, as its main home is western Britain.

Series: *Micantes*

Rubus diversus W. C. R. Watson   Herts Rare
Native.
First record: *c.*1950.

This is a bramble of undisturbed, mildly to strongly acidic soils in ancient woodland, occurring in scattered places in southern Britain. It was first reported *c.*1950 from Hadley Wood (VC21 [Herts.: 1904-1965]) by W. C. R. Watson (in Kent and Lousley, 1952). It was found in VC20 in an old copse at Hertfordshire University, Hatfield (20/D), 1993 *A. D. Marshall* (det. *A. L. Bull*) (Hb. Marshall), and has subsequently been found not far away at

Bush Wood, Welham Green (20/H), 2003 *A. L. B./T. J.* (det. *A. L. B.*) (Hb. HTN).

Rubus erythrops Edees and Newton
Native (U.K. endemic).
First record: before 1988.
Tetrad occurrence: 5 (1%).

A south-eastern bramble of woods and heaths. There are unlocalised 10km records from TL22 and SP90 (Herts.?) in Edees and Newton (1988). An early record of '*Rubus rosaceus*' by Watson from Whippendell Wood (in Kent and Lousley, 1952) may refer to this species, but other records under the same name in Pryor (1887) are more uncertain. During the current survey it was found at Graffridge Wood (22/A), 1993 *A. L. Bull/A. Newton/A. D. Marshall*; and again in 1998 *A. L. B/A. N./T. J.* (Hb. HTN), as well as by Holl Lays Wood nearby. It has also been confirmed at Whippendell Wood (09/T), 1999; Upper Stonyhills Wood (31/D), 2003 *A. L. B./T. J.* (det. *A. L. B.*) (Hb. HTN); and Box Wood, Walkern (22/T), 2006 *T. J.* (det. *A. L. B.*) (Hb. HTN). A recent record from TL21 in Newton and Randall (2004) was from Codicote High Heath (21/E), 1993 *A. Newton.*

Rubus glareosus Rogers   Herts Rare
Native (U.K. endemic).
First record: (*c.*1914?), 1999.

A local bramble of woodlands and heaths in southern Britain. There is a record, which may be correct, from 'Broxbourne' by Miss Trower (*Rep. Bot. Exch. Club*: 66 (1914)). Otherwise, it has been found during the recent survey only at Whippendell Wood (09/T), 1999; and at Symondshyde Great Wood (11/V), 2002 *A. L. B./T. J.* (det. *A. Newton*) (Hb. HTN).

Rubus leightonii Lees ex Leighton   Herts Rare
Native.
First record: *c.*1950?

A bramble of wood borders and heaths in southern England and the west Midlands. A 10km record from TL21 in Edees and Newton (1988) refers to a record from Sherrards Park Wood, 1953 (21/G?) by Watson (Dony ms. index) (and *comm.*: A. Newton). This remains the only record for the County.

Rubus lintonii Focke ex Bab.   Herts Rare
Native (U.K. endemic).
First record: 1953.

A local bramble of hedgerows and wood margins across mainly south-eastern England, but with a stronghold in Norfolk. There is a record from Whippendell Wood *c.*1950 by Watson (in Kent and Lousley, 1952), which was supported by a specimen in Watson's herbarium (Dony, ms. index), and there is a specimen from B. A. Miles, 1964, in Hb. CGE. Edees and Newton (1988) give a 10km record for TQ09, presumably the same record. It was confirmed by Rousebarn Lane, by Whippendell Wood (09/Y), 1999 *A. L. B./T. J.* (det. *A. L. B.*) (Hb. HTN). This remains its only locality in Hertfordshire.

Rubus micans Godron   Herts Rare
Native.
First record: 1979.

A species of hedges and wood borders, mostly in south-western

Britain. This was found in 1979 at Sherrards Park Wood (21/G?), *A. D. Marshall* (det. A. Newton) (Hb. Marshall) (Edees and Newton, 1988), which remains its only record.

Rubus moylei W. C. Barton and Riddelsd.
Native (U.K. endemic).
First record: before 1965.
Tetrad occurrence: 9 (2%).

A woodland and wood margin bramble, frequent in southern England and south Wales. There are old records of '*Rubus lejeunii*' which could be this species. Edees and Newton (1988) give an unlocalised 10km record from TL21, which was made by B. A. Miles before 1965. The current survey has found it in nine tetrads, very widely spread in woodlands and old wooded hedgerows across the County, but with no obvious pattern in its distribution, except that it appears to be limited to ancient woodland habitats.

A bramble Rubus moylei *by Graffridge Wood, Knebworth 2008.*

Rubus norvicensis A. L. Bull and E. S. Edees   Herts Rare
Native (U.K. endemic).
First record: 1993.

A bramble of hedgerows and wood borders, especially in East Anglia. This was found to be frequent in Sherrards Park Wood (21/G), 1993 *A. L. B./A. N./A. D. M.* It was subsequently found to be abundant in old plantations at Panshanger (31/B), 2002; and was also found in small quantity at Bush Wood, Welham Green (20/H), 2003 *A. L. B./T. J.* (det. A. L. B.) (Hb. HTN). In the first two sites, it may have been introduced originally with planted trees.

Rubus percrispus D. E. Allen and R. D. Randall   Herts Rare
Native (U.K. endemic).
First record: 2002.

A recently described species, found on heaths and wood margins, local across mainly southern Britain. A specimen of this was identified from Nomansland Common (11/R), 2002 *A. L. B./T. J.* (det. A. Newton) (Hb. HTN).

Rubus raduloides (Rogers) Sudre   Herts Rare
Native.
First record: 1993.

This is a species of hedgerows and wood margins on dry, moderately acidic or mildly calcareous soils. First recorded from Sherrards Park Wood (21/G), 1993 *A. L. Bull/A. Newton/A. D. Marshall* and more recently at Whippendell Wood (09/T), 1999; Brickground Wood, Bramfield (21/T), 2000 *A. L. B./T. J.* (det. A.

L. B.) (Hb. HTN); and Plashes Wood (32/Q), 2007 *T. J.* (det. A. L. B.) (Hb. HTN).

Rubus trichodes W. C. R. Watson
Native (U.K. endemic).
First record: *c.*1950.
Tetrad occurrence: 6 (1%).

A local woodland or wood margin species, centred on the upper Thames Valley. Recorded (as '*Rubus foliosus*') from Whippendell Wood (09/T?), Croxley Green (09/T), and Oxhey Woods (19/B) by Watson (in Kent and Lousley, 1952). Edees and Newton (1988) also show an unlocalised 10km record from TQ09. The present survey found it at Mardley Heath (21/P), 1993 *A. L. B./A. N./A. D. M.*; Ashridge (91/W), 1997 *A. L. B/A. N.*; Chipperfield Common (00/K), 1998 *A. L. B.* (det. A. Newton) (Hb. A. L. Bull), and 2006 *T. J.* (det. A. Newton) (Hb. HTN); Whippendell Wood (09/T), 1999; Berkhamsted Common (00/E), 2001 *A. L. B./T. J.* (det. A. L. B.) (Hb. HTN); and again at Oxhey Woods (19/B), 2004 *A. L. B./T. J.* (Hb. HTN).

Series: *Anisacanthi*

Rubus adamsii Sudre   Herts Rare
Native.
First record: *c.*1950.

A local plant of heaths and hedge-banks on acidic soils. This was recorded by Watson from Hertford Heath (in Kent and Lousley, 1952); and from Whippendell Wood (specimen in Watson's herbarium, teste Dony, ms. index). It was also recorded from Mardley Heath (21/P), 1993 *A. L. B./A. N./A. D. M.* (det. A. Newton).

Rubus anisacanthos G. Braun   Herts Rare
Native.
First record: 2004.

One record of this rather scarce species of hedgerows and woodland margins, mostly found in northern Britain, has been confirmed from Oxhey Woods (19/B), 2004 *A. L. Bull/T. J.* (conf. A. Newton) (Hb. Bull; Hb. HTN).

[*Rubus cinerosus* Rogers
Native (U.K. endemic).

There is a record from Oxhey Wood (19/B) by W. C. R. Watson given in Kent and Lousley (1952), but no other record from Herts. This may be correct, but needs confirmation.]

Rubus leyanus Rogers   Herts Rare
Native.
First record: 1953.
Tetrad occurrence: 4 (<1%).

This is a rather fine pink-flowered bramble of woodlands, moorland and hedgebanks on acidic soils, which is mainly a feature of south Wales and the south-west. There is an old record by Watson from Sherrards Park Wood (21/H?), 1953 (specimen in Hb. Watson, *teste* Dony ms. index, and the Randall and Newton database). During the survey, it was found in Mutchetts Wood (10/F), 2001; was frequent in Combs and Customs Woods (32/A, F), 2002; and was also at Hoo Wood, Great Gaddesden (01/G), 2003 *A. L. B./T. J.* (det. A. L. B.) (Hb. HTN).

Series: *Radulae*

Rubus bloxamianus Coleman ex Purchas   Herts Rare
Native (U.K. endemic).
First record: 2003.

A very local bramble of the margins of woods and heaths. It is
rather pleasing that this bramble, named by W. H. Coleman later
in life from Leicestershire, its main centre, should now have been
found in his youthful stamping ground of Herts. It was discovered
at Watery Grove and Norton Green (22/G), 2003 *T. J.* (det. A.
Newton) (Hb. HTN).

Rubus cantianus (Watson) Edees and Newton   Herts Rare
Native (U.K. endemic).
First record: before 1988.

A bramble of dry Clay-with-Flints or similar soils. There are
10km records in Edees and Newton (1988) from SP90, TL00 and
TL21. It was found during the survey at Sherrards Park Wood
(21/G), 1993 *A. L. B./A. N./A. D. M.*; Bramfield Woods (21/Y),
2000 *A. L. B./T. J.* (det. A. L. B.); and Pond Wood (20/Q) (VC21
[Herts.]), 2005 *A. L. Bull/T. J.* (det. A. Newton) (Hb. HTN). The
early SP90 record may refer to Pavis Wood, in Bucks, where it is
known to occur.

Rubus echinatoides (Rogers) Dallman
Native (U.K. endemic).
First record: 1849.
Tetrad occurrence: 20 (4%).

This bramble is local but widespread on the margins of woods and
heaths. It was confused with other species by earlier recorders, but
specimens exist from Coleman, collected at Essendon (TL20), and
from Benington High Wood (22/W), 1849 (det. D. P. Earl) (Hb.
BON). There are also several 10km records given in Edees and
Newton (1988). The recent survey found it widely spread across
the centre and south-west of the County on more-or-less acidic
soils in open woods and on commons.

A bramble Rubus echinatus *Furzefield Wood, Symondshyde, 2002.*

may refer here, but could also include other species. Specimens
collected by Coleman from Hertford, 1841 and 1844 (det.
E. F. Linton) are in Hb. CGE. Edees and Newton (1988) show
it occurring throughout the area. The current survey found it to
occur widely, but mainly on gravel. It is, no doubt, still under-
recorded.

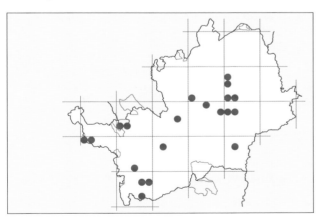

Map 279. *Rubus echinatoides.*

Rubus echinatus Lindley
Native.
First record: 1841.
Tetrad occurrence: 54 (11%).

A fairly common, very prickly, pale pink-flowered bramble of
hedgerows and scrub on more acidic soils, rarely in woods. Early
records in Pryor (1887), given under the name '*Rubus rudis*',

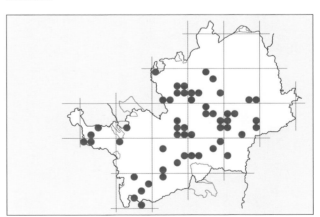

Map 280. *Rubus echinatus.*

Rubus euryanthemus W. C. R. Watson
Native.
First record: *c.*1950 (VC21 [Herts.: 1904-1965]).
Tetrad occurrence: 7 (1%).

This is a bramble of acidic soils under oak-birch woodland or the
margins of heaths. There is a reference to its occurrence in VC20

in Edees and Newton (1988), with records from SP90 and TQ19. It was also recorded by Watson from Hadley (TQ29) (VC21 [Herts.: 1904-1965]) (in Kent and Lousley, 1952). During the survey it has only been found at Harrocks Wood (09/T), 1999; Ermine Street (30/N), 1999; Northaw Great Wood (20/S, X), 2000; Bishop's Wood, Rickmansworth (09/Q), 2003 *A. L. B./T. J.* (det. A. L. B.) (Hb. HTN); and once more at Hadley Common (29/N) (VC21 [Herts.: 1904-1965]), 2005 *A. L. B./T. J.* (det. A. L. B.).

Rubus flexuosus P. J. Mueller and Lef.
Native.
First record: *c*.1950?
Tetrad occurrence: 39 (8%).

A woodland or woodland margin bramble on mildly acidic soils. This was apparently not recorded until Watson reported it, without localities (Kent and Lousley, 1952). Edees and Newton (1988) give 10km records for most of the County. It is in fact widespread across southern and western Hertfordshire.

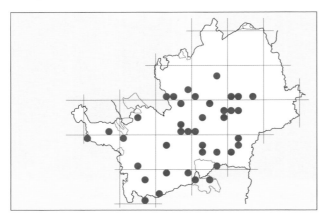

Map 281. *Rubus flexuosus.*

A bramble Rubus flexuosus *Furzefield Wood, Symondshyde, 2002.*

Rubus fuscus Weihe   Herts Rare
Native.
First record: *c*.1950?

Found in woodlands on acidic soils. Specimens named this were collected by Watson from Mardley Heath and Sherrards Park Wood (Hb. Watson, *teste* J. G. Dony ms. index). Watson's use of the name may have been doubtful, but the plant was re-found at Mardley Heath (21/P), 1993 *A. L. B./A. N./A. D. M.* It has also subsequently been found at Northchurch Common (91/Q) and Ashridge (91/W), 1997 *A. L. B./A. N.*

Rubus insectifolius Lef. and P. J. Mueller
Native.
First record: before 1988.
Tetrad occurrence: 16 (3%).

This is a conspicuous, scrambling bramble of heathy woods, with irregularly toothed leaves and white flowers with red styles. It was not reported from Herts. by Watson, but Edees and Newton (1988) give several unlocalised 10km records. It was found widely during the survey, but sparingly, across southern and eastern Hertfordshire, and at Tring in the west, on acidic soils.

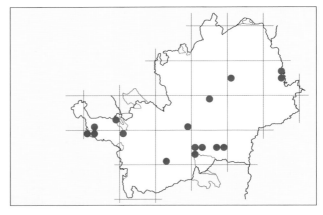

Map 282. *Rubus insectifolius.*

Rubus largificus W. C. R. Watson   Herts Rare
Native (U.K. endemic).
First record: 2000.

The only record of this large bramble of heathy woods is from Northaw Great Wood (20/X), 2000 *A. L. B./T. J.* (det. A. Newton) (Hb. HTN).

Rubus pallidus Weihe in Bluff and Fingerh.
Native.
First record: 1869?
Tetrad occurrence: 5 (<1%).

A species of damp woodlands and hedgerows. This was reported by Babington from Oxhey Woods (19/B) and Easneye (31/W?) in 1869, and also by F. M. Webb from Milwards Park (TL20) and Rickmansworth (= Croxley) Common Moor before 1887 (Pryor, 1887). Although there is possible confusion with *R. euryanthemus*, it is quite possible that most if not all of these are correct. It was later reported from 'Redlands' (= Redwell) Wood/Cangsley Grove (20/B), and from Oxhey Woods by C. Avery, *c*.1950 (Watson, in Kent and Lousley, 1952). Edees and Newton (1988) give 10km records from TL01, 11, 21 and 22. During the current survey it has been found at Chipperfield Common (00/K), 1998 *A. L. B.* (det.

A. Newton) (Hb. Bull); Rousebarn Lane (09/Y), 1999 *A. L. B./T. J.* (det. A. N.) (Hb. HTN); Hedgeswood Common (01/G), 2003 *A. L. B./T. J.* (det. A. N.) (Hb. HTN); Oxhey Woods (19/B), 2004 *A. L. B./T. J.* (Hb. HTN); and Walk Wood, Cokenach (33/Y), 2004 *A. L. Bull/T. J.* (det. A. N.) (hb. HTN). It may be more widespread.

Rubus pannosus Mueller and Wirtgen ex Focke Native. Herts Rare
First record: 1994.

A recently recognised species of bramble in Britain, found in woodlands on acidic soils. This has been recorded from Mardley Heath (21/P), 1994 *A. Newton* (Newton and Randall, 2004 and pers. comm.: A. Newton).

Rubus radula Weihe ex Boenn.
Native.
First record: 1849?
Tetrad occurrence: 19 (4%).

A widespread bramble of woodlands and wood margins. This was recorded first by W. H. Coleman from a number of sites across Hertfordshire (Webb and Coleman, 1849), but many of these are probably errors. A few of Coleman's early records were listed by Pryor (1887). Watson reported it from Whippendell Wood (in Kent and Lousley, 1952). Edees and Newton (1988) give six 10km records. The current survey has recorded it fairly widely, mostly from the less acidic clays in north-east Herts., but also with a few sites on the Chilterns dip-slope, including Whippendell Wood (09/T).

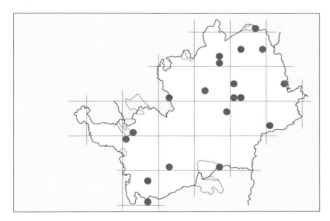

Map 283. *Rubus radula.*

Rubus rudis Weihe
Native.
First record: 1843.
Tetrad occurrence: 26 (5%).

A bramble of heathy scrub and open woodlands on more or less acidic soils. This was recorded by Coleman from a number of sites on gravel in south Herts., and there are specimens to support some of these in Hb. BON, including two from the Panshanger area (21/W), 1843 (det. W. M. Rogers). Pryor (1887) lists more localities, but some may be errors. Watson, however, does not list it for VC20 in Kent and Lousley (1952). It was found to be widespread on lighter gravels and friable clays, especially in central Hertfordshire, during the current survey.

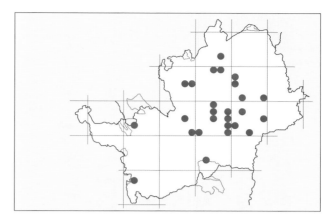

Map 284. *Rubus rudis.*

Rubus rufescens Lef. and P. J. Mueller
Native.
First record: 1840.
Tetrad occurrence: 99 (20%).

This species often forms dense carpets in woodlands, especially Hornbeam woodlands, on moderately acidic loams, where its rough-surfaced leaves, pink flowers and poorly formed fruits are characteristic. Earlier records were often included under '*Rubus rosaceus*', but there are specimens collected by Coleman from a number of sites, including 'Trunks Wood, 2½ miles south of Hitchin' (22/C), 1840 (Hb. BON). It was reported by Watson (in Kent and Lousley, 1952) as 'frequent', and Dony also noted it from

A bramble Rubus rufescens *Furzefield Wood, Symondshyde, 2002.*

Bishop's Wood (TQ09) and by Aldenham Reservoir (TQ19), 1956 (Dony ms. index). Recorded in the current survey mainly on the loams in central and south-eastern Hertfordshire, but it remains under-recorded in the west.

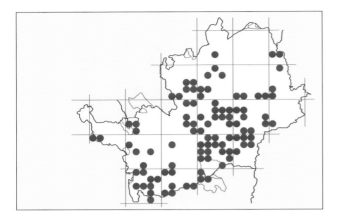

Map 285. *Rubus rufescens.*

[*Rubus sectiramus* W. C. R. Watson

There is a report that there was a specimen from Oxhey Wood, *c*.1950 collected by C. Avery in Watson's herbarium (*teste* Dony, ms. index), but this needs checking. It may be correct.]

Series: *Hystrices*

Rubus asperidens Sudre ex Bouvet (= *R. milesii* Newton)
Native (U.K. endemic).
First record: 1964.

Mainly a woodland or woodland border bramble, this was first collected by B. A. Miles from Whippendell Wood (09/Y), 1964 (Hb. CGE). Edees and Newton also list 10km records from TL31, 41; TQ19, 29. During the current survey it has been found in Northaw Great Wood (20/X), 2000; Panshanger (31/B), 2002; Bishop's Wood (09/Q), 2003 *A. L. B./T. J.* (det. A. Newton) (Hb. HTN); and Oxhey Woods (19/B), 2004 *A. L. B./T. J.* (det. A. L. B.) (Hb. HTN).

Rubus atrebatum Newton   Herts Rare
Native (U.K. endemic).
First record: 1984.

A bramble of heathy woodlands, mainly south of the Thames. The only record from the County is from Aldbury Common (91/R?), 1984 *A. L. Bull* (det. A. Newton, 1995) (Hb. A. L. Bull).

Rubus bercheriensis (Druce ex Rogers) Rogers
Native.
First record: before 1988.
Tetrad occurrence: 4 (<1%).

A bramble of woodlands and wood borders on heathy soils. This is reported from five 10km squares in west Herts. in Edees and Newton (1988). It appears to be limited to this area, because the current survey has only found it at Hastoe (90/E), 1997 *A. L. Bull./A. Newton*; Berkhamsted Common (00/E), 2001; Hoo Wood, Great Gaddesden (01/G), 2003 *A. L. B./T. J.* (det. A. L. B./A. N.) (Hb. HTN); and Chipperfield Common (00/K), 2006 *T. J.* (det. A. L. B.) (Hb. HTN).

Rubus dasyphyllus (Rogers) E. S. Marshall
Native.
First record: *c*.1950.
Tetrad occurrence: 36 (7%).

A widespread bramble of hedgerows, commons and woodlands, usually, but not always, on somewhat acidic soils. This was reported as 'frequent' by Watson (in Kent and Lousley, 1952), and there are seven 10km squares across the area given in Edees and Newton (1988). Earlier records were probably included under '*Rubus koehleri*'. It was found during the survey across most of the County, being absent only on the damper clays and the open Chalk.

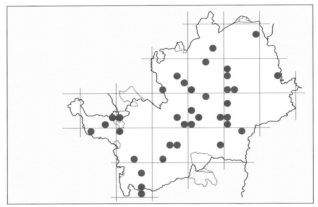

Map 286. *Rubus dasyphyllus.*

Rubus hylocharis W. C. R. Watson   Herts Rare
Native (U.K. endemic).
First record: 1849.

A bramble of especially oak woods on light soils, mainly found in western Britain. This was collected by W. H. Coleman from 'Broxbourne Wood, Bayford' (30/I), 1849 (det. D. P. Earl) (Hb. BON). In the recent survey it was found at Bramfield Woods (21/Y), 2000; Symondshyde Great Wood (11/V), 2002; and Oxhey Woods (19/B), 2004 *A. L. B./T. J.* (det. A. L. Bull) (Hb. HTN).

Rubus iceniensis Newton and H. E. Weber   Herts Rare
Native (U.K. endemic).
First (only) record: 1993.

A bramble of heath margins, mostly in Norfolk. This has only been recorded so far from Mardley Heath (21/P), 1993 *A. L. B./A. N./A. D. M.* (det. A. Newton).

Rubus murrayi Sudre   Herts Rare
Native (U.K. endemic).
First record: *c*.1950.

A local bramble of wood margins and heaths. This was reported by Watson from Whippendell Wood (09/T?) (in Kent and Lousley, 1952), probably correctly. There is a specimen collected by B. A. Miles from Chorleywood Common (09/I), 1964 (Hb. CGE) (*comm.*: R. J. Pankhurst); and Edees and Newton (1988) list it from TQ09 and TQ19. During the recent survey it was re-found at Whippendell Wood (09/T), 1999; and was also found at Oxhey Woods (19/B), 2004 *A. L. B/T. J.* (det. A. L. B./A. N.) (Hb. HTN).

Rubus newbridgensis W. C. Barton and Riddelsd.   Herts Rare
Native (U.K. endemic).
First record: 2003.

Apparently a rather rare bramble, found in woodland, wood
margins and hedgerows. A specimen of this was collected at
Watery Grove (22/G), 2003 *T. J.* (det. A. Newton) (Hb. HTN), the
only record for the County.

Rubus phaeocarpus W. C. R. Watson   Herts Rare
Native.
First record: 1998.
Tetrad occurrence: 4 (<1%).

A bramble of wood margins, mostly in south-east England, this
was first found as a single plant at Hitch Wood Shrubs (12/W),
1998 *A. L. B./A. N./T. J.* (det. A. Newton); later at Bush Wood,
Welham Green (20/H), 2003 *A. L. B./T. J.* (det. A. L. Bull) (Hb.
HTN); and at Sewett's Wood (12/K), as well as nearby Withstocks
Wood (12/F), 2006 *T. J.* (det. A. L. B.) (Hb. HTN).

Rubus proiectus A. Beek   Herts Rare
Native.
First record: 1849.

A bramble of heaths and wood margins, mainly found in
Lincolnshire and East Anglia. This was first collected by W. H.
Coleman from Prae Wood (10/?D), 1849 (det. E. F. Linton) (Hb.
BON). Recently, it has been found at Graffridge Wood (22/A),
1998 *A. L. B./A. N./T. J.* (det. A. N.) (Hb. HTN); Patmore Hall
Wood (42/N), 2001; and Patmore Heath (42/M), 2001 *A. L. B.* At
the last of these, it is the dominant bramble.

Rubus watsonii W. H. Mills
Native (U.K. endemic).
First record: *c.*1950?
Tetrad occurrence: 11 (2%).

A plant of woodlands, heath margins and hedgerows, usually on
mildly acidic, clay soils. This was represented by specimens in
Watson's herbarium from Mardley Heath (21/P) and Berkhamsted
Common (TL00/E?), which may have been correctly identified
(Dony, ms. index); and there is a specimen collected by Dony from
near Zouche's Farm (TL02) (VC20 [Beds.]) in Hb. LTN, (det. W.
C. R. Watson, 1978). Edees and Newton (1988) give seven 10km
records across the west of the County. During the recent survey, it
has been found scattered across the County, with 11 tetrad records.

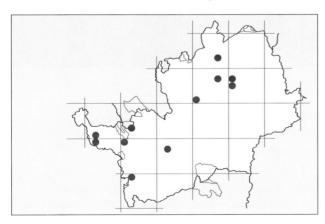

Map 287. *Rubus watsonii.*

Series: *Glandulosi*

Rubus angloserpens Edees and Newton   Herts Rare
Native (U.K. endemic).
First record: 1998.
Tetrad occurrence: 4 (<1%).

A low-growing bramble of ancient woodland, widespread but
local in Britain. This was first found at Graffridge Wood (22/A),
1998 *A. L. B./A. N./T. J.* (det. A. N.) (Hb. Newton); and has
subsequently been confirmed from Bramfield Woods (21/Y),
2000; High Scrubs and Brown's Lane, Hastoe (90/J), 2001; and
Symondshyde Great Wood (11/V), 2002 *A. L. B./T. J.* (det. A. N.)
(Hb. HTN).

Rubus hylonomus Lef. and P. J. Mueller   Herts Rare
Native.
First record: *c.*1950?

A sprawling plant of open woods and heaths. A specimen
named this from Sherrards Park Wood (21/H?) was in Watson's
herbarium (Dony, ms. index), and may have been correct. It has
since been found at Bramfield Park Wood (21/X), 2000; and
at Gustard Wood Common (11/S), 2002 *A. L. B./T. J.* (det. A.
Newton) (Hb. HTN).

Rubus leptadenes Sudre   Herts Rare
Native.
First record: 1999.

A low-growing woodland bramble, apparently very localised
in the U.K. in Bucks. and Herts. This has been identified from
Whippendell Wood (09/T), 1999 *A. L. B./T. J.* (det. A. L. Bull)
(Hb. HTN); and also from Watery Grove (22/G), 2003 *T. J.* (det.
A. Newton) (Hb. HTN).

Rubus pedemontanus Pinkw. in Baenitz   Herts Rare
Native.
First record: 1849.

A low-growing, locally-abundant bramble of damp loam in
woodlands in the Chilterns. This was recorded (as '*Rubus
bellardii*') from 'Tring' by W. H. Coleman (Webb and Coleman,
1851; Pryor, 1887), and there is a specimen in Hb. BON collected
in 1849 (det. D. P. Earl). It was re-discovered at Hastoe (90/E),
1997, and in quantity at High Scrubs and Hare's Garden Wood,
Tring (90/J), 2001 *A. L. B./T. J.* (det. A. L. Bull) (Hb. HTN).

Rubus scaber Weihe in Bluff and Fingerh.   Herts Rare?
Native.
First record: 1851?

A low-growing plant of woods on heathy soils. This was recorded
by C. C. Babington from Prae Wood (TL10), Essendon (TL20)
and Easneye (31/W) (Pryor, 1887). Watson (in Kent and Lousley,
1952) gave records from Whippendell Wood (TQ09) and Northaw
Great Wood (TL20). However, Edees and Newton (1988) only
show 10km records from SP91 and TQ09 in our area. During the
recent survey, it was only recorded once: from Graffridge Wood
(22/A), 1998 *A. L. B./A. N./T. J.* (det. A. Newton) (Hb. HTN).

[*Rubus babingtonianus* W. C. R. Watson

Records of this, as *Rubus althaeifolius*, from Mangrove Lane and Goldings, Hertford from Babington were quoted in Pryor (1887). They may be correct, but need confirmation.]

Rubus britannicus Rogers
Native.
First record: *c.*1950.
Tetrad occurrence: 50 (10%).

A large-leaved and distinctive bramble of damp woodlands and scrub, often on somewhat calcareous clay soils. This was reported by Watson from several sites in south Herts. (in Kent and Lousley, 1952), probably correctly. During the current survey it has turned out to be widespread across the south of the County, with odd records further north.

A bramble Rubus britannicus *Easneye Wood, 2005.*

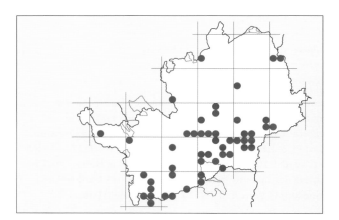

Map 288. *Rubus britannicus.*

Rubus conjungens (Bab.) Rogers in J. B. Warren
Native.
First record: 1841? (1847).
Tetrad occurrence: 6 (1%).

A bramble of hedgerows and scrub. This was apparently first collected by W. H. Coleman from Mangrove Lane, Hertford (31/F), 1841 (det. D. P. Earl, but with some doubt); and later at Bell Bar (20/M), 1847 (det. T. Gibbs and W. Rogers) (Hb. BON). There are records from several localities in south Herts. given by Watson (in Kent and Lousley, 1952), which may be correct. It was found during the current survey in a number of widely scattered localities, at Nomansland Common (11/R), 2002; Bishop's Wood,

Rickmansworth (09/Q), 2003; frequently in the Dancers Hill area (29/J) (VC21 [Herts.]), 2003; by Barkway Road, Royston (33/U), 2004 *A. L. B./T. J.* (det. A. L. Bull/A. Newton) (Hb. HTN); near Long Marston (81/X), 2005 *T. J.* (det. A. L. B.) (Hb. HTN); and near Philpott's Wood, Sandon (33/H), 2005 *T. J.* (det. A. L. B.) (Hb. HTN).

Rubus hindii A. L. Bull
Native.
First record: 1843.
Tetrad occurrence: 71 (15%).

A bramble of hedgerows and scrub, less often of open woodlands, on a wide range of soils. This was not formally described until 1998, but has proved to be one of the commonest brambles in the County, having been subsumed under other names earlier. It was first collected from near Balls Wood (31/K) by W. H. Coleman, 1843 (det. D. P. Earl/A. L. Bull) (Hb. BON); and a paratype was collected by Earl from Brocket Park (21/B), 1993 (Bull, 1998). It is very under-recorded in both west and extreme east Herts., but is genuinely uncommon on the Chalk.

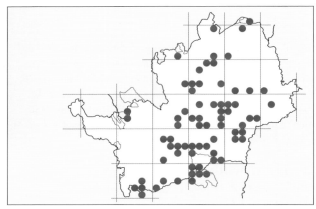

Map 289. *Rubus hindii.*

A bramble Rubus hindii *Langley, June 2008.*

Rubus cantabrigiensis A. L. Bull and A. C. Leslie
Native.
First record: 2004.
Tetrad occurrence: 10 (2%).

A characteristic bramble of the Chalk and dry, calcareous clay soils. It was only formally named at the end of the survey period, and was first found by a green lane at Wallington (23/W), 2004 *T. J.* (det. A. L. B.) (Hb. HTN). It was subsequently found to be widespread in calcareous hedgebanks in the general area between

Baldock and Meesden at least, with records from tetrads 23/L, Q, R, W; 33/A, D, H, X; 43/B, G.

Rubus nemorosus Hayne and Willd.   Herts Rare
Native.
First record: before 1988.

Pryor (1887) gives a number of sites for this, and says that it is 'probably common throughout the county'. However, he also gives other records for its synonym *Rubus balfourianus*, which suggests confusion. Edees and Newton (1988) quote 10km records from TL11 and TQ09. There have been no recent records.

Rubus pruinosus Arrh.
Native.
First record: 1844.

A bramble of scrub, hedgerows and woodland margins. There is a specimen collected by W. H. Coleman from 'Watling Street, 2 miles NW of St Albans', 1844 (det. D. P. Earl) (Hb. BON). Early records of '*Rubus corylifolius*' might include this, but are most likely to be hybrids of *R. caesius*. Records of a more secure synonym, *Rubus sublustris*, are given by Watson (in Kent and Lousley, 1952) from Bishop's Wood (09/Q?), Batchworth Heath (09/R) and Bricket Wood Common (10/F). There are older records from TL10, 1844 *W. H. Coleman*; and TL23, *c.*1980 *A. D. Marshall* included in the Randall and Newton database (Edees and Newton, 1988). The recent survey, however, has only recorded it from Ayot Green (21/C), 1992 *A. D. Marshall* and from Patmore Heath (42/M), 2001 *A. L. Bull*. It may have been overlooked elsewhere.

Rubus tuberculatus Bab.
Native.
First record: 1849.
Tetrad occurrence: 28 (6%).

A widespread bramble of hedgerows, scrub and waste ground, with large white flowers that open early. There is a specimen collected by Coleman from 'Holwell Woods, Hatfield', 1849 and an undated one from Hertford in Hb. BON (det. D. P. Earl). Pryor (1887) lists a number of records, which may be correct. Watson gives records from Whippendell and Broxbourne Woods in VC20, and Mimmshall Woods in VC21 (now Herts.) (in Kent and Lousley, 1952).

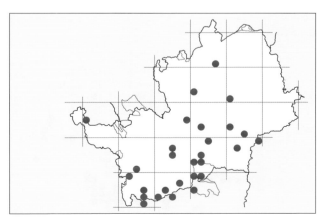

Map 290. *Rubus tuberculatus.*

Section: *Caesii*

Rubus caesius L.
Dewberry
Native.
First record: 1750.
Tetrad occurrence: 294 (60%).
Increasing? (+40%).

A widespread, scrambling bramble with rather insipid fruits, which occurs on more-or-less calcareous soils, in rough grassland, hedgerows and ditches, especially on the Boulder Clay. It may be slightly over-recorded in some areas, as it can be difficult to distinguish from hybrids with other brambles.
(199 tetrads: Dony, 1967; 230 tetrads, 1950-1986)

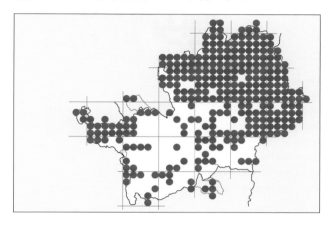

Map 291. *Rubus caesius.*

Unidentifiable hybrids of Dewberry with other brambles occur widely, especially in north Herts. on calcareous soils, and can often be the dominant brambles in hedgerows.

Genus: *Potentilla*

Potentilla fruticosa L.
Shrubby Cinquefoil
Introduced: planted? [native in the U.K.].
First (only) record: 1988.

This was found growing by the old railway line beside Amwell Quarry (31/R), 1988 *T. J.*, but was probably originally planted.

Potentilla palustris (L.) Scop.   Herts Extinct
Marsh Cinquefoil
Native.
First record: 1840.

This was a feature of naturally swampy sites on acidic soils at Croxley (= Rickmansworth) Common Moor (09/X), and in the area of Broxbourne Woods. It was last seen by A. W. Graveson at Franks Field, near Wormley Wood (30/I) about 1919, when it was apparently still 'plentiful' (Dony, 1967 and ms. index).

Potentilla anserina L.
Silverweed
Native.
First record: 1814.
Tetrad occurrence: 350 (71%).
Decreasing (-17%).

This is a plant of trodden damp areas in pastures, waste ground

and by the sides of roads. Although generally thought of as common, it was always thinly scattered on the drier clays and gravels of central and western Hertfordshire, and has now shown signs of retreat elsewhere, especially around towns.
(400 tetrads: Dony, 1967; 408 tetrads: 1950-1986)

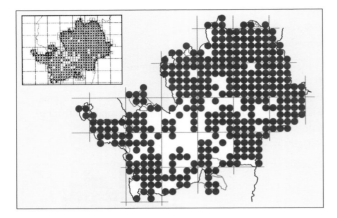

Map 292. *Potentilla anserina.*

Potentilla argentea L.   UK Near Threatened
Hoary Cinquefoil
Native.
First record: 1817.
Tetrad occurrence: 9 (2%).
Decreased sharply (-40%).

This was at one time quite widespread in central Hertfordshire, especially around Hertford and Ware on gravelly ground and in bare pastures. It had become quite rare by the 1960s (Dony, 1967), and is now rarer still. A record from Bricket Wood Common in Burton (1983) may be an error. It was only recorded in nine tetrads during the survey, concentrated on its stronghold around Ware, Hertford and Bramfield. Even in these areas, it is limited to a few plants at odd localities such as the barren grasslands of Panshanger (21/W), and scrubby clearings in Plashes Wood (32/V).
(14 tetrads: Dony, 1967; 15 tetrads: 1950-1986)

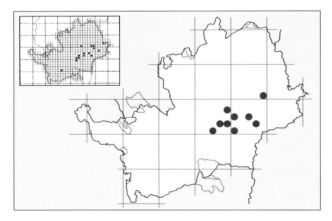

Map 293. *Potentilla argentea.*

Potentilla inclinata Villars
Grey Cinquefoil
Introduced: casual.
First (only) record: 1922.

This has only ever been recorded once, from Bayfordbury (31/A), as an escape (Dony, 1967).

Potentilla recta L.
Sulphur Cinquefoil
Introduced: neophyte.
First record: 1910.
Tetrad occurrence: 6 (1%).

This is an occasionally established escape, found in rough grasslands and on waste ground. During the current survey it has been recorded from six localities: by Hatfield Park, roadside (20/P), 1992 *A. D. Marshall*; Holywell, Watford, rough ground by old car park (09/X), 1994 *T. J.*; Turnford Gravel Pits (30/S), 1994 *G. P. Smith*; Rye House (30/Z), 1995 *G. Hounsome*; Bayfordbury grounds (31/A), 1996 *A. M. Boucher/C. G. Hanson*; Frogmore, old sewage works (10/L), 1997-8 *J. B. Baker*. It has shown a similar pattern of occurrence ever since its first record.

Potentilla hirta L.
Hairy Cinquefoil
Introduced: casual.
First (only) record: 1915.

There is one old record of this rare casual from near 'Hertford Electric Works', 1915 *H. F. Hayllar* (Salisbury, 1917; Dony, 1967, and ms. index).

Potentilla intermedia L.
Russian Cinquefoil
Introduced: casual.
First record: 1915.

Again, there are three records of this, all from Ware, 1915 *G. C. Druce/H. F. Hayllar*; and 1920, 1923 *H. F. H.* (Dony, 1967 and ms. index).

Potentilla norvegica L.
Ternate-leaved Cinquefoil
Introduced: casual.
First record: 1881.

Recorded as a casual, especially in the past at Hitchin, Hertford and Ware; this was recorded during the survey only by the car park at Aldenham Reservoir (19/S), 1990, 1991 *T. D. Walker* (Hb. HTN).

Potentilla erecta (L.) Räusch
Upright Tormentil
Native.
First record: 1822.

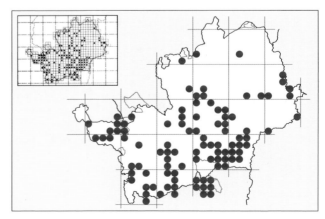

Map 294. *Potentilla erecta.*

Tetrad occurrence: 99 (20%).
Decreasing (-30%).

A plant of unimproved, often heathy pastures, woodland rides and commons on a range of soils. This was widespread and quite common in the 1960s, especially in south-east and west Herts. It has decreased substantially in many areas through loss of old grasslands, scrub encroachment on commons, *etc.*, although it has also continued to be recorded in new localities.
(134 tetrads: Dony, 1967; 160 tetrads: 1950-1986)

Potentilla × *suberecta* Zimm. (*P. erecta* × *P. anglica*)
Native.
First certain record: 2003.

There are a number of earlier records which were attributed to this hybrid (Dony, ms. index; but mistakenly attributed to *P.* × *mixta*), such as around Hertford Heath and Knebworth Woods, where the parents meet. It has only been positively identified once during the survey: Knebworth Park (22/F), 2003 *T. J.* (conf. B. Harold) (Hb. HTN), but has probably been overlooked elsewhere.

[*Potentilla erecta* × *P. reptans*

Although there have been earlier records, and one plant which may have been this was found during the survey at Broxbourne Woods, the occurrence of the plant (originally given the hybrid name *Potentilla* × *italica* Lehm.) in the County is uncertain, because it is difficult to identify from *P.* × *mixta*, and no collection has been confirmed with a chromosome count, the only reliable means of identification.]

Potentilla anglica Laich.
Trailing Tormentil
Native.
First record: 1787.
Tetrad occurrence: 9 (2%).
Rare (stable?).

This appears to have been rare in Hertfordshire for a long time, although many early records may have been confused with *P.* × *mixta*. Evidently Dony had some difficulty with the species, as he only gives two recent records in his *Flora* and other records in his ms. index are mostly probably referable to the hybrid. Records supported by specimens were made subsequently from Barclay Park (30/U), 1978, 1981; and from an old meadow by Goffs Lane (30/G), 1985 *A. M. Boucher* (det. B. Harold). There was also a report from Oxhey Wood (19/B), 1978 *G. Harper* which may be correct. During the current survey it has been confirmed at ten localities: Patmore Hall Wood (42/N), 1988, 1989 *S. Watson* (det. B. H.); Northaw Great Wood (20/S, X), 1988, 1991 *A. M. Boucher/T. J.* (det. B. H.); Symondshyde Great Wood (11/V), 1992 *T. J.*; Rectory Lane Pasture, Shenley (10/V), 1992 *S. M. Hedley*; Ashridge (91/W) (VC24 [Herts.]), 1995 *G. Salisbury/J. Saunders* (det. B. H.); Broxbourne Wood (30/I), 1999 *T. J./G. Salisbury*; Knebworth Park (22/F), 2003 *T. J.* (Hb. HTN); Cowheath Wood (30/I), 2004 *T. J.*; and Chipperfield Churchyard (adjoining Chipperfield Common) (00/K), 2005 *T. J.* It is noteworthy that most of these sites are known to be either former wood pastures or derived from them, and therefore represent the remnants of ancient acid grassland communities.

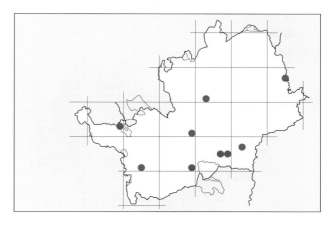

Map 295. *Potentilla anglica.*

Potentilla × *mixta* Nolte ex Reichb. (*P. anglica* × *P. reptans?*)
Hybrid Cinquefoil
Native.
First record: 1910?
Tetrad occurrence: 49 (10%).

There are a number of earlier records made under this name, but owing to taxonomic confusion it is difficult to be sure what was meant (Dony, 1967, and ms. index). The precise parentage of this highly sterile hybrid is uncertain, although it may involve *P. anglica* and a polyploid form of *P. reptans*, and regularly has a chromosome count of 2n=42 (pers. comm.: B. Harold). The hybrid in its broad sense has been recorded in a total of 49 tetrads, concentrated mainly in central and south-eastern Hertfordshire, with a few extra records before 1987. Records attributed with some degree of certainty to the hybrid between *P. anglica* and *P. reptans* were made in 37 of these. The majority of these are from old grasslands, commons or woodland rides on acidic soils.

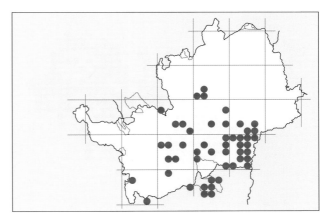

Map 296. *Potentilla* × *mixta.*

Potentilla reptans L.
Creeping Cinquefoil
Native.
First record: 1814.
Tetrad occurrence: 466 (95%).
Stable or slightly decreased (-4%).

A common plant of rough grasslands, roadside verges and waste ground throughout the County. It quite often does not seed very well, spreading vegetatively. Even though it is regarded as native, it is interesting that it was not recorded as early as *P. anglica*, and it may have increased during the last 200 years, although it was

'common' by 1849 (Webb and Coleman, 1849).
(461 tetrads: Dony, 1967, and from 1950-1986)

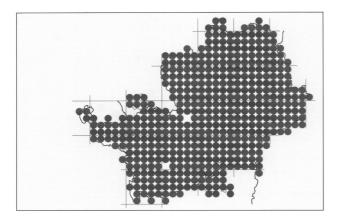

Map 297. *Potentilla reptans.*

Potentilla sterilis (L.) Garcke
Barren Strawberry
Native.
First record: 1814.
Tetrad occurrence: 290 (59%).
Decreased slightly (-8 %).

A plant of nutrient-poor grasslands on road verges, woodland rides, colonising bare ground in gravel pits and waste places. The map shows that it avoids the most intensively agricultural landscapes, and is rare around towns. Otherwise, it is very capable of holding its own on road banks, and is often a pioneer in old gravel pits. Its occurrence is much as it was in the 1960s, but it has appeared in new areas while being lost in others.
(299 tetrads: Dony, 1967; 306 tetrads: 1950-1986)

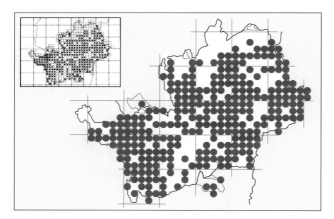

Map 298. *Potentilla sterilis.*

Genus: *Fragaria*

Fragaria vesca L.
Wild Strawberry
Native.
First record: 1748.
Tetrad occurrence: 241 (49%).
Decreasing (-26%).

A frequent plant of somewhat calcareous bare ground, rough grasslands, road banks and woodland rides. It is often a characteristic plant of colonising banks in old gravel and chalk pits, although some records from this kind of habitat may have

been mis-identified *Fragaria × ananassa*. It is only absent on damp clays and in open arable landscapes. Although it is still frequent, it has decreased substantially since the 1960s, possibly as a result of the eutrophication and scrubbing up of roadside banks and the overgrowth of rides in woods.
(308 tetrads: Dony, 1967; 319 tetrads: 1950-1986)

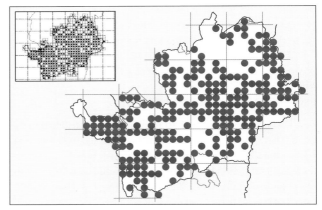

Map 299. *Fragaria vesca.*

Fragaria moschata (Duchesne) Duchesne
Hautbois Strawberry
Introduced: casual.
First (only) record: 1815.

There is one old record from near Tring, 1815 (Dony, 1967) that appears to be correct, but other records are likely to be errors (Dony ms. index).

Fragaria × ananassa (Duchesne) Duchesne
Garden Strawberry
Introduced: neophyte.
First record: 1924?
Tetrad occurrence: 23 (5%).

A hybrid of uncertain origin, confused by earlier botanists both with *F. moschata* and with *F. chiloensis*. It occurs fairly widely on disturbed ground and by railways, but is probably under-recorded in some areas, owing to mis-identification as large *F. vesca*.

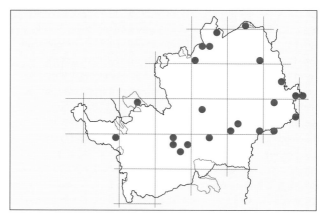

Map 300. *Fragaria × ananassa.*

Geum rivale L.   Herts Rare
Water Avens
Native.
First record: 1814.

A native plant of wet ground by rivers and streams. This was always a rare native, especially of riversides in the Chilterns, with old records from the Latimer/Flaunden area on the Chess, from the Grand Union Canal at Berkhamsted, and from the Ash valley at Easneye (31/R) (Pryor, 1887; Dony, 1967 and ms. index). It was last seen just on the Bucks. side of the border by the Chess at Chenies (09/E) in 1980. However, it has also appeared on chalk grassland at Aldbury Nowers (91/L), 1980 *J. Robertson* and by the main pond at Patmore Heath (42/M), 1981 *B. R. Sawford*, where it was last seen in 1989 by J. Godfree. More recently, it has also appeared on an old, damp trackside bank at Lanterns Lane in Stevenage (22/S), 1992 *G. P. Smith*. It would seem to be an introduction in all three of these locations. Its appearance by the old R. Bulbourne at Berkhamsted town centre (90/Z), 1998 *R. Mabey* could just be a re-appearance of a native colony, but could equally be an escape!

Geum × intermedium Ehrh. (*G. rivale × G. urbanum*)
Native.
First record: *c*.1880

This has occurred at Flaunden, and at Bricket Wood Common (10/F) in the past (Dony, 1967), the latter not being a site where *G. rivale* has been recorded. It was recorded at Lanterns Lane, Stevenage (22/S), 1997 *G. P. Smith*, having replaced *G. rivale*. This may well have been the fate of most of the County's native Water Avens elsewhere.

Geum urbanum L.
Wood Avens
Native.
First record: 1838.
Tetrad occurrence: 464 (95%).
Stable or marginally decreased (-3%).

A very common plant of woodlands, hedgerows, scrub and shady waste ground throughout the County. There is only minor evidence of a decrease in its occurrence since the 1960s, perhaps through eutrophication of some of its habitats.
(454 tetrads: Dony, 1967; 456 tetrads: 1950-1986)

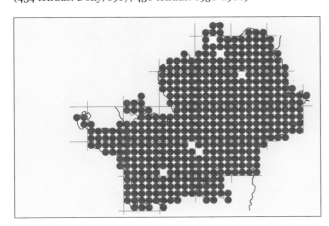

Map 301. *Geum urbanum.*

Agrimonia eupatoria L.
Agrimony
Native.
First record: 1814.
Tetrad occurrence: 375 (76%).
Decreasing (-16%).

A widespread plant of old neutral or somewhat calcareous grasslands, roadside verges and woodland rides. Although still quite frequent, this species is decreasing steadily, owing to a combination of nutrient enrichment of road verges, dereliction or 'improvement' of old pastures and overgrowth of woodland rides. Its tolerance of horse-grazing has allowed it to survive in a good number of sites in south Herts. where it might otherwise have gone.
(423 tetrads: Dony, 1967; 429 tetrads: 1950-1986)

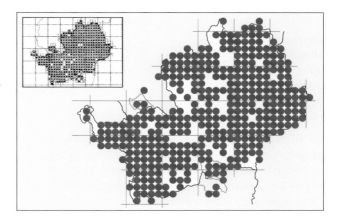

Map 302. *Agrimonia eupatoria.*

Agrimonia procera Wallr.   Herts Rare
Fragrant Agrimony
Native.
First record: 1909.

A plant of more acidic, damp grasslands than its relative. Dony (1967) gives three early records, but had not seen it himself. His ms. index gives two more: an early record from Hertford by D. M. Higgins, and Northaw Great Wood (20/X), without a date [*c*.1950] from B. Jennings. It was re-discovered in a clearing by Cuffley Camp, Northaw Great Wood (20/X), 1999 *J. Easton/ S. Smith* (Hb. HTN). Attempts to re-find it elsewhere have failed, but it may still occur.

Sanguisorba officinalis L.   Herts Rare
Great Burnet
Native.
First record: 1840 (1814?).
Tetrad occurrence: 6 (1%).

Always rare in Hertfordshire, this is a plant of unimproved damp, moderately calcareous or slightly acidic grasslands, such as hay meadows and commons. It was first properly recorded at Ashwell, presumably on Chalk Marl or Gault Clay, as an outlier of its main distribution further north, although Joseph Ransom noted it in his diary somewhere near Hitchin in 1814, but this could have been in

Bedfordshire. There is also a record of it as occurring on Hexton Common (13/A), c.1930 (Whiteman, 1936), which could be correct. It was then discovered at Munden Park (10/F), 1950, *R. B. Benson* (omitted from Dony, 1967), and subsequently at both Totteridge Green and Aldenham Reservoir (Dony, 1967). Dony also reported it from Standon Lordship (32/V), 1956 *L. Lloyd-Evans*. More recently, it was found at North London Cemetery (29/W) (VC20 [Greater London]), 1967 *D. Irvine* (Hb. BM); in small quantity by a track near Barwick (31/U), 1980 *S. Gorton* (not far from Standon Lordship); and at Rye Meads (31/V), 1981 *R. Knightbridge*. The recent survey has found that it persists in a small area, despite mowing, at Totteridge Green (29/L), 1982, 1999 *D. Griffith*, 2003 *T. J.*; and is also in an old damp pasture at South Mimms (20/F), 1989 *T. C. G. Rich*, 1996 *S. Cuming*; rough amenity grass at West Watford (19/C), 1992, 1994 *P. J. Ellison*; in Composers' Park, Elstree (19/S), 2001 *N. Holmes-Smith/J. Moss*; and at Totteridge Fields (29/H), 2003 *J. Carr* (det. R. M. Burton). It also occurs at Meesden Green (43/G), 1992 *J. Godfree*, 2000 *L. Mottram*, where it was originally planted.

Sanguisorba minor Scop.
Salad Burnet
Native.
First record: 1814.
Tetrad occurrence: 155 (32%).
Decreased substantially (-32%).

This is a plant of short grassland on calcareous soils. It is especially common as a major component of chalk grasslands, but also occurs on calcareous clay soils elsewhere. Having been common across most of northern Hertfordshire in the 1960s, it is now increasingly limited to remnant chalk grasslands, some calcareous road banks and churchyards. Outlying sites in south Herts. are usually the latter.
(216 tetrads: Dony, 1967; 234 tetrads: 1950-1986)

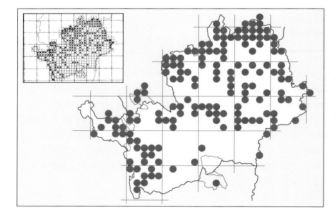

Map 303. *Sanguisorba minor*

The native plant, shown on the map, is ssp. *minor*, but ssp. *muricata* (Gremli) Briq. **Fodder Burnet** is occasionally recorded, originally as a once frequent escape from agricultural cultivation, but now usually as a result of seeding of so-called 'wildflower mixes'. It was first recorded in 1873, and has been found in seven scattered localities during the survey, including its use in mixes for the Baldock bypass (23/L), 2006. It may be under-recorded, and a few records of ssp. *minor* could perhaps refer here.

Genus: *Acaena*

Acaena novae-zelandiae Kirk
Pirri-pirri-bur
Introduced: neophyte.
First record: 1991.

This became established for a while at Hadham Towers tip (41/I), 1991, 1992 *S. Watson* (Hb. HTN). It also appeared in the grounds of Bayfordbury (31/A), 1996 *A. M. Boucher/C. G. Hanson* (Hb. Boucher).

Genus: *Alchemilla*

Alchemilla xanthochlora Rothm.   Herts Rare
Native.
First record: 1915.

This has always been rare in the County, and limited to the western edge, in the Chilterns. It has been recorded in the past at Grove Wood and at Hastoe Hill (90/E); near Hastoe (90/J); and by Phillipshill Wood (09/C) (Dony, 1967). It was found again on a roadside verge near High Scrubs (90/J), 1980 *T. J./A. W. Vaughan* and at High Spring Wood (91/F), c.1980 *A. W. Vaughan*. Its only record during the recent survey was from woods in Tring Park (91/F), 1990 *M. J. Hicks*.

A lady's-mantle Alchemilla xanthochlora *near High Scrubs, Herts, 1980*

Alchemilla filicaulis ssp. *vestita* (Buser) Bradshaw Herts
Common Lady's-mantle Vulnerable
Native.
First record: *c.*1820.
Tetrad occurrence: 15 (3%).
Decreasing rapidly (-68%).

A plant of old, unimproved rough pastures, and woodland rides.
Having been widespread in the 19th century (Pryor, 1887), this
was still 'occasional' in the 1960s (Dony, 1967), but is distinctly
rare now. It was only found in a very few localities during the
recent survey, often limited to small colonies. Even some of
these are now thought to be extinct, often owing to overgrowth
of woodland rides and glades (*e.g.* Hitch Wood (12/W), although
there is some evidence that it can re-appear from buried seed,
such as after tree-felling.
(45 tetrads: Dony, 1967; 49 tetrads: 1950-1986)

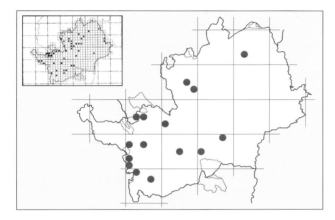

Map 304. *Alchemilla filicaulis* ssp. *vestita.*

Common Lady's-mantle Alchemilla filicaulis *Hitch Wood, 1983.*

Alchemilla mollis (Buser) Rothm.
Introduced: neophyte.
First record: 1988.
Tetrad occurrence: 14 (3%).
Increasing.
An escape from gardens, this was first found on waste ground by
the River Small Lea, Cheshunt (30/R), 1988 *G. P. Smith et al.*
It is increasing steadily in waste places and was recorded in 14
widely-scattered tetrads across the County, but is probably under-
recorded.

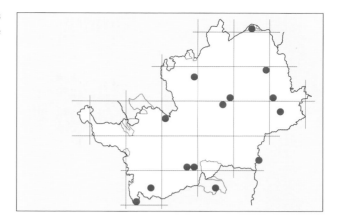

Map 305. *Alchemilla mollis.*

Genus: *Aphanes*

Aphanes arvensis L.
Parsley-piert
Native.
First record: 1821 (Hb. Franks, LTN).
Tetrad occurrence: 280 (57%) for the species.
Probably stable (-4%).

This is a widespread weed of arable farmland, on neutral or more
calcareous soils, and sometimes occurs on bare ground in dry
grassland, or on ant-hills. Its overall occurrence appears to be
stable, but it must have declined in abundance since 1967, owing
to the effects of modern weedkillers. Since the 1960s, it has been
more clearly separated from *A. australis*. The map therefore
shows the strict species, although if unidentified parsley-pierts are
included, it occurred in 312 tetrads (64%).
(278 tetrads: Dony, 1967; 287 tetrads: 1950-1986)

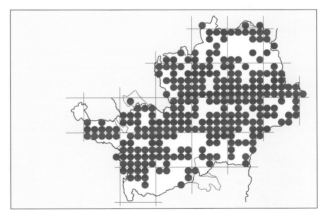

Map 306. *Aphanes arvensis.*

Aphanes australis Rydb.
Slender Parsley-piert
Native.
First record: 1956.
Tetrad occurrence: 64 (13%).

This was not recognised as a separate species until the 1950s, and
so no reliable comparison is possible with Dony's (1967) map. It
occurs usually on gravelly or sandy soils, and is frequent on the
river gravels, as well as on thin glacial drift over Chalk, in similar
habitats to its relative. It may be under-recorded in S.W. Herts.
(30 tetrads: Dony, 1967; 37 tetrads: 1950-1986)

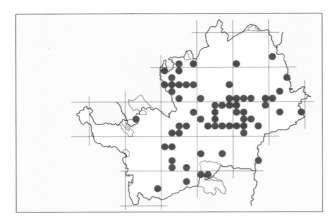

Map 307. *Aphanes australis.*

Genus: *Rosa*

Roses present considerable problems to the field botanist, owing to their frequent hybridisation, and to the fact that the reciprocal crosses between male and female parents produce different hybrid forms. An attempt has been made to record hybrids where possible, and both fieldwork and identification of specimens, including old specimens, have been greatly assisted by Revd. Tony Primavesi, the former BSBI referee for roses, in several areas; while R. Maskew has also named some more recent specimens. However, while the distribution of the more easily recognised species may be fairly accurate, the scarcer species remain under-recorded, and hybrids even more so.

Rosa arvensis Hudson
Field Rose
Native.
First record: *c.*1820.
Tetrad occurrence: 416 (85%).
Stable or increased? (+19%).

This is a readily-recognised rose of old hedgerows, woodland and wood margins throughout most of the County. It does not often occur in recent habitats, and is therefore rare in towns, as well as in areas of arable farmland that have been derived from 19th century inclosures, such as on the Chalk in north Herts. Although noted from significantly more tetrads than in 1967, it was probably better recorded.
(333 tetrads: Dony, 1967; 363 tetrads: 1950-1986)

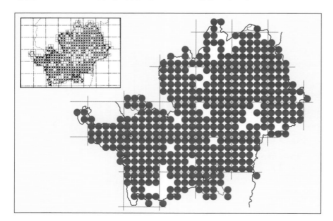

Map 308. *Rosa arvensis.*

Rosa × *irregularis* Désegl. and P. Guillon (= *R.* × *verticillacantha* Mérat) (*R. arvensis* × *R. canina*)
Native.
First record: 1877.

The earliest specimen determined as this by A. L. Primavesi is from New Barnet (TQ29), 1877 *A. Craig-Christie*. The recent survey found it in eleven scattered localities across the County, but it is no doubt much more widespread.

Rosa spinosissima L.
Burnet Rose
Introduced [native in the U.K.].
First record: 1990.

This was first found on the chalky road banks of the A505 at Slip End (23/Y), 1990 *T. J.*, and subsequently on another stretch of the same road to the east, 1992. It had probably been originally planted. It is also reported as planted near the A120 at Wickham Hall (42/R), 2007 *D. Broughton*, and was found as an escape at the Rivers Nursery site, Sawbridgeworth (41/S), 1993 *A. R. Outen*.

Rosa rugosa Thunb. ex Murray
Japanese Rose
Introduced: neophyte.
First record: 1977 (as planted), 1986.

This was first noted as a planted shrub by the old railway at Amwell Quarry (31/R), 1977 *T. J.*, but was found to be self-sown nearby in 1986 *T. J.*, where it survives. The recent survey has also found it in four other localities: Eastbury area (09/W), 1994 *P. J. Ellison*; near Harpendenbury (11/B), 1994, *J. F. Southey*; established by Edgegrove School, Aldenham (19/P), 1995 *J. K. Jackson*; and planted by Rectory Lane, Ridge (20/B), 1998 *T. J.*

Rosa 'Hollandica' hort.
Dutch Rose
Introduced: neophyte.
First record: 1994.

This garden cultivar can establish itself in the wild, and was first found as an escape at Lampits, Hoddesdon (30/U), 1994 *A. M. Boucher* (det. A. L. Primavesi) (Hb. HTN); and later at British Aerospace grounds, Hatfield (20/E), 1995 *A. D. Marshall* (det. A. L. P.) (Hb. Marshall); and Mill Green Golf Course (21/K), 1995 (det. A. L. P.) (Hb. Marshall).

Rosa ferruginea Villars
Red-leaved Rose
Introduced: neophyte.
First (only) record: 1999.

This was found in 1999 as an escape near Hemel Hempstead (TL00) *R. Maskew/A. L. Primavesi* (*comm.*: B.R.C., CEH Monks Wood).

Rosa stylosa Desv.   Herts Rare
Short-styled Field Rose
Native.
First record: *c.*1820.
Tetrad occurrence: 5 (1%).
Rare and apparently decreasing.

This fine, dark-leaved rose occurs naturally in old hedges and edges of woods on clay soils in a limited area in east Herts. It was

Short-styled Field Rose Rosa stylosa *Roads Wood, Watton-at-Stone, 1999.*

noted as rare by Pryor (1887). Dony (1967) gave ten tetrad records, but it is likely that his records from SP91/L and TL13/F at least are errors. With P. M. Benoit, however, he did collect a good specimen from Morley Ponds (31/X), 1962 (det. A. L. Primavesi) (Hb. HTN), which was omitted from his map. It was also recorded from the Potters Bar area (20/L) in Burton (1983), but it is not known if this was checked. During the recent survey, it has only been found as single bushes at Roads Wood (31/I), 1988, 1999 *T. J.* (conf. A. L. P.) (Hb. HTN); Weepings Wood (30/E), 1995 *A. D. Marshall* (det. A. L. P.) (Hb. HTN); Highfield Wood (30/P), 1999 *T. J.* (det. R. Maskew) (Hb. HTN); by Moat Wood (41/B), 2005 *T. J.* (an old site); and in the edge of Vineyards Spring (42/A), 2003 *T. J.* (Hb. HTN). It has also been reported as an introduced bush by the River Stort at Thorley (41/Z), 2002 *S. Watson.*

Rosa × andegavensis Bast. (*R. stylosa × R. canina*)
Native.
First record: 1875.
Rare.

Three old gatherings of this have been confirmed by A. L. Primavesi: Harmer Green (TL21), 1875 *T. B. Blow* (Hb. E); Welwyn (TL21), 1876 *T. B. Blow* (Hb. BIRA); and Broxbourne (TL30), 1927 *E. B. Bishop* (Hb. BM).

Rosa canina L.
Dog-rose
Native.
First record: 1748 (for the aggregate).
Tetrad occurrence: 470 (96%).
Stable (-3%?).

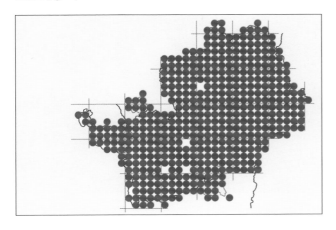

Map 309. *Rosa canina.*

Widespread in hedgerows, scrub, woodland and waste ground across the County, although not recorded for a few tetrads. The map is for the broad concept of the species (but not including evident hybrids or *Rosa obtusifolia*). This itself has four named 'groups', all of which are recorded from the County, but not enough consistent work has been done on these to attempt separate distribution maps. Current records are, however, not strictly comparable with Dony's, as his included other species, notably *Rosa obtusifolia*.
(461 tetrads: Dony, 1967 and from 1950-1986)

Rosa × dumalis Bechst. (*R. canina × R. caesia*)
Native.
First record: 1843? (1988).
Tetrad occurrence: 13 (3%).

'*Rosa dumalis*' was recorded by earlier botanists (Pryor, 1887), but no early records have yet been confirmed from specimens. The hybrid in its presently recognised form was first identified from Weston Hills (23/L), 1988 *T. J.* (conf. A. L. Primavesi) (Hb. HTN). It was also found at Harpenden Common (11/L), 1989 *J. F. Southey* (conf. A. L. P.) (Hb. HTN); and recorded subsequently from Wymondley grid station (22/D), 1994 *A. D. Marshall* (det. A. L. P.); Ashwell Quarry (23/P), 1998 *T. J.* (det. R. Maskew) (Hb. HTN); near Pirton (13/G), 1999 *T. J.* (Hb. HTN); 'California', Dunstable (02/A) (VC20 [Beds.]), 1999 *T. J./ G. P. Smith* (Hb. HTN); Wilbury Hill (23/B) (VC30 [Herts.]), 2001 *T. J.*; Arkley Lane (29/D), 2001 *T. J*; by Long Plantation (24/K), 2003 *T. J.*, (det. R. Maskew) (Hb. HTN); by Moat Wood (41/B), 2005 *T. J.*; near Hedges Farm (10/M), 2005 *T. J.*; Scales Park (43/B), 2005 *T. J.*; and near Philpotts Wood, Sandon (33/H), 2005 *T. J.* (Hb. HTN). It is no doubt widespread.

Rosa × dumetorum Thuill. (*R. canina × R. obtusifolia*)
Native.
First record: 1989.
Tetrad occurrence: 6 (1%).

Rare, but probably overlooked. This was first found at Kinsbourne Green (11/C), and in woodland near Hatching Green (11/G), 1989 *J. F. Southey* (det. A. L. Primavesi) (Hb. HTN). It has also been recorded from Shaw Green (23/V), 1990 *T. J.*; Wilstone (91/C), 1995 *T. J.* (Hb. HTN); Parker's Green, Ardeley (32/H), 1996 *T. J.* (det. R. Maskew) (Hb. HTN); and Hill End, St Albans (10/T), 1998 *T. J.* (Hb. HTN).

Rosa × scabriuscula Sm. (*R. canina × R. tomentosa*)
Native.
First record: 1921.
Tetrad occurrence: 6 (1%).

The first gathering of this, confirmed by A. L. Primavesi, is from Hitchin (TL12), 1921 *J. E. Little* (Hb. CGE). Other early collections are from Great Wymondley (TL22), 1930 *J. E. Little* (Hb. BM), and Little Hyde Wood, Sawbridgeworth (51/C), 1961 *J. L. Fielding* (det. A. L. P.) (Hb. HTN). During the recent survey it has also been found near Moat Wood (41/B), 1989 *S. Watson* (Hb. HTN); Wymondley grid station (22/D), 1994 *A. D. Marshall* (Hb. HTN); South Hatfield (20/D), 1994 *A. D. M.* (Hb. HTN); Dixon's Hill, North Mymms (20/H), 1994 *A. D. M.* (Hb. HTN) (all det. A. L. Primavesi); Potwells, North Mymms (20/B), 2005 *T. J.*; and near Anstey (43/B), 2005 *T. J.* It is probably widespread on the Boulder Clay.

Rosa × *nitidula* Besser (*R. canina* × *R. rubiginosa*)
Native.
First record: 1994.
Rare, but possibly overlooked.

This was first collected from the Smallford Trail (10/Y), 1994
A. D. Marshall (det. A. L. Primavesi) (Hb. HTN). It has also been
collected from Sleapshyde (20/D), 1995 *A. D. M.* (Hb. HTN); and
from Oxshott Hill (22/W), 1998 *T. J./A. L. Primavesi* (Hb. HTN).

Rosa × *toddiae* Wolley-Dod (*R. canina* × *R. micrantha*)
Native.
First record: 2005.
Rare.

A fine bush which displayed good characteristics of this scarce
hybrid was found at Potwells, North Mymms (20/B), 2005 *T. J.*
(Hb. HTN), where both its parents are well known.

Rosa obtusifolia Desv.
Round-leaved Dog-rose
Native.
First record: (1838?) 1953.
Tetrad occurrence: 6 (1%).
Rare, but widespread.

A number of records for '*Rosa tomentella*' were made by W. H.
Coleman and others (Pryor, 1887). Dony (1967) incorporated
records under '*R. canina*', but a record from TL31, made in 1953
and supported by a specimen in the herbarium of Haileybury
College (now in Hb. LTR) has been confirmed by A. L. Primavesi.
During the recent survey, it has been confirmed from an old
meadow south of Codicote (21/D), 1987 *T. J.* (Hb. HTN);
Harpenden Common (11/G), 1989 *J. F. Southey* (Hb. Southey);
Dalmonds (30/P), 1990 *T. J.* (Hb. HTN); Foulwells (30/I), 1995
T. J./A. M. Boucher (Hb. HTN); near Caldecote (23/J), 1995
(Hb. HTN); and from Parker's Green, Ardeley (32/H), 1996 *T. J.*
(Hb. HTN) (all specimens checked by A. L. P). It probably awaits
discovery elsewhere.

Rosa caesia Sm.   Herts Rare
Glaucous Dog-rose
Native.
First record: 1872.
Rare, but possibly overlooked.

The usual subspecies in Herts. is apparently ssp. *vosagiaca* (N.
Despoortes) D. H. Kent, of which the earliest gathering confirmed
from the County is from Preston (TL12), 1872 *E. F. Linton* (det. A.
L. Primavesi) (Hb. E). Other early collections have been confirmed
from New Barnet (TQ29), 1879 *A. Craig-Christie* (Hb. BM); Tring
(SP91), 1930 *E. MacAlister-Hall* (Hb. E); and Clothall (TL23),
1935 *H. Phillips* (Hb. BM). During the survey, it has only been
confirmed from Harpenden Common (11/G), 1989 *J. F. Southey*
(det. A. L. Primavesi) (Hb. HTN); and from Potwells (20/B), 2005
T. J. (Hb. HTN). As the hybrid with *Rosa canina* is apparently
widespread, these records would suggest that *Rosa caesia* was at
one time more widespread further south than it now is.

The more northerly ssp. *caesia* itself (**Hairy Dog-rose**)
has also been confirmed from the County. A gathering from
Sawbridgeworth (TL41), 1953, formerly in the collection of
Bishop's Stortford College (now in Hb. LTR) has been identified
by A. L. Primavesi.

Rosa tomentosa Smith
Harsh Downy-rose
Native.
First record: 1815.
Tetrad occurrence: 71 (15%).

Dony (1967) considered this to be rare. However, Coleman (Pryor,
1887) correctly recognised that it was widespread, especially in
east Herts., and this remains the case, where it is frequent on
the Boulder Clay, and occurs occasionally on Chalk and gravels
elsewhere. Because of the under-recording in the 1960s survey, no
useful assessment of change in its occurrence can be made.
(18 tetrads: Dony, 1967; 26 tetrads: 1950-1986)

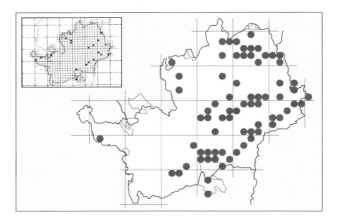

Map 310. *Rosa tomentosa*.

Harsh Downy-rose Rosa tomentosa *Watton-at-Stone, 1990.*

Rosa sherardii Davies   Herts Extinct
Sherard's Downy-rose
Native.
First record: 1877.

This northern and western species has only been confirmed from
Herts. on the basis of historic specimens from 'Ippolits' (12/Y?),
1877 *H. Groves* (Hb. BM); 'Chapel-foot' [the same?] (12/X?), 1877
T. B. Blow (Hb. BM) and a probable specimen from Tingley Wood
(13/F), 1886 *J. Pollard* (Hb. HTN) (all det. A. L. Primavesi). None
of these were known to former botanists.

Rosa rubiginosa L.
Sweet-briar
Native.
First record: *c.*1730 (for the aggregate), 1815.
Tetrad occurrence: 14 (3%).

A species of open, scrubby ground, mainly on the Chalk, but also
on gravels. This was regarded by Pryor (1887) and others as 'rare'.
Dony (1967) only gives five locations, all on the Chalk. It was
found in a number of extra sites during the 1970s and 1980s, while
during the current survey the strict species was recorded from 14
tetrads, widely spread across the County, often, but not always, on
Chalk; and there were another four records of the aggregate which
need proper determination.

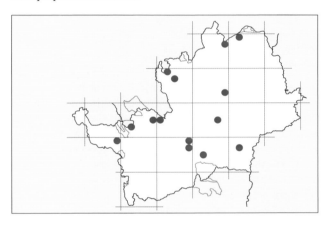

Map 311. *Rosa rubiginosa.*

Rosa micrantha Borrer ex Smith
Small-flowered Sweet-briar
Native.
First record: 1815.
Tetrad occurrence: 15 (3%).

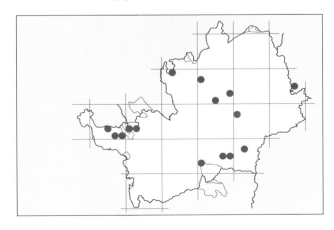

Map 312. *Rosa micrantha.*

As with *Rosa rubiginosa*, this species is also associated with
open, bushy places, but appears to be more usual on clay soils
than on Chalk, just as Coleman and Pryor proposed (Pryor,
1887). Dony (1967) only gave four localities, although another
specimen collected by him has been re-determined as this by A.
L. Primavesi: from Greencroft Barn (01/G) (VC20 [Beds.]), 1963
(Hb. HTN). The current survey has confirmed records from 15
tetrads, with concentrations on the Chilterns dip-slope clays near
Aldbury, on de-calcified Boulder Clay in south Herts. and on Clay-
with-Flints or similar soils around Stevenage.

Rosa agrestis Savi   UK Near Threatened
Small-leaved Sweet-briar
Native [introduced in Herts.?].
First record: 1986.

This rare rose was first discovered, new to Herts., in scrub at
Wymondley grid station (22/D), 1986 *A. D. Marshall*, and was
collected again from the same locality in 1989, 1992, 1994 (conf.
A. L. Primavesi) (Hb. HTN). It is threatened here by overgrowth
of the scrub, although its origin may also be suspect, owing to the
existence of planted shrubs in the area.

Genus: *Prunus*

Prunus cerasifera Ehrh.
Cherry Plum
Introduced: neophyte.
First record: 1912.
Tetrad occurrence: 159 (32%).
Increased (or overlooked?) (+523%).

This native of south-eastern Europe evidently has been greatly
overlooked in the past. In fact it has been used for hedging in
various parts of the County for a long time, although it appears
not to grow from seed very well. It is usually best noticed early
in the Spring, as it is first to flower; while its leaves tend to lose
their characteristic hairy midrib beneath after about June, with
the result that they are easily overlooked as 'Wild Plum'. Dony
only recorded it from a few areas, but the current survey found
it in almost a third of surveyed tetrads. Despite this, it is still
probably under-recorded in many areas, as a glance at the map
willdemonstrate, which shows areas where some botanists have
made a special effort to distinguish it.
(24 tetrads: Dony, 1967; 41 tetrads: 1950-1986)

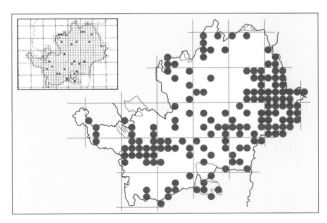

Map 313. *Prunus cerasifera.*

Prunus spinosa L.
Blackthorn *or* **Sloe**
Native.
First record: 1748.
Tetrad occurrence: 476 (97%).
Stable? (-1%).

Common throughout the County in hedgerows, scrub and open woodland on all but the driest soils. However, it is not always as easy to identify as one might think. Much so-called Blackthorn is in fact either Wild Plum, hybrids between them, or even Cherry Plum in disguise! The taxonomy of this complex is far from easy, and although pure Blackthorn is usually obvious, all kinds of intermediates can be found.
(458 tetrads: Dony, 1967; 461 tetrads: 1950-1986)

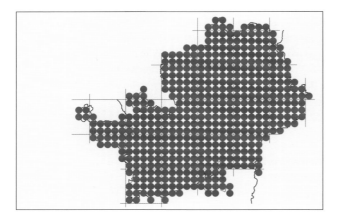

Map 314. *Prunus spinosa.*

Prunus × fruticans Weihe (*P. spinosa × P. domestica*)
Native.
First record: 1919.

This is probably frequent throughout the County, but no detailed study of it has yet been made. J. E. Little recorded it from a number of places around Hitchin, the first near Charlton, 1919 (det. J. Fraser), and he and Fraser published a paper on the hybrid in 1920 (*Rep. Bot. Exch. Club*: 3 (1920)). It has also been recorded as '*P. spinosa* var. *macrophylla*', and is distinguished by its larger leaves, infrequent thorns, ovate fruit, and its larger and later flowers (appearing with the leaves). As it back-crosses with both parents, it actually forms a spectrum between them, and the current survey has probably mis-identified many as either one or the other parent.

Prunus domestica L.
Wild Plum
Introduced: archaeophyte.
First record: 1838.
Tetrad occurrence: 310 (63%).

The account given in Dony (1967) only hints at the difficulties with this 'species'. Plum is now thought to be the product of hybridisation and selection from *Prunus cerasifera* and *P. spinosa*. However, it also appears in a bewildering range of forms (or subspecies), some with yellow, orange or pale green fruits, in part known as ssp. *insititia* (L.) Bonnier and Layens (**Bullace** *or* **Damson**) or ssp. *italica* (Borkh.) Gams ex Hegi (**Greengage**) (Sell, 1991). Most plants, however, form small trees or thickets of suckering shrubs, and have few or no thorns, larger leaves, mostly black or dark purple fruits with flattened stones,

and larger flowers than blackthorn, and may be considered to be ssp. *domestica*. An attempt was made to record the aggregate, based on this understanding of its limits, although many back-crosses with *P. spinosa* (and perhaps with *P. cerasifera*) will have been overlooked. It was recorded widely, predominantly on damper clay soils, and is by no means limited to the neighbourhood of houses.

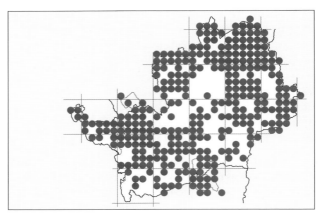

Map 315. *Prunus domestica.*

Prunus avium (L.) L.
Wild Cherry *or* **Gean**
Native (and introduced).
First record: *c.*1730.
Tetrad occurrence: 404 (82%).
Increased markedly (+46%).

A native tree, especially of woodlands and ancient hedgerows on drier loams over Clay-with-Flints in the Chilterns, and on gravels. It would normally be absent on acidic London Clay or on the damper Boulder Clay. However, it has been massively planted by roads and even into semi-natural woodland across much of the County over the last 30 years, and readily colonises disturbed land nearby, with the result that its natural distribution has rapidly been obscured.
(263 tetrads: Dony, 1967; 293 tetrads: 1950-1986)

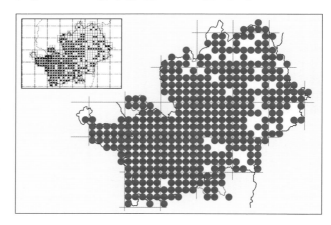

Map 316. *Prunus avium.*

Prunus cerasus L.
Dwarf Cherry
Introduced: archaeophyte.
First record: 1843.
Tetrad occurrence: 5 (1%).

Apparently a rare small tree or large bush, often surviving from former planting in woods and hedges. It has been recorded in the past from a range of places around the County, especially from the Hitchin and Weston areas. However, it can be confused with Gean. The recent survey found it in five localities, although it may have been overlooked elsewhere: near 'The Compasses', Baldock (23/M), 1987 *T. J.*; near Hatfield Station (20/J), 1990 *A. D. Marshall*; S. of St Albans (10/S), 1997 *T. J./G. Salisbury*; Hill Mead Nature Park (19/M), 1997 *J. K. Jackson*; and Sacombe (31/J), 1998 *S. Watson*.

Prunus padus L.
Bird Cherry
Introduced [native in the U.K.].
First record: *c.*1840.
Tetrad occurrence: 9 (2%).

First noted from Panshanger (as 'spontaneous') and near Hatfield Park by Coleman (Webb and Coleman, 1849), this has been ignored consistently by botanists since. It appeared, apparently naturally, at Frogmore Pit, Aston (22/V), 1984 *B. R. Sawford*; but during the current survey has been recorded from nine scattered tetrads, all apparently originally planted trees, although one was at the edge of Milwards Park, Hatfield (20/I), 1989 *A. D. Marshall*, not far from where Coleman saw it!

Prunus serotina Ehrh.
Rum Cherry
Introduced: neophyte.
First record: 1997.

This was noted, possibly as a planted tree, in an old hedge in South Hatfield (20/I), 1997 *P. Harvey* (det. T. J.) (Hb. HTN); and was subsequently found at Berrygrove Wood, Aldenham (19/I), 2001 *T. J.* (Hb. HTN), apparently self-sown. It could be elsewhere, undetected, as it is spreading in other parts of the country.

Prunus lusitanica L.
Portugal Laurel
Introduced: neophyte.
First record: 1977.
Tetrad occurrence: 7 (1%).

An ornamental, evergreen shrub, occurring occasionally in woodlands as an escape. This was first noted self-sown at Gobions Park (20/L), 1977 *H. J. Killick* (Burton, 1978). It was not then seen until the current survey, when it was noted in seven localities: Mutton Wood, Carpenders Park (19/G), 1989 *J. K. Jackson*; Manor Wood, Rothamsted (11/G), 1989 *I. G. Denholm*; north of Hoddesdon (31/Q), 1992; Broxbourne (30/T), 1993 *A. M. Boucher*; woodland, Roehyde (20/D), 1994 *A. D. Marshall*; scrub at Harmer Green (21/N), 1998 *T. J.*; and Chipperfield Common (00/K), 2003 *T. J.*

Prunus laurocerasus L.
Cherry Laurel
Introduced: neophyte.
First record (as escape): 1978.
Tetrad occurrence: 157 (32%).
Probably increasing steadily.

An evergreen ornamental shrub which readily colonises open woodland and scrub. This was first noted as an evidently established escape only in 1978, when large quantities were noted self-sown in woodland at Aldbury Common (91/Q) *T. J.*; and

also by the railway at Bricket Wood (10/F) *ITE Railway Survey*. It was then found in a handful of other tetrads before 1987, but the current survey has demonstrated that it is very widespread, especially on more acidic soils in woodlands across much of the County, only becoming rare on the Boulder Clay and the Chalk. While a number of these records refer to planted shrubberies, many more are escapes. It may also have been overlooked in the past as 'rhododendron'.

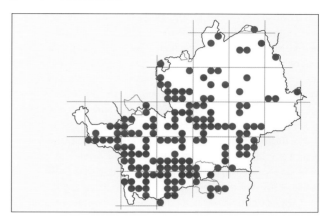

Map 317. *Prunus laurocerasus.*

Genus: *Chaenomeles*

Chaenomeles speciosa (Sweet) Nakai
Chinese Quince
Introduced: neophyte (casual).
First record: 1988.

First noted as an escape in scrub at Dane O'Coys, Bishop's Stortford (42/W), 1988 *J. L. Fielding*; it was subsequently found in scrub by the M1 at Berrygrove Wood (19/J), 2001 *T. J.*

Genus: *Pyrus*

Pyrus communis agg.
Pear
Introduced: neophyte.
First record: 1839.
Tetrad occurrence: 26 (5%).

Escaped garden Pears have been a feature of the Hertfordshire landscape for a long time, occurring mainly in hedgerows and scrub, but records of them are patchy and unreliable, owing to the difficulty of distinguishing them from 'Wild Pears'. Dony scarcely

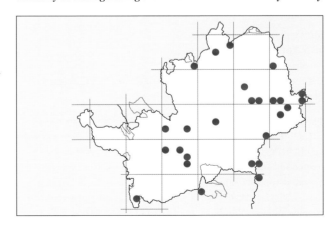

Map 318. *Pyrus communis.*

mentions it, but the current survey has recorded Pear in its broad sense widely spread across the County.

Pyrus pyraster (L.) Burgsd.
Wild Pear
Introduced: archaeophyte?
First record: *c*.1880.

Rackham (1980) made a strong case for the Wild Pear, distinguished by possessing spiny twigs and hard, rounded fruits, to be a relict native species in Britain, although most authors regard it as an ancient introduction. It is hard to identify in the field, because it rarely sets good fruit, and otherwise looks like a native Crab Apple. In Hertfordshire, an old tree which appears to be this was found at Five Acre Wood, Anstey (43/B), 1983 *T. J./B. R. Sawford*; and other possible trees have been seen in Broadfield Wood (33/F) and Moor Hall Great Wood (32/I), but require further study. An old tree was also recorded at Laurel Farm, Totteridge (29/L), 1985 *A. W. Vaughan*. Earlier, A. W. Graveson recorded an old tree, 'apparently quite wild' in the middle of Broxbourne Woods, near Mangrove Lane, (with no date), which was near one of the 19th century localities mentioned in Pryor (1887) (Dony, ms. index); while a very old pear tree, not studied botanically, was felled accidentally by well-meaning conservationists at 'Peartree Pightle', Watery Grove (22/G) in the early 1970s. There are also various localities around the County (including Pirton, and Purwell at Hitchin) whose names, of Saxon origin, refer to pear trees! The present survey received seven records of very old trees: Cheshunt Park (30/M), 1991 *A. M. Boucher*; on an old boundary bank by Monken Hadley Common (29/T), 1992 *A. W. Vaughan*; in the former County boundary hedge, Hyver Hall (29/C), 1993 *A. W. Vaughan*; by lane, Wareside (31/X), 1994 *T. J.*; re-found at Laurel Farm (29/L), 1994 *D. Griffith*; and in an old hedge at Much Hadham, near the Lordship (42/F), 2002 *J. P. Widgery*. While none of the latter are in ancient woodland, they do merit attention, and it would be useful if previously recorded or further old trees of what appear to be the truly 'wild' species could be examined critically.

Pyrus salicifolia Pallas
Willow-leaved Pear
Introduced: casual.
First record: before 1994.

There is a single note of this as an escape at Broxbourne (TL30) in Clement and Foster (1994), but I have no further details.

Genus: *Malus*

Malus sylvestris (L.) Miller
Crab Apple
Native.
First record: 1838 (in the broad sense), *c*.1880 (for the segregate).
Tetrad occurrence for the segregate: 281 (57%).

Native Crab Apples, with spiny branches, hairless leaves and very sour, small green fruits, are mainly a feature of ancient woodland and old hedgerows, where they tend to grow sparsely but widely. A concerted attempt was made to separate these from escaped cultivated apples. Crab apples in general were reported from 444 tetrads, but true *M. sylvestris* was recorded mainly in areas with extensive old woodlands, except in east Herts., where it seems to be more widespread in hedgerows as well. Because Dony (1967)

does not distinguish between wild and escaped apples, it is not possible to make a useful comparison with his records.

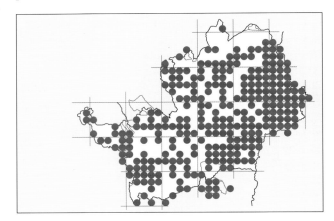

Map 319. *Malus sylvestris.*

Malus domestica Borkh.
Apple
Introduced: archaeophyte.
First record: *c*.1880.
Tetrad occurrence: 372 (76%).

Escaped domestic apples vary from being almost like native Crab Apples with hairy leaves, through to ordinary cultivated apples, even nameable varieties, of which Hertfordshire has a large number. These occur in hedgerows, scrub, by roads, *etc.*, wherever apple cores have been thrown out or birds have spread them! They are reputed to hybridise with the native species, but the records have not distinguished such trees. Domestic Apple was recorded very widely, but can be less common than the native tree in more remote areas with ancient landscapes.

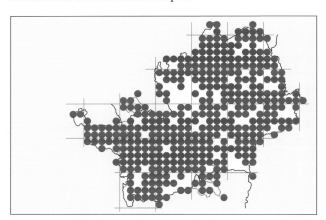

Map 320. *Malus domestica.*

Genus: *Sorbus*

Sorbus aucuparia L.
Rowan
Native (and introduced).
First record: 1657.
Tetrad occurrence: 263 (54%).
Increased substantially (+160%).

This is a native tree of old woodlands on acidic gravels and dry Clay-with-Flints soils in central, south and south-west Herts. It was described by Pryor (1887) as being rather rare, but had become quite common, although still restricted, by the 1960s

(Dony, 1967). Its natural range is rapidly becoming obscured by escapes from cultivation, and it now occurs widely even on Boulder Clay, as well as occasional anaemic trees on Chalk. (96 tetrads: Dony, 1967; 136 tetrads: 1950-1986)

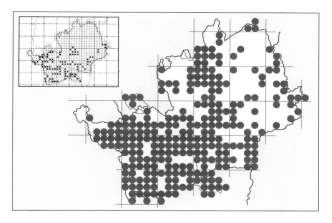

Map 321. *Sorbus aucuparia.*

Sorbus intermedia (Ehrh.) Pers.
Swedish Whitebeam
Introduced: neophyte.
First record: 1955.
Tetrad occurrence: 41 (for the aggregate).
Increasing steadily (+850% as escaped).

Strictly speaking the true Swedish Whitebeam can be difficult to distinguish from some of its close relatives, which is why the records are somewhat difficult to interpret. Trees identified as this occur usually as occasional saplings in mature woodland or scrub, sometimes in more open ground, especially on well-drained, calcareous or gravelly soils. Dony (1967) only recorded it from two localities. By 1986, it had been recorded apparently as an escape in six more places, mostly in south Herts. The current survey recorded the species in its broad sense as self-sown in 19 tetrads, and as planted into 'wild' habitat in a further 22 tetrads. Of these, some 18 records were thought to be the strict species. Most of the self-sown trees are in the south of the County, although the map shows all records.

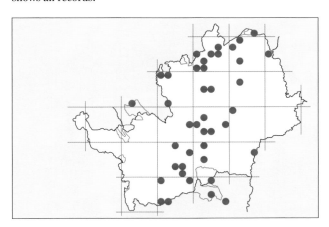

Map 322. *Sorbus intermedia* agg.

Sorbus aria (L.) Crantz
Whitebeam
Native.
First record: 1742.
Tetrad occurrence: 53 (11%) (*sensu stricto*).
Slightly increased (+40%).

This is a conspicuous and characteristic, but local native tree or shrub in hedgerows, scrub and open woodland on the Chalk in west Hertfordshire, occurring as undoubtedly native as far east as Weston, Slip End and Graveley on outliers of the Chalk. It has also very rarely been found on gravels elsewhere, apparently natural, such as in Northaw Great Wood (20/X), 1978 *T. J.* (but not found since). 'Whitebeams' are also sometimes planted, although such trees are not always the native species, but related ones from Europe, which can be difficult to identify. The strict species was recorded from 53 tetrads during the survey, of which trees in four sites may have been planted. However, indeterminate 'whitebeams' were also recorded from a further 24 tetrads, including widely in east and north Herts., outside its native range. (36 tetrads: Dony, 1967; 46 tetrads: 1950-1986, for the native species)

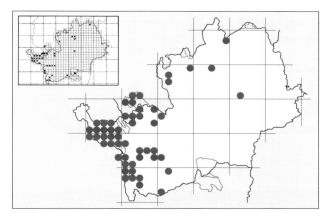

Map 323. *Sorbus aria s. str.*

Sorbus croceocarpa P. D. Sell
Introduced: planted?
First record: 1912.

There is a record of probably planted trees at Temple Dinsley, Preston (12/X), 1912 *J. E. Little* (det. P. D. Sell) (Hb. CGE). Other planted 'whitebeams' could be referable to this.

Sorbus latifolia (Lam.) Pers.
Broad-leaved Whitebeam
Introduced: neophyte.
First record: (1994?) 1996.

Two saplings of the strict species, apparently self-sown, were found in a hedgerow at Merryhills Farm, Bushey (19/H), 1996 *T. J.* Two saplings, which were not confirmed as the segregate, were also found at Croxley Green Station (09/X), 1994 *J. Archer.* Planted trees only identifiable as the aggregate have also been found in Welwyn Garden City (21/L), 1995 *T. J.* It is probably more widespread, but could be confused with *S. croceocarpa.*

Sorbus torminalis (L.) Crantz
Wild Service *or* **Chequer-tree**
Native (and sometimes introduced).
First record: 1815.
Tetrad occurrence: 52 (as native) (11%).
Possibly stable, or increased (+524%).

Occasional in old hedgerows and woodlands on neutral or mildly
acidic clays especially in south Hertfordshire, rare in the west and
north, and on the Boulder Clay. It quite often only reproduces by
suckers, but in a very few woods it can be locally abundant and
setting good seed, such as Great Groves near Bayford (30/E). It
is also increasingly being planted as a 'conservation' exercise,
sometimes in obviously unsuitable habitats outside its native
range. Dony (1967) thought it was restricted to woods on the
London Clay and was 'very rare', although Pryor (1887) had
concluded that it was 'not unfrequent in the south of the County,
but becoming rarer to the north and to the west'. A detailed
survey of the tree, attempting to trace all historical sites for it, as
well as find as many 'new' ones as possible, was carried out by
Geoffrey Harper in 1980 (Harper, 1981). The result demonstrated
that it was indeed quite frequent (although local) across most of
the south of the County, especially the Middlesex fringes, where
it seems to be a genuine 'shadow' of the medieval 'Forest of
Middlesex' and its outlying Hertfordshire commons. The present
survey recorded it from 61 tetrads (of which 7 represented sites
only with planted trees: 90/P; 20/W, X; 22/Q, U; 42/L; 09/L).
The Flora Survey efforts were augmented by a major re-survey
carried out under the auspices of the University of Hertfordshire
in 2000-2001 (Young and Warrington, 2003). Because of the
evident under-recording in the 1960s, it is difficult to compare the
results of the present survey with Dony's.
(8 tetrads: Dony, 1967; 41 tetrads: 1950-1986)

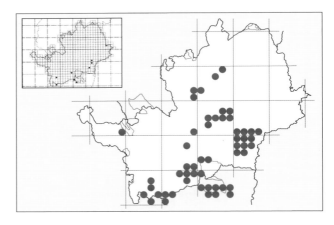

Map 324. *Sorbus torminalis.*

Sorbus domestica L.   [UK Critically Endangered]
Service-tree
Introduced: planted [rare native in the U.K.].
First (only) record: 1996.

This is only known as a planted tree, one mature specimen being
present in Hooks Grove (31/A), 1996 *S. Warrington*, evidently a
relict of the Bayfordbury arboretum.

Genus: *Amelanchier*

Amelanchier lamarckii F. G. Schroeder
Juneberry
Introduced: neophyte.
First record: 1994.

This has only so far been found as an escape on waste ground at
Bury Mead Road, Hitchin (13/V), 1994 *T. J./B. R. Sawford.*

Wild Service Sorbus torminalis *Broxbourne Wood, 1990.*

Genus: *Photinia*

Photinia davidiana (Decne.) Cardot
Stranvaesia
Introduced: planted.
First (only) record: 1994.

This was found as an apparently planted shrub on the edge of Cangsley Grove (20/B), 1994 *C. M. James*, but well away from houses.

Genus: *Cotoneaster*

Cotoneasters present recorders with considerable difficulties, owing to the large number of very similar species which have now been recorded as escapes in Britain. Many appear in scrub and on roadsides or by railways, especially on Chalk, but take some years to mature before they can be readily identified. Most species, however, do not appear to be widespread yet, and when we do find them, we often find several species together where the ground happens to be right for them to become established. With massively increased ornamental plantings of many species around industrial estates and town centres during the last 20 years though, the tendency for them to appear as self-sown in nearby areas is likely to increase.

This account owes much to the interest in the group shown by C. G. Hanson in particular, and also to Jeanette Fryer, who has helped greatly with identifications.

Cotoneaster × watereri Exell (*C. frigidus × C. salicifolius*)
Waterer's Cotoneaster
Introduced: neophyte.
First record: 1991.

One self-sown bush of this was found in a rough field below Redericks Farm, High Wych (41/R), 1991 *T. J.* (det. J. Fryer) (Hb. HTN). It has also appeared self-sown at Elmside Walk, Hitchin (12/Z), 1996 *T. J.* (det. J. Fryer) (Hb. HTN); and in a scrubby chalk pit at 'California', Dunstable (02/A) (VC20 [Beds.]), 1999 *T. J.* (det. J. Fryer) (Hb. HTN). It is probably more widespread, but can be difficult to identify.

Cotoneaster salicifolius Franch.
Willow-leaved Cotoneaster
Introduced: neophyte.
First record: 1993.
Tetrad occurrence: 6 (1%).

First recorded from Hoddesdon (30/U), 1993 *A. M. Boucher* (det. C. G. Hanson) (Hb. Boucher). It has subsequently been found at Bayfordbury (31/A), 1994 *C. G. H.* (Hb. HTN); Bushey Grange (19/I), 1994 *T. J.* (det. J. Fryer) (Hb. HTN); Welwyn Garden City, by railway (21/L), 1996 *A. M. B.*; Tower Road, Ware (31/M), 1996 *C. G. H.* (det. J. Fryer) (Hb. HTN); and old sidings at Royston (34/K) (VC29 [Herts.]), 1998 *T. J.* (conf. J. Fryer) (Hb. HTN).

Cotoneaster henryanus (C. K. Schneid.) Rehder and E. H. Wilson
Henry's Cotoneaster
Introduced: neophyte.
First record: 1997.

Specimens approaching this were identified by J. Fryer from scrub by Napsbury Lane (10/S), *T. J.* 1997; and from old sidings near

Royston Station (34/K) (VC29 [Herts.]), 1998 *T. J.* (Hb. HTN). The precise identity of this plant may need re-examination (Stace, 1997).

Cotoneaster × suecicus G. Klotz (*C. dammeri × C. conspicuus*)
Bearberry Cotoneaster
Introduced: neophyte.
First (only) record: 1996.

The only record is from scrub in the old chalk pit at Little Hadham (42/L), 1996 *C. G. Hanson* (det. J. Fryer) (Hb. Hanson).

Cotoneaster dammeri × C. conspicuus (*C. × suecicus* G. Klotz)
Swedish Cotoneaster
Introduced: neophyte.
First (only) record: 1998 (VC21 [Herts.]).

The only record is from scrub by the Duke of York pub near Potters Bar (29/P) (VC21 [Herts.]), 1998 *T. J.* (det. J. Fryer) (Hb. HTN).

Cotoneaster lacteus W. Smith
Late Cotoneaster
Introduced: neophyte.
First record: 1993.

This was first found as a bird-sown bush in Jefferies Road, Ware (31/S), 1993 *A. M. Boucher* (det. C. G. Hanson) (Hb. Boucher). It has also been found on the site of former greenhouses at Bayfordbury (31/A), 1994 *C. G. Hanson* (det. J. Fryer) (Hb. HTN).

Cotoneaster sherriffii G. Klotz
Sherriff's Cotoneaster
Introduced: neophyte.
First (only) record: 1986.

The only record is of a self-sown bush at Bayfordbury (31/A), 1986 *C. G. Hanson* (det. J. Fryer) (Hb. Hanson).

Cotoneaster integrifolius (Roxb.) G. Klotz
Entire-leaved Cotoneaster
Introduced: neophyte.
First (only) record: 1994.

This was also found as a bird-sown bush on the site of the former greenhouses at Bayfordbury (31/A), 1994 *A. M. Boucher/C. G. Hanson* (det. C. G. H.) (Hb. Hanson).

Cotoneaster linearifolius (G. Klotz) G. Klotz
Thyme-leaved Cotoneaster
Introduced: neophyte.
First (only) record: 1994.

Along with other species, this was at Bayfordbury (31/A), 1994 *A. M. Boucher/C. G. Hanson* (det C. G. H.) (Hb. Hanson).

Cotoneaster horizontalis Decne.
Wall Cotoneaster
Introduced: neophyte.
First record: 1963.
Tetrad occurrence: 34 (7%).
Increasing.

Frequently bird-sown escape from gardens and ornamental plantings, on waste ground, calcareous grassland, road verges and the like, this was already well-established when first noticed at Boxmoor (= Westbrook Hay) Golf Course (00/H) by Dony (Dony, 1967), and was probably present elsewhere as well. By 1986, it had been recorded in four more localities, but during the current survey, it has been found apparently self-sown and often well-established in at least 34 tetrads across the County, with a slight preponderance in the south-east.

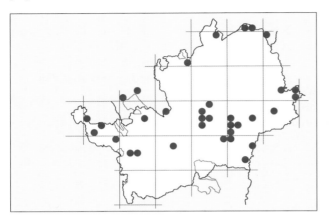

Map 325. *Cotoneaster horizontalis.*

Cotoneaster ascendens Flinck and B. Hylmö
Ascending Cotoneaster
Introduced: neophyte.
First (only) record: 1995.

This is a rare escape from gardens, and its second British record as such was from the scrub at Little Hadham Chalk Pit (42/G), 1995 *C. G. Hanson* (det. J. Fryer) (Hb. Hanson, Hb. HTN).

Cotoneaster divaricatus Rehder and E. H. Wilson
Spreading Cotoneaster
Introduced: neophyte.
First record: 1995.

The only locality so far is with other species at Little Hadham Chalk Pit (42/L), 1995-1996 *C. G. Hanson* (det. J. Fryer) (Hb. HTN).

Cotoneaster simonsii Baker
Himalayan Cotoneaster
Introduced: neophyte.
First record: 1978.
Tetrad occurrence: 19 (4%).

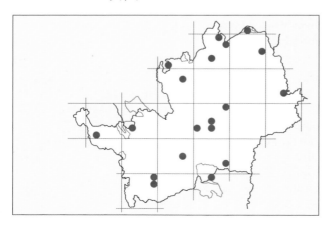

Map 326. *Cotoneaster simonsii.*

A medium-sized shrub becoming a frequent bird-sown coloniser of scrub and secondary woodland in many places. It was first found at Royston Chalk Pit (34/Q), 1978 *T. J.* (Hb. HTN), and the recent survey found it in 19 scattered tetrads across the County.

Cotoneaster bullatus Bois
Hollyberry Cotoneaster
Introduced: neophyte.
First record: 1996.

Along with several other species, this was found to occur in the scrub along the pit margin at Little Hadham Chalk Pit (42/L), 1996 *C. G. Hanson* (det. J. Fryer) (Hb. Hanson; Hb. HTN); and it has also been found in scrub by the old railway at Fleetville, St Albans (10/T), 1998 *T. J.* (det. J. Fryer) (Hb. HTN).

Cotoneaster rehderi Pojark.
Bullate Cotoneaster
Introduced: neophyte.
First record: 1994.

This rather large and conspicuous shrub was first found at Roughdown Common (00/M), 1994 *A. D. Marshall* (det. J. Fryer) (Hb. HTN). It was also found in the scrub at 'California', Dunstable (02/A) (VC20 [Beds.]), 1999 *T. J.* (det. J. Fryer) (Hb. HTN).

Cotoneaster dielsianus E. Pritzel ex Diels.
Diel's Cotoneaster
Introduced: neophyte.
First record: 1989.
Tetrad occurrence: 7 (1%).

This is becoming a fairly frequent escape from gardens. It was first found by the railway at Carpenders Park (19/G), 1989 *J. K. Jackson*; and was found during the survey in seven scattered tetrads, but may be much more widespread.

Cotoneaster franchetii Bois
Franchet's Cotoneaster
Introduced: neophyte.
First record: 1986.
Tetrad occurrence: 4 (<1%).

Rather similar to Diel's Cotoneaster, this was first found at the former greenhouse site at Bayfordbury (31/A), 1986 *C. G. Hanson* (det. E. J. Clement) (Hb. HTN), where it was found again in 1996. It was also found during the survey at Merry Hill Lane, Bushey (19/H), 1994 *J. K. Jackson* (det. J. Fryer) (Hb. HTN); Wengeo Lane, Ware (31/M), 1995 *C. G. Hanson* (det. J. Fryer) (Hb. HTN); and in a derelict garden at Elmside Walk, Hitchin (12/Z), 1996 *T. J.* (det. J. Fryer) (Hb. HTN).

Cotoneaster mairei H. Lév.
Maire's Cotoneaster
Introduced: neophyte.
First record: 1996.

A rare escape from gardens, this was found to be part of the scrub community at Little Hadham Chalk Pit (42/L), 1996, 1997 *C. G. Hanson* (det. J. Fryer) (Hb. HTN).

Cotoneaster sternianus (Turrill) Boom
Stern's Cotoneaster
Introduced: neophyte.
First record: 1992.

First found by the River Lea near Ware Lock (31/M), 1992
C. G. Hanson. It was also recorded at Bowling Road, Ware (31/S),
1993 *A. M. Boucher* (Hb. Boucher); among the scrub on old
sidings near Royston Station (34/K) (VC29 [Herts.]), 1998 *T. J.*
(det. *J. Fryer*) (Hb. HTN); and in scrub on Chadwell Bank, King's
Meads (31/L), 2000 *T. J.* (Hb. HTN). It may well be quite frequent
elsewhere.

Cotoneaster amoenus E. H. Wilson
Beautiful Cotoneaster
Introduced: neophyte.
First record: 1999.

This attractive, low-growing shrub was found to be well-
established on the bare, colonising ground of the chalk pit at
'California', Dunstable (02/A) (VC20 [Beds.]), 1999 *T. J.* (det.
J. Fryer) (Hb. HTN).

Cotoneaster zabelii C. K. Schneid.
Cherryred Cotoneaster
Introduced: neophyte.
First (only) record: 1977.

This was recorded as established on the walls of Hertford Castle
(31/G), 1977 *K. E. Bull* (det. *J. Fryer*) (*comm.*: C. A. Stace). It has
not been recorded again.

Cotoneaster fangianus T. T. Yu
Fang's Cotoneaster
Introduced: neophyte.
First (only) record: 1994.

A rather rare escape, found self-sown at Ware Priory (31/M), 1994
C. G. Hanson (det. *J. Fryer*) (Hb. Hanson).

Genus: *Pyracantha*

Pyracantha coccinea M. Roemer
Firethorn
Introduced: neophyte.
First record: 1990.

This was not noted as an escape until it was found in scrub
at Cheshunt Gravel Pits (30/R), 1990 *A. M. Boucher*. It was
subsequently found, usually as single bushes, at Hertingfordbury
(31/B), 1992 *A. M. B.*; Great Munden (32/L), 1992-3 *S. Watson*;
and in scrub/plantation near Kensworth Quarry (02/A) (VC20
[Beds.]), 1999 *T. J./G. P. Smith*.

Genus: *Mespilus*

Mespilus germanica L.
Medlar
Introduced: planted (and casual?)
First record (planted?): *c.*1880.

This has probably never been a genuinely escaped tree in Herts.
Pryor (1887) recorded it from Stanstead Abbots, but without any
note of its status (but an old tree was known for many years at
Stansteadbury). It occurs as a cultivated tree in a number of old

parks and gardens, such as the grounds of Hatfield House. A single
tree was found on the edge of Park Wood, Weston (22/U), 1997
T. J.; and it has been planted in old grassland at New Barnfield
(20/I), 2004 *J. Moss*.

Genus: *Crataegus*

Crataegus pedicillata Sarg.
Pear-fruited Cockspur-thorn
Introduced: casual.
First record: 1993.

This was recorded as an escape in 1993 from Lime Close, Ware
(31/S) *C. G. Hanson* (det. *B. Wurzell*); and from 'Amersfort', Little
Heath (00/E) *A. D. Marshall* (det. *T. J.*) (Hb. HTN).

Crataegus crus-galli L.
Cockspur-thorn
Introduced: planted?
First (only) record: 1996.

One mature bush was identified at Bernard's Heath, St Albans
(10/P), 1996 *T. J.* It may have been planted.

Crataegus persimilis Sarg.
Broad-leaved Cockspur-thorn
Introduced: neophyte.
First record: 1988.

This was found, as a single mature bush, possibly self-sown, in
a 19th century planted hawthorn hedge at Northfields, Ashwell
(24/R), 1988 *T. J.* (Hb. HTN). It has subsequently been found,
apparently self-sown, at Blackthorn Wood (old bushes) (21/Q),
1992 *A. M. Boucher* (det. *B. Wurzell*) (Hb. Boucher); and at three
places around Hertford (31/F), 1996 *C. G. Hanson* (det. *E. J.
Clement*).

Crataegus monogyna Jacq.
Hawthorn
Native.
First record: 1742 (in the broad sense).
Tetrad occurrence: 486 (99%).
Stable (no measurable change).

A generally ubiquitous plant of hedgerows, scrub and open,
especially secondary, woodland throughout the County. Despite
this, in many areas it is markedly hybridised with Midland
Hawthorn, so that much of the hedgerow material in the main
body of the County may not be the true species. It has also been
planted in large quantities across the enclosed landscapes of
northern Hertfordshire especially, so that its native frequency and
form is possibly doubtful even here. This is now being aggravated
by the planting of other evidently alien 'hawthorns', some of
possibly other taxa altogether, as roadside hedging and amenity
shrubberies. Many of these now flower much earlier than the
'native' form. However, during the drought summers of the 1990s
hawthorn suffered markedly from a dieback caused apparently
by drought-stress, which encourages attack by the jewel beetle
Agrilus sinuatus that in turn introduces a fungal pathogen. This
may also be exacerbated by stress caused by nutrient enrichment
in intensively arable landscapes. In many areas, mature Hawthorns
are dying in large numbers, especially on the Chalk of northern
Herts. Mature thorns in old parkland can be important for insects
(and very old), and often also support Mistletoe. Pink-flowered,

cultivated forms are sometimes found, although the native plant also produces pinkish flowers in drought years or after late frosts. (461 tetrads: Dony, 1967; and from 1950-1986)

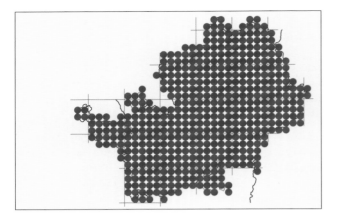

Map 327. *Crataegus monogyna.*

Crataegus × media Bechst. (*C. monogyna × C. laevigata*)
Hybrid Hawthorn
Native.
First record: 1928.
Tetrad occurrence: 74 (15%).

This was mentioned by Dony (1967), but was in fact first recorded by J. E. Little in the Hitchin area in 1928 (Dony, ms. index). The current survey made an attempt to record it, but coverage is probably patchy. It was found widely but patchily across much of the County, with apparent concentrations on the Boulder Clay and in the south, where *C. laevigata* is most frequent. It may form the bulk of hedges in many areas of 'ancient landscape' in south and central Hertfordshire, and is under-recorded especially in west Herts.

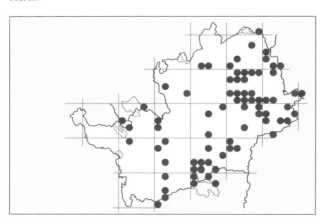

Map 328. *Crataegus × media.*

Crataegus laevigata (Poiret) DC.
Midland Hawthorn
Native.
First record: 1874.
Tetrad occurrence: 278 (57%).
Increased? (+67%).

Early records of this were much confused, and even Pryor's account appears to suggest that *C. monogyna* was the rarer plant! It flowers early, and is found widely in ancient semi-natural woodland, old hedgerows, and mature scrub on commons across the east, south, centre and west of the County on deeper clay

soils, becoming scarce on river valley gravels, and absent on the Chalk. However, despite the best endeavours of our recorders, it is probably over-recorded for the hybrid in many places, especially as the latter can often be markedly similar in leaf form, and have two stigmas.
(158 tetrads: Dony, 1967; 192 tetrads: 1950-1986)

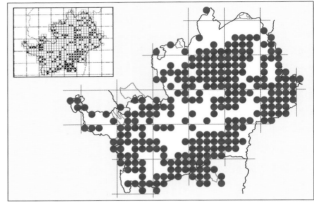

Map 329. *Crataegus laevigata.*

Caesalpiniaceae (Senna family)

Genus: *Senna*

Senna obtusifolia (L.) Irwin and Barnaby
American Sicklepod
Introduced: casual.
First (only) record: 1995.

This was found growing on the sludge beds at Rye Meads Sewage Works (31/V), 1995 *A. M. Boucher/C. G. Hanson* (det.: E. J. Clement) (Hb. Boucher, Hb. Hanson) (Burton, 1996).

Fabaceae (Pea family)

Genus: *Robinia*

Robinia pseudoacacia L.
False Acacia
Introduced: neophyte.
First record: 1916.
Tetrad occurrence: 21 (4%).

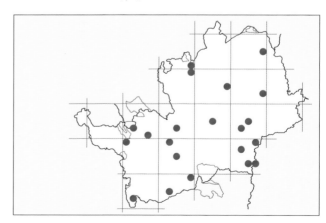

Map 330. *Robinia pseudoacacia.*

This was ignored by Dony (1967), but in fact had been recorded as self-sown as early as 1916, in a copse at Thundridge (TL31) by D. M. Higgins (*Rep. Bot. Exch. Club*: 480 (1916)). It was also reported as escaped at Bishop's Stortford about 1950 (Dony, ms. index). Burton (1983) gives several tetrad records from the south of the County. The current survey has recorded it fairly widely, not all as escapes, but it has been overlooked in many places, especially on the fringes of Middlesex, where Burton found it to be quite frequent. However, it was also widely planted in woodlands in the 19th century, and genuinely naturalised occurrences can be difficult to distinguish from suckers.

Genus: *Sesbania*

Sesbania exaltata (Raf.) Cory
Colorado River-hemp
Introduced: casual.
First record: 1975.

This was identified as a soya waste alien at Rye Meads Sewage Works (31/V), 1975 *C. G. Hanson* (James, 1985). There have been no further records.

Genus: *Phaseolus*

Phaseolus coccineus L.
Runner Bean
Introduced: casual.
First documented record: 1970.

'Beans' are mentioned by Dony (1967) as occurring on tips, but the first actual record of runner bean as an escape is from Blackbridge tip (11/X), 1970 *C. G. Hanson*. It was subsequently recorded from five other tips around the County, and was last seen at Waterford tip (31/C), 1982 *C. G. H.*

Phaseolus vulgaris L.
French Bean
Introduced: casual.
First record: 1959.

A specimen of var. *nanus* (L.) Aschers was collected by Dony from Hoddesdon tip (TL30), 1959 (Hb. HTN). There was also a record of the species from Ware tip (31/M), 1975 *C. G. Hanson.*, but none subsequently.

Genus: *Vigna*

Vigna radiata (L.) Wilczek
Mung Bean
Introduced: casual.
First record: 1973.

This was first reported as a casual at Bulls Mill tip (31/D), 1973 *C. G. Hanson*; and was subsequently recorded at Waterford tip nearby (31/C), 1979, 1984 *C. G. H.*, but not thereafter.

Genus: *Glycine*

Glycine max (L.) Merr.
Soya Bean
Introduced: casual.
First record: 1970.

Although Dony studied soya waste tips near Rickmansworth in the 1960s, the first record of this as an escape itself was not made until 1970, when it was found at Moor Mill tip (10/L) *C. G. Hanson* (Hb. HTN; Hb. LTN). It was subsequently found at Bulls Mill tip (31/D), 1973; two tips at Ware (31/M, N), 1974, 1975; and at Rye Meads Sewage Works (31/V), 1975 *C. G. H.*, after which it has not reappeared.

Genus: *Psoralea*

Psoralea americana L.
Scurfy-pea
Introduced: casual.
First record: 1959.
Only recorded twice: at Pye Corner tip (41/D), 1959 and Hitchin tip (13/V), 1964 (Dony, 1967).

Genus: *Arachis*

Arachis hypogaea L.
Peanut
Introduced: casual.
First record: 1959.

The only occurrence since this was first found at Hitchin tip (Dony, 1967) was at Ware tip (31/M), 1983 *C. G. Hanson*.

Genus: *Galega*

Galega officinalis L.
Goat's-rue
Introduced: neophyte.
First record: 1915.
Tetrad occurrence: 84 (17%).
Increased (+109%).

Having been initially a plant of waste tips, supposedly a garden escape, this has found a niche in gravel pits and similar disturbed ground, where it can become locally established to the exclusion of other plants. It has, however, only become a major part of the flora

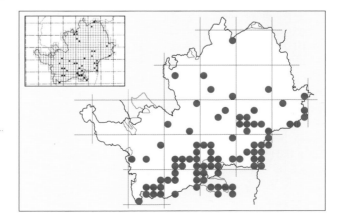

Map 331. *Galega officinalis.*

in a few places, particularly the urban fringes of London, while decreasing elsewhere, such as around Hitchin, as waste tips have been reclaimed. Other species of goat's-rues have been recorded in Britain that could occur in Hertfordshire (Sell and Murrell, 2009), and should be looked for.

(38 tetrads: Dony, 1967; 74 tetrads: 1950-1986)

Genus: *Colutea*

Colutea arborescens L.
Bladder-senna
Introduced: neophyte.
First record: 1913.
Tetrad occurrence: 10 (2%).
Increased slightly? (+18%).

An occasionally more-or-less established shrub of waste ground. Dony thought this was a feature of railway banks (Dony, 1967), but most records have come from waste tips and old gravel pits, scattered across southern and central Hertfordshire, with a persistent colony in the lower Lea Valley, around Waltham Cross. Very few of the current records are from sites where it was recorded in the 1970s or earlier.

(8 tetrads: Dony, 1967; 17 tetrads: 1950-1986)

Colutea × media Willd. (*C. arborescens × C. orientalis*)
Orange Bladder-senna
Introduced: neophyte.
First record: 1992.

This was noted as self-seeding freely from planted bushes at Welwyn Garden City (21/L), 1992 *A. M. Boucher*. It may occur elsewhere.

Genus: *Astragalus*

Astragalus danicus Retz.   UK Endangered
Purple Milk-vetch
Native.
First record: 1690.
Tetrad occurrence: 4 (<1%).
Decreasing rapidly.

This was always limited to a few sites with very thin vegetation on Chalk. It was lost from Sandon Heath when the site was ploughed in the 19th century, and has not been seen by the roadside near Baldock for a long time (Dony, ms. index). It survived until recently at the three localities mentioned by Dony (1967) (except that he erroneously quoted Arbury Banks at Ashwell for Ashwell Quarry (23/P), where it had been known for over a hundred years). It now seems to have gone from here, last seen in 1980 *T. J.*, having been overtaken by rank growth despite concerted conservation action. It was also last seen by the A505 near The Thrift (33/E), in 1988 *B. R. Sawford*; and on the south-facing banks of the Icknield Way at Telegraph Hill (12/E) in 1987 *T. J.* Even on Therfield Heath it has decreased massively, although it was near Sun Hill (34/K), 1993 *T. J.* and is still present at and near Church Hill (33/J), 2006 *C. Cheffings*, 2009 *T. J.* At all its sites, it appears to have succumbed largely to rank growth of coarse vegetation, despite management action, or perhaps to excessively dry springs.

Purple Milk-vetch Astragalus danicus *Thrift road verge, Therfield, 1977.*

Wild Liquorice Astragalus glycyphyllos *Near Holwell, 2009.*

Photo: Brian Sawford

Astragalus glycyphyllos L.   Herts Rare
Wild Liquorice
Native.
First record: 1840 (1814?).
Tetrad occurrence: 4 (as native) (<1%).
Decreasing (-38% as native).

A plant of calcareous clay or chalky soils, where it grows in scrubby grassland and hedgerows, first reliably reported in 1840,

but there is an unlocalised record, possibly from near Hitchin, in Joseph Ransom's diary for 1814. Although it seems to have fared slightly better than its relative, it has also always been rare in the County. Its recent records have been: Tingley Down (13/F), a well-known locality where it has been seen up to 2003 *T. J.*; near Kings Wood (32/R), 1992 *S. Watson*; by the B1368, Braughing (32/X), 1991 *S. W.*; field hedge near Holwell (13/L), 1987 *C. W. Burton*, 2009 (on Beds. border) *B. R. Sawford*. It has also been found as an introduced plant on the roadside at Swanland Road, Water End (20/G) (VC21 [Herts.]), 1988 *P. J. Kerslake-Smith*. It was known in the 1970s and 1980s from several sites around Pirton (13/F, 13/G) *C. W. B.*; from Norton Cross (23/H), 1971 *B. R. Sawford* (given wrongly on the map in Dony (1967) as 23/F); and Westmill Gravel Pit (31/M), 1979 *R. M. Bateman*, but there have been no recent records from these areas.
(6 tetrads: Dony, 1967; 8 tetrads: 1950-1986)

Genus: *Onobrychis*

Onobrychis viciifolia Scop.   UK Near Threatened
Sainfoin
Native (and introduced).
First record: 1814.
Tetrad occurrence: 30 (6%).
Decreasing quite sharply (-47%).

This is likely to be native in old chalk grassland, but is certainly not so as a relict of past cultivation on some road verges and waste ground. Dony (1967) recorded it mainly from the Chalk in north Herts., but the recent survey has shown that small populations occur widely across the County. Unfortunately, records collected for the Flora Survey did not differentiate between the different forms.
(54 tetrads: Dony, 1967; 57 tetrads: 1950-1986)

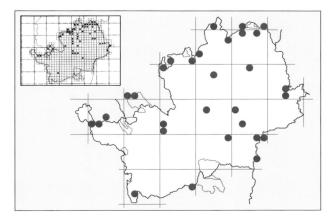

Map 332. *Onobrychis viciifolia.*

Genus: *Anthyllis*

Anthyllis vulneraria L.
Kidney Vetch
Native.
First record: 1748.
Tetrad occurrence: 40 (8%).
Decreasing (-20%).

This is a plant of thin, slightly disturbed chalk grassland. Nineteenth century records show that it was widespread in northern and central Hertfordshire on chalky banks, field margins and roadsides, but it has retreated steadily to the most calcareous soils in northern and north-west Herts., especially since about 1970, as a result of nutrient enrichment. Even here, its native colonies are small and vulnerable, although there are places where it has been sown for 'conservation' on road verges, but usually not with the native form. Not surprisingly, the Small Blue *Cupido minimus* butterfly, which feeds on it, has all but disappeared.
(48 tetrads: Dony, 1967; 58 tetrads: 1950-1986)

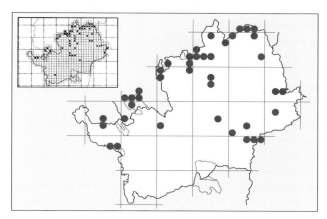

Map 333. *Anthyllis vulneraria.*

The native subspecies is ssp. *vulneraria*, but two alien subspecies have been recorded:

Ssp. *polyphylla* (DC) Nyman. This was first identified by the B1000 near Tewin (21/R), 1982 *A. M. Boucher* (det. J. Akeroyd) (Hb. Boucher); and was later identified as an introduced plant on chalky banks at the former Herts. Environment Centre, Stevenage (22/M), 1998 *F. M. Perring*. It has recently been used extensively in 'wild flower' seeding along Baldock bypass (A505) (23/K,L,S), 2006 (det. T. J.).

Ssp. *carpatica* (Pant.) Nyman. This subspecies was identified as the plant occurring on chalky banks by Ware Road, Hertford (31/L), 1988 *A. M. Boucher* (det. J. Akeroyd) (Hb. Boucher). It may also be a plant used elsewhere as 'wildflower-mix' seeding of road verges. The occurrence of both this and the previous subspecies show the dangers, in terms of conservation of natural vegetation, of employing such species in seed-mixes.

Genus: *Lotus*

Lotus glaber Miller   Herts Rare
Narrow-leaved Bird's-foot Trefoil
Native (and introduced?).
First record: 1845.
Tetrad occurrence: 4 (<1%).

The status of this plant in Hertfordshire is obscure. It may sometimes be misidentified as *L. corniculatus*, but appears to be genuinely native on dry chalky banks and formerly in poor dry, clay grasslands. It also occurs occasionally on waste ground and was at one time a feature of railways. Earlier botanists found it quite widely across most of the County, especially around Hitchin and Royston. Dony (1967) only recorded it from four localities, mostly by railways, although he omitted his record from chalk banks by Upwick Wood (42/M), 1959 (Hb. HTN). It has been recorded more recently from Cedars Park, Cheshunt (30/K), 1982 *M. Crafer*; Mill Green (21/K), 1982 *P. Williams* and from the chalk banks by the A505 at Slip End (23/Y), 1983 *T. J.* (Hb. HTN).

During the current survey, it was re-found at Slip End, 1990, 1999; and also in abundance on chalky banks of the new Offley A505 bypass (12/I), 1992 *T. J.*, near where it was recorded in 1914 by J. E. Little (Dony, ms. index). It has also been found at Cinnamond's Yard, Croxley Green (09/X), 1994 *J. Archer*; and was found to be frequent in a derelict, partially filled old pasture below Croxley Hall Wood (09/S), with a few plants nearby on former sidings, 2006 *T. J.* (Hb. HTN).

Lotus corniculatus L.
Bird's-foot Trefoil *or* **Lady's Slippers**
Native.
First record: 1750.
Tetrad occurrence: 441 (90%).
Decreasing (-8%).

A plant of neutral or calcareous grassland, road verges and waste ground on relatively nutrient-poor, dry soils. This was formerly abundant throughout the County in pastures, on road verges and so on, but has disappeared from many agricultural grasslands, and is now decreasing markedly on road verges through nutrient enrichment and salt-pollution, owing to its habit of growing on the immediate edge of roadside grasslands by the tarmac.
(454 tetrads: Dony, 1967, and from 1950-1986)

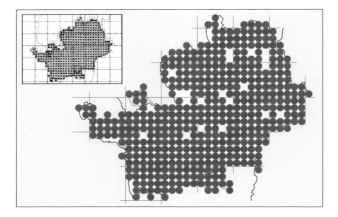

Map 334. *Lotus corniculatus.*

The native subspecies is ssp. *corniculatus*. Ssp. *sativus* Chrtkovà has been recorded from the Herts. section of Pitstone Quarry (91/M) 1995 *T. J./R. Maycock* (Hb. HTN), source unknown, and may have been sown elsewhere in 'conservation' mixes.

Lotus pedunculatus Cav.
Greater Bird's-foot Trefoil
Native.
First record: 1748.
Tetrad occurrence: 177 (36%).
More or less stable (-2%).

This is the wet ground equivalent of *Lotus corniculatus*. It is a plant of old damp clay grasslands, woodland rides and marshy ground throughout much of the County, and retains a similar distribution to that recorded by Dony (1967), although severe disturbance in some river valleys appears to have eliminated it from some areas.
(171 tetrads: Dony, 1967; 191 tetrads: 1950-1986)

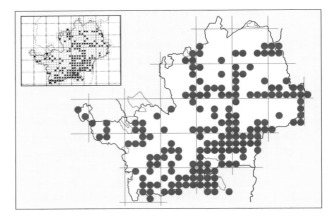

Map 335. *Lotus pedunculatus.*

Genus: *Ornithopus*

Ornithopus perpusillus L.
Bird's-foot
Native.
First record: 1838.
Tetrad occurrence: 11 (2%).
Probably decreased (-8%).

An inconspicuous plant of dry, heathy grassland on old commons or golf courses, occasionally colonising the margins of old gravel and sand pits. Older records show that this was rare, but widespread, across southern Herts., but it had become local and very scarce by the 1960s (Dony, 1967). Although the current survey found it in 11 tetrads, as Dony did, quite a few of the current records are of very small colonies in 'new' sites, while other sites known to Dony have apparently lost it.
(11 tetrads: Dony, 1967; 13 tetrads: 1950-1986)

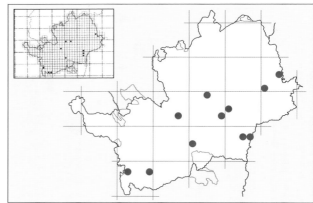

Map 336. *Ornithopus perpusillus.*

Genus: *Coronilla*

Coronilla scorpioides (L.) Koch
Annual Scorpion-vetch
Introduced: casual.
First record: 1915.

This seed contaminant was a plant of waste places and used to be quite frequent around Hertford, but has not been seen in the County since the record from Park Street, 1966 (Dony, 1967).

Genus: *Hippocrepis*

Hippocrepis emerus (L.) Lassen
Scorpion Senna
Introduced: neophyte.
First (only) record: 1993.

This was first recorded for Hertfordshire by the A1(M), South Mimms (20/G) (VC21 [Herts.]), 1993 *G. Wyatt*.

Hippocrepis comosa L.
Horseshoe Vetch
Native.
First record: 1814.
Tetrad occurrence: 12 (as native) (2%).
Decreased (-49%).

This is a plant of old, short, chalk grassland on nutrient-poor soils, and as such has decreased markedly over the last 30 years. It is now confined to steeper slopes on the Chalk in north Herts., mainly Therfield Heath, a small population at Wilbury Hill, Letchworth, and the hills at Pirton and Hexton, except for its re-discovery on chalk banks near Chadwell (31/L), where it was not recorded by Dony, and its survival in two localities in the west: Aldbury Nowers, and Blows Down (VC20 [Beds.]). Its inclusion in seed mixes for the Baldock bypass (23/L), 2006 is perhaps unlikely to result in a viable population, given the disturbed, eutrophic nature of the soils.

(22 tetrads: Dony, 1967; 23 tetrads: 1950-1986)

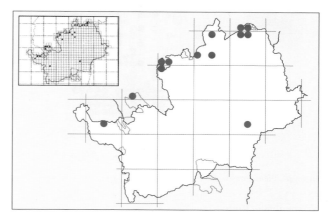

Map 337. *Hippocrepis comosa.*

Genus: *Securigera*

Securigera varia (L.) Lassen
Crown Vetch
Introduced: neophyte.
First record: 1916.

This remains attractive and abundant, although reduced in coverage, on the old railway sidings at Hitchin Station (12/Z), 1997, 2009 *T. J.*, as Dony recorded it in 1958, but it has disappeared from the other two sites he reported. It was found by the River Lea at Dobbs Weir (30/Z), 1981 *C. G. Hanson*; and was also present by the old railway line at Amwell Quarry (31/R), 1982 *G. P. Smith*, where it was last reported in 1993 *G. Hounsome*.

Genus: *Scorpiurus*

Scorpiurus muricatus L.
Caterpillar-plant
Introduced: casual.
First record: 1922.

Dony (1967) listed this under two names: *S. subvillosus* and *S. sulcatus*. It subsequently appeared as a wool shoddy alien at Ramerick, Ickleford (13/R), 1971; and at Newnham (23/N), 1974 *C. G. Hanson*. It was also found at Bulls Mill tip (31/D), 1974 *C. G. H.* (Hb. HTN), and was erroneously stated to be 'new to the County' in James (1985). There have been no recent records.

Genus: Vicia

Vicia cracca L.
Tufted Vetch
Native.
First record: 1748.
Tetrad occurrence: 308 (63%).
Possibly stable (-2%).

A frequent plant of hedgerows, and old neutral or mildly acidic grasslands or fens, especially on damp clay. The distribution of this has changed very little since the 1960s, although its occurrence in old pastures in south Herts. must have reduced substantially.

(299 tetrads: Dony, 1967; 316 tetrads: 1950-1986)

Horseshoe Vetch Hippocrepis comosa *Ashwell Quarry, 1986.*

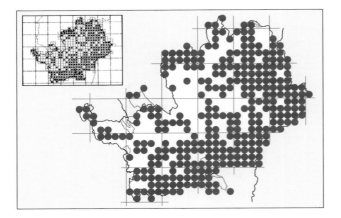

Map 338. *Vicia cracca.*

Vicia tenuifolia Roth
Fine-leaved Vetch
Introduced: casual.
First record: *c.*1900.

In addition to the record from Wheathampstead in Dony (1967), he also reported it (as *V. elegans*) from the dried bed of Startop's End Reservoir (91/B), 1945 *J. E. Dandy* (Hb. BM). It was also found at Hitchin (12/Z), 1934 *J. E. Little* (Hb. CGE). There are no recent records.

Vicia sylvatica L.   Herts Rare
Wood Vetch
Native.
First record: 1815? (1814?)
A plant of open woodland rides and wood margins on well-drained, moderately acidic soils. Despite what Dony (1967) said, it seems that the first record may actually have been in Herts., near Tring (Pryor, 1887). In addition, there is an unlocalised record in Joseph Ransom's diary, possibly from the Hitch Wood area, in 1814. It has always been rare in the County, and was thought to be extinct at its last known site at Wain Wood (12/S), owing to shading, until it was discovered at Harding's Wood, Wigginton (90/P), 1988 *R. Mabey* (Hb. HTN), following clearance of conifers and opening of the ride. This could conceivably have been the 'Tring' site given by Pryor. It would be nice to think it could reappear at Hitch and Wain Woods, given appropriate ride management!

Vicia villosa Roth
Fodder Vetch
Introduced: neophyte.
First record: 1907.

This, including the form formerly named '*Vicia dasycarpa*' (Dony, 1967), occurs occasionally as an established introduction on waste ground, and rarely as a crop weed. It was reported from Roehyde (20/D), 1984 *A. D. Marshall* (Hb. HTN); and during the recent survey it has been found at Holycross Hill, Wormley (30/M), 1990 *A. M. Boucher* (Hb. HTN); on a building site, Hertford (31/G), 1991 *A. M. B.* (Hb. HTN); established at Turnford Gravel Pits, Cheshunt (30/S), 1994 *G. P. Smith*; and in a sainfoin field at Furneux Pelham (42/J), 2000 *K. Robinson* (Hb. HTN).

The usual form is ssp. *villosa*, but ssp. *varia* (Host) Corb. was recorded in Dony (1967), and has since been found at Bulls Mill tip (31/D), 1973 *C. G. Hanson*.

Vicia benghalensis L.
Purple Vetch
Introduced: casual.
First record: 1916.

This was one of a number of vetch species which once occurred as casuals around Ware and neighbouring areas (Dony, 1967). There are no recent records.

Vicia cretica Boiss. and Heldr. in Bois.
Cretan Vetch
Introduced: casual.
First record: 1915.

There have been no records since it was found at Hoddesdon (Dony, 1967).

Vicia monantha Retz.
Introduced: casual.
First record: 1919.

This was another of the casuals from Ware, not recorded since 1928 *G. C. Druce* (Dony, ms. index).

Vicia hirsuta (L.) Gray
Hairy Tare
Native.
First record: 1750.
Tetrad occurrence: 270 (55%).
Probably stable (-3%).

This is a weed of waste places, rough grassland and roadsides, formerly also a cornfield weed. Its distribution remains much the same as it was in the 1960s (Dony, 1967), although it has increased in some areas of wooded country, owing to disturbance and introduction, and it has also now been found more widely on the Boulder Clay.
(265 tetrads: Dony, 1967; 294 tetrads: 1950-1986)

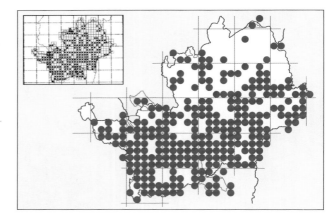

Map 339. *Vicia hirsuta.*

Vicia parviflora Cav.   UK Vulnerable
Slender Tare
Native.
First record: 1843.

Now very rare, having always been scarce in arable field margins and hedge banks on calcareous clay soils. This was only known from a handful of sites around Hertford, Westmill, Pirton, and Letchworth in the 19th and early 20th centuries. Dony (1967) did not know it in the County. It was found at Hexton Chalk

Pit (13/A), 1977 *R. Groom* (Hb. HTN) on dumped clay (James, 1982), where it has remained, having been re-found there 2009 *C. M. James*. It was also found on a grassy field bank west of Letchworth (23/H), 1991 *A. Dean* (Hb. HTN).

Vicia tetrasperma (L.) Schreber
Smooth Tare
Native.
First record: 1838.
Tetrad occurrence: 226 (46%).
Increased markedly (+70%).

A plant of rough, colonising grasslands and waste ground, which has spread along roadsides and in disturbed ground across most of the County, although it remains less common in the west.
(126 tetrads: Dony, 1967; 157 tetrads: 1950-1986)

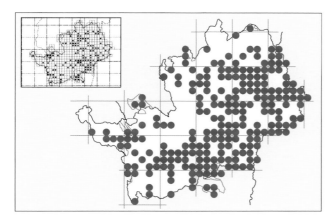

Map 340. *Vicia tetrasperma.*

Vicia sepium L.
Bush Vetch
Native.
First record: 1814.
Tetrad occurrence: 375 (76%).
Decreasing (-15%).

A characteristic plant of roadside hedges, woodland rides, and green lanes on a wide range of soils, only becoming scarce on the Chalk and very acidic clays and gravels. It now appears to be decreasing owing to the overgrowth and dereliction of roadside verges in particular, and is also retreating from over-tidy urban areas.
(418 tetrads: Dony, 1967; 436 tetrads: 1950-1986)

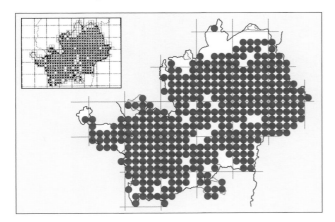

Map 341. *Vicia sepium.*

Vicia grandiflora Scopoli
Large Yellow-vetch
Introduced: casual.
First (only) record: 1993.
This was first identified in Herts. on ground sown with 'Agrimix' at Baas Lane, Hoddesdon (30/T), 1993 *C. G. Hanson* (det. E. J. Clement) (Hb. HTN).

Vicia sativa L.
Common Vetch
Native.
First record: 1750 (as the aggregate).
Tetrad occurrence (for the agg.): 386 (79%).
Probably stable (+1%).

A plant of rough grassland, meadows, road verges and waste places throughout the County, becoming less common on the Boulder Clay and Clay-with-Flints, and absent only in very arable areas. It is very capable of colonising disturbed ground.
(361 tetrads for the aggregate: Dony, 1967; 383 tetrads for the aggregate: 1950-1986)

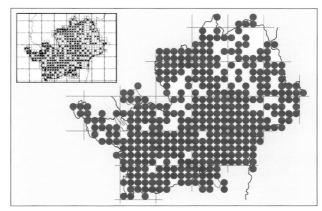

Map 342. *Vicia sativa.*

Dony only recognised two subspecies, and so his distribution map of 'ssp. *sativa*' can only be taken as records for the aggregate. The main subspecies in the County is actually ssp. *segetalis* (Thuill.) Gaudin, but too few records of this have been confirmed to give a separate map. Its first documented record was from Boxmoor (00/I), 1994 *G. Salisbury*. Ssp. *sativa* itself is an introduced fodder plant from southern Europe, and is apparently rare in the County as an escape, with recently confirmed records only from Bulls Mill tip (31/D), 1977; and Ware Station (31/S), 1999 *C. G. Hanson* (Hb. HTN).

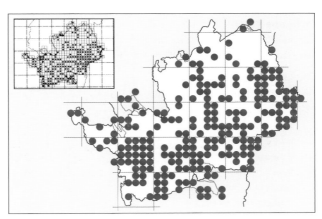

Map 343. *Vicia sativa* ssp. *nigra.*

The other principal subspecies is ssp. *nigra* (L.) Ehrh. **Narrow-leaved Vetch** (Map 343), a native plant of mainly grasslands on lighter, often calcareous clay soils, first recorded by W. H. Coleman in 1838, was found in 224 tetrads during the survey (46%). It is apparently stable or slightly decreased in the County (-1%).
(214 tetrads: Dony, 1967; 225 tetrads: 1950-1986)

Vicia peregrina L.
Introduced: casual.
First record: 1919.

The only records are from Ware (TL31), although Dony (1967) omitted one from dredged mud by the canal, 1932 *A. W. Graveson* (Hb. HTN).

Vicia melanops Sibth. and Sm.
Introduced: casual.
First record: 1920.

Another of the casuals on canal mud at Ware, last recorded in 1928 (Dony, 1967).

Vicia lutea L.
Yellow Vetch
Introduced: casual.
First record: 1887.

There is no confirmed record since this was also found on canal mud near Ware, 1920, 1927 *A. W. Graveson* (Hb. HTN) (Dony, ms. index).

Vicia hybrida L.
Hairy Yellow Vetchling
Introduced: casual.
First (only) record: *c.*1920.

The only record is an undated one from canal mud between Hertford and Ware *A. W. Graveson* (*c.*1920) (Dony, 1967).

Vicia bithynica (L.) L.
Bithynian Vetch
Introduced: casual (native in the U.K.).
First record: 1914.

There is a record by A. W. Graveson given in Dony (1967), who omitted another from a cornfield by Balls Wood (31/K), also 1914 *H. F. Hayllar* (ms. diary).

Vicia narbonensis L.
Narbonne Vetch
Introduced: casual.
First record: 1920.

In addition to the three records given by Dony (1967), it has also been found more recently at Bulls Mill tip (31/D), 1973 *C. G. Hanson*.

Vicia faba L.
Broad Bean
Introduced: casual.
First record as escape: 1970.
Tetrad occurrence: 61 (12%).

This was not even mentioned by Dony (1967), but must have occurred as a casual. It was first noted at Bulls Mill tip (31/D), 1970 *C. G. Hanson*, and was subsequently noticed at three other tips to 1986. The current survey has found that it as a regular casual in many places, almost exclusively in east Herts. on the Boulder Clay, although it has probably been ignored elsewhere!

Genus: *Lens*

Lens culinaris Medikus
Lentil
Introduced: casual.
First record: 1916.

The first was the only record until 1970, when it was found at Cole Green tip (21/Q) and Blackbridge tip (11/X) *C. G. Hanson*. It was later discovered at Ware UDC tip (31/M), 1977; and at Waterford tip (31/C), 1985 *C. G. H*. It has not been seen since.

Genus: *Lathyrus*

Apart from the native species, there are large numbers of casual species recorded, many from Ware, where they appear to have been introduced with grain delivered to maltings beside the canal. Along with vetches and other species, these form an interesting example of past invasions of alien plants that largely no longer occur.

Lathyrus linifolius (Reichard) Bässler   Herts Rare?
Bitter-vetch
Native.
First record: 1838.
Tetrad occurrence: 6 (1%).
Rare and decreasing (-45%).

Bitter-vetch Lathyrus linifolius *Bricket Wood Common, 1983.*

A distinctive plant of heathy grassland, wood borders and woodland rides on moderately acidic soils. This was always local in Herts., but had decreased by the 1960s, and continues to decline, as its habitat is lost to scrub, or through nutrient enrichment. It was only found during the recent survey in six localities: Martin's Green (30/N), 1988 *A. M. Boucher*; Bricket Wood Common (10/F), 1988, 1999 *T. J./G. P. Smith*; Balls Wood (31/K), 1989 *A. M. B.*; road bank by Nicholson's Wood, Bramfield (21/T), 1995 *S. Cuming*; Wormley Wood (30/I), 1998 *S. Davey*; and Robbery Bottom Lane, by the railway (21/N), 2002 *T. J.* In some of these it may no longer be present. Dony (1967) recorded it in 10 tetrads, while it was also found at Hoddesdon Park Wood (30/P), 1978 *Woodland Survey team*; Highfield Wood (30/P), 1985 *T. J.*; and Redwell Wood (20/B), 1986 *T. J.*, before the recent survey began. (10 tetrads: Dony, 1967; 13 tetrads: 1950-1986)

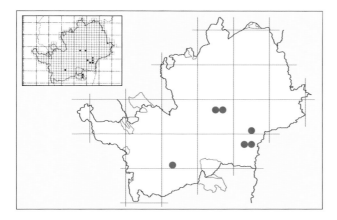

Map 344. *Lathyrus linifolius.*

Lathyrus pratensis L.
Meadow Vetchling
Native.
First record: 1748.
Tetrad occurrence: 435 (89%).
Decreasing (-9%).

This is a common plant throughout most of Hertfordshire in neutral or calcareous grassland, on road verges and waste ground, but usually in established habitats. Its retreat in the face of habitat loss and degradation is beginning to be evident at the tetrad scale, as the map shows.
(452 tetrads: Dony, 1967; and from 1950-1986)

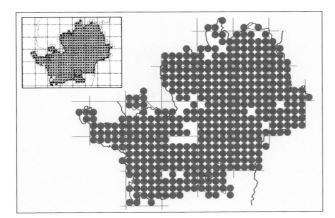

Map 345. *Lathyrus pratensis.*

Lathyrus tuberosus L.
Tuberous Pea
Introduced: neophyte.
First record: 1845.

Dony (1967) recorded this as new to the County from Kensworth (VC20 [Beds.]), but there is a specimen in Hb. CGE from TL21, dated 1845 (*comm.*: B. R. C., CEH Monks Wood). It was found more recently at Kings Langley (00/L), *c.*1974 *R. Hemming*; and by Croxley Common Moor (09/X), *A. V. Moon* (*London Naturalist*, 61). During the recent survey it has only been found once: at two nearby sites adjoining Berrygrove Wood, Aldenham (19/J), 1987 *T. J./G. P. Smith*.

Lathyrus grandiflorus Smith
Two-flowered Everlasting-pea
Introduced: neophyte.
First record: 1978.

This was first reported by A. M. Boucher from beside the car park at Broxbourne Station (30/T), 1978 (Hb. Boucher). It has also recently been found on a disturbed bank by Bedwell Pit, Essendon (20/Z), 2001 *T. J.*

Lathyrus sylvestris L.   Herts Rare
Narrow-leaved Everlasting-pea
Native.
First record: 1805.

This is one of the most enigmatic native plants in the County, occurring in ancient hedges and on wood margins. It has always apparently been rare, but in the 19th century was reasonably widespread across most of the Boulder Clay in east Herts., with one outlying site at Tingley Wood near Pirton (Pryor, 1887). Dony and Little scarcely knew the plant in Herts. (Dony, 1967). Since 1970 it has been recorded by the roadside east of Aston (22/W), 1970 *E. Young* (an historic site); and on the south side of Mardley Heath (21/P), 1973, 1980 *A. D. Marshall/J. Godbey* (Hb. HTN). Records from 20/G, K and N during the 1970s were not supported by specimens, and must remain unconfirmed. There is also a record from Croxley Common Moor (09/S), 1981 given in *London Naturalist*, 61 (Burton, 1982 and 1983), but this may have been an error for *L. tuberosus*, which was recorded from this locality at the same time. During the recent survey, it has only been found once: lane near Gregory's Farm (32/A), 1992 *A. R. Outen* (Hb. HTN), not far from where S. C. Mortis found it in 1951 at Leatherfield Common (Dony, ms. index), a record overlooked in Dony (1967). More recent attempts to re-find this, however, have proved fruitless, following the 'tidying up' of the hedgerow where it grew! It may survive elsewhere.

Lathyrus latifolius L.
Broad-leaved Everlasting-pea
Introduced: neophyte.
First record: 1874.
Tetrad occurrence: 50 (10%).
Increased (+48%).

This attractive, but rather rampant escape from gardens was first recorded by the railway at Hatfield, and was established near Hitchin station by 1920 (Dony, ms. index). Dony (1967) shows it sparsely scattered around the County in hedgerows and waste ground. It is now quite frequent in waste places, especially on

Chalk or gravelly soils around towns. It is, however, strangely absent so far around Stevenage.
(32 tetrads: Dony, 1967; 54 tetrads: 1950-1986)

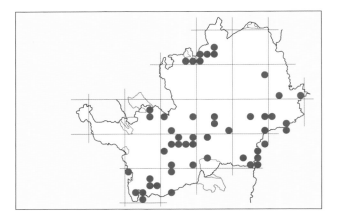

Map 346. *Lathyrus latifolius.*

Lathyrus odoratus L.
Sweet Pea
Introduced: casual.
First record: c.1880.

After its first record at Oughton Head (Pryor, 1887), it was not formally recorded as an escape again until it was found at Moor Mill tip (10/L), 1970 *C. G. Hanson* (det. J. G. Dony). It was also found at Ware tip (31/M), 1977 *C. G. H.* and there is a record from Smallford (10/Y), without date, in Burton (1983). During the present survey it was found on waste ground at Ware (31/M), 1992 *A. M. Boucher*; and by the old R. Lea at Cheshunt (30/R), 1998 *R. M. Burton*.

Lathyrus sphaericus Retz.
Introduced: casual.
First record: 1874.

The only records are from Cole Green (20/V), 1874 (Pryor, 1887), and from Ware (31/M), 1920 (Dony, 1967).

Lathyrus inconspicuus L.
Introduced: casual.
First (only) record: 1920.

The only record is from Ware (Dony, 1967).

Lathyrus cicera L.
Introduced: casual.
First record: 1846.

Omitted by Dony (1967), there is a record from Sawbridgeworth by G. Wolsey (quoted in *Rep. Bot. Exch. Club*: 120 (1920)). Its only other record was from Ware, 1914 (Dony, 1967).

Lathyrus annuus L.
Fodder Pea
Introduced: casual.
First record: 1915.
The only records are from Ware Cemetery (31/M), 1915, 1916 *H. F. Hayllar* (Dony, 1967, and ms. index).

[*Lathyrus hierosolymitanus* Boiss.
Introduced: casual.

There is a record by Trower and Druce, 1914, from Ware (*Rep. Bot. Exch. Club*: 194 (1915)) (Dony, 1967), but this could possibly be *L. annuus*.]

Lathyrus hirsutus L.
Hairy Vetchling
Introduced: casual.
First record: 1894.

This was at one time an occasional casual in waste places, for which Dony (1967) gave two recent records. It was last recorded from a railway bank at Stevenage (22/K), 1968 *A. Rogers* (Hb. HTN); and from a sewage works at New Barnet (29/W) the same year *D. G. Irving* (Dony, ms. records).

Lathyrus ochrus (L.) DC. in Lam. and DC.
Introduced: casual.
First record: 1915.

The only records were from Ware, 1915, 1916 by Trower and Druce (*Rep. Bot. Exch. Club*: 262 (1917)) (Dony, 1967).

Lathyrus nissolia L.
Grass Vetchling
Native.
First record: 1801.
Tetrad occurrence: 46 (9%).
Increased? (+22%).

This is usually a rather inconspicuous plant of unimproved, rough grasslands on well-drained clay, gravel or rarely chalky soils. It can also colonise disturbed ground, *e.g.* around gravel pits. It has always been rather scattered in the County, but can be overlooked, which may explain why it appeared to have increased during the 1980s, but was found in less tetrads again during the present survey.
(36 tetrads: Dony, 1967; 61 tetrads: 1950-1986)

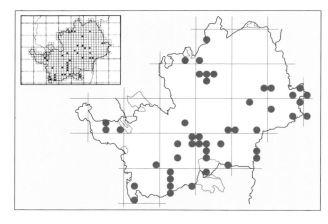

Map 347. *Lathyrus nissolia.*

Lathyrus aphaca L. [UK Vulnerable]
Yellow Vetchling
Introduced [possibly native in the U.K.].
First record: 1841.

There is no evidence that this was ever native in Hertfordshire. It has turned up on a fairly regular basis in rough grassland and waste places across the County. Despite the statement in

Dony (1967) that it had been reported a few times, especially around Welwyn, his manuscript index indicates that he only filed one recent record, from Barnet, 1940 *A. G. Harrold*. There were reliable records after 1967 from Park Street (10/L), 1968 *J. G. Dony* (Hb. HTN); Hitchin tip (13/V), 1968 *H. Bowry*; and from Wormley (30/S), 1985 *B. Nicholson*. During the recent survey it was found at West Hyde (09/F), 1987 *P. J. Ellison*; Cheshunt Gravel Pits (30/R), 1988 *G. P. Smith*; near Elstree (19/X), 1995 *A. R. Outen*; and near Croxley Common Moor (09/S), 1996 *J. Colthup*.

Genus: *Pisum*

Pisum sativum L.
Garden Pea
Introduced: casual.
First record: 1930.

Although Dony (1967) only briefly mentions this, ssp. *arvense* (L.) Poiret was first recorded as an escape on the railway banks at Hitchin (12/Z), 1930 *H. Phillips* (Hb. HTN). There were also subsequent records of the species from Bishop's Stortford and Wheathampstead, and it occurred in six tetrads between 1967 and 1986, mainly on tips. Subspecies arvense was recorded again at Hoddesdon (30/U), 1978 *A. M. Boucher*. During the survey the species was recorded three times: at South Mimms (20/G), 1989 (VC21 [Herts.]) *T. C. G. Rich*; Hertford (31/G), 1990 *A. M. B.*; and a conservation strip by arable, Royston (33/U), 1991 *T. J.*

Genus: *Cicer*

Cicer arietinum L.
Chick Pea
Introduced: casual.
First record: 1913.

This was first noted at Purwell Field, Hitchin (22/E), 1913 *J. E. Little* (det. *H. S. Thompson*) (*Rep. Bot. Exch. Club*: 65 (1914)), and was subsequently found as a casual at Ware, Cole Green and Hoddesdon (Dony, ms. index). More recently it has been found on tips at Hitchin (13/V), 1974; Bulls Mill (31/D), 1977; Ware (31/M), 1977; and Cole Green (21/Q), 1978 *C. G. Hanson*. There have been no records recently.

Genus: *Ononis*

Ononis spinosa L.
Spiny Rest-harrow
Native.
First record: 1843.
Tetrad occurrence: 14 (3%).
Decreasing (-9%).

This was a characteristic plant of unimproved damp grassland on the Chalk Marl and similar soils in north and extreme west Herts., now very limited, owing to loss of habitat. It also occurs rarely on leached Boulder Clay and similar soils elsewhere, and rarely on the Chalk, where it can occur side-by-side with its more widespread relative, such as at Ashwell Quarry (23/P). It may no longer occur in some of its recently recorded sites, such as roadside verges north of Ashwell, which have suffered eutrophication from arable farming.
(15 tetrads: Dony, 1967; 21 tetrads: 1950-1986)

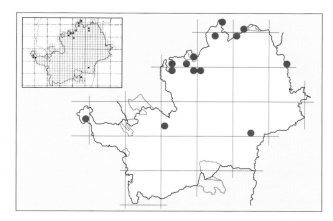

Map 348. *Ononis spinosa.*

Ononis repens L.
Common Rest-harrow
Native.
First record: 1779.
Tetrad occurrence: 183 (37%).
Decreasing (-22%).

A plant of rough grassland, road verges and margins of arable fields on calcareous soils, especially the Chalk and the drier areas of the Boulder Clay. While it appears to have been better recorded in east Herts. than in the 1960s, its loss from many areas is apparent, and where it does occur it is often very limited in quantity.
(224 tetrads: Dony, 1967; 244 tetrads: 1950-1986)

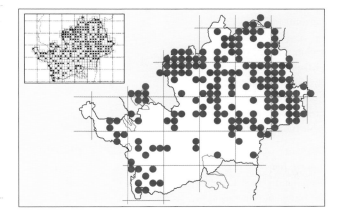

Map 349. *Ononis repens*

Ononis mitissima L.
Mediterranean Rest-harrow
Introduced: casual.
First record: 1987.

This was found as an escape, presumably from bird-seed, at Waterford tip (31/C), 1987 *C. G. Hanson* (Hb. Hanson); and was subsequently found as an escape at South Road Nurseries, Bishop's Stortford (42/V), 1994 *S. Watson* (Hb. HTN).

Ononis baetica Clemente
Andalucian Rest-harrow
Introduced: casual.
First record: 1965.

This was recorded (as *O. salzmanniana*) in Dony (1967); and was also found at Ware tip (31/M), 1976 *C. G. Hanson*. There are no recent records.

Melilotus altissimus Thuill.
Tall Melilot
Introduced: archaeophyte.
First record: 1822.
Tetrad occurrence: 161 (33%).
Increased or stable? (+18%).

Formerly thought of as a native of calcareous rough grasslands, especially on the Boulder Clay, this is now thought to be an ancient introduction. Although it appears to be more widespread than in 1967, it is certainly less abundant where it occurs, having once been a strong feature of road verges and green lanes in east Herts., for example, where it now occurs sparsely.
(130 tetrads: Dony, 1967; 157 tetrads: 1950-1986)

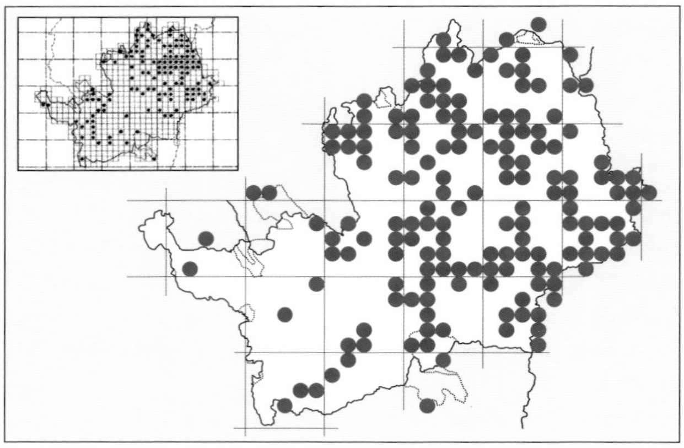

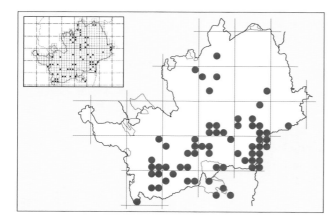

Map 350. *Melilotus altissimus.*

Melilotus albus Medikus
White Melilot
Introduced: neophyte.
First record: 1839.
Tetrad occurrence: 64 (13%).
Stable (no measured change).

A plant of roadsides, bare ground and waste places. Although this has been recorded in the County for a long time, it was rare for over a hundred years. Dony (1967) recorded it as occasional across the County, but the recent survey indicates that it has consolidated its occurrence in the lower Lea and Colne valleys, by main roads and around gravel pits, while it has apparently decreased around Hitchin, Letchworth and Bishop's Stortford, *etc.*
(66 tetrads: Dony, 1967; 88 tetrads: 1950-1986)

Map 351. *Melilotus albus*

Melilotus officinalis (L.) Lam.
Ribbed Melilot
Introduced: neophyte.
First record: 1851.
Tetrad occurrence: 184 (38%).
Increased? (+13%).

A colonist of rough grasslands and waste ground across much of the County, especially on the less calcareous soils on the Clay-with-Flints and river gravels. It is possible that some records in Dony (1967) were misidentified *M. altissima*, as it appears to be much less common in north Herts. than his records suggest.
(154 tetrads: Dony, 1967; 192 tetrads: 1950-1986)

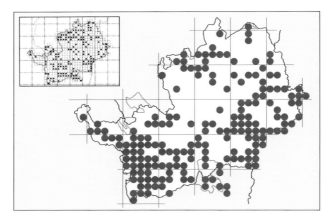

Map 352. *Melilotus officinalis.*

Melilotus indicus (L.) All.
Small Melilot
Introduced: neophyte.
First record: 1887.
Tetrad occurrence: 9 (2%).
Decreased. (-51%).

This is once again a rare casual or short-term colonist of waste places, tips and so on, having shown signs in the 1960s of increasing (Dony, 1967). It was found in only nine scattered tetrads during the survey. The cleaner operation of tips is the primary reason, although it can occur on waste ground around towns.
(17 tetrads: Dony, 1967; 19 tetrads: 1950-1986)

Melilotus sulcatus Desf.
Furrowed Melilot
Introduced: casual.
First record: 1955.

Since its first occurrence at Cole Green tip (Dony, 1967), it has also been found at Bulls Mill tip (31/D), 1973, 1977; Ware tip (31/M), 1975; and again at Cole Green (21/Q), 1977 *C. G. Hanson*. There are no recent records.

Genus: *Trigonella*

Trigonella corniculata (L.) L.
Sickle-fruited Fenugreek
Introduced: casual.
First (only) record: 1876.

The only record is from Hertford (Dony, 1967).

Trigonella polyceratia L.
Introduced: casual.
First (only) record: 1916.

The only record was from Ware (Dony, 1967).

Trigonella caerulea (L.) Ser.
Blue Fenugreek
Introduced: casual.
First record: 1912.

In addition to the records by A. W. Graveson from Ware, 1912, and Hertford, 1920, (Dony, 1967), it appeared as a bird-seed alien by a road in Ware (31/S), 1997 *C. Brown* (det. C. G. Hanson and E. J. Clement) (Hb. Hanson, Hb. HTN).

Trigonella procumbens (Besser) Reichenb.
Introduced: casual.
First (only) record: 1927.

The only record is again from Ware (Dony, 1967).

Trigonella hamosa L.
Egyptian Fenugreek
Introduced: casual.
First record: 1932.

There are two records: specimens from St. Margarets (TL31), 1932 *A. W. Graveson* (Hb. HTN) and *A. H. Carter* (Hb. BM).

Trigonella foenum-graecum L.
Fenugreek
Introduced: casual.
First record: 1919.

Apart from the first record from Hertford (Dony, 1967), it also appeared at Hitchin tip (13/V), 1974; and at Ware tip (31/M), 1977 *C. G. Hanson* (Hb. HTN). During the recent survey it occurred as a bird-seed alien at Ware (31/S), 1996 *C. G. H.* (Hb. HTN).

Trigonella orthoceras Kar. and Kir.
Introduced: casual.
First (only) record: 1991.

A single plant of this was found on the sludge dumps at Rye Meads Sewage Works (31/V), 1991 *C. G. Hanson* (det. E. J. Clement) (Hb. HTN).

Genus: *Medicago*

Medicago lupulina L.
Black Medick
Native.
First record: 1736.
Tetrad occurrence: 456 (93%).
Stable or slightly decreasing (-5%).

This is a plant of more-or-less calcareous grassland, rough ground and waste places, which is frequent throughout most of the County, only becoming scarce on acidic clays or in the most arable landscapes. Although the number of tetrads recorded are almost the same, the distribution map shows that it has become rarer in some of its more marginal habitats, such as in south Herts., since the 1960s.
(457 tetrads: Dony, 1967; 459 tetrads: 1950-1986)

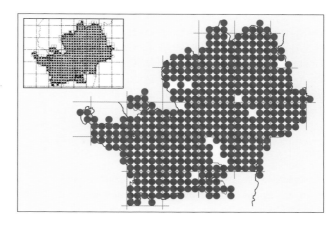

Map 353. *Medicago lupulina.*

Medicago sativa L.
Lucerne *or* **Alfalfa**
Probably introduced: archaeophyte.
First record: 1814.
Tetrad occurrence: 123 (25%).
Decreased (-30%).

Lucerne is subspecies *sativa*, the familiar purple-flowered plant of waste ground, roadsides, and field margins, probably derived from former cultivation, and still sometimes a recent escape, but also very persistent where it occurs. This is the form shown on the map. The present distribution shows it still to occur mostly on more-or-less calcareous clays, as well as on the Chalk, and almost absent on acidic soils, much as Dony (1967) found it to be. However, it does appear less frequently than formerly, judging by the reduced number of tetrads recorded.
(168 tetrads: Dony, 1967; 206 tetrads: 1950-1986)

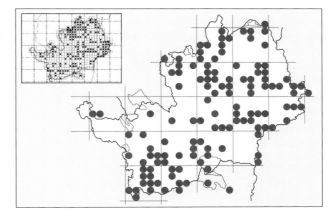

Map 354. *Medicago sativa* ssp. *sativa*

The native yellow-flowered ssp. *falcata* (L.) Arcang. **Sickle Medick** has also been recorded occasionally, having first been noted as early as 1706 (Dony, 1967). Its status in Herts. is usually as a casual, although it does appear in semi-natural habitats from time to time, and is regarded as a native in East Anglia (Preston *et al.*, 2002). It was rare in the 19th century, having only two localities noted in Pryor (1887), but it turned up regularly in various places, especially at Mardley Heath, and in the Hoddesdon and Ware areas earlier in the 20th century. Dony (1967) recorded it from several sites, mostly tips, but some in areas where it had occurred earlier. Since 1970, it has appeared at Brookmans Park (20/L), 1971, 1977 *H. J. Killick*; Amwell Quarry (31/R), 1984 *G. J. White* (Hb. HTN); and it re-appeared at a chalky grassland slope by Upwick Wood (42/M) 1982 *J. L. Fielding*, and again in 1986 *S. Watson*, where Dony had reported it in 1959. During the recent survey, it was re-found by Upwick Wood in 1987 *S. W.* (but not recently); and was found as a casual at Baldock (23/L), 1987 *K. Robinson* (Hb. HTN). Its site at Upwick Wood, which has unfortunately been seriously degraded by scrub growth, may just be a native occurrence, given its location, not that far from its East Anglian stronghold; and the occurrence at Amwell Quarry is interesting, given its past occurrence in the vicinity of old gravel pits around Hoddesdon and Ware.

Ssp. *varia* (Martyn) Arcang. **Sand Lucerne** has also been recorded. It is now considered a hybrid between the two main subspecies, but is still given ssp. status in Stace (1997). It has only been recorded at Hitchin, with the parents, 1959 (Dony, 1967).

Medicago laciniata (L.) Miller
Tattered Medick
Introduced: casual.
First record: 1928.

Dony (1967) mentions the first record of this wool-shoddy alien from Great Wymondley (22/E), 1928 *J. E. Little*, and he re-found it on nearby railway sidings in 1956. The only subsequent record was also as a wool alien at Newnham (23/N), 1973 *C. G. Hanson*.

Medicago minima (L.) Bartal.   [UK Vulnerable]
Bur Medick
Introduced: casual [native in the U.K.].
First record: 1928.

This used to be a fairly frequent casual, introduced with wool shoddy used for bulking soil, around Great Wymondley and the Hitchin area in the early part of the 20th century (Dony, 1967 and ms. index). It was rare by the 1950s, with two records: Wymondley sidings (22/E), 1956 and railway at Hadley Wood (VC21 [Herts.: 1904-1965]), 1958 *J. G. Dony* (Hb. HTN). There were two subsequent records: Newnham (23/N), and Old Ramerick, Ickleford (13/R), 1973 *C. G. Hanson*.

Medicago praecox DC.
Early Medick
Introduced: casual.
First record: 1928.

This was also a wool shoddy alien, first found at Great Wymondley (22/E), 1928 *J. E. Little*, but although Dony (1967) appears to indicate its recurrence there, it was only subsequently recorded once: at Purwell (22/E), 1930-31 *J. E. L.* (Dony, ms. index). It also appeared as a wool shoddy alien more recently at Newnham (23/N), 1973 *C. G. Hanson*.

Medicago polymorpha L.
Toothed Medick
Introduced: casual [native in the U.K.].
First record: 1861.
Tetrad occurrence: 3 (<1%).
Decreased (-65%).

This has been recorded sporadically from a range of sites under a number of different names, especially between 1920 and 1960. Dony (1967) recorded it especially around Hitchin and Letchworth, where it was probably mostly a wool shoddy alien. It subsequently occurred with other medicks on arable fields treated

with shoddy at Newnham (23/N), 1973; and at Old Ramerick, Ickleford (13/R) the same year *C. G. Hanson*. An undated record from Aldenham (19/T), possibly received after the *Flora* was published, was also entered by Dony on his card index. During the present survey period, it was found as a weed of waste ground by Aldenham Golf Course (19/J), 1987 *A. D. Marshall* (Hb. HTN); in Wadesmill (31/N), 1990 *A. M. Boucher* (det. R. M. Burton) (Hb. HTN); and at Hemel Hempstead (00/U), 1994 *G. Salisbury* (det T. J.) (Hb. HTN).
(8 tetrads: Dony, 1967; 11 tetrads: 1950-1986)

Medicago arabica (L.) Hudson
Spotted Medick
Probably introduced [native in the U.K.].
First record: 1861.
Tetrad occurrence: 72 (15%).
Increasing (+213%).

This is a plant of thin grassland and bare, gravelly ground, rarely on other soils, and often associated with seeded areas, or disturbed ground. Its status in Herts. must be doubtful, despite the native designation in Preston *et al.*, (2002), as it was unknown to Coleman, and its only 19th century records were as a cornfield weed and as a casual (Pryor, 1887). J. E. Little noted its great increase (Dony, ms. index), and by the 1960s it was widespread, but not abundant, on gravels from Hitchin to Ware, with a few outliers elsewhere (Dony, 1967). It has since consolidated its occurrence, especially around Hitchin, Stevenage, Ware, Hoddesdon, and up the Stort valley.
(22 tetrads: Dony, 1967; 36 tetrads: 1950-1986)

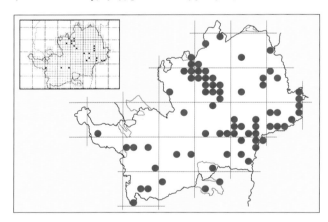

Map 355. *Medicago arabica.*

Genus: *Trifolium*

Trifolium ornithopodioides L.   Herts Extinct
Bird's-foot Clover
Native.
First record: 1846.

The only record for the County would appear to have been from a gravelly roadside bank between Cuffley and Goffs Oak (30/B), 1846 (Pryor, 1887, Dony, 1967). This was an area which was heath until about 1780.

Trifolium repens L.
White Clover
Native.
First record: 1748.
Tetrad occurrence: 479 (98%).
Stable (-1%).

An ubiquitous plant of semi-natural and improved grassland, waste places, roadside verges and similar habitats, except old heathy or chalk grasslands. As it is also a major component of sown grassland, its natural occurrence has long been obscured by introductions. Although it has been recorded in more tetrads during the present survey, its rate of occurrence is overall slightly less, and it is likely to be stable.
(461 tetrads: Dony, 1967; and from 1950-1986)

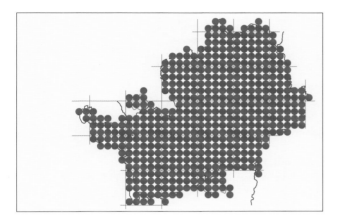

Map 356. *Trifolium repens.*

Trifolium hybridum L.
Alsike Clover
Introduced: neophyte.
First record: *c.*1880.
Tetrad occurrence: 134 (27%).
Decreasing (-58%).

A plant of field margins, rough grassland and waste places, derived from former cultivation as a fodder plant. In the 1960s this was one of the commoner clover species, but it began to decrease noticeably in the 1970s and is now becoming quite scarce in many areas again, being most frequent on river gravels.
(306 tetrads: Dony, 1967; 324 tetrads: 1950-1986)

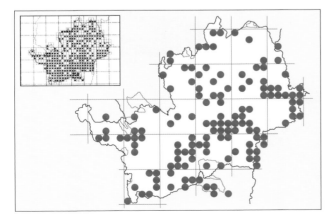

Map 357. *Trifolium hybridum.*

No thorough examination of forms has been carried out, but ssp. *elegans* (Savi) Asch. and Graebn. has been recorded in the

past (Dony, ms. index), in addition to the cultivated form ssp. *hybridum*.

Trifolium michelianum Savi
Annual White Clover
Introduced: casual.
First (only) record: 1875.

The only record of this wool alien was from Welwyn *T. B. Blow* (Dony, 1967).

Trifolium cernuum Brot.
Nodding Clover
Introduced: casual.
First (only) record: 1973.

This was found as a wool shoddy alien at Newnham (23/N), 1973 *C. G. Hanson* (det. E. J. Clement).

Trifolium glomeratum L.
Clustered Clover
Introduced [native in the U.K.].
First record: 1871.

Apart from the first record from Easneye (Pryor, 1887), this has only been found since as a presumed introduction at Bedwell Park Golf Course (20/T), 1978 *A. D. Marshall* (Hb. HTN) (Burton, 1983).

Trifolium fragiferum L.   Herts Vulnerable
Strawberry Clover
Native.
First record: 1838.
Tetrad occurrence: 11 (2%).
Decreased sharply (-72%).

This is now a rare plant of damp, trodden ground on calcareous clay, occurring most often in cart ruts and tracks. It was always rather thinly scattered in grassland on the Boulder Clay, with a few localities elsewhere. Its distribution remains much the same,

Strawberry Clover Trifolium fragiferum *Moor Hall, Ardeley, 1979.*

but its frequency has declined sharply and all colonies appear to be vulnerable. There are two isolated occurrences outside the core area in north-east Herts.: at Thistly Marsh, Cheshunt (30/R), 1994 *A. M. Boucher*; and on a roadside at Marston Gate (81/Y), 2000 *T. J.*

(37 tetrads: Dony, 1967; 41 tetrads: 1950-1986)

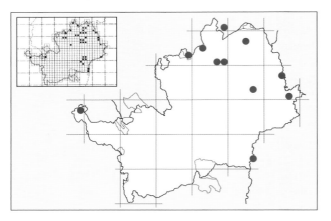

Map 358. *Trifolium fragiferum.*

The usual subspecies is ssp. *fragiferum*, but plants resembling ssp. *bonannii* (C. Presl) Soják were found at Haileybury (31/K), 1995 *A. M. Boucher* (Hb. HTN). Its status as a subspecies is doubtful (Stace, 1997).

Trifolium resupinatum L.
Reversed Clover
Introduced: casual.
First record: 1902.

First recorded by the canal at Broxbourne (30/S), 1902 *C. S. Nicholson* (Kent and Lousley, 1952), this was recorded occasionally in similar localities in the early 20th century, but was not seen after 1926, until one plant was found at Codicote Garden Centre (21/E), 1987 *W. Bishop*. It has now also appeared at Thorley Park Road, Bishop's Stortford (41/Z), 2008 *S. Watson* (Hb. HTN), source unknown.

Trifolium tomentosum L.
Woolly Clover
Introduced: casual.
First (only) record: 1928.

This wool shoddy alien has only ever been recorded at Wymondley *H. Phillips* (Dony, 1967).

Trifolium aureum Pollich
Large Trefoil
Introduced: casual.
First record: *c.*1816.

Apart from its first occurrence at Hitchin (Pryor, 1887), the record from Wymondley in 1931 (Dony, 1967) is the only one.

Trifolium campestre Schreber
Hop Trefoil
Native.
First record: *c.*1820.
Tetrad occurrence: 225 (46%).
Stable, or slightly decreased (-2%).

A plant of open, grassy or disturbed ground on free-draining,

usually calcareous soils. This has always tended to be patchy in its occurrence, and may have decreased in some areas, owing to habitat loss or enrichment, but is still apparently as widespread as it was in the 1960s.

(218 tetrads: Dony, 1967; 256 tetrads: 1950-1986)

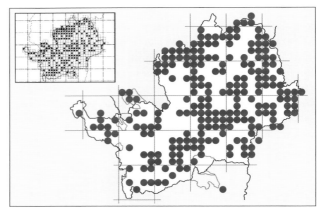

Map 359. *Trifolium campestre.*

Trifolium dubium Sibth.
Lesser Trefoil
Native.
First record: 1823.
Tetrad occurrence: 448 (91%).
Increased? (+8%).

Found in short, rough grassland, lawns, road verges and waste ground throughout the County, usually on less calcareous soils. It seems to be favoured to some extent by moderate enrichment, as it now occurs on the Chalk and calcareous Boulder Clay, where it was formerly absent, although some of the apparent increase may be owing to better recording in east Herts.

(393 tetrads: Dony, 1967; 400 tetrads: 1950-1986)

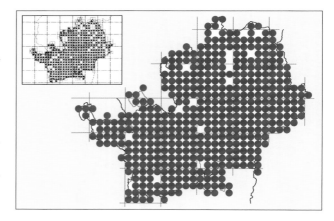

Map 360. *Trifolium dubium.*

Trifolium micranthum Viv.
Slender Trefoil
Native.
First record: *c.*1820.
Tetrad occurrence: 51 (10%).
Increasing? (+39%).

This native of short, thin grassland, usually on acidic, gravelly soils, has been recorded more frequently recently but may to some extent have been overlooked previously. It is particularly characteristic of heavily-mown lawns on acidic soils, although its native habitat is probably acidic grassland on heathy commons, *etc.* It is now widespread across the County on different soil types. (35 tetrads: Dony, 1967; 50 tetrads: 1950-1986)

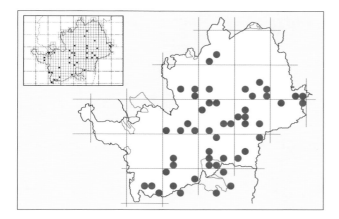

Map 361. *Trifolium micranthum.*

Trifolium pratense L.
Red Clover
Native.
First record: 1748.
Tetrad occurrence: 457 (93%).
Decreasing (-6%).

An often abundant and widespread plant of especially long-established grassland, pastures and roadside verges on all but the most acidic soils, and important for insects, especially bees. There is, however, clear evidence in the most agricultural landscapes that it is becoming very thinly scattered in some places, although it still occurs in most tetrads. Its natural occurrence is also obscured to some extent by the occurrence of agricultural cultivars in new road verge seed mixes.
(461 tetrads: Dony, 1967 and from 1950-1986)

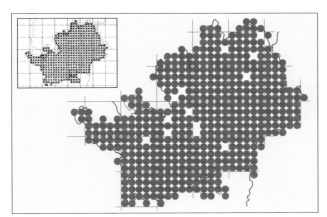

Map 362. *Trifolium pratense.*

Trifolium medium L.
Zigzag Clover
Native.
First record: 1838.
Tetrad occurrence: 62 (13%).
Decreasing sharply (-43%).

This is a plant of long-established rough grassland, road verges, and woodland rides on damper clay soils, or on loamy soils over gravel, but usually avoiding the Chalk, and the drier Boulder Clay. It was formerly quite widespread across the County on

suitable soils, but has increasingly retreated to the London Clay, the damper areas of the Colne gravels, and to some areas on the Boulder Clay, where it is quite scarce. It may be overlooked to some extent in west Herts., but does appear to be rare there. Loss of older grasslands, overgrowth of woodland rides, and eutrophication of road verges appear to be the main causes of its disappearance
(104 tetrads: Dony, 1967; 125 tetrads: 1950-1986)

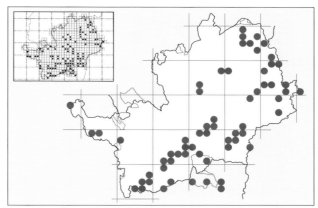

Map 363. *Trifolium medium.*

Trifolium ochroleucon Hudson   UK Near Threatened
Sulphur Clover
Native.
First record: 1787.
Tetrad occurrence: 10 (2%).
Decreased sharply (-37%).

A characteristic but scarce plant of drier unimproved grassland on calcareous Boulder Clay, usually where this is overlain thinly with sands. Found now most often on road verges and field margins, it was always mostly confined to and local in north-east Herts., with

Sulphur Clover Trifolium ochroleucon *Letchworth Golf Course, 1988.*

Photo.: Brian Sawford

almost no former records from west of Stevenage. Its stronghold is now around Letchworth, where it occurs on Letchworth Golf Course (23/A) and Norton Common (23/B) especially. To the east, it only now occurs as scattered colonies in vulnerable sites by arable fields or on road verges, with a small colony on Bishop's Stortford Golf Course (52/A).
(15 tetrads: Dony, 1967; 17 tetrads: 1950-1986)

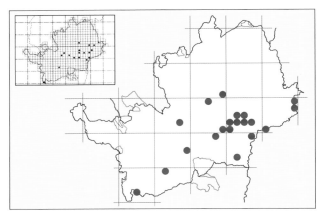

Map 365. *Trifolium striatum.*

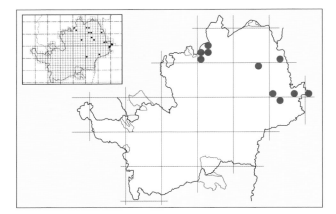

Map 364. *Trifolium ochroleucon.*

Trifolium incarnatum L.
Crimson Clover
Introduced: neophyte.
First record: *c.*1870.

Strictly speaking, 'Crimson Clover' applies only to the introduced subspecies *incarnatum*, formerly grown as fodder and now mostly a seed contaminant, not to the native ssp. *molinerii*, only found in Cornwall and Jersey. Pryor (1887) gives three records, the first by T. B. Blow near Stanborough. There were scattered casual records especially early in the 20th century, but Dony (1967) only gave one record. It was seen during the present survey at Stapleford (31/D), 1991 *K. Robinson*; at Ware (31/R,S), 1993 *C. G. Hanson*; and at Milwards Park (20/N), 1994, 1996 *A. D. Marshall* and *S. Cuming.* In most of these localities it was probably introduced as an impurity in grass seed.

The record from Ware (31/S) was recorded specifically as ssp. *incarnatum.* A white flowered form was collected from Broxbourne (undated) by A. W. Graveson (Hb. HTN) (Dony, ms. index).

Trifolium striatum L.
Striated Clover
Native.
First record: 1838.
Tetrad occurrence: 20 (4%).
Stable or increased? (+11%).

A local plant of open, rough grassland and waste ground on gravel, this was at one time quite frequent in many places on the river valley gravels across the County, but had already decreased substantially by the 1960s (Pryor, 1887; Dony, 1967). It now seems more or less stable in occurrence but few colonies are large. Away from its main stronghold around Ware and Hertford it also seems less frequent. Very rarely it occurs as an introduced plant of sown grasslands, as at Ashwell (23/U), 1986 *T. J.*
(17 tetrads: Dony, 1967; 25 tetrads: 1950-1986)

Trifolium scabrum L.   Herts Rare
Rough Clover
Probably native.
First record: 1914.

Inexplicably, Dony left this plant out of his *Flora*, even though he had collected a specimen from a dry bank at Standon Lordship (32/V), 1956 (Hb. HTN) (Dony, ms. index). He also records in his index that H. F. Hayllar found it in a gravel pit near Rye House (30/Z), 1914, 1915. J. L. Fielding also reported it from the old gravel pit at 'Cornwood Sanctuary' (42/F), *c.*1955. More recently, a single plant was found on a chalky/gravelly field margin at Oxshott Hill, Benington (22/V), 1980 *T. J.* (Hb. HTN) (James, 1989). Some of these may be the result of introductions, but it is known as a native plant of sands and gravels over Chalk in East Anglia, and is conceivably a rare native in Herts. as well.

Trifolium hirtum All.
Rose Clover
Introduced: casual.

The only record is as a wool shoddy alien at Newnham (23/N), 1973 *C. G. Hanson* (Dony, 1975).

Trifolium lappaceum L.
Bur Clover
Introduced: casual.
First record: 1926.

Apart from the two records given by Dony (1967), it has also been found at Hoddesdon (30/U), 1977 *A. M. Boucher* (Hb. Boucher).

Trifolium arvense L.
Hare's-foot Clover
Native.
First record: *c.*1820.
Tetrad occurrence: 30 (6%).
Stable? (+2%).

A characteristic and attractive plant of bare, sandy or gravelly ground, in open rough grasslands and waste places especially on the Lea and Colne valley gravels, where it can be locally frequent, but usually only in small quantities. This is much the same as it was in the 1960s (Dony, 1967), although quite a few sites where it was found then or during the 1980s no longer seem to have it, even though it has now been recorded from 'new' sites elsewhere.
(28 tetrads: Dony, 1967; 42 tetrads: 1950-1986)

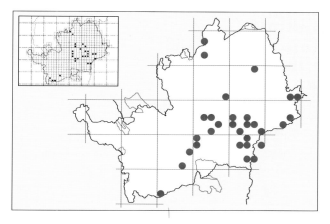

Map 366. *Trifolium arvense.*

Trifolium angustifolium L.
Narrow-leaved Crimson Clover
Introduced: casual.
First record: 1959.

Apart from Dony's record from Wymondley (Dony, 1967), this has also been found as a wool shoddy alien at Ramerick, Ickleford (13/R), 1971 *C. G. Hanson.*

Trifolium echinatum M. Bieb.
Hedgehog Clover
Introduced: casual.
Only record: 1912.

There have been no records other than the occurrence at Ware (Dony, 1967).

Trifolium subterraneum L.   Herts Extinct (as native)
Subterranean Clover
Formerly native, now casual.
First record: 1834.

This was a rare native plant of heathy ground at a number of sites in south Herts. in the 19th century, such as Colney Heath, Bernard's Heath at St Albans, Nomansland Common, Sandridge and Cuffley. It has also occurred rarely as a wool shoddy alien, and it was last seen in this guise at Newnham (23/N), 1973 *C. G. Hanson.*

Genus: *Lupinus*

Lupinus arboreus Sims
Tree Lupin
Introduced: neophyte.
First record: *c.*1975.

This was first noted as an escape at Patmore Heath (42/M), *c.*1975 *J. Godfree*; and subsequently turned up by a road at Braughing (32/X), 1984 *C. G. Hanson*. During the current survey, it was found again at Patmore Heath, 1987 *J. L. Fielding*; near Cheshunt Station (30/R), 1990 *A. M. Boucher/T. J.*; and by the A414 at St Margaret's (31/Q), 1990 *A. M. Boucher.*

[*Lupinus polyphyllus* Lindley
Garden Lupin

It seems likely that all records refer to the Russell Lupin *L.* × *regalis* (see below).]

Lupinus × *regalis* Bergmans (*L. arboreus* × *L. polyphyllus*)
Russell Lupin
Introduced: neophyte.
First confirmed record: 1970.

The first 'garden lupin' to be noted as growing in the wild was found at Moor Mill tip (10/L), 1970 *C. G. Hanson*. It was also found at Waterford tip (31/C), 1982 *C. G. H.*; and during the recent survey it has been found in ten scattered localities on waste ground, road verges, and tips. Although recorded in the field as *L. polyphyllus*, it is very likely that all records refer here.

Lupinus angustifolius L.
Narrow-leaved Lupin
Introduced: casual.
First record: 1934.

A specimen of this collected from Wilbury Hill (23/B), 1934 is in Hb. E. It is probably the same record as the plant found 'near Letchworth', undated, by H. Phillips (*comm.*: Biological Records Centre, CEH Monks Wood).

Genus: *Laburnum*

Laburnum anagyroides Medikus
Laburnum
Introduced: neophyte.
First record: 1915.
Tetrad occurrence: 82 (17%).
Increased substantially.

Only casually noted by Dony (1967), this was actually first noted self-seeding at Hertford in 1915 by C. G. Trower and G. C. Druce (*Rep. Bot. Exch. Club*: 260 (1916)). Dony also mentions it as having been planted at Hexton, where it still occurs quite abundantly in places, especially by the Barton Road (13/A), where it has been revived by thinning of overhanging trees. However, as the map shows, it is now a frequent plant of waste places, tips, and secondary scrub across the County, especially around towns.

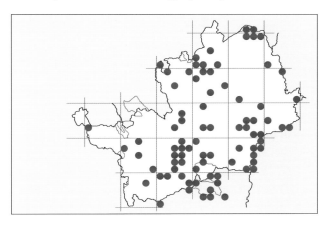

Map 367. *Laburnum anagyroides.*

Genus: *Cytisus*

Cytisus multiflorus (L'Hér. ex Aiton) Sweet
White Broom
Introduced: casual.
First record: 1991.

This was found at Wymondley electricity grid station (22/D), 1991,

1992 *A. D. Marshall* (Hb. HTN), where it may have been planted. It was definitely an escape at Moor Mill tip (10/L), 1994 *T. J.*

Cytisus striatus (Hill) Rothm.
Hairy-fruited Broom
Introduced: casual.
First (only) record: 1995.

A single bush of this was found as an escape near South Mimms (20/G) (VC21 [Herts.]), 1995 *A. D. Marshall*. It may well occur elsewhere, as it can easily be overlooked as common Broom.

Cytisus scoparius (L.) Link
Broom
Native.
First record: 1814.
Tetrad occurrence: 140 (29%).
Increased? (+28%).

A short-lived shrub of more or less acidic sandy or gravelly soils, occurring on heaths, roadside verges, woodland margins and in open scrub. It succumbs rapidly to shading, but can reappear equally rapidly from buried seed following scrub clearance. This may account for the fact that, despite its having all but vanished from many overgrown commons, it is apparently even more widespread now than it was in the 1960s!
(104 tetrads: Dony, 1967; 133 tetrads: 1950-1986)

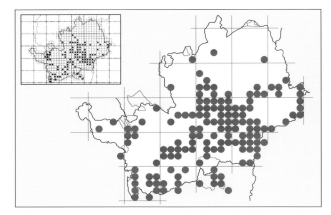

Map 368. *Cytisus scoparius.*

Genus: *Spartium*

Spartium junceum L.
Spanish Broom
Introduced: neophyte.
First record: *c.*1975?

There is an undated tetrad record from Croxley (09/S) in Burton (1983). During the survey it has been found at Wymondley electricity grid station (22/D), 1992 *A. D. Marshall/T. J.*, where it appears to be regenerating from introduced shrubs; on disturbed ground, Wood Green Cemetery, Goffs Oak (30/G), 1993 *A. M. Boucher*; by the railway at Cheshunt (30/R), 1995 *A. M. Boucher*; and by the A414 at Holwell Hyde (21/Q), 2001 *T. J.*

Genus: *Genista*

Genista tinctoria L.   Herts Rare?
Dyer's Greenweed
Native.
First record: 1838.
Tetrad occurrence: 7 (1%).
Strongly decreased (-53%).

This is an especially characteristic plant of unimproved, heathy pasture on moderately acidic or sometimes on neutral clay soils. It was considered to be 'rare' by Pryor (1887), but he lists quite a few sites across the south of the County, as well as a few in the north, on de-calcified Boulder Clay or Clay-with-Flints soils. By the 1960s, it had decreased substantially, and has continued to do so, as sites have either become scrubbed or have succumbed to 'improvement'. It has recently only been found in eight localities: Burleigh Meadow, Knebworth (22/G) (many records), and in a nearby meadow by Norton Green (22/G), 1996 *B. R. Sawford*; old meadows at Dalmonds Farm, Hoddesdon (30/P), 1990 *A. M. Boucher/T. J.*; scrubby field by Bencroft Wood (30/I), 1990 *M. Powell*; Claypits 'meadow', Bayford (30/D), 1988 *M. J. Hicks*; by 'The Dell', Cuffley (20/W), 1993 *A. M. Boucher*; by the canal, Croxley (09/S), 1993 *P. J. Ellison*; and Croxley Common Moor (09/X), 1999 *G. Salisbury*. Very few of these have good populations, and in some it could now be extinct.
(14 tetrads: Dony, 1967; 23 tetrads: 1950-1986)

Dyer's Greenweed Genista tinctoria *Burleigh Meadow, Knebworth, 1975.*

Genista hispanica L.
Spanish Gorse
Introduced: neophyte.
First record: *c*.1980.

There is an undated record of self-sown plants at Loudwater, Rickmansworth (09/M) given in Burton (1983) (but given in error as TQ08). There are no other records.

Genista anglica L.   UK Near Threatened
Petty Whin
Native.
First record: 1834.
Tetrad occurrence: 6 (1%).
Decreased (-49%).

This has never been a common plant, occurring as a sub-shrub in unimproved heathy pastures and on commons. It was recorded by Pryor (1887) from a spread of sites across southern Herts., but by

Petty Whin Genista anglica *Burleigh Meadow, Knebworth, 1980.*

the 1960s it had been reduced to a handful of ancient habitats, in some of which it still survives. It was recorded from five localities during the current survey: The Roundings, Hertford Heath (31/K), 1987, 1989 *A. M. Boucher/T. J.*, where it was re-found in 2001 *P. Hudson*; drier parts of Burleigh Meadow, Knebworth (22/G) (several records); the 'Furze Field' at Colney Heath (20/C) (several records); raised areas on Croxley Common Moor (09/S, X) (many records); and a small hollow on Croxley Green (09/T), 1987, 1991 *P. J. Ellison*. It has apparently disappeared from Hadley Green

(29/N) (VC21 [Herts.: 1904-1965]), where it was last seen in 1986 *A. Haselfoot* (Hb. HTN); and also from Nomansland Common (11/R), where it succumbed to scrub-growth and then overgrazing by rabbits, last being recorded in 1979 *R. M. Bateman*. It had apparently disappeared from other sites known to Dony: Rowley Green (29/D) and Bricket Wood Common (10/F) before 1970 (the latter having been a 1950s record by R. B. Benson omitted in Dony, 1967), as well as from the unidentified site in tetrad 22/I. The record from Sheethanger Common (00/H) (Dony, 1967) may have been an error (Dony, ms. index).
(10 tetrads: Dony, 1967; and from 1950-1986)

Genus: *Ulex*

Ulex europaeus L.
Gorse
Native.
First record: 1742.
Tetrad occurrence: 191 (39%).
Stable or slightly increased? (+2%).

This was always characteristic of Hertfordshire's heathlands and the margins of heathy woods. Some commons were historically yellow with it in the spring, such as Berkhamsted Common, where the commoners used it for fuel. Although this is no longer the case, it is still frequent wherever rather acidic sandy or gravelly soil occurs, even when these are very thin, as at Wilbury Hill (23/B), and even at Fox Covert, Therfield (33/J), where it appeared after windthrow of beeches. It can in fact regenerate rapidly from buried seed after scrub clearance, and its presence in woodland can often indicate a former wood pasture. Its slight increase since Dony's survey may be the product of better recording.
(178 tetrads: Dony, 1967; 215 tetrads: 1950-1986)

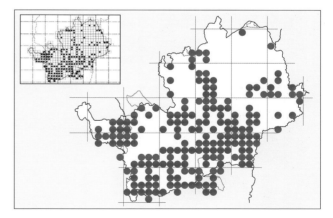

Map 369. *Ulex europaeus.*

Ulex gallii Planchon   Herts Rare
Western Gorse
Native.
First record: 1830.

The status of this plant in Herts. has until now been regarded as problematic. Pryor (1887) gives a record of it having been introduced with planted common Gorse on a road bank south of Hatfield, 1874, and also says that it had increased by 1876. Dony (1967) referred to a record by E. deCrespigny (1877) from Batchworth Heath, which he thought must have been an error. Dony, in his ms. index, also gives a record from Nomansland Common by W. J. Blake in 1830, which had been supplied from

Blake's herbarium (Hb. Druce, OXF) to Edward Salisbury by G. C. Druce (Salisbury, 1914), and reported by Druce in *Rep. Bot. Exch. Club*: 209 (1912). Dony evidently thought that this was also a mistake for *U. minor*. However, examination of some rather etiolated flowering bushes at Nomansland Common in September 2007 *T. J.* (Hb. HTN) revealed the survival of the species under scrub, isolated from but near both its relatives. It would therefore seem very likely to be native after all, and may survive elsewhere. Late-flowering gorse should be examined carefully. The hybrid between *U. gallii* and *U. europaeus* might also occur.

Ulex minor Roth   Herts Rare
Dwarf Gorse
Native.
First record: 1830.
Tetrad occurrence: 3 (<1%).
Stable.

This was always a rare plant of dry heaths in south and west Herts., where it is at the northern limit of its main area of distribution in England. It remains frequent on the north side of the road at Nomansland Common (11/R), having re-appeared vigorously following scrub removal in the 1990s. It also regenerated well on the 'Furze Field' at Colney Heath (20/C) following cessation of mowing in the early 1990s. At its other main site given by Dony (1967), Rowley Green (29/D), it was thought to have disappeared following the development of dense secondary woodland, but two small patches, threatened by scrub, were found there in 2003 *P. J. Attewell* (conf. T. J.) (Hb. HTN). It has long disappeared from its other sites: Batchworth Heath, High Canons and near Abbots Langley. An old specimen from Croxley Common Moor, without a date, in the herbarium of H. Fisher at Grantham Museum is the only record from this locality. Finally, an enigmatic

Dwarf Gorse Ulex minor *Nomansland Common, 2005.*

record in Dony's ms. index from Gustard Wood Common, 1955 may have been an error, as he omitted this from his *Flora*.

Elaeagnaceae (Sea Buckthorn family)

Genus: Hippophae

Hippophae rhamnoides L.
Sea Buckthorn
Introduced: planted and self-seeding.
First record: 1984 (as planted), 1994.

A single bush of this coastal plant was found in scrub by the lagoons at Rye Meads Sewage Works (31/V), 1984 *T. J.*, where it may have been planted, although it just conceivably could have been introduced by birds. It was still there in 1996. Planted bushes in the central reservation of the A505 near Slip End (23/S), 1997 *T. J.* were self-seeding.

Genus: Elaeagnus

Elaeagnus umbellata Thunb.
Spreading Oleaster
Introduced: planted?
First (only) record: 1994.

A single specimen of this garden shrub was found by the old railway at Amwell Quarry (31/R), 1994 *C. G. Hanson*. It may have been planted.

Haloragaceae (Water-milfoils)

Genus: Myriophyllum

Myriophyllum verticillatum L.   UK Vulnerable
Whorled Water-milfoil
Native.
First record: 1843.
Tetrad occurrence: 13 (3%).
Increased? (+80%).

This is the water-milfoil of less eutrophic conditions in rivers, streams and marsh drains, occurring occasionally in old spring-fed field ponds, and in recently excavated gravel pits, reservoirs, *etc.* It was formerly locally frequent in the lower reaches of the

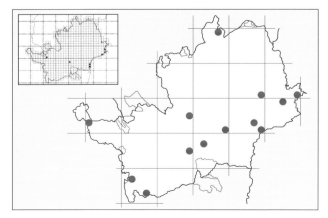

Map 370. *Myriophyllum verticillatum.*

County's rivers, but now appears mostly in middle or upper reaches, and in smaller streams, where eutrophication is less. It is nowhere abundant, although its overall occurrence appears to have increased somewhat.
(7 tetrads: Dony, 1967; 13 tetrads: 1950-1986)

Myriophyllum aquaticum (Vell.) Verdc.
Parrot's-feather
Introduced: neophyte.
First record: 1982.
Tetrad occurrence: 17 (4%).
Increasing.

Originally recorded from the then recently re-excavated pond on Brickendon Green (30/I), 1982 *A. M. Boucher* (Hb. Boucher), this has subsequently appeared, sometimes from deliberate introduction but often accidentally introduced, in a number of ponds across the County. It is potentially a nuisance, producing dominant mats of vegetation at the expense of native aquatic plants.

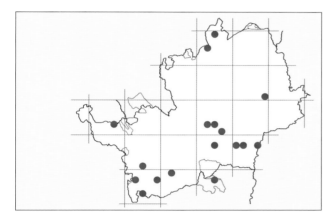

Map 371. *Myriophyllum aquaticum.*

Myriophyllum spicatum L.
Spiked Water-milfoil
Native.
First record: *c*.1810.
Tetrad occurrence: 28 (6%).
Slightly decreased (-8%).

Found in ponds, lakes and flooded gravel pits, as well as in moderately eutrophic rivers and larger ditches across much of the County, especially in the south. It remains occasional, rather than abundant, as Dony (1967) found it, but has apparently

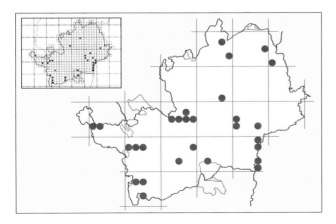

Map 372. *Myriophyllum spicatum.*

disappeared from some areas, while appearing in new water bodies.
(29 tetrads: Dony, 1967; 38 tetrads: 1950-1986)

Myriophyllum alterniflorum DC.   Herts Rare
Alternate Water-milfoil
Native.
First record: 1843.
Tetrad occurrence: 3 (<1%).

A native plant of acidic pools on heathy ground, this has always been rare in the County, and Dony did not know it in the County at all (Dony, 1967). It was found in a pond near Old Fold Manor on Hadley Common (29/N) (VC21 [Herts.: 1904-1965]), 1981 *A. M. Boucher* (Hb. HTN), a completely new site for it in VC21, where it is otherwise thought to be extinct (Kent, 2000). However, during the current survey it has also been found in a former gravel pit pool on acidic gravels at Old Parkbury fishing lake (10/R), 1996 *T. J.* (Hb. HTN), possibly introduced by birds; in the pond on Batchworth Heath (09/R), 2002 *T. J.* (Hb. HTN); and in a pond at the NW side of Hadley Green (29/N) (VC21 [Herts.: 1904-1965]), 2003 *S. M. Hedley/T. J./G. Salisbury* (Hb. HTN). It was not known to 19th century botanists in any of these localities, and may turn up elsewhere.

Gunneraceae (Giant-rhubarb family)

Genus: *Gunnera*

Gunnera tinctoria (Molina) Mirb.
Giant-rhubarb
Introduced: planted?
First record: 2002.

This has been reported as established on the banks of the River Lea at Ware (31/M), 2002 (record *comm.*: R. M. Burton). It may have been planted.

Lythraceae (Purple Loosestrife family)

Genus: *Lythrum*

Lythrum salicaria L.
Purple Loosestrife
Native.
First record: 1814.
Tetrad occurrence: 97 (20%).
Increased (+19%).

An attractive plant of fen, riversides, recently excavated gravel pits and ponds, especially in the Lea and Colne catchments, but also around Hitchin in the River Hiz system. Whereas in America this is a rampant introduced weed of aquatic habitats, it only occasionally takes over sites in this way here, and is characteristic of drawn-down water margins, where it colonises newly-exposed mud rapidly. Recently, though, it has become a garden favourite, and some records may be due to deliberate introduction.
(77 tetrads: Dony, 1967; 90 tetrads: 1950-1986)

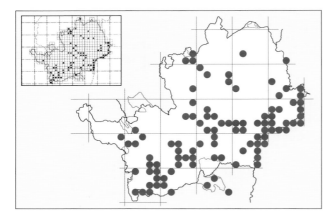

Map 373. *Lythrum salicaria.*

Lythrum junceum Banks and Solander
False Grass-poly
Introduced: casual.
First record: 1914.

In addition to the three records noted by Dony (1967), this has been reported from waste tips at High Leigh, Hoddesdon (30/U), 1970; Waterford (31/C), 1971; near Ware (31/N), 1974 *C. G. Hanson*; and as a casual in a garden at Smallford (10/Y), 1977 *P. Brown*. There are no more recent records.

Lythrum hyssopifolia L.   UK Endangered
Grass-poly   Herts Extinct
Native.
First record: *c.*1848.

This nationally rare plant of seasonally wet places on bare clay soils used to occur on and adjoining Colney Heath, but has not been seen there for over 130 years. Its only other record was from Putteridge (TL12), 1879, *Mr Burkett* as a casual (Hb. LTN) (and see Dony, 1967).

Lythrum portula (L.) D. A. Webb
Water Purslane
Native.
First record: 1838.
Tetrad occurrence: 28 (6%).
Stable? (+2%).

A local but rather inconspicuous plant of wet mud, mostly on acidic soils, found by ponds, and in woodland rides. This apparently occurs much as it did in Dony's survey, although it can

go unnoticed, especially in dry seasons, and may have been missed in some areas during the 1990s drought as a result, just as Dony missed it in some sites in the late 1950s.
(26 tetrads: Dony, 1967; 36 tetrads: 1950-1986)

Thymelaceae (Mezereon family)

Genus: *Daphne*

Daphne mezereum L.   UK Vulnerable
Mezereon
Introduced (or native?).
First record: 1805.

Even in the 19th century, it was presumed that this only ever appeared as a bird-sown escape from cultivation (Pryor, 1887). However, there is an enigmatic record from 'near Gaddesden' by A. Piffard given in Pryor (1875) (Dony, ms. index). This is made even more enigmatic by the find of three small bushes on the edge of Hoo Wood, Great Gaddesden (01/G), 1990 *A. D. Marshall*, but which could not be re-found later. As it is considered native further west in the Chilterns, it could conceivably be so at Great Gaddesden.

Daphne laureola L.
Spurge Laurel
Native (and introduced).
First record: *c.*1730.
Tetrad occurrence: 65 (13%).
Increased (+57%).

Native in scrub, hedgerows and light woodland on chalky soils, this is also occasionally an escape from cultivation, which may account for the quite wide spread of records away from the Chalk. It has recently increased quite markedly in many areas, and long-standing colonies often appear to be thriving and now expanding.
(39 tetrads: Dony, 1967; 61 tetrads, 1950-1986)

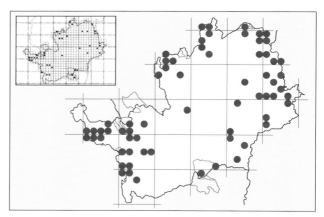

Map 375. *Daphne laureola.*

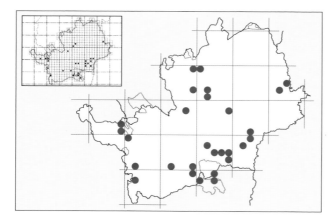

Map 374. *Lythrum portula.*

Onagraceae (Willowherb family)

Genus: *Clarkia*

Clarkia unguiculata Lindl.
Clarkia
Introduced: casual.
First record: c.1980?

The only records are undated tetrad records given from 20/K and 29/U in Burton (1983). It may occur elsewhere as a garden escape.

Clarkia amoena (Lehm.) Nelson and Macbr.
Godetia
Introduced: casual.
First record: 1971.

This was first noted as an escape at Bulls Mill tip (31/D), 1971 *C. G. Hanson*; and was recorded during the survey on roadside gravel at Hitchin (13/V), 1990 *T. J.*

Genus: *Epilobium*

Although the occurrence of hybrids has probably been much overlooked, the difficulties of this group have been greatly lessened during the last 20 years, owing to better keys and a greater understanding of the differences between the species themselves. Help with identification of specimens has been given by T. D. Pennington.

Epilobium hirsutum L.
Great Willowherb *or* **Codlins-and-Cream**
Native.
First record: 1814.
Tetrad occurrence: 459 (94%).
Possibly increased (+5%).

Native of at least seasonally wet or marshy ground by rivers, ponds, in fen swamps, wet woodland rides and the like, but also increasingly recorded from disturbed ground, including set-aside arable and urban waste land. Only rare or absent on the driest Chalk or gravels.
(416 tetrads: Dony, 1967; 424 tetrads: 1950-1986)

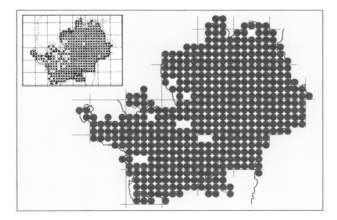

Map 376. *Epilobium hirsutum.*

Epilobium × *subhirsutum* Gennari (*E. hirsutum* × *E. parviflorum*)
Native.
First record: 1933.

There are a few earlier records of this, and it was found at Amwell Quarry (31/R), 1994 *A. M. Boucher* (Hb. HTN), with both parents. It is, no doubt, much commoner than this suggests.

Epilobium × *erroneum* Hausskn. (*E. hirsutum* × *E. montanum*)
Native.
First record: 1998.

One plant of this was found, with the parents, by a pond beside the Duke of York inn, S. of Potters Bar (29/P), 1998 *T. J.* (Hb. HTN). It seems to be a genuinely rare hybrid.

Epilobium × *brevipilum* Hausskn. (*E. hirsutum* × *E. tetragonum*)
Native.
First record: 1989.

One plant of this was detected, with the parents, in set-aside arable, Panshanger (21/W), 1989 *A. D. Marshall* (Hb. HTN). It is probably widespread in this habitat and other disturbed ground.

Epilobium × *novae-civitatis* Smejkal (*E. hirsutum* × *E. ciliatum*)
Native.
First record: 1989.

First found at Town Meads, Bishop's Stortford (42/V), 1989 *S. Watson* where the alien parent had come in with tipped material. It was also found in an urban setting near a natural stream at Osidge (29/W) (VC20 [Greater London]), 1998 *T. J./G. P. Smith/J. Tyler* (det. T. J.); and at Lemsford Springs (21/G), 2005, with both parents *T. J.* (Hb. HTN). It is no doubt widespread.

Epilobium parviflorum Schreber
Hoary Willowherb
Native.
First record: 1814.
Tetrad occurrence: 230 (47%).
Increased substantially (+53%).

This is a plant most naturally at home in natural marshy grassland and fen, where it forms part of the characteristic community, especially in calcareous conditions. It now also occurs frequently in damp set-aside arable, and in waste places, where it hybridises with other species.
(142 tetrads: Dony, 1967; 174 tetrads: 1950-1986)

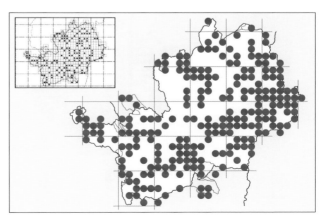

Map 377. *Epilobium parviflorum.*

Epilobium × limosum Schur (*E. parviflorum × E. montanum*)
Native.
First record: 1926.

This was found at the chalk pit by Hitchin Station (12/Z), 1926 *J. E. Little* and later nearby at Benslow (Dony, ms. index), but there have not been any recent records. It is probably overlooked.

Epilobium × dacicum Borbás (*E. parviflorum × E. obscurum*)
Native.
First record: 1992.

First found at Broxbourne Gravel Pit (30/T), 1992 *A. M. Boucher* (det. T. D. Pennington) (Hb. Boucher).

Epilobium parviflorum × E. ciliatum
Native.
First record: 1956.

First detected at Tewin Water (21/M), 1956 *J. G. Dony* (det. G. M. Ash) (Hb. HTN). It has also been found at Broxbourne Gravel Pit (30/T), 1992 *A. M. Boucher* (det. T. D. Pennington); at Cock Lane Gravel Pit, Hoddesdon (30/N), 1992 *A. M. B.* (det. T. D. P.) (Hb. Boucher); and at Potwells, North Mymms (20/B), with both parents, 2005 *T. J.* It is probably common.

Epilobium × rivulare Wahlenb. (*E. parviflorum × E. palustre*)
Native.
First record: 1921?

This was found at the now overgrown St Ippollitts Common (12/Y), 1921 *J. E. Little* (*Rep. Bot. Exch. Club*: 382 (1922)). There is also an undated specimen in the Graveson herbarium (Hb. HTN) from the lost 'Hoddesdon Marsh' (30/Z), which may pre-date this. As *E. palustre* itself is now rare in the County, the occurrence of the hybrid is likely to be even rarer.

Epilobium montanum L.
Broad-leaved Willowherb
Native.
First record: 1814.
Tetrad occurrence: 379 (77%).
Increased? (+9%).

This is a native plant of woodlands, but also occurs widely as a garden weed and as a plant of shady roadsides. It seems to have increased slightly in these habitats.
(331 tetrads: Dony, 1967; 350 tetrads: 1950-1986)

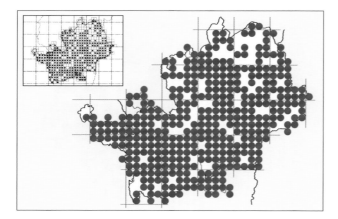

Map 378. *Epilobium montanum.*

Epilobium montanum × E. ciliatum
Native.
First record: 1956.

The first record of this was at Eastwick Wood (41/H), 1956 *J. G. Dony* (det. G. M. Ash) (Hb. HTN), and there is a specimen from TL32 collected by Dony in 1962 in Hb. BM. It was later reported from two tetrads (09/M and 20/B) as well as from a disused railway at Rickmansworth (09/S), 1978 *R. M. Burton* (det. T. D. Pennington) (Burton, 1983). During the recent survey, it was found at Arkley (29/H), 1990 *A. W. Vaughan*; Bishop's Stortford (41/Z), 1994 *S. Watson* (Hb. HTN); Kensworth (01/J) (VC20 [Beds.]), 1996 *T. J.* (Hb. HTN); Watton-at-Stone (22/V), 1997 *T. J.* (Hb. HTN); and Park Wood, Tring (91/F), 2007 *T. J.* It is probably one of the commonest willowherb hybrids in disturbed areas, and one of the more easily detectable.

Epilobium × neogradense Borbás
(*E. montanum × E. lanceolatum*)
Native.

There is an undated, unattributed, pre-1970 record from the Stevenage area (TL22) in the Vascular Plants Database at the Biological Records Centre, about which I have no other information.

Epilobium lanceolatum Sebast. and Mauri
Spear-leaved Willowherb
Native (or introduced?)
First record: 1960.
Tetrad occurrence: 9 (2%).
Rare but increasing (+200%).

This is a native plant of dry ground, mainly in the south-west of Britain, but often thought to be casual elsewhere. It first was noticed in Herts. on a railway bank at Elstree (Dony, 1967), and was later found on another railway bank at Bragbury End, where it survived until at least 1970 *J. G. Dony* (Hb. HTN). It was found in a new shelterbelt, not that far from the railway, at Ashwell (23/U), 1980 *T. J.* (Hb. HTN), and more tetrad records from TQ19 were submitted to the London Natural History Society (Burton, 1983). The recent survey shows that it has apparently consolidated its occurrence in urban areas in south Herts., while its northern outlier has apparently not survived, although with climatic warming, it may well spread further, and may currently be overlooked.
(3 tetrads: Dony, 1967; 5 tetrads: 1950-1986)

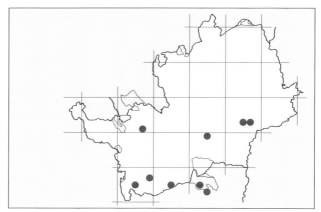

Map 379. *Epilobium lanceolatum.*

Epilobium tetragonum L.
Square-stalked Willowherb
Native.
First record: 1822.
Tetrad occurrence: 302 (62%).
Increased markedly (+212%).

Although Dony (1967) regarded this as a predominantly wet
ground species, it is now more often a weed of waste ground,
set-aside arable land and roadsides, where it has increased
substantially, although the map shows that it favours the damper
clays, and may still be under-recorded in many areas, especially in
the south.
(92 tetrads: Dony, 1967; 116 tetrads: 1950-1986)

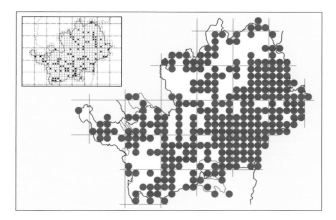

Map 380. *Epilobium tetragonum.*

The usual plant, with narrow sessile leaves, is sometimes
separated from ssp. *lamyi* (F. W. Schultz) Nyman, which was
recorded during the survey from Little Hadham (42/L), 1988
S. Watson; by the pond at Bogs Wood (42/M), 1989 *S. W.*;
Thames Wood (11/L), 1989 *T. J.*; and Sawbridgeworth (41/X),
1990 *S. W.* If it can really be regarded as a definable taxon, it has
probably been overlooked elsewhere.

Epilobium × *mentiens* Smejkal (*E. tetragonum* × *E. ciliatum*)
Native.
First record: 2004.

Apparently a rare hybrid, this was found at Anstey (43/B), with
both parents, 2001 *T. J.* (Hb. HTN); Chorleywood Common
(09/I), 2004 *T. J.*, with both parents; and at Lemsford Springs
(21/G), 2005 *T. J.* (Hb. HTN).

Epilobium obscurum Schreber
Short-fruited Willowherb
Native.
First record: 1874.
Tetrad occurrence: 61 (12%).
Stable or slightly decreased (-8%).

This is a plant mostly of long-established marshy grassland and
wet rides in woods, and does not appear to occur nearly as often
as *E. tetragonum* in disturbed ground. Its distribution remains
much as Dony recorded it, although there are a few more recorded
localities in the east, while it appears to have been either missed or
to have decreased in west Herts.
(63 tetrads: Dony, 1967; 84 tetrads: 1950-1986)

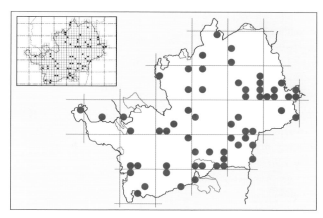

Map 381. *Epilobium obscurum.*

Epilobium obscurum × *E. ciliatum*
Native.
First record: 1957.

This was recorded twice by Dony (ms. index): from wet rides in
Milwards Park (20/I) and Plashes Wood (32/V), 1957. During
the survey, plants identified as this were found at Broxbourne
Gravel Pit (30/T), 1992 *A. M. Boucher* (det. T. D. Pennington)
(Hb. Boucher); and at Hitchin (12/Z), 1997 *T. J.* (Hb. HTN). It is
probably more frequent than these would suggest.

Epilobium roseum Schreber
Pale Willowherb
Native.
First record: 1800.
Tetrad occurrence: 42 (9%).
Apparently increased (+169%).

A native plant of damp woodlands, where it occurs occasionally
by ditches and streams. It was recorded by Pryor (1887) especially
from the wooded streams in south-east Herts. (Pryor, 1887), but
Dony's records did not show this. However, the recent survey
found it especially in the Broxbourne Woods area, which either
suggests it was under-recorded in the 1967 Flora or has increased
again in its native strongholds. It also occurs occasionally in damp
shady places elsewhere, rarely in gardens.
(15 tetrads: Dony, 1967; 33 tetrads: 1950-1986)

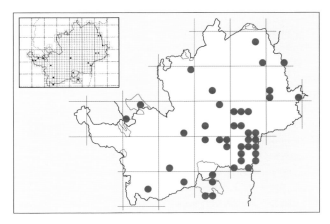

Map 382. *Epilobium roseum.*

Epilobium ciliatum Rafin.
American Willowherb
Introduced: neophyte.
First record: 1937.
Tetrad occurrence: 325 (66%).
Increased (+19%).

This plant of waste ground and disturbed areas has consolidated its occurrence since the 1960s (Dony, 1967), but shows signs of becoming slightly less frequent again in some areas. It hybridises readily with most other native species, and formerly caused much confusion over identification.
(259 tetrads: 1967; 276 tetrads: 1950-1986)

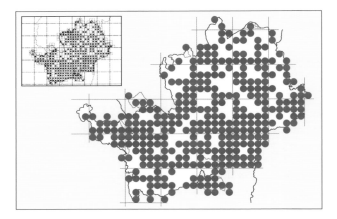

Map 383. *Epilobium ciliatum.*

Epilobium palustre L.   Herts Rare?
Marsh Willowherb
Native.
First record: 1839.
Tetrad occurrence: 6 (1%).
Stable? (+33%).

A plant of grazed swampy ground by rivers and ditches, and in poor-fen. This was never a particularly common plant in Herts., but it has certainly decreased substantially since the 19th century, with the loss of unimproved pastures on swampy ground in the river valleys, and of bogs elsewhere. Of the four localities noted by Dony (1967), it has survived at Patmore Heath (42/M) (re-found in 2008 *J. L. Fielding/T. J./S. Watson*); and at Sawbridgeworth Marsh (41/X), 2003 *S. W.* It has also been found at Sopwell Mill Meadows (10/M), 2000 *M. J. Hicks/L. Mottram*; and Batchworth Heath (09/R), 1988 *J. Colthup*, which re-confirm 19th century records. It was also found on the fen at Commons Wood Nature Reserve, Welwyn Garden City (21/K), 1997 *S. Cuming*, which is a new site for it, but not that far from the 'meadows above Stanborough', where it was recorded in the 19th century; and it has appeared at Bricket Wood Common (10/F), 2005 *J. Edgington*, where it had previously been recorded in 1953, unknown to Dony (Edgington, 2007). It was also found at Purwell Meadows (12/Z, 22/E), 1968 *F. Bentley*; and at Lemsford Meads (21/G), 1972 *L. M. P. Small*, at neither of which has it been seen since. There is also an unlocalised record from tetrad 10/X on Dony's card index, which he queried; and a record from Hadham Towers (41/I), 1985 needed confirmation.
(4 tetrads: Dony, 1967; 7 tetrads: 1950-1986)

Epilobium brunnescens (Cock.) Raven and Engel.
New Zealand Willowherb
Introduced: neophyte.
First record: *c.*1945 (VC21 [Herts.]).

Subsequent to its first occurrence at Potters Bar (Dony, 1967), this has only occurred since at Rabley Heath (21/J), 1981 *P. D. Walton* (Hb. HTN) (James, 1982), where it became a garden weed and survived until at least 1992. There are no other records.

Genus: *Chamerion*

Chamerion angustifolium (L.) Holub
Rosebay Willowherb
Native.
First record: 1787.
Tetrad occurrence: 460 (94%).
Stable or marginally decreased (-5%).

After its explosive spread from its apparently native sites in places like the woods on Berkhamsted Common at the beginning of the 20th century, this has now settled down as a regular member of the woodland flora in most of the County, as well as a common plant of railways and road banks, gravel pits, chalk pits and urban waste ground. However, the survey found it in slightly fewer tetrads relatively than Dony, and it certainly seems to be rather less abundant than it once was.
(460 tetrads: Dony, 1967 and from 1950-1986)

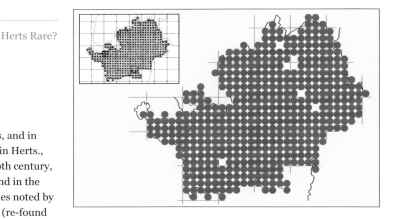

Map 384. *Chamerion angustifolium.*

Genus: *Oenothera*

The evening-primroses are one of our more difficult groups, owing to their propensity to form hybrid swarms, and have not previously been recorded thoroughly, even though they have occurred widely for 160 years or more and can form spectacular stands on waste ground. They remain under-recorded to some extent. I would like to thank Rose Murphy for help with determinations.

Oenothera glazioviana P. Mich. ex C. Martius
Large-flowered Evening-primrose
Introduced: neophyte.
Tetrad occurrence: 59 (12%).
First record: 1923?

Dony (1967) evidently had difficulty with this, as he did not give a map, and the records in his ms. index are limited. He also mistakenly quotes the first record as from Webb and Coleman, who actually only recorded '*O. biennis*', although the application of the name may be wrong. Rostański (1982) mentions specimens collected by J. E. Little from Hitchin, 1923 in Hb. CGE and Hb. BM., which may be the earliest extant gatherings. This species is, however, the most frequent evening-primrose in our area, occurring quite widely on waste ground, railway ballast, in gravel pits, *etc.*, sometimes only as a casual.

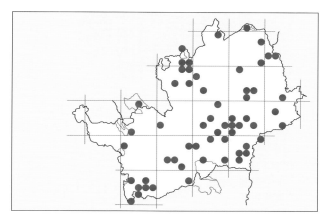

Map 385. *Oenothera glazioviana.*

Oenothera × fallax Renner (*O. glazioviana × O. biennis*)
Intermediate Evening-primrose
Introduced: neophyte.
Tetrad occurrence: 6 (1%).
First record: *c.*1980?

Rostański (1982) mentions a specimen of the hybrid between these two parents collected by J. M. Bryan from Rickmansworth, without a date (Hb. CGE), although Rostański treatment of the genus made *O. fallax* a separate species. During the survey, six records were confirmed: Hoddesdon (30/U), 1996 *A. M. Boucher* (Hb. Boucher); Panshanger (31/B), 1997 *T. J.* (Hb. HTN); Ashwell (23/U), 1997 *T. J.*; Ware (31/S), 1993 *A. M. B.* (det. R. Murphy) (Hb. HTN); near Standon (42/A), 2000 *K. Robinson* (det. R. Murphy) (Hb. HTN); and near Croxley Common Moor (09/S), 1998 *J. Colthup* (*comm.*: R. M. Burton). As it is often cultivated for oil, it is no doubt more widespread.

Oenothera biennis L.
Common Evening-primrose
Introduced: neophyte.
Tetrad occurrence: 4 (<1%).
First record: 1841?

Records are given from Ware, Hertford, Watford and Hitchin in Pryor (1887), several having been made by Coleman and his associates in the 1840s, although their application of the name could conceivably have been wrong. Dony, in his ms. index, lists a few records including one of his own from Cole Green tip (21/Q), 1956. There are also records from 20/K, 29/C and 29/W given in Burton (1983), although he sounds doubtful about the identification of the species by some recorders. It was, however, reported reliably from Waterford (31/C), 1984 *C. G. Hanson/A. L. Grenfell*; Ware tip (31/M), 1986 *C. G. H.*; and from Rye Meads Sewage Works (31/V), 1986 *C. G. H.* From the recent survey, there were records from Roehyde (20/D), 1988 *A. D. Marshall*; Sleapshyde Gravel Pit (20/D), 1991 *A. D. M.*; Goffs Oak (30/G), 1993 *A. M. Boucher*; Lamer Wood (11/X), 1995 *A. D. Marshall* (conf. R. Murphy) (Hb. HTN); and Nineacre Wood,

Bromley (42/A), 2003 *T. J.* (Hb. HTN). All of these were casuals, and the plant can scarcely be called 'common' in our area.

Oenothera biennis × O. cambrica
First record: 1987.

This hybrid has been identified from material collected at Bromley (42/A), 1987 *S. Watson* (det. R. Murphy) (Hb. HTN); and also was collected at Morgan's Road, Hertford (31/F), 1992 *A. M. Boucher* (Hb. HTN).

Oenothera cambrica Rostański
Small-flowered Evening-primrose
Introduced: neophyte.
First record: 1981?

There were records of '*O. parviflora*' from Hoddesdon (30/Z), *c.*1981 *A. M. Boucher* and from near Croxley Common Moor (09/S), 1981 *J. Colthup*, which probably refer to this species. It certainly appeared at Panshanger (21/W), 1997 *T. J.* (Hb. HTN); and by the Grand Union Canal at Dixon's Gap, Tring (91/C), 1998 *S. Hawkins* (det. T. J.) (Hb. HTN). It is possible that hybrids between this and both *O. biennis* and *O. glazioviana* have been overlooked.

Oenothera laciniata Hill
Cut-leaved Evening-primrose
Introduced: casual.
First record: 1926.

The single record of this given by Dony (1967) was by Graveson, from between Ware and St Margarets. This is interesting, because it appeared as a garden weed at Ware (31/S), 1986 *C. G. Hanson* (Hb. HTN).

[*Oenothera rosea* L'Hér ex Aiton
Pink Evening-primrose

This occurs spontaneously in a garden at Ware (31/S), *e.g.* 1984, 1987 *C. G. Hanson* (Hb. HTN), but was originally introduced and cannot be included in the County list as a genuinely wild plant.]

Genus: *Fuchsia*

Fuchsia magellanica Lam.
Fuchsia
Introduced: casual.
First record: 1972.

There are three casual records from tips: Cole Green tip (21/Q), 1972; Pye Corner tip (41/L), 1972; and Rye Meads Sewage Works (31/V), 1985 *C. G. Hanson*.

Fuchsia × hybrida hort. ex Vilm.
Cultivated Fuchsia
Introduced: casual.
First record: 1972.

Outcasts of this were also found at Cole Green tip (21/Q), 1972 and at Rye Meads (31/V), 1985 *C. G. Hanson*.

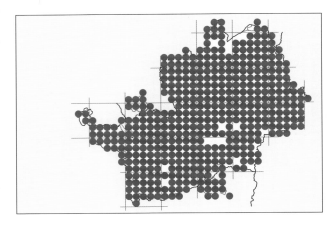

Map 387. *Swida sanguinea.*

Genus: *Circaea*

Circaea lutetiana L.
Enchanter's Nightshade
Native.
First record: *c.*1810.
Tetrad occurrence: 343 (70%).
Increasing? (+6%).

An attractive plant of shady woodlands and mature hedgerows, sometimes also becoming something of a pest as a garden weed. The distribution remains broadly similar to that recorded by Dony (1967), avoiding the Chalk, and becoming thinly spread on parts of the more open Clay-with-Flints and the most arable areas of Boulder Clay. It was recorded in rather more tetrads than in the earlier survey, possibly owing to increasingly overgrown habitats. (306 tetrads: Dony, 1967; 321 tetrads: 1950-1986)

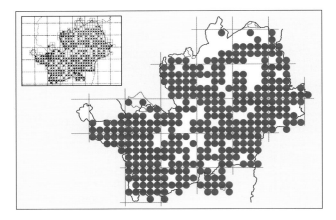

Map 386. *Circaea lutetiana.*

Cornaceae (Dogwood family)

Genus: *Swida*

The adoption of the generic name *Swida* in favour of *Cornus* for the following species follows Sell and Murrell (2009).

Swida sanguinea (L.) Opiz
Dogwood
Native.
First record: 1818.
Tetrad occurrence: 445 (91%).
Stable or marginally decreased (-4%).

A characteristic shrub of old hedgerows, scrub and coppice woodlands on the Boulder Clay and the Chalk, but also found in most other areas where there is enough free calcium in the soil. It shows no significant signs of having changed its occurrence since the 1960s, despite slightly fewer tetrad records in proportion.

Planted specimens of 'Dogwood' need to be re-examined, as there are likely to be both *S. koenigii* (C. K. Schneid) Pojark. **Asian Dogwood** and *S. australis* (C. A. Mey) Grossh. **Southern Dogwood**, as well as the hybrid between them, as supposed 'Dogwood' in amenity plantings (Sell and Murrell, 2009). (441 tetrads: Dony, 1967; 449 tetrads: 1950-1986)

Swida sericea (L.) Holub
Red-osier Dogwood
Introduced: neophyte.
First record: 1969.
Tetrad occurrence: 20 (4%).
Possibly increasing.

This was first noticed as an established plant at Berkhamsted (90/Z), 1969 *P. J. Kingsbury*, where it had become a well-established patch by the canal, and where it remains. However, there is no doubt that it has been planted in landscaped parklands by ponds and rivers for over a hundred years, and was formerly just ignored. It can form extensive patches where it does establish itself.

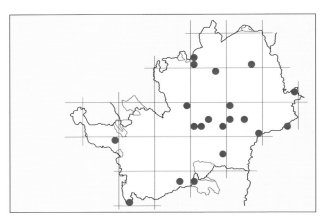

Map 388. *Swida sericea.*

Swida alba (L.) Holub
White Dogwood
Introduced: neophyte.
First record: 1986.

This was first noticed as a planted shrub in a 'wild' situation around the springs below Bingles Wood, Braughing (32/X), 1986 *T. J.* (James, 1989), where it had obviously been present for a long time. It remains at this location, but has now also been found as an introduced ornamental, possibly spreading, at Aldenham Reservoir (19/S), 1996 *J. K. Jackson*; as a few shrubs possibly planted, at Purwell (22/E), 1989 *T. J.* and in a hedgerow at Letchworth (23/G), 1989 *T. J.* As it can be confused easily with Red-osier Dogwood, it may be under-recorded.

Santalaceae (Bastard-toadflaxes)

Genus: *Thesium*

Thesium humifusum DC.   Herts Rare
Bastard-toadflax
Native.
First record: 1840.
Decreased?

A low-growing, inconspicuous plant of short, chalk grassland on the thinnest of rendzina soils, which only occurs now at Therfield Heath (33/J; 34/K). The record from 34/K was from short turf by the first golf course fairway, 1988 *T. J.*, not recorded since. However, it has been re-found at Church Hill (33/J), 2003, 2009 *T. J.* It also used to occur on the lost Sandon Heath, where it grew on the top of Gallows Hill (33/E) in *c.*1840 (Pryor, 1887). These two sites are the most westerly on the Chilterns/East Anglian Heights Chalk ridge, although it does occur on Chalk in south-western Britain.

Bastard-toadflax Thesium humifusum *Church Hill, Therfield Heath, 2009.*

Viscaceae (Mistletoe family)

Genus: *Viscum*

Viscum album L.
Mistletoe
Native.
First record: *c.*1750.
Tetrad occurrence: 93 (19%).
Increasing (+385%).

This strange parasitic plant occurs on a wide range of trees and shrubs, to where its sticky seeds are spread mainly by thrushes. In Herts., it occurs mostly on Hybrid Lime, but also increasingly on poplar, usually the hybrid *Populus* × *canadensis*; as well as on False Acacia, Apple (usually cultivated forms), Rowan and old Hawthorns, *etc.* It was the subject of a national survey during the 1990s, because it was feared it may have been decreasing. Nationally this was inconclusive (Briggs, 2000), but in Herts.,

partly as a result of the attention it then received, and also because the University of Hertfordshire subsequently took an interest in it (Allen-Williams *et al.*, 2002), it has received a thorough examination and has been found to be far more widespread than was thought to be the case, and certainly more than recorded by Dony (1967). Putting all the records from 1987-2003 together, we now know that it occurs in no less than 93 tetrads in the County. It was always common in the Hatfield Park area and around Hertford and Ware (Pryor, 1887), but it is now increasingly abundant in other areas where it was evidently only occasional before, such as Radlett, the Much Hadham area, and Ashwell. Personal observation of its spread at Ashwell since 1975 supports the idea that it is expanding from initial colonies, and has shown that it can completely dominate small apple trees, for example, within ten years.
(18 tetrads: Dony, 1967; 36 tetrads: 1950-1986)

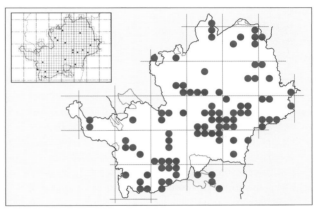

Map 389. *Viscum album.*

Celastraceae (Spindle family)

Genus: *Euonymus*

Euonymus europaeus L.
Spindle
Native.
First record: 1548.
Tetrad occurrence: 328 (67%).
Increasing (+33%).

With its striking fruits, this is an especially attractive shrub, characteristic of calcareous hedgerows and scrub across most of

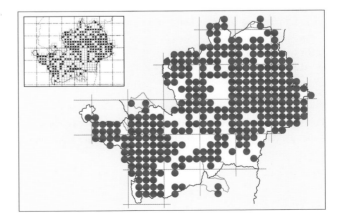

Map 390. *Euonymus europaeus.*

northern and central Hertfordshire, especially on the Clay-with-Flints plateau in the west and the Boulder Clay in the east. It is the first wild plant to have been recorded as such in Hertfordshire, and it still occurs where it was first seen, in the hedgerows by the old road to Cambridge from Puckeridge (Dony, 1967). It also shows clear signs of having increased, possibly because of the increase in scrub habitats.
(234 tetrads: Dony, 1967; 271 tetrads: 1950-1986)

Aquifoliaceae (Hollies)

Genus: *Ilex*

Ilex aquifolium L.
Holly
Native.
First record: 1742.
Tetrad occurrence: 422 (86%).
Increasing? (+10%).

A common and widespread shrub or tree in hedgerows, woodlands and scrub across the County. It is especially dominant in sites which were formerly wood-pasture commons, and it only becomes rare or absent on the open calcareous Boulder Clay and Chalk in north Herts., and on the damp soils north-west of Tring, although it occasionally occurs even here as a bird-sown escape from gardens. There is some evidence of a slight spread since the 1960s, possibly mainly from bird-sown garden escapes, although some old woodlands have also increasingly become dominated by it.
(363 tetrads: Dony, 1967; 381 tetrads: 1950-1986)

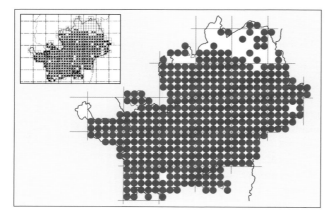

Map 391. *Ilex aquifolium.*

Ilex × altaclerensis (*hort.* ex Loudon) Dallimore
(*I. aquifolium × I. perado*)
Highclere Holly
Introduced.
First record: 2001.

This was found as a long-established shrub in Binghams Plantation, Aldenham (19/J), 2001 *T. J.*; and was also reported as a long-established introduction at Darlands Nature Reserve (29/L), 2002 *R. M. Burton*.

Buxaceae (Box family)

Genus: Buxus

Buxus sempervirens L.
Box
Native? (and introduced).
First record: 1742 (as introduced), 1787.
Tetrad occurrence: 56 (11%).

Dony (1967) gives a good historical account of the occurrence of Box in Hertfordshire, and highlights the fact that its name occurs as an ancient part of various place-names in the County, such as Boxmoor at Hemel Hempstead and Box Wood, Walkern. That it appears to have died out as a genuinely wild tree a long time ago is suggested by the fact that 19th century botanists did not know it in natural conditions. It now occurs as a planted, or sometimes apparently self-sown shrub in game woodlands across the County.

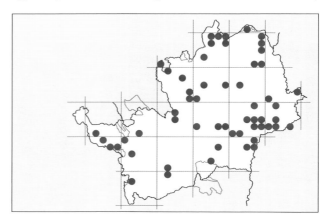

Map 392. *Buxus sempervirens.*

Euphorbiaceae (Spurge family)

Genus: *Mercurialis*

Mercurialis perennis L.
Dog's Mercury
Native.
First record: 1750.
Tetrad occurrence: 440 (90%).
Probably stable (-2%).

Dog's Mercury is especially characteristic of Ash/Maple and Hornbeam woodlands on free-draining, somewhat calcareous loams, where it can form dominant ground-cover almost to the exclusion of other plants. It also occurs in shady woodlands on the Chalk and in less acidic patches by streams in woods on gravels and the London Clay. In old secondary woodlands or scrub it can be locally abundant, despite being thought by some to be an 'ancient woodland indicator'. Its distribution has remained more or less stable, although it appears to have increased in abundance in some woods on the Boulder Clay, at the expense of more species-rich communities over the last 30 years, possibly because deer do not eat it so readily. However, it was recorded from marginally fewer tetrads, proportionately during the survey than in the 1960s.
(426 tetrads: Dony, 1967; 435 tetrads: 1950-1986)

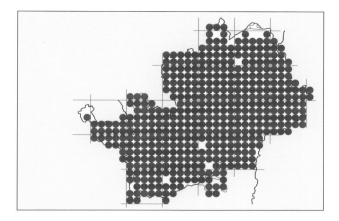

Map 393. *Mercurialis perennis.*

Mercurialis annua L.
Annual Mercury
Introduced: archaeophyte.
First record: 1873.
Tetrad occurrence: 68 (14%).
Probably stable (+2%).

A somewhat unpredictable plant of disturbed ground, tips and cultivation. Although Dony (1967) thought it had increased, there is now no evidence of much further spread, and it still appears to be most frequent on the Lea and Colne gravels, and in an area around Baldock, Letchworth and Hitchin in north Herts.
(63 tetrads: Dony, 1967; 75 tetrads: 1950-1986)

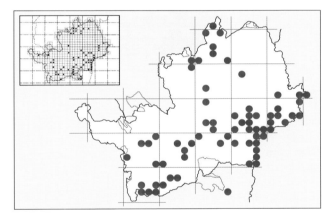

Map 394. *Mercurialis annua.*

Genus: *Euphorbia*

Euphorbia corallioides L.
Coral Spurge
Introduced: casual.
First (only) record: 1997.

This appeared as a garden weed at Kipling Grove, Hemel Hempstead (01/Q), 1997 *C. G. Hanson* (det. E. J. Clement) (Hb. HTN), originating from compost brought in from Ware, where it had been under cultivation.

Euphorbia platyphyllos L.   Herts Vulnerable
Broad-leaved Spurge   (Herts Rare?)
Introduced: archaeophyte.
First record: *c.*1700.
Tetrad occurrence: 8 (2%).
Decreased sharply (-50%).

This species of calcareous Boulder Clay and similar soils is now one of the rarest of our arable weeds, even though, nationally, its status is considered of 'low concern'. It was already scarce and decreasing by the time of Dony's survey, although there were four additional records to his between 1970 and 1986. During the recent survey it was found at eight locations in seven tetrads: at two sites near Little Hormead and Mutton Hall (42/E), 1988 *S. Watson*; near Oxshott Hill (22/V), 1988 *K. Robinson*; arable by Balls Wood (31/K), 1988 *A. M. Boucher/J. Crew*; near Great Hormead (43/A), 1991 *S. W.*; Thundridge Hill (31/T), 1993 *A. M. B.*; Pelham Gate (43/K), 1993 *S. W.*; and in a field by Wormley Wood (30/C), 1998 *R. Dyke*. It is unlikely that it still occurs at all of these. However, a large colony (over 200 plants) was discovered by a rape field near Cottered Warren (32/I), 2009 *G. Salisbury/G. P. Smith/T. J.* (Hb. HTN), which gives hope it might re-appear elsewhere.
(15 tetrads: Dony, 1967; 19 tetrads: 1950-1986)

[*Euphorbia serrulata* Thuill.
Upright Spurge
Introduced? [native in the U.K.].

The only record, which was ignored by Dony (1967), was from Hemel Hempstead in 1883 by A. Gibbs (as *E. stricta*) (Selby, 1884). This was recorded with some doubt in the supplement to Pryor (1887), but there is in fact a specimen in Hb. LIV, undated, collected from there by W. R. Linton. What the status of the plant was we do not know, and without further information the record must remain doubtful.]

[*Euphorbia mellifera* Aiton

This tree-spurge, native to the Canaries, escaped and self-seeded at Coltsfoot Road, Ware (31/S), 1994 *C. G. Hanson*, having originally been cultivated in 1978. As it was adjacent to its source and did not persist, it should not be regarded as a naturally occurring Hertfordshire plant.]

Euphorbia helioscopia L.
Sun Spurge
Introduced: archaeophyte.
First record: 1820.
Tetrad occurrence: 292 (60%).
Stable or slightly decreasing (-6%).

The status of this species remains much as Dony (1967) says: particularly frequent on allotment plots and in gardens, but also

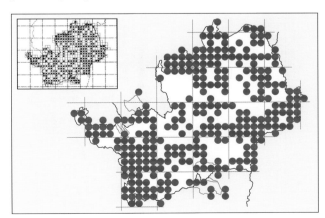

Map 395. *Euphorbia helioscopia.*

occasionally in arable field margins and on waste land.
(294 tetrads: Dony, 1967; 320 tetrads: 1950-1987)

Euphorbia lathyris L.
Caper Spurge
Introduced: archaeophyte.
First record: 1827.
Tetrad occurrence: 60 (12%).
Increasing?

It is difficult to be clear about the spread of this species, because Dony (1967) did not show a map, and there are inadequate records to demonstrate its occurrence in the middle of the 20th century. It had evidently already become fairly widespread by the 1880s (Pryor, 1887), and he reported one wood at Waterford which had thousands of plants. However, most plants are obvious escapes from cultivation, and it is now widespread across the County, usually around villages, or on waste tips.

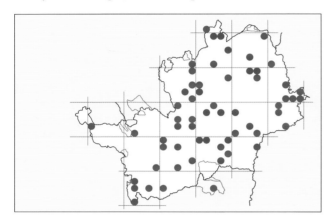

Map 396. *Euphorbia lathyris.*

Euphorbia exigua L.   UK Near Threatened
Dwarf Spurge
Introduced: archaeophyte.
First record: *c.*1820.
Tetrad occurrence: 210 (43%).
Decreased (-27%).

This is an arable weed of dry, calcareous soils, as well as rarely occurring on waste ground. It was formerly abundant in fields on the Chalk across northern Hertfordshire, but is now usually reduced to a few plants in field corners across most of its range, although it does occasionally demonstrate its ability to re-appear

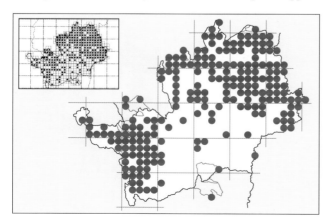

Map 397. *Euphorbia exigua.*

from buried seed, and so its national status may be over-stated. It still occurs most frequently on the Chalk, the Clay-with-Flints (usually where Chalk is showing through), and on the chalky Boulder Clay.
(275 tetrads: Dony, 1967; 289 tetrads: 1950-1986)

Euphorbia peplus L.
Petty Spurge
Introduced: archaeophyte.
First record: 1814.
Tetrad occurrence: 379 (77%).
Decreasing (-18%).

This familiar garden weed, which Dony (1967) thought must be in every garden, has certainly decreased overall since the 1960s, although it is still frequent enough where the ground is cultivated regularly. With the decline in garden vegetable plots and allotments, and the over-tidyness of farmyards, plants like this have suffered somewhat.
(438 tetrads: Dony, 1967; 440 tetrads: 1950-1986)

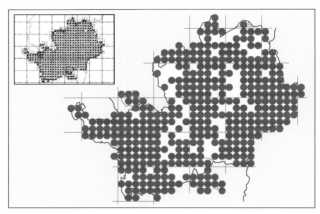

Map 398. *Euphorbia peplus.*

Euphorbia × *pseudovirgata* (Schur) Soó
(*E. esula* × *E. waldsteinii*)
Twiggy Spurge
Introduced: neophyte.
First record: *c.*1810?
Tetrad occurrence: 13 (3%).
Stable or decreasing (-4%).

This is a rather rare, patch-forming colonist of rough grasslands, usually on calcareous soils. Dony (1967) recorded what was mostly

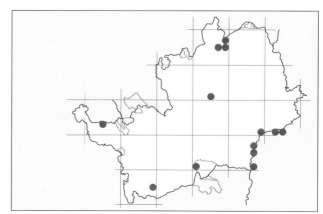

Map 399. *Euphorbia* × *pseudovirgata.*

this as *E. uralensis*, which was considered to be a synonym for the *E. esula* used by Pryor (1887). There were also later records of '*E. esula*' (James, 1982, 1985), which were also probably the same. The taxonomy of the group to which the plant belongs is complex, and it is possible that more than one hybrid is present, although all the material examined closely appears to be the one given here. It was recorded from 13 scattered tetrads during the survey, with clusters around Sandon, and in rough sites in the Lea and Stort valleys. Many of these sites are small, long-standing colonies. (13 tetrads: Dony, 1967; 22 tetrads: 1950-1986)

Euphorbia cyparissias L.
Cypress Spurge
Introduced: casual.
First record: 1918.

Dony listed seven recent tetrad records of this garden escape, and also detailed earlier records. It has remained a rare casual of rough grassland, roadsides, *etc.*, sometimes established for a while. The recent survey produced records from the bank of the A505 at Slip End (23/Y), 1990 *T. J.*; Juniper Hill, Rickmansworth (09/L), 1991 *P. J. Ellison*; and waste ground at Harpenden (11/M), 1997 *I. G. Denholm*.

Euphorbia amygdaloides L.
Wood Spurge
Native.
First record: 1814.
Tetrad occurrence: 67 (14%).
Stable or slightly decreased (-3%).

This plant of glades and ride margins in damp woods on calcareous clays has an interesting distribution. It is very characteristic of the Clay-with-Flints woodlands of the Chilterns dip-slope, but is also quite frequent on damp clays in central and south Hertfordshire, usually rather de-calcified Boulder Clay, not London Clay, as stated by Dony (1967).
(66 tetrads: Dony, 1967; 81 tetrads: 1950-1986)

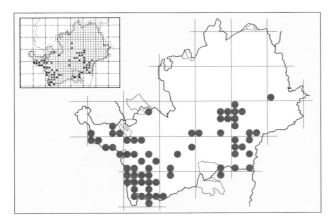

Map 400. *Euphorbia amygdaloides.*

The native subspecies is ssp. *amygdaloides*. Ssp. *robbiae* (Turrill) Stace **Mrs Robb's Bonnet** may occur as a garden outcast, such as in scrub by the Cambridge Road, Walsworth (12/Z), 2005 *T. J.*

Euphorbia characias L.
Mediterranean Spurge
Introduced: casual.
First reord: 2009.

A large clump of this was found in a scrubby hedgerow by an arable field, adjoining Ashwell village (23/U), 2009 *T. J.* Identified as ssp. *characias*.

[*Euphorbia segetalis* L.

This species, native of Tenerife, occurred spontaneously as a garden weed at Ware (31/S), 1996 *C. G. Hanson* (Hb. HTN). As it did not establish itself beyond the garden from which it originated, it cannot be formally regarded as a wild Hertfordshire plant.]

Rhamnaceae (Buckthorns)

Genus: *Rhamnus*

Rhamnus cathartica L.
Buckthorn
Native.
First record: c.1835.
Tetrad occurrence: 210 (43%).
Increased (+44%).

A rather inconspicuous shrub of hedgerows and scrub, most abundant on the Chalk, frequent on the Boulder Clay, and to a lesser extent on the Clay-with-Flints. It also occurs occasionally elsewhere, if the soil is calcareous enough, which would explain why the Brimstone butterfly, whose food-plant it usually is, occurs more widely than the shrub would seem to do. It is evidently increasing, and seems able to cope with nutrient enrichment to some extent.
(139 tetrads: Dony, 1967; 165 tetrads: 1950-1986)

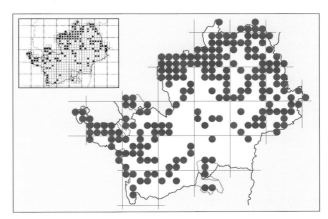

Map 401. *Rhamnus cathartica.*

Genus: Frangula

Frangula alnus Miller   Herts Rare
Alder Buckthorn
Native (and introduced).
First record: 1839.
Tetrad occurrence: 10 (4? as native) (2% (<1%)).
Stable?

In Hertfordshire, this is a rare native shrub of wet, acidic soils on heathy commons, very rarely elsewhere. However, it became fashionable for it to be planted in wet places as an amenity shrub during the 1980s, and there are a few locations where this is known to have been carried out in Herts. Its currently

known native sites are: Bulls Green (21/T), 1991 *T. J.*, where old bushes were hanging on under mature birch scrub; Bricket Wood Common, including west of the railway (10/F), various dates and observers; and Bishop's and Lockwell Woods (09/Q), various records. It has also appeared, apparently spontaneously, in rough acidic grassland at The Commons, near Holwell Hyde Farm (21/K), 1993, 1995 *A. M. Boucher/T. J.* It is known to have been planted by the R. Ver at Drop Lane Pits (10/K); Amwell (31/R); Panshanger (21/R); Lemsford Springs (21/G); Harebreaks Wood, Watford (19/E) and by the Grand Union Canal at Croxley (09/S). There were also records from the long-known native site at Oxhey Woods (19/A, B) in 1978/9 *G. Harper*, and it may survive here, as well as conceivably at other 19th century sites, such as Box Wood at Hoddesdon, Gobions Park or Sherrards Park Wood. Its status at unlocalised sites in tetrads 10/P, 20/Q, 31/K and 19/T, from records supplied between 1970 and 1986 by London Natural History Society, is unknown.
(3 recent tetrads: Dony, 1967; 9 tetrads: 1950-1986)

Vitaceae (Vine family)

Genus: *Vitis*

Vitis vinifera L.
Grape-vine
Introduced: neophyte.
First record: 1964.
Tetrad occurrence: 7 (1%).

Dony (1967) merely notes its occurrence on tips, and gives one record. During the 1970s, it occurred widely on tips, but was also found in wet woodland at Hitchin (12/U), 1975 *T. J./B. R. Sawford*. During the recent survey, it has occurred in seven tetrads, especially at Rye Meads Sewage Works (31/V) 1995-1998 *A. M. Boucher/C. G. Hanson*; but also in scrub at Panshanger (21/W), 1989 *T. J.*; a hedge at Epping Green (20/Y), 1992 *A. M. B.*; hedgerow at Thundridge (31/N), 1993 *A. M. B.*; by Grand Union Canal, Cassiobury (09/L), 1993 *P. J. Ellison*; waste ground at Ascot Road, Watford (09/X), 1994 *T. J.*; and site of old greenhouses, Bayfordbury (31/A), 1994 *A. M. B./C. G. H.*

Genus: *Parthenocissus*

Parthenocissus quinquefolia (L.) Planchon
Virginia-creeper
Introduced: neophyte.
First record: 1988.

The true Virginia-creeper was first confirmed in the wild from Cheshunt Gravel Pits (30/R), 1988 *A. M. Boucher*; and has subsequently been found in scrub by an old railway at St Albans (10/N), 1993 *T. J.*; and by Long Valley Wood, Croxley Green (09/S), 1993 *P. J. Ellison*.

Parthenocissus inserta (A. Kerner) Fritsch
False Virginia-creeper
Introduced: neophyte.
First record: 1986.

This was first found at Turnford Marsh Pit (30/S), 1986 *R. M. Burton*, and was also found nearby at Cheshunt Gravel Pits (30/R), 1994 *G. P. Smith*. It was also found escaped near Albury

Hall (42/H), 1988 *S. Watson*; at Town Meads, Bishop's Stortford (42/V) the same year *S. W.*; and at Totteridge Lane (29/M), 1993 *D. Griffith*.

Linaceae (Flaxes)

Genus: *Linum*

Linum bienne Mill.   Herts Rare
Pale Flax
Native?
First record: 1909.
Tetrad occurrence: 2 (<1%).

This has to be one of the most enigmatic of Hertfordshire's wild plants. There is a record from the files of Bishop's Stortford Natural History Society of the species having been found at the Upper Field, Bishop's Stortford College grounds (42/W), 1909 (recorder unknown), which was regarded by Dony as an error for *L. usitatissimum* (Dony, ms. index), although it was probably correct. A single plant was then found on disturbed ground at Bury Green (42/K), 1988 *S. Watson*; and subsequently another single plant in rough grass at old allotments, Farnham Road, Bishop's Stortford (42/W), 1996 *A. R. Outen*. It may well, therefore, be a rare native in this part of the County.

Linum usitatissimum L.
Flax
Introduced: neophyte.
First record: 1839.
Tetrad occurrence: 40 (8%).
Increased (+173%).

Flax is a relic of cultivation, and as such has occurred sporadically across the County for a long time. In the 1960s, cultivation had all but ceased locally, but it has now resumed for seed oil, and the result is that the plant appears regularly in waste places or by roads, although almost entirely in the east of the County.
(14 tetrads: Dony, 1967; 28 tetrads: 1950-1986)

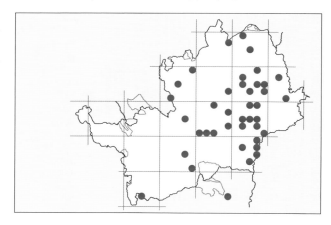

Map 402. *Linum usitatissimum.*

Linum perenne L.   Herts Rare
Perennial Flax
Native.
First record: 1925 (as introduction?), 1972.

Although never having been seen at the site earlier, the first record

Perennial Flax Linum perenne *Therfield Heath, 1992.*

of this on Therfield Heath (33/J) in 1972 by W. H. Darling must be considered a new find of a native plant (although it was not reported at the time to the County recorder). In 1978, the species was found near Fox Covert on Therfield Heath (33/J) *T. J.* (Hb. HTN) and remained here until at least 1982. During the recent survey, it was reported from the same general area, without firm dates, by V. Thompson; but was also found on the banks by the first golf course fairway (34/K), 1992 *T. J.*, where it re-appears sporadically. It has also been found, possibly as an introduction, near Wilbury Hill (23/B), 1925 *H. Phillips* (Hb. HTN) (a record overlooked by Dony); and during the recent survey at Wymondley electricity grid station (22/V), 1991 *A. D. Marshall*, where it must have been introduced.

Linum catharticum L.
Fairy Flax
Native.
First record: 1748.
Tetrad occurrence: 108 (22%).
Decreasing rapidly (-41%).

This inconspicuous but attractive plant of short grassland and sometimes disturbed ground on calcareous soils was frequent and even abundant locally across most of north Hertfordshire in the 1960s, often surviving in otherwise semi-improved pastures. It has since decreased quite severely, being limited to better quality chalk grassland, occasional in old grasslands on Boulder Clay or Clay-with-Flints, and rare elsewhere, although often in old churchyards.
(175 tetrads: Dony, 1967; 190 tetrads: 1950-1986)

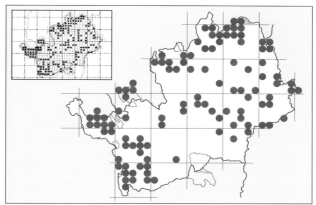

Map 403. *Linum catharticum.*

Genus: *Radiola*

Radiola linoides Roth   UK Near Threatened
Allseed   Herts Extinct
Native.
First record: 1839.

This low-growing annual of bare, eroded places on damp, sandy heaths was found by Coleman at Leggatts, Northaw; and at Colney Heath (Pryor, 1887), but with no subsequent reliable records.

Polygalaceae (Milkworts)

Genus: *Polygala*

Polygala vulgaris L.
Common Milkwort
Native.
First record: 1814.
Tetrad occurrence: 35 (7%).
Decreasing rapidly (-42%).

Having been a widespread and familiar plant of shorter grassland on calcareous soils across most of central and northern Hertfordshire, this is now almost restricted to old chalk grassland. (57 tetrads: Dony, 1967; 69 tetrads: 1950-1986)

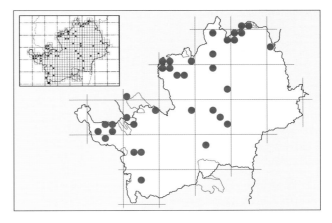

Map 404. *Polygala vulgaris.*

Polygala serpyllifolia Hose   Herts Rare
Heath Milkwort
Native.
First record: 1872.
Tetrad occurrence: 2 (<1%).
Severely decreased (-83%).

Never common in the County, this was known from a wide
range of commons and barren pastures on heathy soils across
southern Hertfordshire after it had first been recognised as a
separate species in the 19th century. Dony (1967) knew it from
several sites as far north as the Knebworth area; while it was
recorded after 1970 from rides in Newton Wood (22/F), 1978,
1982 *T. J./B. R. Sawford*; pastures by Bencroft Wood (30/I),
1980 *A. Woods*; and rides in Bramfield Wood (21/Y), 1980
A. M. Boucher, in all of which it appears to be extinct. During the
recent survey it was only found in the clearings on Bricket Wood
Common (10/F) on various dates *T. J./G. P. Smith et al.*; and at
Claypits Meadow (30/D), 1993 *A. M. Boucher*, where it may also
now be extinct.
(11 tetrads: Dony, 1967; 14 tetrads: 1950-1986)

[*Polygala calcarea* F. W. Schultz
Chalk Milkwort

Reports of this having been recorded at sites like Therfield Heath
are likely to be errors for bright-coloured forms of *P. vulgaris*. It
has never been recorded from the County.]

Staphyleaceae (Bladdernut family)

Genus: *Staphylea*

Staphylea pinnata L.
Bladdernut
Introduced: casual.
First record: 1881.

There is a specimen of this collected from a hedgerow near Hemel
Hempstead (TL00) in 1881 by James Saunders in Hb. LTN. This
record has been overlooked ever since.

Hippocastanaceae (Horse-chestnuts)

Genus: *Aesculus*

Aesculus hippocastanum L.
Horse-chestnut
Introduced: neophyte.
First record: *c*.1713 (as planted tree).
Tetrad occurrence: 402 (82%).
Increased substantially.

Until the 1960s or even later, it was received wisdom that the
conker tree does not naturalise very well in Britain. The map
presented here largely shows records of trees and saplings in
'wild' situations, giving a lie to this perception. It occurs in scrub,
secondary woodland, hedgerows and by streams across most
of the County, except in the most barren arable landscapes. It
appears to be most at home, however, in damp, peaty wooded
ground by streams, which is not surprising, given its native habitat

of peaty wooded hollows in the mountains of south-eastern
Europe. Occasionally it achieves spectacular size, such as the
magnificent old tree with rooting branches which was a familiar
sight near The Gage at Little Berkhamsted until a misguided
landowner lopped its branches! However, since 2006, the invasion
of the Horse-chestnut Leaf-miner moth *Cameraria ohridella* has
resulted in many trees being severely damaged, following which
Horse-chestnut Bleeding-canker *Pseudomonas syringae* var.
aesculi, has also appeared, and the tree's future in many places
must be in doubt.

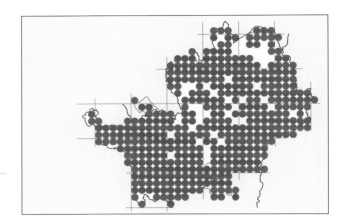

Map 405. *Aesculus hippocastanum.*

Aesculus carnea Zeyher
Red Horse-chestnut
Introduced: neophyte.
First record (as escape): 1995.

This was noted as 'naturalised saplings' at Little Heath (20/R),
1995 *A. D. Marshall*. There are also a number of records of
planted trees elsewhere, and it is a frequent ornamental in parks.

Aceraceae (Maples)

Genus: *Acer*

Acer platanoides L.
Norway Maple
Introduced: neophyte.
First record: 1909.
Tetrad occurrence: 253 (52%).
Increasing substantially.

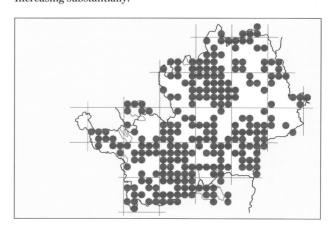

Map 406. *Acer platanoides.*

That Dony (1967) almost ignored this tree is rather strange, given that J. E. Little had recorded it as self-seeding around Hitchin as early as 1909 (Dony, ms. index). As it is a favourite for amenity planting around towns, and now also along main roads, it is bound to spread in much the same way that Sycamore spread earlier. During the recent survey it was found to be extensively naturalised and rapidly increasing, especially on neutral or slightly acidic soils, although in some places it so far only exists as recently planted trees.

Acer campestre L.
Field Maple
Native.
First record: 1742.
Tetrad occurrence: 470 (96%).
Stable: no recorded change.

This tree forms one of the principal native woodland habitat formations in the County, along with Ash, and is an important element of several others. As such, it is abundant in woods and ancient hedgerows especially in north-east Hertfordshire, and is found also on the Chalk, Clay-with-Flints and even on London Clay and gravels where the soil is calcareous enough to support it. It was formerly largely coppiced, or used as a hedgerow species, but occasionally old pollards are found, such as at Panshanger, where one ancient mini-pollard was considered by the arborist J. White to be one of the oldest of its type that he had ever seen (pers. comm. to B. L. Sage). It is also now quite often used for amenity planting, which tends to obscure the fact that it is otherwise a good indicator of old habitat. Recently suggestions have been made (Sell, 2007) that many of these plantings involve non-native subspecies; and ssp. *leiocarpum* (Opiz) Pax, with glabrous fruits, from south-eastern Europe, has now been identified as the plant introduced to Ashwell Quarry Nature Reserve (23/P) some years ago! It has also been recorded from Royston bypass (34/L), and is likely to be widespread (Sell, *op. cit.*).
(446 tetrads: Dony, 1967; 448 tetrads: 1950-1986)

Field Maple Acer campestre *ancient pollard at Cassiobury, Watford, 1992.*

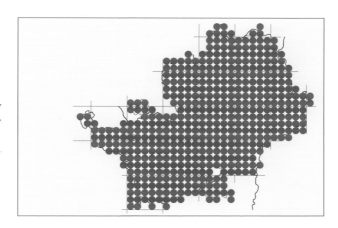

Map 407. *Acer campestre.*

Acer monspessulanum L.
Montpelier Maple
Introduced: planted.
First (only) record: 1997.

This was found as old planted trees at Park Wood, Weston (22/U), 1997 *T. J.*

Acer pseudoplatanus L.
Sycamore
Introduced: neophyte.
First record: 1733.
Tetrad occurrence: 470 (96%).
Probably stable (-1%).

Although there are numerous examples of old parkland trees across the County, it was not until it was treated as a timber tree in the 19th century that it began its spread into 'natural' habitats. It is now one of the most abundant trees in secondary woodland and scrub, as well as forming a major part of native woodlands, especially Ash/Beech woodlands on the Chalk, and damp alder woodlands on fen peat by rivers, where its seedlings can develop so densely as to preclude other species altogether, especially following a felling. However, grey squirrels attack it heavily, and so may check its later dominance in a wood. It was recorded from proportionately slightly fewer tetrads during the survey, but this is not significant.
(453 tetrads: Dony, 1967; 456 tetrads: 1950-1986)

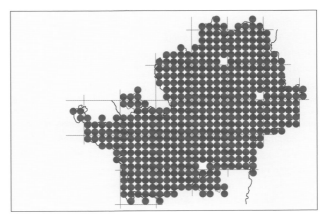

Map 408. *Acer pseudoplatanus.*

Acer saccharinum L.
Silver Maple
Introduced: planted.
First (only) record: 1989.

Old trees were found by Sewett's Wood, Kings Walden (12/K), 1989 *T. J.* It is also occasionally planted for ornament in towns.

Anacardiaceae (Sumach family)

Genus: *Cotinus*

Cotinus coggygria Scop.
Smoke-tree
Introduced: casual.
First (only) record: 1996.

A small, self-sown bush of this was found by the A505, north of Royston (34/Q) (VC29 [Herts.]), 1996, *T. J.* (Hb. HTN).

Genus: *Rhus*

Rhus typhina L.
Stag's-horn Sumach
Introduced: neophyte.
First record: 1970.
Tetrad occurrence: 7 (1%).

This ornamental garden shrub, which suckers profusely, can form small thickets on waste ground, given time, but thankfully does not set seed. It was first found at Moor Mill tip (10/L), 1970 *C. G. Hanson*; and there were subsequent records from Ware tip (31/M), 1984 *C. G. H.* and from the Cheshunt area (30/R) (Burton, 1983). During the recent survey it has been found as an escape at Amwell Quarry (31/R), 1991 *T. J.*; Albury Sewage Works (42/M), 1991; Standon (32/W), 1991; Bishop's Stortford (42/Q), 1992; near Cherry Green (32/T), 1992; near Brent Pelham (43/K), 1993 *S. Watson*; and on railway banks near Baldock Station (23/M), 2007 *T. J.* It may have been overlooked elsewhere.

Simaroubaceae (Tree-of-heaven family)

Genus: *Ailanthus*

Ailanthus altissima (Miller) Swingle
Tree-of-heaven
Introduced: neophyte.
First record: 1983.
Tetrad occurrence: 2 (<1%).

This ornamental tree occurs increasingly around London, where it is potentially a menace, and first appeared in Herts. at Water Hall tip (21/V), 1983 *C. G. Hanson* (det. E. J. Clement). More recently it has been found self-sown at Aldenham Churchyard (19/P), 1993 *J. K. Jackson*; and in the hedge by Rowley Lane, Arkley (29/D), 1997 *T. J./G. P. Smith*. It is likely to increase further.

Rutaceae (Rue family)

Genus: *Citrus*

Citrus auriantium L.
Orange
Introduced: casual.
First record: 1970.

Self-sown seedlings, well-grown enough to be identifiable, were first recorded at Moor Mill tip (10/L), 1970 *C. G. Hanson*, who subsequently found them at various other tips around the County, although with increasing cleanliness of tips, these have reduced, and the last record was from Ware tip (31/M), 1991.

Citrus paradisi Macfad.
Grapefruit
Introduced: casual.
First record: 1970.

As with Orange, this first was recorded at Moor Mill tip (10/L), 1970 *C. G. H.*; and was subsequently found at other sites, the last being Waterford tip (31/C), 1982.

Oxalidaceae (Wood-sorrels)

Genus: *Oxalis*

[*Oxalis valdiviensis* Barnéoud
Chilean Yellow-sorrel

This had become an infesting weed at a garden in Ware (31/S), 1995 *C. G. Hanson*, having originally been cultivated. Unless it appears elsewhere, however, it must remain off the list of 'wild' Hertfordshire plants.]

Oxalis rosea Jacq.
Annual Pink-sorrel
Introduced: casual.
First (only) record: 1978.

Its only occurrence has been as an apparently self-sown weed at Bayfordbury (31/A), 1978 *C. G. Hanson*.

Oxalis corniculata L.
Procumbent Yellow-sorrel
Introduced: neophyte.
First record: 1930 (or possibly *c.*1880).
Tetrad occurrence: 60 (12%).
Increasing.

Of all the alien sorrels, this is the one that occurs mainly as a garden weed, sometimes along pavements, having arrived with potted plants. Although Dony (1967) only gives one record for the species, it was in fact reported from a garden in Hitchin, 1930 *H. Phillips* (Hb. HTN), and Dony's ms. index gives several other early records. There is also a record in Pryor (1887) from Hertford, which was queried at the time, but may well have been correct, and Burton (1983) also gives a number of records in the south of the County. During the recent survey, there was some suggestion of a preference for river valley soils. The most frequent form is var. *atropurpurea* van Houtte ex Planchon.

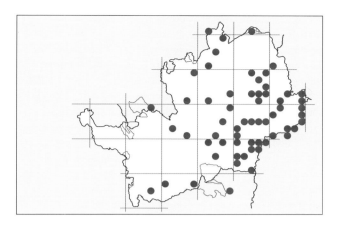

Map 409. *Oxalis corniculata.*

Oxalis exilis Cunn.
Least Yellow-sorrel
Introduced: neophyte.
First record: 1989.
Tetrad occurrence: 15 (3%).

This attractive little plant can become abundant in damp lawns
and by buildings, and so it is strange that it was not until 1989
that it was first found in the gardens of Briggens House (41/A),
S. Watson (det. T. J.) (Hb. HTN). It has subsequently been found
in 15 tetrads, and may well be more widespread, especially round
towns.

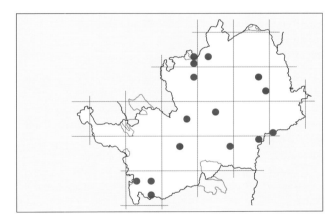

Map 410. *Oxalis exilis.*

Oxalis dillenii Jacq.
Sussex Yellow-sorrel
Introduced: neophyte.
First record: 1993.
Tetrad occurrence: 6 (1%).

This weed, usually of sandy ground, and closely related to
O. stricta, came to be recognised in the early 1990s as occurring
outside Sussex. It was first found in the County at Kingfisher
Nurseries, Bayford (30/D), 1993 *A. M. Boucher* (Hb. Boucher);
and was soon also found in two gardens at Ware (31/M, S) the
same year *A. M. B.*; on a heap of garden rubbish at Herringworth
Hall (32/L), 1993 *S. Watson*; at Bentley Heath (29/P) (VC21
[Herts.]), 1998 *T. J.* (Hb. HTN); and by West Mill, Ware (31/I),
2006 *T. J.* (Hb. HTN). It is probably more widespread.

Oxalis stricta L.
Upright Yellow-sorrel
Introduced: neophyte.
First record: 1856.
Tetrad occurrence: 28 (6%).

Dony (1967) had ignored earlier records of this given by Pryor
(1887), although they are probably correct. It is now thinly but
widely spread as a weed of cultivated ground, both in gardens and
sometimes in arable fields, especially on the Boulder Clay in east
Herts.

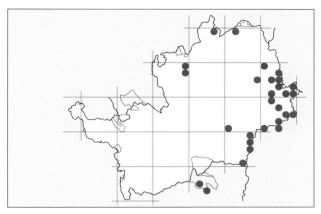

Map 411. *Oxalis stricta.*

Oxalis articulata Savigny
Pink-sorrel
Introduced: casual.
First record: 1971.
Tetrad occurrence: 7 (1%).

With us, there is no real evidence that this becomes genuinely
established as an escape in its sites, which are usually tips or
where garden rubbish has been thrown out. It was first recorded
at Pye Corner tip (41/L), 1971 *C. G. Hanson*; and then from four
other localities until 1986, and in seven tetrads since 1987, mostly
in S. E. Herts.

Oxalis acetosella L.
Wood-sorrel
Native.
First record: 1814.
Tetrad occurrence: 143 (29%).
Stable, or slightly increased (+4%).

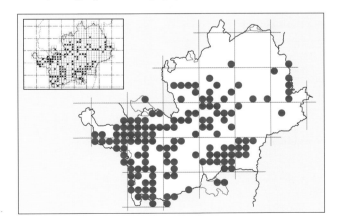

Map 412. *Oxalis acetosella.*

This is a common ground-floor component of shady woodlands on more acidic soils across southern and central Hertfordshire, also on thin acidic clays over Chalk in the Chilterns dip-slope woodlands. As such, it can be a good indicator of woodland continuity, although occasionally it can be an established weed in gardens.

(131 tetrads: Dony, 1967; 150 tetrads: 1950-1986)

Oxalis debilis Kunth
Large-flowered Pink-sorrel
Introduced: neophyte.
First record: *c.*1980.
Tetrad occurrence: 18 (4%).

This can become quite a pernicious weed where it occurs, unlike its relative *O. articulata*. There are tetrad records from Welwyn Garden City and around Hertford in Burton (1983) but without details. The first record available to me was from allotments at Pindar Road, Hoddesdon (30/Z), 1988 *A. M. Boucher*. The usual form with us appears to be var. *corymbosa* (DC.) Lourteig.

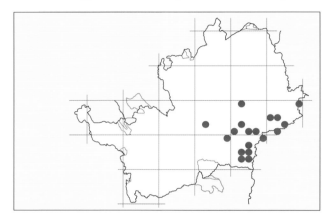

Map 413. *Oxalis debilis.*

Oxalis latifolia Kunth
Garden Pink-sorrel
Introduced: neophyte.
First record: 1971.

Also potentially a pernicious weed, although not apparently in Hertfordshire so far. This was first found at Pye Corner tip (41/L), 1971 *C. G. Hanson*; and later at a number of other tips. Its last record was from Rye Meads Sewage Works (31/V), 1985 *C. G. H.*

Oxalis incarnata L.
Pale Pink-sorrel
Introduced: neophyte.
First record: 1994.

The first record was at Great Amwell (31/R), 1994 *A. M. Boucher*. It has also appeared at Ashwell (23/U), 2009 *T.J.*

Geraniaceae (Crane's-bill family)

Genus: *Geranium*

Geranium endressi Gay
French Crane's-bill
Introduced: neophyte.
First record: 1956.

This occurs rather rarely as an escape from gardens, usually casual, but occasionally established at least for a while in rough grassland on roadsides and waste ground, although the hybrid *G.* × *oxonianum* could be mistaken for it in some cases. Dony (1967) gave three records, the first having been from Gilston. One of the other records was given with an erroneous tetrad reference: Pirton Cross (12/U) (not 12/V). Subsequently it also occurred at Nettleden Farm (00/E), 1967 *J. G. Dony*. During the recent survey it was found five times: Back Lane, Brickendon (30/J), 1992 *A. M. Boucher* (Hb. HTN); abundant on dumped earth, Potwells (20/B), 1994 *T. J.*; roadside near Mimmshall Brook (20/G) (VC21 [Herts.]), 1995 *A. D. Marshall* (Hb. HTN); banks by Bedwell Pit (20/Z), 2001 *T. J.*; and in Bridgefoot Lane, Potters Bar (20/F), 2003 *R. M. Burton*.

Geranium × *oxonianum* Yeo (*G. endressi* × *G. versicolor*)
Druce's Crane's-bill
Introduced: neophyte.
First record: 1921.
Tetrad occurrence: 11 (2%).

Dony (1967) overlooked a record of this, which had been identified in error as *G. endressi*, from Bramfield Road, Hertford, 1921 in the A. W. Graveson herbarium (Hb. HTN). It occurs fairly frequently as a garden outcast, and can persist for long periods, as at Potten End (00/E), where P. Kingsbury reported that it had been established for 20-30 years in 1986.

Geranium versicolor L.
Pencilled Crane's-bill
Introduced: neophyte.
First record: *c.*1880.

Also usually a casual escape from gardens, this was first recorded from Charlton Wellhead, Hitchin (Pryor, 1887). It can also be tricky to separate from the hybrid with *G. endressi*, and so some records may be errors. However, during the current survey it was recorded from Harpenden Common (11/G), 1989 *I. G. Denholm*; Ardeley Churchyard, two patches, probably originally planted (32/D), 1993 *T. J.*: Bricket Wood, by road (10/F), 1999 *T. J./ G. Salisbury/G. P. Smith*; roadside near Radwell Grange (23/I), 2002 *T. J.*

Geranium nodosum L.
Knotted Crane's-bill
Introduced: casual.
First record: 1802.

This is a rare escape from gardens. Dony (1967) notes its first occurrence, but omits to mention the record from 'woodland walks' at Cassiobury (presumably Whippendell Wood), given in Pryor's supplement (1887). It was found once in an apparently 'wild' situation during the survey: roadside verge near 'Button-Snap' cottage, Westmill (32/N), 1993 *S. Watson*. It also occurs as a weed in a garden at Ware (31/S), *C. G. Hanson*, where it was originally cultivated.

Geranium rotundifolium L.
Round-leaved Crane's-bill
Native.
First record: 1874.
Tetrad occurrence: 15 (3%).
Rare, but increasing slowly (+233%).

*Cut-leaved crane's-bills – Cut-leaved Crane's-bill Geranium dissectum (above), see page 269,
and Long-stalked Crane's-bill Geranium columbinum (below), see page 268.*

A plant of open, gravelly ground, most often in warm sites near the sea in southern England, this has an interesting ecology and history in Hertfordshire. It first appeared at the side of the lane to Sopwell Mill, near St Albans (Pryor, 1887). Apparently it was not known to J. E. Little, and Dony first found it at Berkhamsted, by the railway. The ballast of railways appears to have allowed it to spread, probably during the Second World War, when weed-killing was neglected. His *Flora* gives four records, all from this habitat. However, it had appeared in a gravel pit at Waterford (31/C) by the 1970s *A. D. Marshall*. The recent survey found that it had consolidated its occurrences by railways, persisting at or near most of Dony's sites, and appearing at some others that were accessible. It has also spread to other dry, gravelly locations, including more gravel pits and open woodland tracks. It remains local, but may be overlooked, and it is likely to respond to warmer climatic conditions.

(4 tetrads: Dony, 1967; 8 tetrads: 1950-1986)

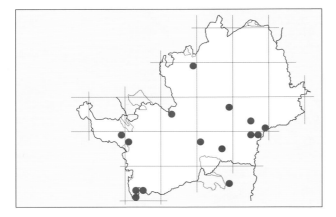

Map 414. *Geranium rotundifolium.*

Geranium pratense L.
Meadow Crane's-bill
Native.
First record: 1814.
Tetrad occurrence: 58 (12%).
Increased (+104%).

This is also an interesting plant. It had become quite scarce in meadows by the 19th century (Pryor, 1887), and was almost extinct in such habitats by the 1960s. Luckily it thrives on rather rank calcareous road verges, as long as these are not sprayed or polluted with salt! It occurs mostly on Boulder Clay or Chalk, but also sparingly in damper areas on Clay-with-Flints. It is also

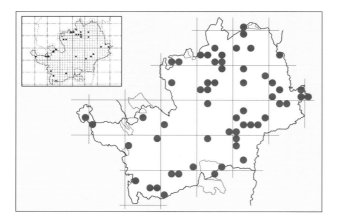

Map 415. *Geranium pratense.*

capable of re-appearing in sites after long absences, and in some can make quite spectacular comebacks, such as the fine show at Chadwell Banks, King's Meads (31/L) in 2003 *A. Reynolds*. Although the survey found it in 58 tetrads, in a few of these it was known to have been introduced. It is also possible that some at least of the escapes were actually *Geranium* 'Johnson's Blue', but none have been confirmed as such.

(27 tetrads: Dony, 1967; 48 tetrads: 1950-1986)

Geranium sanguineum L.
Bloody Crane's-bill
Introduced [native in the U.K.].
First record: 1915.

Dony omitted the first record, which was of an escape on waste ground at the bottom of Gallows Hill, Hertford (31/G), 1915 *H. F. Hayllar* (Dony, ms. index). It was subsequently found as a casual at Ware tip (31/M), 1977 *C. G. Hanson*. During the recent survey, it was found to be well-established at Mardley Heath (21/P), 1992 *A. D. Marshall*, and survived here at least until 1997, when one clump was seen *G. P. Smith*. It also occurred as a relic on former allotments at Farnham Road, Bishop's Stortford (42/W), 1996 *A. R. Outen*; and as a pavement weed at Welwyn Garden City Hospital (21/K), 1997 *T. J.*

Geranium robustum Kuntze
South African Crane's-bill
Introduced: casual.
First record: 1994.

This became established for a while from an unknown source at South Road Nurseries, Bishop's Stortford (42/V), 1994-96 *S. Watson* (det. B. Smith) (Hb. HTN).

Geranium columbinum L.   Herts Vulnerable
Long-stalked Crane's-bill   (Herts Rare?)
Native.
First record: 1838.
Tetrad occurrence: 6 (1%).
Decreased sharply (-54%).

This attractive crane's-bill is native on thin, friable soils over Chalk, often on the edges of disturbed fields or cleared areas. The only such sites where it has been recorded recently (rarely) are chalky field margins adjoining Benington High Wood (22/W), 1993 *G. P. Smith*; field margins by Dawley Warren (21/S), 1990, 1993 *A. M. Boucher* and 2008 *J. Moss*; rabbit-disturbed banks by the old railway at Widford Valley (41/D), 1992 *S. Watson* (where it could not be re-found, 2008); rough grassland by Waterford Marsh (31/C), 1988 (record from the former Nature Conservancy Council). It was also seen on a disturbed railway bank near Welwyn Garden City Station (21/G), 1992 *A. M. B*; and one plant appeared in arable near Graveley (22/P), 2007 *R. Keen/T. J.* Before the survey, it had also been seen at Gravel Hill, Offley (12/P), 1978 *T. J.*; track by Batch Wood (10/J), 1981 *J. Foster*; Cassiobury (09/Y), 1973 *K. Preston-Mafham*; and at Aldenham (19/S), 1981 *O. Linford*. It seems to be disappearing owing to the effects of modern agriculture on the one hand, with the over-fertilising and weed-killing of field margins; and over-growth of rough areas of old grassland and open scrub on the other.

(12 tetrads: Dony, 1967; 16 tetrads: 1950-1986)

Geranium dissectum L.
Cut-leaved Crane's-bill
Introduced: archaeophyte.
First record: 1814.
Tetrad occurrence: 467 (95%).
Stable or slightly increased (+2%).

This weed of arable field margins, secondary grassland and disturbed ground is well able to tolerate the fertilisers and other pollutants we now spread around, and so it remains one of the ubiquitous plants of ruderal habitats.
(435 tetrads: Dony, 1967; 438 tetrads: 1950-1967)

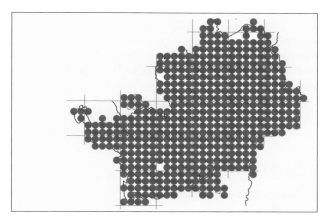

Map 416. *Geranium dissectum.*

Geranium pyrenaicum Burman *f.*
Hedgerow Crane's-bill
Introduced: neophyte.
First record: *c.*1820.
Tetrad occurrence: 179 (37%).
Increased (+119%).

An attractive, but rather unpredictable plant of rough grassy road banks and waste places on neutral or somewhat calcareous, well-drained soils. Its occurrence in such sites, and its absence in more natural habitats, would lend support to the now accepted view of this being a long-standing introduction. It occasionally appears with pale lilac or almost white flowers, which appears to be an increasing recent escape from gardens.
(78 tetrads: Dony, 1967; 91 tetrads: 1950-1986)

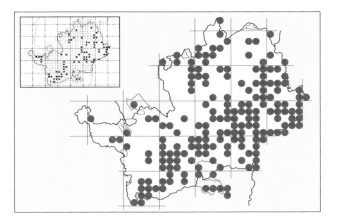

Map 417. *Geranium pyrenaicum.*

Geranium pusillum L.
Small-flowered Crane's-bill
Native.
First record: 1839.
Tetrad occurrence: 123 (25%).
Increased (+149%).

This is a plant of rather dry, short grassland or a colonist of bare ground on gravelly, sandy or sometimes chalky soils. It was rather local in the 1960s (Dony, 1967), unless it had been overlooked, but was quite widespread in the 19th century (Pryor, 1887). It now seems to have greatly consolidated its occurrence on new road banks, by abandoned gravel pits, and in thin lawns across the County, especially on fluvo-glacial gravels around Hertford and Welwyn, and in the Colne valley; and on glacial gravels at Hitchin.
(47 tetrads: Dony, 1967; 74 tetrads: 1950-1986)

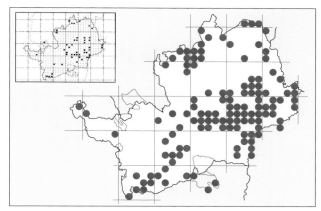

Map 418. *Geranium pusillum.*

Geranium molle L.
Dove's-foot Crane's-bill
Native.
First record: 1814.
Tetrad occurrence: 349 (71%).
Increased (+27%).

Dove's-foot Crane's-bill is more a plant of established, neutral grassland, such as mown roadsides around villages and towns, although it does also appear in bare, colonising habitats. It is also able to withstand some 'improvement' and eutrophication, which probably accounts for it having spread greatly on the Chalk in northern Hertfordshire, and having taken a greater hold on grasslands in the rest of the County.
(262 tetrads: Dony, 1967; 293 tetrads: 1950-1986)

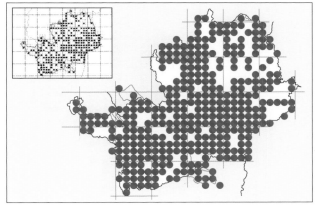

Map 419. *Geranium molle.*

Geranium lucidum L.
Shining Crane's-bill
Probably introduced [native in the U.K.].
First record: 1843.
Tetrad occurrence: 41 (8%).
Increased (+200%).

Earlier botanists considered this to be native in the County, but 19th century records scarcely bear this out. Dony (1967) was more cautious, calling it a 'denizen'. Most of the present records suggest strongly that it is a garden escape, as it can become quite a weed in cobbled paths, and on walls, but is rarely able to compete with native vegetation locally. It is, however, slowly increasing, from the rather low base recorded by Dony, probably only limited by its need for somewhat moist conditions.
(13 tetrads: Dony, 1967; 20 tetrads: 1950-1986)

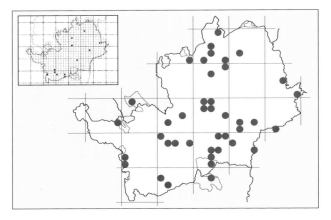

Map 420. *Geranium lucidum.*

Geranium robertianum L.
Herb Robert
Native.
First record: 1814.
Tetrad occurrence: 456 (93%).
Stable: no measurable change.

A familiar plant of shady hedgerows and woodlands, this can occur both in certain types of ancient woodlands, with deep loam on somewhat damp soils, as well as often abundantly under secondary plantation. It also occurs sometimes as a weed of cultivation, and can take off in its other 'natural' habitat, stonework, by buildings, on old walls, in cobbles and so on.
(433 tetrads: Dony, 1967; 441 tetrads: 1950-1986)

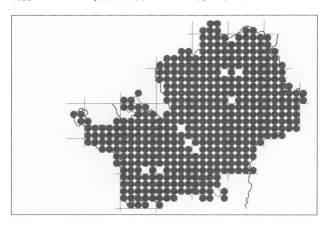

Map 421. *Geranium robertianum.*

Geranium phaeum L.
Dusky Crane's-bill
Introduced: neophyte.
First record: 1840.
Tetrad occurrence: 5 (1%).

At one time quite a frequent and often well-established escape from cultivation, in meadows, copses and road verges, but now becoming rare. A long-standing colony at Clothall (23/Q), first found in a meadow in 1915 (Dony, 1967), survived as a remnant on a road verge until at least 1988 *T. J.*, but appears to have succumbed to over-zealous road verge 'management' since. It has also been present in a damp wood and meadow near Sopwell Mill (10/M) since at least 1958, and was seen there in 1988 *J. Foster*. A colony known to A. W. Graveson at Benington in the 1930s (Dony, ms. index) might have been the same that was found by a lane near Benington Pond (22/W), 1983 *J. W. James*. However, the other three recent records: from Patmore Heath (42/M), 1989 *S. Watson*; from grassland at Rothamsted (11/G), 1989, 2004 *I. G. Denholm*; and from the towpath of the Grand Union Canal, West Hyde (09/K), 2003 *P. J. Ellison* are of unknown longevity.

Genus: *Erodium*

Erodium stephanianum Willd.
Introduced: casual.
First (only) record: 1973.

This Asian species was with other stork's-bills as a wool-shoddy alien at Newnham (23/N), 1973 *C. G. Hanson* (Dony, 1975).

Erodium botrys (Cav.) Bertol.
Mediterranean Stork's-bill
Introduced: casual.
First record: 1928.

At one time a apparently a fairly frequent casual derived from wool shoddy use on arable fields in north Herts. (Dony, 1967). It was first seen at Great Wymondley (TL22) in 1928-9 *J. E. Little* (Dony, ms. index), and was last seen at Newnham (23/N), 1973 *C. G. Hanson*.

Erodium brachycarpum (Godron) Thell.
Hairy-pitted Stork's-bill
Introduced: casual.
First record: *c.*1960.

Dony (1967) noted this as a 'regular wool adventive', along with other alien stork's-bills, but apparently kept no detailed records. There were two later records in similar circumstances: cabbage field at Great Wymondley (22/J), 1972; and arable at Newnham (23/N), 1973 *C. G. Hanson*.

Erodium crinitum Carolin
Eastern Stork's-bill
Introduced: casual.
First record: 1924.

Likewise, this was supposed to be a regular wool alien (Dony, 1967), but he gave no detailed records. However, he did refer two early records from Great Wymondley by J. E. Little (originally identified as *E. cygnorum*) to this species. It was also positively identified at Newnham (23/N), 1973 *C. G. Hanson* (Hb. HTN).

Erodium cygnorum Nees
Western Stork's-bill
Introduced: casual.
First record: 1973?

Assuming Little's two records of this are incorrect, the only record in the 'wild' for this is from Newnham (23/N), 1973 *C. G. Hanson*. However, it has become a persistent weed in a garden at Ware (31/S), 1999, *etc. C. G. H.* (Hb. HTN), and may spread. The latter has been attributed to ssp. *glandulosum* Carolin.

Erodium moschatum (L.) L'Hér.
Musk Stork's-bill
Introduced: archaeophyte.
First record: 1847.
Tetrad occurrence: 9 (2%).

This rather attractive stork's-bill appears to be increasing slowly in its favoured habitat of short, sometimes slightly damp grassland on sandy or gravelly soils, although, because Dony did not keep detailed records, it is not possible to judge precisely. Its first record was also 1847, by R. H. Webb (Pryor, 1887), not 1843, as given by Dony (1967). It is apparently established in several places from Ware south in the Lea valley, and a location at Welwyn Garden City (21/L) appears to have been occupied since at least 1963; it was also recorded as abundant there in 1999 *A. M. Boucher*. However, it no longer occurs as a wool alien, in which habitat it was last seen at Newnham (23/N), 1973 *C. G. Hanson*.

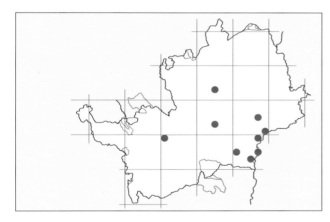

Map 422. *Erodium moschatum.*

Erodium cicutarium (L.) L'Hér.
Common Stork's-bill
Native.
First record: 1814.
Tetrad occurrence: 69 (14%).
Increased (+42%).

A plant of bare, often sandy or somewhat chalky ground, by roads, in mown grassland, and colonising gravel pits. It is widespread on peri-glacial and alluvial sands and gravels around Hertford and Ware, and in gravel pits in the Ver/Colne system. In north Herts., it has increased on thin glacial material over Chalk in several areas, as well as in ruderal habitats around villages.
(46 tetrads: Dony, 1967; 70 tetrads: 1950-1986)

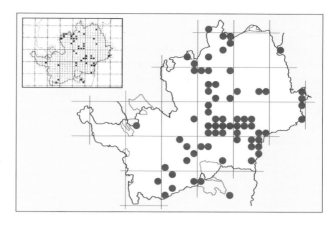

Map 423. *Erodium cicutarium.*

Limnanthaceae (Meadow-foam family)

Genus: *Limnanthes*

Limnanthes douglasii R. Br.
Meadow-foam
Introduced: casual.
First (only) record: 1996.

A few self-sown examples of this American plant were found among the graves at Potters Bar Cemetery (20/K) (VC21 [Herts.]) *A. M. Boucher* (Burton, 1997).

Tropaeolaceae (Nasturtiums)

Genus: *Tropaeolum*

Tropaeolum majus L.
Nasturtium
Introduced: casual.
First record: 1973.

This has occurred as a casual on waste tips, the first record being from Cole Green tip (21/Q), 1973 *C. G. Hanson*. It was last recorded at Pole Hole tip (41/L), 1989 *S. Watson*.

Tropaeolum peregrinum L.
Canary-creeper
Introduced: casual.
First (only) record: 1979.

The only record is from Waterford tip (31/C) *C. G. Hanson*.

Balsaminaceae (Balsam family)

Genus: *Impatiens*

Impatiens capensis Meerb.
Orange Balsam
Introduced: neophyte.
First record: [1821?] 1875.
Tetrad occurrence: 54 (11%).
Increased (+72%).

This is confined to the borders of rivers and streams, growing usually with sedges or Reed Sweet-grass, *etc*. Although there is an early specimen in Hb. LTN from 'Harewood', 1821, whose location is uncertain, it was first properly recorded in Herts. by the Grand Union Canal near Hunton Bridge, 1875 (Pryor, 1887). It then spread throughout the Bourne and Grand Union Canal system by the 1960s, and first appeared in the Lea Valley near Dobbs Weir (30/Z), and Amwell (31/R), 1977 *A. M. Boucher* (having been just in Essex the year before). It had arrived at Purwell Meadows, in the Hiz catchment (22/E) by 1993 *Mrs. Mitchell*, although has not yet spread much; and finally appeared upstream in the Stort valley at Sawbridgeworth Marsh (41/X), 2003 *S. Watson*.
(30 tetrads: Dony, 1967; 34 tetrads: 1950-1986)

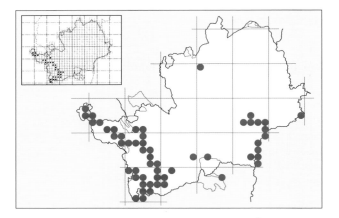

Map 424. *Impatiens capensis.*

Impatiens parviflora DC.
Small Balsam
Introduced: neophyte.
First record: 1874.
Tetrad occurrence: 51 (10%)
Stable or slightly increased (+11%).

This has established itself especially in wooded gardens and secondary woodland in west Herts., as well as similar habitat in the Lea Valley. Its casual occurrences elsewhere, however, seem to have declined, so that its core distribution is only slightly wider now than it was in the 1960s.
(44 tetrads: Dony, 1967; 56 tetrads: 1950-1986)

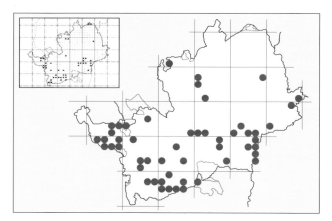

Map 425. *Impatiens parviflora.*

Impatiens glandulifera Royle
Indian (*or* Himalayan) Balsam
Introduced: neophyte.
First record: 1932.
Tetrad occurrence: 124 (25%).
Increasing (+209%).

Occurs in swampy ground by rivers, in wet woodland and by lakes, sometimes as a casual on waste ground elsewhere. Unfortunately the hope (Dony, 1967) that it would not spread further was in vain. It has strongly consolidated its position in the Lea and Stort Valleys, and has spread to west and north Herts. However, it only occasionally forms dominant stands, as long as river banks are not disturbed by dredging, which was formerly its main agent of spread.
(38 tetrads: Dony, 1967; 74 tetrads: 1950-1986)

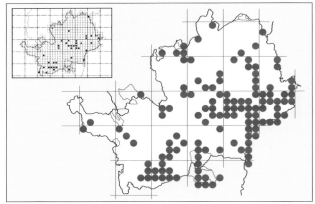

Map 426. *Impatiens glandulifera.*

Araliaceae (Ivy family)

Genus: *Hedera*

Hedera colchica (K. Koch) K. Koch
Persian Ivy
Introduced: neophyte.
First record: 1995.
Tetrad occurrence: 7 (1%).
Increasing.

The variegated form is an attractive but aggressive invader of waste ground and roadside hedges, if allowed out of the gardens in which it is so frequently planted. It was first noted in the 'wild' by a track near Sarratt Mill (09/J), 1995 *T. J.*, where it was already rampant. It has since been noted at a range of other sites, usually, but not always, near houses.

Hedera helix L.
Ivy
Native.
First record: 1742.
Tetrad occurrence: 475 (97%).
Probably stable (-2%).

This is an ubiquitous climber across the County, on roadside hedges, trees, in secondary woodland, scrub and on buildings. Only in ancient semi-natural woodland and on heaths does it tend not to occur. Its ripe berries are an important source of food for birds in late winter, and its autumn flowers are important for insects needing nectar late in the season. There may have been a tendency for it to become more dominant in many ruderal habitats recently, although this has not affected its overall frequency of occurrence.

(458 tetrads: Dony, 1967; 460 tetrads: 1950-1986)

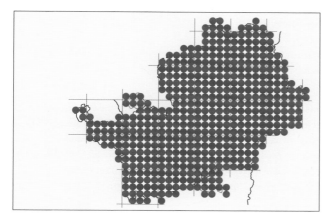

Map 427. *Hedera helix.*

The usual form is ssp. *helix*, but the cultivar 'Hibernica' of ssp. *hibernica* (G. Kirchn.) DC (**Irish Ivy**) (Map 427a) is also frequent, especially around towns, where it has long been used as a rather sombre ground-cover, as opposed to climbing plant, in shrubberies, from which it rapidly escapes into scrub and secondary woodland. First formally recorded as an escape at Berkhamsted (90/Z), 1988 *P. and S. Kingsbury*; it has been recorded from 25 tetrads, but is probably overlooked elsewhere. It is taxonomically separate from wild ssp. *hibernica* proper and should not be confused with that native ivy of western Britain's maritime cliffs.

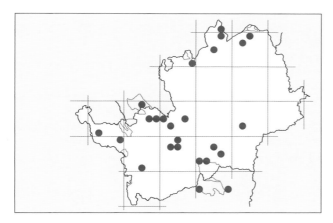

Map 427a. *Hedera helix* 'Hibernica'.

Apiaceae (Carrot family)

Genus: *Hydrocotyle*

Hydrocotyle vulgaris L.
Marsh Pennywort
Native.
First record: 1838.
Tetrad occurrence: 8 (2%).
Decreasing (-33%).

In the 1960s this was already a rare species of natural bogs in a number of long-known locations, mainly in south Hertfordshire, often on peat over spring seepages. It is now steadily decreasing as these habitats are being damaged by drainage, 'improvements', and pond-dredging. It was recorded from eight localities during the survey, but at least one of these sites, by Nyn Pond, Northaw (20/R) is known to have been damaged by over-raised water levels since it was last seen there in 1989 *T. J.*

(11 tetrads: Dony, 1967; 13 tetrads: 1950-1986)

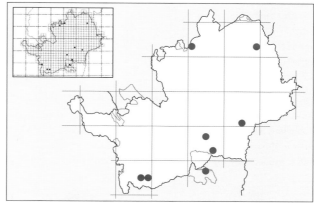

Map 428. *Hydrocotyle vulgaris.*

Hydrocotyle ranunculoides L. *f.*
Floating Pennywort
Introduced: neophyte.
First record: 1999.

This pernicious, mat-forming weed of open water in slow-moving rivers and ponds first made its unwelcome appearance in the River Stort at Town Meads, Bishop's Stortford and above South Mill Lock (42/V), 1999 *B. Tranter*. There were unconfirmed reports from elsewhere along the Stort later, and it had appeared in two ponds at Monken Hadley (29/N), by 2003 *T. J.* (VC21 [Herts: 1904-1965]).

Genus: *Sanicula*

Sanicula europaea L.
Sanicle
Native.
First record: *c.*1730.
Tetrad occurrence: 161 (33%).
Decreasing (-20%).

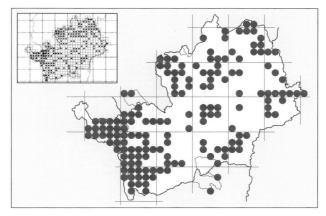

Map 429. *Sanicula europaea.*

An attractive woodland herb on more-or-less calcareous soils, often under Beech. It appears to be holding its ground on the Clay-with-Flints and Chalk of west Herts., but has retreated in north-east Herts., mainly as a result of the steady eutrophication of small coppices in this area, giving way to Nettles and Dog's Mercury. (192 tetrads: Dony, 1967; 203 tetrads: 1950-1986)

Genus: *Chaerophyllum*

Chaerophyllum temulum L.
Rough Chervil
Native.
First record: 1814.
Tetrad occurrence: 389 (79%).
Decreasing (-14%).

A frequent plant of shady, moderately nutrient-enriched hedge banks, scrub and roadsides. It appears to have started to decrease somewhat, possibly owing to competition from Nettles and rank herbs in the increasingly-enriched habitat it favours. (428 tetrads: Dony, 1967; 432 tetrads: 1950-1986)

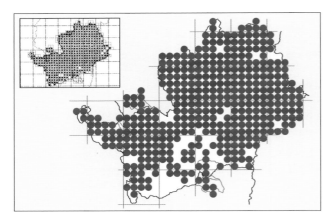

Map 430. *Chaerophyllum temulum.*

Genus: *Anthriscus*

Anthriscus sylvestris (L.) Hoffm.
Cow Parsley
Native.
First record: 1750.
Tetrad occurrence: 483 (98%).
Stable (-1%).

Almost ubiquitous in rank, nutrient-enriched roadsides,

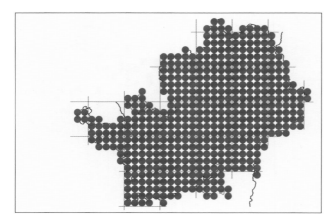

Map 431. *Anthriscus sylvestris.*

hedgerows, scrub and secondary woodland across the County on all soils, also increasingly in ancient woodland. It has increased massively in quantity since the 1960s in many places, although it was always common, and this does not show up at the tetrad level. (463 tetrads: Dony, 1967; 464 tetrads: 1950-1986)

Anthriscus caucalis M. Bieb.
Bur Chervil
Native.
First record: 1838.
Tetrad occurrence: 12 (2%).
Increased? (+60%).

This has always been a rather scarce plant in the County, occurring mainly on bare sandy ground in the Hertford/Ware area, but also rarely on sandy material over Chalk in north Herts. and on river gravels elsewhere. However, it is easily overlooked, and may not actually have increased as much as the records suggest. (7 tetrads: Dony, 1967; 13 tetrads: 1950-1986)

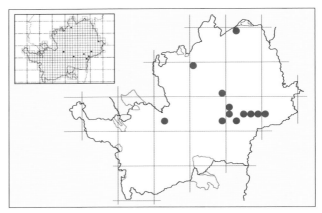

Map 432. *Anthriscus caucalis.*

Anthriscus cerefolium (L.) Hoffm.
Garden Chervil
Introduced: casual.
First record: *c.*1880.

In addition to the old records given in Pryor (1887), it also occurred at Little Amwell (31/K), 1914; occasionally at Hitchin (12/Z), 1922-1931; *J. E. Little*; and Norton (23/H) *c.*1920 *T. A. Dymes* (Hb. HTN). There are no recent records.

Genus: *Scandix*

Scandix pecten-veneris L.   UK Critically Endangered
Shepherd's-needle
Introduced: archaeophyte.
First record: 1733.
Tetrad occurrence: 23 (5%).
Decreased markedly (-71%).

This attractive, if potentially noxious arable weed was considered to be all but extinct by the late 1970s, but notices of its demise were rather premature. It became increasingly recorded again in various localities during the 1980s, and the recent survey found it rarely, but widely spread across much of its former range, with a concentration on the chalky Boulder Clay in north-east Herts., where it can sometimes be abundant, such as the massive colony extending over about ½ a mile found near Scales Park (43/B, C, H), 1993, 1995 *S. Watson*; *M. Gurney/T. J./G. P. Smith.*

(77 tetrads: Dony, 1967; 83 tetrads: 1950-1986)

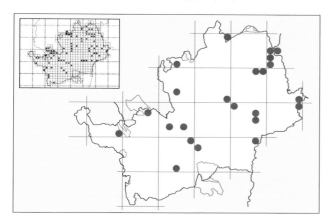

Map 433. *Scandix pecten-veneris.*

Genus: *Myrrhis*

Myrrhis odorata (L.) Scop.
Sweet Cicely
Introduced: neophyte.
First record: 1953.
Tetrad occurrence: 4 (<1%).
Increasing? (+100%).

This handsome plant of mountain meadows is limited by climate
in our part of the country. It survived in the damp scrub on
Norton Common (23/B), where it was first found (Dony, 1967),
the most recent record being 1994 *T. J.* It was also reported to
Dony at Bulbourne (91/G), 1957 *J. Harper* (Dony, ms. index),
and became established at Castle Hill, Berkhamsted (90/Z),
1986 *P. J. Kingsbury*. During the survey, apart from Norton
Common, it was also found at Harpenden Common (11/G), 1989
I. G. Denholm; Bower Heath (11/N), 1995 *T. J.*; and Appspond
(10/C), 1997 *G. Salisbury*. Most of these sites are within the higher
rainfall area adjoining the Chilterns. The sources of introduction
are unknown.

Genus: *Coriandrum*

Coriandrum sativum L.
Coriander
Introduced: casual.
First record: 1873.

This occurs quite frequently on tips and as a bird-seed alien on
waste ground, although its occurrence on waste tips has decreased
as waste management has improved. It was recorded during the
survey from Ware tip (31/M), 1987 *C. G. Hanson*; Rye Meads
Sewage Works (31/V), 1996 *C. G. Hanson*; and a farm dump,
Newgate Street (20/X), 1998 *J. Crew*.

Genus: *Smyrnium*

Smyrnium olusatrum L.
Alexanders
Introduced: archaeophyte.
First record: 1824.
Tetrad occurrence: 11 (2%).
Increasing (+450%).

This has been a feature of a few places as a long-established

escape from cultivation for a very long time, such as around Pirton
(13/K), where it was first noted in 1841, and by the old North
Road at Baldock (23/M), where it was present *c.*1840, although it
comes and goes even in these sites. It is now beginning to appear
by major roads in a few places, encouraged by salt, as well as in
apparently new village locations.
(2 tetrads: Dony, 1967; 8 tetrads: 1950-1986)

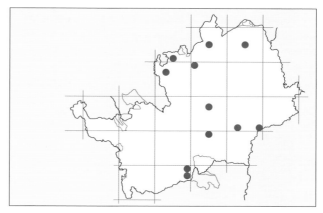

Map 434. *Smyrnium olusatrum.*

Genus: *Bunium*

Bunium bulbocastanum L.   Herts Vulnerable?
Great Pignut
Native.
First record: 1840.
Tetrad occurrence: 9 (2%).
Decreasing (-44%).

This local plant of rough chalk grassland is especially important
in Hertfordshire, as the only area in which it occurs in Britain is
along the Chiltern and East Anglian Heights Chalk ridge. It was

Great Pignut Bunium bulbocastanum *Whiteley Hill, Barkway, 1977.*

formerly also an arable weed, but has long ceased to be so in our area. Owing to the small size of almost all its populations in the County, the species is extremely vulnerable, because plants are often limited to narrow strips of ancient chalky banks by roads. Quite apart from direct destruction from road works, they are also prone to scrub encroachment, and especially from increased pollution from the road, including both traffic exhausts and especially over-liberal dosing with salt. Another threat might also be to successful germination because of climate warming, as it germinates strongly following sharp winter frosts, which may be necessary for its re-appearance.

(15 tetrads: Dony, 1967; 19 tetrads: 1950-1986)

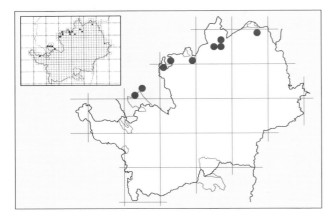

Map 435. *Bunium bulbocastanum.*

Genus: *Conopodium*

Conopodium majus (Gouan) Loret
Pignut
Native.
First record: *c.*1820.
Tetrad occurrence: 252 (51%).
Stable? (-1%).

This is a characteristic plant of free-draining loam soils in ancient woodland and old grassland, especially on the Clay-with-Flints. Its occurrence in places in north-east Hertfordshire, formerly thought to have been on Boulder Clay, has now often been demonstrated to represent outlying exposures of the underlying Clay-with-Flints deposits. While its woodland sites have remained stable, its occurrences in old grassland have decreased, as this habitat has been systematically destroyed since the 1960s.

(242 tetrads: Dony, 1967; 261 tetrads: 1950-1986)

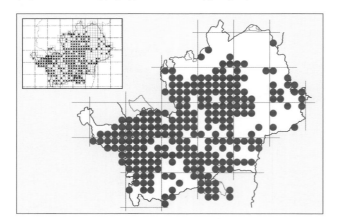

Map 436. *Conopodium majus.*

Genus: *Pimpinella*

Pimpinella major (L.) Hudson
Greater Burnet-saxifrage
Native.
First record: 1748.
Tetrad occurrence: 99 (20%).
Stable or slightly decreasing (-5%).

Occasional in rough grassland, on roadsides and in ditches, by woods and in green lanes, usually on a damp clay soil, but not always so. As Dony (1967) found, it has a peculiar distribution, with a primary population centred on the Boulder Clay, but with other local centres, such as on the London Clay in south Hertfordshire, and on damp alluvium over gravel around St Albans and neighbouring areas. Given the greater level of recording, the similar number of tetrad records may reflect a slight decrease.

(99 tetrads: Dony, 1967; 108 tetrads: 1950-1986)

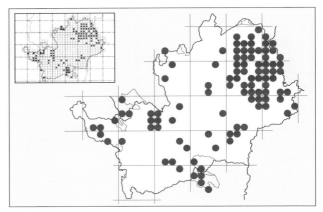

Map 437. *Pimpinella major.*

Pimpinella saxifraga L.
Burnet-saxifrage
Native.
First record: 1819.
Tetrad occurrence: 328 (67%).
Decreasing (-17%).

A plant of thin, nutrient-poor grassland on more or less calcareous soils. It shows signs of having diminished markedly around the more heavily urban parts of the County, as well as retreating in more intensive arable areas. On road verges, its occurrence has

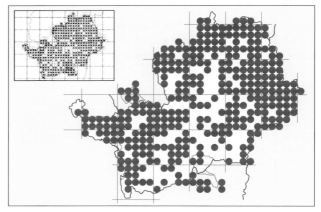

Map 438. *Pimpinella saxifraga.*

declined markedly as they become dominated by rank herbs. Quite often it is increasingly limited to old lawns and churchyards. (376 tetrads: Dony, 1967; 389 tetrads: 1950-1986)

Genus: *Aegopodium*

Aegopodium podagraria L.
Ground Elder
Introduced: archaeophyte.
First record: 1814.
Tetrad occurrence: 432 (88%).
Probably slightly decreased (-9%).

While this may have been a culinary herb at one time, it is now a very persistent weed of disturbed ground, in gardens, on road verges and waste ground. Despite this, it shows signs of some decrease, especially in the more open, arable landscapes, where it may have succumbed to mechanical hedge trimming and tidying. (449 tetrads: Dony, 1967; and from 1950-1986)

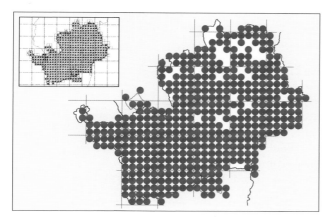

Map 439. *Aegopodium podagraria.*

Genus: Sium

Sium latifolium L.   UK Endangered
Greater Water-parsnip
Native, or introduced? [native in the U.K.].
First confirmed record: (1911?) 1965.

This is an enigmatic plant in Hertfordshire. Blackstone (1746) had recorded it from the 'Harefield River', but other early botanists did not find it across the County boundary here in Herts. (Webb and Coleman, 1849), although there are records from Harefield up to at least 1945, and there is a record from Tolpits Lake (09/X), 1911 in the U.K. Biological Records Centre database. It was also reported from the banks of the River Stort at Bishop's Stortford, 1910 by H. F. Hayllar (Hayllar diary, North Herts. Museums), and included in a list of local plants by the Bishop's Stortford Natural History Society in 1951 (Dony, ms. index). However, Dony dismissed these records as errors, and there do not appear to be supporting specimens, although the Tolpits Lake record at least is quite likely to be correct. D. H. Kent then discovered it by the lake at Rydal Mount School, Potters Bar (20/K) (VC21 [Herts.]) (Hb. HTN) (Dony, 1967), where Dony supposed it to have been planted, although there is no evidence of this. It probably still occurs here, having last been recorded in 1986 *I. D. Marshall* (Hb. HTN).

Genus: *Berula*

Berula erecta (Hudson) Cov.
Lesser Water-parsnip
Native.
First record: 1822.
Tetrad occurrence: 61 (12%).
Increased (+65%).

This is a plant of flowing calcareous streams, ditches and river margins, and occasionally by old flooded gravel pits, where it is usually an indicator of good water quality. This is encouraging, as it has shown signs of re-appearing in previously quite polluted lower stretches of rivers and streams, especially the Lea. (35 tetrads: Dony, 1967; 47 tetrads: 1950-1986)

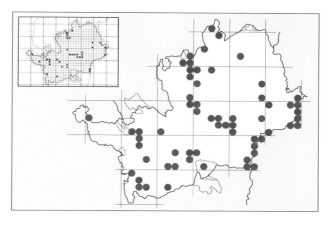

Map 440. *Berula erecta.*

Genus: *Seseli*

Seseli libanotis (L.) Koch   UK Near Threatened
Moon-carrot   Herts Extinct
Native.
First record: 1841.

This rare plant of ancient chalk grassland was only ever known from Arbury Banks, Ashwell (23/U), and was last recorded as

Moon Carrot Seseli libanotis *Arbury Banks, Ashwell, 1974.*

a single specimen struggling against rank herbage and scrub in 1976 *B. R. Sawford*. The habitat has since continued to degrade, having been firstly adjacent to intensive arable farming, and later enclosed and heavily disturbed by cattle.

Genus: *Oenanthe*

Oenanthe fistulosa L.   UK Vulnerable
Tubular Water-dropwort
Native.
First record: 1737.
Tetrad occurrence: 6 (1%).
Decreased (-37%).

This has always been rather a rare plant of two different habitats: fen dykes or peaty ground around springs; and the margins of ponds on moderately acidic clay. It is steadily disappearing from all but the most well-managed sites, and was only recorded during the survey from sites in six tetrads: spring pool, Purwell Meadows (22/E), 1989 *T. J.*, 1996 *B. Hedley* and 2009 *A. Harris/T. J. et al.*; Tednambury Meadows (41/Y), 1990 *S. Watson*; Heath Farm Pond, Breachwood Green (12/L), 1993 *T. J.*, where it appeared following clearance of the pond; pond in Burleigh Meadow, Knebworth (22/G), various dates; ditch, Knebworth Park (22/F), 1994 *G. P. Smith*; and Rye Meads (31/V), 1995 *G. J. White*. (9 tetrads: Dony, 1967; 10 tetrads: 1950-1986)

Oenanthe pimpinelloides L.   Herts Extinct?
Corky-fruited Water-dropwort
Native.
First record: (1925?) 1962.

A very rare plant of unimproved damp or dry neutral grassland, hay meadows or horse-pastures, usually on gravelly or sandy substrates. There was a record, unsupported by a specimen, from Water End, Gaddesden (TL01), 1925, in the diary of Mrs R. I. Sworder (Dony, ms. index), but the species was finally confirmed for the County at Bulls Mill (31/C) in 1962 by A. R. Paterson (Dony, 1967). As Hertfordshire is on the very edge of its U.K. range, it has probably always been rare, and despite a lack of further records may still re-appear.

Oenanthe lachenalii C. Gmelin   Herts Rare
Parsley Water-dropwort
Native.
First record: 1841.

This used to be a feature of a number of ancient grazing commons on the Chalk Marl or the Gault Clay in northern Hertfordshire. Its last known site is Norton Common, Letchworth (23/B), where it has remained frequent in a small area on the main marsh, just as Dony knew it, thanks to concerted conservation effort over a long period.

Oenanthe crocata L.
Hemlock Water-dropwort
Native.
First record: (1840?) *c.*1950.
Tetrad occurrence: 10 (2%).
Increasing (+233%).

A rare, but increasing native of river and canal-sides and other wet places. R. H. Webb thought he had found this at Rickmansworth as long ago as 1840 (Webb and Coleman, 1849), but it was not

confirmed. It was then recorded at Watford and Rickmansworth by D. H. Kent (Kent and Lousley, 1953), as well as at Sarratt Bottom by R. F. Turney about the same time, although Dony (1967) omitted the latter record. It has now consolidated its position in the Colne and Gade valleys, and has also extended its range in the Lea Valley gravel pits. A record from a pond near Westmill (32/N), 1993 *S. Watson* may be of an introduction. (2 -3 tetrads: Dony, 1967 and from 1950-1986)

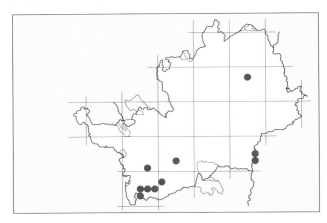

Map 441. *Oenanthe crocata.*

Oenanthe fluviatilis (Bab.) Coleman
River Water-dropwort
Native.
First record: 1843.
Tetrad occurrence: 16 (3%).
Probably decreased , if better recorded (+38%).

A mostly submerged aquatic plant of clean, nutrient-poor flowing waters, for which Hertfordshire has some responsibility, because

River Water-dropwort Oenanthe fluviatilis *Hertford, 1844.*
(W. H. Coleman specimen, North Herts. Museums)

it contains one of the larger populations left in England. It was also one of the areas in which Coleman originally recognised it as a species, and a specimen named by him survives in North Herts. Museums (HTN), originally from the herbarium of Haileybury College, 1844. However, although the plant was at one time quite widespread in rivers in southern Hertfordshire, it appears to have retreated from most of these, owing to eutrophication and low flows. It is now abundant only in the New River canal, from its source at Ware to Waltham Cross, where it leaves the County. Otherwise, the plant has recently been found in the R. Ash at Easneye (31/R, W) on various dates; in the Small Lea at Cheshunt and Waltham Cross (30/Q; 39/U), 1992, 1995 *A. M. Boucher*; in the Colne near Croxley Common Moor (09/X), 2003 *G. Hounsome*; and in the R. Beane at Waterford Marsh (31/C) on various dates. It was also recorded in the R. Beane at Goldings (31/B) 1986 *T. J.*; and in the R. Colne at Bushey Hall (19/D), 1984 *B. P. Pickess*. A detailed survey of the species carried out by Barry Tranter for Hertfordshire Biological Records Centre in 2004 failed to re-find it in the Small Lea, and in the Beane at Goldings, but did discover it in the Lea by Amwell Quarry (31/R), and from the Ash below Watersplace (31/X). Including the 2004 survey, it is now known from more tetrads in the County than in the 1960s, but this is almost certainly down to better recording.

(11 tetrads: Dony, 1967; 15 tetrads: 1950-1986)

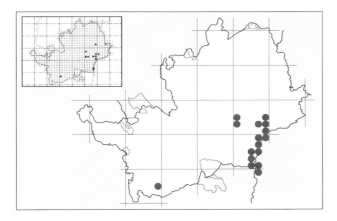

Map 442. *Oenanthe fluviatilis.*

Oenanthe aquatica (L.) Poiret   Herts Rare
Fine-leaved Water-dropwort
Native.
First record: 1824.
Tetrad occurrence: 2 (<1%).
Very rare and decreasing sharply (-69%).

Now a very rare plant of silted ponds on clay soils, tolerating some shading, but not heavy nutrient-enrichment. This was known by Dony (1967) from a number of ponds across central and southern Hertfordshire, and to earlier botanists from more. Quite a few of its previous sites were destroyed by the construction of Welwyn Garden City, but others seem to have succumbed either to the drying out, eutrophication or infilling of ponds, or to over-zealous pond management. It is now only known to occur in ponds at Watery Grove, Knebworth (22/G), various dates (very few non-flowering plants, 2009) *T. J.*; and at a pond in Bush Wood, Welham Green (20/H), 2003 *S. Murray/T. J.* (Hb. HTN), where it was known by earlier botanists. It appears to have been lost from the pond at Burleigh Meadow (22/G), where it was last seen in 1991 *T. J.*

(6 tetrads: Dony, 1967; 8 tetrads: 1950-1986)

Fine-leaved Water-dropwort Oenanthe aquatica *Watery Grove, Knebworth, 1991.*

Genus: *Aethusa*

Aethusa cynapium L.
Fool's Parsley
Native or introduced.
First record: 1819.
Tetrad occurrence: 407 (83%).
Decreasing (-14%).

A widespread and hitherto common weed of arable land, gardens and bare, waste places. It was once ubiquitous, but the recent survey has found that it appears to be retreating, especially from drier, gravel soils in the river valleys and south Herts. Its abundance has also been sharply reduced around arable fields elswewhere.

(447 tetrads: Dony, 1967; 449 tetrads: 1950-1986)

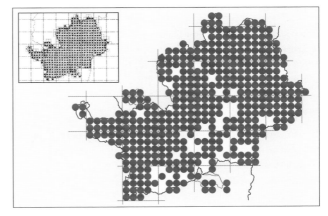

Map 443. *Aethusa cynapium.*

The usual plant appears to be ssp. *cynapium*. Ssp. *agrestis* (Wallr.) Dostál has only been positively identified once, at Harpenden (11/C), 1990 *J. F. Southey*, but may be widespread. The recently introduced ssp. *cynapioides* (M. Bieb.) Nyman was also found at Little Berkhamsted (20/Y), 2001 *T. J.* (Hb. HTN).

Genus: *Foeniculum*

Foeniculum vulgare Miller
Fennel
Introduced: archaeophyte.
First record: 1849.
Tetrad occurrence: 37 (8%).
Increased (+120%).

From having been quite a rare plant of railway banks and waste places, this appears to be steadily increasing by major roads and on waste ground, especially in south-east Hertfordshire.
(16 tetrads: Dony, 1967; 27 tetrads: 1950-1986)

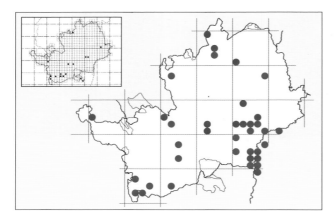

Map 444. *Foeniculum vulgare.*

Genus: *Anethum*

Anethum graveolens L.
Dill
Introduced: casual.
First record: 1920.

This was occasional as an escape on tips. It was recorded during the 1970s from several localities, but was last recorded at Rye Meads Sewage Works (31/V), 1982; and at Ware tip (31/M), 1984 *C. G. Hanson.*

Genus: *Silaum*

Silaum silaus (L.) Schinz and Thell.
Pepper-saxifrage
Native.
First record: *c.*1820.
Tetrad occurrence: 57 (12%).
Decreasing (-36%).

This is a particularly characteristic plant of old semi-natural neutral grassland on damp clay or alluvial soils, and as such its decrease clearly indicates the steady loss of this kind of grassland. It only remains abundant at a few major sites, such as Hunsdon Mead (41/A), and parts of King's Meads (31/L). Elsewhere, it may persist as a few plants in an otherwise degraded pasture, or in a road verge.
(84 tetrads: Dony, 1867; 111 tetrads: 1950-1986)

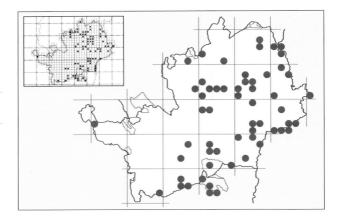

Map 445. *Silaum silaus.*

Genus: *Conium*

Conium maculatum L.
Hemlock
Introduced: archaeophyte.
First record: 1814.
Tetrad occurrence: 342 (70%).
Increased substantially (+117%).

Dony (1967) considered this to be especially found by rivers, perhaps owing to the prevalence of extreme dredging that once occurred, but Pryor (1887) and others considered it to be a waste ground, hedgerow and coppice woodland species. It is now often an abundant tall herb on waste ground, roadsides, tips and disturbed ground, especially on damp gravels or calcareous soils, where nutrient levels may be high.
(150 tetrads: Dony, 1967; 183 tetrads: 1950-1986)

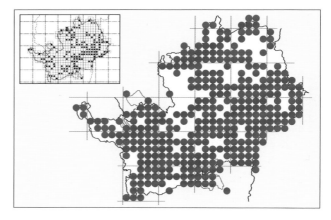

Map 446. *Conium maculatum.*

Genus: *Bupleurum*

Bupleurum petraeum L.
Rock Hare's-ear
Introduced: casual.
First (only) record: 1934.

The only record remains the casual occurrence on a waste tip at Welwyn (Dony, 1967).

Bupleurum rotundifolium L.   UK Critically Endangered
Thorow-wax   Herts Extinct
Introduced: archaeophyte.
First record: *c.*1730.

This was apparently never an especially common weed of
cornfields, except in certain places on the Chalk in north
Hertfordshire, such as fields west of Odsey. It had decreased
markedly before 1930; was last seen in any abundance near Lilley
Hoo (12/J) in 1934 *R. Morse* (Dony, ms. index); and last recorded
at Allen's Green (41/N), 1941 *H. W. Pugsley* (Dony, 1967).

Bupleurum subovatum Link ex Sprengel
False Thorow-wax
Introduced: casual.
First record: 1839.

Despite the statement by Dony (1967) that this had increased as
a bird-seed alien, there are few confirmed records. It was found
three times in the vicinity of Hitchin in the 1970s and early 1980s,
the last being from Ickleford (13/W), 1982 *H. Schearer* (det. T. J.)
(Hb. HTN). It was also grown from bird-seed at Ware (31/S), 1992
C. G. Hanson (Hb. HTN).

Genus: *Apium*

Apium graveolens L.
Celery
Introduced: casual.
First record: *c.*1840.

There is no evidence that genuine wild Celery has ever been
recorded in the County. Records in Pryor (1887) refer to
occurrences of the cultivar *dulce* (Miller) DC as an escape, and
there were one or two subsequent records of similar plants. There
are no recent records.

Apium nodiflorum (L.) Lagasca
Fool's Water-cress
Native.
First record: 1819.
Tetrad occurrence: 238 (49%).
Apparently increased (+14%).

A frequent plant of silted streams and ditches, river margins
and ponds on more or less calcareous substrates. This may have
genuinely increased, partly because it colonises new gravel pits
when colonisation has progressed, but also because it is able to

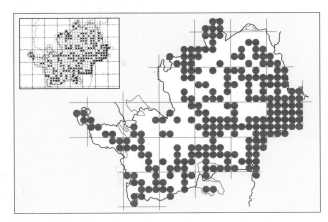

Map 447. *Apium nodiflorum.*

tolerate some eutrophication of watercourses.
(198 tetrads: Dony, 1967; 222 tetrads: 1950-1986)

Apium inundatum (L.) Reichb. *f.*   Herts Rare
Lesser Marshwort
Native.
First record: 1838.
Tetrad occurrence: 5 (1%).
Decreased (-33%).

A rare, but inconspicuous plant of the muddy margins of heathy
ponds. Never common, this has increasingly become restricted
to ponds on ancient commons. Its only known recent sites are:
pond, Rectory Lane Meadows, Shenley (10/V), 1992 *S. M. Hedley*
(Hb. HTN); Bride's Farm Pond, Hertford Heath (31/K), 1995
T. J. (Hb. HTN); pond on Bricket Wood Common (10/F), 1999
T. J./G. Salisbury/G. P. Smith; pond, Hadley Green (29/N) (VC21
[Herts. 1904-1965]), 2003 *T. J./G. Salisbury et al.*; pond on
Berkhamsted Common (00/E), 2004 *T. J./G. Salisbury et al.*
(6 tetrads: Dony, 1967; 7 tetrads: 1950-1986)

Genus: *Trachyspermum*

Trachyspermum ammi (L.) Sprague
Ajowan
Introduced: casual.
First record: 1965.

This is a rare casual of tips. Apart from an undocumented record
from 09/G (Burton, 1983), I have only received records since 1970
from Cole Green tip (21/Q), 1978 *C. G. Hanson* (det. J. G. Dony);
and Waterford tip (31/C), 1979, 1987 *C. G. H.* (det. E. J. Clement)
(Hb. Hanson).

Genus: *Petroselinum*

Petroselinum crispum (Mill.) Nym. ex A. W. Hill
Garden Parsley
Introduced: casual.
First record: *c.*1840.

Occasionally found as an escape from gardens, it was found in
five tetrads during the survey, the last being from a roadside at
Newnham (23/N), 1997 *T. J.*

Petroselinum segetum (L.) Koch
Corn Parsley
Native.
First record: 1841.
Tetrad occurrence: 13 (3%).
Increased? (+575%).

This was always a rather rare plant of bare, grassy banks on
dry, calcareous soils, often on road verges, but may have been
overlooked, because it can remain as a non-flowering rosette of
leaves in adverse conditions. It is mainly found on the Chalk in
north Hertfordshire, but was also found on a roadside at High
Wych (41/L), 1992 *S. Watson*; and in two localities by the M25
near Sarratt (09/N, P), 1991 *G. Salisbury/J. Saunders.*
(2 tetrads: Dony, 1967; 11 tetrads: 1950-1986)

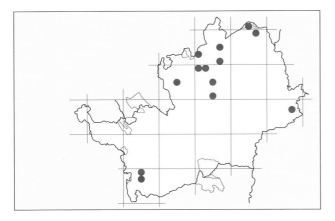

Map 448. *Petroselinum segetum.*

Ridolfia segetum (Guss.) Moris
False Fennel
Introduced: casual.
First record: 1926.

A rare casual from bird-seed on tips. It was found at Hitchin tip (13/V), 1973; Waterford tip (31/C), 1978, 1979; and in Welwyn Garden City (21/G), 1977 *C. G. Hanson* (det. E. J. Clement) (Hb. HTN).

Genus: *Sison*

Sison amomum L.
Stone Parsley
Native.
First record: 1822.
Tetrad occurrence: 155 (31%).
Increasing (+44%).

This is a plant of somewhat damp, usually neutral or mildly acidic clay soils, where it grows in tall herbs alongside scrub, particularly Blackthorn. It is mainly found in south Herts., and becomes rarer on the Chalk and on the drier Clay-with-Flints. It has increased particularly in northern Hertfordshire, perhaps reflecting nutrient enrichment of calcareous habitats.
(102 tetrads: Dony, 1967; 125 tetrads: 1950-1986)

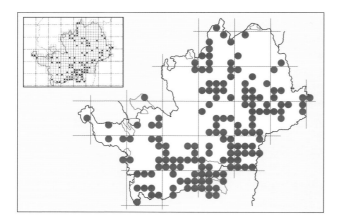

Map 449. *Sison amomum.*

Genus: *Cicuta*

Cicuta virosa L.   Herts Extinct
Cowbane
Native.
First record: 1625.

Apart from a very early record from Moor Park, all the historic sites for this were small swampy ponds in the Brickendon/ Wormley Wood area, where it was last seen in 1929 (Dony, 1967).

Genus: *Ammi*

Ammi visnaga (L.) Lam.
Toothpick Plant
Introduced: casual.
First record: *c.*1980?

There are tetrad records given for 30/N, U, without further details by Burton (1983). Otherwise, the only record is from Waterford tip (31/C), 1985 *C. G. Hanson* (det. E. J. Clement) (Hb. Hanson).

Ammi majus L.
Bullwort
Introduced: neophyte.
First record: 1876.
Tetrad occurrence: 5 (1%).
Increasing slightly?

This is now usually a casual of bird-seed origin, although Dony (1967) knew it as a wool-shoddy alien, but gave no detailed records. It was recorded as a wool alien at Newnham (23/N), 1973 *C. G. Hanson*. It was then found as a weed in a nursery at St Margaret's (31/Q), 1986 *A. M. Boucher*; and during the current survey was found at Sleapshyde, (20/D), 1988 *P. Brown* (det. Nat. Hist. Mus.); Bishop's Stortford (42/V), 1993 *J. L. Fielding* (Hb. HTN); Hitchin (12/Z), 1993 *A. M. B.*; Baldock (23/L), 1994 *B. R. Sawford* (Hb. HTN); and Verulamium Park (10/M), 1994 *A. M. B.*

Longleaf Falcaria vulgaris *Ash Hill, Ashwell, 1982.*

Photo: Brian Sawford

Genus: *Falcaria*

Falcaria vulgaris Bernh.
Longleaf
Introduced: neophyte.
First record: 1899.
Tetrad occurrence: 2 (<1%).
Decreased? (-33%).

This has never become a widespread plant. It occurs by hedges and in scrub or young plantations on Chalk. Having first been noticed at Hertford (Dony, ms. index), it became a feature of a short stretch of road verge at White Hall, Aston (22/V), *c.*1920 *A. W. Graveson*, where it remains, last having been recorded here in 2000 *T. J.* Dony (1967) also recorded it from Lilley Bottom (12/I); and from near Arbury Banks (23/U). It has subsequently become established at nearby Ash Hill, Ashwell (23/P), where, in 1996, it was plentiful in a new plantation *T. J.* It also appeared for a time at Reed Chalk Pit (33/N), 1978 *T. J.* (Hb. HTN), but did not apparently become established.
(3 tetrads: Dony, 1967; 5 tetrads:1950-1986)

Genus: *Carum*

Carum carvi L.
Caraway
Introduced: casual.
First record: *c.*1870.

In addition to the few records noted by Dony (1967), he also

reported it at St Ippollitts (12/Y), 1967. During the recent survey it has been found as a casual on a roadside spoil heap near Standon (42/A), 1987 *S. Watson*; and at Rye Meads Sewage Works (31/V), 1991 *C. G. Hanson* (det. E. J. Clement) (Hb. Hanson).

Genus: *Angelica*

Angelica archangelica L.
Garden Angelica
Introduced: neophyte.
First record: 2000.

One plant of this spectacular riverside herb was found by the Lee Navigation at Ware (31/M), 2000 *T. J.* (Hb. HTN), but not thereafter. Another plant was then found by the Tykes Water at Aldenham Country Park (19/S), 2001 *T. J.* As the plant is reasonably frequent by rivers and canals around London, it could spread.

Angelica sylvestris L.
Wild Angelica
Native.
First record: 1737.
Tetrad occurrence: 251 (51%).
Stable (+1%).

This is a plant of calcareous fen, damp woodland rides and riversides, occurring especially on the Boulder Clay in east Herts., and in river valleys elsewhere. The evidence for increase is slight, and may be down to better recording, in east Herts. especially.
(235 tetrads: Dony, 1967; 255 tetrads: 1950-1986)

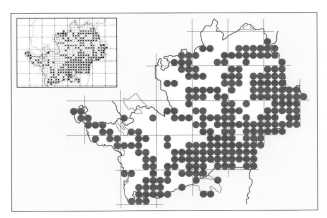

Map 450. *Angelica sylvestris.*

Genus: *Pastinaca*

Pastinaca sativa L.
Wild Parsnip
Native.
First record: 1820.
Tetrad occurrence: 115 (23%).
Decreasing (-20%).

A plant of rough calcareous grassland on downs, road verges, railway banks and similar localities. Although it has taken advantage of some of the recently constructed new roads across the County, its native strongholds on downland, railway banks and older road verges have often been lost to scrub growth or to over-mowing.
(137 tetrads: Dony, 1967; 157 tetrads: 1950-1986)

Garden Angelica Angelica archangelica, *R. Lea, Ware, 2000.*

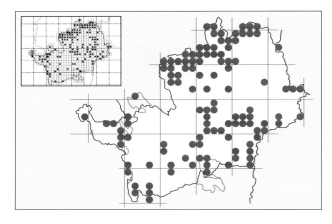

Map 451. *Pastinaca sativa.*

Genus: *Heracleum*

Heracleum sphondylium L.
Hogweed
Native.
First record: 1696.
Tetrad occurrence: 482 (98%).
Stable? (-1%).

An abundant tall herb of rank road verges, rough ground, railway banks, woodland rides and re-vegetated gravel pits. As such, it is an important nectar source for mid-summer insects. It remains fairly ubiquitous across the County, but may be retreating in favour of nettles in some of its steadily eutrophicating road verge sites, and to scrub overgrowth on railway banks.
(463 tetrads: Dony, 1967 and from 1950-1986)

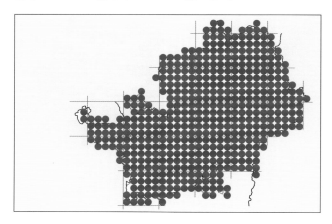

Map 452. *Heracleum sphondylium.*

'*Heracleum sphondylium* × *H. mantegazzianum*'

This hybrid, of now uncertain parentage, was recorded at Darlands Nature Reserve, Totteridge (29/L), 2002 *R. M. Burton*. It or others may well occur elsewhere.

Heracleum mantegazzianum auct.
Giant Hogweed
Introduced: neophyte.
First record: *c.*1950 (for the aggregate).
Tetrad occurrence: 71 (15%).
Increased.

Giant Hogweed has hitherto been regarded as one species: *H. mantegazzianum* Somm. and Lev. Sell and Murrell (2009)

have alerted us to the fact that there are possibly three different species masquerading under this name in Britain. The most widespread of these is probably *H. trachyloma* Fisch. and C. A. May **Giant Hogweed**, with basal leaves having broad overlapping segments and very hairy mature fruits. However, plants with lower leaves more narrowly lobed and less hairy mature fruits may be either *H. grossheimii* Manden. and Grossh. **Grossheim's Hogweed**, or *H. lehmannianum* Bunge **Lehmann's Hogweed**, both of which occur in Cambridgeshire, and the former of which has been identified from near Furneux Pelham, in Essex (Sell and Murrell, *op. cit.*). All of these plants are native of the Caucasus or western Asia area. Hertfordshire records have not as yet been assessed for any of these species, and therefore the following account has to be based on the aggregate, recorded under the erroneous name of '*H. mantegazzianum*', a plant that does not appear to occur in Britain at all. Dony (1967) only mentions these potentially quite noxious, if spectacular plants as occasional garden escapes. They had probably been cultivated in large estate parklands and gardens since the end of the 19th century, but no note of them having established themselves came until they were reported from Totteridge by D. J. Hinson, and from Furneux Pelham, Baldock and Bayfordbury shortly afterwards (Dony, ms. index). Plants were evidently well-established in a number of areas, especially on calcareous clays in north-east Herts., during the 1970s, such as in the Therfield and Sandon areas, and around Weston Park (where they had long been growing by the lake). They also continued to turn up in new sites, although some of these proved impermanent. During the recent survey, plants were found to be focused especially on the valleys of the rivers Rib, Beane, Quin, *etc.*, and their tributaries, where they have spread downstream with flood waters. They also occur on tips, and in some urban open spaces, notably in and around Stevenage. Recent systematic attempts to halt their spread on public health grounds may affect the species' future distribution and the occurrence of one or more of these taxa in the County.
(37 tetrads for the aggregate: 1950-1986)

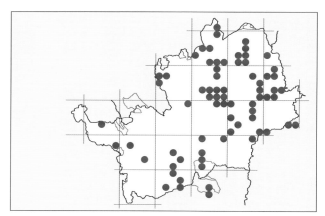

Map 453. *Heracleum mantegazzianum auct.*

Genus *Tordylium*

[*Tordylium maximum* L.
Hartwort
Introduced: casual.

This appeared spontaneously in a garden at Ware (31/S), 1996 *C. G. Hanson*, having been cultivated some time before. Unless it appears elsewhere it cannot be regarded as a true addition to the Hertfordshire flora.]

Torilis japonica (Houtt.) DC.
Upright Hedge-parsley
Native.
First record: 1822.
Tetrad occurrence: 398 (81%).
Apparently decreasing (-7%).

This is a familiar late-summer plant of rough grassland and scrub, woodland rides and waste ground. However, there is some evidence of a decline in both distribution and abundance. The relatively less rank, flower-rich rough grasslands that it favours are retreating in the face of rank vegetation dominated by Nettles and scrub.
(407 tetrads: Dony, 1967; 419 tetrads: 1950-1986)

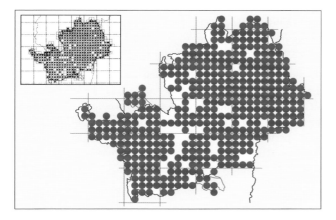

Map 454. *Torilis japonica.*

Torilis arvensis (Hudson) Link   UK Endangered
Spreading Hedge-parsley
Introduced: archaeophyte.
First record: 1821.
Tetrad occurrence: 8 (2%).
Decreased sharply (-79%).

Having once been a widespread weed of arable fields, usually on a calcareous clay or Chalk soil, this had become very local by the 1970s, and has continued to decrease. The recent survey received records from eight tetrads, but in none of these is the species thought to have a large population. The most robust populations were along a roadside ditch and field margin at High Wych (41/N), 1992 *S. Watson*; and with other scarce arable weeds near

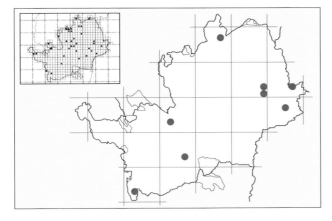

Map 454. *Torilis arvensis.*

Napsbury Hospital (10/R), 1998 *F. Hall/G. J. White*, 2005 *D. Bevan*. At Broadbalk, Rothamsted (11/G), where it had been abundant in 1985, it was reduced to one plant by 1989 *I. G. Denhom*, despite apparently beneficial management practices.
(35 tetrads: Dony, 1967; 42 tetrads: 1950-1986)

Torilis nodosa (L.) Gaertner
Knotted Hedge-parsley
Native.
First record: 1839.
Tetrad occurrence: 16 (3%).
Increased? (+74%).

A plant of short, bare grassy banks and field margins, especially on the Chalk. This species had become rare by the 1960s (Dony, 1967), but there is some evidence either of an increase, or that it was overlooked to some extent. It is still rare, but was recorded during the survey from a range of habitats, including scrubby road verges, banks of old chalk pits, secondary sheep pasture and waste ground.
(9 tetrads: Dony, 1967; 12 tetrads: 1950-1986)

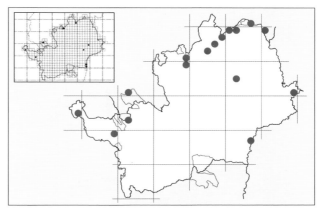

Map 456. *Torilis nodosa.*

Caucalis platycarpos L.
Small Bur-parsley
Introduced: neophyte.
First record: 1821.

This was quite a frequent weed of bare, chalky fields around Ashwell, Sandon, Royston and a few other places, mainly in north Herts. during the 19th century (Pryor, 1887), but had become a casual of waste places by 1920 (Dony, ms. index). It was last recorded from Haileybury (TL31), 1937 *A. G. Harrold* (Dony, ms. index).

Turgenia latifolia (L.) Hoffm.
Greater Bur-parsley
Introduced: casual.
First record: *c.*1840.

Apart from its first occurrence in a field of tares near Ashwell (Webb and Coleman, 1849), and an unreported record from near Baldock, *c.*1850 *A. M. Barnard* (Hunnybun mss., Hb. CGE), it was also recorded as a casual around Ware, Tewin and Hoddesdon early in the 20th century. Its last records were from Ware and Hoddesdon in 1915 *H. F. Hayllar* (Dony, ms. index).

Genus: *Daucus*

Daucus carota L.
Wild Carrot
Native.
First record: 1814.
Tetrad occurrence: 248 (51%).
Increased slightly? (+3%).

Wild Carrot is a plant of rough, calcareous grassland on road verges, chalk downs, old pits, and waste ground. It can rapidly colonise new habitats, but does not persist in enriched ones. As a result, its pattern of distribution shows evidence of both expansion and retraction. It has largely gone from intensive arable landscapes, where it once occurred on grassy field banks, but has increased substantially both around old gravel pits, and in new towns, where it can colonise bare grassy banks by roads.
(228 tetrads: Dony, 1967; 244 tetrads: 1950-1986)

The wild plant is ssp. *carota*. The cultivated carrot, ssp. *sativus* (Hoffm.) Arcang., occurs rarely as a casual, other than as a relic of cultivation. It has been recorded from Ware tip (31/M), 1986; and from Rye Meads Sewage Works (31/V), 1993 *C. G. Hanson*.

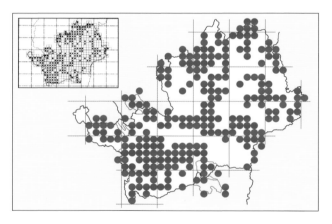

Map 457. *Daucus carota.*

Gentianaceae (Gentian family)

Genus: *Centaurium*

Centaurium erythraea Rafn.
Common Centaury
Native.
First record: 1730.
Tetrad occurrence: 145 (30%).
Apparently increased (+42%).

This is a somewhat enigmatic plant, occurring in poor, rough grasslands on neutral or slightly calcareous soils, in woodland rides, and occasionally colonising new habitats in old gravel and, rarely, chalk pits. It can also appear by arable field margins on poor soils, and is quite capable of regenerating after scrub clearance, from a long period of dormancy, or during periods of arable set-aside. For this reason, its increase, to some extent, may be more apparent than real.
(97 tetrads: Dony, 1967; 123 tetrads: 1950-1986)

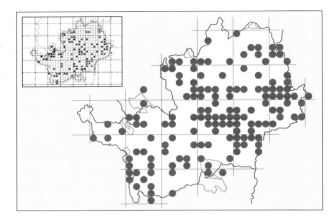

Map 458. *Centaurium erythraea.*

Centaurium pulchellum (Sw.) Druce   Herts Extinct
Lesser Centaury
Native.
First record: 1805.

This was a very rare plant of bare, damp pasture on gravel near East End Green (21/V) in the early 19th century (Pryor, 1887); and was also found until the 1930s in the damp, heathy grassland which once occupied Ermine Street, by Broxbourne Woods (TL30) (Dony, ms. index) (not clearings in the woods, as Dony (1967) indicates). There is also a record from 'Marden Heath' [Mardley Heath?] (TL21), 1957 *C. Leach* (Dony, ms. index), but this needs confirmation.

Genus: *Blackstonia*

Blackstonia perfoliata (L.) Hudson
Yellow-wort
Native.
First record: 1805.
Tetrad occurrence: 33 (7%).
Apparently increased (+81%).

This is an especially unmistakeable plant of chalk grassland. It also occurs occasionally in clearings in woods on calcareous clays, and sometimes in damp, calcareous grassland around spring seepages. More recently, it has also appeared, rarely, as a colonist on recently-created road banks on calcareous soils. Owing to its propensity for just 'turning up', it is difficult to know whether its increase is down to genuine spread, or if buried seed can make an appearance, given the right circumstances.
(17 tetrads: Dony, 1967; 26 tetrads: 1950-1986)

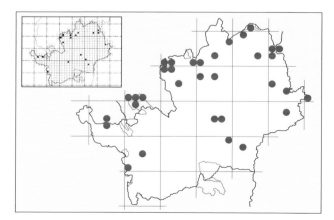

Map 459. *Blackstonia perfoliata.*

Gentianella campestris (L.) Börner   UK Vulnerable
Field Gentian   Herts Extinct
Native.
First record: 1597.

This plant of short, heathy grassland was only ever known from
a roadside bank near Gorhambury (TL10), Colney Heath (20/C),
and Nomansland Common (11/R). It was last seen at Colney
Heath in 1875 (not 1877) by E. de Crespigny (Dony, 1967 and ms.
index). A mention of it as occurring at Hexton (Whiteman, 1936)
is probably an error.

Gentianella germanica (Willd.) Börner   Herts Rare?
Chiltern Gentian
Native.
First record: probably *c.*1700.
Tetrad occurrence: 9 (6) (2 (1) %).
Decreasing (as native) (-29%).

Never common, this has occurred on a very few chalk grassland
sites in west Herts. for a long time. The recent survey found
it in nine tetrads, one more than recorded by Dony (1967).
However, in three of these, it is thought to be an introduction,
and its continued survival in these sites is mostly threatened.
It is therefore considered to have been found in six native
sites, of which one is likely to have been lost recently. These
sites were: scrub by Beechengrove Wood (09/N), 1991
G. Salisbury/J. Saunders; Oddy Hill, Tring (91/F), various
dates; lower slopes of Tring Park (91/F), 1990 *M. J. Hicks/
T. J./M. Beaton*; slopes by Pitstone Quarry (91/L) (just in VC20),
1998 *G. S./J. S.*; Flaunden Quarry (00/A), 1989 *G. S./J. S.* (Hb.
HTN) (site apparently since lost); Old Hill, near Studham (01/C)
(VC20 [Beds.]), 1997 *P. Baker*; and meadow by Hoo Wood, Great

Chiltern Gentian Gentianella germanica *Bedwell Chalk Pit, 1973.*

Gaddesden (01/G), 1998 *B. Harold/F. Hall* (only one plant at a
formerly rich site). The sites where it has been introduced are:
Chadwell Bank, King's Meads (31/L), 1989 *A. M. Boucher/T. J.*
(but apparently not seen recently); Little Hadham Chalk Pit
(42/L), 1988 *S. Watson* (since when the site has greatly scrubbed
up, and its floor been disturbed); and Bedwell Pit (20/Z),
1991, 2004 *T. J.* (where the species has a precarious existence
surrounded by heavily disturbed land). At other sites where it was
recorded after 1970, such as at Jack's Dell, Flaunden (01/W); and
the slopes below Aldbury Common (91/R), the habitat has largely
been lost to scrub and rank growth.
(8 tetrads: Dony, 1967; 10 tetrads: 1950-1986 (as native))

Gentianella × pamplinii (Druce) E. Warb.
(*G. germanica × G. amarella*)

First apparently recorded at Tring (SP91), 1912 *E. J. Salisbury*
(Salisbury, 1914), this fertile hybrid can form swarms where the
two species co-exist, ultimately possibly threatening either one
or other of the parents. During the survey, it was found to be
occasional at Oddy Hill (91/F), 1988 *M. Demidecki* (conf. T. J.).

Gentianella amarella (L.) Börner
Autumn Gentian
Native.
First record: 1640.
Tetrad occurrence: 25 (5%).
Stable? (+9%).

Autumn Gentian is an inconspicuous plant of short, open
chalk grassland and other similar calcareous grasslands, often
colonising old chalk pits. It has always occurred rather locally in
Herts., mainly on the long-established chalk grassland sites, where
it was at one time especially favoured by rabbit grazing, which
kept its habitat open. Having decreased during the 1950s and
1960s owing to the outbreak of myxomatosis and the cessation
of sheep-grazing on downland, it made some sort of a comeback
during the 1970s, with the conservation of many sites. More
recently, it appears to have started to lose ground again, as its sites
become increasingly rank from atmospheric nitrogen deposition,
causing competition from coarse herbs.
(22 tetrads: Dony, 1967; 32 tetrads: 1950-1986)

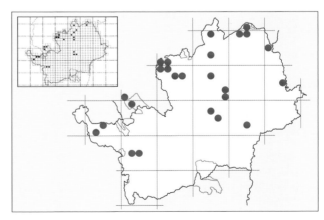

Map 460. *Gentianella amarella.*

[Gentianella anglica (Pugsley) E. Warb.
Early Gentian

As Dony (1967) pointed out, neither the early record from 'Tring' by E. Forster, nor the unlocalised record by C. Oldham (Salisbury, 1916) can be accepted without further evidence. In any case, there is a suggestion that this plant cannot be reliably separated from *G. amarella* genetically.]

Apocynaceae (Periwinkle family)

Genus: *Vinca*

Vinca minor L.
Lesser Periwinkle
Introduced: archaeophyte.
First record: 1814.
Tetrad occurrence: 116 (24%).
Increased (+121%).

Lesser Periwinkle is a patch-forming herb of especially secondary woodland and scrub, often spreading from road verges, where it has been introduced from gardens. It occasionally occurs well away from habitation in older woodland, and such occurrences led in the past to the idea that it was native. It was widespread even in the 19th century, and Dony recorded it fairly evenly across the County. It appears to be still increasing, and is showing signs of preferring damper clay soils in east and south-east Hertfordshire. (50 tetrads: Dony, 1967; 78 tetrads: 1950-1986)

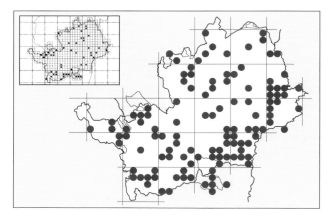

Map 461. *Vinca minor.*

Vinca difformis Pourr.
Intermediate Periwinkle
Introduced: neophyte.
First record: 1989.

This was found as an escape from cultivation at Hadham Towers tip (41/I), 1989 *S. Watson.* It was also noted as planted at Furneux Pelham (42/P) the same year *S. W.*

Vinca major L.
Greater Periwinkle
Introduced: neophyte.
First record: 1657.
Tetrad occurrence: 104 (21%).
Probably increased substantially.

Dony (1967) makes only a brief mention of this, and comments

that it is rarely established, although there are several early records suggesting that it was well-established, both in settlements, and in wilder habitats (Dony, ms. index). It is still most frequent in roadside hedges, and on old walls, but is also found in a wide range of especially secondary woodland locations elsewhere, showing some preference for calcareous soils. (21 tetrads: 1950-1986)

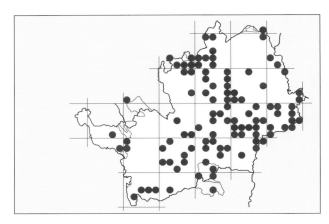

Map 462. *Vinca major.*

Var. *oxyloba* Stearn, with its very distinctive, narrow-petalled flowers, was found at Thundridge (31/N), 1996 *C. G. Hanson* and was also found to be well-established at Long Green, near Ashlyns (90/Y, 00/D), 2006 *T. J.* (Hb. HTN).

Asclepiadaceae (Milkweed family)

Genus: *Vincetoxicum*

Vincetoxicum nigrum (L.) Moench
Black Swallow-wort
Introduced: casual.
First (only) record: 2009.

Several plants matching the description of the strict species in *Flora Europaea* were found in a rough hedge by Bayfordbury (31/A), 2009 *A. Cooper* (det. T. J.) (Hb. HTN). How this south-western European plant got there is unknown.

Solanaceae (Nightshade family)

Genus: *Nicandra*

Nicandra physalodes (L.) Gaertner
Apple-of-Peru
Introduced: neophyte.
First record: 1946.

The first documented record of this appears to be from a potato field near Little Hadham (42/G), 1946 *H. J. Killick.* Dony (1967) gave five records, and it was subsequently found quite frequently at most of the tips in southern Hertfordshire between 1970 and 1979, with records from 11 tetrads. With the increased sanitisation of tips, its occurrences drastically reduced, so that it was then only recorded at Rye Meads Sewage Works (31/V), 1984 *C. G. Hanson* before the current survey began. During the survey, apart from regular records to 1996 from Rye Meads, it was only found on

disturbed ground by the A602 near Stevenage (22/R), 1994
A. M. Boucher; and on a manure heap near Ware (31/T), 2000,
2001 *C. G. H.*

Genus: *Lycium*

Lycium barbarum L.
Duke of Argyll's Teaplant
Introduced: neophyte.
First record: 1917.
Tetrad occurrence: 34 (7%).

Dony (1967) referred all earlier records of the Duke of Argyll's
Teaplant to this species. Most specimens critically examined do
seem to refer here, but some records may be *L. chinense*, and
therefore the map must be regarded as an aggregate. It is rarely
genuinely escaped, having been allowed to spread from its original
site of introduction, in a hedgerow or by houses. However, plants
do seem to occur mostly on the calcareous clay soils of east Herts.

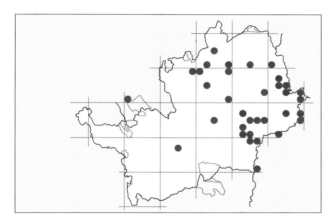

Map 463. *Lycium barbarum.*

Lycium chinense Mill.
Chinese Teaplant
Introduced: neophyte.
First record: 1926.

A specimen from TL31 (site details not reported), collected by J.
E. Little in 1926 has been determined as this by F. H. Perring (Hb.
CGE) (*comm.*: BRC, CEH Monks Wood). The BSBI's Vascular
Plants Database also has a record from Hertford (31/G), 1962
K. A. Beckett, which may be correct, and plants meeting its
description have been found at Ashwell (23/U), spreading from a
hedge into an arable field, 2009 *T. J.* (Hb. HTN). However, Stace
(1997) queries the taxonomic status of this plant.

Genus: *Atropa*

Atropa belladonna L.
Deadly Nightshade
Native (and introduced).
First record: 1737.
Tetrad occurrence: 31 (6%).
Stable or increased? (+54%).

Probably only genuinely native in scrub and woodlands on the
Chalk in W. Hertfordshire, where it occurs occasionally. Elsewhere
it is probably an escape from past cultivation as a medicinal herb,
especially near Hitchin, where it was grown until the 1940s.
(19 tetrads: Dony, 1967; 42 tetrads: 1950-1986)

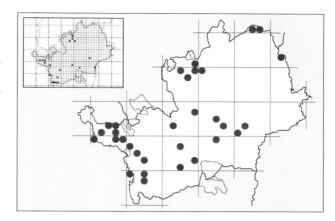

Map 461. *Atropa belladonna.*

Genus: *Hyoscyamus*

Hyoscyamus niger L.   UK Vulnerable
Henbane
Introduced: archaeophyte.
First record: 1814.
Tetrad occurrence: 15 (3%).
Decreased (-28%).

This is an occasional colonist of waste places, particularly
manured ground, and is found most frequently in alluvial habitats
near rivers, or on the Chalk. It was formerly quite frequent when
farmyard manure was widely in use, but has declined as the
rearing of livestock has also declined, although it can regenerate
from buried seed after long periods of apparent absence.
(20 tetrads: Dony, 1967; 31 tetrads: 1950-1986)

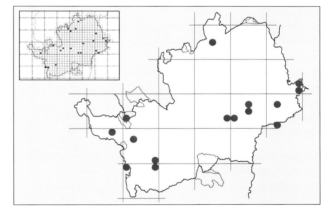

Map 465. *Hyoscyamus niger.*

Hyoscyamus albus L.
White Henbane
Introduced: casual.
First (only) record: 1934.

The only record remains that from roadworks at Pirton Road,
Hitchin (12/U), 1934 *J. Lamb* (det. J. E. Little) (*Rep. Bot. Exch.
Club*: 833 (1935)).

Genus: *Physalis*

Physalis alkekengi L.
Japanese Lantern
Introduced: neophyte.
First record: 1955.

This has remained a rare escape in our area. Its only recent records have been from Waterford tip (31/C), 1969; roadside at Hoddesdon (30/U), 1973 *C. G. Hanson*; path, Royston (34/K) (VC29 [Herts.]), 1998 *T. J.*

Physalis peruviana L.
Cape Gooseberry
Introduced: neophyte.
First record: 1939.

This has become a particular feature of sludge tips at Rye Meads Sewage Works (31/V), where it was first recorded in 1975 *C. G. Hanson*. It occurred regularly at this site as an established part of the vegetation at least until 1998, one of the only such sites in Britain (Hb. HTN). It also occurred on Cole Green tip (21/Q), 1978 *C. G. H.*; on set-aside at Bedmond (10/C), 1997 *G. Salisbury* (det. *E. J. Clement*) (Hb. HTN); and as a casual by West Alley, Hitchin (12/Z), 2007 *T. J.*

Physalis pubescens L.
Low Ground-cherry
Introduced: casual.
First record: 1996.

This was found, with *P. peruviana*, at the sludge tip, Rye Meads Sewage Works (31/V), 1996 *C. G. Hanson/A. M. Boucher/ T. J.* (det. *E. J. Clement*) (Hb. HTN). The specimens were referred to var. *grisea* Waterfall. A further plant was found in a garden at Cuffley (20/W), 2005 *comm.: H. J. Killick* (det. *C. G. Hanson*) (Hb. Killick).

Physalis philadelphica Lam.
Large-flowered Tomatillo
Introduced: casual.
First record: 1984.

One plant of this was found at Rye Meads Sewage Works (31/V), 1984 *A. M. Boucher/C. G. Hanson* (det. *E. J. Clement*) (Hb. HTN). It then made regular appearances at the site from 1989 to 1994 *A. M. B./C. G. H.*

Physalis angulata L.
Cut-leaved Ground-cherry
Introduced: casual.
First (only) record: 1929.

The only record remains that of a wool-shoddy alien from Great Wymondley (TL22), 1929 *J. E. Little* (det. *G. Taylor*) (Dony, 1967; and ms. index).

Genus: *Capsicum*

Capsicum annuum L.
Sweet Pepper
Introduced: casual.
First record: 1967.

This was first found as an escape at Hitchin tip (13/V), *C. M. Dony*. It was subsequently found at several tips in the Hertford/Hoddesdon area during the 1970s and early 1980s, but during the recent survey it has only been recorded at Rye Meads Sewage Works (31/V), 1989, 1997 *A. M. Boucher/C. G. Hanson*.

Genus: *Lycopersicon*

Lycopersicon esculentum Mill.
Tomato
Introduced: neophyte.
First record: *c.*1880.
Tetrad occurrence: 28 (6%).

Dony (1967) ignored this altogether, but it was first recorded by Pryor (1887). During the 1970s it was widely recorded on tips, and especially around Rye Meads Sewage Works, where it often formed a monoculture on sludge heaps. However, the recent survey showed that it is increasingly occurring as a casual in waste places in many areas, sometimes surviving over mild winters, especially in the Lea and Stort valleys.

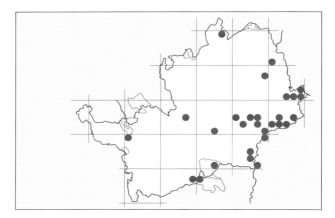

Map 466. *Lycopersicon esculentum.*

Genus: *Solanum*

Apart from the two widely-occurring species, this genus includes a range of weedy introductions, which suffer from confusing taxonomy. The current treatment owes much to the researches of Gordon Hanson.

Solanum nigrum L.
Black Nightshade
Native (or introduced).
First record: 1814.
Tetrad occurrence: 288 (59%).
Stable, or slightly decreasing (-6%).

This is particularly a plant of disturbed, nutrient-enriched soils, often on cultivated ground. It occurs especially where manuring is carried out, but also on waste ground. As such, its occurrence is sporadic and unpredictable, which may account for its strangely patchy distribution. The current distribution shows considerable changes from that given by Dony (1967), who found it especially around Hitchin and Letchworth, as well as in south-east and central Herts., while the current survey found it mainly on the Clay-with-Flints soils of the Chilterns, and on the Boulder Clay in east Herts.

(290 tetrads: Dony, 1967; 316 tetrads: 1950-1986)

The usual plant is ssp. *nigrum*. The neophyte ssp. *schultesii* (Opiz) Wessely has been found at least twice: at Cole Green tip (21/Q), 1979 *C. G. Hanson* (det. E. J. Clement); and at Waterford tip (31/C), *C. G. H.* (det. J. M. Edmonds). The specimen '*cf.* var. *chlorocarpon*' recorded by Dony (1967) from Blackbridge tip may also refer to this.

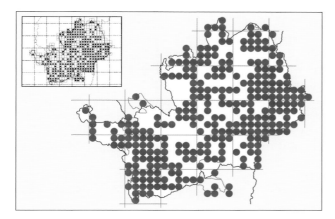

Map 467. *Solanum nigrum.*

Solanum villosum Mill.
Red Nightshade
Introduced: casual.
First record: 1978.

This appeared as a wool shoddy alien at Newnham (23/N), 1978 *C. G. Hanson*. It also turned up in his garden at Ware (31/S), 1985 *C. G. H.* (Hb. HTN), having been introduced there earlier.

Solanum scabrum Mill.
Garden Huckleberry
Introduced: casual.
First record: 1992.

Two plants of this were found at Rye Meads Sewage Works (31/V), 1992 *A. M. Boucher* (det. C. G. Hanson) (Hb. HTN). A few plants were subsequently found at the same location in 1993, 1994 and 1996 *C. G. H.* (Hb. HTN).

[*Solanum chenopodioides* Lam.
Tall Nightshade

This appeared spontaneously in a garden at Ware (31/S), 1997, 1998 *C. G. Hanson* (Hb. HTN), but was originally from seed collected in London, 1990. Unless it appears elsewhere, it cannot be regarded as part of the naturally occurring flora.]

Solanum physalifolium Rusby
Green Nightshade
Introduced: neophyte.
First record: 1973.
Rare, but increasing.

This was first found as a wool shoddy alien at Newnham (23/N),

1973 *C. G. Hanson*. It was found during the current survey near Bishop's Stortford (42/W), 1992 *J. L. Fielding* (det. T. J.) (Hb. HTN); on waste ground at Hitchin (12/Z), 1998 *T. J.* (Hb. HTN); and at the old station yard, Ware (31/S), 2001 *C. G. H.*

Solanum sarachoides Sendtner
Leafy-fruited Nightshade
Introduced: neophyte.
First record: 1955.

Dony first found this at Blackbridge tip (11/X), 1955 (Dony, 1967 and ms. index). More recently, it was also found there in 1970, 1974, and 1976 *C. G. Hanson*, but not since.

Solanum triflorum Nutt.
Small Nightshade
Introduced: neophyte.
Only record: 1919.

There have been no further reports since A. W. Graveson found this at Hertford (Dony, 1967).

Solanum americanum Mill.
Small-flowered Nightshade
Introduced: neophyte.
First record: *c.*1960.

Dony (1967) recorded it 'regularly' at Blackbridge tip (11/X), but it is unclear when he first found it there. It was last seen there in 1976 *C. G. Hanson*. He also recorded it from a number of other tips in central Herts., between 1970 and 1979. Its only record during the survey was from Waterford tip (31/C), 1987 *C. G. H.*

Solanum dulcamara L.
Bittersweet *or* **Woody Nightshade**
Native.
First record: 1814.
Tetrad occurrence: 472 (96%).
Probably stable (-3%).

This ubiquitous plant of damp, shady places appears to be a natural component of watersides and damp woodland in eutrophic conditions, but is also a weed of waste places elsewhere. The current survey found it in a similar proportion of tetrads to those reported in Dony (1967), although it was missed in two.
(461 tetrads: Dony, 1967; and from 1950-1986)

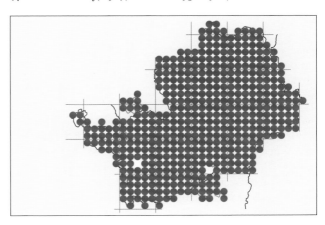

Map 468. *Solanum dulcamara.*

Solanum tuberosum L.
Potato
Introduced: casual.
First record: *c.*1950?
Tetrad occurrence: 20 (4%).

Dony (1967) does not mention this, although it must have occurred regularly as a relic of cultivation. It was reported to him from Bishop's Stortford, *c.*1950 *D. McClintock.* It was then recorded from tips in 11 tetrads between 1970 and 1986 *C. G. Hanson*; and has been recorded from 20 scattered tetrads during the survey, sometimes in field situations, but is not known to persist.

Solanum stoloniferum Schltdl.
Wild Potato
Introduced: casual.
First record: 1985.

This was found as a greenhouse weed at Bayfordbury (31/A), 1985 *C. G. Hanson*; and it survived the removal of the greenhouses, being found on the same site in 1994, 1996 *A. M. Boucher/C. G. H.* (det. E. J. Clement) (Hb. HTN).

Solanum diflorum Vell.
Winter-cherry
Introduced: casual.
First record: 1993.

A record of *S. pseudocapsicum* agg. is probably this, recorded from Rye Meads Sewage Works (31/V), 1993 *C. G. Hanson* (Clement and Foster, 1994).

Solanum melongena L.
Aubergine
Introduced: casual.
First (only) record: 1984.

This was found growing at Waterford tip (31/C), 1984 *C. G. Hanson.*

Solanum sisymbrifolium Lam.
Red Buffalo-bur
Introduced: casual.
First record: 1942.

There have been no further records since the two given by Dony (1967).

Solanum rostratum Dunal
Buffalo-bur
Introduced: casual.
First record: 1970.

This was first reported from the tip at High Leigh, Hoddesdon (30/P), 1970 *J. G. and C. M. Dony* (Hb. HTN; Hb. LTN); and was subsequently found by them at Rickmansworth tip (09/L, M), 1976 (Hb. HTN). Burton (1983) mentions repeated records from Cole Green (21/Q), but I have no details. It has been found during the present survey at Garston (19/E), 1989 *O. Linford*; and at Rye Meads Sewage Works (31/V), 1989, 1990 *A. M. Boucher/ C. G. Hanson.*

Genus: *Datura*

Datura stramonium L.
Thorn-apple
Introduced: neophyte.
First record: 1814.
Tetrad occurrence: 14 (3%).
Decreasing (-26%).

This is a rather uncommon, but widely distributed weed of cultivated or waste ground, tips and the like, and can be intermittently persistent for long periods, re-appearing from buried seed, although its occurrences appear to be declining, especially on tips.
(18 tetrads: Dony, 1967; 33 tetrads: 1950-1986)

The distinct variety *chalybaea* W. J. Koch (= var. *tatula* (L.) Torr.) has been recorded a number of times at Rye Meads Sewage Works (31/V), the last being 1996 *C. G. Hanson.* It has also been recorded from Ware tip (31/M), 1985 *A. M. Boucher*; Wadesmill (31/N), 1989 *A. M. B.*; and from Puckeridge (32/W), 1991 *S. Watson.* Var. *inermis* (Juss. ex Jacq) Schinz and Thell. was recorded from Mead Lane Gravel Pit, Hertford (31/G), 1922 *A. W. Graveson* (det. at Kew) (*Rep. Bot. Exch. Club*: 739 (1923)).

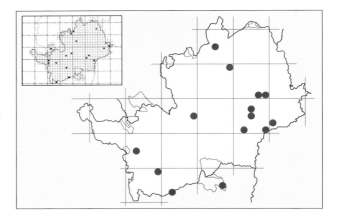

Map 469. *Datura stramonium.*

Datura innoxia Mill.
Recurved Thorn-apple
Introduced: neophyte.
First record: 1999.
This has become an established weed in a garden at Ware (31/M), 1999 *C. G. Hanson* (det. E. J. Clement) (Hb. HTN), source unknown.

Genus: *Nicotiana*

Nicotiana alata Link and Otto
Sweet Tobacco
Introduced: neophyte.
First record: 1970.

This was apparently not noticed until C. G. Hanson found it on tips at Moor Mill (10/L), Blackbridge (11/X) and Cole Green (21/Q), 1970. It was then found several times at a number of other sites during the 1970s and 1980s (Hb. HTN). During the recent survey it has been found at Rye Meads Sewage Works (31/V), 1989, 1995 *C. G. H./A. M. Boucher*; and on tipped spoil, Vicars Grove, St Ippollitts (12/X), 1999 *T. J.*

Nicotiana × *sanderae* W. Watson (*N. alata* × *N. forgetiana*)
Introduced: casual.
First (only) record: 1995.

This was also found at Rye Meads Sewage Works (31/V), 1995 *A. M. Boucher/C. G. Hanson* (Hb. HTN).

Genus: *Petunia*

Petunia × *hybrida* (Hook.) Schinz and Thell.
(*P. axillaris* × *P. integrifolia*)
Petunia
Introduced: casual.
First record: 1971.

This was first recorded as an escape at Hitchin tip (13/V) *C. G. Hanson*; and was subsequently found by him at Ware tip (31/M), 1984, and Rye Meads Sewage Works (31/V), 1985. Its only records during the survey were from dumped soil at Blackthorn Wood (21/Q), 1992 *A. M. Boucher*; and on disturbed ground at Chorleywood Common (09/I), 2004 *T. J.* It is almost certainly more frequent, but is overlooked as planted.

Convolvulaceae (Bindweed family)

Genus: *Convolvulus*

Convolvulus arvensis L.
Field Bindweed
Native.
First record: 1814.
Tetrad occurrence: 462 (94%).
Stable or decreasing slightly (-4%).

This ubiquitous and tenacious weed of disturbed or cultivated ground and waste places also occurs in grassland that has been disturbed in the past, and occasionally in scrub or woodland. It remains much as Dony (1967) recorded it, although its abundance in arable fields must have decreased.
(459 tetrads: Dony, 1967 and 1950-1986)

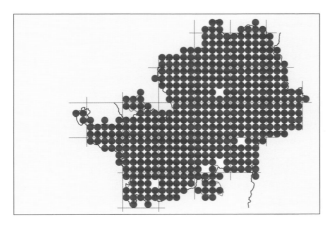

Map 470. *Convolvulus arvensis.*

Genus: *Calystegia*

Calystegia sepium (L.) R. Br.
Hedge Bindweed *or* **Bellbine**
Native.
First record: 1750.
Tetrad occurrence: 384 (78%).
Decreased (-10%).

In its natural habitat, this grows among tall herbs, usually in damp places. It also occurs commonly in unmanaged hedgerows, scrub and waste ground. The recent survey suggests a noticeable decline in distribution, and it seems to have suffered somewhat from the tidying of hedgerows in particular.
(405 tetrads: Dony, 1967; 423 tetrads: 1950-1986)

The usual subspecies is ssp. *sepium*, but the introduced ssp. *spectabilis* Brummitt was found by the River Lea at Cheshunt (30/S), 1988 *A. M. Boucher* (Hb. Boucher).

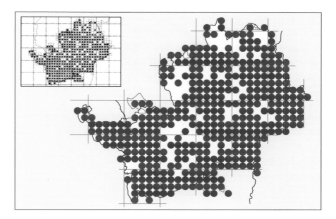

Map 471. *Calystegia sepium.*

Calystegia × *lucana* (Ten.) Don (*C. sepium* × *C. silvatica*)
Native.
First record: c.1960.

Although Dony (1967) noted the widespread occurrence of the hybrid, it was not recorded properly in Herts. until E. B. Bangerter gave one record from Herts. in his London survey (Bangerter, 1967) and Burton (1983) gave five tetrad records from the Barnet area. It is still very under-recorded, but the survey found it in seven scattered tetrads in south and west Herts. However, it does still seem to be particularly a feature of the Barnet area.

Calystegia pulchra Brummitt and Heyw.
Hairy Bindweed
Introduced: neophyte.
First record: 1957?

It is uncertain from Dony's records (Dony, 1967) where this first occurred, as he did not include most of them in his ms. index, although there is one from Bragbury End (22/Q), 1957. It was found subsequently at East Barnet (29/S), c.1967 (*comm.*: J. G. Dony) where it was re-found in 1977 *A. M. Boucher* (conf. R. K. Brummitt) (Hb. Boucher); Ashwell (23/U), 1981, *etc. T. J.* (Hb. HTN); and Harmer Green (21/M), 1981 *T. J.* In addition to the Ashwell colony, which persisted until c.2000, it was also found during the recent survey at Puckeridge (32/W), 1991 *S. Watson*;

Baker's End (31/Y), 1993 *S. W.*; and Rabley Heath (21/J), 1992 *P. D. Walton* (where it may have been planted).

Calystegia × howittiorum Brummitt (*C. pulchra × C. silvatica*)

This rare hybrid was found at Latchford, near Standon (32/V), 1992 *S. Watson* (conf. T. J.) (Hb. HTN). The locality is not that far from the colony of *C. pulchra* found earlier at Puckeridge.

Calystegia silvatica (Kit.) Griseb.
Large Bindweed
Introduced: neophyte.
First record: 1916.
Tetrad occurrence: 317 (65%).
Increased (+85%).

Large Bindweed was introduced in the early 19th century as a garden plant, and has escaped into ruderal habitats widely across the County. However, it was only recognised as a separate species botanically in 1948 and its first recorded occurrence in Herts. is from an herbarium specimen. Its exact distribution may still be uncertain, because it is impossible to identify when not in flower, and it also hybridises with *C. sepium*. It was recorded largely on clay soils, and shows expansion from centres recorded by Dony (1967).
(163 tetrads: Dony, 1967; 214 tetrads: 1950-1986)

The usual plant is ssp. *silvatica*, but ssp. *disjuncta* Brummitt was found by a car park at Hoddesdon (30/Z), 1996 *A. M. Boucher* (det. R. K. Brummitt) (Hb. Boucher). The scarce variety *quinquepartita* N. Terrace was found and photographed near Stanstead Abbotts, by the Lee Navigation (31/V), 2007 *S. Hawkins*, its only record so far in Herts.

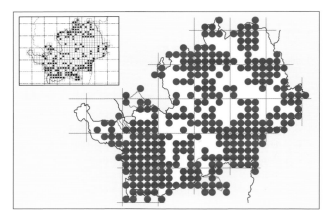

Map 472. *Calystegia silvatica.*

Genus: *Ipomoea*

Ipomoea batatas (L.) Lam.
Sweet-potato
Introduced: casual.
First record: 1964.

There has been only one other record since it was first found at Hitchin (Dony, 1967): at Bulls Mill tip (31/D), 1976 *C. G. Hanson*.

Ipomoea hederacea Jacq.
Ivy-leaved Morning-glory
Introduced: casual.
First record: 1968.

This escape first appeared at Latchford, Standon (32/V), 1968 *C. G. Hanson*, and was subsequently found at Rickmansworth tip (09/L, M), 1976 *J. G. and C. M. Dony* (Hb. LTN); Bulls Mill tip (31/D), 1976; and Rye Meads Sewage Works (31/V), 1976 *C. G. H.* During the survey, it was only found at Rye Meads in 1995 and 1996 *A. M. Boucher/C. G. H.*

Ipomoea lacunosa L.
White Morning-glory
Introduced: casual.
First (only) record: 1976.

The only record is from Rickmansworth tip (09/L) *J. G. and C. M. Dony* (Hb. LTN).

Ipomoea purpurea Roth
Common Morning-glory
Introduced: casual.
First record: 1970.

This was first found at High Leigh tip (30/P), 1970 *J. G. and C. M. Dony* (Hb. LTN); and has subsequently been found at Rye Meads Sewage Works (31/V), 1991 *C. G. Hanson* (det. E. J. Clement) (Hb. Hanson).

Cuscutaceae (Dodders)

Genus: *Cuscuta*

Cuscuta campestris Yuncker
Yellow Dodder
Introduced: neophyte.
First record: 1970.

This was first found in a flower bed at Newgate Street (30/C), 1970 *H. J. Killick* (det. at Natural History Museum); and was subsequently found at Rye Meads Sewage Works (31/V), 1976 *C. G. Hanson*. It re-appeared at Rye Meads in 1983 *A. M. Boucher/C. G. H.* (Hb. Boucher).

Cuscuta europaea L.   Herts Extinct
Greater Dodder
Native.
First record: 1750?

Genuine occurrences of this in Herts. are hard to determine because early records may not always have been correctly identified. There is a record by W. Ellis from Little Gaddesden, *c.*1750, omitted by Dony and others. It was evidently always rare, found mainly in west Herts. in river valleys, and was last recorded *c.*1880.

Cuscuta epilinum Weihe
Flax Dodder
Introduced: casual.
First record: *c.*1839.

There have been no further records since it was last seen near Ashwell in 1921 (Dony, 1967), despite the upsurge in cultivation of its host.

Cuscuta epithymum (L.) L.   UK Vulnerable
Common Dodder
Native.
First record: *c.*1836.
Extinct in Herts.*?*

This was always a rare plant, found as a native on Gorse and Broom on dry heaths, mainly in west Herts. It is also recorded as a parasite on clovers, *etc.*, and its last record was on *Trifolium dubium* by Hoo Wood, Great Gaddesden (01/G), 1985 *R. Crossley.*

[*Cuscuta suaveolens* Ser.
Lucerne Dodder

There is a record from Thundridge (TL31) in Pryor (1887), attributed to this, but without a specimen it must be regarded as doubtful.]

Menyanthaceae (Bogbean family)

Genus: *Menyanthes*

Menyanthes trifoliata L.
Bogbean
Native (and introduced).
First record: *c.*1730.
Tetrad occurrence: 22 (5%).
Increased (as introduced) (+309%).

As a native plant, this was formerly widespread in peaty swamps in river valleys throughout the County. It was also probably native in mildly acidic swamps on clay in the south-east of the County, from where it came to occur in ponds in the same area. Unfortunately, for students of natural plant communities, it has become an increasing favourite of the aquatic gardener, with the result that the distribution map largely shows non-native sites. It is known to survive in one swampy river valley meadow near Sopwell Mill (10/M), 2000 *L. Mottram/M. J. Hicks*, but it is apparently no longer at similar sites mentioned by Dony (1967). It still occurs sporadically at Bayford Pond (30/E), although this may not be a native site, despite it having been here since at least 1920. It is possibly more natural at Brickendon Green Pond (30/I), where it appeared, apparently from buried seed, when the pond was re-excavated in the early 1980s. It was also found in a small pond by White Stubbs Lane (30/I), 1989 *A. M. Boucher*, which is probably a survivor of the swamps around Wormley

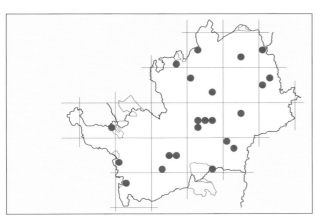

Map 473. *Menyanthes trifoliata.*

Wood, where it was formerly noted as abundant (Pryor, 1887). Other sites are more doubtful, such as the pond at Bovingdon Green (00/B), despite having been known there since *c.*1950 *G. Salisbury*; and the pond at Bricket Wood Common (10/F), 1988 *P. Baker*. Owing to the doubt about so many sites, it is not listed as a 'Herts Rare' species, although it probably is as a native plant.
(5 tetrads: Dony, 1967; 8 tetrads: 1950-1986)

Genus: *Nymphoides*

Nymphoides peltata Kuntze
Fringed Water-lily
Introduced [native in the U.K.].
First record: 1855.
Tetrad occurrence: 24 (5%).
Increasing.

Unlike its relative, this has never had any claim to be a native plant in Hertfordshire. Its natural habitat of calcareous fen pools does not occur in the County. It has, however, become a frequent feature of gravel pit lakes, and some other smaller ponds, across southern Hertfordshire since Dony published his *Flora*, because he gave no recent records at all. It can sometimes become quite dominant in these habitats.

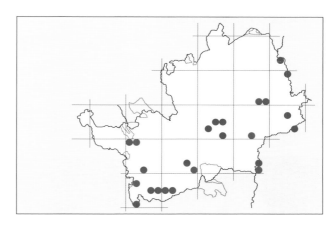

Map 474. *Nymphoides peltata.*

Polemoniaceae (Jacob's-ladder family)

Genus: *Polemonium*

Polemonium caeruleum L.
Jacob's-ladder
Introduced [native in the U.K.].
First record: 1847.

This is only ever a rare garden escape, although some 19th century records were from damp calcareous grassland near rivers, more like its native seepages in limestone scree grassland. It was recorded at Oakleigh Park (29/W), 1968 *P. E. G. Irvine*; and more recently near Herringworth Hall (32/L), 1993 *S. Watson*; and near Hitch Wood (12/W), 1996 *A. D. Marshall*.

[*Collomia grandiflora* Douglas ex Hook.
Large-flowered Collomia
This has self-sown in a garden at Ware (31/S), 1996 *C. G. Hanson*.
It was originally cultivated, and, unless it spreads, cannot be
regarded as a naturally occurring species in the County.]

Hydrophyllaceae (Phacelia family)

Genus: *Phacelia*

Phacelia tanacetifolia Benth.
Phacelia
Introduced: neophyte or casual.
First record: 1991.
Tetrad occurrcence: 11 (2%).
This was first found, possibly as a sown plant for bees, at Law
Hall, Kings Walden (12/R), 1991 *C. R. Boon* (Hb. HTN). It has now
been found in eleven scattered tetrads, in most of which it may
originally have also been sown.

Boraginaceae (Borage family)

Genus: *Lithospermum*

Lithospermum purpureocaeruleum L.
Purple Gromwell
Introduced [native in the U.K.].
First record: 1978.

Purple Gromwell Lithospermum purpureocaeruleum *Gravel Hill, Hexton, 1980.*

Four plants of this scarce native of bushy places on limestone
were found, presumably as garden outcasts, on a disturbed chalky
roadside at Gravel Hill, Hexton (12/E), 1978 *G. Crompton* (Hb.
HTN). It re-appeared here at sporadic intervals, last being seen in
1992 *T. J.*, when there was a fair-sized patch.

Lithospermum officinale L.   Herts Rare
Common Gromwell
Native.
First record: *c.*1839.
Tetrad occurrence: 3 (<1%).
Very rare but stable (no measurable change).

This is a strange plant of scrubby places, usually on a calcareous
marl soil, or Chalk. It has occurred in various places across the
County for a long time, but is never common. Dony (1967) gave
three localities. It was at one time fairly frequent in the Easneye
area (31/R), but was last seen there by the old railway in 1977 *T. J.*
It also appeared at Telegraph Hill (Hoo Bit) (12/E), 1975 *T J.*
(being a feature of scrub on nearby Pegsdon Hills, Beds.), and was
reported from 'near Hinxworth' (TL24), 1977 *E. de Boer*. During
the recent survey it was found in three places: green lane on the
County boundary at Long Plantation (24/K), 1989, 2008; roadside
hedge, Hinxworth Road (23/J), 1997 *T. J.*; and by The Meg
plantation, Hexton (12/E), 2009 *T. J.*, not far from Hoo Bit.

Lithospermum arvense L.   UK Endangered
Field Gromwell
Native.
First record: 1814.
Tetrad occurrence: 36 (7%).
Decreased strongly (-60%).

This is a plant of disturbed, calcareous clay or Chalk soils, usually
found as an arable weed. As such, it has decreased drastically since
the 1960s, and is now only ever found in small numbers, surviving
on the margins of fields. The survey still found it across much of
its range, however, and it appears to survive as buried seed quite
well.
(85 tetrads: Dony, 1967; 102 tetrads: 1950-1986)

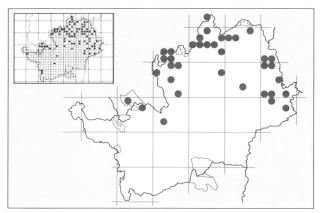

Map 475. *Lithospermum arvense.*

Cerinthe major L.
Greater Honeywort
Introduced: casual.
First (only) record: 1943.

There have been no further additions to its self-sown occurrence at Great Amwell, 1943 (Dony, 1967).

Genus: *Echium*

Echium italicum L.
Pale Bugloss
Introduced: casual.
First record: 1907.

Dony (1967) reported one record, from Ware, 1907. It had also been reported from near Ware in 1908 *A. W. Graveson* (Hb. HTN); and from a gravel pit near Ware Park, 1917 *H. G. Hayllar* (Dony, ms. index). There are no recent records.

Echium vulgare L.
Viper's-bugloss
Native.
First record: 1750.
Tetrad occurrence: 19 (4%).
Increased? (+50%).

This attractive plant was said by Pryor (1887) to be 'frequent', although the records he reported were not that numerous. Dony (1967) regarded it as rare, but noted that it occurred on both the river and glacial gravels (especially where the latter overlie Chalk). It is often found as one or two plants, usually in somewhat open, disturbed, gravelly or somewhat chalky places. Some of its sites are long-standing, while others seem to be ephemeral, although it may appear from buried seed. Following Dony's survey, it continued to be found in 'new' sites, and the current survey showed the same pattern, with widely scattered records from most parts of the County. Unfortunately there has recently been a fashion to sow it as part of 'wild-flower' mixes, which obscures its real ecology, such as the vast stands by Baldock bypass (23/L), 2007 (not mapped).
(12 tetrads: Dony, 1967; 20 tetrads: 1950-1986)

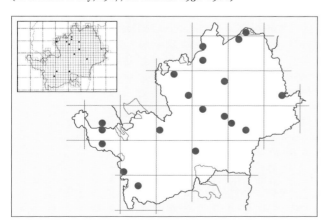

Map 476. *Echium vulgare.*

Genus: *Pulmonaria*

Pulmonaria officinalis L.
Lungwort
Introduced: neophyte.
First record: *c*.1870.
Tetrad occurrence: 10 (2%).

This is a rather rare escape from gardens, which sometimes persists for a while in shady roadsides. It occurs more often on damper neutral or mildly acidic clays than elsewhere. It was first recorded in Pryor (1887). Dony (1967) only mentions it, and it was only recorded once between 1970 and 1986. The recent survey found it in ten scattered localities, mostly in south Herts. Other lungworts occur as escapes in the U.K., and should be watched for.

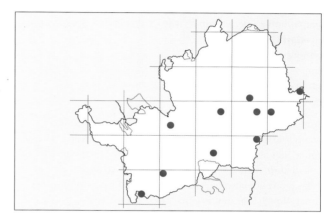

Map 477. *Pulmonaria officinalis.*

Genus: *Nonea*

Nonea lutea (Desr.) DC.
Yellow Nonea
Introduced: casual.
First (only) record: 1980.

This appeared as a weed in a garden in Ware (31/S) *C. G. Hanson* (Hb. HTN), source uncertain.

Genus: *Symphytum*

Comfreys can be a confusing group, not least because of the occurrence of variable colour forms of the same taxa, garden escapes, and complex hybrids. Attempts have been made to give a thorough account of these, but problems remain with some populations.

Symphytum officinale L.
Common Comfrey
Native.
First record: 1819.
Tetrad occurrence: 120 (24%).
Increasing? (+60%).

Despite its name, this is not the commonest comfrey in the County. With us it is usually a pale cream-flowered species found in damp situations, often near or by rivers or streams, but also in moist places along road verges on the clays in southern Hertfordshire. It may have genuinely increased, although better recording may account for some of this.
(71 tetrads: Dony, 1967; 93 tetrads: 1950-1986)

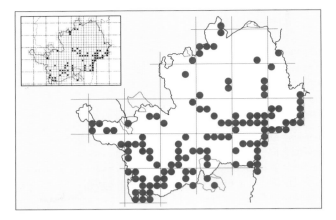

Map 478. *Symphytum officinale.*

Symphytum × uplandicum Nyman (*S. officinale × S. asperum*)
Russian Comfrey
Introduced: neophyte.
First record: 1909.
Tetrad occurrence: 230 (47%).
Increasing (+112%).

This introduced fodder plant is the regular roadside comfrey, usually with purple flowers, occurring in rough herbage on waste ground, but also beside rivers, especially where their banks have been disturbed. As it is a hybrid with the native plant, in these places it forms confusing back-crosses with its parent. Its other parent, Rough Comfrey, is much rarer, but where it has occurred, it also seems to have created back-crosses, with more blue flowers. Rarely, it can also have reddish flowers. It was found widely across the County, most frequently on the damper clay or marl soils, or near rivers. It appears recently to have genuinely increased.
(103 tetrads: Dony, 1967; 122 tetrads: 1950-1986)

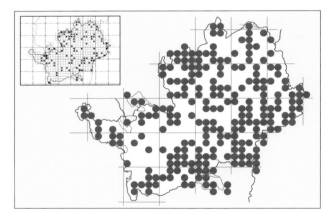

Map 479. *Symphytum × uplandicum.*

Symphytum 'Hidcote Blue' *hort.* ex G. Thomas
(*S. officinale × S. asperum × S. grandiflorum*)
Hidcote Comfrey
Introduced: casual.
First record: 1984.

This escape was first found as an established plant near the gardens of the Glaxo factory, Ware (31/M), 1984 *C. G. Hanson* (Hb. HTN), originally mis-reported as *S. grandiflorum* (James, 1989). It was also found by a road at Welwyn (21/I), 1994 *A. M. Boucher* (Hb. HTN). It may be more widespread, and blue-flowered comfreys with spreading stems need to be recorded with care.

Symphytum asperum Lepechin
Rough Comfrey
Introduced: neophyte.
First record: *c.*1950.

The only certain occurrences of this relate to the colony discovered by D. McClintock at Easneye (31/R, W) that was recorded in Dony (1967). Convincing material was collected from the banks of the Lee Navigation at Easneye (31/R), 1977 *T. J.*, and from the roadside at Hollycross Road (31/R, W), 1993 *A. M. Boucher* (Hb. HTN), but there are also substantial quantities of hybrids with *S. officinale* in the area as well.

Symphytum tuberosum L.
Tuberous Comfrey
Introduced [native in the U.K.*?*].
First record: 1843.
Tetrad occurrence: 4 (1%).

This is a patch-forming plant of damp, shady woodland, supposed to be native in the north (but see Braithwaite *et al.*, 2006). Its few occurrences in Hertfordshire are certainly in more secondary habitats, such as hedgerows or plantations. It has not been recorded recently from its original site at Thundridge (Dony, 1967), nor at Symondshyde Great Wood and Newfield Hill. It was found in Roundabouts Plantation, Kings Walden (12/L), 1978 *B. R. Sawford* (Hb. HTN), but apparently did not persist. During the current survey, it was found at Gaddesden Row (01/L), 1989 *P. J. Ellison*; Winding Hill, Much Hadham (41/J), 1991 *S. Watson* (Hb. HTN); and in a more natural state in Coldharbour Wood, Newgate Street (20/S, X), 2002 *T. J.* (Hb. HTN).

Symphytum grandiflorum DC.
Creeping Comfrey
Introduced: neophyte.
First record: 1991.
Tetrad occurrence: 6 (1%).
Increasing.

The report of its occurrence in the County in James (1989) was an error for *S.* 'Hidcote Blue'. However, during the recent survey, the real thing has been found in a number of shady road verges, *etc.*: Chorleywood (09/M), 1991, 1995 *P. J. Ellison*; green lane, Wallington (23/W), 1993 *T. J.*; Moor Lane, Rickmansworth (09/R), 1997 *P. J. Ellison*; Kensworth Lynch (01/P) (VC20 [Beds.], 1997 *C. R. Boon/T. J./G. Salisbury*; by Courts Farm, Ardeley (32/H), 1998 *T. J.*; Gaddesden Row (01/L), 2005 *T. J.*

Symphytum orientale L.
White Comfrey
Introduced: neophyte.
First record: 1927.
Tetrad occurrence: 17 (4%).
Increasing (+1650%).

This early-flowering garden escape has slowly increased since its first appearance at Hitchin (Dony, 1967). It usually occurs in dappled shade by roads, where it can be quite attractive, and persists.
(1 tetrad: Dony, 1967; 8 tetrads: 1950-1986)

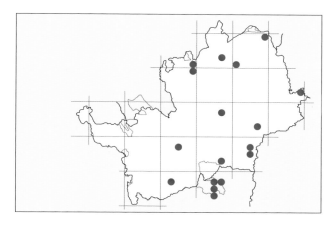

Map 480. *Symphytum orientale.*

Genus: *Brunnera*

Brunnera macrophylla (Adams) I. M. Johnston
Great Forget-me-not
Introduced: neophyte.
First record: 1995.
Tetrad occurrence: 4 (1%).

This first appeared in the wild in a hedgerow at Harmer Green (21/N), 1995 *A. M. Boucher*, who also found it in a copse at Morley Hall (31/X), 1996. It has subsequently appeared as an escape at St Albans (10/N), 1997 *A. R. Outen*; and at Sandon (33/C), 2005 *T. J.* It may well be elsewhere.

Genus: *Anchusa*

Dony (1967) outlines the occurrence of a number of species of *Anchusa* that were discovered by A. W. Graveson in and near an old sand pit near Ware Park in 1907, and which continued to be recorded, under various names, for nearly 20 years, giving rise to the botanists' name for the pit as the 'Anchusa Pit', a site now lost. Modern treatments of the genus show that these can be reduced to a number of recognisable taxa, and specimens for some of these records exist. Dony's dismissal of all these records therefore needs to be reviewed, and the following account is an attempt to unravel the details of these bizarre occurrences. That so many species were at the site might suggest deliberate introduction, but it is of note that many are fodder or grain aliens, and that Ware was the County's main centre for the grain trade by barge into London.

Anchusa ochroleuca M. Bieb.
Yellow Alkanet
Introduced: casual.
First (only) record: 1914.

This species is recorded from the pit at Ware (31/M), 1914, only on the evidence of G. C. Druce (*Trans. Herts. N.H.S.*, 15, p. 172).

Anchusa officinalis L.
Alkanet
Introduced: neophyte.
First record: 1907.

A. W. Graveson first found this species at the 'Anchusa Pit' in 1907 (Hb. HTN), where it was found at least until 1926 *E. Graham* (*comm.*: Biological Records Centre, CEH Monks Wood). It also occurred on waste ground near Ware Cemetery (31/M), 1915 *H. F. Hayllar* (ms. diary, North Herts. Museums). Dony (1967),

notes it as a casual from Hitchin (12/Z), *c.*1952 *G. L. Evans*. There are no more recent records.

Anchusa azurea Miller
Garden Anchusa
Introduced: neophyte.
First record: 1908.

This also appeared at the 'Anchusa Pit', 1908 *A. W. Graveson* (Hb. HTN); and there were subsequent records from the area until *c.*1917 *H. F. Hayllar*. Dony (1967) also notes that he found it in the same locality, actually in 1955 (Hb. HTN). More recently it was found as a casual at Blackbridge tip (11/X), 1971 *C. G. Hanson*; and during the recent survey it was recorded from bare, scrubby calcareous grassland on a roadside bank, Radwell (23/I), 2002 *T. J.*, a newcomer to the site.

Anchusa undulata L.
Undulate Anchusa
Introduced: casual.
First record: 1909.

This was also at the 'Anchusa Pit' in 1909 *A. W. Graveson*, and was re-found there in 1915 *H. F. Hayllar* (*Rep. Bot. Exch. Club*: 274 (1916)). There are no other records.

Anchusa arvensis (L.) M. Bieb.
Bugloss
Introduced: archaeophyte (?).
First record: 1814.
Tetrad occurrence: 13 (3%).
Decreasing (-13%).

This is now considered to be an ancient introduction (Preston *et al.*, 2002), although Stace (1997) listed it as native. It does seem to have a genuinely natural distribution, occurring consistently on bare, gravelly ground on the fluvo-glacial gravels mostly in central and southern Hertfordshire, where it is now a rather rare plant of gravel pits and arable field margins. Its occurrences are usually as a few plants, and although the current survey found it in 13 tetrads, it is probably genuinely scarcer now than in the 1960s. (Dony: 14 tetrads; 25 tetrads: 1950-1986)

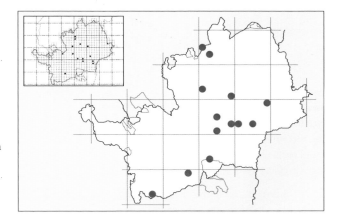

Map 481. *Anchusa arvensis.*

Cynoglottis barrelieri (All.) Vural and Kit Tan
False Alkanet
First record: (1909?) 1996.

One of the plants growing in the 'Anchusa Pit' was listed as
a synonym for this by Dony (1967), but may have referred to
Anchusa undulata. It was genuinely reported as an established
garden weed at Berkhamsted (90/Y), 1996 *E. M. Evans* (det. T. J.)
(Hb. HTN).

Genus: *Pentaglottis*

Pentaglottis sempervirens (L.) Tausch ex L. Bailey
Green Alkanet
Introduced: neophyte.
First record: 1843.
Tetrad occurrence: 174 (35%).
Increased massively (+3118%).

This was evidently still a casual escape from gardens in only a
few localities in the 1960s, although Dony (1967) does note that it
had become well-established at Barley. It has massively increased
in frequency since then, and is now often a persistent, invasive
weed in gardens, on roadside verges and waste ground elsewhere,
especially on river gravels and the Chalk.
(5 tetrads: Dony, ms. index; 30 tetrads: 1950-1986)

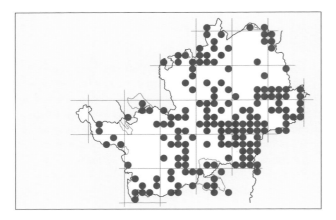

Map 482. *Pentaglottis sempervirens.*

Genus: *Borago*

Borago officinalis L.
Borage
Introduced: neophyte.
First record: *c.*1840.
Tetrad occurrence: 35 (7%).
Increased (+545%).

This has much increased over the last 20 years or so, as a result of
its cultivation in some areas as a crop for seed oil, but it is seldom
persistent for long periods. It has also remained a popular herb in
gardens, and is sometimes sown as a nectar source for bees. As a
result some of the records may be from deliberate introduction,
although most are of escapes on tips, waste ground and road
verges, or as crop relics round field margins.
(5 tetrads: Dony, ms. index; 10 tetrads: 1950-1986)

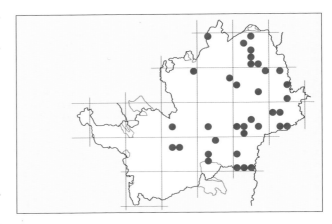

Map 483. *Borago officinalis.*

Genus: *Trachystemon*

Trachystemon orientalis (L.) Don
Abraham, Isaac and Jacob
Introduced: casual.
First (only) record: 1991.

This was found as an escape in Sherrards Park Wood (21/G), 1991
C. G. Hanson.

Genus: *Amsinckia*

Amsinckia lycopsoides (Lehm.) Lehm.
Scarce Fiddleneck
Introduced: neophyte.
First record: 1915.

Dony (1967) only gives one record, from Ware, 1915 *H. F. Hayllar*,
but his ms. index records its occurrence at Mead Lane Gravel Pit,
Hertford (31/G), 1919 and Ware tip (31/M), 1920 *A. W. Graveson*
(Hb. HTN), as well as a further occurrence at Stanstead Road
Gravel Pit, near Hertford (TL31), 1915 *H. F. Hayllar*. There have
been no more recent records.

[*Amsinckia calycina* (Moris) Chater

Dony (1967) reports a record of this, under the name
A. angustifolia Lehm., but it seems likely that this was an error for
A. micrantha.]

Amsinckia micrantha Suksd.
Common Fiddleneck
Introduced: neophyte.
First record: 1915.

In contrast to some other areas in eastern England, this has never
been common in the County. It was first seen at Ware (TL31),
1915 *A. Trower/G. C. Druce* (Dony, 1967), and was also seen at
Hertford (TL31), 1920 *A. W. Graveson* (*Rep. Bot. Exch. Club*:
136 (1921)), and again at Ware, 1923 *G. C. Druce* (*Rep. Bot. Exch.
Club*: 200 (1924)). The only recent record has been from a small
tip of garden refuse on Gustard Wood Common (11/S), 1999
T. J./G. P. Smith (Hb. HTN), although it is an occasional weed
in a garden at Ware (31/S), *C. G. Hanson*, where it was originally
introduced.

Asperugo procumbens L.
Madwort
Introduced: casual.
First record: *c.*1873.

The first record of this (Pryor, 1887) was from Easneye, and it was found as a rare casual from bird-seed until its last record in 1922 (Dony, 1967).

Genus: *Myosotis*

Myosotis scorpioides L.
Water Forget-me-not
Native.
First record: 1814.
Tetrad occurrence: 199 (41%).
Apparently increasing (+36%).

This is the usual forget-me-not by rivers and streams, and it is frequent in this habitat throughout the County. It also occurs by eutrophic ponds, and appears to have increased in such places. The recent survey showed it to be much more widespread than in the 1960s, with many more occurrences away from rivers, although some of this may be down to better recording.
(139 tetrads: Dony, 1967; 165 tetrads: 1950-1986)

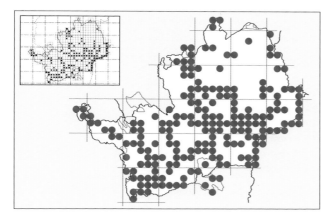

Map 484. *Myosotis scorpioides.*

Myosotis × *suzae* Domin (*M. scorpioides* × *M. laxa*)
Native.
First documented record: 1965.

The only records remain the one from Braughing (32/X), 1965 *P. Benoit* (Dony, 1967) and another reported, without a date, from Colney Heath (Stace, 1975). It may be frequent on the less calcareous soils, where the two plants meet.

Myosotis secunda A. Murray   Herts Rare
Creeping Forget-me-not
Native (and introduced?).
First record: 1844.

Never a common plant in the County, this was recorded in the 19th century from a few bogs around Little Berkhamsted, Bell Bar and Hatfield Woodside, and was thought to have become extinct, being last seen in Hatfield Park, *c.*1880 (Dony, 1967). However, it was found to be locally frequent in muddy patches in heathy ground recently opened up at Mardley Heath (21/P), 2008

T. J. (Hb. HTN), a most extraordinary re-appearance. However, heather seed was imported to this site in the 1990s, possibly from Thursley in Surrey, so it may have been introduced.

Myosotis laxa Lehm.
Tufted Forget-me-not
Native.
First record: 1820.
Tetrad occurrence: 44 (9%).
Decreasing quite markedly (-37%).

This is the native forget-me-not of naturally marshy places, ditches and old ponds, most often on the more acidic clays of south Hertfordshire, but also scattered in old habitats across the Boulder Clay. As such, it has decreased markedly since the 1960s, with the loss of marshy pastures and old ponds. It is now rare in west Herts., and has always been rare beside rivers.
(66 tetrads: Dony, 1967; 77 tetrads: 1950-1986)

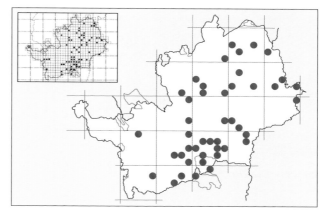

Map 485. *Myosotis laxa.*

Myosotis sylvatica Hoffm.
Wood Forget-me-not
Native (and introduced).
First record: 1875.
Tetrad occurrence: (143, overall; 9 as native) (29%; 2%).
Stable as a native; increased enormously as an introduction (+1113%).

As a presumed native, this was always apparently rare, and limited to damp, shady woodlands and by shaded water in the valley of the River Ash, from Easneye to Little Hadham (Pryor, 1887; Dony, 1967). Dony notes its occurrence elsewhere as an escape, but did not think it became established (his ms. index gives two such

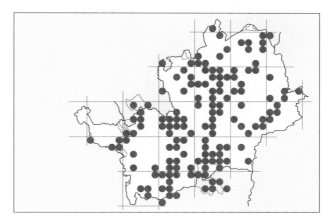

Map 486. *Myosotis sylvatica (overall distribution).*

records). From the mid-1970s, its garden form began to occur much more frequently in secondary woodland, scrub and by shaded roadsides, until the present survey has recorded the broad species across the County. However, the garden escape tends to have brighter blue, slightly smaller flowers, and the plant is usually less straggling than the native form, although care has to be taken to distinguish these from a garden form of *M. arvensis*. Map 486 shows the overall distribution and Map 486a shows its natural distribution in woodlands along the Ash Valley in east Herts., where it has remained constant since 1967. Elsewhere its occurrence is entirely owing to escapes or introductions from cultivation.

(9 tetrads: Dony, 1967 and 11 tetrads: ms. index; 42 tetrads: 1950-1986)

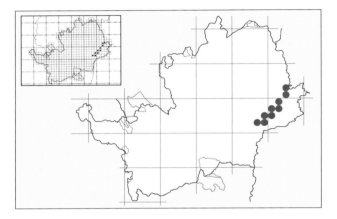

Map 486a. *Myosotis sylvatica (native distribution).*

Myosotis arvensis (L.) Hill
Field Forget-me-not
Introduced: archaeophyte.
First record: 1838.
Tetrad occurrence: 445 (91%).
Probably decreasing (-7%).

Until recently considered a native (Preston *et al.*, 2002), this is a familiar weed of cultivated ground, as well as occurring in disturbed habitats elsewhere, such as waste ground and tracks in woodland. It remains common throughout the County, and is probably present in every tetrad, although in some it can be scarce. It still occurs widely as an arable weed, but is far less abundant than it once was.

(452 tetrads: Dony, 1967; 460 tetrads: 1950-1986)

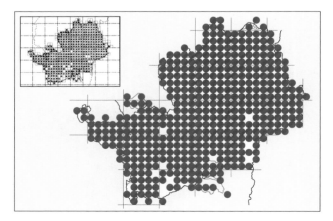

Map 487. *Myosotis arvensis.*

Myosotis ramosissima Rochel
Early Forget-me-not
Native.
First record: 1838.
Tetrad occurrence: 32 (7%).
Probably increased (+51%).

Although not common, this is a plant that is easily overlooked, owing to its early flowering. It grows in bare places on sandy or somewhat chalky soil, such as disturbed roadside banks, and the edges of gravel pits. As such, potential habitats have increased during the last 30 years, with the rash of gravel extraction in its strongholds on the fluvo-glacial gravels of central Herts. However, better recording has found it sparsely elsewhere, such as on road verges in north Hertfordshire.

(20 tetrads: Dony, 1967; 36 tetrads: 1950-1986)

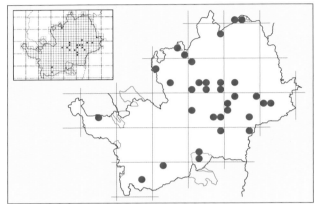

Map 488. *Myosotis ramosissima.*

Myosotis discolor Pers.
Changing Forget-me-not
Native.
First record: 1838.
Tetrad occurrence: 25 (5%).
Stable? (+13%).

This is an uncommon and rather enigmatic plant, found in rather open, bare places, usually on gravelly ground, sometimes in damp habitat, such as over-grazed river valley pastures, rarely in open forestry rides. Its occurrences can also be unpredictable, which may account for the fact that many of the recorded localities for it during the recent survey were not those where it was found in the 1960s, making assessment of change in its status difficult.

(21 tetrads: Dony, 1967; 32 tetrads: 1950-1986)

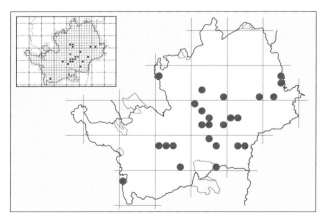

Map 489. *Myosotis discolor.*

Genus: *Lappula*

Lappula squarrosa (Retz.) Dumort.
Bur Forget-me-not
Introduced: casual.
First record: 1841.

This was first recorded at Ware (Webb and Coleman, 1849), and was subsequently found in a few scattered localities as a bird-seed alien until its last record in 1925 at Totteridge (Dony, 1967).

Genus: *Omphalodes*

Omphalodes verna Moench
Blue-eyed Mary
Introduced: casual.
First record: *c.*1844.

There are only two records for this: the first at Panshanger Park, 1844 *J. Ansell* (see: *Rep. Bot. Exch. Club*: 135 (1920)), and the sole record known to Pryor (1887) from a meadow at Bushey Hall (TQ19).

Genus: *Heliotropium*

Heliotropium europaeum L.
Heliotrope
Introduced: casual.
First (only) record: 1920.

This has been recorded once: at Ware (TL31), 1920 *M. L. Wedgwood* (*Rep. Bot. Exch. Club*: 389 (1921)).

Genus: *Cynoglossum*

Cynoglossum officinale L.   UK Near Threatened
Hound's-tongue
Native.
First record: 1751.
Tetrad occurrence: 7 (1%).
Rare, but possibly stable (+27%).

This has never been a common plant in the County (Pryor, 1887; Dony, 1967), occurring in disturbed, bare chalky and gravelly places. It seems to have gone from most of the area around Ware and Hertford where Dony recorded it, although it was found at Hatfield Park (20/J), 1971 *A. D. Marshall*; and also in Waterford Gravel Pit (north) (31/C), 2006 *T. J.* In north Herts., it was found at Reed Chalk Pit (33/N), 1977 *T. J./B. R. Sawford*, where it was last recorded in 1992 *T. J.*, but may persist. It has also been a feature of the area around Tingley Wood, Pirton (13/F) since at least the 1920s, where it occurs sporadically on disturbed chalk grassland, field margins and by an old chalk pit. Seven plants also appeared by a green lane at nearby Gravel Hill, Offley (12/P), 1997 *A. Dean*. One plant flowered following ditch clearance by the road at Heath Farm, Kelshall (33/D), 1998 *T. J.*, but has not been seen since; and it also occurred as a casual pavement weed at Berkhamsted (90/Y), 1995 *E. Evans*.
(5 tetrads: Dony, 1967; 8 tetrads: 1950-1986)

Cynoglossum germanicum Jacq.   UK Critically Endangered
Green Hound's-tongue   Herts Extinct
Native.
First record: 1857.

Dony (1967) seems to almost dismiss this as a native plant, merely noting that its 'only certain record was from Cassiobury Park, 1857' by S. Pidcock. However, Pryor (1887) also noted a record of it from a 'field by Digswell Water' (*c.*1880?) by W. Earley, which sounds implausible for a plant of woodland glades on loamy soils (Preston *et al.*, 2002), until we find that there is a specimen in Hb. OXF from nearby Lockley's Warren (21/M?) collected by a Dr Hodgson, undated. As both Cassiobury and Lockley's Warren were ancient wood pasture sites, it might indicate that glades in wood pasture were its lost natural habitat in the County.

Verbenaceae (Vervains)

Genus: *Verbena*

Verbena officinalis L.
Vervain
Introduced: archaeophyte.
First record: 1814.
Tetrad occurrence: 29 (6%).
Decreased slightly (-8%).

Vervain occurs occasionally as an ancient relic of cultivation, on roadside banks, rough pastures and waste ground, often near houses, preferring a free-draining, calcareous soil. Where it does occur, it can persist for long periods. The distribution map shows much the same spread of localities as Dony (1967) recorded, although some are new and others have been lost.
(30 tetrads: Dony, 1967; 34 tetrads: 1950-1986)

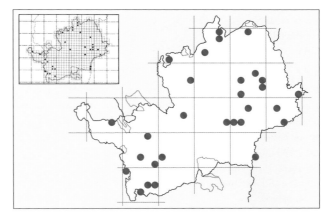

Map 490. *Verbena officinalis.*

Verbena bonariensis L.
Argentinian Vervain
Introduced: casual or neophyte.
First record: 2005.

This appeared as an escape from gardens half a mile away at Mymms Woods (20/B), 2005 *T. J.* Given hotter summers it will no doubt appear elsewhere.

Lamiaceae (Dead-nettle family)

Genus: *Stachys*

Stachys officinalis (L.) Trev. St Léon
Betony
Native.
First record: 1787.
Tetrad occurrence: 68 (14%).
Decreasing steadily (-42%).

This is a characteristic plant of mildly acidic unimproved grassland in pastures, hay meadows and woodland rides. With the overgrowth of woodland rides and the loss of old grassland, it is not entirely surprising that this attractive plant is decreasing quite fast. Many of its colonies are now very small, and nowhere is it common.
(112 tetrads: Dony, 1967; 138 tetrads: 1950-1986)

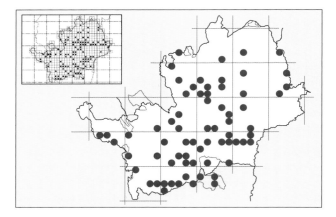

Map 491. *Stachys officinalis.*

Stachys byzantina K. Koch
Lamb's-ear
Introduced: neophyte.
First record: 1991.
Tetrad occurrence: 5 (1%).

This has become increasingly popular in gardens, and is consequently now being found as an outcast, sometimes persisitng on road verges. It was first found at Hadham Towers tip (41/I), 1991 *S. Watson*; and was subsequently found by a road at Stags End (01/Q), 1992 *T. J./G. Salisbury*; in Roundhill Wood (90/P), 1996 *A. D. Marshall*; on waste ground at Chorleywood (09/N), 2002 *P. J. Ellison*; and near Croxley Common Moor (09/X), 2003 *G. Hounsome.*

[*Stachys germanica* L.
Downy Woundwort

There is a record of this endangered native species of rough grasslands from a gravel pit at Great Amwell in the diary of H. F Hayllar, but without confirmation it must be doubted.]

Stachys sylvatica L.
Hedge Woundwort
Native.
First record: 1814.
Tetrad occurrence: 465 (95%).
Stable or marginally decreased (-3%).

This is a common component of the flora of rank hedgerows, scrub, secondary woodland and less abundantly in old woodland glades and rides. It is probably present in every tetrad, although a few produced no records.
(457 tetrads: Dony, 1967; and from 1950-1986)

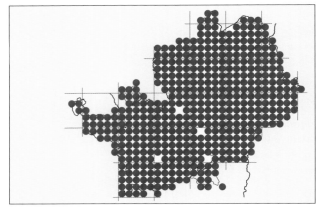

Map 492. *Stachys sylvatica.*

Stachys × *ambigua* Smith (*S. sylvatica* × *S. palustris*)
Hybrid Woundwort
Native.
First record: 1849.

This has never been a common plant in the County. Dony gave three 20th century records, but omitted one from Foxley's Wood, Stapleford (31/D), 1921 *A. W. Graveson* (Hb. HTN); while the specimen from Norton (Hb. HTN) collected by T. A. Dymes appears to be a form of *S. sylvatica*. A patch was also discovered at Marshmoor Meadow (20/I), 1988 *A. D. Marshall*.

Stachys palustris L.
Marsh Woundwort
Native.
First record: 1838.
Tetrad occurrence: 76 (16%).
Slightly increased (+17%).

This is a local plant of riversides, canals, ditches and damp places, mostly on neutral clay or alluvial soils. Its distribution shows that it might have increased somewhat, especially along ditches in central Hertfordshire, while it appears to have become less common by canals, where bank engineering works may have reduced opportunities for it to survive.
(62 tetrads: Dony, 1967; 78 tetrads: 1950-1986)

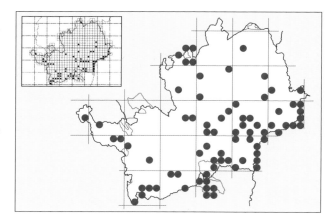

Map 493. *Stachys palustris.*

Stachys annua (L.) L.
Annual Yellow Woundwort
Introduced: casual.
First record: 1896.

There were a number of scattered records of this contaminant of grain subsequent to its first occurrence near Pirton, and it was last seen by J. G. Dony next to Sawtrees Wood (31/Z), 1956 (Dony, 1967).

Stachys arvensis (L.) L.   UK Near Threatened
Field Woundwort
Introduced: archaeophyte.
First record: 1838.
Tetrad occurrence: 3 (<1%).
Decreasing? (-44%).

This has never been a common plant in the County, found in cultivated fields, on a range of free-draining soils, including calcareous ones. Dony (1967) found it in a number of places, and there were records from Ridge (20/B), 1970 *J. P. Widgery*; and from Croxley (09/X), 1973 *J. A. Moore* prior to the survey. It has been found recently especially in a field below Bogs Wood, Albury (42/M), 1987 *J. L. Fielding*, where it remained abundant in 2001 *S. Watson* (Hb. HTN). It was also found on thin calcareous clay by Scales Park (43/H), 1989 *T. J./I. D. Marshall* (Hb. HTN); and on vegetable plots at Highcroft Farm, Bovingdon (00/C), 1999 *R. Keen* (det. T. J.) (Hb. HTN).
(5 tetrads: Dony, 1967; 7 tetrads: 1950-1986)

Genus: *Ballota*

Ballota nigra L.
Black Horehound
Introduced: archaeophyte.
First record: *c.*1820.
Tetrad occurrence: 417 (85%).
Possibly increased (+8%).

A frequent plant of hedgerows, scrub and woodland margins throughout the County. It may have increased slightly, although it remains scarce in the most open, arable landscapes on the Boulder Clay, and on parts of the Clay-with-Flints of the Chilterns dip-slope.
(366 tetrads: Dony, 1967; 386 tetrads: 1950-1986)

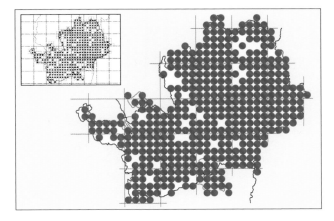

Map 493. *Ballota nigra.*

Genus: *Molucella*

Molucella laevis L.
Bells of Ireland
Introduced: casual.
First (only) record: 1986.

This was found as an established relic in a garden, on the site of an old greenhouse at Little Wymondley (22/D), 1986 *J. Short* (det. at Natural History Museum).

Genus: *Lamiastrum*

Lamiastrum galeobdolon (L.) Ehrend. and Polatschek
Yellow Archangel
Native.
First record: 1597.
Tetrad occurrence: 226 (46%).
Probably stable or slightly increased (+5%).

This is especially characteristic of ancient woodlands on the free-draining Clay-with-Flints soils of the Chilterns dip-slope, also occurring in old hedgerows in the same area, alongside Bluebells. Elsewhere it is less abundant, but occurs quite widely on the less acidic clays of south-eastern Hertfordshire, and on loams over Reading Beds or fluvo-glacial gravel. In north-eastern Hertfordshire, its scattered occurrences are almost always on isolated outcrops of Clay-with-Flints in the Boulder Clay zone. It is rare on the Chalk itself. The recent survey proved it to have remained remarkably stable. Map 495 shows the native subspecies *montanum* (Pers.) Ehrend. and Polatschek.
(205 tetrads: Dony, 1967; 224 tetrads: 1950-1986)

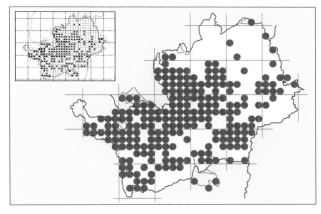

Map 495. *Lamiastrum galeobdolon* ssp. *montanum.*

The ornamental, silver-leaved ssp. *argentatum* (Smejkal) Stace, of uncertain horticultural origin (Map 495a), was first recorded at Potten End (00/E), 1986 *P. J. Kingsbury*. It is now a frequent escape across the County, especially on neutral or mildly acidic loams over gravel, more rarely on Clay-with-Flints. It rapidly becomes established vegetatively to form dense carpets in many roadside hedgerows, as well as in woodlands where garden refuse is dumped. It is not certain how much it may threaten the native subspecies in such places. It was recorded from 78 tetrads during the survey.

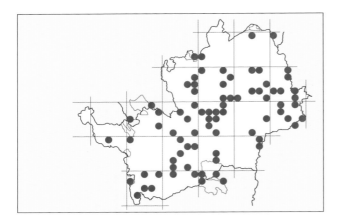

Map 495a. *Lamiastrum galeobdolon* ssp. *argentatum*.

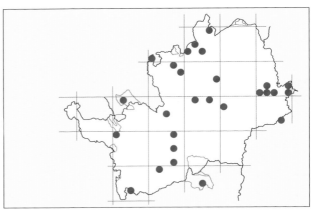

Map 497. *Lamium maculatum*.

Genus: *Lamium*

Lamium album L.
White Dead-nettle
Introduced: archaeophyte.
First record: 1814.
Tetrad occurrence: 474 (97%).
Stable (+1%).

This is a more or less ubiquitous plant of waysides, waste
ground and scrub throughout the County, forming one of the
characteristic plants of eutrophic ruderal vegetation, but not
usually occurring in ancient woodland or old grassland. Its habit
of flowering in winter makes it quite valuable for insects at that
time of year.

(447 tetrads: Dony, 1967; 448 tetrads: 1950-1986)

Lamium purpureum L.
Red Dead-nettle
Introduced: archaeophyte.
First record: 1748.
Tetrad occurrence: 461 (94%).
Probably stable (-3%).

This is an especially characteristic plant of disturbed ground and
waysides, particularly in the Spring. Its habit of becoming difficult
to find in high summer probably accounts for the few tetrads
where it was missed, although it is also less abundant than it once
was, owing to the decrease in vegetable cultivation in gardens, and
drastic losses from arable farmland.

(451 tetrads: Dony 1967; and from 1950-1986)

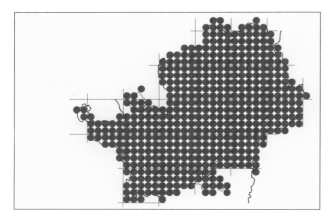

Map 496. *Lamium album*.

Lamium maculatum (L.) L.
Spotted Dead-nettle
Introduced: neophyte.
First record: 1910.
Tetrad occurrence: 27 (6%).
Increasing?

A plant of waysides and waste ground, usually near houses. The
first record was from near Haileybury (31/K), 1910 *J. E. Little*
(Dony, 1967). From records submitted to Dony (ms. index), it was
evidently quite widespread by the 1960s, but precise details are
lacking. It was recorded from 19 tetrads between 1970 and 1986;
and during the recent survey it was found in more, although in few
of these is it likely to be more than a casual.

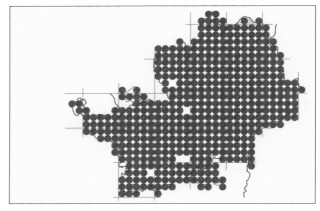

Map 498. *Lamium purpureum*.

Lamium hybridum Villars
Cut-leaved Dead-nettle
Introduced: archaeophyte.
First record: 1840.
Tetrad occurrence: 60 (12%).
Increased (+171%).

This is a rather unpredictable weed of cultivated or disturbed
ground on rich soils, sometimes where manure has been spread,
especially on the Boulder Clay. It was evidently also frequent
in the Hitchin area in the early 20th century (J. E. Little: ms.
notebooks), but Dony (1967) only recorded it sparsely across
northern Hertfordshire. Subsequent records showed it also to
occur occasionally in the south, while the recent survey found it
mainly as a plant of north-east Herts., thinly scattered elsewhere.
(21 tetrads: Dony, 1967; 28 tetrads: 1950-1986)

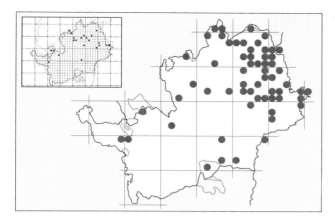

Map 499. *Lamium hybridum*

Lamium amplexicaule L.
Henbit Dead-nettle
Introduced: archaeophyte.
First record: 1814.
Tetrad occurrence: 106 (22%).
Stable or slightly increased? (+7%).

This was once a frequent weed of arable fields on the Chalk in northern Hertfordshire, also occurring elsewhere where the Chalk outcrops, as well as on calcareous gravels around Ware and Hertford. Although its distribution remains much as it was in the 1960s, if not slightly expanded, its abundance has drastically reduced where it occurs, through the use of weedkillers. It is often found in a cleistogamous form (with closed flowers), but when in full bloom is particularly attractive.
(94 tetrads: Dony, 1967; 115 tetrads: 1950-1986)

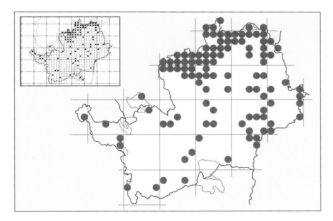

Map 500. *Lamium amplexicaule*.

Henbit Dead-nettle Lamium amplexicaule *with fully open flowers, Ashwell, 1997.*

Genus: *Sideritis*

Sideritis lanata L.
Introduced: casual.
First (only) record: 1915.

This was recorded from waste ground by Ware Cemetery (31/M), 1915 *H. F. Hayllar*, not at Hoddesdon, as given in Dony, 1967 (H. F. Hayllar diary, North Herts. Museums).

Sideritis romana L.
Introduced: casual.
First (only) record: 1909.

This was recorded from a disused gravel pit at Hoddesdon, (TL30), 1909, *H. F. Hayllar* (Salisbury, 1916) not 1915, as given by Dony, (1967).

Genus: *Galeopsis*

Galeopsis angustifolia Ehrh. ex Hoffm.   UK Critically Endangered
Red Hemp-nettle
Introduced: archaeophyte.
First record: 1819.
Tetrad occurrence: 2 (<1%).
Very rare, and decreased greatly (-93%).

This is an attractive plant of nutrient-poor, disturbed calcareous soils, and was formerly mainly an arable weed on the Chalk, but also occasionally on chalky Boulder Clay. It was evidently widespread in the 19th century (Pryor, 1887), and was still at least occasional in arable fields in the 1960s. Records since 1970 have been extremely few, and some of these might also have been mis-identifications of *G. tetrahit* or *G. bifida* in arable margins. Reliable records subsequent to Dony (1967) include: Loudwater (09/N), 1966 *P. J. Ellison*; near Great Wymondley (22/E), *c.*1970 *J. G. Dony*; near Batch Wood (10/J), *c.*1970 *D. J. Hinson*; by a canal towpath, Rickmansworth (09/L), 1976 (Burton, 1983); Hitches Valley, Therfield (33/J), 1978 *T. J./B. R. Sawford*; and near Stump Cross, Kelshall (33/D), 1981 *T. J./B. R. S.* The picture is also somewhat clouded by the fact that Dony's ms. index gives possibly uncertain records from tetrads 11/M, Y; 13/A; 21/E; and 42/Q which were not included on his map, while there were also records from elsewhere during the 1950s in 09/P and 12/E (*comm.*: Biological Records Centre, CEH Monks Wood). Since 1987 it has only been recorded twice: locally frequent in barley stubble at New Model Farm, Sarratt (09/P), 1991 *G. Salisbury/J. Saunders*; and a single plant on thin chalky soil by a wheat field at Deadman's Hill, Sandon (23/Y), 1999 *T. J.* It has no doubt succumbed to both weedkillers and nutrient enrichment.
(28 tetrads: Dony, 1967; 41 tetrads: 1950-1986)

Galeopsis speciosa Miller   UK Vulnerable
Large-flowered Hemp-nettle
Introduced: archaeophyte.
First record: 1843.
Decreased (-80%).

This has always been an uncommon plant in the County, occurring as an unpredictable weed of manured, cultivated fields, rarely in old gravel pits. Dony (1967) found it in a number of places in south-west Herts., and once near Reed. It appeared at Kings Langley Lake (00/R), 1971 *B. Ing* (record from former South Herts. Environmental Records Centre files); and in some quantity by the Hambridge Way at Pirton (13/K), 1986 *C. W. Burton*, an area where it had been recorded in the 19th century (Pryor, 1887). During the recent survey, it was only recorded once: again by the Hambridge Way, 1987 *C. W. B.*, but not thereafter.

Galeopsis tetrahit L.
Common Hemp-nettle
Native.
First record: (1824, as the aggregate), 1838.
Tetrad occurrence: 163 (for the species) (33%); 273 (for the aggregate).
Probably stable.

This is now a characteristic species of tall herb communities in woodland glades, hedgerows and arable field margins, mainly on the Clay-with-Flints, occasionally on gravel, London Clay or Boulder Clay, rarely on the Chalk itself. However, it is interesting to note that Pryor (1887) did not give many records from west Herts., and regarded it as more a plant of waste ground, occurring in coppices when they were cut. It may therefore not have been a woodland plant as such. Earlier records were also much confused with *G. bifida*, so the distribution map given here is the first attempt to map its true occurrence. However, owing to the difficulty of identifying it early in the season, it remains under-recorded. The map of the aggregate is also given (Map 501a), as a comparison with that given by Dony (1967).
(244 tetrads for the aggregate: Dony, 1967; 275 tetrads: 1965-1986)

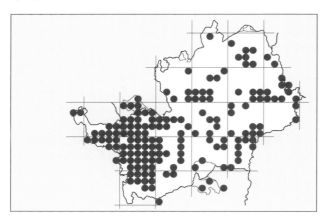

Map 501. *Galeopsis tetrahit s. str.*

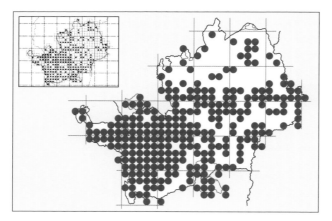

Map 501a. *Galeopsis tetrahit agg.*

Galeopsis bifida Boenn.
Bifid Hemp-nettle
Native.
First record: *c.*1880.
Tetrad occurrence: 93 (19%).
Pryor (1887) had recorded this fairly widely as a variety of *G. tetrahit*, but with some doubt about all but one of his records. Dony (1967) also appeared to be doubtful about it, although it is clearly distinct when in flower, except for hybrids (which have not been identified in the County). The current survey showed that it seems to be less clearly associated with the Clay-with-Flints than its relative, otherwise occurring in similar places, sometimes together with it.

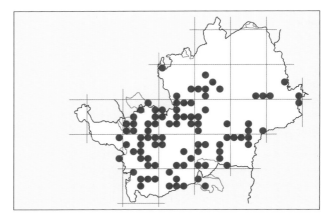

Map 502. *Galeopsis bifida.*

Genus: *Marrubium*

Marrubium vulgare L.   Herts Extinct
White Horehound
Introduced (formerly probably native).
First record: *c.*1820.

Dony (1967) thought that this had probably been a native of gravelly banks in the 19th century (Pryor, 1887), but had himself only seen it as a casual. Its 19th century records show that it occurred rarely but quite widely in semi-natural habitat on dry, gravelly commons, as well as on road verges. It appeared at Great Wymondley (22/J), 1972; and at Newnham (23/N) 1973 *C. G. Hanson*, on both occasions as a wool shoddy introduction. There have been no further records.

Genus: *Scutellaria*

Scutellaria galericulata L.
Skullcap
Native.
First record: 1814.
Tetrad occurrence: 65 (13%).
Decreasing (-12%).

Most frequently now found by larger rivers and canals, often growing from damp brickwork or lock-gates, this is really a native of wet woodland, tall fen and seasonally flooded unimproved grassland, where it often occurs as an opportunist on sedge tussocks. It has always been local in Hertfordshire, being largely restricted to the main river valleys in the south, where it seems to prefer neutral or even mildly acidic conditions. This might explain why it has always been rare in the north of the County, where

the only record recently has been from the River Hiz at Ickleford (13/W), 1982 *M. Yeo*.
(70 tetrads: Dony, 1967; 87 tetrads: 1950-1986)

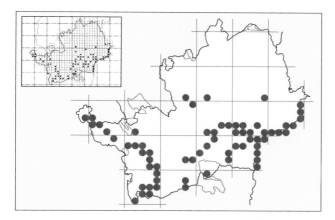

Map 503. *Scutellaria galericulata.*

Scutellaria minor L.   Herts Rare
Lesser Skullcap
Native.
First record: 1839.
Tetrad occurrence: 3 (<1%).
Rare, decreasing?

This has always been rare in the County since recording began, having been found on a few wet heaths and in the rides of heathy woodland in south Herts. during the 19th century. Dony (1967) thought it was relatively frequent in Bishop's Wood (09/Q), and also found it in Northaw Great Wood (20/X). It has survived in both these localities, although its occurrence in Bishop's Wood has apparently greatly diminished, owing to the loss of open heathy spaces following re-planting in the 1980s; while it has been found in two new localities in Northaw Great Wood (20/S, X), 2002, *etc. various observers*. It could perhaps re-appear in other old localities, if management allowed it to germinate, such as wet areas in Milwards Park.

Genus: Teucrium

Teucrium scorodonia L.
Wood Sage
Native.
First record: 1789.
Tetrad occurrence: 77 (16%).
Probably decreasing (-2%).

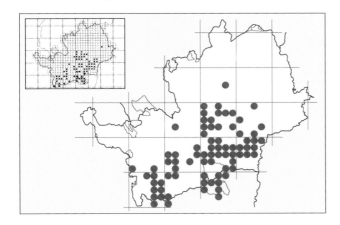

Map 504. *Teucrium scorodonia.*

A plant of heathy commons and scrubby, heathy woodland, this is probably an excellent indicator of the past extent of wood-pasture in south and central Hertfordshire, as it seems to occur wherever such sites were known to have existed in those parts of the County. Interestingly, however, it is apparently entirely absent from the Ashridge area. There is some evidence of a decrease, mainly from the loss of open spaces in woodlands through scrub growth, and occasionally through habitat destruction.
(75 tetrads: Dony, 1967; 91 tetrads: 1950-1986)

Genus: *Ajuga*

Ajuga reptans L.
Bugle
Native.
First record: 1814.
Tetrad occurrence: 305 (62%).
Stable (-2%).

Bugle is an important plant of woodland rides, damp neutral or mildly acidic grassland, often in wet flushes, as well as in scrub, providing a valuable nectar source for insects. It occurs across most of the County, but becomes rare or absent in the most intensively arable landscapes, as well as on the Chalk and on very acidic soils. Its occurrence at the tetrad level remains stable, because it can tolerate some habitat deterioration, but it is being lost from derelict grasslands and some overgrown woodland rides.
(296 tetrads: Dony, 1967; 313 tetrads: 1950-1986)

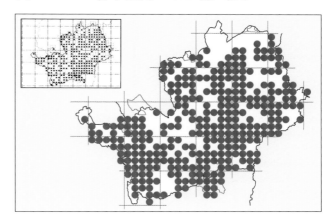

Map 505. *Ajuga reptans.*

Ajuga chamaepitys (L.) Schreber   UK Endangered
Ground Pine   Herts Extinct?
Native.
First record: 1805.

The native habitat of this plant is nutrient-poor, open places on dry, disturbed or friable soils over Chalk. It has always been rare in the County, but was at one time locally frequent on suitable ground around Ashwell, Pirton and Lilley especially. It was still in some quantity on disturbed arable beside Tingley Wood (13/F) as late as 1964 (Dony, 1967 and ms. index), but, despite frequent searches, has not been found here or elsewhere in the County, despite being present within yards of the County boundary at Barton, Beds., and until recently not far away at Morden Grange in Cambs. It has occurred as an escape at Rothamsted (11/G), 1989 *I. Denholm*.

Genus: *Nepeta*

Nepeta cataria L.   UK Vulnerable
Catmint
Introduced: archaeophyte.
First record: 1813.
Tetrad occurrence: 8 (2%).
Decreasing (-57%).

Formerly considered to be a native plant of scrub and hedgerows on Chalk, this is now thought to be an ancient introduction. It is now rare on the Chalk in north Herts., except near Barley (34/V), where it remains locally frequent beside shelterbelts. It also appeared at Rye Meads Sewage Works (31/V), 1996 *A. M. Boucher/C. G. Hanson/T. J.*, presumably of garden origin.
(17 tetrads: Dony, 1967; 22 tetrads: 1950-1986)

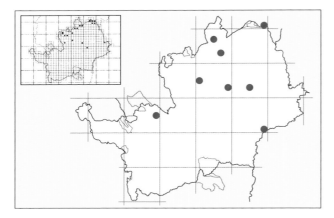

Map 506. *Nepeta cataria.*

Genus: *Glechoma*

Glechoma hederacea L.
Ground-ivy
Native.
First record: 1814.
Tetrad occurrence: 473 (96%).
Stable (-2%).

This is an abundant plant of nutrient-enriched woodlands, scrub, roadside verges and rough grassland across the County. It thrives especially in grassland where rabbits are abundant, because they do not like it. There is little evidence at the tetrad level that the species has changed in occurrence, but there are suggestions that

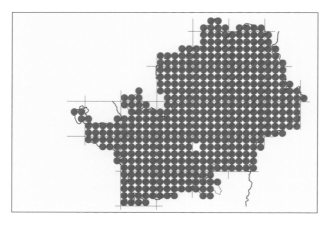

Map 507. *Glechoma hederacea.*

it may be more frequent now in ancient woodlands than formerly, perhaps from increased atmospheric deposition of nitrogen, or as a response to deer or rabbit pressure.
(458 tetrads: Dony, 1967; 460 tetrads: 1950-1986)

Genus: *Dracocephalum*

Dracocephalum parviflorum Nutt.
American Dragonhead
Introduced: casual.
First record: 1920.

The only records remain those by A. W. Graveson from Mead Lane, Hertford (31/G), 1920; and Cole Green (21/V), 1924 (Dony, 1967).

Genus: *Prunella*

[*Prunella grandiflora* (L.) Scholler
Large Self-heal

There is a mention of this as an escape in Hertfordshire in Sell and Murrell (2009), but I have no further information and its status is doubtful.]

Prunella vulgaris L.
Self-heal
Native.
First record: 1748.
Tetrad occurrence: 452 (92%).
Stable (-1%).

This is an almost ubiquitous plant of long-established lawns, but is also found in woodland rides and semi-improved grasslands on most soil types elsewhere, where it can be quite handsome and is a valuable nectar source. Although generally it shows no real signs of reduction in distribution, it is probably much less frequent now than formerly in agricultural grasslands, and its woodland ride habitats have also decreased.
(432 tetrads: Dony, 1967; 443 tetrads: 1950-1986)

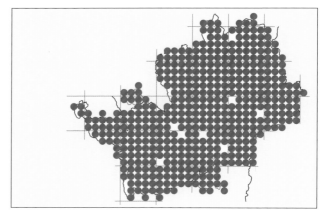

Map 508. *Prunella vulgaris.*

Prunella × *intermedia* Link (*P. vulgaris* × *P. laciniata*)
First record: 1912.

This was found with the parents at Therfield Heath (TL33) by C. E. Moss (Dony, 1967); and there is also a specimen collected by J. E. Little from Great Wymondley (TL22), 1927 in Hb. BM.

Prunella laciniata (L.) L.
Cut-leaved Self-heal
Introduced: neophyte.
First record: 1912.

A plant of calcareous grasslands, this was first found at the west end of Therfield Heath (33/J), 1912 *C. E. Moss* (Dony, 1967); and was subsequently found at Great Wymondley Springs (22/E), 1927 *J. E. Little*; near Berkhamsted, 1937 *M. Hoare*; and near Radlett (TQ19?), 1920 *R. S. Adamson* (Dony, ms. index). There have been no subsequent records.

Genus: *Melissa*

Melissa officinalis L.
Balm
Introduced: neophyte.
First record: *c.*1860.
Tetrad occurrence: 35 (7%).
Increasing.

Dony (1967) barely mentions this, although Pryor (1887) had given two early records. It was recorded up to 1986 in 6 scattered localities, usually near habitation or where garden refuse had been dumped. During the recent survey it was found in no less than 35 tetrads, with an apparent preference for calcareous, gravelly ground, especially around Watford and Rickmansworth.

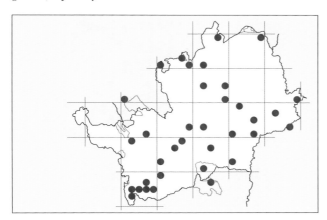

Map 509. *Melissa officinalis.*

Genus: *Ziziphora*

Ziziphora taurica M. Bieb.
Introduced: casual.
First (only) record: 1909.

The only record of this Asiatic species, cultivated for its volatile oils, is that from waste ground at Ware, 1909 by H. F. Hayllar (Salisbury, 1916) (not 1915, as given by Dony (1967)).

Genus: *Clinopodium*

Clinopodium ascendens (Jordan) Samp.
Common Calamint
Native.
First record: 1838.
Tetrad occurrence: 20 (4%).
Increased (or actually declining?) (+86%).

This attractive plant is an unpredictable, late-flowering and rather local herb of rough banks, wood margins and hedgerows on chalky

soils. Owing to its late flowering, it may have been overlooked in the 1967 survey, because it now seems to be more frequent than Dony reported it to be. However, old records suggest it was widespread across the County wherever dry chalky soils occurred, and more recent records would support this, also showing it to be most frequent in the north, around Hitchin, Stevenage and Baldock. It may now actually be slightly decreasing, because several sites where it was found during the 1980s no longer seem to have it.
(10 tetrads: Dony, 1967; 27 tetrads: 1950-1986)

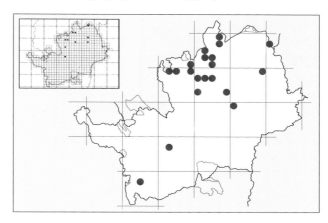

Map 510. *Clinopodium ascendens.*

Clinopodium calamintha (L.) Stace   UK Vulnerable
Lesser Calamint
Native.
First record: 1737.
Stable but very rare.

This was always a rare plant in the County, with old records from a number of sites on dry, calcareous gravels or loams over Clay-with-Flints, from Rickmansworth in the south-west to Datchworth, with one record from Pirton. It was reduced to one site on a road verge at Maple Cross (09/L) by the 1960s (Dony, 1967). During the survey, it was reported a number of times from the same locality, the latest being in 1999 *B. Harold/ J. Williamson/S. Bose.*

Clinopodium vulgare L.
Wild Basil
Native.
First record: *c.*1820.
Tetrad occurrence: 314 (64%).
Decreasing (-11%).

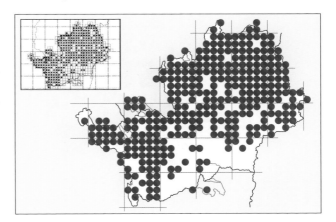

Map 511. *Clinopodium vulgare.*

Characteristic of rough grassland, scrub and hedgerows on a fairly nutrient-poor, moderately to strongly calcareous soil, this is a plant which is vulnerable to the degradation of road verges, and the nutrient-enrichment of scrub. As such, it is showing signs of retreat in many areas, although it remains widespread at the tetrad level.

(336 tetrads: Dony, 1967; 350 tetrads: 1950-1986)

Clinopodium acinos (L.) Kuntze   UK Vulnerable

Basil Thyme

Native.

First record: *c.*1820.

Tetrad occurrence: 10 (2%).

Decreasing markedly (-65%).

This is especially characteristic of short, nutrient-poor, sometimes slightly disturbed turf over Chalk. However, with nutrient-enrichment of road verges and loss of chalk grassland, it is not surprising it is rapidly disappearing. It was only found in small quantity in a few sites during the survey, mainly around Royston, but with outliers near Benington and elsewhere.

(27 tetrads: Dony, 1967; 36 tetrads: 1950-1986)

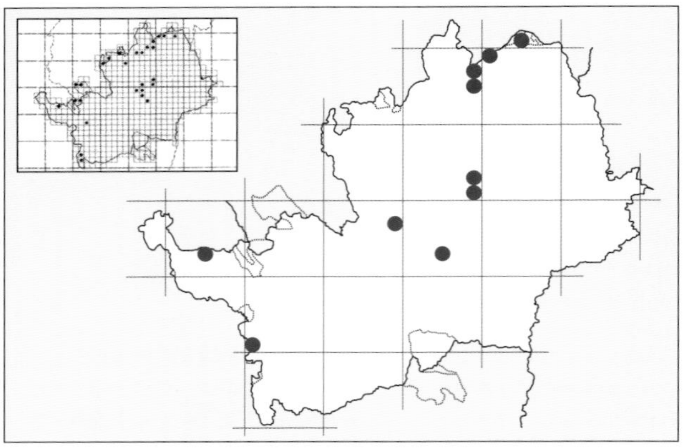

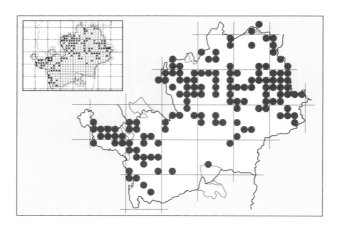

Map 512. *Clinopodium acinos.*

Genus: *Origanum*

Origanum vulgare L.

Wild Marjoram

Native.

First record: 1657.

Tetrad occurrence: 138 (28%).

Possibly increasing (+13%).

Found on chalky soils, in scrub on roadside verges, field banks and rough grassland, this plant seems to be at least moderately tolerant of nutrient-enrichment, and its apparent increase may reflect its better flowering in roadside banks following reduced mid-summer mowing. During the survey it was found mainly in the north of the County.

(116 tetrads: Dony, 1967; 130 tetrads: 1950-1986)

Genus: *Thymus*

Thymus pulegioides L.

Large Thyme

Native.

First record: (1748, for the agg.), 1903.

Tetrad occurrence: 51 (10%).

Decreasing (-28%).

A plant of nutrient-poor, short turf on Chalk and on calcareous sandy soils, which is also declining, but perhaps less markedly than other species of such habitats. It was once quite frequent in short turf on roadside banks, as well as on its more characteristic chalk grassland sites. It can be especially frequent on old anthills. Dony (1967) probably under-recorded it, because it is now known to occur alongside its rarer relative in several sites, including Therfield Heath, where Dony did not record it.

(67 tetrads: Dony, 1967; 75 tetrads: 1950-1986)

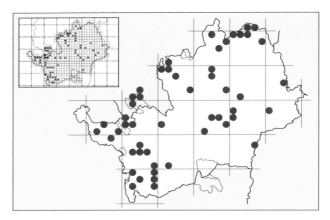

Map 514. *Thymus pulegioides.*

Thymus polytrichus A. Kerner ex Borbás

Wild Thyme

Native.

First record (as segregate): *c.*1880.

Tetrad occurrence: 21 (4%).

Probably decreasing.

It is almost impossible to judge any change in occurrence in this species, owing to past confusion with its relative, although it must be doubtful that it can have survived any better than *T. pulegioides*. It does seem to be generally rarer than *pulegioides* however. It is very often in the same habitat, usually slightly earlier flowering, although it is apparently rarely away from Chalk, the only site on moderately acidic soils (and here on anthills) being Patmore Heath (42/M), where it was confirmed by C. D. Pigott in the 1950s (Dony, 1967), and where it remained until recently alongside its relative, although neither could be found in 2008.

(3 tetrads: Dony, 1967; 7 tetrads: 1950-1986)

Map 513. *Origanum vulgare.*

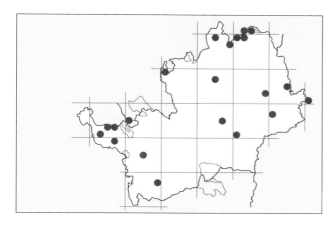

Map 515. *Thymus polytrichus.*

Genus: *Lycopus*

Lycopus europaeus L.
Gypsywort
Native.
First record: 1820.
Tetrad occurrence: 205 (42%).
Increased (+17%).

This is a characteristic plant of more or less permanently wet, neutral to mildly acidic habitats, such as pond margins and wet woodland. It can also tolerate quite significant levels of eutrophication, which is probably why it survives in heavily shaded ponds and wooded swamps long after most other wetland herbs have succumbed. Its increase appears to have been into new areas away from the river valleys, possibly as a response to eutrophication, but judging by the fact that it had apparently increased almost to current levels by 1986, it may no longer be spreading.
(166 tetrads: Dony, 1967; 197 tetrads: 1950-1986)

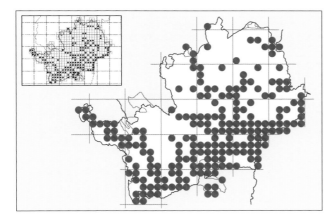

Map 516. *Lycopus europaeus.*

Genus: *Mentha*

This genus still presents some difficulties in identification, especially the various hybrids, and an attempt has been made to get difficult material expertly named. There seems, however, to have been a decrease in the occurrence of some of the rarer hybrids noted by earlier botanists.

Mentha arvensis L.
Corn Mint
Native.
First record: 1838.
Tetrad occurrence: 115 (23%).
Decreased markedly (-34%).

The common name of this is rapidly becoming a misnomer, because it is retreating into what is probably its natural habitat of damp mixed herbaceous vegetation, especially on clay soils, often in woodland rides, or now sometimes colonising seasonally inundated ground round gravel pits. Formerly it was widespread in damp arable fields on clay, where it was an important nectar source for late summer insects, but it is now rare in such places, being very vulnerable to weedkillers.
(165 tetrads: Dony, 1967; 186 tetrads: 1950-1986)

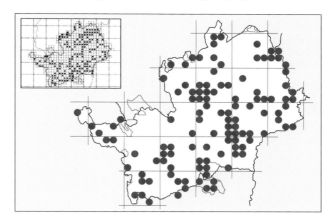

Map 517. *Mentha arvensis.*

Mentha × *verticillata* L. (*M. arvensis* × *M. aquatica*)
Whorled Mint
Native.
First record: *c*.1810.
Tetrad occurrence: 24 (5%).
Probably stable (+20%).

This sterile hybrid was formerly considered to be a separate species. It remains scattered across the County, much as Dony (1967) recorded it, being more common where *M. arvensis* remains frequent, although it can survive for long periods in some sites in the absence of its parents, reproducing vegetatively. It is usually in damp marshy habitats in woodland rides or by ponds, but can occur in disturbed habitats elsewhere.
(19 tetrads: Dony, 1967; 25 tetrads: 1950-1986)

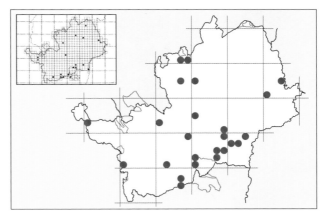

Map 518. *Mentha* × *verticillata.*

Mentha × *smithiana* R. A. Graham
(*M. arvensis* × *M. aquatica* × *M. spicata*)
Tall Mint
Introduced: neophyte.
First record: 1800.

A specimen of this rare escape from cultivation from the
Beechwood area (TL01), 1800, collected by Miss F. Sebright,
has been identified as this by R. A. Graham (*comm.*: Biological
Records Centre, CEH Monks Wood). Dony (1967) gave three
records, and there are single old records from TL31, 41 and TQ19/I
in the database at the B.R.C., all identified by R. A. Graham. The
most recent record is from Chorleywood (09/H), undated, given in
Burton (1983).

Mentha × *gracilis* Sole (*M. arvensis* × *M. spicata*)
Bushy Mint
Introduced: neophyte.
First record: 1912.

This is a rarely occuring natural hybrid, but is also often an
escape. The first record was from near Hertford (TL31), 1912
A. W. Graveson (conf. R. A. Graham) (Hb. HTN) (Dony, ms.
index). Dony (1967) also gave three other recent records. It
has since been found at a few tip sites: Purwell (22/E), *c.*1970
F. Bentley; Hitchin tip (13/V), 1970; Cole Green tip (21/Q), 1973,
1979; Ware tip (31/M), 1981; Waterford tip (31/C), 1982; and
lastly by the A1 at Stevenage (22/G), 1986 *C. G. Hanson*. There
have been no further records, although it could be overlooked or
mis-identified as *M.* × *verticillata*.

Mentha aquatica L.
Water Mint
Native.
First record: 1819.
Tetrad occurrence: 291 (59%).
Apparently increased (+23%).

In its natural habitat, this is frequent in permanently wet places,
by streams, and wet rides in woods. It also colonises new wetlands
readily, such as by gravel pits. Its apparent increase may be in
part due to better recording, but it does appear to have genuinely
increased away from river valleys.
(225 tetrads: Dony, 1967; 242 tetrads: 1950-1986)

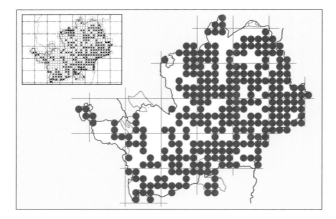

Map 519. *Mentha aquatica.*

Mentha × *piperita* L. (*M. aquatica* × *M. spicata*)
Peppermint
Introduced: neophyte.
First record: 1690.
Tetrad occurrence: 5 (1%).

This can occur as a natural hybrid in wetlands but is most often an
escape from cultivation on waste ground, although it has always
been rare. Dony (1967) gave a couple of records and there were
earlier ones given by Pryor (1887). It was found by the railway at
Hitchin (12/Z), 1977 (*comm.*: ITE Railway Survey) and on waste
ground at Baldock (23/L), 1985 *K. Robinson* (det. T. J.) (Hb.
HTN). During the recent survey, it was also found at St John's
Road Cemetery, Hitchin (12/Z), 1987 *S. Gorton*; Birchall Lane
(21/Q), 1990 *A. M. Boucher*; Elstree (19/X), 1995 *A. R. Outen*;
Wormley West End (30/M), 1995 *A. M. Boucher*; and Sopwell
Meadows, by R. Ver (10/M), 2005 *T. J.* (Hb. HTN).

Var. *citrata* (Ehrh.) Briq. **Eau-de-Cologne Mint** has been
recorded from Northaw (20/R), 1921 *A. W. Graveson* (det. R. A.
Graham) (Hb. HTN); and from Bishop's Stortford (42/V), 1961
J. L. Fielding (Hb. HTN) (Dony, 1967 – who gave the tetrad in
error as 41/V).

Mentha spicata L.
Spearmint
Introduced: archaeophyte.
First record: *c.*1806.
Tetrad occurrence: 32 (7%).
Decreased (-28%).

This cultivated mint, derived from hybrids between Round-leaved
Mint *M. suaveolens* and the non-native Horse Mint *M. longifolia*
Hudson, has been the source of many errors of identification,
because it comes in various forms, glabrous and hairy. The current
distribution map shows the continued wide scatter of escapes
across the County, but there is evidence for a decrease, especially
as Dony probably under-recorded it, owing to the confusion with
M. longifolia.
(42 tetrads: Dony, 1967; 59 tetrads: 1950-1986)

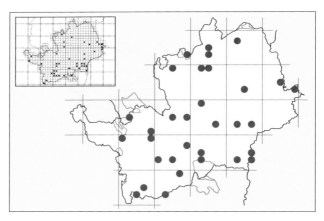

Map 520. *Mentha spicata.*

Mentha × villosa Hudson (*M. spicata × M. suaveolens*)
Apple Mint
Introduced: neophyte.
First record: 1919.
Tetrad occurrence: 20 (4%).
Apparently increased substantially (+583%).

This is a favourite garden mint, and frequently occurs as a throw-out, which can persist. The usual form is var. *alopecuroides* (Hull) Briq., which may have been mistaken formerly for the true *M. suaveolens*. Var. *villosa* has also been recorded in the past. (3 tetrads: Dony, 1967; 11 tetrads: 1950-1986)

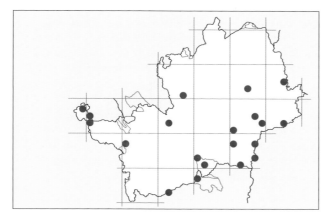

Map 521. *Mentha × villosa.*

Mentha × villosonervata Opiz (*M. spicata × M. longifolia*)
Sharp-toothed Mint
Introduced: neophyte.
First record: 1950.

Dony (1967) does not mention this plant, which is essentially a back-cross with *M. spicata*, although it was collected from Croxley Hall (09/S), 1950 *R. A. Graham* (Hb. Graham) (*comm.*: Biological Records Centre, CEH Monks Wood); and there is also a record from a tip at Welwyn Garden City (TL21), 1958 *C. C. Townsend* in the BSBI's Vascular Plant Database. Dony himself also collected what he named as '*M. longifolia* var. *horridula*', probably this, from Whitwell (12/V), 1959 (Hb. HTN). A record has also been reported from TL22, without locality details, 1970 (det. R. A. Graham) (*comm.*: B.R.C.). During the current survey, the plant was only found at New England Moor (43/C), 1999 *R. Keen* (det. T. J.) (conf. R. M. Harley) (Hb. HTN).

Mentha suaveolens Ehrh.
Round-leaved Mint
Introduced? [native in the U.K.].
First record: 1846.

Dony (1967) cast doubt on all earlier records of this, owing to the likely confusion with *M. × villosa*. However, there is apparently a specimen that I have not seen in Hb. OXF from TL21, 1846 (det. R. M. Harley) (*comm.*: B.R.C.), possibly from the Archer's Green site given by W. H. Coleman (Webb and Coleman, 1849). Dony did, however, give the record from near Hertford (20/Z), 1933 *J. E. Lousley*, which is from the same area (Water Hall) as other records listed in Pryor, suggesting it may have been a long-standing site, if not native. Finally, a specimen from Pole Hole tip (41/L), 1990 *S. Watson* has been named as this by R. M. Harley (Hb. HTN).

Mentha pulegium L.   UK Endangered
Pennyroyal
Native.
First record: 1839.
Extinct as native?

Coleman knew this as a rare plant on wet, muddy ground by ponds on old commons in south Herts., and with one or two records from elsewhere, such as Little Wymondley. It survived at Brickendon (30/J) and Goose Green (30/N) until about 1926; and at Tewin Upper Green (21/S) until at least 1915. Loss of horse and cattle grazing on commons was no doubt the reason for its demise. Its appearance on disturbed ground near the R. Hartsbourne at Carpenders Park (19/G), 2003 *M. Spencer* (Hb. HTN) suggests an introduction, although the colony appeared natural enough. The area has subsequently been regularly mown, and very few plants survived in 2005 *T. J.*

Genus: *Lavandula*

Lavandula angustifolia Mill.
English Lavender
Introduced: casual.
First record: 1996.

This is no doubt more frequent as an escape than the three current records suggest, as it readily seeds into stony, barren ground. It was first recorded as a pavement weed at Watton-at-Stone (21/Z), 1996; and was subsequently found at Hitchin (12/Z), 1997 *T. J.* and S. of Dunstable (02/A) (VC20 [Beds.]), 1999 *T. J./G. P. Smith*. There is some doubt about whether the hybrid Garden Lavender *L. × intermedia* Loisel., which some suggest can be fertile, may also be involved with some of these occurrences (Sell and Murrell, 2009).

Genus: *Rosmarinus*

Rosmarinus officinalis L.
Rosemary
Introduced: casual.
First (only) record: 1995.

This has been found once only 'in the wild': as a pavement weed in St Albans (10/N) *A. M. Boucher*.

Genus: *Salvia*

This large genus contains a wide range of often showy plants which escape from gardens, as well as deriving from importations with grain, which may explain the large number of species which have occurred around Ware and Hertford. Their identification can often be difficult.

Salvia officinalis L.
Sage
Introduced: casual.
First record: 1996.

This was first noted, probably as a relict of cultivation, at a former allotment site at Farnham Road, Bishop's Stortford (42/W), 1996 *A. R. Outen*. It was also found in a more natural setting on a rough road verge at Bedmond Lane, St Albans (10/I), 2003 *A. Harris* (det. T. J.) (Hb. HTN).

Salvia splendens Ker Gawler
Scarlet Sage
Introduced: casual.
First (only) record: 1971.

This garden bedding plant was found as a throw-out at Bulls Mill tip (31/D) *C. G. Hanson*.

Salvia reflexa Hornem.
Mintweed
Introduced: casual.
First record: 1958.

This bird-seed alien has a more genuinely 'wild' place in the County flora. It was first found at Hoddesdon tip (30/U) and at Bulls Mill tip (31/D), 1958 *J. G. Dony* (ms. index), and he also found it at Pye Corner tip (41/L), 1964 (Dony, 1967). More recently it turned up at Grove Pit, Hitchin (13/V), 1968 *J. G. D.* and on waste ground at Ware Station (31/S), 1985 *C. G. Hanson*.

Salvia sclarea L.
Clary
Introduced: casual.
First (only) record: 1945.

This fine Mediterranean plant was found as an escape near Tring (SP91) *J. E. Dandy* (Dony, 1967). There were no subsequent records.

Meadow Clary Salvia pratensis *Ware Road, Hertford, 1989.*

Salvia pratensis L. UK Near Threatened
Meadow Clary
Introduced? [native in the U.K.].
First record: 1909.
Tetrad occurrence: 3 (<1%).

The first record of this somewhat enigmatic plant was from a chalk pit near Hertford, 1909 *A. W. Graveson*, where it also occurred in 1919 (Dony, 1967 and ms. index). It was also recorded from Hoddesdon in 1910 *H. F. Hayllar* (Dony, ms. index). In 1957, it was found on railway banks at Letchworth Station (23/B) *I. Spalding* (det. S. M. Walters) (Hb. CGE). In 1967 it turned up in rough grass over an old pit at St Ippollitts (12/Y) *F. Bentley* (Dony, 1969, where it was erroneosly recorded as new to the County, having previously been recorded under the name *S. bertolonii*). More recently, it was found, interestingly, near an old chalk pit at Ware Road, Hertford (31/L), 1988 *A. M. Boucher* (Hb. HTN), suggesting this may have been the site of its earlier records. It has also been found, just in Herts., by Farnham Quarry (42/W), 1994, 2004 *S. Watson* (Hb. HTN); and as locally frequent on an area of dumped ground in horse pastures at Whippendell Bottom, Chipperfield (00/L), 1991 *G. Salisbury/J. Saunders* (Hb. HTN). Whether any of these sites represent genuinely 'native' occurrences is doubtful.

Salvia nemorosa L.
Balkan Clary
Introduced: casual.
First (only) record: 1984.

This was found as a casual on disturbed ground by the old railway at Amwell Quarry (31/R), 1984 *T. J.* (Hb. HTN).

Salvia × *sylvestris* L. (*S. nemorosa* × *S. pratensis*)
Introduced: casual.
First record: 1875.

This was first found at Ware Park Mill (31/G), 1875 *T. B. Blow*, no doubt as a garden escape. There were a number of subsequent records from the same area until 1917 (Dony, 1967 and ms. index).

Salvia villicaulis Borbás.
Introduced: casual.
First (only) record: 1920.

There is a specimen from a field near Bulls Mill (31/D), 1920 collected by A. W. Graveson (Hb. HTN) (Dony (1967), as *S. amplexicaulis* Lam.). How it got there is unknown.

Salvia verbenaca L. Herts Rare
Wild Clary
Native.
First record: 1814.
Tetrad occurrence: 5 (1%).
Rare, but possibly stable (+11%).

Wild Clary has always apparently been rare in Herts., but the often small size of its colonies means it is particularly vulnerable. It often relies on frequent mowing of the calcareous banks where it grows for survival in the face of rank vegetation, but this also means it only occasionally manages to set seed. The most reliable colony in the County occurs on the steep lower slopes of Windmill Hill, Hitchin (12/Z), where it has been known since at least 1907. During the recent survey it was also found on old lawns at

Bayfordbury (31/A), 1996 *A. M. Boucher/C. G. Hanson*, where it was known in the 1950s (Dony, 1967); by a ditch at Cabbage Green, Benington (32/C), 1997 *G. P. Smith*; in thin grass under a new plantation at Barley (34/V), 1997 *T. J.*, possibly introduced; and on a road bank at Claybush Hill, Ashwell (23/U), 1988, *etc.* *T. J.*, where it has been known on and off for 160 years (Pryor, 1887), as well as on a bank by Station Road in the village. It was also present on a road verge by the entrance to the lane to Holwell on the A600 N. of Hitchin (13/R), 1985 *T. J./B. R. Sawford*, but has not been seen there recently. Two other sites known to Dony have been lost in the last 30 years.
(4 tetrads: Dony, 1967; 7 tetrads: 1950-1986)

Salvia virgata Jacq.
Meadow Sage
Introduced: casual.
First (only) record: 1914.

The only record remains that from a gravel pit at Ware (Dony, 1967).

Salvia viridis L.
Annual Clary
Introduced: casual.
First record: 1922.

This occurs rarely on waste tips. It was recorded (as *S. horminum*) in Dony, 1967; and more recently has been found at Bulls Mill tip (31/D), 1971; Waterford tip (31/C), 1981 *C. G. Hanson*; Potten End (00/E), 1986 *P. J and S. Kingsbury* (Hb. HTN); and on waste ground at Kinsbourne Green (11/C), 1989 *J. F. Southey* (Hb. HTN).

Salvia verticillata L.
Whorled Clary
Introduced: neophyte.
First record: 1857.
Decreased (-85%).

Dony (1967) gives six recent sites for this, often by railways, although its first record was from a canal bank near Hertford (Pryor, 1887). It was last seen at the railway sidings at Hitchin (12/Z), 1978 *B. Wurzell*; but otherwise it only seems now to survive at a long-standing colony on railway banks at Kings Langley (00/R), where it was recorded in 1992 *G. Salisbury/ J. Saunders* (Hb. HTN).

Hippuridaceae (Mare's-tail family)

Genus: *Hippuris*

Hippuris vulgaris L.
Mare's-tail
Native.
First record: 1737.
Tetrad occurrence: 21 (4%).
Decreasing (-28%).

Native in ponds and slow-flowing streams, this also can colonise new water bodies, such as gravel pits, but is probably affected by eutrophication. It is most frequent in water bodies associated with the upper Lea and its tributaries.
(28 tetrads: Dony, 1967; 36 tetrads: 1950-1986)

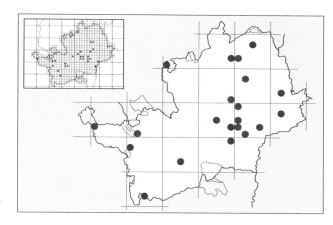

Map 522 *Hippuris vulgaris.*

Callitrichaceae (Water Starworts)

Genus: *Callitriche*

This genus is readily recognised in both still and flowing waters, but identification of species can be problematic, even with flowering and fruiting material. The accounts given here are an attempt to name material based initially on the understanding of species concepts given in Stace (1997), updated by Lansdown (2006), and from aids to identification provided by R. V. Lansdown in Rich and Jermy (1998). More recently, the taxonomy has been stabilised by the publication of Landsown (2008), but too late to influence recording. All species are under-recorded, especially in west Herts. Records of the genus in aggregate were made from 294 tetrads during the Flora Survey.

Callitriche stagnalis Scop.
Common Water-starwort
Native.
First record: (1823, for the aggregate), *c.*1840.
Tetrad occurrence: 198 (40%).
Probably stable (+98%).

This is the most widespread species in the County, occurring most often in ponds, but also in muddy backwaters of streams, and often on muddy ground in woodland rides, where it can be difficult to identify with certainty because of its altered appearance and lack of fruits. Its distribution appears to reflect a preference for neutral to moderately acidic conditions. Dony (1967) gave a map which is very uneven, and it is therefore difficult to compare

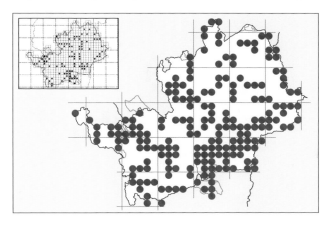

Map 523 *Callitriche stagnalis.*

with the current survey.
(95 tetrads: Dony, 1967; 157 tetrads: 1950-1986)

Callitriche platycarpa Kütz.
Various-leaved Water-starwort
Native.
First record: 1843.
Tetrad occurrence: 20 (4%).
Decreased? (-29%).

Regarded by a number of earlier botanists as a variety of
'*Callitriche verna*', although recognised by W. H. Coleman as
a separate species (Webb and Coleman, 1849). Dony (1967)
made some attempt to separate records of this, with help from
P. M. Benoit. Its distribution, however, remains uncertain, as it is
not always easy to identify, especially when not in fruit. It appears
to prefer running streams and more calcareous water. It was
reported from 22 tetrads during the survey, although two of these
need further examination. It certainly does not appear to be the
'most abundant species' (Lansdown, in Preston *et al.*, 2002), in
Hertfordshire at least.
(27 tetrads: Dony, 1967; 32 tetrads: 1950-1986)

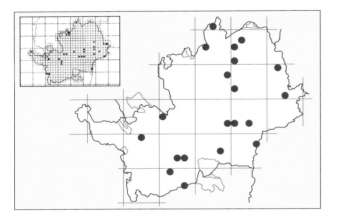

Map 524 *Callitriche platycarpa.*

Callitriche obtusangula Le Gall
Blunt-fruited Water-starwort
Native.
First record: 1876.
Tetrad occurrence: 32 (7%).
Probably stable (+38%).

This is apparently most frequent in deeper calcareous rivers and
streams, although it does occasionally occur in still water. It is
especially characteristic of the upper reaches of the R. Lea and its

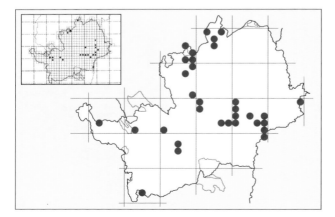

Map 525 *Callitriche obtusangula.*

tributaries around Hertford. It is also now known to be frequent in
both the Hiz and Ivel systems, and in the Rhee around Ashwell. It
is probably very under-recorded in the rivers Gade and Ver, *etc.*
(22 tetrads: Dony, 1967; 30 tetrads: 1950-1986)

Callitriche brutia Petagna
Intermediate Water-starwort
Native.
First record: 1846.
Tetrad occurrence: 40 (8%).
Increased? (+215%).

The taxonomic treatment of this plant has been confused for
a long time. Lansdown (2006, 2008) has returned to the 19th
century view that *C. hamulata* and *C. brutia* are the same species,
differing at varietal level, and this treatment is followed here.
The principal variety recorded in Hertfordshire appears to be
var. *hamulata* (Kütz. ex Koch), although there are old records of
'*Callitriche brutia*' which suggest that the pedunculate form may
also exist, although I know of no specimens to support this. Webb
and Coleman (1849) regarded the plant as one of spring sources,
but records suggest it is most frequent in still or slow-flowing,
less calcareous waters. It also shows signs of having increased,
possibly through enrichment of watercourses.
(12 tetrads: Dony, 1967; 21 tetrads: 1950-1986)

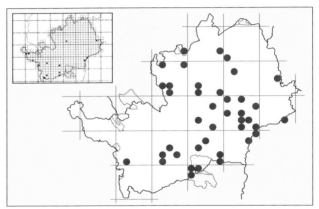

Map 526 *Callitriche brutia.*

Plantaginaceae (Plantain family)

Genus: *Plantago*

Plantago coronopus L.
Buck's-horn Plantain
Native [and introduced].
First record: 1814.
Tetrad occurrence: 50 (10%).
Increased substantially (+685%).

This was apparently entirely a very rare native species by the
1960s, limited to a few remnant gravelly, heathy sites, such as
Mardley Heath (21/P), where it remains in its more natural
habitat of thin, bare, mildly acidic grassland (Dony, 1967).
However, it had occurred quite frequently on bare ground by
gravelly roads in the 19th century, and it is therefore interesting
to find that, encouraged by salt, it has re-appeared in such places
across much of the County since the early 1990s.
(6 tetrads: Dony, 1967, and from 1950-1986)

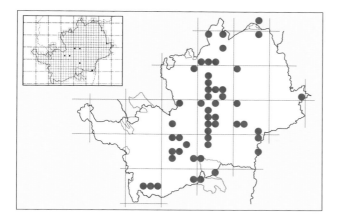

Map 527. *Plantago coronopus.*

Plantago maritima L.
Sea Plantain
Introduced [native in the U.K.].
First record: 1983.

Plants of this were found by the A414 at Boxmoor (00/N), 1983 *A. D. Marshall* (Hb. HTN), but there have not been any further records. It should be looked for by salted roads.

Plantago major L.
Great Plantain
Native.
First record: 1724.
Tetrad occurrence: 480 (98%).
Stable (-2%).

An abundant weed of lawns, roadsides, waste ground and short grassland throughout the County. Although recorded in slightly fewer tetrads proportionately than in the 1960s, there is no evidence of any decrease. No attempt has been made to study the subspecies in the County.
(464 tetrads: Dony, 1967 and from 1950-1986)

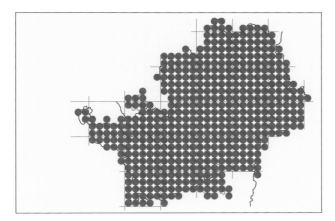

Map 528. *Plantago major.*

Plantago media L.
Hoary Plantain
Native.
First record: 1748.
Tetrad occurrence: 237 (48%).
Decreasing (-17%).

This is still mostly a plant of the Chalk and the calcareous Boulder Clay in north and north-east Herts., and is increasingly often

limited especially to churchyards and mown road verges. There is quite strong evidence of a decrease in its occurrence, owing to the loss of short, unimproved grassland across much of its range.
(270 tetrads: Dony, 1967; 293 tetrads: 1950-1986)

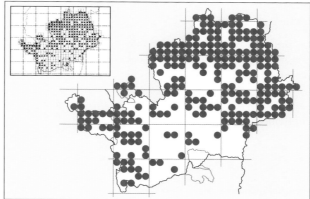

Map 529. *Plantago media.*

Plantago lanceolata L.
Ribwort Plantain
Native.
First record: 1724.
Tetrad occurrence: 479 (98%).
Stable (-2%).

Mainly a plant of semi-improved or unimproved neutral or calcareous grassland, but tolerating a wide range of conditions, and often colonising waste ground. The proportional recorded decrease is not significant.
(463 tetrads: Dony 1967, 464 tetrads: 1950-1986)

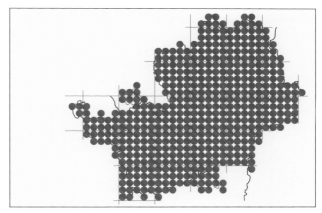

Map 530. *Plantago lanceolata.*

Plantago arenaria Waldst. and Kit.
Branched Plantain
Introduced: casual.
First record: 1916.

This was recorded from Ware and Little Dudswell in Dony (1967). There was also a record from Royston, 1926 *A. W. Graveson* (Hb. HTN). It is just possible that one or other of these may have been *P. afra* L. There have been no recent records.

Genus: *Littorella*

Littorella uniflora (L.) Asch.   Herts Extinct
Shoreweed
Native.
First (only) record: 1843.

This formerly occurred in 'wet spots towards the S. end of Berkhamsted Common' (Webb and Coleman, 1849), but has not been seen since.

Buddlejaceae (Butterfly-bush family)

Genus: *Buddleja*

Buddleja davidii Franchet
Butterfly-bush
Introduced: neophyte.
First record: *c.*1950.
Tetrad occurrence: 183 (37%).
Continuing to increase steadily (+3291%).

This was apparently first noticed as an escape at Bishop's Stortford about 1950 *D. McClintock*, although the exact date is not known. It was certainly at Wormley by 1955 *R. M. Payne* (Dony, ms. index). Unfortunately Dony (1967) scarcely mentions the plant, and so there is no real record of its early spread, although his ms. index does give five records. It was certainly appearing by railways in the 1970s, and by 1980 it was beginning to appear in old gravel pits and on road verges, *etc.* The current survey found it to be widespread and locally abundant on waste ground, especially on the river gravels in the Lea and Colne valleys, but also around Hitchin and Royston on Chalk. It forms a dominant part of a characteristic Buddleia/Birch/Sallow/Sycamore scrub alongside railways and on stony waste ground elsewhere. It also colonises decaying buildings, where it accelerates the process of dilapidation. Most recently it has begun to appear in clearings in open woods on gravelly soils.
(5 tetrads: Dony, ms. index; 45 tetrads: 1950-1986)

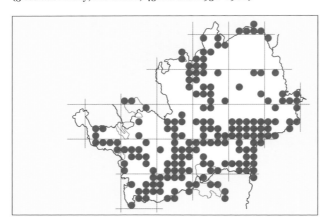

Map 531. *Buddleja davidii.*

Buddleja × *weyeriana* Weyer (*B. davidii* × *B. globosa*)
Weyer's Butterfly-bush
Introduced: casual.

This was found, possibly deliberately introduced, on Harpenden Common (11/G), 2001 *E. Anderson/L. Mottram.*

Oleaceae (Ash family)

Genus: *Forsythia*

Forsythia × *intermedia* hort. ex Zabel
(*F. suspensa* × *F. viridissima*)
Forsythia
Introduced: casual.
First record: 1995.

Forsythia was noted as having 'been there years' near the carpark at Bencroft Wood (30/I), 1995 *A. M. Boucher*. It was also noted during the survey as an escape at Warrengate Farm (20/G) (VC21 [Herts.]), 1996 *A. D. Marshall.*

Genus: *Fraxinus*

Fraxinus excelsior L.
Ash
Native.
First record: 1657.
Tetrad occurrence: 475 (97%).
Stable (-2%).

An abundant and widespread tree of semi-natural woodlands, especially on more calcareous soils, but also a frequent colonist of calcareous scrub and waste ground. Although the frequency at the tetrad level gives no evidence of increase, its occurrence in scrub and waste ground has probably grown substantially since the 1960s.
(462 tetrads: Dony, 1967; 464 tetrads: 1950-1986)

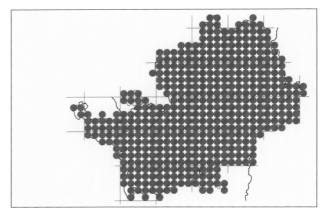

Map 532. *Fraxinus excelsior.*

Genus: *Syringa*

Syringa vulgaris L.
Lilac
Introduced: neophyte.
First record: 1920.
Tetrad occurrence: 33 (7%).
Increasing slowly.

J. E. Little recorded this from the Hitchin area, and in a plantation by Therfield Heath (= Fordham's Wood) (Dony, ms. index), but Dony himself ignored it. An escape was noted at Purwell (22/E), *c.*1970 *F. Bentley*, but only during the recent survey was any attempt made to map the species properly. It has been found to occur quite widely, especially on railway banks, and including the old bushes which still exist at Fordham's Wood (33/J).

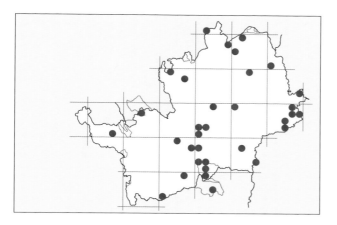

Map 533. *Syringa vulgaris.*

Genus: *Ligustrum*

Ligustrum vulgare L.
Wild Privet
Native.
First record: 1814.
Tetrad occurrence: 341 (70%).
Increased? (+31%).

Wild Privet is very much a feature of dry scrub on the Chalk in
north Hertfordshire, but is also surprisingly frequent on other
soils. It occurs widely on calcarous gravels, and on drier areas of
Boulder Clay. It also occurs quite widely, if thinly, in hedgerows
and woodlands even on the neutral to mildly acidic soils in south-
east Hertfordshire, and on the Clay-with-Flints in the west. It is
only really sparse on the more strongly acidic gravels and clays of
central and southern Hertfordshire. Compared with Dony's map,
it does appear to have increased, although some of this may be
down to better recording.
(247 tetrads: Dony, 1967; 285 tetrads: 1950-1986)

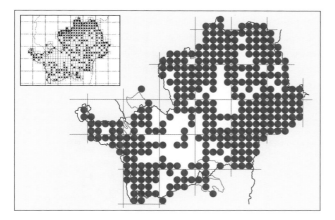

Map 534 *Ligustrum vulgare.*

Ligustrum ovalifolium Hassk.
Garden Privet
Introduced: neophyte.
First record: 1978.
Tetrad occurrence: 55 (11%).
Increasing?

Dony (1967) stated that this did not occur as a wild plant, and
somewhat similar views were expressed by Burton (1983). It
was first properly recorded as an escape at Oxhey Woods (19/B),

1978 *G. Harper*, but judging by the age of some bushes in various
places, it has been present in scrub for much longer than this. It
occurs quite frequently by railways and in old scrub around towns,
derived no doubt from garden refuse. It has also been found
apparently self-sown in a number of localities, and may have been
mis-identified as *L. vulgare* in some.

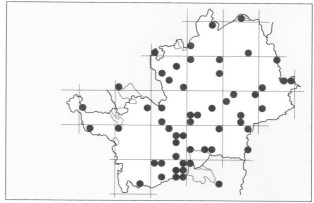

Map 535. *Ligustrum ovalifolium.*

Scrophulariaceae (Figwort family)

Genus: *Verbascum*

Mulleins become more difficult to identify as more cultivated
species are recorded as escapes, and the potential for hybrids
increases. Four species are reckoned to be native in Britain (two
in Herts.), but the rest are mostly casuals of disturbed ground,
usually on calcareous, free-draining soils.

Verbascum blattaria L.
Moth Mullein
Introduced: neophyte.
First record: 1856.
Tetrad occurrence: 5 (1%).
Increasing.

This has been recorded at intervals for the last 150 years, and
remains a rare, although apparently increasing, escape from
gardens. Dony gave two recent records, and there was an
additional one from an unrecorded site in TL33, 1955 (*comm.*:
Biological Records Centre, CEH Monks Wood). It was found at
Hadham Towers tip (41/I), 1967 *D. J. Hinson*; and nearby at
Thorley (41/P,U), 1976 *D. J. H.* During the recent survey it has
also been recorded from Picotts End (00/P), 1997 *P. G. Stapleton*;
from Old Welbury (12/P), 1999 *P. G. S*; by the A414 at Mill Green
(20/P), 2005 *T. J.*; beside Lilley Hoo Lane (12/I), 2007 *T. J.*
(Hb. HTN); and from a railway bank near Tring (91/G), 2008
P. Shipway (det. T. J.). The usual form found recently has been
var. *albiflora* (Don) House, with pinkish-white flowers.

Verbascum virgatum Stokes
Twiggy Mullein
Introduced: casual.
First record: 1849.

This has always been a rare escape. Dony gave one record from
Hitchin. There was also another post-1950 record from SP90 by
Miss H. Miller (*comm.*: Biological Records Centre, CEH Monks

Wood). It was seen at Royston tip (34/L), 1967 *J. G. Dony*; and at a disused railway siding at Stevenage (22/L), 1978 *A. D. Marshall* (det. E. J. Clement). There have been no subsequent records.

Verbascum bombyciferum Boiss.
Broussa Mullein
Introduced: casual.
First record: 1982.

This was first found at Waterford tip (31/C), 1982 *C. G. Hanson* (James, 1985). During the recent survey two plants were also found at the top of an old chalk pit by the railway at Knebworth Golf Course (22/K), 1998 *T. J.* (Hb. HTN).

Verbascum phlomoides L.
Orange Mullein
Introduced: neophyte.
First record: 1926.
Tetrad occurrence: 16 (3%).
Increasing (+267%).

Since the 1960s, this has become more or less established on the gravels around Hertford and Ware, where it appears on road verges and waste ground, and it also occurs occasionally in the lower Lea Valley and elsewhere.
(4 tetrads: Dony, 1967; 9 tetrads: 1950-1986)

Orange Mullein Verbascum phlomoides *Hertingfordbury, 1997.*

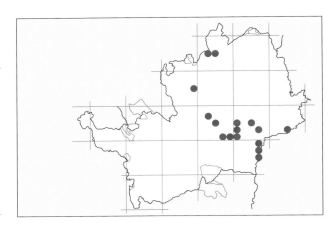

Map 536. *Verbascum phlomoides.*

Verbascum × kerneri Fritsch (*V. phlomoides* × *V. thapsus*)

This was found at a gravel pit at Ware (31/M), 1982 *A. M. Boucher* (Hb. Boucher), with the parents (James, 1985). It is probably elsewhere.

Verbascum densiflorum Bertol.
Dense-flowered Mullein
Introduced: casual.
First record: 1995.

The only record so far is from rough ground at Goldings, near Hertford (31/C), 1995 *T. J.* (Hb. HTN). It could be mistaken for other species.

Verbascum thapsus L.
Great Mullein
Native.
First record: 1736.
Tetrad occurrence: 244 (50%).
Increasing (+41%).

Dony (1967) expressed some doubt about the real native status of this plant, and its occurrence as a casual in disturbed ground throughout the County certainly suggests it is now mostly a colonist of such places, as disturbance to long-standing habitats increases.
(164 tetrads: Dony, 1967; 201 tetrads: 1950-1986)

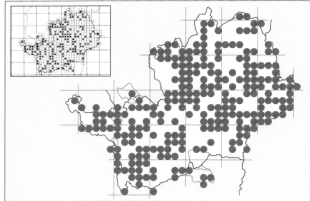

Map 537. *Verbascum thapsus.*

Verbascum × semialbum Chaub. (*V. thapsus × V. nigrum*)
Native.
First record: 1919.

This was identified by A. W. Graveson at an old chalk pit by Ware Park (31/G), 1919 (Hb. HTN), although Dony (ms. index) appeared to be doubtful. It was also reported from Benslow, Hitchin (12/Z), 1931 *J. E. Little* (*Rep. Bot. Exch. Club*: 132 (1932)), which may be the source of the record given in Stace (1975) for VC20. It may be more widespread.

Verbascum × thapsi L. (*V. thapsus × V. lychnitis*)
This was also recorded by J. E. Little from the chalk pit at Benslow, Hitchin (12/Z), 1931-2 (Dony, 1967).

Verbascum × godronii Boreau (*V. thapsus × V. pulverulentum*)

This was recorded in the chalk pit by Ware Park Mill (31/G), 1908-1911 *A. W. Graveson* with the parents (Dony, ms. index), but omitted from Dony (1967).

Verbascum chaixii Villars
Nettle-leaved Mullein
Introduced: casual.
First (only) record: 1919.

There have been no further records than the one from Ware (TL31) *J. W. Higgens* (Dony, 1967). It could be overlooked as a branched form of *V. nigrum*.

Verbascum nigrum L.
Dark Mullein
Native.
First record: 1756.
Tetrad occurrence: 73 (15%).
Stable or increasing (+16%).

The increase may be apparent rather than real, as this plant has always been a rather scattered and erratic species of rough, calcareous grassland on road verges, *etc.* It also escapes from gardens. It appears to have decreased somewhat in south-west Herts., but may have increased in central and eastern areas on disturbed ground.
(60 tetrads: Dony, 1967; 77 tetrads: 1950-1986)

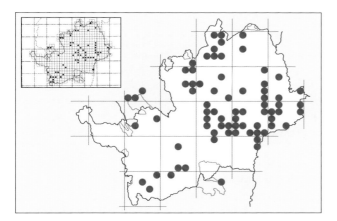

Map 538. *Verbascum nigrum.*

Verbascum speciosum Schrader
Hungarian Mullein
Introduced: casual.
First record: 1927.

This was reported from Purwell Field (12/Z), 1927 and Windmill Hill, Hitchin (12/Z), 1929 *J. E. Little* (det. W. B. Turrill) (Dony, 1967 and ms. index). It was also present as an escape by a car park at Hoddesdon (30/Z), 1996 *A. M. Boucher* (Hb. HTN). It is probably more widespread.

Verbascum pulverulentum Villars
Hoary Mullein
Introduced: casual [native in the U.K.].
First record: 1908.

This was found at the old chalk pit at Ware Park (31/G), 1908 *A. W. Graveson*, where it apparently persisted until at least 1916 (Dony, 1967). There have been no other records.

Verbascum lychnitis L.
White Mullein
Introduced: casual [native in the U.K.].
First record: 1839.

There is no real evidence of this being native in Herts., although it was present in the Hatfield/Brocket Park area for a while in the 19th century (Pryor, 1887). A few later records are given by Dony (1967). It was also reported from Ware (31/M), 1979 (recorder unknown?) (Burton, 1983); and most recently from Hemel Hempstead (00/Z), 1992 (*comm.*: Industrial Environmental Management consultants), although the latter was not confirmed.

Genus: *Scrophularia*

Scrophularia nodosa L.
Common Figwort
Native.
First record: 1814.
Tetrad occurrence: 319 (65%).
No measured change.

This is a widespread, if sometimes thinly occurring species characteristic of ancient woodland and old hedgerows, especially on neutral or mildly acidic loams, absent on the Chalk.
(303 tetrads: Dony, 1967; 323 tetrads: 1950-1986)

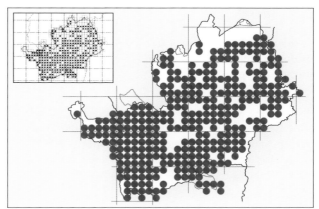

Map 539. *Scrophularia nodosa.*

Scrophularia auriculata L.

Water Figwort

Native.

First record: 1814.

Tetrad occurrence: 282 (57%).

Increased slightly (+11%).

Mostly a plant of riversides, pond margins and ditches, but also occasionally found in damp scrub elsewhere, even rarely in old chalk pits. It is frequent on the Boulder Clay and London Clay in east Herts., but is limited to water margins in the west of the County.

(242 tetrads: Dony, 1967; 256 tetrads: 1950-1986)

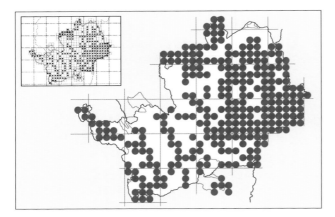

Map 540. *Scrophularia auriculata.*

Scrophularia vernalis L.

Yellow Figwort

Introduced: neophyte.

First record: 1843.

Tetrad occurrence: 3 (<1%).

Stable.

This has been a feature of the Hatfield Park area for 150 years, but elsewhere it has only been a casual introduction. Dony (1967) gave two recent records. It was also seen at Norton (23/H?), 1937 *T. A. Dymes* (Hb. HTN). More recently, it was found as a garden weed at St Albans (10/T), 1985 *J. Foster*. During the survey, it was recorded from Hatfield Home Farm (20/I), 1988; around Hatfield House (20/J), 1988 *A. D. Marshall*; and Woodside Place Farm (20/N), 1988 *B. Tranter*.

Genus: *Paulownia*

Paulownia tomentosa Sieb. and Zucc.

Foxglove Tree

Introduced: neophyte.

First record: 1997.

One tree of this exotic Chinese species was by the settling tanks at Rye Meads Sewage Works (31/V) *C. G. Hanson*, who noted that there were many suckers and seedlings nearby, although the tree itself had been cut down. Given that it is increasing around London, it may appear elsewhere in the County.

Genus: *Mimulus*

Monkeyflowers can be difficult to identify, owing to hybridisation, and some records, especially earlier ones, may have been erroneous.

Mimulus moschatus Douglas and Lindley

Musk

Introduced: casual.

First record: 1920.

Dony (1967) gives a record of it appearing on dredged mud from the River Lea, Hertford (TL31), 1920 *A. W. Graveson* (Hb. HTN). He omitted to report another occurrence at Watersplace Farm (31/X), 1943 *D. McClintock* (Dony, ms. index).

Mimulus guttatus DC.

Monkeyflower

Introduced: neophyte.

First record: *c.*1843.

Tetrad occurrence: 17 (4%).

Decreased (-15%).

At one time, this was a frequent and quite striking spectacle along especially the banks of the rivers Lea and Mimram above Hertford, and also downstream towards Cheshunt in a number of places. There is evidence of a decrease, especially along the lower Lea, although it still appears in new localities, such as at Bishop's Stortford. It also occurs occasionally elsewhere, often only casually.

(19 tetrads: Dony, 1967; 29 tetrads: 1950-1986)

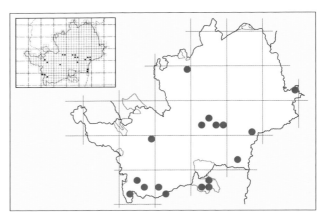

Map 537. *Mimulus guttatus.*

Mimulus × robertsii Silverside (*M. guttatus × M. luteus*)

Hybrid Monkeyflower

Introduced: neophyte.

First record: 1994.

Monkeyflowers in the River Gade at Gadebridge Park, Hemel Hempstead (00/P) 1994 *G. Salisbury/J. Saunders* (Hb. HTN) were found to be this sterile hybrid, making earlier records of *M. guttatus* from this area possibly doubtful. It was also found to occur further south in 00/N and at Picotts End (00/P), 1994; at Great Gaddesden (01/F); and at Water End (01/K), 1996 *GS/JS*.

[*Mimulus luteus* L.

Blood-drop-emlets

Burton (1983) gives an undated record from Lemsford (21/G), but queries whether it was in fact *M. × robertsii*. As *M. guttatus* also occurs nearby, its identity must be questionable. It was also reported from a habitat-creation pond at Buncefield, Hemel Hempstead (00/Z), 1992 (*comm.*: Industrial Environment Management consultants), no doubt introduced. The identity of this might also have been questionable, but as the site was destroyed in 2004, this is rather academic.]

Genus: *Limosella*

Limosella aquatica L.   Herts Rare
Mudwort
Native.
First record: 1843.
Tetrad occurrence: 2 (<1%).
Rare, but probably recently stable.

Even in the 19th century, this inconspicuous annual plant of
wet mud by ponds, and muddy tracks was rare in the County.
It was formerly at Bricket Wood (10/F), Mymms Woods and
North Mymms Park (20/B), and at Aldenham Reservoir (19/S?)
(Pryor, 1887). A. W. Graveson found it at Sarratt Green (09/P),
1919 (Dony, ms. index). There is also a record of it occurring in
some quantity in cart ruts on Berkhamsted Common (00/E?),
1931 *C. Oldham* (*Trans. Herts. N.H.S.*, 19: xxxv). It was
found at Tringford Reservoir (91/B) in 1919 *E. J. Salisbury*;
and subsequently at Startop's End Reservoir (91/B), 1961
H. J. M. Bowen, where Dony knew it. It was found at Wilstone
Reservoir (91/B), 1982 *A. J. Showler*; and was still at the muddy
inlet on the south side of this reservoir in 1989, 2009 *T. J.*, as well
as being found at Marsworth Reservoir (91/G), 1989; and again
at Startop's End Reservoir, 1990, 2009 *T. J./G. Salisbury* and
in 1997 *G. J. White*. It could still re-appear on muddy cart ruts
somewhere.

Genus: *Calceolaria*

Calceolaria chelidonioides Kunth
Slipperwort
Introduced: casual.
First (only) record: 1994.

This was found as an escape at a garden centre at Goffs Oak
(30/G) *A. M. Boucher* (Hb. HTN).

Genus: *Antirrhinum*

Antirrhinum majus L.
Snapdragon
Introduced: neophyte.
First record: 1838.
Tetrad occurrence: 61 (12%).
Increasing?

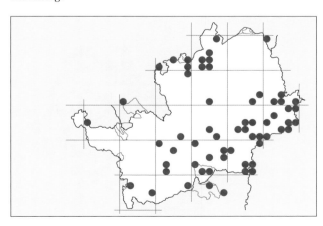

Map 542. *Antirrhinum majus.*

Dony's brief statement of its occurrence at Hertford Castle,
where it has been known for over 150 years, and Rickmansworth
obscures the fact that this garden escape must have occurred
more widely. His ms. index gives six locations. It is now a frequent
escape on walls and on bare, stony ground around most towns and
many villages in the County, usually in its wild red-flowered form.
(18 tetrads: 1970-1986)

Antirrhinum nuttallianum Benth.
Violet Snapdragon
Introduced: casual.
First (only) record: 1983.

This was identified from a grown-on seedling found at the site of
old greenhouses at Bayfordbury (31/A), 1983 *C. G. Hanson* (det.
E. J. Clement) (Hb. Hanson).

Genus: *Chaenorhinum*

Chaenorhinum minus (L.) Lange
Small Toadflax
Introduced: archaeophyte.
First record: 1787.
Tetrad occurrence: 104 (21%).
Decreasing (-41%).

Most frequent now as a casual weed of waste places and less
frequently in the margins of arable fields, mainly on the Chalk,
where it has severely decreased owing to fertilisation and
weedkillers. It also occurs on disturbed calcareous gravels and by
railways, although the latter are less open and weed-rich now than
they were in the 1960s, when Dony found it to be a frequent plant
in such habitats.
(167 tetrads: Dony, 1967; 186 tetrads: 1950-1986)

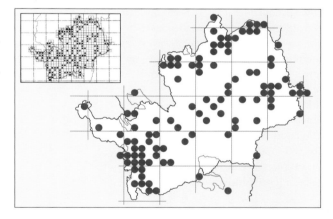

Map 543. *Chaenorhinum minus.*

Genus: *Misopates*

Misopates orontium (L.) Raf.   UK Vulnerable
Weasel's-snout   Herts Extinct?
Introduced: archaeophyte.
First record: 1838.

This was formerly a rare, but constant plant of gravelly arable
fields, especially in central Herts. It had decreased by the
beginning of the 20th century, and Dony (1967) only gave one
recent record. It was last seen at Hunsdon (41/A), 1966 *G. Thomas*
(*comm.*: J. Fielding).

Genus: *Cymbalaria*

Cymbalaria muralis P. Gaertner, Meyer and Scherb.
Ivy-leaved Toadflax
Introduced: neophyte.
First record: 1640.
Tetrad occurrence: 144 (29%).
Increased slightly (+11%).

Frequent on old walls, and occasional on stony, bare ground in waste places. This attractive plant shows some signs of having increased, consolidating its position around towns and villages, although it is prone to be 'tidied up'. It does not tolerate competition in semi-natural vegetation.
(123 tetrads: Dony, 1967; 146 tetrads: 1950-1986)

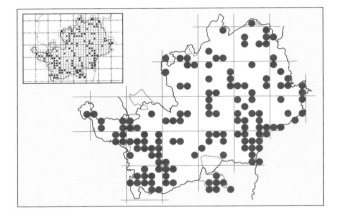

Map 544. *Cymbalaria muralis.*

Genus: *Kickxia*

Although both fluellens have been considered by some to have been affected by weedkillers, their late flowering appears to have saved them from some of the worst ravages of the arable enterprise, with the result that they are not as rare as people feared. They also often occur together.

Kickxia elatine (L.) Dumort.
Sharp-leaved Fluellen
Introduced: archaeophyte.
First record: 1820.
Tetrad occurrence: 119 (24%).
Stable or possibly decreasing (-4%).

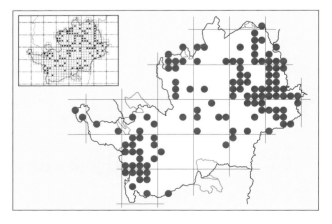

Map 545. *Kickxia elatine.*

Although this frequently grows with its relative in the margins of chalky arable fields, it does seem to have a slightly different habitat – preferring more friable, dry calcareous soils, often on Clay-with-Flints, sometimes on superficial calcareous gravels. Its apparent absence in some areas in north-central Herts., may be due to less concerted attempts to record the arable habitat.
(117 tetrads: Dony, 1967; 135 tetrads: 1950-1986)

Kickxia spuria (L.) Dumort.
Round-leaved Fluellen
Introduced: archaeophyte.
First record: 1805.
Tetrad occurrence: 152 (31%).
Slightly decreased (-8%).

Although still a fairly frequent field weed on the chalky Boulder Clay, this does appear to have decreased somewhat on the Chalk itself in the north; while better recording in south-west Herts. shows that it is more frequent on the Clay-with-Flints than formerly appeared to be the case (Dony, 1967). It remains the commoner of the two fluellens.
(158 tetrads: Dony, 1967; 178 tetrads: 1950-1986)

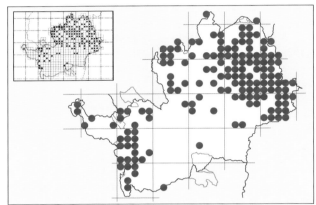

Map 546. *Kickxia spuria.*

Genus: *Linaria*

Linaria vulgaris Miller
Common Toadlfax
Native.
First record: 1822.
Tetrad occurrence: 351 (72%).
Increased slightly (+8%).

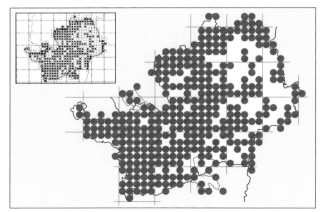

Map 547. *Linaria vulgaris.*

Whereas this was formerly quite a frequent arable weed on the Chalk, the main habitats this now grows in are roadside verges and waste ground. It occurs in most areas, but tends to be uncommon on the damper Boulder Clay, and on the wet London Clay.
(309 tetrads: Dony, 1967; 328 tetrads: 1950-1986)

Linaria × *sepium* Allman (*L. vulgaris* × *L. repens*)
First record: 1924.

This fertile hybrid occurs where the parents meet, such as on old railways and in chalk pits. Dony (1967) gave two records, and it was recorded during the recent survey on the 'Nicky Line', Harpenden (11/B), 1989 *B. Tranter*; and at Rickmansworth Station car park (09/S), 1998 *G. Salisury* (Hb. HTN).

Linaria purpurea (L.) Miller
Purple Toadflax
Introduced: neophyte.
First record: *c*.1880.
Tetrad occurrence: 146 (30%).
Increased markedly.

Dony (1967) merely notes this as occurring 'frequently' on tips, although his ms. index only gives about nine records. It was evidently quite widespread by the time Burton (1983) reported on the flora of the London area, but not until the current survey has there been an attempt to map its true occurrence in the County. It was found widely in urban waste places and roadsides, mostly on the Chalk and gravels.
(30 tetrads: 1950-1986)

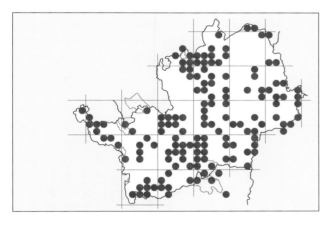

Map 548. *Linaria purpurea.*

Linaria × *dominii* Druce (*L. purpurea* × *L. repens*)
First record: 1999.

This rather rare hybrid was found at an old chalk pit at 'California', near Dunstable (02/A) (VC20 [Beds.]), 1999 *T. J./G. P. Smith* (Hb. HTN); and it was subsequently recorded from Rickmansworth Station car park (09/M), 2001 *B. Harold* (*comm.*: R. M. Burton).

Linaria repens (L.) Miller
Pale Toadflax
Introduced: archaeophyte.
First record: 1696.
Tetrad occurrence: 18 (4%).
Stable? (no percentage change).

This is a local plant of mineral-rich, well-drained ground, and has been a feature of some old railway lines and sidings for a long

time, growing on ballast. It also occasionally occurs in old chalk pits, and on walls. It is most frequent around Harpenden, and also in the Rickmansworth/Croxley area. It may have decreased in the north of the County, although access to railway land is less easy now than formerly, and it may have been overlooked.
(17 tetrads: Dony, 1967; 22 tetrads: 1950-1986)

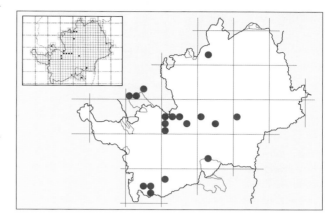

Map 549. *Linaria repens.*

[*Linaria supina* (L.) Chaz.
Prostrate Toadlfax
Introduced: casual.

This appeared spontaneously in a garden at Ware (31/S), 1997 *C. G. Hanson* (Hb. HTN), but was from an originally introduced source, and so cannot be considered as genuinely wild.]

Linaria maroccana Hook. *f.*
Annual Toadflax
Introduced: casual.
First record: 1959.

This was noted as an escape at Bayfordbury in 1959 (Dony, ms. index), although he omitted it from his *Flora*. It was also found as a presumed bird-seed escape at Hoddesdon (30/U), 1990 *A. M. Boucher* (Hb. HTN). It probably occurs occasionally elsewhere.

Genus: *Digitalis*

Digitalis purpurea L.
Foxglove
Native (and introduced).
First record: 1657.
Tetrad occurrence: 293 (60%).
Increased substantially (+117%).

Found as a native mainly in ancient semi-natural woodland on acidic soils, as well as on wooded commons and in old hedgerows. It has been used as a garden plant and herb for centuries, from which it escapes, when it can be found on roadsides, and waste ground, even sometimes on the Chalk. The survey showed that it has increased quite markedly since the 1960s, having consolidated its natural distribution across southern and western Hertfordshire on the more acidic London Clay, river gravels and Clay-with-Flints, where it forms a characteristic association with bracken in woodland glades and hedgerows. It has also spread around settlements in northern Hertfordshire, but remains uncommon or rare on the Boulder Clay and the Chalk.
(128 tetrads: Dony, 1967; 166 tetrads: 1950-1986)

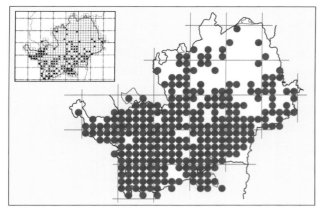

Map 550. *Digitalis purpurea.*

Digitalis lutea L.
Straw Foxglove
Introduced: casual.
First (only) record: 1933.

There is one record of this having occurred as an escape: at Letchworth, 1933 H. Phillips (Hb. HTN), overlooked by Dony (1967).

Genus: *Veronica*

Veronica serpyllifolia L.
Thyme-leaved Speedwell
Native.
First record: 1814.
Tetrad occurrence: 345 (70%).
Increased substantially (+49%).

This is a frequent plant of slightly nutrient-enriched, neutral to moderately calcareous grassland, often secondary, such as on roadsides, waste ground and old pits, as well as in more natural grassland in woodland rides. As such, it has apparently responded to the general enrichment of these habitats.
(220 tetrads: Dony, 1967; 259 tetrads: 1950-1986)

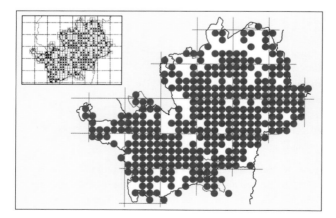

Map 551. *Veronica serpyllifolia.*

Veronica officinalis L.
Heath Speedwell
Native.
First record: 1657.
Tetrad occurrence: 117 (24%).
Probably more or less stable (+4%).
Despite its name, this is a plant of dry, mildly acidic or neutral

soils, and is most frequent on sunny banks, or in woodland glades on the loams of central Hertfordshire. The loss of managed woodland rides and the eutrophication of roadside verges has affected this species to some extent, but it has also colonised gravel pits in some places.
(106 tetrads: Dony, 1967; 129 tetrads: 1950-1986)

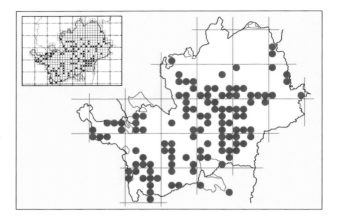

Map 552. *Veronica officinalis.*

Veronica chamaedrys L.
Germander Speedwell *or* **Bird's-eye**
Native.
First record: 1814.
Tetrad occurrence: 455 (93%).
More or less stable (-3%).

A characteristic and important member of neutral or mildly calcareous grassland communities, both ancient and secondary, on most soils, only becoming rare on thin rendzinas over Chalk, or on strongly acidic soils. Although its occurrence at tetrad level remains substantially the same as in 1967, there are signs that it is becoming increasingly localised, resulting in a failure to find it in some tetrads.
(448 tetrads: Dony, 1967; 453 tetrads: 1950-1986)

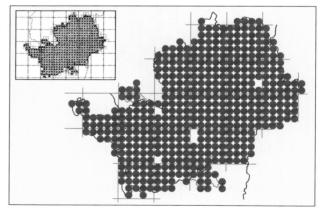

Map 553. *Veronica chamaedrys.*

Veronica montana L.
Wood Speedwell
Native.
First record: 1838.
Tetrad occurrence: 214 (44%).
Apparently increasing (+30%).

This is a plant of usually fairly damp semi-natural woodland, usually on neutral or mildly acidic soils and tolerating fairly deep shade. Its apparent increase may to some extent be owing to better recording, although it does appear to have spread into more Boulder Clay woodlands, possibly responding to soil acidification. (156 tetrads: Dony, 1967; 181 tetrads: 1950-1986)

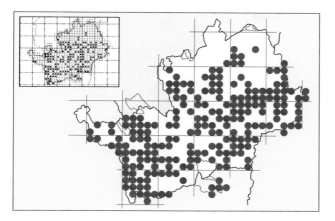

Map 554. *Veronica montana.*

Veronica scutellata L.
Marsh Speedwell
Native.
First record: 1814.
Tetrad occurrence: 22 (5%).
Rare, but increased? (+73%).

At one time this was most usually found by ponds on heathy commons, *etc.*, although it was also in fen ditches in river valleys (Pryor, 1887). It is probably capable of being spread to new habitats by birds, because it seems to appear at new sites, such as short, marshy vegetation in gravel pits. It can also go unnoticed at sites during periods of unfavourable habitat status, reappearing when conditions improve. However, it remains genuinely rather rare, just as its habitat is rare.

(12 tetrads: Dony, 1967; 22 tetrads: 1950-1986)

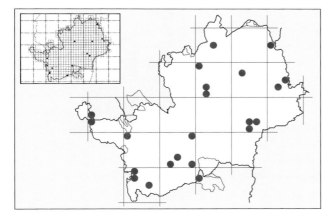

Map 555. *Veronica scutellata.*

Veronica beccabunga L.
Brooklime
Native.
First record: 1814.
Tetrad occurrence: 316 (64%).
Increased? (+17%).

Found in damp ground, by ponds, in ditches, by streams and gravel pits throughout much of the County, being the only wetland speedwell that can tolerate much grazing, and also being quite

tolerant of enriched sites. It only becomes rare on the Chalk and on the drier areas of the Clay-with-Flints in west Herts., much as Dony found. It appears to have genuinely increased, although some of this may be down to better recording.

(257 tetrads: Dony, 1967; 290 tetrads: 1950-1986)

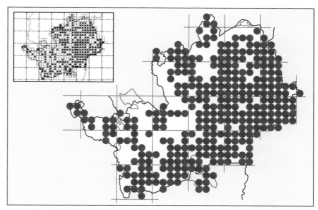

Map 556. *Veronica beccabunga.*

Veronica anagallis-aquatica L.
Blue Water-speedwell
Native.
First record: 1838.
Tetrad occurrence: 132 (27%).
Increased? (+63%).

This is the frequent water speeedwell of calcareous streams and rivers across the County, only occasionally appearing in ponds, and colonising bare mud by gravel pit lakes. It was probably seriously under-recorded in the 1960s survey, because it is difficult to see how it could have increased as much as it would appear to have done, although the development of new gravel pits in some areas will have helped.

(77 tetrads: Dony, 1967; 105 tetrads: 1950-1986)

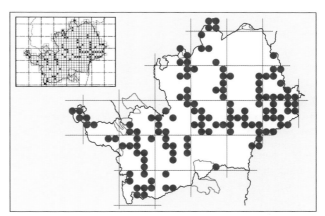

Map 557. *Veronica anagallis-aquatica.*

Veronica × lackschewitzii Keller
(*V. anagallis-aquatica* × *V. catenata*)
Native.
First record: 1909.

The first record of this derives from re-determined herbarium material collected from Rye House (30/Z), 1909 *P. H. Cooke* (det. J. H. Burnett). Subsequent to the notes in Dony (1967), it was also found at Lemsford Springs (21/G), 1972 *T. J.* (conf. J. G. Dony); and at King's Meads (31/L), 1978 *T. J.* It is probably overlooked, and a number of records of *V. anagallis-aquatica* in particular may refer here. It was positively identified three times during the survey: at Amwell Quarry (31/R), 1987 *T. J.*; by the River Gade, Water End (01/F), 2002 *A. Harris* (det. T. James), where it has been known for many years; and at Lemsford Springs again (21/F, G), 2005 *T. J.*

Veronica catenata Pennell
Pink Water-speedwell
Native.
First record: 1911.
Tetrad occurrence: 47 (10%).
Increased (or stable)? (+50%).

Following its taxonomic separation from *V. anagallis-aquatica*, the first record of this was from Cadwell, near Ickleford (13/R), 1911 *J. E. Little*, although hybrid material of this with *V. anagallis-aquatica* had been collected earlier at Rye House (see above). Dony (1967) gave a brief account of it, and considered that it occurred mostly in the east. Subsequent recording has suggested that it is most frequent on mud by shallow ponds in pasture on the Boulder Clay, as well as by slow streams, ditches and gravel pits, especially in the Ash, Lea and Stort valleys, but also scattered elsewhere. However, it remains relatively rare.
(30 tetrads: Dony, 1967; 50 tetrads: 1950-1986)

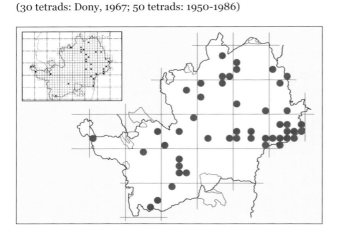

Map **558.** *Veronica catenata.*

Veronica triphyllos L.   UK Endangered
Fingered Speedwell
Introduced: casual [archaeophyte in U.K.].
First (only) record: 1978.

A single plant of this Breckland rarity was identified from a garden at Mannicotts, Welwyn Garden City (21/G), 1978 *J. Corfield*, where it appeared in a newly-created heather bed (James, 1982).

Veronica arvensis L.
Wall Speedwell
Native.
First record: 1820.
Tetrad occurrence: 434 (88%).
Probably stable (+2%).

As in the 19th century, this is a frequent or even quite common plant of old walls, bare stony banks and field margins, although its abundance has probably decreased with the effects of modern agriculture. It tends to be overlooked, owing to its early flowering.
(402 tetrads: Dony, 1967; 411 tetrads: 1950-1986)

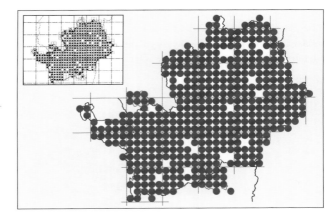

Map **559.** *Veronica arvensis.*

Veronica agrestis L.
Green Field-speedwell
Introduced: archaeophyte.
First record: (1748?) 1838.
Tetrad occurrence: 130 (27%).
Probably stable, or slightly increased (+20%).

This is a rather overlooked plant, usually found more in gardens and allotments than in arable fields, and avoiding calcareous soils unless they are well-manured. Dony (1967) queried its first record by Kalm, but on what grounds is uncertain. It is almost certainly under-recorded in some places, particularly on the more acidic gravels and clays in south Hertfordshire, because the records display a decided bias in favour of the south-east, which, while reflecting the fact that it is commonest here, nevertheless does not match very well with the distribution recorded in the 1960s.
(103 tetrads: Dony, 1967; 121 tetrads: 1950-1986)

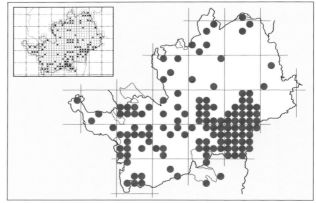

Map **560.** *Veronica agrestis.*

Veronica polita Fries
Grey Field-speedwell
Introduced: neophyte.
First record: 1820.
Tetrad occurrence: 151 (31%).
Increased, or stable? (+28%).

At one time this was the main larger-flowered speedwell found in arable fields, although it was apparently never abundant (Pryor, 1887). Both Dony and Pryor thought it was most frequent on poorer, sandy soils, but the present survey suggests it is widespread in arable, especially in the east, and has decreased in the south, probably owing to the cessation of arable farming in much of this area. It is certainly less common than its relative *V. persica*, and unpredictable in its appearance. It could also be overlooked to some extent.

(112 tetrads: Dony, 1967; 126 tetrads: 1950-1986)

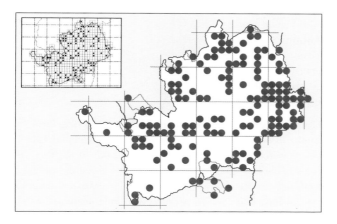

Map 561. *Veronica polita.*

Veronica persica Poiret
Common Field-speedwell
Introduced: neophyte.
First record: 1843.
Tetrad occurrence: 463 (94%).
Stable (-3%).

This is now an ubiquitous weed of cultivated ground and waste places throughout the County, having originally been introduced in the early 19th century from Asia. It has been missed in a few tetrads, although modern agricultural weedkillers have certainly affected its abundance.

(453 tetrads: Dony, 1967; 455 tetrads: 1950-1986)

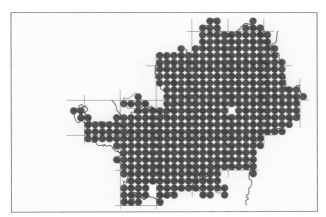

Map 562. *Veronica persica.*

Veronica filiformis Smith
Slender Speedwell
Introduced: neophyte.
First record: 1946.
Tetrad occurrence: 298 (61%).
Increasing markedly (+287%).

An introduced, self-incompatible clone of a montane speedwell from the south-east of Europe, this was first actually recorded at Letchworth (23/A), 1946 *H. J. Killick*. It is a rather attractive spreading species that occurs most often in mown lawns and road verges, where, in damper years, it can become very invasive. The patchy distribution map may reflect the effects of drought years

during the survey period, when it lay dormant without flowering, rather than its true current extent.

(73 tetrads: Dony, 1967; 133 tetrads: 1950-1986)

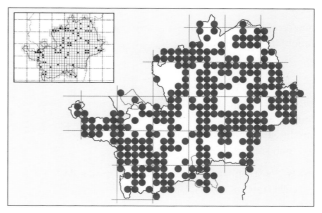

Map 563. *Veronica filiformis.*

Veronica hederifolia L.
Ivy-leaved Speedwell
Introduced: archaeophyte.
First record: 1814.
Tetrad occurrence: 415 (85%).
Decreasing slightly (-10%).

The early flowering of this species tends to mean that it is often not found later in the season, which may account for a few of its apparent losses, although it has also decreased in arable, owing to the effects of pre-emergent weedkillers. However, the species still occurs widely and commonly in arable fields, hedgebanks and gardens on disturbed fertile soils.

(436 tetrads: Dony, 1967; 437 tetrads: 1950-1986)

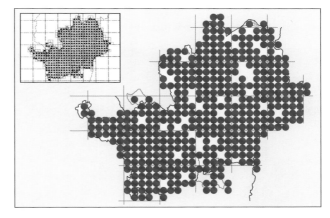

Map 564. *Veronica hederifolia.*

Of the two subspecies in the County, ssp. *lucorum* (Klett and Richter) Hartl is probably the commoner of the two overall, occurring most frequently in shaded hedgerows, woodland *etc*; while ssp. *hederifolia* is the usual form in arable fields and open cultivated ground. Records of the two sspp. were not submitted uniformly enough to give separate distribution maps.

Veronica longifolia L.
Garden Speedwell
Introduced: casual.
First (only) record: 1994.

A few escaped plants of this were noted on a railway bank at Watford (09/X) *J. Archer*.

Genus: *Hebe*

Hebe × *franciscana* (Eastw.) Souster (*H. elliptica* × *H. speciosa*)
Hedge Veronica
Introduced: neophyte or casual.
First (only) record: 1990.

Variety 'Blue Gem' was noted as a self-sown escape at Cheshunt Gravel Pits (30/R), 1990 *A. M. Boucher/T. J.*

Genus: *Melampyrum*

Melampyrum cristatum L.   UK Vulnerable
Crested Cow-wheat
Native.
First record: 1838.
Decreased, almost extinct (-67%).

This was never common, but occurred reasonably frequently in newly cut coppices and by fields on the drier soils over Chalk in north-east Hertfordshire (not on deeper Boulder Clay, as Dony (1967) indicated). With the cessation of coppicing, it had become rare by the 1960s, only found on a few road verges. Since then, it had also vanished from these, having been overtaken by rank growth, so that it was considered extinct until a small colony was found in a newly-established conservation margin by an ancient hedgebank at Nuthampstead (43/C), 2001 *K. Robinson* (Hb. HTN).
(3 tetrads: Dony, 1967; and from 1950-1986)

Crested Cow-wheat Melampyrum cristatum *Nuthampstead, 2001.*

Melampyrum arvense L.   UK Pending Red List
Field Cow-wheat   Herts Extinct
Introduced: neophyte?
Only record: 1840.

Regarded as an introduction in Preston *et al.* (2002), possibly even an archaeophyte, although precise evidence for this is lacking (C. D. Preston, pers. comm.), but thought by some to be a specially rare native weed of dry calcareous clays. Henry Fordham found

this right on the County boundary near Odsey, in Ashwell parish (23/Y), where Coleman also saw it (Webb and Coleman, 1849). It was on a small area of characteristic, friable dry clay over Chalk, similar to ground where it occurs, rarely, in Bedfordshire.

Melampyrum pratense L.
Common Cow-wheat
Native.
First record: (1814?) 1838.
Tetrad occurrence: 14 (3%).
Decreasing (-15%).

The first record may have been from near Hitch Wood, as there is an unlocalised record from the Hitchin area in Joseph Ransom's diary, now in North Herts. Museums, for 11th June 1814. It is specially characteristic of former wood-pasture woodlands and commons on moderately acidic soils in south-eastern and central Hertfordshire, where it is fairly widespread and sometimes locally abundant, although not generally common. It also occurs rarely elsewhere, such as at High Scrubs near Tring. It is an important indicator of long habitat continuity. The record from tetrad 23/F given in Dony (1967) may have been an error, as the habitat is unsuitable in this area.
(17(16?) tetrads: Dony, 1967; 23 tetrads: 1950-1986)

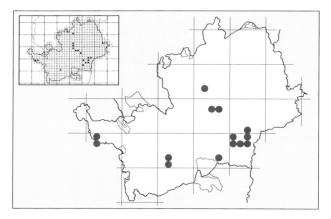

Map 565. *Melampyrum pratense.*

Genus: *Euphrasia*

Eyebrights in general are difficult to identify, although those occurring locally appear only to fall into two or perhaps three species. It is not inconceivable that one or two others have also occurred in the past, although in general they are declining, through loss of old grasslands.

[*Euphrasia anglica* Pugsley   UK Endangered
Native?

There are records of specimens from 'Wormley Wood' (TL30), 1910, collected by P. H. Cooke (det. D. H. Kent), in Hb. London Natural History Society; and from 'Broxbourne' (TL30), 1924 by E. B. Bishop (also det. D. H. Kent) in Hb. Bishop (Kent and Lousley, 1954). Dony did not notice these records, and in any case, further study of the specimens would probably be needed before they could be formally accepted to the Hertfordshire flora, although the species has occurred in Epping Forest, and might also have occurred in our area.]

Euphrasia arctica Lange ex Rostrup   Herts Extinct
Northern Eyebright
Native.
First (only) record: 1911.

Subspecies *borealis* (F. Towns.) Yeo was found in old calcareous pasture, now lost, at Welbury Farm (12/P), 1911 *J. E. Little* (det. C. Bucknall). This is the only record of the species from the County. There is, however, an old record from Harefield Moor, just in Middlesex (Kent, 1975), which supports its survival so far south until recent times.

Euphrasia nemorosa (Pers.) Wallr.
Common Eyebright
Native.
First record: 1814? (1914).
Tetrad occurrence: 42 (9%).
Local and decreasing (-20%).

This quite variable species is the most likely eyebright to be found across the County, occurring in short chalky grassland, as well as mildly heathy ground. It is still reasonably frequent in the main areas of old chalk grassland, but has become increasingly rare on road verges or in other types of grassland. Quite a few of the localities shown on the maps now probably do not support it, although it can be overlooked, owing to its late flowering. (50 tetrads: Dony, 1967; 63 tetrads: 1950-1986)

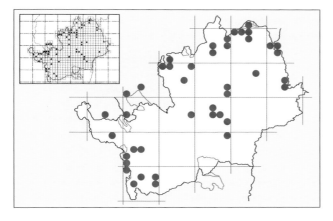

Map 566. *Euphrasia nemorosa.*

Euphrasia pseudokerneri Pugsley   UK Endangered
Chalk Eyebright
Native.
First record: 1922.
Tetrad occurrence: 9 (2%).
Stable? (+20%) (may now be decreasing).

This has probably always been a rare species, limited by its habitat to thin, open grassland on Chalk. It was recorded by Dony from old downland sites in seven tetrads, and after 1970, it was seen additionally at Ravensburgh Castle (02/Z), just in Herts, 1979 *T. J./B. R. Sawford*. During the current survey it was found in seven localities: at Markham's Hill, Offley (12/J), 1987 *T. J.*; Therfield Heath (33/J, P, 34/K), 1988, 1991 *T. J.*; Telegraph Hill (12/E), 1988 *T. J.*; Tingley Downs (13/F), 1988 *C. W. Burton*; Oddy Hill (91/F), 1988 *T. J.*: Roughdown Common (00/M), 1993 *G. Salisbury*; and Pitstone Quarry (VC20) (91/L), 1998 *G. Salisbury*. It is now probably decreasing because of nutrient enrichment of chalk grassland, but the recent survey results do not yet demonstrate this.

Chalk Eyebright Euphrasia pseudokerneri *Tring, 1972.*

[*Euphrasia micrantha* Reichb.
Native?

Pryor (1887) gives a record of '*E. officinalis* var. *gracilis*' from a 'lane near Thistley Farm' (Gosmore?) (12/Y?), *c.*1850 collected by Prof. Robert Bentley. If this was the locality, it is a most unlikely locality for a plant of wet heaths, and so the record must remain very doubtful. There is also a slightly more plausible record by R. D. S. English from Bricket Wood Common (English, 1955), but without further evidence, this must also remain in doubt, especially as he records it in a neutral plant community. Dony (1967) ignored both records.]

Genus: *Odontites*

Odontites vernus (Bellardi) Dumort
Red Bartsia
Native.
First record: 1810.
Tetrad occurrence: 295 (60%).
Stable or slightly increased (+12%).

This hemi-parasite of grasses in semi-improved or unimproved rough grassland is widespread on more calcareous soils across the County, becoming rarer on the London Clay in the south and on gravels in central Herts. It may have increased slightly in less intensively managed grasslands.
(251 tetrads: Dony, 1967; 277 tetrads: 1950-1986)

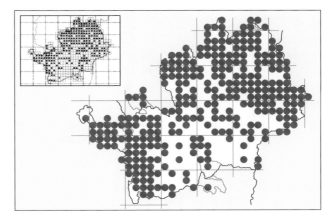

Map 567. *Odontites vernus.*

The map shows records of ssp. *serotinus* (Syme) Corbière, which is by far the commoner ssp. in the County. Ssp. *vernus* has only been recorded from a ride in Wain Wood (12/S), 1990 *T. J./A. Parry*; Bromley (42/A), 1987 *S. Watson*; and from scrub at York Way, Royston (34/K) (VC29 [Herts.]), 1998 *T. J.* Dony gave no records for *vernus*, while commenting that it was less common.

Genus: *Parentucellia*

Parentucellia viscosa (L.) Caruel
Yellow Bartsia
Introduced [native in the U.K.].
First record: 1937.

This appeared in marshy grassland adjoining recently-created ponds at The Node, Codicote (22/A) in 1937 *E. J. Salisbury* (Dony, 1967). More recently, it appeared in thin, rough grassland by Commons Wood (21/K), 1974 *A. D. Marshall*. It had increased by 1991, but the site was subsequently bulldozed for a new golf course in 1992. How it came to be introduced to either site is unknown.

Genus: *Rhinanthus*

[*Rhinanthus angustifolius* C. Gmelin
Greater Yellow-rattle
Introduced: archaeophyte?

Dony (1967) questioned the few earlier records of this species from Herts., and there do not appear to be any reliably named specimens in herbaria from the County. It was deliberately introduced to rough ground near buildings at Rothamsted (11/G), 1981 *R. M. Bateman*, where it remained for a while.]

Rhinanthus minor L.
Yellow-rattle
Native (and introduced).
First record: 1733.
Tetrad occurrence: 45 (9%).
Increased (+136%).

As a native plant of old grasslands, and occasionally as a weed in cornfields, this was widespread in the 19th century, but had decreased markedly by the 1960s (Dony, 1967). It may have been slightly under-recorded in the 1967 'Flora', but it does appear to have increased slightly in some areas during the 1970s and early 1980s. More recently, it has become the fashion to include it in seed mixes for 'conservation' purposes, and so its natural occurrence is now obscured, although some well-known native

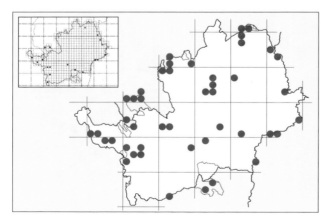

Map 568. *Rhinanthus minor.*

sites, such as Hunsdon Mead (41/A, F) still have it in fair quantity. (18 tetrads: Dony, 1967; 34 tetrads: 1950-1986)

No proper study of the subspecies of Yellow Rattle has ever been undertaken in Herts. Ssp. *calcareus* (Wilmott) Warb. was identified from Therfield Heath (33/J), 1963, 1966, 1972 *P. D. Sell* (Hb. CGE).

Genus: *Pedicularis*

Pedicularis palustris L.   Herts Extinct
Marsh Lousewort *or* **Red Rattle**
Native.
First record: 1838.

As Dony (1967) outlined, this was formerly widespread in old flood-plain meadows, such as King's Meads, Croxley Common Moor, Hoddesdon Marsh, Sopwell Meadows, Bayfordbury, Tewin Mill, Walsworth Common and other localities. He was shown it at Sarratt Bottom (09/J) 1955 by R. B. Benson, and that was its last record. As a plant of permanently wet, unimproved pastures, its loss graphically describes the dereliction and degradation of such habitat across the County since about 1920.

Pedicularis sylvatica L.   Herts Rare
Lousewort
Native.
First record: 1787.
Tetrad occurrence: 3 (<1%).
Decreasing rapidly (-70%).

This now only survives, apparently, in three localities: Burleigh Meadow, Knebworth (22/G), where it was still present in some quantity in 2009 *T. J. et al.*; clearings in Broxbourne Wood (30/I), where it was found to be locally frequent in a newly opened up clearing, 2007 *T. J.*; and the former common pasture, now enclosed, at Crouch Green, Knebworth (22/A), where it was recorded by L. Mottram in 2000, and is reported by the owner to be still present (2008). Apparently it has disappeared from Hertford Heath (31/K), last being seen in 1972 (observer unknown); Croxley Common Moor (09/S), 1983 *R. A. Palmer*; Claypits Meadow, Bayford (30/D), present in increasing scrub in 1979 *Herts. and Middx. Trust Meadow Survey*, but where the site has since suffered severe disturbance; and a clearing in Newsetts Wood (90/P), 1984 *P. A. Kingsbury*.

Lousewort Pedicularis sylvatica *Burleigh Meadow, Knebworth, 1977.*

Orobanchaceae (Broomrape family)

Genus: *Lathraea*

Lathraea squamaria L.
Toothwort
Native.
First record: 1813.
Tetrad occurrence: 13 (3%).
Probably stable (+13%).

This is a rather inconspicuous plant, parasitising the roots of hazel, elm and other trees in old hedgerows, and because it dies down rapidly following flowering in Spring, it may still be overlooked. However, many of its known sites are very long-standing, such as the margins of Wain Wood, Preston (12/S), where it has been known for over 160 years. It now appears to be restricted to the Chilterns dip-slope.
(11 tetrads: Dony, 1967; 15 tetrads: 1950-1986)

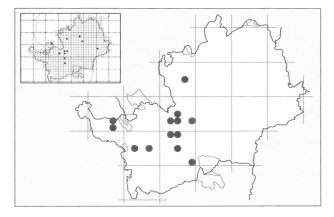

Map 569. *Lathraea squamaria.*

Toothwort Lathraea squamaria *by Wain Wood, 1991.*

Lathraea clandestina L.
Purple Toothwort
Introduced: neophyte.
First record: 1935.

Dony (1967) gave two records. It was last properly recorded at one of his localities, Whitney Wood (22/I), in 1970 *B. R. Sawford*, although it may still occur there. It was subsequently found established by a pond at Bayfordbury (31/A), 1979 *C. G. Hanson*, where it was also recorded in 1994 *A. M. Boucher/C. G. H.*

Genus: *Orobanche*

Orobanche purpurea Jacq.   UK Vulnerable
Yarrow Broomrape   Herts Extinct
Native.
First record: 1839.

This was only ever recorded from banks in unenclosed fields near the Hertford road north of Hoddesdon, where it was last seen in 1938 by H. F. Hayllar (Dony, 1967).

Orobanche rapum-genistae Thuill.   UK Near Threatened
Greater Broomrape
Native.
First record: 1838.

At one time quite widespread, although rare, parasitising Broom on commons and in hedgebanks across south-east Hertfordshire (Pryor, 1887). It was rare by the 1920s and Dony (1967) only knew it from a hedgerow adjacent to arable near Burleigh Meadow (22/G), where it still occurs sporadically, often eaten by rabbits.

Great Broomrape Orobanche rapum-genistae *by Burleigh Meadow, Knebworth, 1998.*

Orobanche elatior Sutton
Knapweed Broomrape
Native.
First record: 1815.
Tetrad occurrence: 41 (8%).
Stable? (+6%).

This is a particularly characteristic plant of usually quite old, rough chalky grasslands in the drier north-east of the County, where it can occur commonly on some roadside banks and field borders. It also occurs on chalk outcrops south towards Stevenage, but is rare elsewhere, its only record from W. Herts. being from a road verge at Hastoe Hill (91/F), 1992 *A. D. Marshall*. Often such road banks and field balks are known to be ancient in origin, and its presence is therefore of some importance for historical ecology. (37 tetrads: Dony, 1967; 47 tetrads: 1950-1986)

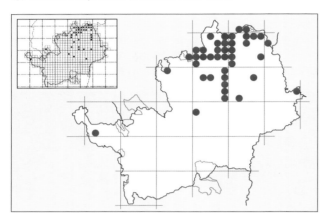

Map 570. *Orobanche elatior.*

Ivy Broomrape Orobanche hederae *Weston Churchyard, 1984.*

Orobanche hederae Duby   Herts Rare
Ivy Broomrape
Native? (possibly introduced).
First record: 1984.
Tetrad occurrence: 5 (1%).
Increasing.

Ivy Broomrape was first found in fair quantity around Ivy-covered tombstones at Weston Churchyard (22/U), 1984 *J. Welsh* (Hb. HTN), as well as among Ivy by a drive not far away in the adjoining tetrad (23/Q). It remains in this area, but has subsequently turned up at Oaklands College (21/G), 1997 *A. Davidson* (det. T. James) (Hb. HTN); and at Totteridge Churchyard (29/M), 2003 *R. Keen*. It was also introduced to a garden at Ware Road, Hertford (31/L), 1999 *J. C. Doyle*, where it is well-established and spreading. It has long occurred in cemeteries in north London and elsewhere, so it is possible that seed may have blown naturally, but it may also have been introduced with the ornamental variety 'Hibernica' of Ivy to gardens.

[*Orobanche artemisiae-campestris* Vaucher ex Gaudin
Oxtongue Broomrape

As Dony (1967) explains, a specimen of *O. minor* collected by W. J. Blake at Welwyn (Salisbury, 1916) was wrongly reported as this by Druce in *Rep. Bot. Exch. Club* (1912). Specimens seeming to be this were also found at Hertford (31/L), 1992 *J. C. Doyle*, but were subsequently identified as a form of *O. minor* also.]

Orobanche minor Smith
Common Broomrape
Native.
First record: 1822.
Tetrad occurrence: 54 (11%).
Stable? (+7%).

In the 1960s, this species was mainly found in the more calcareous areas of the County, where it occurred mainly on clover (Dony, 1967). Its current distribution is more widespread, mainly as a result of its quite frequent occurrence on disturbed ground, particularly where seed mixes containing clover have been used. However, these colonies are often ephemeral, and it may now be decreasing again.
(48 tetrads: Dony, 1967; 72 tetrads: 1950-1986)

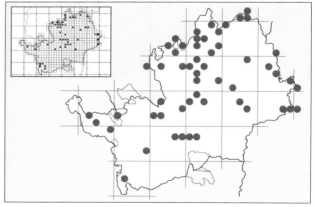

Map 571. *Orobanche minor.*

This highly variable plant has a number of subspecies recognised. The usual form is ssp. *minor*. Ssp. *compositarum* Pugsley, with more erect flowers, and often more slender, grows mainly on Asteraceae. It was recorded a few times during the survey: at

Ledgeside, Graveley (22/P), 1997 *C. M. James/T. J.*; Hitchin (13/Q), 1992 *C. M. James* (det. T. J.) (both on *Crepis capillaris*); Watford, (19/D), 1993 *O. Linford* (det. T. J.) and 2002 *P. J. Ellison* (on *Senecio ambigua* in gardens).

Acanthaceae (Bear's-breech family)

Genus: [*Acanthus*]

[*Acanthus spinosus* L.
Spiny Bear's-breech

There is one unlocalised and undated record of this given from the Cheshunt area (30/R), in Burton (1983), but the B.S.B.I. Vascular Plant Database gives this as an Essex record.]

Pedaliaceae (Sesame family)

Genus: *Sesamum*

Sesamum orientale L.
Sesame
Introduced: casual.
First record: 1983.

This was found at Rye Meads Sewage Works (31/V), 1983 *A. M. Boucher/C. G. Hanson*. It also occurred on the sludge dump in small numbers in 1989, 1990 and 1994 *C. G. H./A. M. B.* (Hb. HTN).

Lentibulariaceae (Butterwort family)

Genus: *Pinguicula*

Pinguicula vulgaris L.   Herts Extinct
Common Butterwort
Native.
First record: 1597.

Dony (1967) barely mentions this, but Pryor (1887) lists a number of sites: Norton and Walsworth Commons; by Wilstone Reservoir (presumably Rushy Meadow); Croxley (as Rickmansworth or Watford) Common Moor; Barkway Moor; and 'boggy meadows about Hatfield'. It is also known to have occurred at Oughton Head Common in the 19th century (James, 1980a). That it had vanished from all of these by the end of that century tells us much about the deterioration of moorish wetland habitats, even as early as 1900.

Genus: *Utricularia*

Utricularia vulgaris L. (s. str.)   Herts Rare
Greater Bladderwort
Native.
First record: (1820 for the aggregate), 1973.

Always very rare, in base-rich pools, now only known at the lake in Balls Park (31/F), where it was first properly reported in 1973 by N. Underwood. It was still present in 2000 *A. P. Reynolds*. The

record given by Dony (1967) from Batchworth Heath probably refers to *U. australis*. Unfortunately the colony of bladderwort in a pond on Broxbourne Common (30/N), recorded until *c*.1960 (Dony, *op. cit.*) appears not to have survived, and therefore its specific identity must remain doubtful. Bladderworts have not been seen elsewhere for a very long time, although they could persist in a vegetative state. The record given in Burton (1983) for a 'gravel pit' in the Lea Valley, 1972, probably refers to the Balls Park site. Early records from Beechwood (TL01), Stanstead Abbotts (TL31), Hoddesdon Marsh (30/Z) and Broxbournebury (30/N) (Pryor, 1887) may or may not have been this species, although those in the Lea Valley at least may well have been.

Utricularia australis R. Br.   Herts Rare
Bladderwort
Native.
First record (for the segregate): 1988.

Following pond clearance, this was specifically identified from material collected at Batchworth Heath (09/R), 1988 *O. Linford* (det. T. J., conf. P. Taylor) (Hb. HTN), which would indicate that the plant recorded by B. P. Pickess there in 1965 was also this species (Dony, 1967), as well as an unpublished record from the same site in 1969 by S. E. Crooks. It was present there in fine flower in 1992 *P. J. Ellison*; and has also appeared at a pond on Chorleywood Common (09/I), 1990 *G. Salisbury* (det. T. J.) (Hb. HTN). It could conceivably be elsewhere in acidic ponds on commons, undetected.

Campanulaceae (Bellflower family)

Genus: *Campanula*

Campanula patula L.   UK Endangered
Spreading Bellflower
Introduced: casual? [native in the U.K.].
Only record: 1874.

The only proper record for Herts. remains the single plant found in a cornfield at Pirton Cross (12/U), 1874 by J. Pollard (Hb. HTN) (Dony, 1967), although there is an unlocalised record by Joseph Ransom of Hitchin in his diary for 1814 that might be a local occurrence.

Campanula rapunculus L.
Rampion Bellflower
Introduced: casual.
First record: 1844.

This was also recorded in the 19th century from a few sites on gravelly ground in south Herts. There are no recent records of it in the wild, but it has established itself in a lawn at Ware (31/S), originally brought from France *C. G. Hanson*.

Campanula persicifolia L.
Peach-leaved Bellflower
Introduced: neophyte.
First record: 1946.
Tetrad occurrence: 10 (2%).
Increasing (+150%).

First noticed at Welwyn Garden City (Dony, 1967), this has now appeared in a number of places, sometimes fairly persistent, as at Weston Hills (23/L), where it was first found in 1984 *K. Robinson*, and was still present in 1988.

(2 tetrads: Dony, 1967; 3 tetrads: 1950-1986)

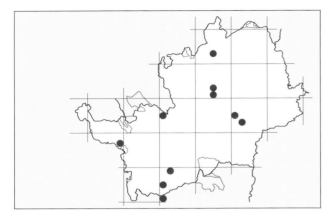

Map 572. *Campanula persicifolia.*

Campanula medium L.
Canterbury-bells
Introduced: casual.
First record: *c.*1880.

This was said to have been naturalised by the railway at Berkhamsted (Pryor, 1887). There has been only one subsequent record of an escape: at Napsbury Lane, St Albans (10/S), 1997 *T. J./G. Salisbury.*

Campanula glomerata L.
Clustered Bellflower
Native.
First record: 1597.
Tetrad occurrence: 41 (8%).
Decreasing quite markedly (-35%).

A plant of rough chalky grassland, this was formerly widespread across the north of the County, and occurred wherever chalk outcrops exist elsewhere, on road banks and field borders. It has tended to retreat to better quality chalk grassland sites, and has been lost from most road verges owing to salt pollution, rank growth or badly timed road verge cutting.

(60 tetrads: Dony, 1967; 68 tetrads: 1950-1986)

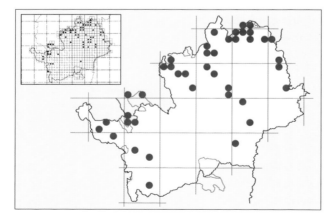

Map 573. *Campanula glomerata.*

Campanula portenschlagiana Schult.
Adria Bellflower
Introduced: neophyte.
First record: 1994.
Tetrad occurrence: 3 (<1%).

A plant of waste ground and walls, this was first noted at the former Hitchin railway sidings (22/E), 1994 *T. J.* It has also appeared on a wall at Kneesworth Street, Royston (34/K) (VC29 [Herts.]), 1996 *T. J.*; and near Broxbourne Lido (30/T), 1997 *C. G. Hanson.* It is likely to be under-recorded.

Campanula poscharskyana Degen
Trailing Bellflower
Introduced: neophyte.
First record: 1996.
Tetrad occurrence: 3 (<1%).

Like its relative, this is a plant of rockeries, old walls and urban wastelands, and was only recently recognised in published floras. This explains why we only have three records: from Hitchin (12/Z), 1996; Berkhamsted (90/Z), 1996 *T. J.*; and Bishop's Stortford (42/W), 2003 *S. Watson.* It is, no doubt, much more widespread, but may not yet be recognised for the escapee it is in other places.

Campanula latifolia L.
Giant Bellflower
Native (and introduced?)
First record: 1843.
Tetrad occurrence: 11 (2%).
Slightly decreased (-15%).

Just as Dony (1967) found, this is occasional in old copses, by ditches and in old hedgerows that survive in the arable landscape north of Buntingford, towards Sandon, as well as in the Quin valley near Braughing. Elsewhere, it is found in scattered places in old woods in west Herts., some of these being sites known for over 100 years, a few of which at least might be long-standing introductions. It appears to have been lost in one or two localities recently.

(12 tetrads: Dony, 1967; 16 tetrads: 1950-1986)

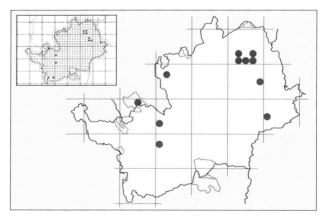

Map 574. *Campanula latifolia.*

Campanula trachelium L.
Nettle-leaved Bellflower
Native.
First record: 1597.
Tetrad occurrence: 38 (8%).
Possibly increasing (+64%).

In the 19th century, Pryor (1887) gave a range of sites, especially in the north of the County, but Dony's survey only found it rather sparsely, except near Wallington and Sandon. It was found during the recent survey to be sporadic, but well-established, in woodlands, old hedges, and green lanes in most of the places known to 19th century botanists, which suggests that the 1960s survey may have missed it. It is certainly a feature of hedgerows around Wallington, Sandon and at Throcking, where it was reported in Pryor to 'make the place where it grows blue'. It has also turned up in some new sites, such as by the A505 near Slip End (23/Y), where it is certainly a new arrival, and by Therfield Heath (33/J).
(22 tetrads: Dony, 1967; 33 tetrads: 1950-1986)

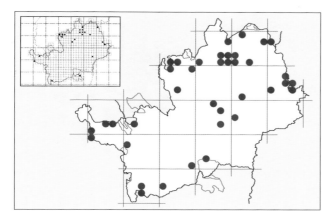

Map 575. *Campanula trachelium.*

Campanula rapunculoides L.
Creeping Bellflower
Introduced: neophyte.
First record: 1868.
Tetrad occurrence: 19 (4%).
Increased (+39%).

An escape from gardens, this was first reported at High Down (13/F) by J. Pollard (Dony, 1967), where it still occurs. It is more often an impermanent plant of hedgerows and rough ground, but can occasionally appear and remain in large quantities, such as

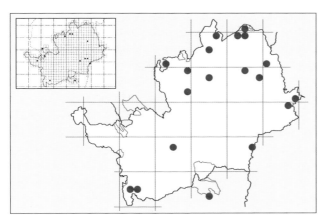

Map 576. *Campanula rapunculoides.*

in derelict set-aside by Arbury Banks, Ashwell (23/U), where it occurred in thousands, despite occasionally being mown, until the site was ploughed again in 2009.
(13 tetrads: Dony, 1967; 21 tetrads: 1950-1986)

Campanula rotundifolia L.
Harebell
Native.
First record: 1696.
Tetrad occurrence: 129 (26%).
Decreasing (-21%).

A charismatic plant of dry, nutrient-poor chalky or heathy grassland. As such, it is not surprising that it is decreasing quite markedly on rank road verges and in pastures, especially in the north and east of the County, although it remains quite widespread. It can, however, reappear from buried seed, given the right conditions.
(156 tetrads: Dony, 1967; 181 tetrads: 1950-1986)

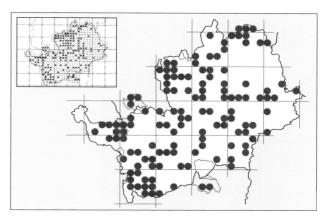

Map 577. *Campanula rotundifolia.*

Genus: *Legousia*

Legousia hybrida (L.) Delarbre
Venus's Looking-glass
Introduced: archaeophyte.
First record: 1640.
Tetrad occurrence: 59 (12%).
Decreasing (-20%).

This rather inconspicuous but attractive cornfield weed has declined quite substantially in quantity, but is still widespread, and occasionally locally abundant in arable margins on the Chalk

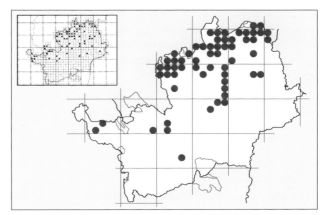

Map 578. *Legousia hybrida.*

in north Herts. It appears to have decreased in the west, although possibly overlooked in places, but occurs quite frequently along the chalk outcrop east of the River Beane south to Watton-at-Stone.
(70 tetrads: Dony, 1967; 80 tetrads: 1950-1986)

Legousia speculum-veneris (L.) Chaix
Large Venus's Looking-glass
Introduced: casual.
First (only) record: 1907.

The only record is of a presumably casual plant found at Lilley Hoo in 1907 (Dony, 1967).

[Genus: *Wahlenbergia*]

[*Wahlenbergia hederacea* (L.) Reichb.
Ivy-leaved Bellflower

A rather unsatisfactory record of this was included in Pryor (1887), on the strength of a specimen supposed to have been collected in Herts., and shown at the Whetstone Flower Show some time before 1876. If this was correct, it must have been a casual introduction.]

Genus: *Jasione*

Jasione montana L.   Herts Extinct
Sheep's-bit
Native.
First record: c.1820.

There are a number of old records of this from thin, acidic grasslands, especially around Bramfield, but also from Hoddesdon, Hertford, Colney Heath and near Rickmansworth. It was apparently last seen at Bulls Green (21/T) about 1914 (Dony, 1967 and ms. index).

Genus: *Lobelia*

Lobelia erinus L.
Garden Lobelia
Introduced: casual.
First record: 1979.

This was found on the old tip at Waterford (31/C), 1979 *C. G. Hanson*; since when it has also been found at Hadham Towers tip (41/I), 1989 *S. Watson*; on waste ground at Archer's Ride Open Space, Welwyn Garden City (21/K), 1995 *T. J.*; as a pavement weed in Wheathampstead (11/S), 1999 *T. J./G. P. Smith*; and on dumped soil at Chorleywood Common (09/I), 2004 *T. J.* Given that it frequently self-seeds from window boxes and hanging baskets, it must be more frequent as a genuine escape in urban areas.

Rubiaceae (Bedstraw family)

Genus: *Sherardia*

Sherardia arvensis L.
Field Madder
Native.
First record: 1814.
Tetrad occurrence: 163 (33%).
Stable (-1%).

Mainly a weed of arable field margins on light, calcareous and often gravelly soils, this also turns up on waste ground, and in slightly disturbed, thin grassland. It usually avoids bare chalk, and is now most frequent on thin, calcareous clays and gravel. It appears to have decreased on the Boulder Clay, probably through intensive agriculture, but has been found to be more widespread than formerly on the Clay-with-Flints.
(156 tetrads: Dony, 1967; 180 tetrads: 1950-1986)

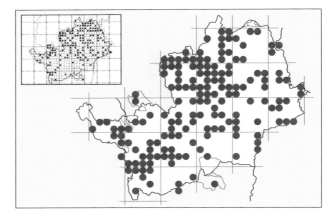

Map 579. *Sherardia arvensis.*

Genus: *Asperula*

Asperula cynanchica L.
Squinancywort
Native.
First record: 1814.
Tetrad occurrence: 14 (3%).
Decreasing (-22%).

In the 19th century, this attractive species of short, grazed chalk grassland was considered to be 'common' in the north of the County. Coleman found it to be 'plentiful' south of Hitchin, and 'in vast abundance' on Therfield Heath (Pryor, 1887). It occurred widely on chalky road banks, as well as on the established chalk grassland sites where it still is found. Dony (1967) regarded it as 'rare, but constant', but now it appears to be more or less decreasing generally, and is nowhere 'abundant', except maybe in good years on Therfield Heath.
(17 tetrads: Dony, 1967; 19 tetrads: 1950-1986)

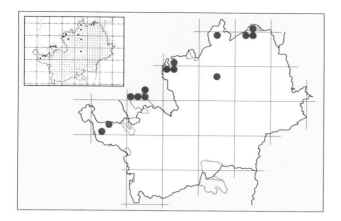

Map 580. *Asperula cynanchica.*

Asperula arvensis L.
Blue Woodruff
Introduced: casual.
First record: 1841.

Dony (1967) gave one recent record as a bird-seed alien, although some earlier records were more 'wild'. It was also found as a bird-seed escape at both Letchworth (23/B) and Baldock (23/L) in 1970 *B. R. Sawford*. There are no recent records.

Genus: *Galium*

Galium odoratum (L.) Scop.
Woodruff
Native.
First record: 1814.
Tetrad occurrence: 87 (18%).
Decreasing (-16%).

Dony (1967) surmised that the occurrence of this interesting woodland herb is more controlled by climate than by soils. It maintains its westerly distribution in the County, being particularly characteristic of woodlands on the Clay-with-Flints and similar soils over Chalk. However, it is also constant in woodlands in south-east Hertfordshire, on more acidic clays, where Chalk is not far below the surface. It also occasionally occurs as a probable escape, having been used as a garden plant for centuries. The survey results indicate that it may now be retreating somewhat, although this may have been the result of drought summers in the 1990s reducing its apparency.
(98 tetrads: Dony, 1967; 116 tetrads: 1950-1986)

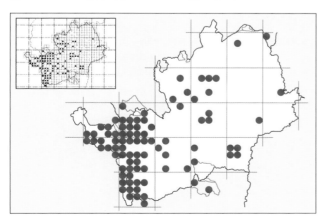

Map 581. *Galium odoratum.*

Galium uliginosum L.
Fen Bedstraw
Native.
First record: 1820.
Tetrad occurrence: 38 (8%).
Probably stable or slightly increased (+20%).

This is a highly characteristic plant of ancient fen-meadow communities, where the water supply is more or less calcareous. It can survive for a long time in rank, ungrazed swampy habitat, which probably accounts for its survival despite the degradation of wetland sites generally across much of the County. The recorded increase may be more a function of better recording.
(30 tetrads: Dony, 1967; 41 tetrads: 1950-1986)

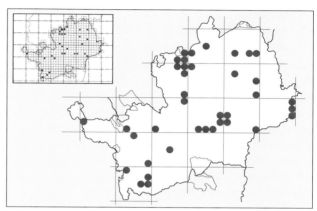

Map 582. *Galium uliginosum.*

Galium palustre L.
Marsh Bedstraw
Native.
First record: 1814.
Tetrad occurrence: 161 (33%).
Increased but now probably stable (+18%).

More widespread than its wetland cousin *G. uliginosum*, this is found in marshes, wet woodland rides, gravel pits, and by ponds across the damper areas of the County, only becoming rare or local in the west, where there is little standing water. The increase in gravel pits has benefited the species, but there are signs it has disappeared from some areas in the more arable parts of the County.
(130 tetrads: Dony, 1967; 165 tetrads: 1950-1986)

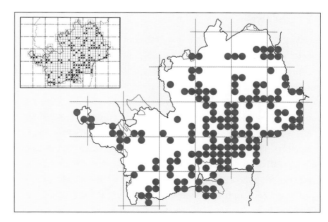

Map 583. *Galium palustre.*

The usual subspecies in wet woodland rides and marshy grassland appears to be ssp. *palustre*, while ssp. *elongatum*

(C. Presl.) Arcang. is probably the main subspecies in swamps beside rivers and gravel pit lakes, and was recorded at a number of places in the 19th century, when it was considered to be a separate species (Pryor, 1887). However, recent records of it, determined using Stace (1997), have only been obtained from Redbournbury Meadows (11/A), 1988 *T. J.*; North Metropolitan Pit (30/R), 1994 *T. J.*; and by the River Lea, Rye House (31/V), 1999 *T. J/G. P. Smith*. Sell and Murrell (2006) have now also recognised ssp. *tetraploideum* A. R. Clapham ex Franco, and claim that it is common in calcareous habitats, but we have no records.

Galium verum L.
Lady's Bedstraw
Native.
First record: 1750.
Tetrad occurrence: 340 (69%).
Decreasing (-11%).

A particularly characteristic plant of better quality calcareous grassland, found on Chalk, Boulder Clay and more calcareous gravelly soils especially, but becoming scarce or absent on the more acidic Clay-with-Flints and London Clay. With the steady loss and degradation of natural grasslands across the County, the plant is often now difficult to find in some areas, although it can survive in abundance on mown road verges, unless these are destroyed by salt.
(362 tetrads: Dony, 1967; 382 tetrads: 1950-1986)

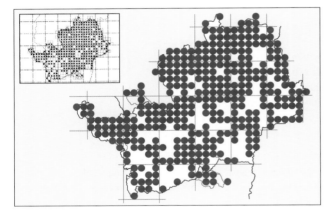

Map 584. *Galium verum.*

Galium × *pomeranicum* Retz. (*G. verum* × *G. mollugo*)
Native.
First record: 1849.

Despite the frequent occurrence together of both species, especially ssp. *erectum* of the latter, it is surprising how rare this appears to be, although when it does arise it can persist for a long time. Pryor (1887) gave two records, but Dony (1967) does not mention it. It was found on the old railway by Croxley Common Moor (09/X), 1977 *M. V. Marsden* (Burton, 1983) (Hb. HTN), where it has persisted, last reported in 1998 (*comm.*: R. M. Burton). The survey also found it on a small island in the R. Gade near Croxley Common Moor (09/S), 1990; at Croxley Hall Wood (09/S), 1996 *J. Colthup*; Langleybury Churchyard (00/V), *G. Salisbury/J. Saunders*; Ashwell Quarry (23/P), 1989 (Hb. HTN); and near Reed (33/S), 1993 *T. J.* (Hb. HTN).

Galium mollugo L.
Hedge Bedstraw
Native.
First record: 1657.
Tetrad occurrence: 387 (79%).
Decreasing slightly (-9%).

This common plant of rough hedgerows, field borders and ungrazed grassland shows some signs of decrease, but remains widespread. It is found across most of the County, except on the most acidic soils.
(403 tetrads: Dony, 1967; 413 tetrads: 1950-1986)

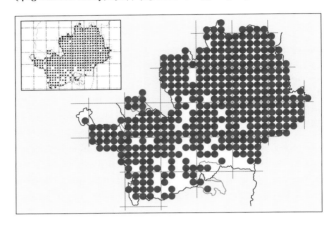

Map 585. *Galium mollugo.*

Stace (1997) admits two subspecies, which Dony (1967) also recognised, while Sell and Murrell (2006) list three, one of which is rare. The usual hedgerow plant is ssp. *mollugo*. Subspecies *erectum* Syme, with larger flowers and denser, more narrow panicles, is also quite widely recorded. Dony gave a separate map for this, considering it to occur most often on disturbed ground, railway banks, *etc.*, and even possibly being an alien. In the 19th century, it was regarded as a separate species (Pryor, 1887), and it was also treated as such (as *Galium album* Mill.) in the 1980s, when a number of records were made, especially on more calcareous ground in central and northern Hertfordshire. The recent survey found it widely scattered in 22 tetrads, mostly on calcareous soils, although it was probably overlooked in many places. Its real status in the County remains to be determined.

Galium pumilum Murray   UK Endangered
Slender Bedstraw
Native.
First record: *c.*1942.
Extinct in Herts.?

This plant of species-rich chalk grassland is another of the more enigmatic plants in the Hertfordshire flora. E. Milne-Redhead recorded it near Blows Downs, Dunstable (TL02) (VC20 [Beds.]), *c.*1942 (*Rep. Bot. Exch. Club*: 728 (1943-4)) (Hb. LTN), but Dony did not see it there. However, he did find it in Royston Churchyard (34/K), 1964 (Hb. HTN). Recent searches have failed to find it in either locality. It was, however, reported to be 'plentiful' on chalk grassland just in Bucks. near Tring in 1897 (G. C. Druce, in *Rep. Bot. Exch. Club*: 550 (1898)) and could occur in Herts. in this area.

Galium saxatile L.
Heath Bedstraw
Native.
First record: 1838.
Tetrad occurrence: 88 (18%).
Stable, or now decreasing? (-1%).

This is an especially characteristic plant of acidic, heathy grassland, usually found on old commons, in parkland, or in glades and rides in woodlands on acidic soils, rarely in enclosed pastures. It is widespread across south Hertfordshire, where it is effectively a 'ghost' of former wood-pasture, along with plants like heather and gorse, but is very rare in the north. It occasionally appears as a result of introduction on lawns. It was recorded from a similar number of tetrads to those that Dony (1967) found, but he had evidently under-recorded it, judging by the number of extra tetrads it had been found in by 1986. The steady loss of old acidic grassland must by now be affecting it in many areas.
(84 tetrads: Dony, 1967; 103 tetrads: 1950-1986)

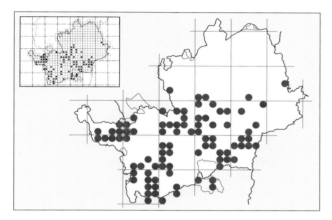

Map 586. *Galium saxatile.*

Galium aparine L.
Cleavers *or* **Goosegrass**
Native.
First record: 1750.
Tetrad occurrence: 483 (98%).
Stable? (-1%).

Native in nutrient-rich, somewhat disturbed and often damp habitats, such as woodland rides and drier areas of fen, this had become an ubiquitous weed by the 1960s, and has continued to expand in response to excessive use of fertilisers, and to atmospheric nitrogen deposition. It now occurs virtually

everywhere except in nutrient-poor chalk grassland, heath or aquatic habitats, although the overall proportion of tetrads in which it was recorded is marginally less.
(464 tetrads: Dony, 1967; and from 1950-1986)

Galium spurium L.
False Cleavers
Introduced: casual.
First record: 1907.

A plant of cultivated ground, this was first found at Rye House (30/Z), 1907 *G. C. Druce* (Hb. OXF), a record which was overlooked by Dony (1967). Its only other record was as a wool-shoddy alien at Newnham (23/N), 1973 *C. G. Hanson.*

Galium tricornutum Dandy   UK Endangered
Corn Cleavers
Introduced: archaeophyte.
First record: 1838.
Tetrad occurrence: 1 (<1%).
Almost extinct, decreased dramatically (-78%).

Having been a fairly widespread cornfield weed in the 19th and early 20th centuries, especially on more calcareous soils, this decreased rapidly after 1950, so that by the time Dony surveyed the flora, it had become very rare, owing to its susceptibility to weedkillers. It now only occurs on the untreated plots at Broadbalk, Rothamsted (11/G), where it has appeared rather erratically, with only 10 plants in 1987, but 'hundreds' in 2009 *I. G. Denholm*, following its adoption as a Biodiversity Action Plan species. This is almost the only remaining naturally occurring locality in Britain.
(4 tetrads: Dony, 1967; 5 tetrads: 1950-1986)

Corn Cleavers Galium tricornutum *Broadbalk, Rothamsted, 2008.*

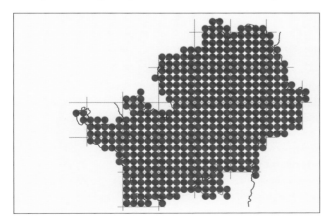

Map 587. *Galium aparine.*

Photo: Ian Denholm

Galium parisiense L.   UK Vulnerable
Wall Bedstraw
Native? (or introduced).
First record: 1857.

This rare native British plant of bare, gravelly ground and old
walls was a feature of the old park wall at Brocket Park, near
Lemsford Mill (21/B) in the 19th century, where it was last seen
in 1875 by A. R. Pryor (Hb. BM). Interestingly, it re-appeared
not that far away on the old railway near Cole Green (21/V),
1978 *B. Wurzell*, although there are no recent records. Its status
in the County could be either as a rare native on gravels, or an
introduction.

Genus: *Cruciata*

Cruciata laevipes Opiz
Crosswort
Native.
First record: c.1730.
Tetrad occurrence: 21 (4%).
Probably stable (+16%).

This has always been a scarce plant in the County, and has always
had a rather disjunct distribution. It occurs most frequently in
rough grassland and by rivers on somewhat calcareous gravels
over Chalk in the valleys of the upper Colne, Mimmshall Brook
and Catherine Bourne near Shenley and Potters Bar. It also
used to occur in the Lea Valley near Wheathampstead; while
its appearance at Chadwell Bank, King's Meads (31/L), 2007
A. Reynolds may be as a result of introduction. Elsewhere, it
has been known as a feature of the rough calcareous grassland
along field balks on the Chalk Marl at Ashwell for a long time,
although Dony never found it here; while it has also been recorded
consistently around Hexton. The recent survey found it in many of
the areas where it was known to Dony, but not in others, especially
in central Hertfordshire. Overall, it is probably as frequent as it
has ever been.
(17 tetrads: Dony, 1967; 27 tetrads: 1950-1986)

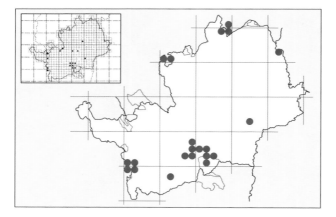

Map 588. *Cruciata laevipes.*

Caprifoliaceae (Honeysuckle family)

Genus: *Sambucus*

Sambucus racemosa L.
Red-berried Elder
Introduced: neophyte.
First record: c.1926.

This was first noted from Berkhamsted Common by J. A. Williams
(Dony, 1967 and ms. index), and was subsequently reported from
Ashridge, 1936 *H. Phillips* (Hb. HTN). It also appeared as an
outcast in the chalk pit by Hitchin Station (12/Z), 1928 *J. E. Little*.
The persistence of this around Ashridge apparently continued,
because J. Wilson reported it from several localities in 91/X, 1968
(Hb. HTN; Hb. LTN); and it was found at Cromer Wood, Little
Gaddesden (01/A), 1982 *P. J. Kingsbury* (Hb. HTN). It was also
reported at Barkway (33/W), 1979 *C. G. Hanson*. These records
are all the more interesting because there were no reports during
the recent survey. It is probably being overlooked.

Sambucus nigra L.
Elder
Native.
First record: 1733.
Tetrad occurrence: 480 (98%).
Stable (-2%).

This has always been a common plant in woodlands, hedgerows
and scrub across the County, but there may have been some
increase, especially on waste ground, despite the relatively lower
proportion of tetrads in which it was recorded, having been
missed in one complete tetrad. It can be adversely affected by
drought years.
(463 tetrads: Dony, 1967; 464 tetrads: 1950-1986)

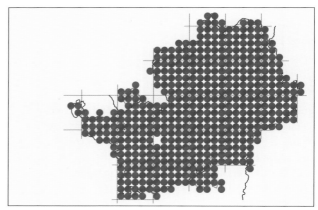

Map 589. *Sambucus nigra.*

Green or white-berried forms have been recorded, such
as at Norton Common (23/B), 1980 *B. R. Sawford*; and at
Childwickbury (11/F), 1979 *P. Barton*; while cut-leaved forms are
widespread, and a form with variegated leaves also occurs.

Sambucus canadensis L.
American Elder
Introduced: casual.
First (only) record: 1972.

The only record is from Boxmoor (00/H), 1972 *B. H. S. Russell*. Its
status is uncertain.

Sambucus ebulus L.
Dwarf Elder *or* **Danewort**
Introduced: archaeophyte.
First record: 1657.
Tetrad occurrence: 6 (1%).
Stable?

This odd plant has always been rare, although it has been known in some of its sites on and off for a very long time, such as at Barkway, Weston and Shephall, where it was known on roadsides and in some hedges for well over 170 years (Pryor, 1887; Dony, 1967), although in a few it has not been seen recently. During the survey, it was found at six localities: Marshcroft Farm, Tring (91/G), 1992 *T. J.*; near Biggin Manor (33/W), 1995 *E. Bell*; S. of Weston (22/U), 1995 *J. P. Widgery*; W. of Weston (22/P), 1997 *G. P. Smith*; Aldenham Park (19/T), 1998 *T. J./G. P. Smith*; Symonds Green (22/C), 1999 *M. Falvey.*

Genus: *Viburnum*

Viburnum opulus L.
Guelder Rose
Native.
First record: 1838.
Tetrad occurrence: 235 (48%).
Apparently increased markedly (+35%).

Normally a native shrub of damp woodland, riversides and fen, but sometimes found in drier woodlands and hedgerows. It is found most frequently in north-east and west Hertfordshire, on damper clay soils or by streams and ditches. However, it also occurs widely on less calcareous soils in south-east and central Hertfordshire, often in areas of damp woodland and scrub, as well as around flooded gravel pits. More recently, 'Guelder Rose' has become popular in amenity roadside shrubberies, which may account for some of the apparent increase, but not all. With these, though, there could be confusion with its near relatives *V. sargentii* Koehne **Asian Guelder Rose** or *V. trilobum* Marsh. **American Guelder Rose** (Sell, 2007), which are widely used for ornamental planting, and which should be looked for in such situations.
(166 tetrads: Dony, 1967; 192 tetrads: 1950-1986)

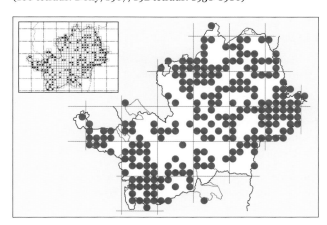

Map 590. *Viburnum opulus.*

Viburnum lantana L.
Wayfaring Tree
Native.
First record: 1787.
Tetrad occurrence: 237 (48%).
Increased (+17%).

This is an especially characteristic shrub of old hedgerows on calcareous soils on the Boulder Clay and Chalk in north-east and west Hertfordshire, but occurring elsewhere wherever Chalk comes to the surface. In a few places it forms thickets of scrub with other calcicoles like Privet, as at Ravensburgh Castle, Hexton (12/E). Like its relative *V. opulus*, it has also been used as an amenity shrub in many places, although some of these might be misidentified plants of *V. rhytidophyllum*, or possibly the hybrid between the two.
(193 tetrads: Dony, 1967; 209 tetrads: 1950-1986)

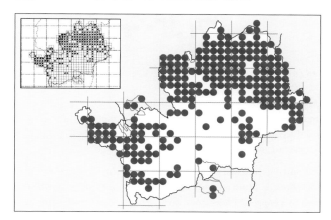

Map 591. *Viburnum lantana.*

Viburnum tinus L.
Laurustinus
Introduced: neophyte.
First record: *c.*1980.

The first record is an undated one from Darlands Nature Reserve, Totteridge (29/L), where it was noted as 'established' (Burton, 1983). It has more recently been found as a solitary bush in an old planted hedgerow by a green lane near Royston (33/P), 1996 *T. J.*

Viburnum rhytidophyllum Hemsley
Wrinkled Viburnum
Introduced: casual or planted.
First record: 1993.

Possibly planted bushes were found by the A505 at Slip End, Ashwell (23/Y), 1993 *T. J.* It may well occur elsewhere in roadside shrubberies, and could spread.

Genus: *Symphoricarpos*

Symphoricarpos albus (L.) S. F. Blake
Snowberry
Introduced: neophyte.
First record: *c.*1880.
Tetrad occurrence: 233 (48%).
Increasing.

Strangely almost ignored by Dony (1967), although his ms. index indicates he did actually record it from at least 24 tetrads. It was apparently well established even by the early years of the 20th century in many places (G. C. Druce in *Rep. Bot. Exch. Club*: 268 (1915), and J. W. Higgens *ibid*.: 489 (1916)). It forms thickets in woodland and scrub, especially where formerly introduced for game cover, although it appears not to spread readily from seed. (64 tetrads: 1970-1986)

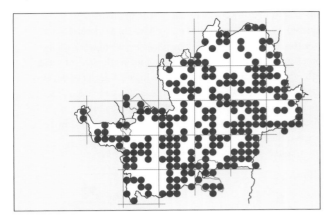

Map 592. *Symphoricarpos albus.*

Symphoricarpos orbiculatus Moench
Coralberry
Introduced: neophyte.
First record: 1982.

First noted as a casual on a tip at Waterford (31/C), 1982 *C. G. Hanson*. More recently it has been found as an established patch in a copse at Woodstock Road, Broxbourne (30/T), 1991 *A. M. Boucher* (Hb. Boucher).

Symphoricarpos × chenaultii Rehder
(*S. microphyllus × S. orbiculatus*)
Hybrid Coralberry
Introduced: casual.
First record: 1993.

The only record during the survey period was of a single bush at Sleapshyde Gravel Pit (20/D), 1993 *A. D. Marshall*. It was also noted subsequently as an escape on banks by a road at Ashwell (23/U), 2007 *T. J.*

Genus: *Leycesteria*

Leycesteria formosa Wallich
Himalayan Honeysuckle
Introduced: neophyte.
First record: 1987.

This was first noted as an escape at Bayfordbury (31/A), 1987 *C. G. Hanson* (det. B. Wurzell) (Hb. Hanson). It has subsequently been encountered at Cuffley (30/B), 1994 *T. J.*, where it had become established in a decaying wall; in scrub at The Gorse, Radlett (19/U), 1995 *A. D. Marshall* (Hb. HTN); Little Hadham (42/F), 1997 *S. Watson*; and in scrub on an old chalk pit by the railway at Knebworth (22/K), 1998 *T. J.*

Genus: *Lonicera*

Lonicera pileata Oliv.
Box-leaved Honeysuckle
Introduced: casual.
First (only) record: 1996.

The only record is of a self-sown plant in a car park gutter, Welwyn Garden City (21/G) *A. M. Boucher* (Burton, 1997). It probably occurs elsewhere, given its frequency as an ornamental shrubbery plant.

Lonicera nitida E. Wilson
Wilson's Honeysuckle
Introduced: neophyte.
First record: 1985.
Tetrad occurrence: 25 (5%).
Increasing.

This had been established for a long time in an old hedge at White Hill, Berkhamsted (90/Z) by the time P. J. Kingsbury reported it in 1985. Recent study has shown that it is widespread, mainly as a planted shrub for game cover in woods, but also apparently self-sown or as a result of outcasts in several places.

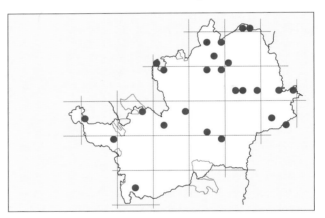

Map 593. *Lonicera nitida.*

Lonicera involucrata (Rich.) Banks ex Sprengel
Californian Honeysuckle
Introduced: casual.
First (only) record: 1987.

This was found on a rubbish tip at Wymondley electricity grid station (22/D), 1987 *A. D. Marshall* (det. B. Wurzell) (Hb. HTN).

Lonicera xylosteum L.
Fly Honeysuckle
Introduced: neophyte (or native?).
First record: (1841) c.1880.

Webb and Coleman (1849) recorded what were almost certainly planted bushes from near Hertford in 1841. Pryor (1887) gives an undated record from Northchurch. Several very old bushes were found by a stream in Hook Wood (20/Q), 1990 *A. M. Boucher* (Hb. HTN), but may originally have been planted, in association with the nearby old ornamental lake.

Lonicera henryi Hemsley
Henry's Honeysuckle
Introduced: neophyte.

This rather pernicious escape was found well-established
in different places in Sherrards Park Wood (21/G), 1992
independently by *T. J.* and *A. D. Marshall* (Hb. HTN); and in a
third place in 1999 *T. J.* It is apparently steadily increasing there,
but has not so far been recorded elsewhere.

Lonicera japonica Thunb. ex Murray
Japanese Honeysuckle
Introduced: neophyte.
First record: 1992.
Tetrad occurrence: 8 (2%).
Increasing.

First reported as an escape near Radlett (19/Z), 1992 *L. E. Perrins*.
It has subsequently been found on waste ground at Hitchin
railway sidings (22/E), and at Bury Mead Road, Hitchin (13/V),
1994 *T. J.*; by the old railway below Blows Downs, Dunstable
(02/L) (VC20 [Beds.]), 1995 *C. R. Boon/T. J.*; on waste ground
near houses, Osidge (29/W) (VC20 [Greater London]), 1998
T. J./G. P. Smith/J. Tyler; by Hadley Golf Course (29/T), 1999
T. J./G. P. Smith; Tyttenhanger Gravel Pits (10/X), 2000 *T. J.*;
and in a rough field at Broxbournebury (30/N), 2004 *T. J.*

Lonicera periclymenum L.
Honeysuckle *or* **Woodbine**
Native.
First record: 1724.
Tetrad occurrence: 375 (76%).
Possibly increased (+6%).

Wild Honeysuckle forms a constant and characteristic part of
woodland plant communities, especially on neutral to mildly
acidic soils across much of the County. It also occurs widely in old
hedgerows, and to some extent in secondary woodland and scrub.
There is evidence of a decrease in more intensively arable parts of
north-east Hertfordshire, but elsewhere it has either been poorly
recorded in the past, or has increased, especially in suburban
areas. A few of the records from such areas may be errors for
escaped garden honeysuckles of one sort or another.
(337 tetrads: Dony, 1967; 347 tetrads: 1950-1986)

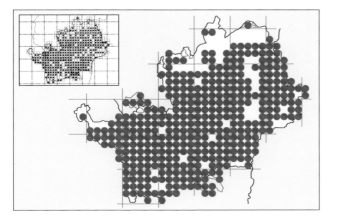

Map 594. *Lonicera periclymenum.*

Lonicera caprifolium L.
Perfoliate Honeysuckle
Introduced: neophyte.
First record: 1854?

A specimen of this, wrongly determined as *L. periclymenum*, is
in the herbarium of Miss Lucas, from 'near Pegsdon', but possibly
in Herts., 1854 (Hb. HTN). There are also undated records in
Pryor (1887), as well as others in Dony's ms. index. A solitary
bush was present for some years around 1977 at Ashwell Springs
(23/U), *T. J.*, probably an introduction; and it was noted as an
escape at Berkhamsted (90/Z), 1985 *P. J. Kingsbury*. During the
recent survey, it was recorded at Blackfan Wood (30/D), 1989
K. Robinson. It is possible that one or two of these records may
have been the hybrid with *L. etrusca*, the usual garden plant.

Lonicera × *italica* Schmidt ex Tausch
(*L. caprifolium* × *L. etrusca*)
Garden Honeysuckle
Introduced: casual.
First record: 2005.

This was positively identified as an escape in scrub at Lemsford
Springs (21/F) *T. J.* It is no doubt much more frequent.

Adoxaceae (Moschatel family)

Genus: *Adoxa*

Adoxa moschatellina L.
Moschatel *or* **Town-hall Clock**
Native.
First record: 1814.
Tetrad occurrence: 51 (10%).
Increasing or stable? (+24%).

This is an easily overlooked, but very characteristic and fascinating
plant of slightly damp, calcareous woodlands and long-establishd
scrub. It is especially found in the Chilterns, but also around
Tewin and Bramfield, and in some parts of south Hertfordshire,
with scattered records elsewhere. Outlying sites in the north-east
have been found to indicate the presence of Clay-with-Flints soils
at the surface. Owing to its early flowering, it may be overlooked
in many places, and therefore it is difficult to be sure that it has in
fact increased.
(39 tetrads: Dony, 1967; 66 tetrads: 1950-1986)

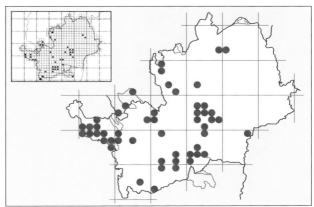

Map 595. *Adoxa moschatellina.*

Valerianaceae (Valerian family)

Genus: *Valerianella*

Valerianella locusta (L.) Laterr.
Common Corn-salad
Native.
First record: 1814.
Tetrad occurrence: 56 (11%).
Decreasing (-38%).

As a native plant, this occurs, rather rarely, as an ephemeral of bare patches in rough grassland, especially on roadside banks. It also occurs more widely as a weed of arable field margins on calcareous, often gravelly soils, and on waste ground, railway ballast, *etc*. Its current distribution indicates that it may have been under-recorded in some areas in the 1960s, because it is evidently quite frequent around Hertford, as Pryor (1887) indicated, although Dony (1967) only had one record from the area. However, it does not appear to be anywhere near as frequent around St Albans, and its occurrence on railway ballast has probably declined substantially, although this habitat is now much less easy to survey.
(86 tetrads: Dony, 1967; 97 tetrads: 1950-1986)

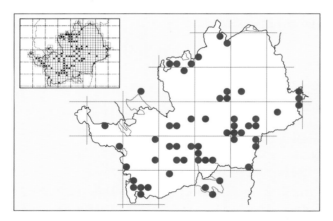

Map 596. *Valerianella locusta.*

Valerianella carinata Lois.
Keeled-fruited Corn-salad
Introduced: archaeophyte.
First record: 1847.
Tetrad occurrence: 6 (1%).
Increasing?

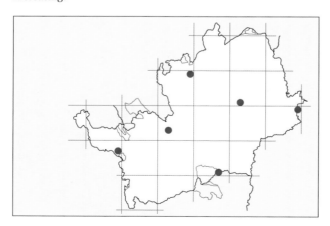

Map 597. *Valerianella carinata.*

This has always been a rather rare colonist of waste ground, but can persist locally for some time, and become quite abundant where it does occur. Dony (1967) had one record, from West Leith, near Tring. There were no further records until it was found at Harpenden Common (11/G), 1989, 1990 *I. G. Denholm* (Hb. HTN); and subsequently abundantly in gardens at Dane End (32/F), 1994 *T. J.* (Hb. HTN); in a garden at Bishop's Stortford (41/Z), from 1995-1998 *S. Watson* (Hb. HTN); on disturbed ground at Brickhill Green (90/Y), 2006 *T. J.*; at Fir and Pond Woods N. R. (20/Q), 2006 *D. Gompertz* (conf. T. J.); and by an alleyway at Hitchin (12/Z), 2007 *T. J.*

Valerianella rimosa Bast.   UK Endangered
Broad-fruited Corn-salad
Introduced: archaeophyte.
First record: 1724.
Possibly extinct.

This was formerly a rare, but occasionally locally frequent cornfield weed on gravelly ground, particularly in the Colne Valley area and near Bramfield. Dony (1967) gave two records: from Benington and near Sarratt (where it had been reported as locally abundant) (Dony, ms. index). There was a record, unfortunately not confirmed, from near Benington (22/W), 1977 *M. Hooper*, which may have been correct; but otherwise the last confirmed record was from Park Street Gravel Pits, Colney Street (10/L), 1965 *E. S. Bradford* (*Proc. S. Lond. Ent. and N.H.S.*, 3, p. 90).

Valerianella dentata (L.) Poll.   UK Endangered
Sharp-fruited Corn-salad
Introduced: archaeophyte.
First record: 1839.
Tetrad occurrence: 12 (2%).
Decreasing markedly (-66%).

Formerly quite widespread as a cornfield weed on chalky soils across northern and western Hertfordshire, as well as occasionally occurring on Boulder Clay, this has now become a rare plant except at a few favoured localities, such as around Benington High Wood and Oxshott Hill (22/V, W). It is very susceptible to weedkillers, and does not tolerate over-enriched ground.
(33 tetrads: Dony, 1967; 41 tetrads: 1950-1986)

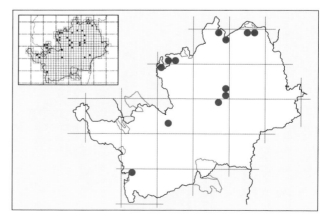

Map 598. *Valerianella dentata.*

Valerianella eriocarpa Desv.
Hairy-fruited Corn-salad
Introduced: neophyte.
First (only) record: *c.*1880.

The only record was as a garden weed from Hatfield (Pryor, 1887).

Genus: *Valeriana*

Valeriana officinalis L.
Common Valerian
Native.
First record: 1814.
Tetrad occurrence: 31 (6%).
Decreasing (-41%).

There are two fairly distinct subspecies: ssp. *collina* (Wallr.)
Nyman is a plant of scrubby ground on dry chalk; while ssp.
sambucifolia (Mikan ex Pohl) Hayward is a plant of damp, more
or less calcareous or even mildly acidic ground near streams and
rivers. The plant of the Chalk has always apparently been quite
limited in its occurrence, occurring especially around Tring,
Pirton, Weston and Barkway, while the damp ground plant was
formerly widespread, especially in and around the woodlands in
south-east Hertfordshire, and along the banks of the rivers Lea,
Colne and Stort. Both have decreased quite markedly since the
1960s, mainly through loss of habitat, although they can respond
to management, such as the increase in population at Aldbury
Nowers (91/L), following scrub clearance in the early 1990s.
(43 tetrads: Dony, 1967; 55 tetrads: 1950-1986)

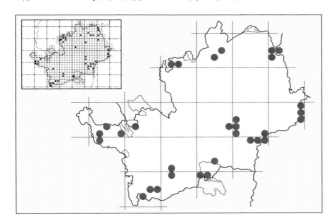

Map 599. *Valerianella officinalis*.

Valeriana dioica L.
Marsh Valerian
Native.
First record: 1814.
Tetrad occurrence: 18 (4%).
Local, but possibly stable (+32%).

Marsh Valerian is a particularly characteristic plant of open,
naturally wet ground, usually where this is fed by emerging
springs. As such, it became quite rare in the County following
the loss of many wet meadows in the late 19th and early 20th
centuries. It is vulnerable to the degradation of such habitats, both
through lowered water tables, and lack of grazing or overgrowth
of scrub, although it quite often survives vegetatively for long
periods in adverse conditions, which may account for its periodic
're-appearance' at sites where it was thought to have vanished.
(13 tetrads: Dony, 1967; 21 tetrads: 1950-1986)

Marsh Valerian Valeriana dioica *Moor Hall, Ardeley, 1998.*

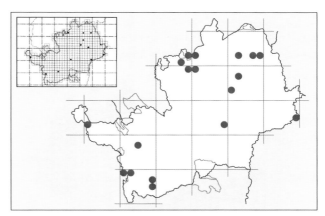

Map 600. *Valeriana dioica*.

Genus: *Centranthus*

Centranthus ruber (L.) DC.
Red Valerian
Introduced: neophyte.
First record: *c.*1880.
Tetrad occurrence: 38 (8%).
Increasing.

Dony (1967) dismissed this as a casual, but the recent survey has
shown that it is well-established on walls and on bare, dry, waste
ground around towns and villages, especially around Hitchin and
Hertford.

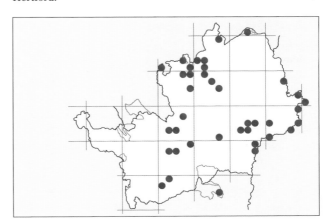

Map 601. *Centranthus ruber*.

Dipsacaceae (Teasel family)

Genus: *Dipsacus*

Dipsacus fullonum L.
Wild Teasel
Native.
First record: 1819.
Tetrad occurrence: 375 (76%).
Increased markedly (+46%).

As a native plant, this was formerly especially characteristic of ditch sides and rough grassland on calcareous Boulder Clay and on the Aylesbury Vale clays in the extreme west of the County. Elsewhere it occurred more patchily in river valleys and on waste ground (Dony, 1967). The recent survey has shown that it has greatly increased its range and frequency, especially in the centre and west of the County, now occurring widely on rough road verges and disturbed, waste ground throughout the area. It has invaded ancient woodland areas as a result of rubble dumping on tracks, and is a frequent plant around gravel pits.
(244 tetrads: Dony, 1967; 271 tetrads: 1950-1986)

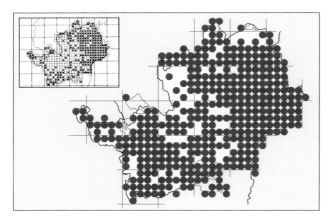

Map 602. *Dipsacus fullonum.*

Dipsacus sativus (L.) Honck.
Fuller's Teasel
Introduced: casual.
First record: 1874.

At one time used in the cloth fulling industry at Hertford and elsewhere, this was formerly a rare casual on waste tips in various localities (Dony, 1967). Its last record was at Long Green (90/Y), 1985 *R. Mabey*. It is just possible that it has been overlooked in some localities as a robust form of *D. fullonum*.

Dipsacus laciniatus L.
Cut-leaved Teasel
Introduced: casual.
First record: 2005.

A substantial colony of this imposing southern species was found in an abandoned field by the Icknield Way at Baldock (31/M), 2005 *J. L. Sharman* (*comm.*: A. C. Leslie) (Hb. HTN). It is slowly increasing, but vulnerable to land use change.

Dipsacus pilosus L.
Small Teasel
Native.
First record: 1657.
Tetrad occurrence: 25 (5%).
Increased? (+168%).

A local plant of damp, shaded ground in woodland rides, or by rivers, on more or less calcareous soils, this was recorded in the 19th century from quite a number of sites in east Hertfordshire, and also from a few places in the Colne Valley. Dony (1967) only found it in a handful of places, but subsequent recording has found it again more widely, although it remains uncommon. It may therefore have been overlooked in the 1960s survey, making any change difficult to assess.
(9 tetrads: Dony, 1967; 19 tetrads: 1950-1986)

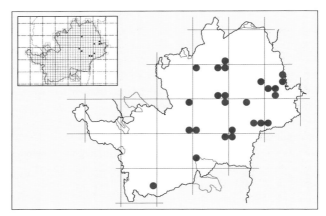

Map 603. *Dipsacus pilosus.*

Genus: *Cephalaria*

Cephalaria gigantea (Ledeb.) Bobrov
Giant Scabious
Introduced: neophyte.
First record: 1918.

This garden escape remains rare, but may be slowly increasing nationally. Its first occurrence at Ware was short-lived, but the colony on railway banks at Letchworth (23/B), first noticed in 1997 *T. J.* is increasing steadily. It was also found in scrub at Bernards Heath, St Albans (10/P), 1990 *A. D. Marshall* (Hb. HTN).

Genus: *Knautia*

Knautia arvensis (L.) Coulter
Field Scabious
Native.
First record: 1814.
Tetrad occurrence: 363 (74%).
Decreasing slightly (-11%).

A familiar plant of calcareous rough grassland across the County, only absent on the most acidic soils in south Hertfordshire. There is evidence, however, of a steady decline in abundance, mainly owing to the poor management of road verges and the loss of unimproved rough grasslands.
(388 tetrads: Dony, 1967; 398 tetrads: 1950-1986)

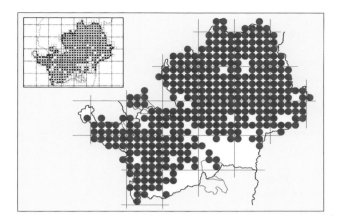

Map 604. *Knautia arvensis.*

Genus: *Succisa*

Succisa pratensis Moench
Devil's-bit Scabious
Native.
First record: 1820.
Tetrad occurrence: 66 (13%).
Decreasing (-24%).

This is found in a range of different natural grassland communities, ranging from dry chalk downland, to damp calcareous Boulder Clay pasture, old moderately acidic grassland on London Clay, and herbaceous vegetation on loams in open woodland rides. It was formerly quite common, especially on the London Clay in south Herts., but it has steadily decreased, owing to the loss of old grassland, and many of its recent records are of small colonies, just surviving.
(82 tetrads: Dony, 1967; 108 tetrads: 1950-1986)

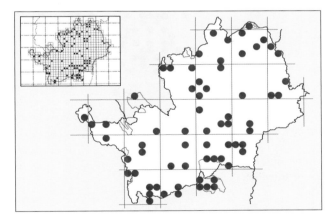

Map 605. *Succisa pratensis.*

Genus: *Scabiosa*

Scabiosa columbaria L.
Small Scabious
Native.
First record: 1838.
Tetrad occurrence: 57 (12%).
Decreased substantially (-33%).

This is a frequent plant of old chalk grassland, occurring wherever Chalk comes to the surface, formerly rarely on old walls and on gravel. It is also another plant which has succumbed to the loss of

old grassland habitats, retreating to the remaining better quality sites, having formerly been quite widespread on chalky roadside banks and field margins, as well as downland. Its few occurrences in southern Hertfordshire are usually where small outcrops of Chalk occur, but it has occurred as an introduced plant on rough ground near Cheshunt Station (30/R), 1990 *A. M. Boucher* (det. E. J. Clement).
(80 tetrads: Dony, 1967; 90 tetrads: 1950-1986)

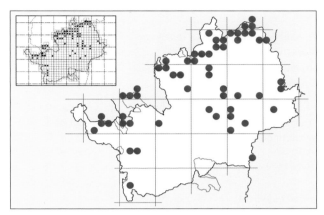

Map 606. *Scabiosa columbaria.*

Succisa atropurpurea L.
Sweet Scabious
Introduced: casual.
First (only) record: 1921.

There is a solitary record of this garden plant, introduced from Europe, as an escape in a Lucerne field at Buckland *A. W. Graveson* (Dony, 1967, and ms. index).

Asteraceae (Daisy family)

Sub-family: Lactucoideae (Thistles and relatives)

Genus: *Echinops*

Echinops sphaerocephalus L.
Glandular Globe-thistle
Introduced: neophyte.
First record: *c.*1980.
Tetrad occurrence: 3 (<1%).

This was first noted as a well-established stand in scrub and a hedgerow by Wilbury Road, Letchworth (23/B), *c.*1980 *B. R. Sawford*, and this colony persists to the present day (Hb. HTN). It was also recorded from the old railway by Croxley Common Moor (09/X), 1981 *A. V. Moon*; and during the recent survey from Town Meads, Bishop's Stortford (42/V), 1988 *S. Watson*; and on a chalky roadside, Stotfold Road, Letchworth (23/A), 1996 *A. Dean*, and 1997 onwards *T. J.*, where it is spreading (Hb. HTN).

Echinops exaltatus Schrad.
Globe-thistle
Introduced: neophyte.
First record: 1989.
Tetrad occurrence: 3 (<1%).

First noted at a derelict coal yard by Ware Station (31/R), 1989 *A. M. Boucher* (Hb. Boucher); and at Purwell, Hitchin (22/E), 1989 *T. J.*, where it has persisted (Hb. HTN). It was also found in scrub by Ivel Springs, Baldock (23/H), 1996 *T. J.* (Hb. HTN).

Echinops bannaticus Rochel ex Schrad.
Blue Globe-thistle
Introduced: neophyte.
First record: 2003.

This has been found as an escape by the A414, St Margarets (31/Q) *S. Oakes-Monger* (det. P. Perkins). As it is frequent in gardens, it may occur elsewhere.

Genus: *Carlina*

Carlina vulgaris L.
Carline Thistle
Native.
First record: 1820.
Tetrad occurrence: 24 (5%).
Decreasing quite markedly (-46%).

Mostly found in short, dry, chalk grassland, but also occasionally in old chalk pits, and on bare gravelly ground. Pryor (1887) did not regard it as very common, although he listed a good number of localities. It was fairly frequent across the north and west of the County in the 1960s (Dony, 1967), but has decreased substantially, mostly in marginal sites on roadsides, *etc.*
(42 tetrads: Dony, 1967; 47 tetrads: 1950-1986)

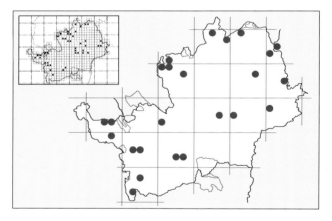

Map 607. *Carlina vulgaris.*

Genus: *Arctium*

This difficult group has had different treatments over the years, with the result that earlier records cannot always be assigned to more recent concepts of species. The Flora Survey recording and this treatment follow Stace (1997), especially recognising *Arctium nemorosum* as a separate species, which seems to be more useful than having all taxa lumped as subspecies under '*Arctium lappa*' as proposed by Sell and Murrell (2006). The supposedly distinct '*Arctium pubens*', which Dony mapped, was considered a form of *A. minus* by Stace, but has been resurrected as a subspecies (of

lappa) by Sell and Murrell (although they admit its variability, and also suggest a possible hybrid origin).

Arctium tomentosum Miller
Downy Burdock
Introduced: casual.
First (only) record: 1964.

This was recorded once at Dobbs Weir (30/Z), 1964 *J. G. Dony*. There have not been any subsequent records.

Arctium lappa L.
Greater Burdock
Introduced: archaeophyte.
First record: 1874.
Tetrad occurrence: 171 (35%).
Increased substantially (+142%).

In this account, the strict definition of the species, according to Stace (1997) is followed, which appears to be most useful, as it is a readily-recognised plant with a fairly clear habitat preference. Both Pryor (1887) and Dony (1967) considered it to be relatively common, even though Dony's records show it to have been rather limited in occurrence, by streams, mostly in east Hertfordshire. It is now frequent across much of the County on damper ground, although it is still generally absent from the Clay-with-Flints and the Chalk, as well as in less disturbed habitats elsewhere.
(67 tetrads: Dony, 1967; 78 tetrads: 1950-1986)

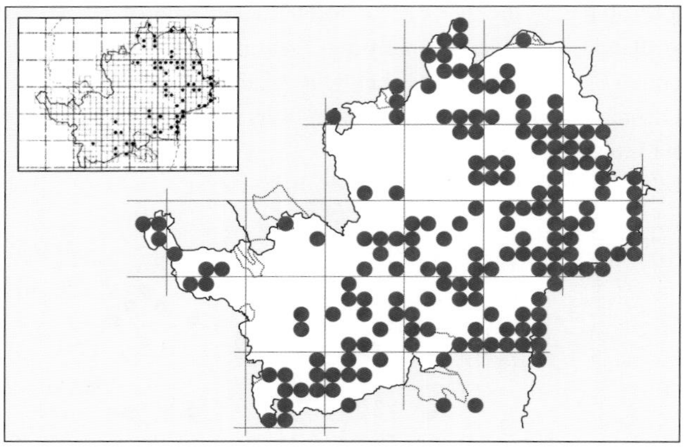

Map 608. *Arctium lappa.*

Arctium minus (Hill) Bernh.
Lesser Burdock
Native.
First record: (1822 for the aggregate), 1840.
Tetrad occurrence: 455 (93%).
Increasing? (+6%).

This is the principal burdock found in scrub, waste ground and roadsides through much of the County. The treatment of this and the next species over the years has caused much confusion. In addition, it is likely that hybrids with *A. lappa* occur, although there are no confirmed records. Dony (1967) also recorded *Arctium minus* separately from '*A. pubens*', which has been considered by Stace (1997) to be a form of *A. minus*. For the sake of comparison, Dony's records of '*pubens*' and *minus* have been amalgamated, although the former almost certainly include some records of *A. nemorosum*, which was for a time also considered to be a separate subspecies of *minus*. The records from the current survey were often recorded as the aggregate, although attempts were made to separate *A. nemorosum.*

(406 tetrads: Dony, 1967 (for the aggregate); 416 tetrads: 1950-1986)

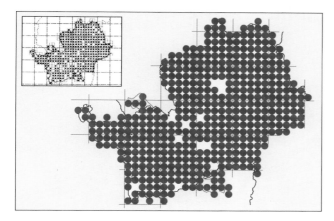

Map 609. *Arctium minus.*

Arctium nemorosum Lej.
Wood Burdock
Native.
First record: 1868 (Pryor, 1887).
Tetrad occurrence: 47 (10%).

This fine and quite distinctive burdock usually occurs in glades and borders of old woods, occasionally along hedgerows and green lanes, where it appears to be a genuinely native taxon. Records made during the Flora Survey were made on the basis of the treatment by Stace (1997), as well as earlier accounts, where it was recognised as a separate subspecies of *minus.* It was clearly recognised by Pryor (1887), but unfortunately Dony (1967) regarded Pryor's records as referring to '*Arctium pubens*', while he did not separate out records of what has recently been thought of as this species. The account of it in Burton (1983) also displays confusion between '*Arctium pubens*' and *nemorosum.* As a result, no measure of its changing status can be made. More recently, it has again been ignored in Preston *et al.* (2002). The survey produced enough records to suggest that it is most widespread on the Clay-with-Flints and gravels in west Herts., becoming quite rare in the north and east, and apparently absent on the damper and more acidic London Clay. This closely mirrors its occurrence as given by Pryor.

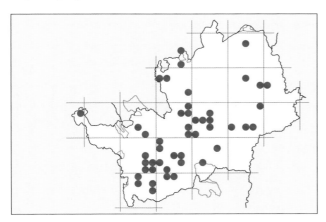

Map 610. *Arctium nemorosum.*

Carduus tenuiflorus Curtis
Slender Thistle
Introduced? [native in the U.K.]
First record: *c.*1873.
Tetrad occurrence: 5 (1%).

This is an interesting plant, being mainly a coastal species in Britain. It appeared first in large quantity by the Grand Union Canal at Boxmoor (00/N), where Dony (1967) also found it in 1956, and where it persists, having been found there in 1994 *G. Salisbury/J. Saunders.* It is interesting that Dony also found it by the Grand Union Canal at Croxley Common Moor (09/X), 1958 (a record omitted from his *Flora*), suggesting that the canal was probably one means of its introduction. Elsewhere it seems to have been introduced with wool shoddy, and this may be the source of records at Newnham (23/N), 1973 *C. G. Hanson*; and near Stevenage (22/H), *c.*1974 *R. D. Hawkins.* Other records from farmland may also represent wool shoddy introductions in the past, such as by Beeches Wood (43/K), 1987 *K. Robinson.* It was found, rarely, at waste ground by the R. Colne, Watford (19/D), 1989 *O. Linford*; in a field near Grove Mill, Watford (09/Z), 1992 *T. J.* (Hb. HTN); and a small colony at Cooper's Green Gravel Pit near St Albans (10/Z), 1995 *T. J./G. P. Smith* (Hb. HTN). It is, however, rather surprising that a plant of shingle by the sea should not have been found more often in the County's many gravel pits.

Carduus crispus L.
Welted Thistle
Native.
First record: 1787.
Tetrad occurrence: 358 (73%).
Increased slightly (+8%).

This plant is particularly common on calcareous soils, and is abundant on the Chalk and Boulder Clay, as well as on more calcareous gravels. However, Sell and Murrell (2006) have now suggested that we have in Britain not only Welted Thistle, but also *Carduus acanthoides* L. **Broad-winged Thistle**. As earlier records of Welted Thistle would have been recorded under the name '*C. acanthoides*', following general usage in Britain in the 1960s and subsequently, there is much scope for confusion. As yet, there are no properly verified records of *C. acanthoides* L. from the County, which only seems to differ from *C. crispus* in its robustness and size of flower capitulum. Welted Thistle, as hitherto understood, has expanded especially in the south, as

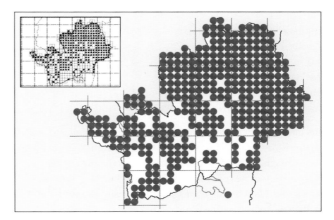

Map 611. *Carduus crispus.*

a result of the increase in waste land, disturbed ground and the dumping of building rubble, *etc*. It is also very capable of withstanding enrichment of arable field margins, with the result that it is doing well in the farm landscape. Our plant is thought to be ssp. *multiflorus* (Gaudin) Franco.

(315 tetrads: Dony, 1967; 338 tetrads: 1950-1986)

Carduus nutans L.
Musk *or* **Nodding Thistle**
Native.
First record: *c*.1820.
Tetrad occurrence: 58 (12%).
Decreased (-8%).

Dony (1967) did not recognise any particular distribution pattern, while 19th century botanists thought it was most frequent on the Chalk. Its present distribution suggests it is more a plant of calcareous gravels, being found most frequently in the flood-plain grasslands and waste ground of the middle reaches of the Lea, and the lower Colne valleys. It may also occur as a result of manuring on calcareous soils elsewhere. Hybrids with *C. crispus* probably occur, and should be looked for.

(60 tetrads: Dony, 1967; 78 tetrads: 1950-1986)

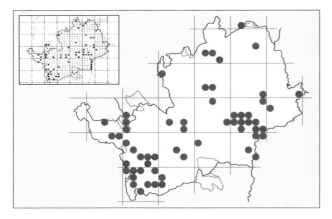

Map 612. *Carduus nutans.*

Carduus thoermeri J. A. Weinm.
Introduced: casual.
First (only) record: 1934.

There is a record of this grain-seed alien having been collected from a waste heap at Welwyn (TL21), 1934 *H. Phillips* (det. J. E. Lousley) (Hb. HTN). This was overlooked by Dony (1967).

Genus: *Cirsium*

Cirsium eriophorum (L.) Scop.
Woolly Thistle
Native.
First record: 1820.
Tetrad occurrence: 8 (2%).
Rare, but possibly increasing (+78%).

This magnificent thistle has always been a rare plant in Hertfordshire, probably because the County's climate is not quite moist enough, its main distribution being on the calcareous clays and limestones of central and western England. With us it is a scarce plant of rough grassland and bushy places on the Chalk in northern Hertfordshire, with recent records, some confirming older reports, from Hartham Common, Brent Pelham

Woolly Thistle Cirsium eriophorum *Hexton, 1985.*

(43/F), 1978 *T. Bell* (Hb. HTN); Birkett Hill, Offley (12/I), 1978 *T. J./B. R. Sawford*, where it survives despite ploughing of the old chalk grassland in 1979; Ravensburgh, Hexton (12/E), 1985 *T. J./B. R. S.*; by Gravel Hill, Offley (12/P), 1987 *S. Gorton*; Danesbury Park, Welwyn (21/I), 1987 onwards *P. Watt*; Anstey Chalk Pit (33/W), 1992 *T. J.*, also 1999 *J. Murray*; by Knott Wood (11/B), 1997 *I. G. Denholm*; by A505, Lilley (12/C), 1993 *T. J.*; banks at Old Hill (01/C) (VC20 [Beds.]), 2000 *P. Baker*; and Tring Park (91/F), 2005 *R. Mabey*.

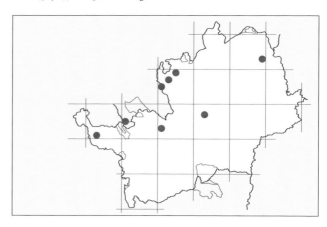

Map 613. *Cirsium eriophorum.*

AtH 09

Scarce thistles – Woolly Thistle Cirsium eriophorum *(left), see opposite, and Slender Thistle* Carduus tenuiflorus *(right), see page 353.*

Hybrid Woolly × Creeping Thistle Cirsium × sennenii *Danesbury, September 2007, 1st U.K. record.*

Cirsium × sennenii Rouy (*C. eriophorum × C. arvense*)
Native.
First (only) record: 2007.

A specimen of this rare hybrid was found in association with both its parents at Danesbury Park (21/I), 2007 *P. Watt* (provisional det. T. J.; conf: K. J. Walker) (Hb. HTN). This is the first British record.

··

Cirsium vulgare L.
Spear Thistle
Native.
First record: 1750.
Tetrad occurrence: 476 (97%).
Probably stable (-2%).

A very common weed of waste places, rough grassland, *etc.* throughout the County, although not as abundant as *C. arvense*. There is no evidence of any change from the previous survey. (460 tetrads: Dony, 1967; 461 tetrads: 1950-1986)

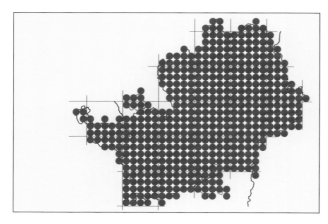

Map 614. *Cirsium vulgare.*

Cirsium dissectum (L.) Hill   Herts Extinct
Meadow Thistle
Native.
First record: 1838.

This plant of species-rich, permanently wet pasture on peaty soils was always rare in the County, but was recorded from a number of sites in the 19th century, such as boggy meadows near Little Berkhamsted, Croxley Common Moor, by Wilstone Reservoir, by Knebworth Woods, and Hertford Heath, among other places. It had decreased substantially by the early 20th century, and was last seen, non-flowering, at Burleigh Meadow (22/G), in 1980 *M. Hooper*. It is noteworthy that it also failed at other sites earlier in the same way, attributed by Coleman to drought.

··

Cirsium heterophyllum (L.) Hill
Melancholy Thistle
Introduced [native in the U.K.].
First documented record: 1986.

A small colony of this species was established for a while following deliberate introduction to Meesden Green (43/G) in the early 1980s. 13 plants were recorded in 1986 *B. R. Sawford*. Unless it shows signs of re-appearing, it scarcely merits inclusion in the County list.

··

Cirsium acaule (L.) Scop.
Dwarf or **Stemless Thistle**
Native.
First record: 1814.
Tetrad occurrence: 81 (17%).
Decreasing (-17%).

Particularly characteristic of short chalk grassland, this thistle used to occur more frequently than it now does in unimproved calcareous pasture on Boulder Clay and Clay-with-Flints as well. It remains quite widespread on the Chalk, but is disappearing from some marginal sites elsewhere.

(93 tetrads: Dony, 1967; 111 tetrads: 1950-1986)

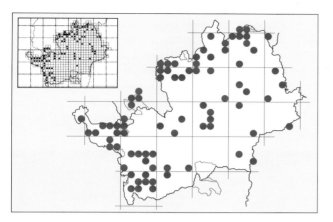

Map 615. *Cirsium acaule.*

Cirsium palustre (L.) Scop.
Marsh Thistle
Native.
First record: 1814.
Tetrad occurrence: 271 (55%).
Decreasing slightly (-10%).

Widespread and locally abundant in wet, marshy grassland, woodland rides and around old flooded gravel pits throughout much of the County. It is particularly frequent in older pasture on the Boulder Clay and London Clay, becoming scarce on the Clay-with-Flints, and absent on the Chalk, except around seepages. There is increasing indication of a decrease, possibly owing to the loss of old damp grassland and the overgrowth of woodland rides. White-flowered forms are quite frequent.

(286 tetrads: Dony, 1967; 305 tetrads: 1950-1986)

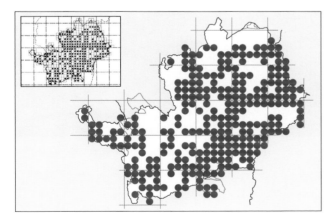

Map 616. *Cirsium palustre.*

Cirsium arvense (L.) Scop.
Creeping Thistle
Native.
First record: c.1820.
Tetrad occurrence: 486 (99%).
Stable (no measurable change).

An abundant weed in waste places, rough grassland, arable fields and roadsides throughout the County, except on the most acidic or wet soils and in undisturbed woodland. It has probably spread in disturbed habitats and poorly managed grassland in some areas,

while having decreased in abundance in arable farmland through the use of weedkillers.

(463 tetrads: Dony, 1967; 464 tetrads: 1950-1986)

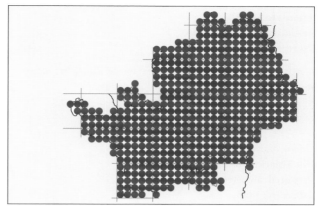

Map 617. *Cirsium arvense.*

Genus: *Galactites*

Galactites tomentosa Moench
Galactites
Introduced: casual.
First record: 1916.

This Mediterranean plant was found on a waste tip at Ware (TL31), 1916 *A. W. Graveson* (Hb. HTN) (not 1910, as stated in Dony, 1967). As it self-seeds in gardens, it could spread with climate warming.

Genus: *Onopordum*

Onopordum acanthium L.
Cotton Thistle
Introduced: archaeophyte.
First record: 1838.
Tetrad occurrence: 35 (7%).
Increasing?

Cotton Thistle, or Scottish Thistle, as it is mis-named, can be spectacular when it appears, often by houses as an obvious escape, but also not infrequently remote from houses on chalky road banks, and in old pits, where some have suggested it might be native. It is most frequent in the drier areas of the County, on the Chalk in north Hertfordshire, and around Hertford, *etc.* It may

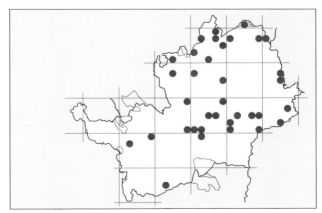

Map 618. *Onopordum acanthium.*

have increased, although Dony kept few detailed records of its occurrence.

Onopordum nervosum Boiss.
Reticulate Thistle
Introduced: casual?
First record: 1986?

There is a note of this as apparently established in 'Herts.' since 1986 in Stace (1997), but I have no other details.

Genus: *Silybum*

Silybum marianum (L.) Gaertner
Milk Thistle
Introduced: archaeophyte.
First record: 1828.
Tetrad occurrence: 12 (2%).
Increasing? (+1100%).

Earlier botanists recorded this quite frequently, but usually as a short-lived casual, and it has broadly retained this status in the County. It appears to be most regular around Hertford, and has also made an appearance by new roads, particularly the A505 and A602 between Offley and Stevenage, and on waste tips, such as Rye Meads (31/V), where it was established from at least 1975 to 1981 *C. G. Hanson*.
(1 tetrad: Dony, 1967; 9 tetrads, 1950-1986)

Map 619. *Silybum marianum.*

Genus: *Serratula*

Serratula tinctoria L.   Herts Rare
Saw-wort
Native.
First record: 1748.
Tetrad occurrence: 5 (1%).
Probably decreasing.

In Herts., this is a rare plant of old, somewhat damp rough grassland on neutral or slightly acidic clay soils. While its first record was from Little Gaddesden (Dony, ms. index), most of its later records have been made from the London Clay near Potters Bar and Barnet. In addition, earlier botanists found it around remote woodlands near Barley, and there is a mention of it apparently occurring (presumably on glacial soils on the hills) at Hexton (12/E?) c.1930 (Whiteman, 1936), which may be correct. Dony recorded it from Barkway Airfield (Dony, 1967), but unfortunately he did not detail most of his other records, which

makes assessing change difficult. There were also four pre-1980 records supplied to him for which no details are available, from tetrads 20/K, L; 29/M, W. Its more recent records have been: pasture by Peplins Wood (20/M), 1984 *T. J.* (possibly now extinct here); Dollis Valley, Totteridge (29/H) (VC20 [Greater London]), 1987 *D. Griffith* (Hb. HTN) and 1990, 1992 *A. W. Vaughan*; by Gobions Wood (20/L) (VC21 [Herts.]), 1987 *I. D. Marshall*; Waterfall Walk, Osidge (29/W) (VC20 [Greater London]), 1997 *R. Blades* and 1998 (including a white-flowered variant) *T. J./G. P. Smith/J. Tyler*; scrub by Arkley Lane (29/D), 1997 *T. J./G. P. Smith* (but not re-found 2008); meadows S. of 'Lyndhurst', Elstree (19/Z), 1999 *S. Murray*.

Saw-wort Serratula tinctoria, *white and purple forms, Osidge, Barnet, 1998.*

Genus: *Centaurea*

Centaurea scabiosa L.
Greater Knapweed
Native.
First record: 1814.
Tetrad occurrence: 242 (49%).
Probably stable (+3%).

Wherever Chalk outcrops, particularly across north Hertfordshire, this plant is a characteristic species of rough grassland, on roadside verges, downland, rough fields and old chalk pits. It becomes less frequent west of Hitchin, where the presence of Clay-with-Flints at the surface restricts it. In central Hertfordshire, it occurs generally wherever Chalk outcrops through clay or gravel.

It may have suffered somewhat recently from roadside verge degradation through winter salting and enrichment, but this has not so far resulted in losses at the tetrad scale.

(223 tetrads: Dony, 1967; 238 tetrads: 1950-1986)

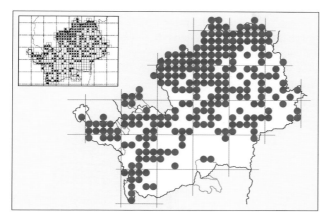

Map 620. *Centaurea scabiosa.*

Centaurea montana L.
Perennial Cornflower
Introduced: neophyte.
First record: 1916.
Tetrad occurrence: 21 (4%).
Increasing?

It seems strange that this was not recorded after its first occurrence at Ware (Dony, 1967) until 1970. It was found as an escape at four localities from 1970-1986, mostly on tips; while the recent survey has recorded it widely as occasional clumps from garden outcasts, predominantly in the south of the County, and usually near habitation.

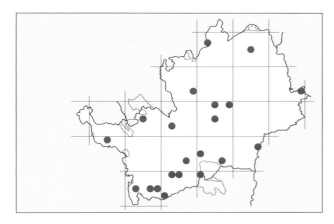

Map 621. *Centaurea montana.*

Centaurea cyanus L.
Cornflower *or* **Bluebottle**
Introduced: archaeophyte.
First record: 1814.
Tetrad occurrence: 17 (4%).
Decreased? (-10%).

This charismatic cornfield weed had already decreased substantially by the 1960s (Dony, 1967), although even in the 19th century the number of areas where it was common appears to have been rather limited (Pryor, 1887). It prefers dry soils, either on Chalk or gravels. After 1970, it was recorded quite frequently, mostly as a casual on tips, but was especially noted from a field

Cornflower Centaurea cyanus *Napsbury, 2004.*

near Colney Street (10/R), 1981 *E. Bowman*, and again in the same area by the newly constructed M25 at Napsbury in 1986 *T. J.* Other earlier records away from tips were from High Down, Pirton (13/K), 1981 *C. W. Burton*; and a field by the R. Lea, Essendon (20/U), 1973 *T. J.* During the survey, it was recorded mostly as a casual, but the colony at Barley Mo Farm, Napsbury (10/R) was found to be very substantial in good years, with the result it has recently been the focus of considerable attention to conserve it, including harvesting seed for re-introduction elsewhere. In addition, apart from occurrences on tips and as suspected sown seed-mixes, it has also appeared at Rothamsted (11/G), 1997, 1998 *I. G. Denholm*; near Harpenden (11/H), 1998 *A. McGlynn*; by Johnson's Spring, Colney Heath (20/D), 1989 *A. D. Marshall*; on Colney Heath (disturbed soil) (20/C), 1999 *R. Keen*; near Sandon, by A505, on disturbed ex-arable (33/E), 1991 *T. J.*; at Baldock allotments (23/M), 1998 *T. J.*; roadside bank, Ashwell (23/U), 1991 *T. J.*; near Rossway, on disturbed ground by A41(M) (90/U), 1993 *R. Mabey*; and near Shenley Hall (10/W), 1996 *D. DeVos*. Despite being recorded so widely, it has been regarded as a conservation priority, especially for its occurrence in long-established sites.

(18 tetrads: Dony, 1967; 28 tetrads: 1950-1986)

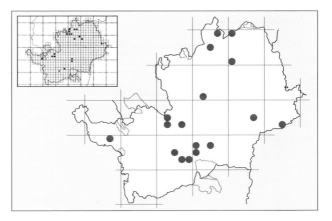

Map 622. *Centaurea cyanus.*

Centaurea calcitrapa L.   [UK Endangered]
Red Star-thistle
Introduced: casual [archaeophyte in U.K.].
First record: 1843.

None of the Hertfordshire records for this suggests a permanent population. It has occurred rarely on waste or disturbed ground, the only recent record being as a wool alien at Newnham (23/N), 1973 *C. G. Hanson*.

Centaurea solstitialis L.
Yellow Star-thistle
Introduced: casual.
First record: 1825.

Formerly a rare, but regularly reported casual in waste places, or as a seed contaminant in fields, this was last seen in a Lucerne field at Lemsford in 1952 *E. G. Kellett* (Dony, 1967 and ms. index).

Centaurea melitensis L.
Maltese Star-thistle
Introduced: casual.
First record: *c*.1916.

Apart from its first record from Rye House (31/V) (Dony, 1967), it was also recorded from Ware (TL31), 1922 *A. W. Graveson*; and from Walsworth Bridge, Hitchin (12/Z), 1928 *J. E. Little*.

Centaurea diluta Aiton
Lesser Star-thistle
Introduced: casual.
First record: 1933.

Following its first record at a waste tip near Welwyn (TL21) (Dony, 1967), this was recorded at Cole Green tip (TL21), 1957; Wheathampstead dump (= Blackbridge tip) (11/X), 1959 *J. G. Dony*; and in a yard at Sawbridgeworth (41/X), 1959 *J. L. Fielding*. More recently it was also found on tips at Pye Corner (41/L), 1969; Hitchin (13/V), 1973; Rye Meads (31/V), 1977 *C. G. Hanson*; near Hertford (TL31), 1978 *A. D. Marshall* (Hb. HTN); and Waterford (31/C), 1979 *C. G. H.* There have been no subsequent records.

Centaurea nigra agg.
Common Knapweed *or* **Hardheads**
Native.
First record (for the aggregate): 1748.
Tetrad occurrence: 471 (96%).
Stable or slightly decreased (-4%).

Hardheads (as these plants are often called in Herts.) is common throughout the County in old grassland, road verges and long-established waste ground, tolerating moderate grazing. As Dony (1967) indicated, this has been a problematic species, and attempts have been made at times to distinguish between narrow and paler-leaved, small-flowered forms with brownish capitular scales named variously as '*Centaurea nemoralis* Jord.' or as a subspecies of *Centaurea debeauxii* Gren. and Godron, **Chalk Knapweed**, and of *nigra* itself. Sell and Murrell (2006) have now adopted *C. debeauxii* as a recognised British species, and therefore future recording will need to account for these more carefully. There does appear to be a distinctive form on calcareous soils in the north of the County, and a number of records of it have been made in the past, and during the Flora Project, but the treatment

has not been followed through systematically and records do not allow a satisfactory separation. A rayed form has also sometimes been recorded, possibly back-crosses of the hybrid with *C. jacea*, or hybrids between *nigra* and *debeauxii*, of which more studies are needed. There is no statistical evidence of an overall decrease of the aggregate at tetrad level, but there is no doubt Hardheads is much less abundant than formerly, following the loss of old pasture and the overgrowth of road verges. Its inclusion in so-called 'conservation seed-mixes' is likely to lead to blurring of the natural occurrence of the different forms.
(465 tetrads: Dony, 1967; and from 1950-1986)

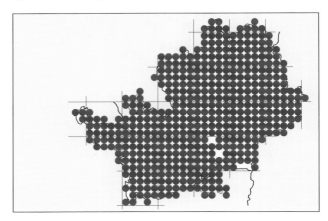

Map 623. *Centaurea nigra.*

Centaurea jacea L.
Brown Knapweed
Introduced: casual.
First (only) record: 1913.

There is one old record of this, identified as ssp. *jungens* Gugler, collected from an old waste tip north of Welwyn Tunnels (21/N), 1913 *J. E. Little* (*Rep. Bot. Exch. Club*: 476 (1914)), which was overlooked by Dony (1967). It is possible that hybrids between this and *C. nigra* occur, recorded as occasional rayed forms of the latter, but these need confirmation.

Genus: *Carthamus*

Carthamus tinctorius L.
Safflower
Introduced: casual.
First record: 1911.

This occurs almost exclusively on waste tips, and has been found at most of the older tips, such as those around Ware, Hertford, Pye Corner, Moor Mill, Hatfield and Radlett between 1970 and 1986. During the survey, however, it was only recorded regularly at Rye Meads Sewage Works sludge tips (31/V), last being seen there in 1996 *C. G. Hanson*. It has otherwise been found at two sites around Ware (31/R, S), 1994 *C. G. H.* (Hb. HTN).

Carthamus lanatus L.
Downy Safflower
Introduced: casual.
First (only) record: 1929.

There is only one record of this: as a casual at Stotfold Road, Letchworth (23/A) *H. Phillips* (Hb. HTN).

Genus: *Cnicus*

Cnicus benedictus L.
Blessed Thistle
Introduced: casual.
First (only) record: 1928.

This has been recorded once, at Hitchin (Dony, 1967).

Genus: *Cichorium*

Cichorium intybus L.
Chicory
Introduced: archaeophyte.
First record: *c*.1820.
Tetrad occurrence: 57 (12%).
Decreased? (-15%).

Found sporadically and most often as a weed in rough field margins, by tracks or near manure heaps. It was at one time thought to be native on chalky soils, and it is still most frequent on these, as well as on calcareous gravels. It has apparently increased around Hertford, where it is now frequent, while having disappeared from other areas.
(64 tetrads: Dony, 1967; 70 tetrads: 1950-1986)

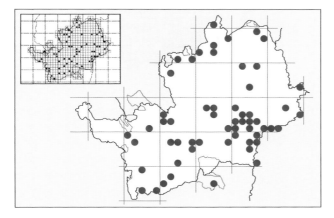

Map 624. *Cichorium intybus.*

Cichorium endivia L.
Endive
Introduced: casual.
First record: 1979.

This was found on the sludge tips at Rye Meads Sewage Works (31/V), 1979 *C. G. Hanson* (Hb. HTN); and re-appeared there in 1995.

Genus: *Arnoseris*

Arnoseris minima (L.) Schweigg. and Körte   Extinct in UK
Lamb's Succory
Introduced: archaeophyte.
First record: 1871.

Only ever known in Herts. on barren, gravelly soil at Easneye (TL31), it was initially found to be quite plentiful, but apparently did not persist for long (Pryor, 1887).

Genus: *Lapsana*

Lapsana communis L.
Nipplewort
Native.
First record: 1819.
Tetrad occurrence: 468 (95%).
Stable (-4%).

Common in shady hedgerows, woodland, scrub and waste ground throughout the County. It is able to withstand considerable nutrient enrichment, so is often found in rank herbage. Its status has not altered since the 1960s survey , despite a few missed tetrads.
(461 tetrads: Dony, 1967; 468 tetrads: 1950-1986)

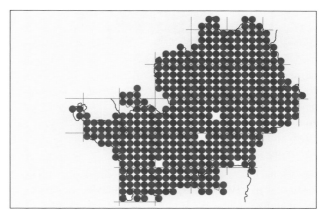

Map 625. *Lapsana communis.*

The usual subspecies is ssp. *communis*. Subspecies *intermedia* (M. Bieb.) Hayek has appeared spontaneously in a garden at Ware (31/S), 1999 *C. G. Hanson*. It had originally been grown from seed seven years earlier. Subspecies *adenophora* (Boiss.) Rech. *f.* was identified from material collected beside the M1 near Berrygrove Wood (19/J), 1996 *A. D. Marshall* (det. R. M. Burton) (Hb. Marshall), which may be the first U.K. record for this eastern race, presumably 'off the back of a lorry'!

Genus: *Hedypnois*

Hedypnois cretica (L.) Dum. Cours.
Scaly Hawkbit
Introduced: casual.
First (only) record: 1917.

There is one old record of this from Ware (Dony, 1967).

Genus: *Hypochaeris*

Hypochaeris radicata L.
Common Cat's-ear
Native.
First record: *c*.1820.
Tetrad occurrence: 415 (85%).
Probably stable (+5%).

A frequent plant of unimproved and semi-improved pastures on neutral to mildly acidic soils, also found on roadside banks and sometimes on bare waste ground. Its wiry stems resist grazing by livestock, and its flattened leaf-rosettes allow it to survive close-shaving by mowers. Its distribution remains much as Dony found, common in southern Hertfordshire, but becoming rare on the Chalk and calcareous Boulder Clay soils. Although it was found in more tetrads than in the 1967 survey, this may be a function of better recording in the north-east and far west of the County. (376 tetrads: Dony, 1967; 383 tetrads: 1950-1986)

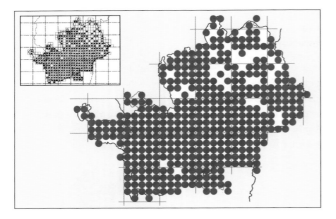

Map 626. *Hypochaeris radicata.*

Hypochaeris glabra L. [UK Vulnerable]
Smooth Cat's-ear
Introduced: casual [native in the U.K.].
First record: 1840.

Although the first record was from a pasture on gravelly soils near Bramfield (TL21) (Webb and Coleman, 1849), it seems highly likely that this was introduced with grass seed (Pryor, 1887). The only other record was as a probable wool shoddy alien, from between Baldock and Clothall (TL23), 1927 *M. S. Phillips* (*comm.*: H. Phillips) (Hb. HTN).

Hypochaeris maculata L. UK Threatened
Spotted Cat's-ear
Native.
First record: 1924.

A very rare plant of old, species-rich chalk grassland. This was first confirmed by a photograph of a rosette on Therfield Heath, taken in April 1924 by A. W. Graveson (coll.: North Herts. Museums) (James, 1980b). However, Henry Fordham had thought he had seen it there in the 1840s (Dony, 1967). It has apparently never flowered very frequently here, and detailed searching on Church Hill (33/J) by G. Crompton in 1978 found only five plants. By 1985 there were only two rosettes *G. C./T. J.* and it was apparently last seen in 1993 *T. C. E. Wells*. However, plants were grown from seed collected by the late Terry Wells of the then Institute of Terrestrial Ecology at Monks Wood during a rare flowering at Therfield Heath and planted into trial chalk grassland restoration plots nearby (34/K), where they were still reported to be present in 1999 *V. Thompson*, although not formally recorded by ecologists from Monks Wood after 1974.

Genus: *Scorzoneroides*

The treatment of this genus as separate from *Leontodon* follows Sell and Murrell (2006).

Scorzoneroides autumnalis L.
Autumn Hawkbit
Native.
First record: c.1820.
Tetrad occurrence: 427 (87%).
Decreasing (-10%).

A widespread and locally abundant plant of churchyards, old lawns, pastures and roadside verges. Whereas in the 1960s survey this was found to be fairly well ubiquitous, it is not so now. The recent survey failed to find it in a significant number of tetrads, especially in more arable landscapes, and even in some where older habitats persist. Churchyards are a particularly notable habitat for it, because grass-mowing later in the summer tends to be limited. It is also becoming far less abundant in pastures as these become rank or have been 'improved'.
(452 tetrads: Dony, 1967 and from 1950-1986)

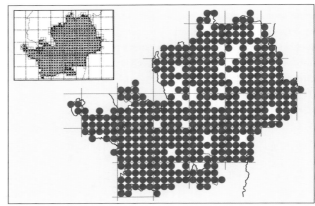

Map 627. *Scorzoneroides autumnalis.*

Genus: *Leontodon*

Leontodon hispidus L.
Rough Hawkbit
Native.
First record: 1814.
Tetrad occurrence: 210 (43%).
Decreasing markedly (-32%).

This was a common plant of rough grassland on more calcareous soils, especially on the Chalk itself, but also elsewhere. With the degradation of road verges in particular, but also the loss of rough grassland elsewhere to scrub, it is losing its habitat across much of the northern part of the County, and in the south it is becoming

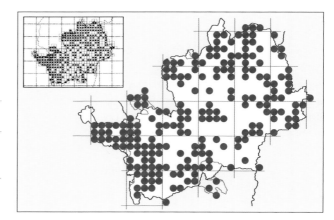

Map 628. *Leontodon hispidus.*

very scarce. Only in the Chilterns does it appear to be holding its own, possibly because road verges are less under pressure from intensive agriculture. Old churchyards are also increasingly important for it.

(293 tetrads: Dony, 1967; 301 tetrads: 1950-1986)

Leontodon saxatilis Lam.
Lesser Hawkbit
Native.
First record: 1838.
Tetrad occurrence: 100 (20%).
Stable or increased? (+28%).

This is apparently a plant of old grazed grassland on a range of soil types. Pryor (1887) considered it to occur on damp soils, while Dony (1967) thought it occurred especially on calcareous soils. Examination of records suggests its main requirements are for old, relatively short grassland on most soil types, and it would seem possible that it has always tended to be overlooked where its commoner relative *L. hispidus* also occurs. The recent survey showed it to be widespread across the County, and to have apparently retreated from some areas, while having been found to occur in others. It may have decreased in some places, owing to the loss of old grassland, but this has not been confirmed by the survey.

(74 tetrads: Dony, 1967; 97 tetrads: 1950-1986)

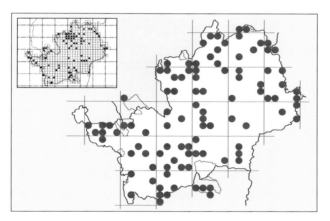

Map 629. *Leontodon saxatilis.*

Genus: *Picris*

Picris echioides L.
Bristly Oxtongue
Introduced: archaeophyte.
First record: 1759.
Tetrad occurrence: 348 (71%).
Increased massively (+160%).

Having been quite a scarce plant in the 19th century (Pryor, 1887), and limited mostly to the Boulder Clay and Chalk in north Hertfordshire in the 1960s, this weed of waste places, arable field margins and roadsides is rapidly becoming almost ubiquitous.
(127 tetrads: Dony, 1967; 152 tetrads: 1950-1986)

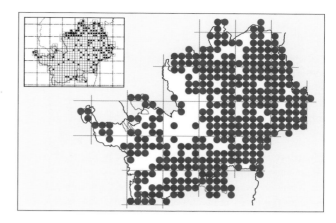

Map 630. *Picris echioides.*

Picris hieracioides L.
Hawkweed Oxtongue
Native.
First record: 1821.
Tetrad occurrence: 101 (21%).
Decreasing? (-7%).

As a native, this is a plant of rough calcareous grassland, and as such has always occurred on road verges, and round old chalk pits. It seems to be becoming much less common in such places than previously, owing to the loss of nutrient-poor rough grassland, while it now appears to have found a niche in the rough ground around recent gravel pits, as well as by new motorways, where these are on calcareous substrates.

(103 tetrads: Dony, 1967; 119 tetrads: 1950-1986)

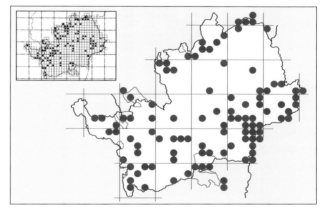

Map 631. *Picris hieracioides.*

Genus: *Scorzonera*

Scorzonera hispanica L.
Scorzonera
Introduced: casual.
First (only) record: 1992.

This relic of cultivation was found on long-abandoned allotments at Nast Hyde (20/D) *A. D. Marshall* (det. T. J.).

Genus: *Tragopogon*

Tragopogon pratensis L.
Goat's-beard
Native.
First record: 1814.
Tetrad occurrence: 405 (83%).
Stable (-4%).

Although considered rather uncommon in the 19th century (Webb and Coleman, 1849), it is now a frequent plant of rough grassland, road verges and waste ground throughout the County. Its habit of closing its flowers at midday gives it its local name of 'Jack-go-to-bed-at-noon'. Its occurrence remains similar to that recorded by Dony (1967).
(401 tetrads: Dony, 1967; 420 tetrads: 1950-1986)

The native form is ssp. *minor* (Miller) Wahlenb., which is shown on the map. The Continental ssp. *pratensis*, with larger flowers, is occasionally found, recent records being from Cheshunt Gravel Pits (30/R), 1987 *D. Bevan*; and Broad Oak End (31/B), 1991 *A. M. Boucher*.

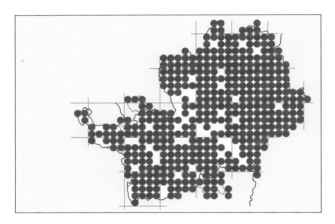

Map 632. *Tragopogon pratensis.*

Tragopogon porrifolius L.
Salsify
Introduced: neophyte.
First record: 1838.
Tetrad occurrence: 13 (3%).

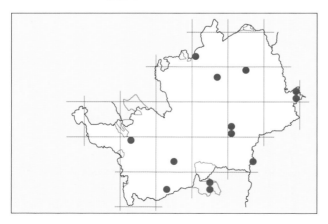

Map 633. *Tragopogon porrifolius.*

An occasional relic of cultivation, sometimes establishing a colony that persists. Dony noted that it was formerly quite frequent

around Hitchin, while recent records have been widespread. The longest-persisting colony appears to be that on the roundabout and roadsides of the A414 at Hertingfordbury (31/B), where it was first noted as over 100 plants in 1985 *A. M. Boucher/C. G. Hanson.*

Genus: *Sonchus*

Sonchus arvensis L.
Perennial Sow-thistle
Native.
First record: 1839.
Tetrad occurrence: 448 (91%).
Stable or decreasing slightly (-6%).

A widespread and often common plant of damp ground, roadside ditches, arable field margins and scrub. It has not changed its status much since recording began, although it may not be quite so frequent as it was in the 1960s.
(451 tetrads: Dony, 1967; 453 terads: 1950-1986)

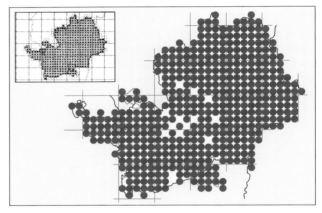

Map 634. *Sonchus arvensis.*

Plants corresponding to ssp. *uliginosus* (M. Bieb.) Nyman have been identified at Wilstone (91/B), 1999 *T. J.* (Hb. HTN), but its status as a taxon is uncertain (Stace, 1997).

Sonchus oleraceus L.
Smooth Sow-thistle
Native.
First record: 1814.
Tetrad occurrence: 465 (95%).
Probably stable (-2%).

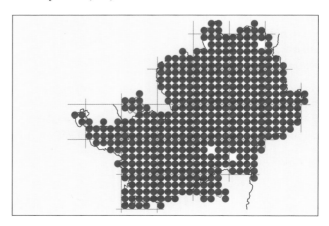

Map 635. *Sonchus oleraceus.*

An abundant weed of cultivation, waste places, gardens, roadsides, *etc.* throughout the County, particularly on enriched soils.
(451 tetrads: Dony, 1967; 452 tetrads: 1950-1986)

Sonchus asper L. (Hill)
Prickly Sow-thistle
Native.
First record: *c.*1820.
Tetrad occurrence: 471 (96%).
Stable (-2%).

An abundant weed of bare, waste places, often on gravelly or ruderal ground, roadsides, *etc.* The increase in abandoned agricultural land, derelict ground around old quarries, roadworks, *etc.* has encouraged some expansion, although overall it remains stable in occurrence.
(456 tetrads: Dony, 1967; 457 tetrads: 1950-1986)

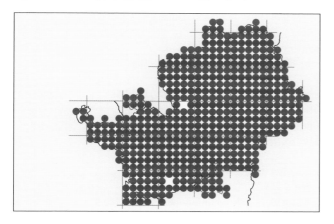

Map 636. *Sonchus asper.*

Genus: *Lactuca*

Lactuca serriola L.
Prickly Lettuce
Introduced: archaeophyte.
First record: 1922.
Tetrad occurrence: 402 (82%).
Increased massively (+277%).

A weed of ruderal land, waysides and waste places, which is still spreading steadily since A. W. Graveson first recognised it in the County (Dony, 1967). Dony gave a clear picture of its progress up to the mid-1960s, having colonised the gravel pits and waste ground of the lower Lea Valley first, as well as roadsides around

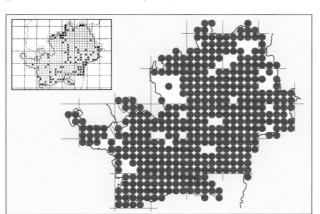

Map 637. *Lactuca serriola.*

Hitchin, Letchworth and elsewhere. It has since spread substantially, including into most rural areas, along roads, where it tolerates salt and nitrogen pollution.
(101 tetrads: Dony, 1967; 142 tetrads: 1950-1986)

Lactuca virosa L.
Great Lettuce
Introduced [native in the U.K.].
First record: 1841.
Tetrad occurrence: 105 (21%).
Increased substantially (+161%).

Apparently a native of coastal areas, this first appeared on roadside banks around Baldock, possibly having derived from medicinal herb cultivation, but spread along newly-constructed railways in the 19th century. By the 1960s, it had begun to colonise gravel pits (Dony, 1967). More recently, it has also begun to spread along motorways, especially the M25, where its ability to withstand salt pollution and enrichment gives it an advantage in rough herbage.
(38 tetrads: Dony, 1967; 50 tetrads: 1950-1986)

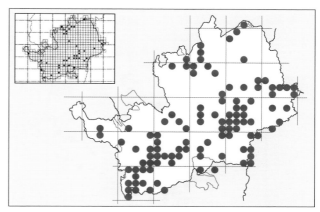

Map 638. *Lactuca virosa.*

Genus: *Cicerbita*

Cicerbita macrophylla (Willd.) Wallr.
Common Blue Sow-thistle
Introduced: neophyte.
First record: 1954.
Tetrad occurrence: 27 (6%).
Increased (+72%).

First recorded at a disused brickfield in Welwyn Garden City

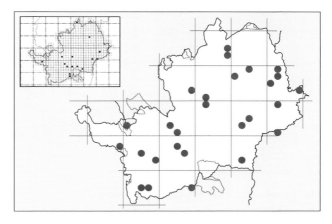

Map 639. *Cicerbita macrophylla.*

(21/B) (Dony, 1967 and ms. index), this has slowly increased in occurrence, forming discrete colonies in scattered localities across the County, usually on roadside verges, not all of which persist, as there does not seem to be a colony at Welwyn any more!
(15 tetrads: Dony, 1967; 30 tetrads: 1950-1986)

Genus: *Mycelis*

Mycelis muralis (L.) Dumort
Wall Lettuce
Native.
First record: 1746.
Tetrad occurrence: 86 (18%).
Increased? (+28%).

This delicate and attractive plant is particularly associated with the dry, shady woodlands of the Chilterns dip-slope, where it is locally quite common. Elsewhere, it occurs here and there in shady woodland or roadsides, often with Beech trees, as well as sometimes long-established colonies on old walls, such as that round Baldock Churchyard (23/L). In east and central Hertfordshire it is rare, but may have increased slightly.
(64 tetrads: Dony, 1967; 74 tetrads: 1950-1986)

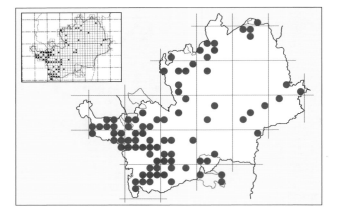

Map 640. *Mycelis muralis.*

Genus: *Taraxacum*

Dandelions are ubiquitous across the County in grassland, waste places, road verges, gardens and woodland rides. Many are common species of ruderal ground, but there are a number of species limited to old grassland, commons and heaths. A fair number are also reckoned to be native, while many others are thought to be introduced, particularly those of disturbed habitats. The group presents great identification difficulties, with the result that very little concerted attention has been given to them in the County. More work, especially, is needed on the species of semi-natural habitats. The current survey did not attempt to differentiate them, and I take no credit for any of the information presented here. Accounts given in previous floras are also based on what is now a very out-of-date understanding of the genus, and therefore, with few exceptions usually based on herbarium material, earlier records are unusable. For these reasons, and because I do not hold full details of all records, I have also been unable to quote first dates of recording for most species.

Despite these difficulties, J. E. Little's specimens at Hb. CGE provide the basis for some earlier records, and material was collected during the 1980s especially by Ann Boucher,

mainly in the Hoddesdon area, determined by A. J. Richards or C. C. Haworth. Some visiting national experts, notably A. J. Richards around Harpenden, have also supplied records, including lists during the recent survey period. The following account is based mostly on the 10km records held in the national database maintained by A. A. Dudman and A. J. Richards, together with records supplied by Ann Boucher, and some notes on more notable species where useful information is available. Details of the individual records are held by the author, as well as in the national database. In this account, records are mostly summarised by 10km squares. **Records given in italics are from before 1970**. All other records are post-1970. Dandelions in general ('*Taraxacum officinale*' agg.) were recorded in 481 tetrads during the recent survey.

Section: *Erythrosperma*

Taraxacum lacistophyllum (Dahlst.) Raunk.
Native.
Frequent on calcareous soils.
SP91; TL00, *12*, 21, 22, 30, 31, 33.

Taraxacum brachyglossum (Dahlst.) Dahlst.
Native.
Widespread in dry habitats.
TL*12*, 30, 31, 33.

Taraxacum argutum Dahlst.
Native.
Uncommon, usually on limestone.
TL30.

Taraxacum rubicundum (Dahlst.) Dahlst.
Native.
Widespread but local, usually on chalk grassland or heaths.
TL21, 30, 31, 33.

Taraxacum proximum (Dahlst.) Dahlst.
Native.
Local, in dry grassland.
TL*12*, 30 (det. C. C. Haworth).

Taraxacum oxoniense Dahlst.
Native.
Locally common on chalk downland and similar old grassland.
TL*12*, 33, 34, 43.

Taraxacum fulviforme Dahlst.
Native
Rare, in calcareous grassland. Old records only.
TL*12*.

Taraxacum fulvum Raunk.
Native.
Scarce, in rich calcareous grassland. Old records only.
TL*12*.

Taraxacum retzii Soest
Native.
Very local on heaths. Old record only.
TL*12*.

Taraxacum glauciniforme Dahlst.
Native.
Widespread on calcareous grassland, lawns, *etc.*
TL11, 22, 30, 32, 33.

Taraxacum acutum A. Richards   UK Rare Endemic
Native.
Limited apparently to Therfield Heath (*33/J*, 34/K), one of few
sites known in Britain.

A dandelion Taraxacum acutum *Therfield Heath, 2002.*

Section: *Palustria*

Taraxacum palustre (Lyons) Symons   Herts Rare
Native.
First record: 1842 (1814?).
Extinct?

A species of old, natural wetlands; this is the only species for
which earlier records are more or less reliable. It was recorded
from the now lost Ashwell Common (24/R), 1842 *W. H. Coleman*
(Hb. OXF) and *I. Brown* (Hb. LTR) (the latter record mis-
attributed to TL23). An unlocalised record by Joseph Ransom
in 1814 may have been from Hitchin also. There are also records
by J. E. Little from Oughton Head Common (13/Q); Burleigh
Meadow, Knebworth (22/G); Colney Heath (20/C) and Walsworth
Common (13/V) before 1930, which are likely to be accurate. It
appears to have been seen last at Oughton Head Common, 1933
H. Phillips (Dony, 1967).

Section: *Spectabilia*

[*Taraxacum faeroense* (Dahlst.) Dahlst.
Native.

Records by earlier workers of *T. spectabile* Dahlst. (Dony, 1967)
may refer here, but need confirmation. There are no reliable
recent records.]

Section: *Naevosa*

Taraxacum euryphyllum (Dahlst.) Hjelt
Native.
In wet, base-rich habitats.
TL11, 33.

Taraxacum richardsianum C. C. Haworth   UK Endemic
Native.   Herts Rare
Local, in damp, herb-rich grasslands.

Blagrove Common (33/G), 1986 *A. M. Boucher* (det. A. J.
Richards).

Section: *Celtica*

Taraxacum gelertii Raunk.
Native.
In semi-natural grasslands.
TL*13*; TQ09.

Taraxacum bracteatum Dahlst.
Native.
Widespread in damp habitats.
TL30, 33.

Taraxacum subbracteatum Richards   UK Endemic
Native.
Widespread.
TL*11*, 30, 31, 43.

Taraxacum duplidentifrons Dahlst.
Native.
Widespread.
TL11.

Taraxacum excellens Dahlst.
Native.
Widespread.
TL30, 31; TQ09.

Taraxacum fulgidum G. E. Haglund
Native.
Local, in damp hay meadows.
TL20, 31, 41.

Taraxacum tamesense A. J. Richards   Herts Rare?
Native.
Scarce, in water meadows.

Rothamsted (11/G), 1978 *A. O. Chater* (det. A. J. Richards).

Taraxacum haematicum Haglund
Native.
Local, in damp, herb-rich grassland.
TL30.

Taraxacum nordstedtii Dahlst.
Native.
Widespread, in wet grassland, roadsides, *etc.*
TL20, 33, 34.

Taraxacum hamatum Raunk.
Native.
Widespread in shaded habitats.
TL00, 01, 30, 31, 33, 41; TQ29.

Taraxacum hamatulum Hagend., Soest and Zev.
Doubtfully native.
Scattered in disturbed habitats.
TL30, 31.

Taraxacum subhamatum M. Christ.
Native.
Grassy places, roadsides, waste ground.
TL11, 30, 31.

Taraxacum marklundii Palmgren
Native.
Grassy places, roadsides, waste ground.
TL*12*, 33, 41.

Taraxacum hamiferum Dahlst.
Doubtfully native.
Waste places.
TL02 (VC20).

Taraxacum quadrans Øllgaard
Probably introduced.
Widespread.
TL01, 11, 20, 30, 41.

Taraxacum pseudohamatum Dahlst.
Native.
Very common: the most widespread dandelion.
SP91, TL01, 10, 11, 12, 20, 21, 23, 30, 31, 33, 34.

Taraxacum boekmanii Borgv.
Probably native.
Grassy places, roadsides, waste ground.
TL11, 30; TQ09, 19.

Taraxacum atactum Sahlin and Soest
Native.
Grassy places, roadsides, waste ground.
TL11.

Taraxacum hamatiforme Dahlst.
Native.
Locally common in hedgebanks, road verges, *etc.*
TL01, 10, 11, 12, 20, 21, 30, 31, 41.

Taraxacum kernianum Soest, Hagend. and Zev.
Introduced.
Waste places.
TL31.

Taraxacum lamprophyllum M. Christ.
Possibly introduced.
Scattered in waste ground.
TL30, *42*.

Taraxacum macrolobum Dahlst.
Probably introduced.
Grassy places, road verges.
TL30, 32.

Taraxacum pannucium Dahlst.
Probably introduced.
Widespread in grassy places, waste ground.
TL21, 30, 33, 34.

Taraxacum subexpallidum Dahlst.
Probably introduced.
Locally common in grassy places, roadsides.
TL*12*, 30, 41.

Taraxacum alatum Lindb. *f.*
Native.
Widespread and locally common in waste places.
TL00, 01, 11, 30, 33, 43.

Taraxacum horridifrons Rail.
Introduced.
Roadsides: local.
TL11.

Taraxacum densilobum Dahlst.
Introduced.
Road verges: uncommon.
TL30, 31.

Taraxacum insigne Ekman ex M. Christ. and Wiinst.
Native.
Dry, grassy places, roadsides: widespread.
TL11, 22, 30, 42.

Taraxacum pannulatiforme Dahlst.
Native.
Locally common in grassy roadsides, *etc.*
TL12, 30.

Taraxacum laticordatum Markl.
Native.
Grassy roadsides, waste ground.
TL30; TQ19, 29.

Taraxacum pallescens Dahlst.
Probably introduced.
Occasional on road verges and in grassland.
TL32, 43.

Taraxacum necessarium Øllgaard
Possibly introduced.
Grassy ground, roadsides: uncommon.
TL11.

Taraxacum expallidiforme Dahlst.
Native?
Grassland, waste places: widespread.
TL11, 12, 30, 31, *33*, 41; TQ09, 19, 29.

Taraxacum pallidipes Markl.
Probably introduced.
Road verges, *etc.*, often semi-shaded.
TL11; TQ09.

Taraxacum croceiflorum Dahlst.
Native.
Widespread on road verges, waste ground.
TL30, 41; TQ09, 29.

Taraxacum lacerifolium Haglund
Probably introduced.
Scattered on road verges, *etc.*
TL30, 32.

Taraxacum stenacrum Dahlst.   UK Endemic
Native.
Grassland, roadsides, waste ground.
TL30; TQ09.

Taraxacum undulatiflorum M. Christ.
Probably introduced.
Waste ground, road verges: common.
TL01, 11, 20, 21, 23, 30, 32; TQ09, 29.

Taraxacum piceatum Dahlst.
Probably introduced.
Waste ground, road verges: widespread.
TL31, 43; TQ09, 19.

Taraxacum cyanolepis Dahlst.
Native.
Damp grasslands: decreasing?
TL11, 12.

Taraxacum acutifrons Markl.
Introduced.
Road verges: uncommon.
TL10.

Taraxacum chrysophaenum Rail.
Introduced.
Waste ground: rare.
TL11.

Taraxacum tumentilobum Markl. ex Puol.
Probably introduced.
Grassy places, roadsides, waste ground.
TL23, 30, 31, 32.

Taraxacum sellandii Dahlst.
Native.
Grassland, roadside verges, *etc.*: common.
TL01, 30, 31, 41; TQ09.

Taraxacum angustisquameum Dahlst. ex Lindb. *f.*
Probably introduced.
Grassland, road verges: occasional.
TL31, 43.

Taraxacum adiantifrons Ekman ex Dahlst.
Probably introduced.

Grassland, waste ground: locally common.
TL11, 30, 31, 32.

Taraxacum retroflexum Lindb. *f.*
Introduced.
Waste ground: rare.
TL30.

Taraxacum aequilobum Dahlst.
Probably introduced.
Waste ground, gardens, roadsides: widespread.
TL11.

Taraxacum latissimum Palmgren
Introduced.
Waste ground: widespread.
TL10, 11.

Taraxacum exsertum Hagend., Soest and Zev.
Introduced.
Waste ground.
TL23, 30, 31.

Taraxacum exacutum Markl.
Probably introduced.
Waste ground, rubbish tips.
TL11, 30; TQ19.

Taraxacum valens Markl.
Introduced.
Waste ground: uncommon.
TL34.

Taraxacum pannulatum Dahlst.
Probably introduced.
Grassy places, road verges: widespread.
TL21, 30.

Taraxacum lingulatum Markl.
Native.
Grassland, waste ground, common.
TL11, 20, 23, 30, 31, 32, 41, 42; TQ09, 19, 39.

Taraxacum rhamphodes G. E. Haglund.
Introduced.
Grassland, roadsides, waste ground: locally common.
TL11, 30, 31, TQ29.

Taraxacum procerisquameum H. Øllgaard
Introduced.
Road verges.
TL31; TQ19.

Taraxacum vastisectum Markl. ex Puol.
Introduced.
Road verges, waste ground: occasional.
TL33.

Taraxacum cordatum Palmgren
Native.
Grassland, waste places on sandy soils.
TL31, 33; TQ09, 29.

Taraxacum sagittipotens Dahlst. and Ohlsen ex G. E. Haglund
Probably native.
Grassland, waste ground: locally common.
TL34; TQ39.

Taraxacum ekmanii Dahlst.
Possibly native.
Grassland, gardens: common.
TL11, 20, 23, 30, 31, 32, 41, 42; TQ09, 19, 29.

Taraxacum aurosulum Lindb. *f.*
Probably introduced.
Shaded road verges, *etc.*: uncommon.
TL30, 43; TQ29.

Taraxacum aberrans Hagend., Soest and Zev.
Probably introduced.
Roadsides, *etc.*: uncommon.
TL11.

Taraxacum oblongatum Dahlst.
Native.
Damp pastures: widespread.
TL11, 12, 20; TQ19.

Taraxacum cophocentrum Dahlst.   UK Endemic
Native.
Grassland, wood margins, scrub.
TL11, 23, 30; TQ09, 29.

Taraxacum pachymerum Haglund
Probably introduced.
Grassland, waste ground: locally common.
TL10.

Taraxacum sinuatum Dahlst.
Possibly native.
Grassy roadsides, *etc.*: scattered in U.K.
TL11.

Taraxacum laciniosifrons Dahlst.
Probably native.
Grassland, road verges: local.
TL11.

Taraxacum dahlstedtii Lindb. *f.*
Native.
Grassland, roadsides, *etc.*: locally common.
TL43.

Taraxacum fagerstroemii Såltin
Introduced.
Grassy waste places: rare.
TL11.

Taraxacum subundulatum Dahlst.
Native.
Species-rich meadows, roadsides: occasional.
TL30, 31, 41.

Taraxacum pectinatiforme Lindb. *f.*
Probably introduced.

Waste ground, road verges, *etc.*: local.
TL41.

Taraxacum trilobatum Palmgren
Introduced.
Waste ground, grassland, *etc.*: uncommon.
TL11, 20, 30, 33.

Taraxacum polyodon Dahlst.
Native or introduced.
Grassland, roadsides, *etc.*: common.
SP91; TL11, *12*, 23, 30, 31, 32, 33, *42*, 43; TQ19, 29.

Taraxacum incisum H. Øllgaard
Introduced.
Grassland.: common around London.
TL12, 21, 30, 31; TQ09, 29.

Taraxacum xanthostigma Lindb. *f.*
Possibly introduced.
Grassland, roadsides, *etc.*: locally common.
TL11, 23, 30.

Taraxacum 'anceps'
A species similar to *T. xanthostigma*, so far without a properly
published name, is recorded from TL30.

Taraxacum longisquameum Lindb. *f.*
Native.
Mainly semi-natural grassland: locally common.
TL00, 10, 21, 33.

Taraxacum scotiniforme Dahlst. ex G. E. Haglund
Introduced?
Grassland: local.
TL11, 32.

Taraxacum sublongisquameum M. Christ.
Introduced.
Road verges: rare.
VC20 record in Dudman and Richards, 1997.

Taraxacum fasciatum Dahlst.
Possibly native.
Road verges: locally common.
TL11, 30, 31.

Genus: *Crepis*

Crepis biennis L.
Rough Hawk's-beard
Native.
First record: 1724.
Tetrad occurrence: 14 (3%).
Stable? (+4%).

This has always been a rare, and rather enigmatic plant. It has
been said to favour rough grassland on Chalk (Pryor, 1887), but
examination of the records indicates that it mostly grows on thin,
free-draining Clay-with-Flints, or gravelly soils over Chalk. This
has been very clearly demonstrated in north-east Herts., where
apparently anomalous records from near Sandon have been found

Rough Hawksbeard Crepis biennis *Wheat Hill, Sandon, 1990.*

to coincide with outcrops of Clay-with-Flints appearing from underneath the overlying Boulder Clay. It may be overlooked elsewhere, or mis-recorded as *C. vesicaria*.

(13 tetrads: Dony, 1967; 18 tetrads: 1950-1986)

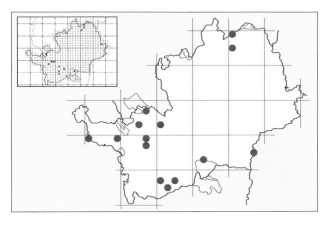

Map 641. *Crepis biennis.*

Crepis tectorum L.
Narrow-leaved Hawk's-beard
Introduced: casual.
First record: 1974.

This grass seed alien was first found by the R. Colne at Rickmansworth (09/M) in 1974 (observer unknown) (Burton, 1983). Several plants were also found in newly-sown grass at Gardiner's Lane, Ashwell (23/U), 1989 *T. J.* (Hb. HTN). The colony was mown off later, before seeding.

Crepis nicaeensis Balbis
French Hawk's-beard
First record: *c.*1880.
Introduced: casual.

There does not seem any real reason, as Dony thought, to doubt Pryor's record from a presumably re-seeded meadow at Stevenage (Pryor, 1887), but its inclusion in a list of plants from Bayfordbury in the 1950s may be more suspect (Dony, ms. index).

Crepis capillaris (L.) Wallr.
Smooth Hawk's-beard
Native.
First record: 1821.
Tetrad occurrence: 458 (93%).
Stable or marginally decreased (-5%).

A common plant of rough, somewhat enriched grassland on road verges, waste ground, pastures, *etc.* throughout the County. It is very variable and its occurrence seems to have remained very similar to that recorded by Dony (1967).
(457 tetrads: Dony, 1967; 458 tetrads: 1950-1986)

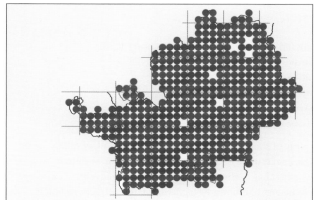

Map 642. *Crepis capillaris.*

Crepis vesicaria L.
Beaked Hawk's-beard
Introduced: neophyte.
First record: 1874.
Tetrad occurrence: 345 (70%).
Stable (-2%).

A plant of rough grasslands, road verges and waste ground throughout the County, having increased rapidly in the early 20th

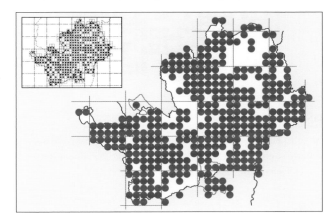

Map 643. *Crepis vesicaria.*

century. The recent survey showed that it has consolidated its position in some areas, but has decreased in especially the most intensely arable landscapes.

(336 tetrads: Dony, 1967; 355 tetrads: 1950-1986)

Crepis setosa Haller *f.*
Bristly Hawk's-beard
Introduced: casual.
First record: 1844.

At one time an occasional casual of cultivation, with a few records in the 19th century around Hitchin and Baldock, *etc.* Dony (1967) mentions an occurrence at Dunstable, but the tetrad he gave falls outside VC20 [Beds.], so it is uncertain if this relates to our area at all. There have been no recent records.

[*Crepis foetida* L.   UK Extinct in the Wild
Stinking Hawk's-beard

This was recorded as occurring at Hexton, *c.*1930 in Whiteman (1936), but without better evidence, the record cannot be accepted.]

Genus: *Pilosella*

Pilosella officinarum F. W. Schultz and Sch. Bip.
Mouse-ear Hawkweed
Native.
First record: 1690.
Tetrad occurrence: 259 (53%).
Decreasing (-17%).

A plant of short, dry grassland on Chalk, gravel, or mildly acidic loamy soils, often on sunny roadside banks or in churchyards. As its habitat has declined, through the eutrophication of road verges and the loss of unimproved grassland, this attractive plant has retreated from many arable areas, even on the Chalk, and has also lost ground around villages to excessive tidying or 'improvement' of roadside grassland and lawns.

(295 tetrads: Dony, 1967; 315 tetrads: 1950-1986)

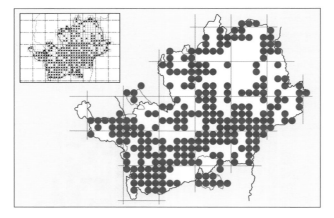

Map 644. *Pilosella officinarum.*

The subspecies defined in Sell and Murrell (2006) have not been properly studied in the County, although some specimens have been collected (Hb. HTN).

Pilosella praealta (Villars ex Gochnat) F. W. Schultz and Sch. Bip.
Tall Mouse-ear Hawkweed
Introduced: casual.
First record: 1955.

There are apparently only two records of this, one for each subspecies. Subspecies *thaumasia* (Peter) P. D. Sell was found at Chorley Wood (09/H), 1955 *R. H. Turney*; while ssp. *praealta* itself was recorded from Borehamwood (19/X), 1965 *J. G. Dony* (Hb. HTN) (Dony, 1967).

Pilosella aurantiaca (L.) F. W. Schultz and Sch. Bip.
Fox-and-cubs
Introduced: neophyte.
First record: 1912.
Tetrad occurrence: 31 (6%).
Increasing (+110%).

An attractive garden escape which can establish long-lasting colonies on dry grassland and road banks, as well as occurring casually on waste ground and walls. It was recorded widely but sparsely across the County during the survey.

(14 tetrads: Dony, 1967; 23 tetrads: 1950-1986)

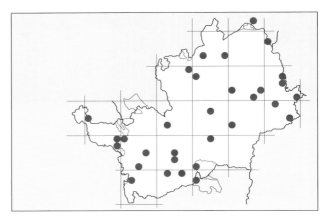

Map 645. *Pilosella aurantiaca.*

Where the subspecies has been determined, this has been found to be ssp. *carpathicola* (Nägel and Peter) Soják.

Genus: *Hieracium*

The hawkweeds comprise a taxonomically very difficult group of plants in Britain, although in the lowlands, the difficulties are mostly rather less than in the uplands (but see below). The following account stems mainly from a thorough review of all the herbarium material readily available for the County, and is based on species concepts that have been revised recently by P. D. Sell and others (Sell and Murrell, 2006), whose English names and sequence have been adopted here. Herbarium material from Hb. HTN and from the recent Flora Survey, including all of Dony's extant Hertfordshire material, was re-examined by D. J. McCosh, to whom I am indebted for his help, and for supplying further records and comments on this text. For most species, earlier records that were not supported by specimens have been rejected, owing to the recent revision of names in hitherto accepted groups. Railways have obviously been important in the spread of many of the introduced species. In addition to these sources, a study by Peter Sell, based on work by the late Swedish hawkweed specialist Nils Hylander, of a puzzling array of plants belonging to Section *Hieracium* on the chalky road banks beside and adjoining the A505 at Royston, largely in VC29 but administratively Hertfordshire, has produced no less than 10 named taxa, in addition to those recorded by myself and named by David McCosh. The results of this study were summarised by A. C. Leslie (2007); and notes on their occurrence are also included in the account of *Hieracium* in Sell and Murrell (2006). Where all these exotic hawkweeds came from, many of which are thought to be grassland specialists from across Europe, is a mystery!

Section: *Sabauda*

Hieracium vagum Jordan
Glabrous-headed Hawkweed
Probably introduced [native in the U.K.].
First record: 1957.

Dony (1967) gave four tetrad records for this, of which that from 30/S is unsupported by a specimen, and the record for 19/P is in error for 19/U, but otherwise correct. It was re-found on the railway embankment at Brookmans Park (20/L), 1977 *R. M. Burton*, having first been found there in 1965 by Dony, and then re-recorded in 1994 by A. D. Marshall (Hb. HTN). It has also been found at Hatfield Home Park (20/J), 1995 *A. D. M.* (det. D. J. McCosh) (Hb. HTN).

[*Hieracium rigens* Jordan
Rigid Hawkweed

The record given by Dony (1967) was in error for *H. salticola* (re-det. D. J. McCosh, 2004). A specimen in Hb. A. W. Vaughan, collected at Barnet Gate (29/C), 1987 *A. Vaughan* (det. R. M. Burton, 2005) might need re-examination.]

Hieracium salticola (Sudre) Sell and C. West
Bluish-leaved Hawkweed
Introduced.
First record: 1958.

This was first found at Oakleigh Park Station (19/S) (VC20 [Greater London]), 1958 *J. G. Dony* (det. D. J. McCosh) (Hb. HTN), originally reported as *H. rigens* (Dony, 1967). He also gave four records of *H. salticola* itself, of which three have also been confirmed (his record for tetrad 10/Y appearing to lack a specimen). There have been a number of subsequent records, and during the recent survey it was found in seven tetrads: near Cheshunt Station (30/R), 1990 *A. M. Boucher* (Hb. HTN); Chorleywood Common (09/I), 1991 *P. J. Ellison* (Hb. HTN); Milwards Park (20/N), 1993 *A. D. Marshall* (Hb. HTN); Berkhamsted (00/D), 1994 *G. Salisbury* (Hb. HTN); North Watford Cemetery (19/E), 1994 *J. K. Jackson* (Hb. HTN); Rowley Lane, Borehamwood (29/D), 1997 *T. J.* (Hb. HTN); Hadley Green (29/N) (VC21: [Herts, 1904-1965]), 2003 *T. J./G. Salisbury* (Hb. HTN) (all det. D. J. McCosh).

Hieracium virgultorum Jordan   Herts Rare
Long-leaved Hawkweed
Native.
First record: 1920.

The only confirmed records for the County are from Berkhamsted Common (SP91), 1920 *R. S. Adamson* (det. D. J. McCosh) (Hb. BM); and from nearby Little Heath, Potten End (00/E), 1955 *C. J. Bruxner* (Hb. HTN). The reference to 09/E in Dony (1967) is an error.

Hieracium sabaudum L.
Autumn Hawkweed
Native.
First record: (1696) 1868.
Tetrad occurrence: 23 (5%).

This is the commonest many-leaved hawkweed found on wood banks, roadsides, *etc.* on neutral or mildly acidic soils across southern and central Hertfordshire, and many of the 109 un-named tetrad occurrences of '*Hieracium*' during the recent survey were probably this, especially in south Herts. The first reference to what was probably this species was by L. Plukenet, from near Rickmansworth (Pryor, 1887). Following Webb and Coleman (1849), he also gives a number of other early records under the name '*H. boreale*'. Many of these are probably accurate, but the earliest recently examined specimen is from Hitch Wood (12/W), 1868 *J. Pollard* (Hb. HTN). Dony (1967) gave 12 tetrad records, of which specimens from nine have been verified. The recent survey recorded it quite widely, but it is probably still under-recorded.

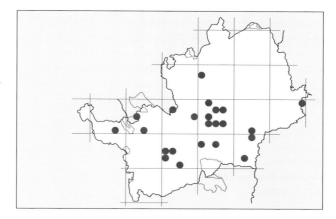

Map 646. *Hieracium sabaudum.*

Two forms occur: the nominate f. *sabaudum* being apparently less common in Herts. than f. *bladonii* (Pugsley) P. D. Sell, although not all records have been determined to this level.

Section: *Hieracioides*

Hieracium umbellatum L.   Herts Rare
Umbellate Hawkweed
Native.
First record: (1839) 1913.

A plant of acidic, heathy soils. There are early records from Coleman and others in the 19th century that may be correct, but the first confirmed specimen is from near Knebworth Woods (TL22), 1913 *A. W. Graveson* (Hb. HTN). It was found on a railway bank near Brookmans Park (20/L), 1977 *R. M. Burton*; and again in 1994 *A. D. Marshall* (Hb. HTN). It has also been found in clearings at Bricket Wood Common (10/F), 1992, *G. Salisbury* and 2002 *T. J.* (Hb. HTN) (conf. D. J. McCosh). All Hertfordshire specimens have been identified as ssp. *umbellatum*.

Section: *Tridentata*

Hieracium trichocaulon (Dahlst.) Johansson   Herts Rare
Hairy-stemmed Hawkweed
Native.
First record: 1956.

Dony found this at Aldenham Reservoir (19/S) (det. P. D. Sell) (conf. D. J. McCosh, 2004) (Hb. HTN). There is also a record from a garden near East Barnet Station (29/S), 1981 *D. Bevan* (det. C. West), but the specimen has not been checked recently. It is usually a plant of sandy soils.

Hieracium calcaricola (F. Hanb.) Roffey   Herts Rare
Toothed Hawkweed
Native.
First record: 1958.

First found by the railway at Northchurch (90/Z), 1958 *J. G. Dony* (det. P. D. Sell; conf. D. J. McCosh). Dony (1967) also gives a record from tetrad 19/Y (det. P. D. Sell and C. West), which is supported by a specimen from Elstree, 1963 *J. G. Dony,* (Hb. LTN) (*comm.*: D. J. McCosh). During the recent survey, the species was found at Wymondley electricity grid station (22/D), 1994 *A. D. Marshall* (Hb. HTN); and at Bricket Wood Common (10/F), 1999 *T. J.* (Hb. HTN) (both det. D. J. McCosh, 2004).

Section: *Vulgata*

Hieracium vulgatum Fries.   Herts Rare
Common Hawkweed
Possibly native.
First record: 1956.

Dony found this at Mardley Heath (21/P), 1956 (det. P. D. Sell; conf. D. J. McCosh, 2004). This is in fact the record that Dony (1967) gave as from tetrad 29/P, in error. He also found it by the railway at Borehamwood (19/Y), 1965 (det. C. Andrews; conf. D. J. McCosh, 2004) (Hb. HTN). It is most common in northern Britain.

Hieracium lepidulum Stenstroem
Irregular-toothed Hawkweed
Introduced.
First record: (1911?) 1957.

The record given in Dony (1967) has been re-determined as *H. anglorum.* However, a specimen collected from 'Chalk Hill, near Weston' (23/L?), 1911 *D. W. Brunt* (Hb. HTN) was determined as 'possibly this' by D. J. McCosh. Also, there is a specimen from Tring (SP91), 1957 *F. Rose* (det. D. J. McCosh) (Hb. NMW) (*comm.*: D. J. McCosh).

Hieracium naevuliferum Jordan
Baldock Hawkweed
Introduced.
First record: 1912.

A specimen from Weston Hills, Baldock (23/L), 1912 *J. E. Little* (Hb. CGE) (*comm.*: D. J. McCosh) is the first of several records from this site, the first from which it was recorded in Britain, and still one of its few locations. It was subsequently found in 1931 by H. Phillips (Hb. HTN), and another specimen from 'Weston' (23/L?), 1925 *R. Morse* (Hb. HTN) was also said probably to be

this. These specimens were previously called '*H. maculatum*' as were other records of similar plants elsewhere. The colony at Weston Hills was re-found 2009 *T. J.* (Hb. HTN), but other records need re-examining.

[**Hieracium spilophaeum** Jordan ex Boreau
Spotted Hawkweed
Introduced.

A maculate hawkweed collected from the roadside at Waltham Cross (30/Q), 1991 *A. M. Boucher* was thought possibly to be this by D. J. McCosh, 2004 (Hb. HTN).]

[**Hieracium diaphanum** Fries.
Dark-leaved Hawkweed
Introduced?

Records given under this name in Dony (1967) could refer to *H. anglorum*, *H. diaphanum* or *H. daedalolepioides*, of which *anglorum* is the species most likely to be involved. There is a specimen from the railway bank at Brookmans Park (20/L), 1994 *A. D. Marshall* that has been provisionally named as the true *diaphanum* by D. J. McCosh (Hb. HTN).]

[**Hieracium daedalolepioides** (Zahn) Roffey
Petite-leaved Hawkweed

A specimen collected from the roadside of the A507, Windmill Hill, Clothall (23/R), 1997 *T. J.* has been provisionally determined as this by D. J. McCosh (Hb. HTN).]

Hieracium anglorum (Ley) Pugsley
Anglian Hawkweed
Introduced.
First record: 1921.

The earliest known collection is from Hitchin (TL12), 1921 *J. E. Little* (Hb. CGE) (*comm.*: D. J. McCosh). Records attributed to *diaphanum* by Dony (1967) have now been re-determined as this. Other confirmed records are: Hitchin railway sidings (12/Z), 1963 *J. G. Dony* and again in 1974 *F. Bentley* (probably Little's site); Wheathampstead (11/X), 1966 *J. G. D.*; by railway, Potters Bar (20/K), 1965 *J. G. D.* (originally det. *H. lepidulum*); Hatfield Station (20/J), 1988 *A. D. Marshall*; near the railway, Hatfield (20/J), 1990 *A. D. M.*; railway by Sailor's Grove, Bayfordbury (30/J), 1995 *A. D. M.* There are also specimens from Ayre's End (11/L), 1989 *T. J.*; and Anstey Chalk Pit (33/W), (33/W), 1992 *T. J.* which are probably this. All determined by D. J. McCosh, 2004 (Hb. HTN).

Hieracium acuminatum Jordan
Tall Hawkweed
Introduced [native in the U.K.].
First record: 1975.

Dony's concept of *H. strumosum* included both this species and others, as did earlier records included under '*H. vulgatum*' by Pryor (1887). The record given in James (1985) is also unconfirmed. The only recently confirmed record is: by the railway, Deard's End Lane, Knebworth (22/K), 1998 *T. J.* (det. D. J. McCosh, 2004) (Hb. HTN). Records determined originally by P. D. Sell, but not reviewed by D. J. McCosh, include: on old railway near Watford (19/C), 1975 *J. Rogerson*; and from Potters Bar (20/K, L), *c.*1980 *J. P. Widgery*, but are probably referable to *H. argillaceum*. There is also a specimen in Hb. HTN from Panshanger (21/W), 1990 *A. M. Boucher*; and in Hb. A. Vaughan from Barnet (29/N) *A. V.* (VC21 [Herts. 1904-1965]) both determined by R. M. Burton, that may need confirmation.

Hieracium consociatum Jordan
Sociable Hawkweed
Introduced?
First record: 1965.

One of the former *H. strumosum* aggregate, this was collected from scrub above the railway tunnels, Harmer Green (21/N), 1965 *J. G. Dony*; and from Evergreen Wood, Panshanger (21/W), 1990 *A. M. Boucher* (det. D. J. McCosh, 2004) (Hb. HTN).

Hieracium argillaceum Jordan
Southern Hawkweed
Introduced.
First record: 1913.
Tetrad occurrence: 11 (2%).

Previously confused with other species under the name *H. strumosum*, this is one of the more widespread species, especially on gravelly, calcareous soils. Earlier records confirmed by D. J. McCosh from specimens in Hb. HTN are: Snailwell, Ickleford (13/V), 1913 *J. E. Little*; Whippendell Wood (09/T?), 1954 *J. G. Dony*; by Bayford Wood (30/D), 1955 *J. G. D*; Broxbourne Woods (30/D), 1956 *J. G. D.*; Stubbings Wood (91/A), 1963 *J. G. D.*; Ashridge (91/Q), 1963 *J. G. D.*; by railway, Kings Langley (00/V), 1965 *J. G. D.*; disused railway, St Albans (10/M), 1965 *J. G. D.*; by railway, Carpenders Park (19/G), 1965 *J. G. D.*; Turnford (30/S), 1966 *J. G. D*; and near Potters Bar (20/K?), 1970 *J. P. Widgery* (Hb. BM).

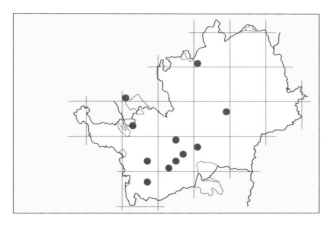

Map 647. *Hieracium argillaceum.*

Hieracium nemophilum Jordan ex Boreau   Herts Rare
Grassland Hawkweed
Native.
First record: 1997.

This is a species of semi-natural chalk grassland. Specimens of this from Stotfold Road, Letchworth (23/A), 1997 *T. J.*; and from scrubby calcareous grassland N. of Royston (34/R) (VC29 [Herts.]), 1998 *T. J.* have been determined as this by D. J. McCosh, 2004.

Hieracium aviicola Jordan
Many-toothed Hawkweed
Introduced.
First record: (1963?) 1988.

Another of the group previously confused under the name *H. strumosum*, this has been determined from specimens collected from Marlin Hill, Wigginton (90/J), 1963 *J. G. Dony* ('probably this': D. J. McCosh); and from the railway at Hitchin (13/V), 1988 *T. J.*, (det. D. J. McCosh, 2004) (Hb. HTN).

Hieracium cheriense Jordan ex Boreau
Cher Hawkweed
Introduced.
First record: 1963.

This was first found at Bushey Heath (19/M), *J. G. Dony* (det. P. D. Sell and C. West) (conf. D. J. McCosh) (Hb. HTN). Dony also collected a specimen, originally determined as *H. strumosum*, from Whippendell Wood (09/T?), 1965 (Hb. HTN). During the recent survey, it was collected from Bush Wood, Welham Green (20/H), 1989; and from the gardens at Hatfield House (20/J), 1989 *A. D. Marshall* (both det. D. J. McCosh, 2004) (Hb. HTN).

Section: *Hieracium*

Hieracium scotostictum Hylander
Dappled Hawkweed
Introduced.
First record: 1995.

First collected from the site of old greenhouses at Bayfordbury (31/A), 1995 *C. G. Hanson* (det. P. D. Sell) (conf. D. J. McCosh, 2004) (Hb. HTN). It was also identified from specimens sent from a garden at Bushey (19/H), 1999 *J. Joseph* (det. T. J.) (conf. D. J. McCosh) (Hb. HTN), where it was a persistent weed. Plants derived from this source have since become established in a garden at Ashwell (23/U), 2000, *etc. T. J.*; and the species is also established in a garden at Gubblecote (91/C), 2005 *T. J.*, although neither of these have spread elsewhere.

Hieracium grandidens Dahlst.
Grand-toothed Hawkweed
Introduced.
First record: 1950?

The first reported record of this was from the roadside at Royston (34/Q), 1950 *P. D. Sell* (Dony, 1967). It was found in the same area at Burloes (34/Q), 1994 *T. J.* (Hb. HTN) (det. D. J. McCosh), although it was not listed by Sell in his list of species from the area in Leslie (2007), suggesting that his earlier record may have referred to another species in this complex. Specimens confirmed by D. J. McCosh have also been collected from The Meg, Hexton (12/E), 1985 *T. J.*; and from Westmill Chalk Pit (32/T), 1992 *S. Watson* (Hb. HTN). There is also a published record from Redbournbury Chalk Pit (11/F), 1974 *B. N. K. Davis* (*Watsonia*, 11 (4), p. 346 (1977)).

Hieracium sylvularum Jordan ex Boreau
Ample-toothed Hawkweed
Introduced.
First record: 1999.

One of the species found on the cutting of the old Newmaket Road,

E. of Royston (34/Q) (VC29 [Herts.]), 1999 *P. D. Sell* (Hb. CGE).
This may be the species previously referred to *H. grandidens* by
Sell in 1950.

Hieracium firmiramum Hylander
Dense-branched Hawkweed
Introduced.
First record: 1999.

Under the Beeches on the N. side of Newmarket Road, Royston
(34/Q) (VC29 [Herts.]), 1999 *P. D. Sell* (Hb. CGE). This is so far
the only known British locality. Otherwise it is only known from
Sweden, where it is also thought to be introduced.

Hieracium onychodontum Hylander
Giant-toothed Hawkweed
Introduced.
First record: 1999.

Recorded from under Beech trees on the N. side of the old
Newmarket Road, Royston, and also on nearby chalk cutting
banks (34/Q), 1999 (VC29 [Herts.]) *P. D. Sell* (Hb. CGE). This
could also be the species previously referred to *H. grandidens*.

Hieracium quadridentatum Hylander
Four-toothed Hawkweed
Introduced.
First record: 1999.

Also found on the chalk cutting by the A505, E. of Royston (34/Q)
(VC29 [Herts.]), 1999 *P. D. Sell* (Hb. CGE), but evidently not
named until after his account in Sell and Murrell (2006) was
produced, as it is not mentioned there.

Hieracium seriflorum Hylander
Gigantic-toothed Hawkweed
Introduced.
First record: 1999.

Another of the plants found at the chalk cutting E. of Royston
(34/Q) (VC29 [Herts.]), 1999 *P. D. Sell* (Hb. CGE).

Hieracium koehleri Dahlst.
Koehler's Hawkweed
Introduced.
First record: 1953.

A specimen collected from beside the cutting of the old
Newmarket Road, E. of Royston (34Q) (VC29 [Herts.]), 1953
P. D. Sell was named as this by Sell, 1999 (Hb. CGE).

Hieracium aterrimum Hylander
Patent-toothed Hawkweed
Introduced.
First record: 1956.

Another specimen collected from the A505 E. of Royston (34/Q)
(VC29 [Herts.]), 1956 *P. D. Sell* (Hb. CGE) was named as this by
Sell, 1999.

Hieracium cardiophyllum (Jord. ex Sudre) Juxip
Heart-leaved Hawkweed
Introduced.
First record: 1999.

Also found on the N. side of the old Newmarket Road, E. of

Royston (34/Q) (VC29 [Herts.]), 1999 *P. D. Sell* (Hb. CGE).

Hieracium exotericum agg.
Jordan's Hawkweed
Introduced.
First confirmed record: 1979.

Two records under the name *H. exotericum* Jord. ex Boreau were
published by Dony (1967), but neither is confirmed. A specimen
from the railway near Marshcroft Farm, Tring (91/L), 1979,
collected during a Herts. and Middx. Wildlife Trust farm survey,
was identified as the aggregate by D. J. McCosh, 2004 (Hb. HTN).

Hieracium neosparsum (Zahn) P. D. Sell
Bank Hawkweed
Introduced.
First record: 1956.

This was collected from the bank of the A505, E. of Royston
(34/Q) (VC29 [Herts.]), 1956 *P. D. Sell* and named by him, 1999
(Hb. CGE).

Hieracium gentile Jordan ex Boreau
Foreign Hawkweed
Introduced.
First record: 1956.

The last of the taxa found on the banks of the chalk cutting by the
A505, E. of Royston (34/Q) (VC29 [Herts.]), 1956 *P. D. Sell* (Hb.
CGE) and determined by him, 1999.

**Sub-family: Asteroideae (Asters, fleabanes, daisies
and allies)**

Genus: *Filago*

Filago vulgaris Lam.
Common Cudweed
Native.
First record: 1820.
Tetrad occurrence: 12 (2%).
Decreased (-35%).

A plant of bare ground on a range of dry soils, on waste ground,
trackways and arable field margins. This had become quite rare
even by the 1960s (Dony, 1967), and has continued to decrease.
Dony had recorded it especially in the Bramfield and Welwyn

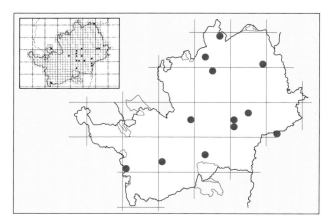

Map 648. *Filago vulgaris.*

areas on gravel, while 19th century botanists evidently found it to be widespread. In the recent survey, it was found, usually as a few plants only, in widely scattered localties, often on gravel, but also on Chalk and Boulder Clay.

(17 tetrads: Dony, 1967; and from 1950-1986)

Filago lutescens Jordan   UK Endangered
Red-tipped Cudweed   Herts Extinct
Introduced: archaeophyte.
First record: 1848.

Found in the 19th century as a rare plant on barren, gravelly ground at a number of localities in central Herts., from Grub's Lane, Hatfield (20/N), where it was first collected by Coleman, to Lemsford (21/B), Codicote (21/E), Woolmer Green (21/P), Hertford (31/H) and Rye House (30/Z). It was last seen in the County at Waterford (31/C), 1919 *A. W. Graveson* (Hb. HTN) (Dony, 1967; Rich, 1999).

Filago pyramidata L.   UK Endangered
Broad-leaved Cudweed
Introduced: archaeophyte.
First record: *c.*1828.

This nationally rare plant was never common, but at one time occurred occasionally, especially on the Chalk near Hitchin and Baldock, but also on calcareous gravel near Hertford and Hoddesdon. It was only seen by Dony at Cock Lane dump near Hoddesdon (30/U), 1958 (Dony, 1967), and was thought to be extinct until it was found on a rubble track through Roundhill Wood, Wigginton (90/P), 1997 *G. Salisbury/J. Saunders* (Hb. HTN), presumably introduced with the rubble. More recently, it was re-discovered on disturbed former gravel workings beside Broxbournebury Park (30/N), 2004 *T. J.* (Hb. HTN), not far from where Dony last saw it.

Filago minima (Smith) Pers.   Herts Rare
Small Cudweed
Native.
First record: 1821.
Tetrad occurrence: 3 (<1%).
Rare, and decreased sharply (-45%).

A plant of very barren, gravelly or sandy ground, on heathy grassland sites. In the 19th century, this was apparently locally abundant in parts of south Herts. on heaths and in gravel pits around Hertford, and also on roadsides in the days when horse traffic kept the verges of unsurfaced roads bare of vegetation. It was rare by the 1960s, when Dony recorded it from only five recent localities. Recently it was thought to be extinct, but a small colony was found by a field path near Albury Hall (42/H), 2000 *K. Robinson* (Hb. HTN); another on a bare, rabbit-chewed bank by Fish Wood (21/C), 2005 *J. P. Widgery* (Hb. HTN); and further plants by Bardon Clumps (31/C), 2005 *K. Robinson*, 2006 *T. J.* It may hang on elsewhere in similar places.
(5 tetrads: Dony, 1967; and from 1950-1986)

Filago gallica L.   UK Extinct in the Wild
Narrow-leaved Cudweed
Introduced: archaeophyte.
First record: 1847.

At one time locally frequent, with other cudweeds, between Hertford and Welwyn on gravelly soils, this has long been extinct,

last having been seen in 1878 (Dony, 1967).

Genus: *Antennaria*

Antennaria dioica (L.) Gaertn.   Herts Extinct
Mountain Everlasting
Native.
First record: 1841.

This charismatic plant of montane and coastal lime-rich grasslands was only ever a rare plant on Therfield Heath, in two localities, as relics of a time when northern plants were more frequent in the south. It was last seen there in 1947 by C. D. Pigott, and succumbed following the cessation of sheep-grazing after the 1930s (Dony, 1967).

Genus: *Gnaphalium*

Gnaphalium sylvaticum L.   UK Endangered
Heath Cudweed
Native.
First record: *c.*1820.
Extinct in Herts.?

A plant of heathy rides in woods, borders of commons, *etc.*, this was never common in the County, having been found especially round Colney Heath, Welwyn, Tewin and Bramfield. Dony had not seen it locally. The only record he quoted was from Whippendell Wood (09/T), 1954 *A. W. Exell* (Dony, 1967), although he missed a mention of it apparently occurring at Hexton, presumably on gravels on the summit of the hills south of the village, *c.*1930 (Whiteman, 1936). After his *Flora* was published, it was also found in a ride near Thunderdell Lodge, Ashridge (91/W), 1967 *J. Wilson*. It was not seen again until a small colony was found by

Heath Cudweed Gnaphalium sylvaticum *Harmergreen Wood, 1979.*

a ride in Harmergreen Wood (21/N), 1979 *T. J.* (Hb. HTN), also found independently by M. Hooper. This remains its most recent record, although it could reappear following ride management elsewhere.

Gnaphalium uliginosum L.
Marsh Cudweed
Native.
First record: 1820.
Tetrad occurrence: 192 (39%).
Stable? (+2%).

A plant of trodden, muddy ground, by tracks and in pastures, usually on more acidic soils. It also occurs in mud around arable field margins and on waste ground, which may explain its apparent slight increase, especially on the Clay-with-Flints in west Herts., although it may have been under-recorded earlier.
(178 tetrads: Dony, 1967; 198 tetrads: 1950-1986)

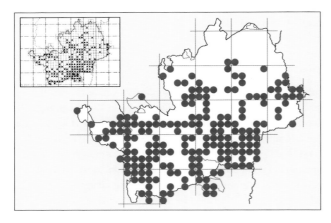

Map 649. *Gnaphalium uliginosum.*

Genus: *Helichrysum*

Helichrysum bracteatum (Vent.) Andrews
Everlasting Flower
Introduced: casual.
First (only) record: 1981.

Found once only: at Waterford tip (31/C) *C. G. Hanson* (James, 1985).

Genus: *Inula*

Inula helenium L.
Elecampane
Introduced: archaeophyte.
First record: 1820.

Only ever really a casual of waste places, escaping from cultivation. It was last seen at Letchworth (23/B), *c.*1960 (Dony, 1967).

Inula conyzae (Griess.) Meikle
Ploughman's Spikenard
Native.
First record: 1814.
Tetrad occurrence: 65 (13%).
Increased (+54%).
A plant of scrubby rough ground on calcareous soils, especially on the Chalk in north Hertfordshire. It is able to take advantage of

disturbed sites, and so is a ready colonist of new roadsides when scrub begins to develop, or of similar ground around chalk pits. It also occurs in south Herts. where the substrate is calcareous enough, such as in old gravel pits, and on old railways.
(40 tetrads: Dony, 1967; 58 tetrads: 1950-1986)

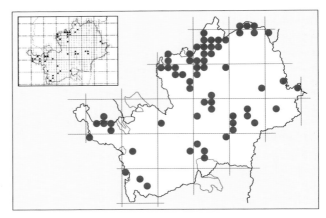

Map 650. *Inula conyzae.*

Genus: *Pulicaria*

Pulicaria dysenterica (L.) Bernh.
Common Fleabane
Native.
First record: 1819.
Tetrad occurrence: 158 (32%).
Probably stable (+10%).

Characteristically a plant of marshy ground, ditches, damp tracks, and damp woodland rides, usually on wet clay, both Boulder Clay and London Clay. It is usually a plant of reasonably old, species-rich habitats, but it also occurs, rarely, as a weed of arable field margins and waste ground. The apparent increase in the species may be down to better recording in east Herts. during the latest survey.
(135 tetrads: Dony, 1967; 156 tetrads: 1950-1986)

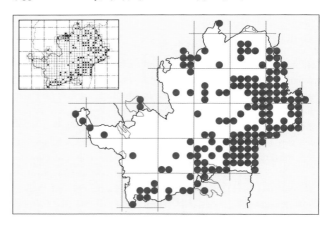

Map 651. *Pulicaria dysenterica.*

Pulicaria vulgaris Gaertner   UK Vulnerable
Small Fleabane   Herts Extinct
Native.
First record: *c.*1820.

This was a plant of well-grazed and trodden ground around ponds, especially on old commons in south Hertfordshire, such as Bricket Wood Common, Hertford Heath, Colney Heath, *etc.* It was last seen at Colney Heath in 1923 (Dony, 1967), about the time when grazing of commoners' livestock ceased in such places.

Genus: *Grindelia*

Grindelia squarrosa (Pursh) Dunal
Curly-cup Gumweed
Introduced: casual.
First (only) record: 1923.

There is only one record of this American plant: from Ware (TL31) *A. W. Graveson* (Dony, 1967).

Genus: *Solidago*

Solidago virgaurea L.   Herts Rare
Golden-rod
Native.
First record: 1838.

This was always a rare plant in Hertfordshire, found around heathy woods, especially in south-east Herts., but also on the Clay-with-Flints in the west. Dony never saw it, but it has persisted, erratically, along open rides at Broxbourne/Claypits Woods (30/I), being seen there in 1967 *P. R. Greenwood*; 1974 *H. J. Killick*; and in 1978 *A. M. Boucher* before the current survey. It was last seen here in 1999 *T. J./G. Salisbury*; but in 2004 a few non-flowering plants were found in the ride at Brambles Wood (30/J) *A. Harris/T. J.*, which gives hope it may persist elsewhere, although it is very vulnerable to neglect or over-management of rides.

Solidago canadensis L.
Canadian Golden-rod
Introduced: neophyte.
First record: 1919.
Tetrad occurrence: 151 (31%).
Increased markedly.

First collected from a lane at Marshmoor (TL20), 1919 *A. W. Graveson* (Hb. HTN) (Dony, ms. index), this was evidently occasional by the 1960s, but Dony (1967) did not really account for it. Burton (1983) showed that it was widespread in south Herts., and the current survey has also demonstrated this. It is now found widely on rough ground, by roads, and on tips across much of the County, but especially on damper soils, near rivers, *etc.*
(26 tetrads: 1950-1986)

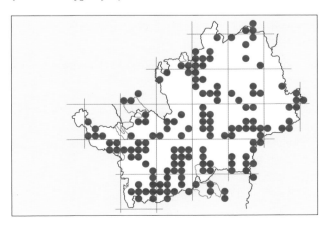

Map 652. *Solidago canadensis.*

Solidago gigantea Aiton
Early Golden-rod
Introduced: neophyte.
First record: 1954.
Tetrad occurrence: 38 (8%).
Increasing.

Although Dony (1967) says this was 'frequent' as a garden escape, his ms. index only gives one record: Welwyn tip (TL21), 1954, observer unknown. There were seven scattered records between 1970 and 1986, but it was found widely scattered across the County during the recent survey, mostly in damper, often shady habitats.

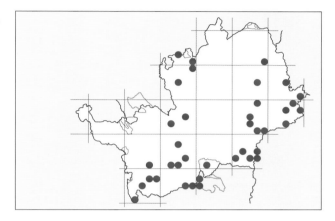

Map 653. *Solidago gigantea.*

Genus: *Aster*

The Michaelmas daisies are a fairly difficult group which, until recently, were much misunderstood, and usually ignored as 'garden escapes', despite first having been seen in the wild as early as the late 1880s near Easneye (Pryor, 1887). Burton (1983) gave a very useful account of the group, with illustrations, allowing much more accurate identification, and so records have shown that several taxa, and especially one hybrid, are widespread. Earlier records are therefore very inadequate, as well as being unreliable. As a group, they are widespread in rough grasslands, by roads, and on waste-tips, often near water, and are increasing steadily, recorded in the broad sense from 125 tetrads during the recent Flora Survey. They are valuable as nectar sources for insects in late summer.

Aster novae-angliae L.
Hairy Michaelmas-daisy
Introduced: casual.
First (only) record: 2004 (VC21 [Herts.]).

This rather rare species was found as an escape at Fir and Pond Woods Nature Reserve (20/Q) (VC21 [Herts.]), 2004 *G. Salisbury.*

Aster laevis L.
Glaucous Michaelmas-daisy
Introduced: casual?
First (only) record: 1992.

There is only one record of this species so far: from beside Mill Wood, Much Hadham (41/I), 1992 *S. Watson.*

Aster × *versicolor* Willd. (*A. laevis* × *A. novi-belgii*)
Late Michaelmas-daisy
Introduced: neophyte.
First record: 1982.
Tetrad occurrence: 8 (2%).

First positively identified from Ware (31/S), 1982 *C. G. Hanson* (det. B. Wurzell). The recent survey found it sparsely scattered across the County, especially in the south and east, but it is probably under-recorded.

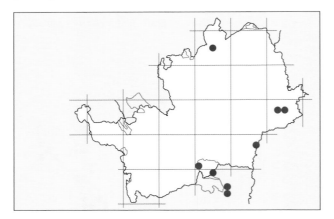

Map 654. *Aster* × *versicolor*.

Aster novi-belgii L.
Confused Michaelmas-daisy
Introduced: neophyte.
First record: 1972.
Tetrad occurrence: 9 (2%).

Although many earlier records of 'Michaelmas Daisy' were assigned to this species, it became clear that most were actually *A.* × *salignus*. The first confirmed record was from Moor Mill tip (10/L), 1972 *C. G. Hanson* (det. E. J. Clement), and he susbequently recorded it from Cock Lane tip (30/T) and Waterford tip (31/C). There was also a record from beside the railway at Woolmer Green (21/N), 1977 *J. M. Way* that was probably correct. Burton (1983) gave a map showing many records in south Herts., but acknowledged that many were likely to be wrong.

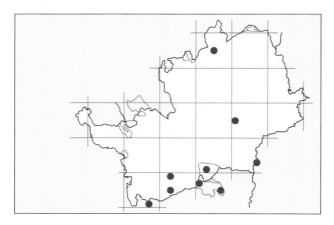

Map 655. *Aster novi-belgii*.

Aster × *salignus* Willd. (*A. novi-belgii* × *A. lanceolatus*)
Common Michaelmas-daisy
Introduced: neophyte.
First record: 1953.
Tetrad occurrence: 41 (8%) (for the segregate).
Increasing steadily.

This was first identified (as *A. salignus*) from Wood Lane, Pirton (13/K?), 1953 *G. L. Evans* (Hb. HTN). Dony (1967) ignored this record, and dismissed the group as a whole. The map given here is for the hybrid, although by far the majority of records of '*Aster*' are likely to refer to this. The map records are biased to the south and east, where identification was tackled by certain field workers more thoroughly. It clearly shows that the plant is especially common on the damper clay soils in south Herts., where derelict land around towns and motorways allows it to thrive.

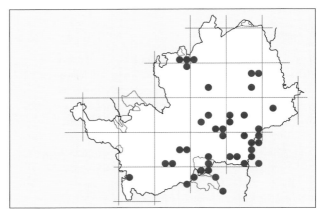

Map 656. *Aster* × *salignus*.

Aster lanceolatus Willd.
Narrow-leaved Michaelmas-daisy
Introduced: neophyte.
First record: c.1970.

First specifically identified at Purwell, Hitchin (22/E), c.1970 *F. Bentley*, this remains quite rare, with only six subsequent records: Twyfordbury (41/Z), 1989 *S. Watson* (det. T. J.) (Hb. HTN); Broxbourne (30/T), 1994 *A. M. Boucher*; near Tingley Wood, by Hitchin Road (13/F), 1997 *T. J.*; by road, Gustard Wood (11/S), 1999 *T. J./G. P. Smith*; Mead Lane, Hertford (31/G), 2008 *T. J.* (Hb. HTN); and Cadwell Lane, Hitchin (13/V), 2008 *T. J.*

Aster squamatus (Sprengel) Hieronymus
Narrow-leaved Aster
Introduced: casual.
First record: 2008.

This South American weed of waste places and bare ground, which is abundant in parts of southern Europe, and which only arrived in Britain in 2006, appeared spontaneously in a garden at Hatfield Road, St Albans (10/N), 2008 *L. Gravestock* (det. E. J. Clement). It is likely to spread by roads, and should be watched for, with small, white daisy flowers on tall, branched, spreading stems, carrying narrow, appressed leaves.

Erigeron karvinskianus DC.
Mexican Fleabane
Introduced: neophyte.
First record: 1993.

First noted as a possible escape from hanging baskets in Ware (31/M), 1993 *A. M. Boucher* and 1994 *C. G. Hanson* (Hb. HTN); this has since been found as a fairly persistent escape at a plant nursery at St Margarets (31/V); by a wall at Hertford Heath (31/K), 1996 *A. M. B.*; along a wall by the River Lea at Wheathampstead (11/S), 1999 *T. J./G. P. Smith*, where it was still present in 2007; and on a wall at Hitchin (12/Z), 2007 *T. J.* It could become a widespread plant in such places, in response to climatic warming.

Erigeron annuus (L.) Pers.
Tall Fleabane
Introduced: casual.
First (only) record: 1977.

The only record is of a plant growing on waste ground at Old Hale Way, Hitchin (13/V) *T. J.* (det. at Natural History Museum) (Hb. HTN) (James, 1982).

Erigeron acer L.
Blue Fleabane
Native.
First record: 1814.
Tetrad occurrence: 117 (24%).
Increased substantially (+87%).

This attractive plant was considered to be rare in the 19th century (Pryor, 1887), and only 'occasional' in the 1960s (Dony, 1967). Its original habitat was probably bare, overgrazed pasture on calcareous or gravelly soils. Even during the 19th century it was evidently most frequent on the then recently-created railway embankments, and it is this kind of secondary, poor grassland that it favours now, being frequent on rough banks by new roads, chalk or gravel pits. It is most frequent on the river gravels, and also on the Chalk and chalky Boulder Clay.
(59 tetrads: Dony, 1967; 70 tetrads: 1950-1986)

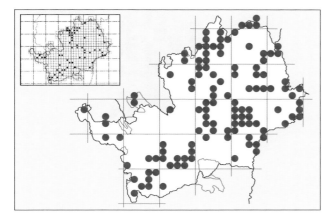

Map 657. *Erigeron acer.*

Until fairly recently, it was assumed that we only had one species, *C. canadensis*, in Britain. Others have since been discovered, and Sell and Murrell (2006) now give six species, comprising numerous forms, and their hybrids. Their treatment is followed here. It is quite possible that more taxa than those listed below will appear with further study, and that some records for one or other of *canadensis* and *sumatrensis* are actually for other taxa. However, there is still much debate about the validity of some of these taxa amongst taxonomists.

Conyza canadensis (L.) Cronq.
Canadian Fleabane
Introduced: neophyte.
First record: 1859.
Tetrad occurrence: 257 (52%).
Increased, now decreasing again? (+57%).

This has become a common plant of bare, impoverished waste ground, by roads, railways, and tips, and occasionally as a weed of cultivation. It is very variable in both size and form, and Sell and Murrell (2006) describe several different named varieties that have not been studied locally. Dony (1967) noted that it had only started to increase about 1920, and it had then become frequent in the south of the County. It consolidated its position, especially on river gravels and around towns, but remains scarce on damper soils, especially the Boulder Clay and London Clay, as well as on the Clay-with-Flints. Most recently, however, it appears to have retreated around larger towns in favour of its relative *C. sumatrensis*.
(155 tetrads: Dony, 1967; 173 tetrads: 1950-1986)

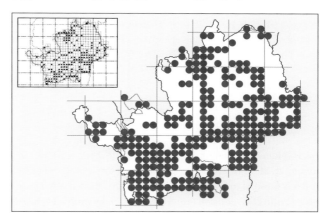

Map 658. *Conyza canadensis.*

Conyza sumatrensis (Retz.) E. Walker
Guernsey Fleabane
Introduced: neophyte.
First record: 1991.
Tetrad occurrence: 39 (8%).
Increasing steadily.

Found in similar places to *C. canadensis*, but usually in warm, sheltered places, often by walls, flowering somewhat later. This was first encountered at Standon (32/V) and Hare Street (32/Z), 1991 *S. Watson* (det. T. J.) (Hb. HTN). Shortly afterwards, it was encountered in a number of places in the Lea Valley and at Welwyn Garden City, so that, by 1993 it had been found in eight tetrads. By the end of the main survey it had been found in 33 tetrads, mostly in the Lea Valley, but as far north as Hitchin and Anstey. There are some signs that its spread has slowed since the 1990s droughts eased, although it has recently been found in a woodland clearing at Balls Wood (31/K), a habitat which it specially favours around London.

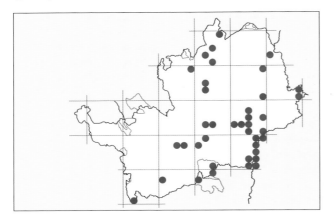

Map 659. *Conyza sumatrensis.*

Conyza daveauiana Sennen
Small-flowered Fleabane
Introduced: neophyte.
First record: 2007.

Attention was drawn to the existence of this in Britain by Sell and Murrell (2006), although its distinction from late-flowering *C. sumatrensis* can be difficult. Specimens agreeing with its description were first noticed at Hitchin (12/Z), 2007 *T. J.* (Hb. HTN), mixed with *C. sumatrensis* in a few localities, especially associated with supermarket carparks. It was then quickly found in small quantity at Baldock (23/L) and around Stevenage Old Town (22/H) (Hb. HTN). It is no doubt elsewhere, and is probably spreading rapidly, aided by vehicles. It appears to flower later than most of its relatives.

Conyza bonariensis (L.) Cronq.
Argentine Fleabane
Introduced: neophyte.
First record: 1981.

This was found at Smallford (10/Y?), in 1981 *P. Brown* (Hb. BM) (*comm.*: R. M. Burton, 2005), but was not recorded subsequently until it was found to have established itself in a garden at Ware (31/S), 2000 *C. G. Hanson* (Hb. HTN), originally from introduced seed. It has more recently been found alongside *Senecio inaequidens* by the Lee Navigation, Rye House (30/Z), 2008 *T. J.*, and may spread elsewhere into similar habitats to *C. sumatrensis*, although it is less adapted to our climate.

Genus: *Bellis*

Bellis perennis L.
Daisy
Native.
First record: 1748.
Tetrad occurrence: 467 (95%).
Stable? (-4%).

A well-loved and familiar plant of garden lawns, amenity grassland, mown roadsides and older pastures. There is no significant evidence at the tetrad level of any decrease, but in some areas, it can now be hard to find if there are no houses with lawns, because old pastures are rapidly disappearing, and road verges have become increasingly rank. Hence, the apparent absence in tetrad 10/Z is probably an oversight, but the absence from 33/W was despite quite careful recording.
(461 tetrads: Dony, 1967; and from 1950-1986)

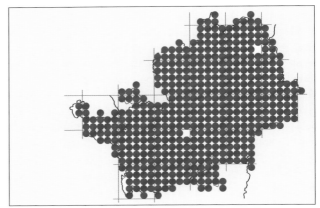

Map 660. *Bellis perennis.*

Genus: *Tanacetum*

Tanacetum parthenium (L.) Schultz Bip.
Feverfew
Introduced: archaeophyte.
First record: 1820.
Tetrad occurrence: 234 (48%).
Increased substantially (+162%).

Dony (1967) considered this scarcely to be 'wild'. Used for hundreds of years as a cure-all herbal remedy, it occurs on waste ground, roadsides, tips and occasionally as a weed of cultivation, usually on fairly enriched soils. The recent survey confirmed the impression from Burton (1983) that it had increased.
(85 tetrads: Dony, 1967; 137 tetrads: 1950-1986)

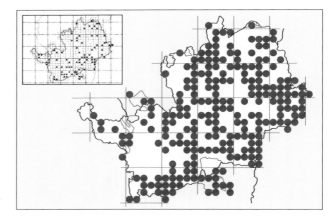

Map 661. *Tanacetum parthenium.*

Tanacetum vulgare L.
Tansy
Native (or introduced).
First record: 1819.
Tetrad occurrence: 104 (21%).
Increasing (+110%).

Although considered native in Britain, its status in much of Hertfordshire has to be questioned. It almost always occurs on

rough grassy road verges, occasionally on waste ground elsewhere, sometimes near rivers, and usually forms small, discrete patches, having probably long-escaped from gardens in many cases. It was quite rare in the 19th century (Pryor, 1887), and 'occasional' in the 1960s (Dony, 1967). Since then, it has continued to increase, and is now widespread, especially in the river valleys.
(47 tetrads: Dony, 1967; 79 tetrads: 1950-1986)

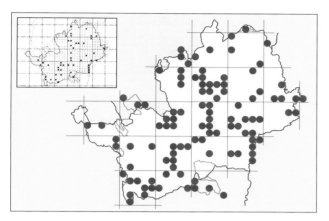

Map 662. *Tanacetum vulgare.*

Genus: *Artemisia*

Artemisia annua L.
Annual Mugwort
Introduced: casual.
First (only) record: 1916.

The only record remains that from Ware by D. M. Higgens (Dony, 1967).

Artemisia dracunculus L.
Tarragon
Introduced: casual.
First record: *c.*1960.

Apart from the undated record by F. M. Day given by Dony (1967), this was also found at Broxbourne Gravel Pit (30/T), 1968 by J. G. Dony himself. (Hb. HTN).

Artemisia vulgaris L.
Mugwort
Introduced: archaeophyte.
First record: *c.*1820.

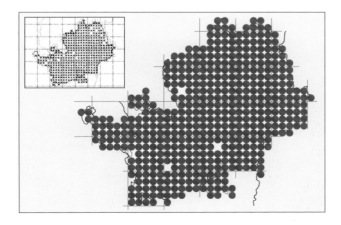

Map 663. *Artemisia vulgaris.*

Tetrad occurrence: 473 (96%).
Increased slightly (+3%).

This is a plant of nutrient-enriched rough ground, often by roadsides, where it tolerates salt as well as responding to nitrogen enrichment. It has expanded substantially since the 1960s, although at the tetrad scale this only shows as a modest increase.
(437 tetrads: Dony, 1967; 439 tetrads: 1950-1986)

Artemisia verlotiorum Lamotte
Chinese Mugwort
Introduced: casual.
First record: 1953.

Dony (1967) considered this to be increasing, but it has not maintained its populations, and the last record was from High Leigh (30/U), 1970 *C. G. Hanson*, although it may be overlooked in urban areas in south Herts.

Artemisia absinthium L.
Wormwood
Introduced: archaeophyte.
First record: *c.*1820.
Tetrad occurrence: 13 (3%).
Decreased (-37%).

Never abundant, this has decreased substantially since the 19th century (Pryor, 1887). Dony found it mostly on river gravels, but recent records have been widely scattered, with no apparent distribution pattern. It usually occurs in bare, waste places, beside roads, *etc.*, but was formerly found as an established plant on gravelly banks in various localities.
(20 tetrads: Dony, 1967; 27 tetrads: 1950-1986)

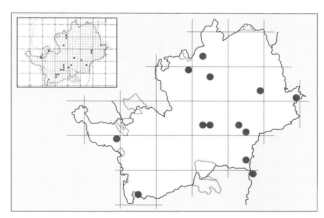

Map 664. *Artemisia absinthium.*

Artemisia stelleriana Besser
Hoary Mugwort
Introduced: casual.
First (only) record: 1995.

Usually an introduced plant of coastal areas, this was found on waste ground at the British Aerospace grounds, Hatfield (20/E) *A. D. Marshall* (Hb. HTN).

Artemisia biennis Willd.
Slender Mugwort
Introduced: casual.
First record: 1913.

Dony (1967) gave this as recorded from Hertford by Trower and

Druce in 1915, but omitted to say that it had first been found there in 1913 by *A. W. Graveson*, and that it persisted there until 1916. It was subsequently also found at Ware by Graveson in 1926 (Hb. HTN). There are no recent records.

Genus: *Achillea*

Achillea ptarmica L.
Sneezewort
Native.
First record: 1820.
Tetrad occurrence: 59 (12%).
Decreasing (-12%).

A characteristic plant of unimproved, moorish pasture on neutral to mildly acidic clays, this has evidently decreased, although Dony (1967) seriously under-recorded it in especially north-east Herts. and failed to find it at all in the Berkhamsted area, which therefore makes it appear to have remained relatively stable in terms of the number of tetrads recorded. Its disappearance from many areas in south-east Herts. is as a direct result of the loss of old pastures in this part of the County.
(64 tetrads: Dony, 1967; 83 tetrads: 1950-1986)

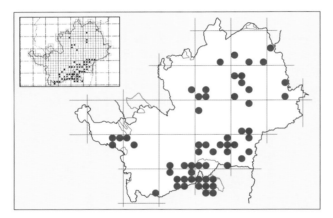

Map 665. *Achillea ptarmica.*

Achillea decolorans Schrader
Introduced: casual.
First (only) record: 1857.

This was reported from Ayot Green (TL21) (Pryor, 1887), but there have been no subsequent records.

Achillea millefolium L.
Yarrow
Native.
First record: 1748.
Tetrad occurrence: 477 (97%).
Probably slightly decreased (-2%).

A widespread and locally abundant plant of rough grasslands and roadside verges on a wide range of soils. It has probably decreased in old pastures, along with the habitat generally, but remains widespread elsewhere.
(463 tetrads: Dony, 1967; and from 1950-1986)

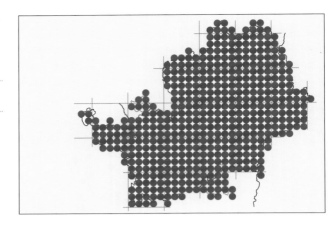

Map 666. *Achillea millefolium.*

Achillea nobilis L.
Noble Yarrow
Introduced: casual.
First (only) record: 1914.

The only record remains that from Mead Lane, Hertford *A. W. Graveson* (Hb. HTN) (Dony, 1967).

Achillea filipendulina Lam.
Fern-leaf Yarrow
Introduced: casual.
First record: 1909.

First found at Ware [recorder unknown] (Dony, 1967, and ms. index). The only other sighting on record is as a pavement weed at Ashwell (23/U), 2006, *etc. T. J.*, but it must have occurred elsewhere in between times!

Genus: *Chamaemelum*

Chamaemelum nobile (L.) All.   UK Vulnerable
Chamomile
Native.
First record: *c*.1820.

At one time a constant feature of short, grazed heaths and greens in southern Hertfordshire, but it had become rare by the 1960s, when Dony (1967) only knew it at Gustard Wood Common and Totteridge Green. J. P. Widgery found it 'near Welwyn Garden City' (21/F), 1974; and during the recent survey it was found as a native on a heathy road verge, Sele Hill, Hertford (31/B), 1998 *T. J.* (Hb. HTN); and as a probable introduction at old allotments, Bushey (19/I), 1996 *S. Cuming*.

Chamomile Chamaemelum nobile *Sele Hill, Hertford, 1998.*

Anthemis punctata Vahl
Sicilian Chamomile
Introduced: casual.
First (only) record: 1999.

A few plants of this were found on waste ground by Aldwicks Plantation, Offley (12/N), 1999 *S. Hawkins* (det. T. J.) (Hb. HTN).

Anthemis arvensis L.   UK Endangered
Corn Chamomile
Introduced: archaeophyte.
First record: 1838.

Possibly extinct in Herts. as a truly wild plant. This was rare, but widely scattered on both calcareous and non-calcareous gravels across the County in the 19th century, occurring by arable fields, and on grassy banks. Dony (1967) only knew it from a gravelly roadside at Rye Meads (31/V), and from a railway bank at Bragbury End (22/K, Q). The only relatively recent records of apparently wild plants are from Potters Bar (20/Q), 1970 *J. P. Widgery*; and from a disturbed bank by the A41, Barnet (29/D), 1993 *P. J. Ellison*. It was also recorded as apparently introduced at Throcking (33/A), 2002 *K. Robinson*; and as a sown plant at the former Herts. Environment Centre, Lonsdale Road, Stevenage (22/M), 1998 *F. M. Perring/S. Smith*.

Anthemis ruthenica Bieb.
Eastern Chamomile
Introduced: casual.
First (only) record: 1919.

Only recorded from Ware *A. W. Graveson* (Dony, 1967).

Anthemis cotula L.   UK Vulnerable
Stinking Chamomile
Introduced: archaeophyte.
First record: 1814.
Tetrad occurrence: 40 (8%).
Decreasing markedly (-59%).

An arable weed and plant of damp waste ground on clay soils, this was formerly quite frequent across much of southern Hertfordshire, but is becoming increasingly rare.
(93 tetrads: Dony, 1967; 109 tetrads: 1950-1986)

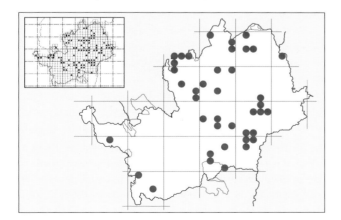

Map 667. *Anthemis cotula.*

Anthemis tinctoria L.
Yellow Chamomile
Introduced: neophyte.
First record: 1860.

The first record at Mead Lane, Hertford (31/G) (Pryor, 1887) is backed up by a specimen in Hb. BM. It persisted here to at least 1909 *A. W. Graveson* (Dony: ms index). Elsewhere it was apparently occasional as a casual until at least the 1980s, but has become rather rare. The only records during the survey were from the disused railway, the 'Nicky Line', between Redbourn and Harpenden (11/B,C), 1985-1989 *J. F. Southey* and 1997 *I. G. Denholm*. However, more recently it has become fashionable in 'conservation seed mixes' and has been sown by the A505 at Baldock (23/S), 2007 *T. J.*, apparently the eastern ssp. *australis* R. Fernand; as well as possibly the same subspecies near Plashes Wood, by the A10 bypass (32/Q), 2007 *T. J.*

Anthemis altissima L.
Southern Chamomile
Introduced: casual.
First (only) record: 1916.

The only record is from Ware (TL31) *A. W. Graveson* (Hb. HTN) (Dony, 1967).

Anthemis austriaca Jacq.
Austrian Chamomile
Introduced: casual.
First (only) record: 1916.

Also recorded from Ware *A. W. Graveson* (Dony, 1967).

Genus: *Xanthophthalmum*

Xanthophthalmum segetum L.   UK Vulnerable
Corn Marigold
Introduced: archaeophyte.
First record: 1750.
Tetrad occurrence: 13 (3%).
Decreased (-27%).

Having once been a fairly frequent arable weed on loamy soils, this is now mostly a rare casual, although it can still appear occasionally in some quantity in crops, apparently sometimes as a seed contaminant, although a few records might be from 'wildflower mixes'.
(17 tetrads: Dony, 1967; 29 tetrads: 1950-1986)

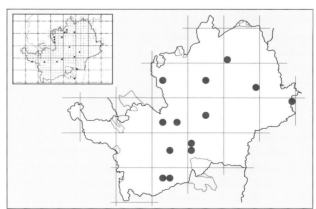

Map 668. *Xanthophthalmum segetum.*

Xanthophthalmum coronarium L.
Crown Daisy
Introduced: casual.
First record: 1929.

The only records remain those from an allotment at Purwell, Hitchin (22/E), 1929 *J. E. Little* and a waste tip at Welwyn (TL21), 1932 *H. Phillips* (Dony, 1967).

Genus: *Leucanthemella*

Leucanthemella serotina (L.) Tzvelev
Autumn Oxeye
Introduced: casual.
First (only) record: 1915.

The only record remains that from Hertford *G. C. Druce* (Dony, 1967).

Genus: *Leucanthemum*

Leucanthemum vulgare Lam.
Oxeye Daisy
Native (and introduced).
First record: 1748.
Tetrad occurrence: 402 (82%).
Stable or slightly decreased (-3%).

Native in old grassland on most soils, this also occurs widely as a colonist of secondary rough grasslands, such as around old gravel pits. It is also frequently sown with amenity seed-mixes, which makes its natural distribution and frequency uncertain.
(394 tetrads: Dony, 1967; 406 tetrads: 1950-1986)

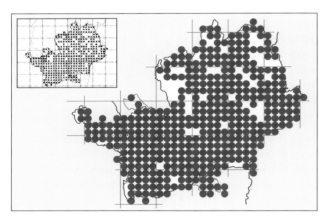

Map 669. *Leucanthemum vulgare.*

Leucanthemum lacustre (Brot.) Samp.
Shasta Daisy
Introduced: neophyte.
First record: *c.*1950.
Tetrad occurrence: 25 (5%).

This garden escape can become thoroughly established in rough grassland and waste places, where it can sometimes be misidentified as Oxeye Daisy. Dony (1967) ignored it, although it had been reported from Bishop's Stortford (TL42), *c.*1950 *D. McClintock*, as *Chrysanthemum maximum*. Recent doubt about its specific identity has resulted in many records being given as *L.* × *superbum*, but recent study has identified this with *L. lacustre* itself.

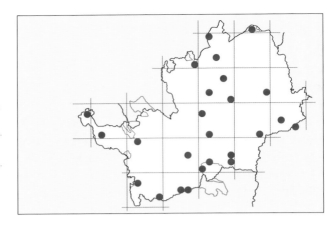

Map 670. *Leucanthemum lacustre.*

Genus: *Matricaria*

Matricaria recutita L.
Scented Mayweed
Introduced: archaeophyte.
First record: 1814.
Tetrad occurrence: 238 (49%).
Increased? (+11%).

A weed of waste places and arable field margins, especially on neutral clay or loam soils. It may have increased on the more calcareous Boulder Clay since the 1960s, although it may also have decreased on the London Clay, with the reduction of arable agriculture in some areas.
(204 tetrads: Dony, 1967; 237 tetrads: 1950-1986)

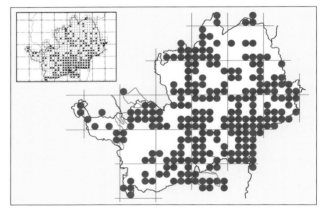

Map 671. *Matricaria recutita.*

Matricaria discoidea DC.
Pineapple Weed
Introduced: neophyte.
First record: 1907.
Tetrad occurrence: 462 (94%).
Stable? (-4%).

A particularly characteristic plant now of trodden wet mud in farm tracks and field gateways. This invaded Britain rapidly after its first record in 1871, so that, although J. E. Little had not seen it in Herts. before 1917, it had become ubiquitous by the 1960s.
(456 tetrads: Dony, 1967 and from 1950-1986)

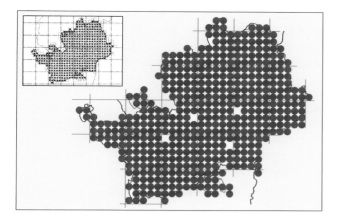

Map 672. *Matricaria discoidea.*

Genus: *Tripleurospermum*

Tripleurospermum inodorum (L.) Schultz Bip.
Scentless Mayweed
Introduced: archaeophyte.
First record: 1820.
Tetrad occurrence: 447 (91%).
Decreasing (-8%).

Retained here as a separate species, following Stace (1997), but variously recorded as a subspecies of *T. maritimum*, which can cause confusion in records. Formerly a very abundant weed of arable fields and waste places everywhere, but showing some signs of decreasing. It is only occasional now by arable fields in many places, owing to effective weedkillers, and the tetrad distribution map shows that it is sometimes not being found at this scale. (459 tetrads: Dony, 1967; 461 tetrads: 1950-1986)

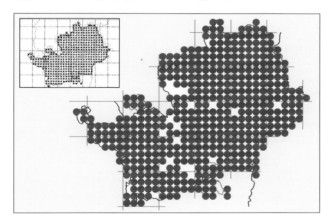

Map 673. *Tripleurospermum inodorum.*

Genus: *Senecio*

Senecio ambiguus (Biv.) DC.
Silver Ragwort
Introduced: neophyte.
First record: 1992.

A weed of rough grassland and waste places, usually near the gardens from which it has escaped. It was first noted in the wild on waste ground at Harpenden (11/H), 1992 *J. F. Southey*. It was then found at Bishop's Stortford (42/W), 1994 *S. Watson*; at Rye House (30/Z), 1995 *A. M. Boucher*; and on the road bank of the A505 at Royston (34/Q) (VC29 [Herts.]), 1996 *T. J.* In none of

these localities was there more than one or two plants, but it could be unnoticed as an escape elsewhere.

Senecio × albescens Burb. and Colgan (*S. ambiguus × S. jacobaea*)
Native.
First record: 1984.

This rather striking hybrid was first confirmed from a roadside at Cottered (32/E), 1984 *S. and C. Watson* (det. B. Swain) (Hb. HTN). It was subsequently found near Bishop's Stortford (42/Q), 1991 *S. Watson* (Hb. HTN), and was later recorded at Cheshunt Wash (30/S), 1995 *A. M. Boucher* (Hb. Boucher); and at Willow Mead, Hertford (31/B), 1995 *A. M. B.* It is no doubt elsewhere.

Senecio inaequidens DC.
Narrow-leaved Ragwort
Introduced: neophyte.
First record: 1971.
Tetrad occurrence: 5 (1%).
Increasing steadily.

At first recorded as a casual wool-shoddy alien, this has begun to appear recently as a weed of waste places by roads and on waste urban sites. It was first found as a shoddy alien at Ramerick, Ickleford (13/R), 1971 *C. G. Hanson*, and re-appeared nearby (13/S) in 1985 (Hb. HTN). More recently it appeared on gravelly ground by the 'Traveller's Inn' at Welwyn Garden City (21/F), 1991 *A. M. Boucher* (Hb. HTN); and she recorded it as a pavement weed in the town itself (21/G), 2005; since when there have been one or two other records from the area. A single plant was also noted at Bessemer Road, (21/L), 2002 *W. Bishop*. Most recently, a clump was found by the Lee Navigation near Rye House (30/Z), 2008 *T. J.*, marking its outward spread elsewhere.

Senecio fluviatilis Wallr.
Broad-leaved Ragwort
Introduced: neophyte.
First record: *c.*1870.

This only occurs as a slowly-expanding patch by the side of Rushy Meadow, by Wilstone Reservoir (91/B), where it was originally planted by H. Harpur-Crewe (Dony, 1967).

[*Senecio paludosus* L.   UK Critically Endangered
Fen Ragwort
Native.

There is a genuine specimen of this, purportedly collected from a gravel pit at Ware (TL31) in 1932, in the Enid McAllister Hall Herbarium at Edinburgh (Hb. E). It was originally determined *Solidago canadensis* in error. The source and status of this specimen is very doubtful, and therefore, without further information, Fen Ragwort cannot rightly be included on the list of Hertfordshire plants.]

Senecio jacobaea L.
Common Ragwort
Native.
First record: 1750.
Tetrad occurrence: 460 (94%).
Increasing (+11%).

A widespread and sometimes locally abundant plant of rough

grasslands, roadsides, and waste ground. Despite being a 'notifiable weed' it has become more abundant in over-grazed pastures as the effective management of these has declined. It has also increased overall since Dony's survey, but remains quite scarce in parts of north-east Herts, just as he found. Despite being a poisonous plant for livestock, it is an important nectar plant for insects in autumn.

(395 tetrads: Dony, 1967; 402 tetrads: 1950-1986)

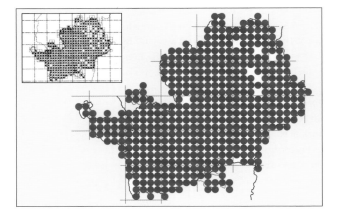

Map 674. *Senecio jacobaea.*

Senecio × *ostenfeldii* Druce (*S. jacobaea* × *S. aquaticus*)
Native.
First record: 1964.

First recognised in the County by P. M. Benoit (Dony, 1967), this has only been firmly recorded since at Sawbridgeworth (41/X), 1989 *S. Watson* (Hb. HTN); and at Hadley Green (29/N) (VC21 [Herts: 1905-1964]), 2003 *T. J./G. Salisbury/S. M. Hedley* (Hb. HTN). It is probably much more frequent than this in old river valley meadows, in places where Common Ragwort has taken a hold following dereliction of pasture.

Senecio aquaticus Hill
Marsh Ragwort
Native.
First record: 1838.
Tetrad occurrence: 38 (8%).
Possibly stable (+20%).

Given the better recording in many areas, and the fact that this plant seems to be remarkably stable where it occurs, it was probably previously under-recorded in some areas in the previous survey (Dony, 1967). It is uncommon in old marshy pasture and

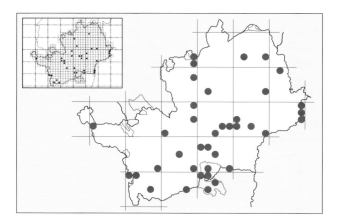

Map 675. *Senecio aquaticus.*

wet woodland rides, especially on the London Clay and alluvial soils. Some records may be mis-identifications of the hybrid with *S. jacobaea*.

(30 tetrads: Dony, 1967; 43 tetrads: 1950-1986)

Senecio erucifolius L.
Hoary Ragwort
Native.
First record: 1820.
Tetrad occurrence: 310 (63%).
More or less stable (-3%).

This is a specially characteristic plant of rough grasslands on clay soils, although it prefers the Boulder Clay and London Clay to the well-drained Clay-with-Flints. It is also a frequent colonist of rough grasslands on disturbed ground, such as round old gravel pits or new road verges. This probably explains why it has disappeared in some areas, owing to loss of older grasslands, while having increased in others, particularly the south and west of the County, where formerly it was uncommon.

(303 tetrads: Dony, 1967; 310 tetrads: 1950-1986)

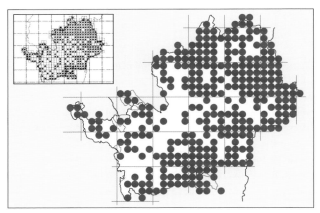

Map 676. *Senecio erucifolius.*

Senecio squalidus L.
Oxford Ragwort
Introduced: neophyte.
First record: 1921.
Tetrad occurrence: 249 (51%).
Increased (+12%).

This might have taken some time to get going, but is now in built-up areas, waste ground and beside main roads across the County, occurring on walls, bare gravelly ground, *etc.* However, it cannot

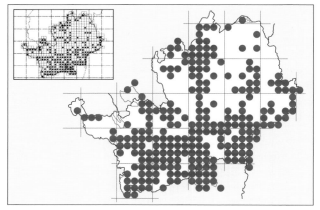

Map 677. *Senecio squalidus.*

compete with closed native vegetation and has not spread into the open countryside much, remaining very much an urban feature.
(211 tetrads: Dony, 1967; 245 tetrads: 1950-1986)

Senecio × baxteri Druce (*S. squalidus × S. vulgaris*)
Native.
First record: 1966.

First found at Turnford (30/S), 1966 *J. G. Dony* (Hb. HTN), this has appeared sporadically since at Park Street tip (10/L), 1967 *J. G. D.* (Hb. HTN); Cole Green tip (21/Q), 1978 *B. Wurzell*; Hoddesdon (30/U), 1987 *A. M. Boucher* (det. H. Noltie) (Hb. HTN); Brunswick Park Cemetery (29/W), 1996 *D. Furley* (conf. *T. J.*) (Hb. HTN); and by M25 at Ridgehill (20/B), 1998 *T. J.* (Hb. HTN). An apparent back-cross with *S. squalidus* was determined from a specimen collected at Welwyn Garden City (21/G), 1987 *A. M. Boucher* (det. H. Noltie) (Hb. HTN).

Senecio × subnebrodensis Simonkai (*S. squalidus × S. viscosus*)
Native.
First record: 1957.

Occasional in waste places with the parents. Dony (1967) listed it from nine tetrads. It was recorded between 1970 and 1986 from four more: Harpenden (11/M), 1979 [recorder unknown] (*comm.*: J. G. Dony); Hitchin railway sidings (12/Z), 1978 *B. Wurzell*; Wymondley electricity grid station (22/D), 1978 *A. D. Marshall*; and Rye House power station (30/Z) [undated] *A. D. M.* (*comm.*: J. G. Dony). During the recent survey, it was found at Hatfield (20/E), 1995 *A. D. Marshall* (Hb. HTN); Letchworth (23/G), 1988 *A. D. M.* (Hb. HTN); Broxbourne Gravel Pit (30/T), 1988 *A. M. Boucher*; Hoddesdon (30/Z), 1993 *A. M. B.* (Hb. HTN); Hertford (31/B, G), 1991 *A. M. B.* (Hb. HTN); Hunsdon Lodge Farm (41/H), 1989 *S. Watson* (Hb. HTN); and Bishop's Stortford (42/V), 1994 *S. W.* (Hb. HTN).

Senecio vulgaris L.
Groundsel
Native.
First record: 1814.
Tetrad occurrence: 473 (96%).
Stable (-3%).

Ubiquitous in cultivated ground and waste places across the County, and an important source of seed food for some birds. There is no significant change in its occurrence.
(462 tetrads: Dony, 1967 and from 1950-1986)

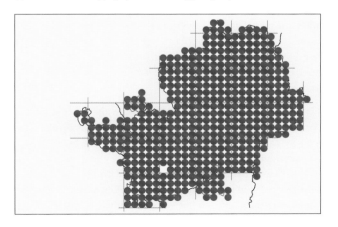

Map 678. *Senecio vulgaris.*

Senecio sylvaticus L.
Heath Groundsel
Native.
First record: 1833.
Tetrad occurrence: 53 (11%).
Decreasing? (-12%).

A plant of heathy woodland clearings, and occasionally in heathy grassland, scattered across the southern and central areas of the County. It is particularly frequent in the Broxbourne Woods area. Its apparent decrease may be more a function of its ability to lie dormant in the seed-bank until coppicing or woodland clearance is carried out.
(60 tetrads: Dony, 1967; 76 tetrads: 1950-1986)

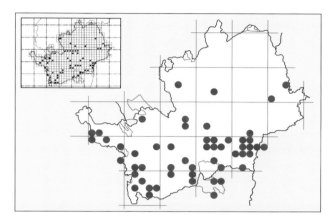

Map 679. *Senecio sylvaticus.*

Senecio vernalis Waldst. and Kit.
Eastern Groundsel
Introduced: neophyte.
First (only) record: 1992.

This was found on a rubble-filled area in fields near Cuffley (20/V) *T. J.* (Hb. HTN), but has apparently not established itself elsewhere.

Senecio viscosus L.
Sticky Groundsel
Introduced: neophyte.
First record: 1874.
Tetrad occurrence: 141 (29%).
Decreasing (-24%).

This is mainly a weed of bare, gravelly or sandy ground. Dony

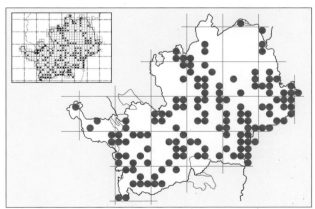

Map 680. *Senecio viscosus.*

found it particularly by railway tracks, but this habitat is now difficult to survey, and its recent records have been mostly from gravel pits, new road verges, waste ground and building sites. It appears to have decreased somewhat, especially in the London fringes, and remains a rare casual in rural areas.
(176 tetrads: Dony, 1967; 193 tetrads: 1950-1986)

Genus: *Tephroseris*

Tephroseris integrifolia (L.) Holub   UK Endangered
Field Fleawort
Native.
First record: 1812.

This plant of short, grazed chalk grassland was known historically from Therfield Heath, Aldbury Nowers, chalk slopes below the Bridgewater Monument at Ashridge, and Ravensburgh Castle at Hexton. There is also a specimen lablelled 'Hitchin' from Isaac Brown in Hb. BM, but its precise locality is doubtful. Dony (1967) only knew it at Therfield Heath and Aldbury Nowers, although there was a record by H. and D. Meyer from Barkway Chalk Pit (33/Y), 1951 (Meyer ms. records, North Herts. Museums), which is probably correct. It was found in small quantity by the Icknield Way at Telegraph Hill (12/E), 1980 *R. M. Bateman/T. J.*, as well as on the County boundary at Pegsdon tumulus (13/F) the same year *T. J./B. R. Sawford*. It was last seen at Telegraph Hill in 1987

Field Fleawort Tephroseris integrifolia *Church Hill, Therfield Heath, 1978.*

Photo: Brian Sawford

T. J., when the slopes here were being damaged by motorcycles. It has only recently been found at two localities on Therfield Heath (33/J; 34/K), where its last actual record was from near the first hole on the golf course (34/K), 1993 *T. J.* Hopefully it survives here and at its long-standing location on Church Hill (33/J), despite the lack of recent records.

Genus: *Doronicum*

Doronicum pardalianches L.
Leopard's-bane
Introduced: neophyte.
First record: *c.*1875.

Pryor (1887) gives a number of undated records of this, and Dony recorded several occurrences (Dony, ms. index), in addition to the record at Whippendell Wood he gave in his *Flora*. There is a suggestion that a colony at Ayot St Peter (21/C) may have survived from about 1880, when T. B. Blow recorded it, to the present, as it was found in a green lane near the church here in 1997 *T. J.* Otherwise, recent records have been from Harpenden Common (11/L), 1989 *J. F. Southey*; Hatfield Park (20/P), 1991-1992 *A. D. Marshall* (also conceivably a 19th century survival), and Southern Green (33/A), 1990 *T. J.*

Doronicum × *willdenowii* Rouy
(*D. pardalianches* × *D. plantagineum*)
Willdenow's Leopard's-bane
Introduced: neophyte.
First record: 1991.

A single clump of this has been established on the road verge at Morden Road, Ashwell (24/Q) since 1991 *C. M. James* (det. T. J.) (Hb. HTN).

Doronicum plantagineum L.
Plantain-leaved Leopard's-bane
Introduced: neophyte.
First record: *c.*1875.

Despite what Dony (1967) said, there was one extra record since the first by R. T. Andrews from Ware: from a Beech copse at Berry Lane, Chorleywood (09/H), *c.*1950 *R. F. Turney* (Dony, ms. index). There are no others.

Genus: *Tussilago*

Tussilago farfara L.
Colt's-foot
Native.
First record: 1748.
Tetrad occurrence: 424 (86%).
Decreasing (-11%).

This familiar and attractive weed of roadsides and waste ground is beginning to show signs of disappearing from some places. Its native habitat is probably exposed mud by rivers, but it has successfully colonised new gravel pits, the muddy edges of recently-cleared roadside ditches, and arable field edges on wet ground throughout the County. Now some of its habitat is affected by road salt, ditches are left uncleared and arable margins are eutrophic, while gravel pits become colonised by shrubberies, gradually eliminating the colonising plant communities.
(453 tetrads: Dony, 1967 and from 1950-1986)

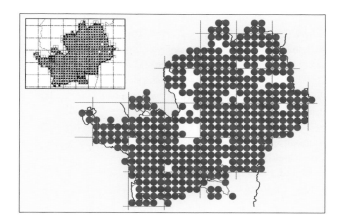

Map 681. *Tussilago farfara.*

Genus: *Petasites*

Petasites hybridus (L) P. Gaert., Mey. and Scherb.
Butterbur
Native.
First record: 1737.
Tetrad occurrence: 72 (15%).
Stable? (+2%).

A native plant of marshy margins of rivers, spring seepages
and seasonally wet hollows in meadows, this has a very similar
distribution to that known by Dony (1967), although it has
colonised new gravel pits in places, particularly silt fans, and some
extra sites have been found, while it has apparently gone from
others. The female plant is very rare in the County, the only recent
records being from the Aquadrome, Rickmansworth (09/L), 1997
M. Simpson; and from a ditch near Ashwell End (24/K), 2008
T. J. The latter may just have been introduced accidentally with
aquatic plants earlier, although the male form occurs not that far
away.
(67 tetrads: Dony, 1967; 80 tetrads: 1950-1986)

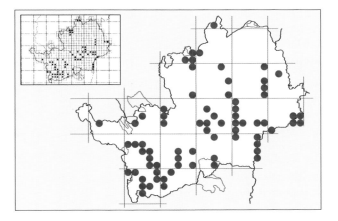

Map 682. *Petasites hybridus.*

Petasites japonicus (Sieb. and Zucc.) Maxim.
Giant Butterbur
Introduced: neophyte.
First record: 1952.

As this plant forms long-persistent stands when it establishes
itself from ornamental grounds, the actual date it became
established in the 'wild' is doubtful. It has been known in the
grounds of Chorleywood House (09/I) for a long time; and it was

also previously recorded from Aldenham Park, where no doubt
it survives, but has not recently been reported. Its other recent
records have been from Weston Park Lake (22/U), 1997, *etc.*
G. P. Smith/T. J.; roadside ditch, Bell Bar (20/M), 1998 *T. J.*;
Parkfield, Potters Bar (20/Q) (VC21 [Herts.]), 1995 *J. P. Widgery.*
There are also older records from Croxley (09/S) and Bayfordbury
(31/A), at both of which it could still be present.

Petasites fragrans (Villars) C. Presl
Winter Heliotrope
Introduced: neophyte.
First record: *c.*1880.
Tetrad occurrence: 37 (8%).
Increasing.

Dony scarcely makes mention of this, but, although only the
male plant occurs in Britain, it can establish itself and spreads
vegetatively, now occurring on roadside banks and similar places
across the County. In some localities it can persist for a long time.
For example, the massive colony by the Great North Road south of
Hatfield (20/I) has been known there for at least 120 years.
(16 tetrads: 1950-1986)

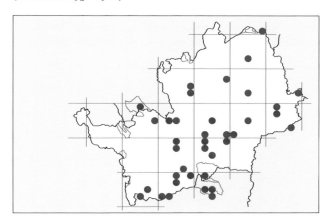

Map 683. *Petasites fragrans.*

Genus: *Calendula*

Calendula arvensis L.
Field Marigold
Introduced: casual.
First record: 1916.

This was first reported as a casual at Ware (TL31), 1916
A. W. Graveson (Hb. HTN), and subsequently by J. W. Higgens
from the same locality. More recently it has occurred on tips at
Moor Mill (10/L), 1972; Waterford (31/C), 1981; Ware (31/M),
1981; and Water Hall (21/V), 1983 *C. G. Hanson*. During the
survey period it has been found at Waterford tip again (31/C),
1987 *C. G. H.*; and on tipped soil near Wheathampstead (11/X),
1994 *T. J.*

Calendula officinalis L.
Pot Marigold
Introduced: neophyte.
First record: *c.*1840.
Tetrad occurrence: 23 (5%).
Increasing.

Although the first record of this in the wild was made by J. Ansell
(Webb and Coleman, 1849), Dony (1967) did not pay much

attention to the plant. From the recent survey, it is evident that it is widespread, if sporadic, on disturbed soils, tips, and around villages, and may persist in some localities where it is warm enough.

Genus: *Ambrosia*

Ambrosia trifida L.
Giant Ragweed
Introduced: casual.
First record: 1923.

Recorded from three localities early in the 20th century (Dony, 1967 and ms. index), but not subsequently.

Ambrosia artemisiifolia L.
Ragweed
Introduced: neophyte.
First record: 1906.
Tetrad occurrence: 8 (2%).
Increasing.
The first record was actually made at Harpenden Common (TL11) in 1906 *E. J. Salisbury*, not 1911 (Dony, 1967). It has increased as a weed of waste tips, and more recently as a bird-seed casual in various places. As a potentially very noxious plant, causing severe hay-fever, its increase is unwelcome.

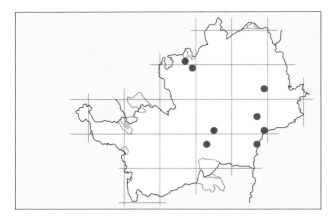

Map 684. *Ambrosia artemisiifolia.*

[Genus: *Iva*]

[*Iva xanthiifolia* Nutt.
Marsh-elder
Introduced: casual.

A record of this is held on the Biological Records Centre database, CEH Wallingford, from a garden at Ware (31/S), 1996-7 *C. G. Hanson*, but it was not a genuine escape.]

Genus: *Xanthium*

Xanthium strumarium L.
Rough Cockle-bur
Introduced: casual.
First record: 1974.
Tetrad occurrence: 6 (1%).

First found at two separate tips at Ware (31/M, N), 1974 *C. G. Hanson* (Dony, 1975), this was not found again until the recent survey, when it was recorded from the banks of Wilstone

Reservoir (91/B), 1990 *T. J.* (det. A. M. Boucher) (Hb. HTN); Puckeridge tip (32/W), 1991 *S. Watson* (Hb. HTN); in a garden at Broxbourne (30/T), 1995 *A. M. Boucher*; near Hoddesdon (30/N), 1995 *C. G. Hanson* (det. E. J. Clement) (Hb. Hanson); Hitchin (12/Z), 1995 *T. J.*; and in a garden, Ashwell (23/U), 1997 *T. J.* (Hb. HTN). In all of these localities it was probably the result of introduction with bird seed.

Xanthium spinosum L.
Spiny Cockle-bur
Introduced: casual.
First record: 1846.

Although this was first noticed at Hertford in 1846 (Pryor, 1887; Dony, 1967), it was rather rarely recorded subsequently, usually as a wool shoddy alien, and has not been recorded since it was found on a shoddy heap at Ramerick, Ickleford (13/R), 1971 *C. G. Hanson*.

Genus: *Guizotia*

Guizotia abyssinica (L. *f.*) Cass.
Niger
Introduced: casual.
First record: 1926.

Considering that this is now frequently sold as bird-seed, it is surprising it is not widespread. Dony (1967) gave a few recent records; and in the 1970s it became frequent on tips, with records between 1970 and 1985 from 13 tetrads. Since then, however, modern tip management has reduced its occurrence in these sites, and it was only recorded during the recent survey from Waterford tip (31/C), 1987 *C. G. Hanson* and from Rye Meads Sewage Works (31/V), where it was regular until at least 1997 *A. M. Boucher/C. G. H.* (Hb. HTN).

Genus: *Sigesbeckia*

Sigesbeckia serrata DC.
Western St Paul's-wort
Introduced: casual.
First record: 1992.

This was cultivated at Ware (31/S), originally from wool waste collected in Bedfordshire, and became locally established from at least 1992 to 1997 *C. G. Hanson* (Hb. HTN).

Genus: *Rudbeckia*

Rudbeckia hirta L.
Black-eyed Susan
Introduced: casual.
First (only) record: 1988.

The only record is from Ware tip (31/M), 1988 *C. G. Hanson.*

Genus: *Helianthus*

Helianthus petiolaris Nutt.
Lesser Sunflower
Introduced: casual.
First record: 1979.

First noted as an escape at Waterford tip (31/C), 1979 *C. G. Hanson*, where it re-appeared until 1984 (James, 1985).

Recently it has also been noted as a casual in a garden at Ashwell (23/U), 2000 *T. J.*, where it was presumably introduced from bird seed; and as probable game cover at Standon Lodge (42/A), 2003 *T. J.* It is probably overlooked elsewhere, and could establish in warm years.

Helianthus annuus L.
Sunflower
Introduced: casual.
First record: *c.*1880.
Tetrad occurrence: 17 (4%).
Increasing?

A spectacular garden plant, this is also now cultivated for both game cover and bird seed, so it is not surprising it turns up occasionally as an escape, often by roads, having fallen off the back of a lorry! It was first recorded at Ware (Pryor, 1887), but Dony ignored it. From 1970-1986 it was recorded in 14 tetrads, mostly on tips, but during the recent survey it was found in 17 tetrads, interestingly in much the same areas.

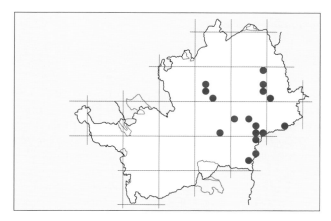

Map 685. *Helianthus annuus.*

Helianthus × multiflorus L. (*H. annuus × decapetalus*)
Thin-leaved Sunflower
Introduced: casual.
First record: 1987.

This garden flower was also found at Waterford tip (31/C), 1987 *C. G. Hanson* (det. E. J. Clement) (Hb. Hanson). A plant reported as *H. decapetalus* from Rickmansworth (09/L) in Burton (1983) could also have been this, as he suspected.

Helianthus × laetiflorus Pers. (*H. rigidus × tuberosus*)
Perennial Sunflower
Introduced: casual.
First record: *c.*1950?

This is the usual perennial sunflower grown in gardens, and was recorded as an escape at Waterford tip (31/C), 1979 and at Ware tip (31/M), 1987 *C. G. Hanson* (det. E. J. Clement) (Hb. Hanson). Plants of supposed *H. rigidus* itself, recorded since at least 1950 (Dony, ms. index; Burton, 1983) were also probably this hybrid.

Helianthus tuberosus L.
Jerusalem Artichoke
Introduced: casual.
First record: *c.*1880.
Tetrad occurrence: 10 (2%).

First recorded as an escape at Hertford (Pryor, 1887). It is

occasionally grown as a crop, and is also sometimes used as game cover, becoming locally established from tubers for a while.

Genus: *Galinsoga*

Galinsoga parviflora Cav.
Gallant-soldier
Introduced: neophyte.
First record: 1912.
Tetrad occurrence: 12 (2%).
Decreased (-38%).

A weed of waste places, Dony (1967) recorded this from 18 tetrads, but noted that it appeared to have stabilised in occurrence. There were nine extra tetrad records between 1970 and 1986, but the recent survey would suggest it is now quite uncommon.
(18 tetrads: Dony, 1967; 27 tetrads: 1950-1986)

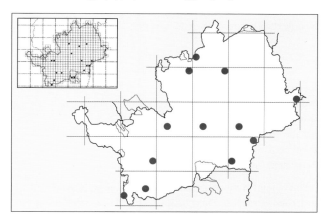

Map 686. *Galinsoga parviflora.*

Galinsoga quadriradiata Ruiz, Lopez and Pavón
Shaggy-soldier
Introduced: neophyte.
First record: 1921.
Tetrad occurrence: 36 (7%).
Increasing (+62%).

Like its relative, this occurs in waste ground, on tips, as a pavement weed and also occasionally as a weed in allotments. It may tolerate higher nutrient levels than its cousin, as it was recorded much more often during the survey, with strongholds in the lower Lea Valley, and around Rickmansworth in the Colne Valley.
(21 tetrads: Dony, 1967; 29 tetrads: 1950-1986)

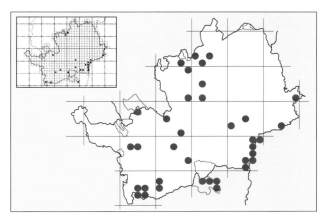

Map 687. *Galinsoga quadriradiata.*

Hemizonia pungens Torrey and A. Gray
Common Spikeweed
Introduced: casual.
First record: 1920.

Apart from the record from Ware mentioned by Dony (1967), where it apparently persisted to 1924 *A. W. Graveson*, it was also found at Hitchin (13/V), 1924 *J. E. Little* (Hb. BM) (but assigned to *Centromadia* [= *Hemizonia*] *fitchii* by Dony, in error). There are no modern records.

Hemizonia kelloggii E. Greene
Kellogg's Spikeweed
Introduced: casual.
First (only) record: 1917.

The only record is from Ware (Dony, 1967).

Genus: *Bidens*

Bidens cernua L.
Nodding Bur-marigold
Native.
First record: 1838.
Tetrad occurrence: 54 (11%).
Decreasing (-30%).

A plant of mud at the margins of freshwater, usually on less calcareous substrates. This remains in much the same areas as Dony (1967) recorded it, but it has shown strong evidence of decrease as old ponds have become neglected, polluted or lost.
(73 tetrads: Dony, 1967; 70 tetrads: 1950-1986)

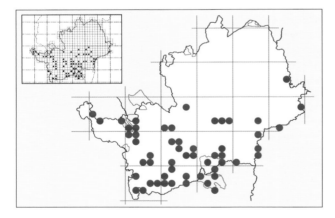

Map 688. *Bidens cernua.*

Bidens tripartita L.
Trifid Bur-marigold
Native.
First record: *c.*1820.
Tetrad occurrence: 65 (13%).
Stable or slightly decreased (-4%).

Dony thought that this was a plant of the margins of shallower water than *B. cernua*, but its occurrence alongside rivers rather than by ponds would suggest this is not the case. It remains almost restricted to the lower reaches of rivers in south Herts., except that it now appears to be commoner than formerly in the Gade/Bulbourne valleys, and to have disappeared from the lower Lea

Valley, presumably through the almost total loss there of marshy river margins.
(64 tetrads: Dony, 1967; 79 tetrads: 1950-1986)

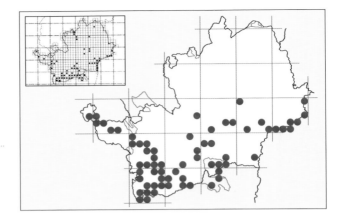

Map 689. *Bidens tripartita.*

Bidens connata Mühlenb. ex Willd.
London Bur-marigold
Introduced: neophyte.
First record: 1978.

Burton (1983) recorded this from one tetrad in Hertfordshire (09/L), but it had in fact been recorded in 1978 in two different places by Mrs M. V. Marsden and Dr J. H. Chapman: by a gravel pit at Rickmansworth (09/L), and by the Grand Union Canal near Rickmansworth (09/S). This was only one year after its first discovery in Britain, further south by the Grand Union Canal. There were no subsequent records until the present survey, when P. J. Ellison found it still by the canal in tetrads 09/K, L, S and X, between 1991 and 1994. This apparently remains the only area where it occurs in the County.

Bidens frondosa L.
Beggarticks
Introduced: neophyte.
First record: *c.*1965?

The exact date of the first occurrence of this at Dobbs Weir (30/Z) (Dony, 1967) does not seem to have been recorded. It was still there in 1984 *C. G. Hanson* (Hb. HTN). Dony also found it by the Grand Union Canal at Berkhamsted (90/Z), 1967; and it was later found by the same canal at Croxley Common Moor (09/X), 1977 (*comm.*: London N.H.S.) and again in 1980, *J. R. Phillips*. The recent survey found it again in the Rickmansworth area, where it occurred at four localities in 09/L and 09/S between 1992 and 1994, *P. J. Ellison*; and it also turned up at a recently dredged pond by Oxley's Wood, Hatfield (20/I), 2006 *C. James* (det. T. J.) (Hb. HTN).

Bidens bipinnata L.
Spanish Needles
Introduced: casual.
First record: 1961.

The only records of this appear to be the first, from Wymondley (22/D), 1961 *J. G. Dony* (Dony, 1967); and from Ramerick (13/R), 1971 *C. G. Hanson*. Both were from wool shoddy waste.

Bidens ferulifolia (Jacq.) DC.
Apache Beggarticks
Introduced: casual.
First (only) record: 1997.

The only record of this is of seedlings spontaneously regenerating from plants in hanging baskets at Bishop's Stortford (42/V) *S. Watson* (Hb. HTN).

Genus: *Cosmos*

Cosmos bipinnatus Cav.
Mexican Aster
Introduced: casual.
First record: *c.*1960?

Dony (1967) mentions occurrences of this, but does not give any details. Burton (1983) mentions that it was recorded from tetrads 10/X and 29/P some time between 1965 and 1976. There were also casual records from tips at Moor Mill (10/L), 1970, 1971; Waterford (31/C), 1979 and Ware (31/M), 1981 *C. G. Hanson*. The only recent record was at Ware tip again, 1987 *C. G. H.*

Genus: *Dahlia*

Dahlia × cultorum hort.
Garden Dahlia
Introduced: casual.
First (only) record: 1975.

This artificial hybrid occurred as a casual on Cole Green tip (21/Q) *C. G. Hanson*. It probably occurs as a throw-out elsewhere.

Genus: *Tagetes*

Tagetes patula L.
French Marigold
Introduced: casual.
First record: 1933.

Since this was reported as an escape at Welwyn (Dony, 1967), it has appeared at Waterford tip (31/C), 1984 *C. G. Hanson/ A. L. Grenfell*; Ware tip (31/M), 1985 *C. G. H.*; and at Rye Meads Sewage Works (31/V), 1985 *C. G. H.* There are no more recent records, although it almost certainly does persist occasionally from garden throw-outs elsewhere.

Tagetes minuta L.
Southern Marigold
Introduced: casual.
First record: 1928.

This wool adventive species was reported by Dony at Little Wymondley (22/D) in 1959, not far from where it was first recorded. It was then recorded from Newnham (23/N), 1973 *C. G. Hanson*, but has not been reported since.

Genus: *Eupatorium*

Eupatorium cannabinum L.
Hemp-agrimony
Native.
First record: *c.*1820.
Tetrad occurrence: 77 (16%).
Stable or increasing (+16%).

An attractive and characteristic plant of somewhat calcareous, damp situations, especially drier areas of fens, riversides where the water supply is calcareous; also a valuable late-flowering plant for insects. It has a somewhat unusual distribution in the County, much as it had in the 1960s. It occurs commonly in the Hitchin area, associated with the fen vegetation around the spring sources of the streams that feed into the River Hiz. Similarly, it is quite widespread around Rickmansworth, and in the vegetation along the rivers Lea and Stort. However, it seems strangely scarce in the Bulbourne/Gade system, while occurring quite widely in scattered ditches and pond margins elsewhere, even in woodland clearings with seepage areas, such as in the Broxbourne Woods. The apparent increase could partly be explained by better recording, although it appears to have disappeared in some areas, while increasing around gravel pits.
(63 tetrads: Dony, 1967; 71 tetrads: 1950-1986)

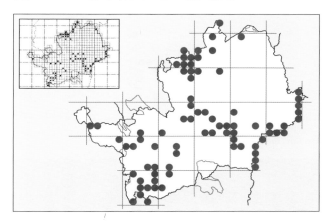

Map 690. *Eupatorium cannabinum.*

Hemp Agrimony Eupatorium cannabinum *By R. Gade, Watford, 1982.*

Liliidae (Monocotyledons)

Butomaceae (Flowering-rush family)

Genus: *Butomus*

Butomus umbellatus L.
Flowering-rush
Native.
First record: 1597.
Tetrad occurrence: 23 (5%).
Stable or slightly decreased (-10%).

An attractive, local and rather unpredictable plant of tall fen by
and in rivers and lakes, this has always been rather a feature
of the Colne system in south Herts.; also occurring in the Lea/
Stort system and around Tring Reservoirs, as well as occasionally
elsewhere.
(24 tetrads: Dony, 1967; 29 tetrads: 1950-1986)

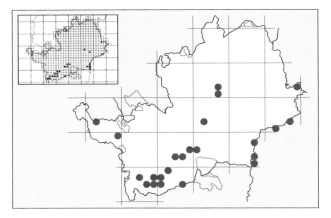

Map 691. *Butomus umbellatus.*

Flowering Rush Butomus umbellatus *Cheshunt, 1989.*

Alismataceae (Water-plantains)

Genus: *Sagittaria*

Sagittaria sagittifolia L.
Arrowhead
Native.
First record: 1838.
Tetrad occurrence: 27 (6%).
Decreasing (-14%).

This rather uncommon plant has remained a feature of the cleaner
stretches of rivers in the Colne and Stort catchments, but has
decreased substantially in most of the lower Lea. Lowered water
levels and chronic pollution from nutrient enrichment are steadily
reducing populations.
(30 tetrads: Dony, 1967; 36 tetrads: 1950-1986)

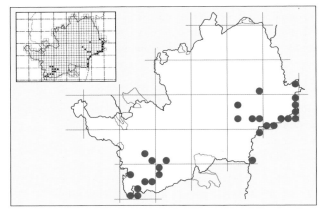

Map 692. *Sagittaria sagittifolia*

Sagittaria latifolia Willd.
Duck Potato
Introduced: casual?
First record: 2003.

Strictly speaking this North American plant has not been recorded
from Hertfordshire. It was found in one of the ponds on Hadley
Green (29/N), 2003 *T. J.* (Hb. HTN) (VC21 [Herts., 1904-1965]).
However, reports of '*S. sagittifolia*' from the same pond in 1992
suggest that it has been established there for some time.

Genus: *Baldellia*

Baldellia ranunculoides (L.) Parl.   Herts Extinct
Lesser Water-plantain
Native.
First record: 1845.

The only record from VC20 is from a shallow ditch on the lost
Ashwell Common (24/R) in 1845 (Dony, 1967). It was also
reported from Hadley Common (29/N) (VC21 [Herts.: 1904-
1965]) as recently as 1947 (Kent and Lousley, 1955), a record
overlooked by Dony (1967).

Genus: *Alisma*

Alisma plantago-aquatica L.
Water-plantain
Native.
First record: 1814.
Tetrad occurrence: 184 (37%).
Stable (+1%).

A widespread plant of exposed mud by ponds and slow-flowing streams across the County. It is quite capable of colonising new sites rapidly, and therefore has benefited from gravel pits, especially in W. Herts., where it was formerly scarce. However, it has disappeared from many field ponds through dereliction and loss of habitat.
(173 tetrads: Dony, 1967; 198 tetrads: 1950-1986)

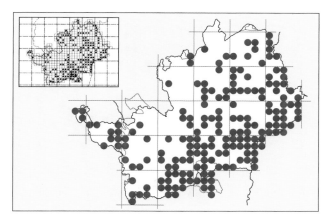

Map 693. *Alisma plantago-aquatica.*

Alisma lanceolatum With.
Narrow-leaved Water-plantain
Native.
First record: *c.*1874.
Tetrad occurrence: 16 (3%).
Decreased quite markedly (-43%).

Dony (1967) considered this to be particularly common along the Gade and Bulbourne valleys, with a few outlying records elsewhere. The recent survey, however, shows no clear pattern, which suggests that either there have been a number of misidentifications, or it has decreased in some areas, notably in the west of the County. In east Herts., it tends to occur most

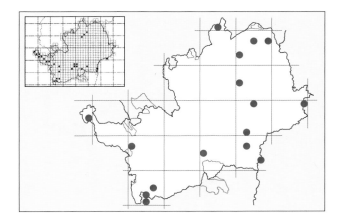

Map 694. *Alisma lanceolatum.*

frequently in shallow ditches or by ponds on calcareous substrates.
(27 tetrads: Dony, 1967; 35 tetrads: 1950-1986)

Genus: *Damasonium*

Damasonium alisma Miller UK Critically Endangered
Star-fruit Herts Extinct
Native.
First record: 1805.

This used to occur at the muddy margins of shallow ponds on acidic clay on some of the commons in south Herts. in the 19th century, notably Totteridge Green (29/L) and Hadley Green (29/N) (VC21 [Herts.: 1904-1965]). It was last seen at a pond on the west side of the latter in 1928 (Kent and Lousley, 1955; Dony, ms. index).

Hydrocharitaceae (Frogbit family)

Genus: *Hydrocharis*

Hydrocharis morsus-ranae L. UK Vulnerable
Frogbit
Native (and introduced).
First record: 1841.

The status of this plant in Hertfordshire has always been a bit problematical. It would seem to have been a feature of peaty

Frogbit Hydrocharis morsus-ranae *Cheshunt Gravel Pits, 1989.*

dykes in the marshes of the lower Colne and Lea valleys in the historic past (Pryor, 1887; Dony, 1967, Burton, 1983, *etc.*). It was also present in a similar situation at Oughton Head (13/Q) in the 19th century (Dony, 1967). There are old records from ponds at Potters Bar (20/K?) (Kent, 1975); Redcoats Pond (22/D), 1921 *J. E. Little*; Wymondley (22/D), 1925 (Hb. Phillips, HTN) (same as Redcoats?); and more recently from a peaty pond at Northaw (20/R), 1984 *T. J.*, where it remained until at least 1991. It is known to have been planted at Batlers Green Farm pond (19/P), 1982 *D. Graham*. In 1975 it was at Broad Colney Gravel Pit (10/R) *T. J.*, assumed to have been planted, although there is also a record from Park Street Gravel Pits (10/L), 1965 *B. Goater*, and a 19th century one from Cassio Bridge at Watford (09/X) (Dony, ms. index) which might indicate a more natural origin. The same might apply to the record given in Dony (1967) from below Cheshunt Lock (30/R), 1966. It was certainly still at the North Metropolitan Gravel Pit, Cheshunt (30/R) as late as 1989 *T. J.* The plants at Bury Green Pond (42/K), 1992 *T. J.*, however, were almost certainly introduced.

Genus: *Stratiotes*

Stratiotes aloides L.
Water-soldier
UK Near Threatened

Native? (usually introduced).
First record: 1695.
Tetrad occurrence: 10 (2%).
Increasing (as an introduction).

Even more than Frogbit, the status of this plant in Hertfordshire is doubtful. It was first recorded from the then newly-created water features at The Broadwater in Hatfield Park (20/P), possibly having spread there naturally from marsh dykes in the Lea valley. Its only other regular occurrences until recently were around Hitchin, where it is known to have been originally introduced in the 19th century (Dony, ms. index). Burton (1983) shows a record from Cheshunt (30/R), without further details, and it was recorded from a pond at Hadley Green (29/N) (VC21 [Herts.: 1904-65]), 1979 *A. M. Boucher*, where it was still present in 1988. It has also become increasingly introduced to ponds for ornament, such as at Meesden Green (43/G), 1979 *T. J.*, where it remained until at least 1987 *S. Watson*; and a pond by the road at Hitchin Priory (12/Z), 1980 *T. J.*

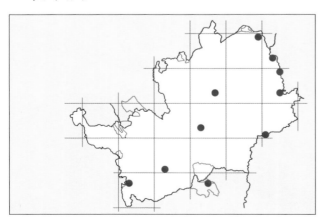

Map 695. *Stratiotes aloides.*

Genus: *Elodea*

Elodea canadensis Michaux
Canadian Waterweed
Introduced: neophyte.
First record: 1856.
Tetrad occurrence: 79 (16%).
Decreased (-15%).

Following its introduction, this became a dominant plant of most ponds and lakes across the County, but has decreased substantially, and is still decreasing. It is now most frequent in larger water bodies, especially old gravel pits, although its more recently arrived relative *E. nuttallii* appears to be replacing it in many places.
(88 tetrads: Dony, 1967; 106 tetrads: 1950-1986)

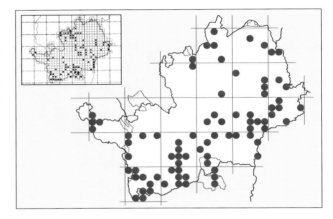

Map 696. *Elodea canadensis.*

Elodea nuttallii (Planchon) H. St. John
Nuttall's Waterweed
Introduced: neophyte.
First record: 1976.
Tetrad occurrence: 54 (11%).
Increasing.

This was first found in the County in the River Gade at Watford (09/Y), 1976 *I. G. Smith* (*comm.*: London N.H.S.). It spread slowly at first, especially in rivers and recent gravel pits, being found in nine tetrads by 1986. It was recorded during the survey mostly in the rivers Lea, Colne and Stort, as well as old gravel pits, where it appears to have begun to replace *E. canadensis*.

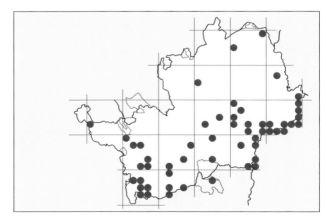

Map 697. *Elodea nuttallii.*

Elodea callitrichoides (Rich.) Caspary
South American Waterweed
Introduced: casual.
First (only) record: 1948.

Plants named this were recorded from the River Colne near Harefield (09/F), in Hertfordshire, 1948 by H. C. Grigg. This was apparently the first U.K. record of the species, probably discarded by aquarists. It does not seem to have persisted, as there were no subsequent records. Burton (1983) queried the taxonomy of records for this species, but Simpson (1984) and Preston and Croft (1997) confirm its former status as an introduction locally.

Genus: *Lagarosiphon*

Lagarosiphon major (Ridley) Moss
Curly Waterweed
Introduced: neophyte.
First record: 1966.
Tetrad occurrence: 24 (5%).
Increasing.

First recorded at Potten End Pond (00/E), 1966 *J. G. Dony* (Dony, 1967), this has become something of a menace in a number of ponds across the County, usually as the result of throw-outs from garden ponds and aquaria, although it does not always persist. It was recorded from six tetrads between 1970 and 1986, but during the current survey it has been found in 24 tetrads, almost certainly an under-estimate.

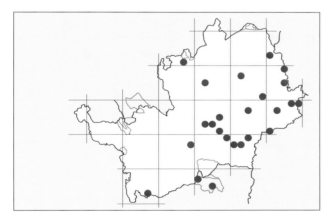

Map 698. *Lagarosiphon major.*

Genus: *Vallisneria*

Vallisneria spiralis L.
Tapegrass
Introduced: neophyte.
First record: 1970.
Extinct?

This was found to be plentiful in the Lee Navigation between Aqueduct Lock and Waltham Abbey (30/R, S), 1970 *S. S. Harris/T. Lording* (Hb. HTN; Hb. LTN), and was subsequently also found in the River Lea by Rye Meads Sewage Works (30/Z), 1980 *B. Wurzell*. It was last seen near Waltham Cross (30/Q), 1981 *J. H. Bratton*. The recent survey failed to re-find it.

Juncaginaceae (Arrowgrass family)

Genus: *Triglochin*

Triglochin palustre L.
Marsh Arrowgrass
Native.
First record: 1820.
Tetrad occurrence: 10 (2%).
Decreased sharply (-41%).

A native plant of high quality grazed marshy pasture with seepages, often on peat domes, and in grazed stream or ditch margins. Because of the sensitive nature of this plant's habitats, and the severe degradation of most such habitat in the County, it is hardly surprising that it is disappearing. It was found in only 10 tetrads during the survey, with a concentration in the Panshanger/ Poplars Green area by the Mimram, and in the Chess Valley around Sarratt.
(16 tetrads: Dony, 1967; 19 tetrads: 1950-1986)

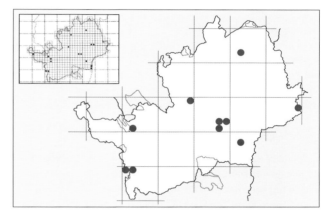

Map 699. *Triglochin palustre.*

Potamogetonaceae (Pondweeds)

Genus: *Potamogeton*

As a group, these plants are taxonomically difficult as well as hard to sample, and therefore tend to be under-recorded. Dony had the benefit of a concerted effort at recording carried out by J. E. Dandy and G. Taylor in the 1930s and 1940s. More recently, some attempt to record them was made, especially during the 1980s, with the result that a fair picture of their occurrence was obtained before recent deterioration in river and canal quality and the increasing eutrophication of gravel pits and other water bodies during the 1990s. Comparison with 19th and earlier 20th century records indicates just how poor most of Hertfordshire's aquatic habitats now are compared with their 'natural' state.

Potamogeton natans L.
Floating Pondweed
Native.
First record: 1820.
Tetrad occurrence: 107 (22%).
Stable? (-2%).

This is the common floating-leaved species of ponds, gravel pits, reservoirs, or slow-moving rivers. It is tolerant of moderately eutrophic conditions, as well as being able to colonise new sites through the movement of waterfowl, although there is also evidence of it being introduced quite often. It was recorded during the survey mostly in the river valleys and clay country of the south-east.

(104 tetrads: Dony, 1967; 123 tetrads: 1950-1986)

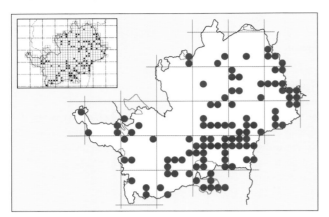

Map 700. *Potamogeton natans.*

Potamogeton polygonifolius Pourret   Herts Rare
Bog Pondweed
Native.
First record: 1843.
Tetrad occurrence: 4 (<1%).
Stable? (+33%)

This plant of acidic bogs has always been rare in the County, and remains so. Dony (1967) listed three recent sites, in two of which it has been recorded during the recent survey: Hertford Heath (Brides Farm Pond) (31/K), 1987 *T. J.* (Hb. HTN); Bricket Wood Common (10/F), 1997 *T. J.* (Hb. HTN), in both of which it has been known for more than 150 years. It has also been found recently at a pool in Sherrards Park Wood (21/G), 1994 *A. D. Marshall* (det. T. J.) (Hb. HTN); and in a pond at Milwards Park (20/I), 2003 *T. J.* (Hb. HTN), both of which are new sites. It could conceivably be elsewhere on acidic soils in south-east Hertfordshire. A record in Whiteman (1936) from the Hexton area must be an error.

Potamogeton coloratus Hornem.   Herts Extinct
Fen Pondweed
Native.
First record: 1838.

This plant of high quality calcareous water in fen dykes was only ever known from the former Ashwell Common (24/R), where it was last recorded in 1841 by W. H. Coleman (Hb. BM), before the site was destroyed.

Potamogeton lucens L.   Herts Rare?
Shining Pondweed
Native.
First record: 1839.
Tetrad occurrence: 9 (2%).
Decreasing rapidly (-47%).

At one time a familiar feature of some sections especially of the rivers Lea and Stort, as well as nearby gravel pits, and at Tring Reservoirs with its associated canals, this plant has rapidly

vanished from most sites, so that even the map depicted here is now out of date. For example, the last record in the Stort valley was in the Stort backwater at Tednambury (41/Y), 2003 *S. Watson.* It now appears to have vanished from the Stort Navigation entirely.

(16 tetrads: Dony, 1967; 17 tetrads: 1950-1986)

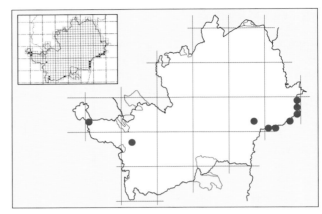

Map 701. *Potamogeton lucens.*

Potamogeton alpinus Balbis   Herts Extinct?
Red Pondweed
Native.
First record: 1843.

At one time rather a feature of the River Colne near Colney Heath and at Rickmansworth, as well as in the Stort, this had become rare by the 1960s. Dony (1967) had 20th century records of it from three sites: a pond at Marshmoor (20/H); the R. Colne at Rickmansworth (TQ09); and a recent one from the Stort Navigation at Hunsdon Mill (41/F). It was last reported from the Stort near Roydon (Herts.?), 1971 (Burton, 1983), and has not been seen since.

Potamogeton perfoliatus L.   Herts Rare?
Perfoliate Pondweed
Native.
First record: 1838.
Tetrad occurrence: 12 (2%).
Decreasing rapidly (-29%).

Formerly a frequent species in the Lea, especially below Hertford, as well as the Stort, the Grand Union Canal, the Ver, the Colne and some other rivers, this had decreased quite markedly by the 1960s (Dony, 1967), and was mainly limited to the Grand Union Canal

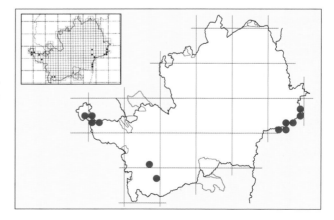

Map 702. *Potamogeton perfoliatus.*

and the Stort Navigation. Since then, the advent of motorised canal boats has virtually destroyed it throughout much of these systems. The current survey found it almost solely in the Grand Union Canal at Tring, and in the Stort. However, the last record I have received was from the Gade at Cassiobury (09/Y), 1996 *P. J. Ellison*, and it is now likely to be very rare indeed. (16 tetrads: Dony, 1967; 20 tetrads: 1950-1986)

Potamogeton × cooperi (Fryer) Fryer (*P. perfoliatus × P. crispus*)
Native.
First record: 1915.

This was at one time a feature of the Grand Union Canal between Berkhamsted and Wilstone, but the last actual record appears to be that made by Dony in 1959 (Hb. BM).

Potamogeton friesii Rupr.   UK Near Threatened
Flat-stalked Pondweed
Native.
First record: 1875.
Decreased markedly (-67%).

This is another plant that was formerly frequent in the Grand Union Canal and at Tring Reservoirs, but is now apparently extinct there. Dony (1967) had three tetrad records for it: in the Aylesbury Arm of the Grand Union Canal (81/W, X); and in the Lee Navigation (31/V). It was found in the River Lea at Rye Meads (30/Z), 1981 *B. Wurzell*; and then in gravel pits at Cheshunt, with records from the Metropolitan Police Pit (30/R), 1989 *T. J.* (Hb. HTN); North Metropolitan Pit (30/R), 1990 *T. J.* (Hb. HTN); and again at the latter in 1994 *D. Bevan*.

Potamogeton pusillus L.   Herts Rare
Lesser Pondweed
Native.
First record: (1838?) 1881.
Tetrad occurrence: 6 (1%).
Now decreasing? (+67%).

Owing to past confusion with *P. berchtoldii*, the real frequency of this is uncertain. It occurs usually in fairly deep, clean water, in gravel pits, reservoirs, and lakes, occasionally in smaller ponds. It seems to have gone from Tring Reservoirs, where Dandy and Taylor knew it, but has appeared occasionally, sometimes in abundance, at recently excavated gravel pits in the Lea Valley, among other areas, although it disappears from these as they become more eutrophic. It was recorded in abundance at Amwell Quarry (31/R), 1984 *T. J.* (conf. N. Holmes) (Hb. HTN); and from a pond at Bedwell Park (20/T), 1978 *A. D. Marshall* (det. N. Holmes) (Hb. HTN). During the recent survey, it was still at Amwell until at least 1987 *T. J.*; and was found at North Metropolitan Pit, Cheshunt (30/R), 1988, 1990 *D. Bevan/T. J.* (Hb. HTN); Metropolitan Police Pit (30/R), 1988 *G. J. White*; at a new pond at Standon Lordship (32/V), 1992 *S. Watson* (det. C. D. Preston) (Hb. HTN); in a newly re-excavated moat at Lawns Wood (41/H), 1990 *S. Watson*; and in plenty in the main pond on Rowley Green (29/D) (VC20 [Greater London], 2008 *T. J.* (Hb. HTN).

Potamogeton obtusifolius Mert. and Koch   Herts Rare
Blunt-leaved Pondweed
Native.
First record: 1840.

This has always been a rare plant in the County, and its real frequency has also been confounded by earlier misidentifications as *P. friesii* and *P. gramineus*. Dony (1967) gave two records (one of which, for the pond at Hook Wood, may have been an error for Devitt's Pond, near Northaw Place). It was subsequently found in the River Colne at Broad Colney (10/R), 1976 *J. G. and C. M. Dony* (conf. N. Holmes) (Hb. HTN). During the recent survey, it was found in a flood pound by the A414 at Nast Hyde (20/D), 1992 *A. D. Marshall* (det. T. J.) (Hb. HTN); in a concrete water cistern at Wrotham Park (29/P) (VC21 [Herts.]), 1998 *T. J.* (Hb. HTN); and in a newly re-excavated part of Pond Wood Pond (20/V) (VC21 [Herts.]), 2000 *G. J. White* (det. T. J.) (Hb. HTN). Another record from the Metropolitan Police Pit (30/R), 1988 *G. J. W.* was not confirmed.

Potamogeton berchtoldii Fieber
Small Pondweed
Native.
First record: 1836.
Tetrad occurrence: 12 (2%).
Stable, or increased? (+60%).

This is usually a plant of moderately deep ponds, flooded gravel pits and lakes, and can colonise new sites relatively readily, as long as the water quality is good. Early records had been misidentified as other grass-leaved species, and Dony's ms. index includes a number of records re-identified from herbarium material, including the first from Hoddesdon (TL30) in the herbarium of Lucy Manser of Hertford (Hb. HTN). The recent survey found it mostly in ponds and old gravel pits across the south of the County. (7 tetrads: Dony, 1967; 12 tetrads: 1950-1986)

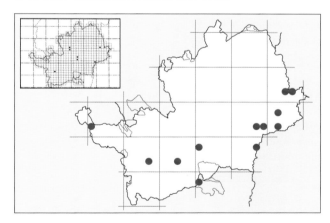

Map 703. *Potamogeton berchtoldii.*

Potamogeton trichoides Cham. and Schlecht.
Hairlike Pondweed
Native.
First record: 1939.
Tetrad occurrence: 8 (2%).
Stable, or increased? (+300%)

Like other grass-leaved species, this was overlooked in the 19th century, and it was not until Dandy and Taylor carried out their surveys that it was first recorded, mainly around Tring (Dony, 1967). Dony himself only ever saw it once, at Tring. It was subsequently found at Rye Meads gravel pit (31/V), 1980 *B. Wurzell*; Stockers Lake (09/L), 1983 *J. Welsh* (det. N. Holmes); and at Cheshunt Lake (30/R), 1985 *A. M. Boucher*. During the recent survey, it was recorded from eight tetrads: Turnford Pit (30/S), 1987 *R. M. Burton*; pond near Bury Green (32/K), 1989 *S. Watson* (det. K. J. Adams) (Hb. HTN); North Metropolitan Pit, Cheshunt (30/R), 1994 *A. M. B.* (Hb. HTN); Bowyers Water (30/Q), 1992, *A. M. B.* and 1999 *T. J./G. P. Smith* (Hb. HTN); Tumbling Bay Gravel Pit, Amwell (31/R), 1994 *A. M. B.* (Hb. HTN); Pitstone Quarry (91/M), 1995 *T. J.* (Hb. HTN); Holwell Pit (13/R), 1996 *J. Welsh* (det. T. J.); and a new pond at Saffron Green (29/D), 2008 *T. J.* (Hb. HTN).

(1 tetrad: Dony, 1967; 4 tetrads: 1950-1986)

Potamogeton compressus L.   UK Endangered
Grass-wrack Pondweed   Herts Extinct
Native.
First record: 1935.

This decreasing plant of still, nutrient-poor calcareous water was only ever recorded from the canal at Little Tring (91/B), where it survived until about 1944 (Dony, 1967).

Potamogeton acutifolius Link   UK Critically Endangered
Sharp-leaved Pondweed   Herts Extinct
Native.
First record: 1844.

This was collected by W. H. Coleman and others from the River Colne at Colney Heath (TL21) and London Colney (TL10); and from one of the rivers at Hertford (TL31) (a record overlooked by Dony, 1967), but was lost after 1846 (Pryor, 1887; Dony, ms. index).

Potamogeton crispus L.
Curled Pondweed
Native.
First record: 1843.
Tetrad occurrence: 62 (13%).
Decreasing (-10%).

A plant of moderately eutrophic shallow ponds and ditches. As such, it has been able to hold its own better than most of its relatives in the modern landscape, and can turn up in newly-created ponds quite readily, although there is evidence of an overall decrease. The current survey found it to be fairly widespread, but with a strange abundance in parts of east Herts.,

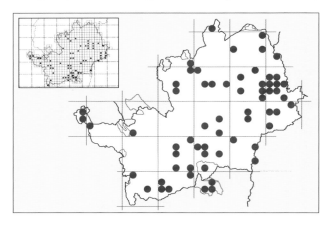

Map 704. *Potamogeton crispus.*

unlike the distribution recorded by Dony (1967).
(65 tetrads: Dony, 1967; 84 tetrads: 1950-1986)

Potamogeton pectinatus L.
Fennel Pondweed
Native.
First record: 1843.
Tetrad occurrence: 47 (10%).
Stable? (+7%).

This species is found in moderately eutrophic, even turbid water, and is therefore the last to disappear from heavily churned canals. It has always been a feature of the Grand Union Canal, where it remains. It is also widespread in the Stort, but may have decreased in the lower Lea. The recent survey also found it to be frequent in the River Hiz.
(42 tetrads: Dony, 1967; 49 tetrads: 1950-1986)

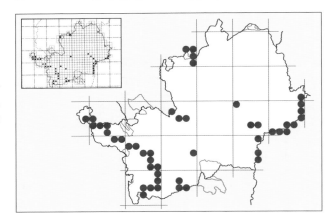

Map 705. *Potamogeton pectinatus.*

Genus: *Groenlandia*

Groenlandia densa (L.) Fourr.
Opposite-leaved Pondweed
Native.
First record: 1838.
Tetrad occurrence: 11 (2%).
Decreasing (-21%).

Dony regarded this as a species of fast-flowing, clear streams, although his survey probably under-recorded it. It still occurs in a few such places, as well as in clear, spring-fed pools, but its habitats were damaged considerably during the 1990s droughts,

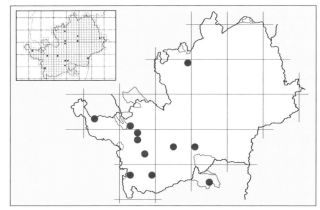

Map 706. *Groenlandia densa.*

as well as by eutrophication, so that the recent survey showed a clear decline, especially in east Herts., from the early 1980s, where many sites were streams in arable land.

(13 tetrads: Dony, 1967; 21 tetrads: 1950-1986)

Zannichelliaceae (Horned pondweeds)

Genus: *Zannichellia*

Zannichellia palustris L.
Horned Pondweed
Native.
First record: *c.*1810.
Tetrad occurrence: 22 (5%).
Stable? (+5%).

A rather scarce, but probably also very much overlooked plant of streams, gravel pits, ponds, *etc.* Remarkably, it was recorded from almost the same number of tetrads as in the 1960s, although not always in the same places, which suggests it can appear and disappear in any one locality. It also does not appear to suffer as much from eutrophication as the *Potamogeton* species.

(20 tetrads: Dony, 1967; 30 tetrads: 1950-1986)

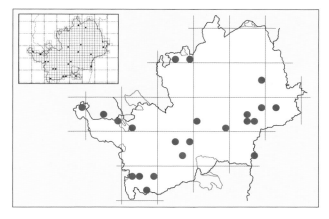

Map 707. *Zannichellia palustris.*

Arecaceae (Palms)

Genus: *Phoenix*

Phoenix dactylifera L.
Date Palm
Introduced: casual.
First record: 1955.

Probably present on tips well before its first record, this has actually turned up quite frequently in such places. The first record was at Aldenham tip (TQ19), 1955 *J. G. Dony* (although he overlooked this in his *Flora*) (Dony, ms. index). Subsequently there were records from Moor Mill tip (10/L) and Cole Green tip (21/Q), 1970 *C. G. Hanson*; and it was then recorded from six tetrads up to 1986. Since then it has only been recorded from Rye Meads Sewage Works (31/V), 1995 *A. M. Boucher/C. G. H.*, owing to cleaner disposal methods.

Araceae (Arum Lily family)

Genus: *Acorus*

Acorus calamus L.
Sweet-flag
Introduced: neophyte.
First record: 1838.
Tetrad occurrence: 23 (5%).
Probably increasing slowly (+57%).

A plant of riversides and lake margins, where it can exist inconspicuously amongst other fen vegetation without flowering for long periods. As a result, its large increase may be rather more apparent than real.

(14 tetrads: Dony, 1967; 22 tetrads (1950-1986)

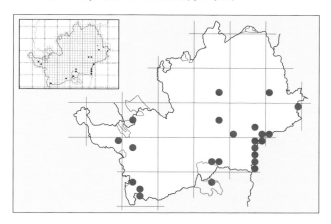

Map 708. *Acorus calamus.*

Genus: *Arum*

Arum maculatum L.
Lords-and-ladies *or* **Cuckoo-pint**
Native.
First record: 1814.
Tetrad occurrence: 462 (94%).
Decreasing slightly? (-4%).

An almost ubiquitous plant of shady hedgebanks, scrub, overgrown gardens and especially secondary woodlands. Characteristically it has spotted leaves, but not always. Despite being common, there are some signs it may be decreasing,

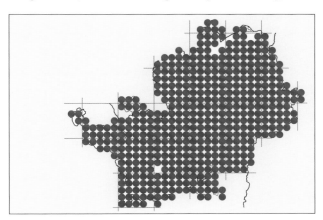

Map 709. *Arum maculatum.*

especially in the dry, open north of the County, and also perhaps in urban areas.
(458 tetrads: Dony,1967; and from 1950-1986)

Arum italicum Miller
Italian Lords-and-ladies
Introduced: neophyte.
First record: 1969.
Tetrad occurrence: 6 (1%).

First recorded from Roxford (31/A), 1969 *M. Kennedy/ P. C. Holland* (Lousley, 1970), this is still probably overlooked, but is apparently well-established as a garden escape in several places: north-west Barnet (29/I) (VC20 [Greater London]), 1992 *A. W. Vaughan*; near Brent Pelham Hall (43/F), 1992-3 *S. Watson*; Aspenden (32/P), 1993 *S. W.* (Hb. HTN); High Leigh (30/U), 1996 *A. M. Boucher*; Danesbury (21/I), 2005 *T. J.*; and Graveley (22/J), 2007 *T. J.* Our plant is ssp. *italicum*, although it does not always have white-veined leaves.

Genus: *Dracunculus*

Dracunculus vulgaris Schott
Dragon Arum
Introduced: casual.
First record: 1990.

This spectacular plant appeared spontaneously in a garden at Southsea Road, Stevenage (22/H), 1990 *Mr Rawlinson* (det T. J.). It has since also appeared at Old Charlton Road, Hitchin (12/Z), 1999 *B. R. Sawford*; and in a garden at Bovingdon (00/B), 2007 *G. Salisbury*. In none of these was it deliberately planted.

Genus: *Orontium*

Orontium aquaticum L.
Golden Club
Introduced: casual.
First record: 1990.

This has been established, possibly originally planted, in a pond at Chorleywood Common (09/I) since at least 1990 *P. S. Mosley, P. J. Ellison*.

Genus: *Pistia*

Pistia stratiotes L.
Water-lettuce
Introduced: casual.
First (only) record: 2006.

This sub-tropical aquatic was found in a pond at Goldingtons, Hertford Heath (31/K) *T. J.*, well away from houses.

Lemnaceae (Duckweeds)

Genus: *Spirodela*

Spirodela polyrhiza (L.) Schleiden
Greater Duckweed
Native.
First record: 1839.
Tetrad occurrence: 11 (2%).
Decreasing (-35%).

Found in ponds and still backwaters of watercourses, usually in less eutrophic, or mildly acidic water. As such, it has always been relatively uncommon in the County, although it was at one time found in north Herts. as well as the south. Its strongholds now are the ponds on Berkhamsted Common, and similar places elsewhere in south Herts.
(16 tetrads: Dony, 1967; 20 tetrads: 1950-1986)

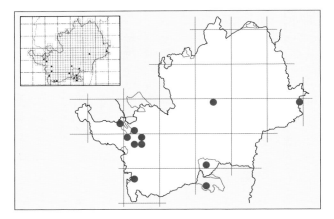

Map 710. *Spirodela polyrhiza.*

Genus: *Lemna*

Lemna gibba L.
Fat Duckweed
Native.
First record: 1839.
Tetrad occurrence: 11 (2%).
Probably decreasing (-15%).

Never very common, this occurs mainly in low-lying shallow ponds and ditches, where it often occurs alongside *L. minor*, and can be rather inconspicuous. It was found during the survey

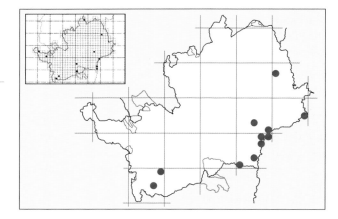

Map 711. *Lemna gibba.*

mostly in the south-east, around Hoddesdon.
(12 tetrads: Dony, 1967; 15 tetrads: 1950-1986)

Lemna minor L.
Common Duckweed
Native.
First record: 1824.
Tetrad occurrence: 320 (65%).
Increased (+14%).

Found in still, eutrophic water across the County. It seems this species is doing rather well. New gravel pits, as well as garden ponds, will all be aiding its spread. It has also benefited from the dereliction of field ponds, allowing it to increase in abundance and become more obvious.
(267 tetrads: Dony, 1967; 294 tetrads: 1950-1986)

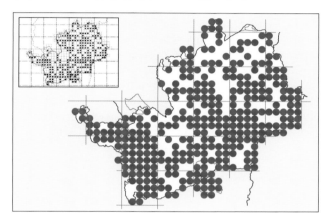

Map 712. *Lemna minor.*

Lemna trisulca L.
Ivy-leaved Duckweed
Native.
First record: 1838.
Tetrad occurrence: 69 (14%).
Probably decreased (-5%).

This is a species of clean water in ponds, and still backwaters of rivers. It is often rather inconspicuous, as it does not come to the surface like its relatives. It seems to have decreased quite markedly in the more arable areas, as ponds have become derelict; while in south Herts. it has benefited from new gravel pits. It also seems to occur more frequently now in rivers, possibly as their flows have decreased.
(69 tetrads: Dony, 1967; 86 tetrads: 1950-1986)

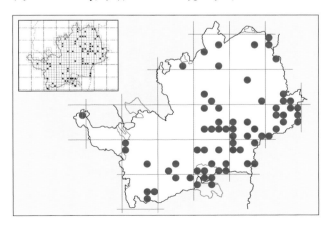

Map 713. *Lemna trisulca.*

Lemna minuta Kunth
Least Duckweed
Introduced: neophyte.
First record: 1981.
Tetrad occurrence: 38 (8%).
Increasing steadily.

This American plant was first found in the Grand Union Canal at Croxley (09/X,Y), 1981 *K. W. Page* (conf. A. C. Leslie) (Leslie and Walters, 1983), having first been found in Britain in 1977, but probably overlooked for some time before. By 1993, it had established itself in two main centres: around Hertford, and in the Colne valley, being recorded then from 23 tetrads. It has since steadily colonised many of the gravel pits in south Herts., as well as more eutrophic ponds elsewhere, where it can form a dense mat across the surface. It has, however, generally remained in these two areas, apparently being absent from the north of the County.

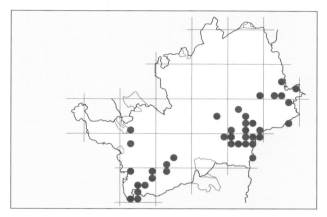

Map 714. *Lemna minuta.*

Commelinaceae (Spiderworts)

Genus: *Tradescantia*

Tradescantia fluminensis Vell.
Small-leaf Spiderwort
Introduced: casual.
First (only) record: 1994.

Plants of this were found on the site of former greenhouses at Bayfordbury (31/A) *A. M. Boucher/C. G. Hanson* (det. J. P. M. Brennan) (Hb. Hanson).

Tradescantia zebrina hort. ex Bosse
Wandering Jew
Introduced: casual.
First (only) record: 1972.

This familiar house-plant was found escaped on Blackbridge tip (11/X) *C. G. Hanson.*

Juncaceae (Rushes)

Genus: *Juncus*

Juncus squarrosus L.   Herts Rare
Heath Rush
Native.
First record: 1839.
Tetrad occurrence: 4 (<1%).

Always a rare plant in Hertfordshire, this occurred in the 19th
century on relict heathland sites at Leggatts near Northaw (20/R);
Milwards Park (TL20); Colney Heath (20/C); and Bushey Heath
(19/M). Dony (1967) says that Edward Salisbury last saw it at
Colney Heath about 1930, but his ms. index gives a record from
there about the time of World War II by A. W. Graveson; and an
unconfirmed record by E. G. Kellett from Brocket Park at about
the same time. It was then thought to have become extinct in the
County, until a colony was found at Patmore Heath (42/M), 1968
J. L. Fielding, where it remains, although diminished by drought.
In 1991, a very small colony was found in a damp ride in Northaw
Great Wood (20/S) *T. J.* (Hb. HTN), not that far from the Leggatts
site. It was also found in small quantity in a newly re-opened
damp ride in the wood (20/X), 1997 *K. Seaman*. Finally, a single
clump was found at Hadley Green (29/N) (VC21 [Herts., 1904-
1965]), 2003 *G. Salisbury/T. J./S. M. Hedley* (Hb. HTN). This
was a completely new site for the plant, and the only remaining
locality in Greater London (pers. comm.: R. M. Burton).

Juncus tenuis Willd.
Slender Rush
Introduced: neophyte.
First record: 1952.
Tetrad occurrence: 15 (3%).
Increased (+63%).

From its initial introduction to Nuthampstead Airfield (43/C),
1952 *J. G. Dony*, where it had probably been brought during
World War II by the American bomber squadron based there,
it quite rapidly began to turn up across the County in bare,
trodden paths, *etc.*, often on acidic soils. However, although it has
consolidated its position, its rapid expansion did not continue,
and it is only found in any quantity on the towpath of the Grand
Union Canal.
(9 tetrads: Dony, 1967; 12 tetrads: 1950-1986)

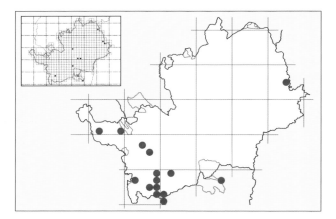

Map 715. *Juncus tenuis.*

Juncus compressus Jacq.   UK Near Threatened
Round-fruited Rush
Native?
First record: 1915.

Although Dony (1967) says this was first seen at Startop's End
Reservoir (91/B, G), date uncertain, his ms. index also gives
a record from Wilstone Reservoir (91/B), 1955 *R. I. Sworder*.
It also contains a record from a pond in a marshy pasture at
Ettridge Farm (30/I), 1915 *H. F. Hayllar*, both of which he
apparently overlooked. Subsequent records give a picture of its
odd occurrence. Dony mentions that he found it by the roadside
at Shaftenhoe End (43/B), 1955, a most extraordinary habitat,
on Chalk. More recently, it was found by the Icknield Way near
the R. Hiz at Ickleford (13/V), 1982 *M. Yeo* (Hb. HTN), but did
not persist; and was also found in the marshy meadow at Rye
Meads (31/V), 1979 *K. Roberts* (det. at Kew). The last of these
sites is at least a reasonably natural habitat. It has remained
at Tring Reservoirs, where it was fairly abundant at Startop's
End Reservoir (91/B), 2009 *T. J./G. Salisbury*. Recently,
it occurred just in Bucks., near Long Marston (81/S), 2008
G. Salisbury/P. Shipway, in a marshy patch by arable; and
in 2009 R. Maycock found it nearby on the canal towpath at
Puttenham (81/W), just in Herts. It appears, therefore, to be a
colonist of damp, muddy places, and may depend on being moved
around by wildfowl.

Juncus foliosus Desf.   Herts Rare
Leafy Rush
Native.
First record: 2001.

The only site known so far for this plant, which looks superficially
similar to *J. bufonius*, was from a permanently marshy patch in
an entrance to the sedge meadow at Purwell Ninesprings Nature
Reserve (22/E), 2001 *T. J.* (Hb. HTN), a locality which has
unfortunately become very overgrown. It is very rare regionally,
but probably under-recorded.

Juncus bufonius L.
Toad Rush
Native.
First record: 1838.
Tetrad occurrence: 259 (53%).
Increasing (+24%).

A frequent plant of wet, muddy ground in tracks, woodland rides
and edges of fields. It has evidently increased quite substantially

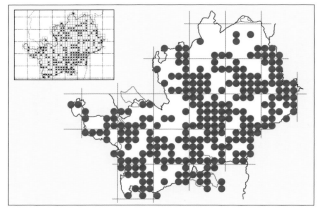

Map 716. *Juncus bufonius.*

throughout its range. It seems to tolerate relatively eutrophic conditions, and therefore takes advantage of muddy tracks in arable land.

(198 tetrads: Dony, 1967; 231 tetrads: 1950-1986)

Juncus subnodulosus Schrank

Blunt-flowered Rush

Native.

First record: 1843.

Tetrad occurrence: 20 (4%).

Scarce, but increased (+46%).

A plant of wet flushes and swamps with a calcareous water supply in fen meadows, and the margins of reed beds. This has never been a common plant in the County, limited by its habitat preference, although it can colonise new sites where the water supply is from chalk springs, such as the swamp at Hollycross Lake, Amwell Quarry (31/R), which developed on a back-filled pit. It remains in most of the sites known to Dony, and has been found in a few more.

(13 tetrads: Dony, 1967; 20 tetrads: 1950-1986)

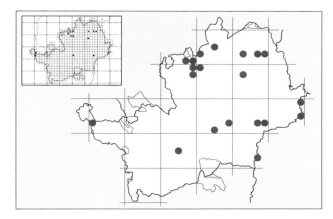

Map 717. *Juncus subnodulosus.*

Juncus articulatus L.

Jointed Rush

Native.

First record: 1838.

Tetrad occurrence: 200 (41%).

Increasing? (+16%).

A frequent plant of cattle-grazed marshy pasture, pond margins, ditches and swamps on mostly neutral soils. The apparent increase in this plant may be due to past under-recording,

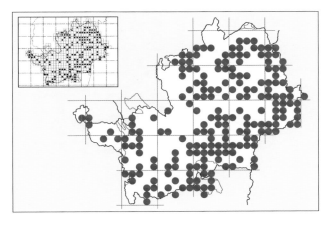

Map 718. *Juncus articulatus.*

although it is capable of colonising new localities. It is, nevertheless, most often found in long-established habitat.

(164 tetrads: Dony, 1967; 200 tetrads: 1950-1986)

Juncus × *surrejanus* Druce ex Stace and Lambinon
(*J. articulatus* × *J. acutiflorus*)

Native.

First record: 1961.

Since the two records by P. M. Benoit given in Dony (1967), this has been positively identified only at Moor Hall Meadow (32/I), 1975 *T. J.* (Hb. HTN); Oughton Head Common (13/Q), 1983 *T. J.* (det. A. C. Leslie); and Potwells (20/B), 2006 *J. Williamson/J. Moss* (det. T. J.) (Hb. HTN). It is almost certainly being overlooked elsewhere.

Juncus acutiflorus Ehrh. ex Hoffm.

Sharp-flowered Rush

Native.

First record: 1820.

Tetrad occurrence: 49 (10%).

Increased? (+45%).

A rather local plant of marshes, wet woodland rides, *etc.*, mostly on moderately acidic soils over clay or gravel, although sometimes present in swamps elsewhere. It can be difficult to identify from *J. articulatus* in tall vegetation, and also from hybrids, which have recently been suggested to be commoner than the species. The apparent increase may in part be due to better recording, although it was not found in some areas from which records were received in the 1970s.

(32 tetrads: Dony, 1967; 55 tetrads: 1950-1986)

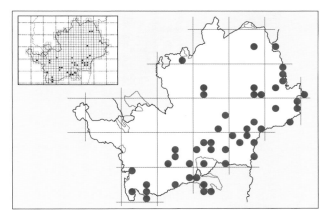

Map 719. *Juncus acutiflorus.*

Juncus bulbosus L.

Bulbous Rush

Native.

First record: 1839.

Tetrad occurrence: 17 (4%).

Increased? (+84%).

A plant of wet places on heaths, heathy woodland rides, and by or in boggy ponds, perhaps increasing, although possibly under-recorded in the past. Owing to its varied growth forms, it tends to be overlooked, but is not common. It occurs mostly on the acidic London Clay in south Herts.

(9 tetrads: Dony, 1967; 13 tetrads: 1950-1986)

Plants previously identified as '*Juncus kochii*' (Dony, 1967) are now no longer considered to be a separable taxon by Stace (1997).

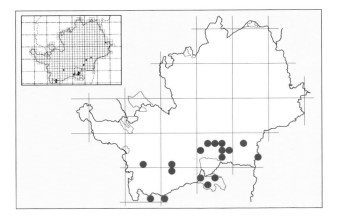

Map 720. *Juncus bulbosus.*

Juncus inflexus L.
Hard Rush
Native.
First record: 1838.
Tetrad occurrence: 340 (69%).
Stable or slightly increased (+2%).

A common plant where water stands at least part of the year on moderately calcareous to neutral soils, most frequent on the clays in east and south Hertfordshire, becoming scarce on the Chalk, and on the free-draining Clay-with-Flints in west Herts. It occurs in both long-established, semi-natural wetlands, as well as in recently created habitats.
(316 tetrads: Dony, 1967; 333 tetrads: 1950-1986)

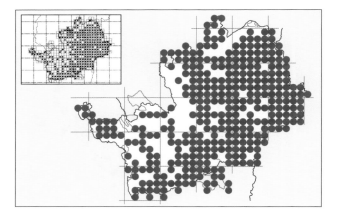

Map 721. *Juncus inflexus.*

Juncus × diffusus Hoppe (*J. inflexus × J. effusus*)
Native.
First record: 1843.

Early botanists regarded this as a separate species, and it is listed as such in Pryor (1887). Dony (1967) lists earlier specimens collected by Coleman and others, but says he found no satisfactory material in the County. Plants with intermediate characters were found with the parents at Vicar's Grove Gravel Pit (12/X), 1982 *T. J.* (Hb. HTN). During the survey, the hybrid was also found at a ride in Newsetts Wood (90/P), 1992 *T. J.* (Hb. HTN); ride in Row Wood (21/Y), 1993 *T. J.*; derelict field near Woodside (20/N), 1993 *T. J.*; Rush Green Airfield (22/C), 1994 *K. Hall* (det. T. J.) (Hb. HTN); by Aldenham Reservoir (19/S), 2001 *T. J.* (Hb. HTN); in Berrygrove Wood (19/J), 2001 *T. J.* (Hb. HTN); and at Lemsford Springs (21/G), 2005 *T. J.*

Juncus effusus L.
Soft Rush
Native.
First record: *c.*1820.
Tetrad occurrence: 377 (77%).
Increased (+8%).

Widespread in damp ground of all kinds on neutral to moderately acidic soils, only becoming scarce or absent on the more calcareous clays, and on the Chalk. The usual form is easily identified, but var. *subglomeratus* DC., with its compact flower heads, is sometimes mistaken for *J. conglomeratus* or the hybrid. (330 tetrads: Dony, 1967; 343 tetrads: 1950-1986)

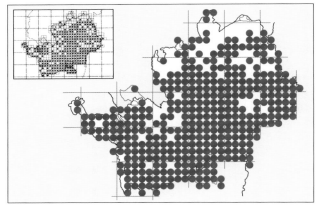

Map 722. *Juncus effusus.*

Juncus × kern-reichgeltii Jansen and Wacht. ex Reichg.
(*J. effusus × J. conglomeratus*)
Native.
First record: 2001.

This was first detected with the parents in a secondary grass field adjoining Watery Grove, Knebworth (22/G), 2001 *T. J.* (Hb. HTN). It was subsequently also found with the parents at Cowheath Wood (30/I), 2004 *T. J.* It may well be more frequent, and could have been misidentified as *J. conglomeratus*.

Juncus conglomeratus L.
Clustered Rush
Native.
First record: *c.*1820.
Tetrad occurrence: 179 (37%).
Decreased? (-14%).

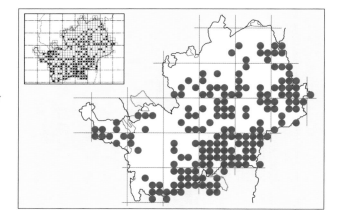

Map 723. *Juncus conglomeratus.*

This is mainly a plant of semi-natural habitats on acidic soils, especially open woodland rides, commons and old damp pastures. It has probably been over-recorded for forms of *J. effusus* or for its hybrid with that species, especially in the past, which may account for its apparent decrease, although old habitat is steadily disappearing. It occurs widely on the acidic clays in south Herts., as well as on the Reading gravels, and less calcareous areas of Boulder Clay.

(197 tetrads: Dony, 1967; 222 tetrads: 1950-1986)

Genus: *Luzula*

Luzula forsteri (Smith) DC.
Southern Wood-rush
Native.
First record: 1838.
Tetrad occurrence: 9 (2%).
Stable or increasing? (+100%).

This has always been scarce in Herts. on the edge of the plant's range in Britain, and remains so, although it is locally frequent in the south-west of the County, and has been recorded in more tetrads than it had been previously. It occurs especially on dry, bare, calcareous gravelly soils on wood margins, by tracks and clearings, often beneath beech trees. Dony (1967) gave four recent sites for it, and he also found it at Oxhey Woods (19/B), 1979. During the recent survey records were received from Limeshill Wood (09/J), 1997, 1998 *G. Salisbury/T. J.*; Derry's Wood and Westfield Grove (30/C), 1998 *S. Davey* (a new site for it); Ladywalk Wood (09/G), 1991 *P. J. Ellison*, 2002 *G. S.*; Shire Lane by Phillipshill Wood (09/C), 1999 *G. S.*; Shire Lane at Chorleywood (09/C), 1999 *G. S.*; Bishop's Wood (09/Q), 1991, 1992 *P. J. E.* and (09/R), 2002 *G. S.*; Nanscot Wood, Oxhey Woods (19/A), 2003 *G. S.*; Roundhill Wood (90/J), 2003 *T. J.* After several attempts to re-find it at Easneye Wood (31/W), where Dony saw it, and where it was recorded by Coleman as plentiful, it was found in small quantity at the north end in 2009 *T. J.* (Hb. HTN).

(4 tetrads: Dony, 1967; 6 tetrads: 1950-1986)

Luzula × borreri Bromf. ex Bab. (*L. forsteri × L. pilosa*)
Native.
First (only) record: 2003.

This was found at Nanscot Wood, Oxhey Woods (19/A), 2003 *G. Salisbury* (det. G. Kay) (Hb. HTN), with the parents, new to the County.

Luzula pilosa (L.) Willd.
Hairy Wood-rush
Native.
First record: *c.*1820.
Tetrad occurrence: 115 (23%).
Stable or slightly decreased (-5%).

A widespread plant of shady banks in ancient semi-natural woodland, and old wooded hedgerows throughout much of the County, mainly on less calcareous soils, although it was not found in a few sites on the Boulder Clay where it was formerly known.
(115 tetrads: Dony, 1967; 129 tetrads: 1950-1986)

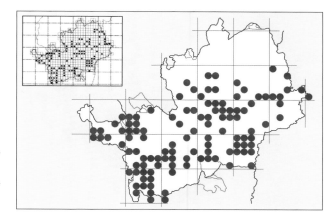

Map 724. *Luzula pilosa.*

Luzula sylvatica (Hudson) Gaudin
Great Wood-rush
Native.
First record: 1814.
Tetrad occurrence: 14 (3%).
Probably stable (-3%).

This is a very localised plant of damp, shady banks on gravelly soils in ancient woodland. As such, it may have suffered from drought, as it seems to have decreased in some areas, notably around Knebworth and Stevenage, and in outlying sites in the Broxbourne Woods complex. It was, however, found on the edge of Sun's Wood at Bromley (42/A), 2003 *T. J.*, a new site for the species.

(14 tetrads: Dony, 1967; 22 tetrads: 1950-1986)

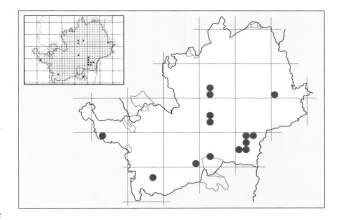

Map 725. *Luzula sylvatica.*

Luzula campestris (L.) DC.
Field Wood-rush
Native.
First record: 1838.
Tetrad occurrence: 306 (62%).
Stable or increased? (+3%).

Widespread and often abundant in old grassland, in lawns, churchyards, old pastures, commons and open woodland rides throughout much of the County, avoiding only the most calcareous and dampest soils. Although old pastures have declined, and it has become less abundant in many areas, it does seem to have maintained its position or even increased elsewhere, possibly through colonising amenity grasslands.
(283 tetrads: Dony, 1967; 314 tetrads: 1950-1986)

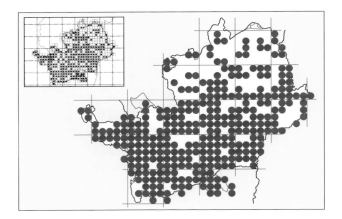

Map 726. *Luzula campestris.*

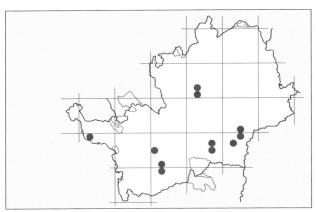

Map 727a. *Luzula multiflora* ssp. *congesta.*

Luzula multiflora (Ehrh.) Lej.
Heath Wood-rush
Native.
First record: 1737.
Tetrad occurrence: 35 (7%).
Decreasing (-28%).

A local plant of rough, heathy grasslands, old commons, woodland clearings and rides on acidic soils. This seems to have decreased rather rapidly since the 1980s, as it was found to be under-recorded in the 1967 survey, and was found in many new sites by the Hertfordshire and Middlesex Wildlife Trust's Woodland Survey team in 1978. It has not been re-found in quite a few of these sites, and even where it does still occur, it is apparently succumbing to scrub growth, loss of woodland rides, or eutrophication. Some earlier records may be misidentifications of tall specimens of *L. campestris*, but this would not account for all the change in status.
(46 tetrads: Dony, 1967; 70 tetrads: 1950-1986)

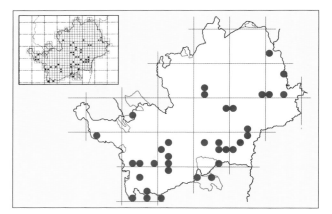

Map 727. *Luzula multiflora.*

The main map shows the aggregate species. However, it consists of two distinct subspecies, not always named by recorders in the field. The plant of ancient woodland rides, *etc.* is usually ssp. *multiflora*. In more heathy areas, especially on former wood-pastures or commons in south Herts., ssp. *congesta* (Thuill.) Arcang. is met with, regarded by some as a separate species (Map 727a). This was first recorded as a separate taxon by J. E. Little at Mardley Heath (21/P), 1913 (ms. diary, North Herts. Museums).

Cyperaceae (Sedges and allies)

The classification and nomenclature used for this family follows the revised taxonomy published in Jermy *et al.* (2007).

Genus: *Eriophorum*

Eriophorum angustifolium Honck.   Herts Rare
Common Cottongrass
Native.
First record: c.1730.
Extinct?

This has twice been lamented as extinct in Hertfordshire (Dony, 1967; James and Goldsmith, 1993), but may well now be so. At least, it is extremely rare. In the 19th century, it was a local plant of semi-natural raised mires supported by ground water, especially in wet valley pastures around Hertford, and also in similar places elsewhere. It also occurred rarely in similar habitats around spring sources in upland pastures on the Boulder Clay, both in north-east Herts., and in the south. The catastrophic decline of ground water tables throughout the County during the early 20th century resulted in its loss from most of these sites. It remained in a few upland spring-fed mires until more recently. James and Goldsmith listed recorded sites in detail. The last known sites were the spring-fed mire in Moor Hall Meadow SSSI (32/I), 1975 *T. J.*; and the mire adjoining a pond at Patmore Heath (42/M), 1979 (*comm.*: Herts. and Middx. Trust Meadow Survey team); until a single plant was re-discovered at Moor Hall Meadow in 1998 *T. J./G. P. Smith*, although, as this site was badly damaged in 2009, its survival is now in doubt. It has also been planted in wetland plots at Ickleford (13/W), but is hardly likely to survive.

Eriophorum latifolium Hoppe   Herts Extinct
Broad-leaved Cottongrass
Native.
First (only) record: 1849.

This plant of fen peat was only ever known from a lost spring-fed 'moor' at Barkway, where it was found by W. H. Coleman in 1849. The exact location of the site is unknown, although 'Bogmoor Road' (33/Y) may mark its former existence.

Scirpus sylvaticus L.   Herts Rare
Wood Club-rush
Native.
First record: 1805.
Tetrad occurrence: 2 (<1%).
Rare and decreasing (-50%).

This is only known now from a very few patches by the Spital Brook at Hoddesdon Park Wood and downstream to Barclay Park, Hoddesdon (30/P, U), in all of which it appears to be decreasing, possibly partly through excessive shading, but also from loss of the swampy areas by the stream where it used to occur. It has not been traced in the Bayford area, along the Wormleybury Brook, or in the upper reaches of the Spital Brook in Broxbourne Woods, where Dony knew it. It was also formerly known at Totteridge (Pryor, 1887).

Genus *Bolboschoenus*

Bolboschoenus maritimus (L.) Palla
Sea Club-rush
Introduced [native in the U.K.].
First record: 1958.

This is apparently brought in accidentally by waterfowl to various ponds, and can persist for a while. After the first records (Dony, 1967), it has appeared at Smallford Gravel Pits (10/Y), 1984 *T. J.* (Hb. HTN); Hollycross Lake, Amwell Quarry (31/R), 1986 *G. J. White*; and at a recently re-excavated pond at Goose Green (30/P), 1989 *A. M. Boucher*.

Genus: *Schoenoplectus*

Schoenoplectus lacustris (L.) Palla
Common Club-rush
Native.
First record: 1838.
Tetrad occurrence: 60 (12%).
Increased (+82%).

Frequent in silty rivers and gravel pits, occasionally in smaller ponds. It has apparently increased substantially, perhaps as a result of reduced river maintenance. It certainly also now seems to flower more frequently than in the past, possibly owing to reduced river levels, or reduced levels of cutting.
(31 tetrads: Dony, 1967; 43 tetrads: 1950-1986)

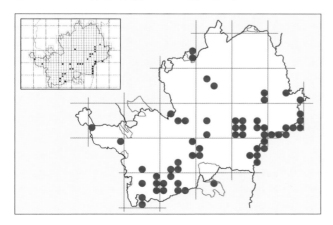

Map 728. *Schoenoplectus lacustris.*

Schoenoplectus tabernaemontani (Gmelin) Palla
Grey Club-rush
Introduced? [native in the U.K.].
First record: 1988.

At one time mostly a maritime plant, this has spread inland over recent decades (Preston *et al.*, 2002), and was first found in Hertfordshire in marshy depressions on the back-filled Moor Mill Gravel Pit (10/L), 1988 *T. J.* (Hb. HTN), where it remained in 1991. It was also introduced to a new pond at Tewin Orchard (21/S), 1993 *T. J.*, and has been found planted by the R. Stort canal (41/F), 2006 *T. J.*

Genus: *Eleocharis*

Eleocharis palustris (L.) Roemer and Schultes
Common Spike-rush
Native.
First record: 1838.
Tetrad occurrence: 77 (16%).
Decreasing (-19%).

Characteristic of the draw-down areas around ponds and lakes, and also in grazed marshy pasture, particularly by ditches or in seasonally wet hollows. While the distribution of this remains much as found by Dony (1967), the species is showing strong signs of decline, especially around ponds, as these have become eutrophic or shaded. It is, however, able to colonise new sites, presumably moved around by waterfowl.
(90 tetrads: Dony, 1967; 106 tetrads: 1950-1986)

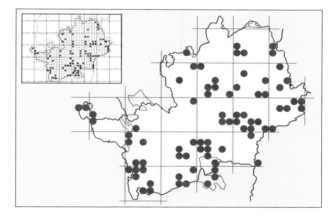

Map 729. *Eleocharis palustris.*

The common subspecies appears to be ssp. *vulgaris* Walters. Ssp *palustris* was recorded at Sawbridgeworth Marsh (41/X) in Dony (1967); but no attempt has been made to find it otherwise.

Eleocharis multicaulis (Smith) Desv.   Herts Extinct
Many-stalked Spike-rush
Native.
First record: 1839.

This was only ever known from peat bogs near Bell Bar (TL20), where it was last seen in 1843 (Dony, ms. index).

Eleocharis acicularis (L.) Roemer and Schultes   Herts Extinct?
Needle Spike-rush
Native.
First record: 1843.

A plant of exposed mud by lakes. Dony (1967) managed to

find this at several sites: Tring Reservoirs (91/B), Hilfield Park Reservoir (TQ19), Aldenham Reservoir (19/S), and by the canal at Hunton Bridge (00/Q). There were also earlier records from Tring and Totteridge. Repeated attempts to find it at the reservoirs have failed, since it was last seen at Aldenham Reservoir in 1975 *M. E. Kennedy.*

Eleocharis quinqueflora (Hartmann) Schwarz   Herts Rare
Few-flowered Spike-rush
Native.
First record: 1805.
Stable?

This rare plant of base-rich flushes was known to 19th century botanists from Colney Heath (20/C), bogs near Kentish Lane (TL20), Cheshunt Common (30/B), and at an untraced locality: 'Chalk Lodge'. More recently, it was found by A. W. Graveson at Foulwells (30/I); and by J. G. Dony at Blagrove Common, Sandon (33/G) (Dony, 1967). It remained at these last two sites into the present survey, having been last recorded at Blagrove Common in 1989 *T. J.*; and at Foulwells in 1999 *T. J./G. Salisbury.*

Genus: *Isolepis*

This genus has now been expanded to include the species previously known as *Eleogiton fluitans.*

Isolepis setacea (L.) R. Br.
Bristle Club-rush
Native.
First record: 1838.
Tetrad occurrence: 19 (4%).
Increased or possibly stable (+39%).

An inconspicuous, and therefore often under-recorded plant of bare, damp and slightly muddy places in old grassland and damp woodland rides. The distribution map from the recent survey shows that it was re-found in most of the places where it was found in the 1960s (Dony, 1967), and also in some new sites. It was also found in a few others between the two surveys. As it can lie dormant for a long while, awaiting the return of satisfactory conditions, it often goes unnoticed.
(13 tetrads: Dony, 1967; 19 tetrads: 1950-1986)

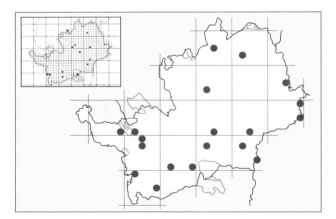

Map 730. *Isolepis setacea.*

Isolepis fluitans (L.) R. Br.   Herts Rare
Floating Club-rush
Native.
First record: 1843.

A rare plant of acidic ponds on heathy ground, this was only known in the 19th century from Colney Heath (20/C), White Stubbs Lane (TL30), Brickendon Green (30/I), Northaw (20/W) and Woodside (20/N) (Pryor, 1887). Dony (1967) found it at Arkley (= Rowley Green) (29/D), and at a pond at Cheshunt. The latter he appears to have quoted in error as having been at Cheshunt Marsh (30/Q), because his ms. index gives the record as from a pond at Cheshunt Common (30/B), a much more likely locality, being enclosed land from former wood-pasture. It was also found at a pond at Epping Green (20/Y) 1962 *I. Hodson* (det. F. H. Perring) (*comm.*: B.R.C.: CEH Monks Wood), a record unknown to Dony. More recently, it has been found at a pond by White Stubbs Lane near Kingfisher Nurseries, Bayford (30/D), 1993, 1994 *A. M. Boucher* (Hb. HTN); and also again at the pond on Rowley Green (29/D) (VC20 [Greater London]), 1988 *M. J. Smith* (Hb. HTN), still there 2008 *T. J.* (Hb. HTN). Both these sites were known to earlier botanists. Its propagules appear able to remain dormant in silt for long periods, and so it may yet remain at several other localities in south-east Herts.

Genus: *Cyperus*

Cyperus longus L.   [UK Near Threatened]
Galingale
Introduced [native in the U.K.].
First record: 1959?
Tetrad occurrence: 15 (3%).
Increasing (+675%).

Dony (1967) gave two records of colonies of garden origin. After 1970, it was reported from the main pond at Patmore Heath (42/M), 1986 *J. L. Fielding*, where it had apparently been present 'many years', and where it remains. It was also found at Cock Lane tip (30/T), 1982 *C. G. Hanson*, but did not persist. Since 1990, it has increasingly been reported from ponds, where it is usually either a throw-out or deliberately planted.

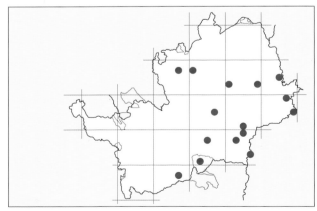

Map 731. *Cyperus longus.*

Cyperus eragrostis Lam.
Pale Galingale
Introduced: casual.
First record: 1914.

First recorded from Batchworth Heath, not 'Batchworth Lake'

(Dony, 1967), this garden escape and grain alien occurs rarely. It was found subsequently at Waterford tip (31/C), 1984 *A. L. Grenfell/C. G. Hanson*; and during the recent survey also turned up at Hadham Towers tip (41/I), 1993 *S. Watson* (Hb. HTN). It is a weed in Gordon Hanson's garden at Ware (31/S), but scarcely counts as 'wild' here.

Blysmus compressus (L.) Panzer ex Link   Herts Rare
Flat Sedge
Native.
First record: *c.*1835.
Very rare and decreased (-50%).

A plant of wet marshy pasture in river valleys. Always very rare, both Pryor (1887) and Dony (1967) considered the first record to have been made by E. de Crespigny from Croxley (= Rickmansworth) Common Moor, 1877. However, there is an annotation by J. D. Morell in a copy of Turner and Dillwyn's '*Botanist's Guide*' in Hitchin Museum giving an undated record from Oughton Head Common (13/Q), presumed to be about 1835. Dony found it at Sarratt Bottom (09/J) and it was found by P. J. Ellison at Boxmoor (Dony, 1967). It was re-found during the recent survey at Fishery Moor, Boxmoor (00/N), 1999 *G. Salisbury* (Hb. HTN), although more recent attempts to re-find it have failed.

Genus: *Schoenus*

Schoenus nigricans L.   Herts Extinct
Black Bog-rush
Native.
Only record: 1843.
This was only ever known from (presumably) a peaty flush at the same lost 'Barkway Moor' (Webb and Coleman, 1849) where *Eriophorum latifolium* was recorded, whose exact location is now unknown.

Genus: *Carex*

Carex paniculata L.
Greater Tussock-sedge
Native.
First record: 1838.
Tetrad occurrence: 44 (9%).
Possibly increasing (+30%).

This is a characteristic sedge of flushed, calcareous mire, often associated with spring sources or by rivers and streams where ground water is upwelling. As such, some of its colonies are small and probably previously overlooked. However, there does seem to have been a genuine increase of the species in some areas, notably in the upper Lea Valley, which is hard to explain.
(32 tetrads: Dony, 1967; 39 tetrads: 1950-1986)

Carex × *boenninghausiana* Weihe (*C. paniculata* × *C. remota*)
Native.
First record: 1843.

There have been no further records of this rare hybrid from Herts. since its discovery at Easneye (31/W) in 1959 (Dony, 1967).

Carex appropinquata Schum.   UK Vulnerable
Fibrous Tussock-sedge   Herts Extinct
Native.
First record: 1885.

There have been no records of this rare native plant of rich fen since it was found in 'meadows near Harefield in Herts.' (Pryor, 1887). These were probably on the site of one or other of the Colne Valley gravel pits. Repeated attempts to re-find the species by these have failed.

Carex diandra Schrank   UK Near Threatened
Lesser Tussock-sedge   Herts Extinct
Native.
First record: 1843.

A plant of peaty habitats, this was only ever properly recorded from two ponds near Broxbourne Woods (TL30), but was not seen again after Coleman found it. A record from Oughton Head Common *c.*1880 by T. B. Blow, published by him in the *Hitchin Gazette*, is unconfirmed.

Carex otrubae Podp.
False Fox-sedge
Native.
First record: *c.*1810.
Tetrad occurrence: 199 (41%).
Probably increased (+19%).

A plant of more or less calcareous clay soils, frequent in damp woodland rides and ditches on the Boulder Clay, less acidic places on the London Clay, and to a lesser extent on alluvial soils in river valleys. It appears to have increased overall, especially on back-

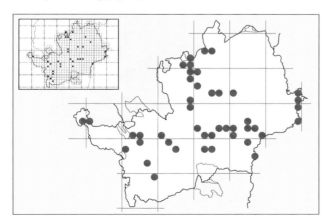

Map 732. *Carex paniculata.*

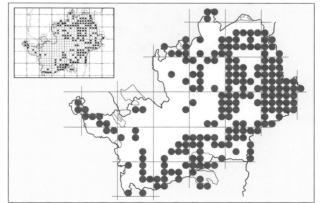

Map 733. *Carex otrubae.*

filled gravel pits in central Hertfordshire. In the east, its apparent increase may be partly down to previous poor recording, although there are also some signs it has disappeared from heavily arable landscapes. Old records of 'Carex vulpina' appear to refer to this species, as the true Fox Sedge has never been confirmed for the County.
(159 tetrads: Dony, 1967; 184 tetrads: 1950-1986)

Carex × *pseudoaxillaris* K. Richt. (*C. otrubae* × *C. remota*)
Native.
First record: 1838.

Originally thought to be a separate species: *Carex axillaris*, this was recorded from a number of localities in the 19th century (Pryor, 1887), and Dony (1967) also lists five recent records. It was subsequently found at Burleigh Meadow (22/G), 1967 *J. G. and C. M. Dony* (Hb. HTN); in 'sand pits by Watford Road', Hatfield (20/D), 1972 *A. D. Marshall* (Hb. HTN); and at Broad Colney Gravel Pits (10/R), 1976 *J. G. and C. M. Dony* (Hb. HTN). During the recent survey it was found by Beanfield Road, High Wych (41/S), 1989 *S. Watson* (Hb. HTN); at the entrance to Scales Park (43/B), 1992 *S. Watson* (det. T. J.) (Hb. HTN); by a pond at High Wych (41/T), 1994 *S. W.* (Hb. HTN); and at Sleapshyde Gravel Pits (20/D), 1988 *A. D. Marshall* (Hb. HTN), presumably the same site at which he had found it in 1972. It is probably overlooked elsewhere.

Carex spicata Hudson
Spiked Sedge
Native.
First record: (1838, for the aggregate) 1921.
Tetrad occurrence: 178 (36%).
Apparently increasing (+25%).

A plant of rough grassland on more or less calcareous soils, this appears to have increased somewhat across the County, possibly as a result of an increase in rough ground on road verges and elsewhere. Owing to past confusion with *Carex muricata*, it is not possible to judge its 19th century occurrence with any certainty.
(135 tetrads: Dony, 1967; 157 tetrads: 1950-1986)

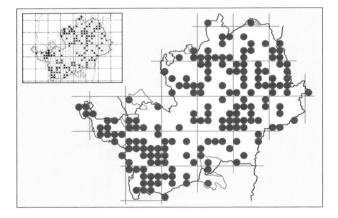
Map 734. *Carex spicata.*

Carex muricata L.
Prickly Sedge
Native.
First record: 1924 (for the segregate).
Tetrad occurrence: 27 (6%).
Increased? (or possibly stable) (+112%).

This sedge was formerly confused with *Carex spicata*, with the result that early records are unreliable. Dony (1967) only gave 12 records. He may well have under-recorded it, although it is not common, and seems to be especially found on free-draining, more or less acidic soils over sand or gravel, usually in long-standing old grassland. The Hertfordshire plant is ssp. *pairae* (F. W. Schultz) Čelak.
(12 tetrads: Dony, 1967; 22 tetrads: 1950-1986)

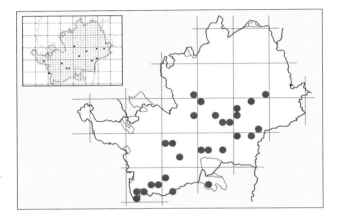
Map 735. *Carex muricata.*

Carex divulsa Stokes
Grey Sedge
Native.
First record: *c.*1810.
Tetrad occurrence: 194 (40%).
Increasing? (+45%).

Grey Sedge is a plant of somewhat shaded rough grassland by roads, on wood banks and along hedgerows, on dry, moderately calcareous or neutral loam soil. It is widespread across most of central, eastern and western Hertfordshire, becoming scarcer on the more open Chalk, and on the acidic clays in the south-east. Although there are areas where it appears to have declined since the 1960s, such as around Sandon, it was also found to be more consistently spread across the Clay-with-Flints, and in eastern

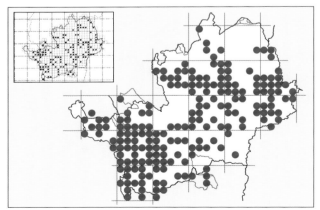
Map 736. *Carex divulsa.*

Hertfordshire than Dony found. Whether this is down to more effective recording, or some past errors is uncertain. (127 tetrads: Dony, 1967; 159 tetrads: 1950-1986)

The main subspecies in the County is ssp. *divulsa*. Ssp. *leersii* (Kneuck.) W. Koch has been identified on a number of occasions, the first record being from a specimen collected at Easneye (31/R), 1871 *J. F. Duthie* (det. R. W. David) (Hb. BM). Recently it has been found by the A10 near Braughing (32/X), 1986 *T. J.* (Hb. HTN); at Bovingdon (00/B), 1999 *R. Keen* (det. T. J.) (Hb. HTN); near Croxley Hall Wood (09/S), 2006 *T. J.* (Hb. HTN); and at Bull's Wood, Tring Park (91/F), 2007 *T. J.* Most of these are not on sites that could be called chalky, contrary to the habitat specified in the literature.

Carex disticha Hudson
Brown Sedge
Native.
First record: 1838.
Tetrad occurrence: 43 (9%).
Increased? or now possibly declining (+21%).

Forming sometimes quite extensive patches in wet pasture, fen swamp or wet meadows, this is a characteristic plant of old, long-established wetlands with more or less calcareous water supply. As such, it is local in the County, but, despite its apparent increase since the 1960s survey, the records suggest it was previously under-recorded in some areas, and may now be showing signs of decline, as high quality wetlands are lost. (34 tetrads: Dony 1967; 57 tetrads: 1950-1986)

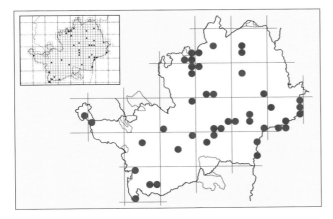

Map 737. *Carex disticha.*

Carex remota L.
Remote Sedge
Native.
First record: 1838.
Tetrad occurrence: 217 (44%).
Increased (+52%).

A plant of wet woodland rides, shaded ditch or pond banks, and hedgerows on wet clays, especially more acidic substrates. It seems to have genuinely increased since the 1960s, possibly as a result of the increase in shaded habitats, although there may be an element of past under-recording. (135 tetrads: Dony, 1967; 164 tetrads: 1950-1986)

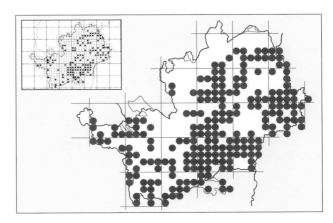

Map 738. *Carex remota.*

Carex leporina L.
Oval Sedge
Native.
First record: 1838.
Tetrad occurrence: 72 (15%).
Slightly increased, or stable? (+16%).

A plant of somewhat damp, heathy grassland in old pastures, on commons, and sometimes in open woodland rides, mostly in central, south and west Hertfordshire. It probably declined over the last 100 years, as unimproved grassland has been lost, although recent tetrad records show a slight increase, which is not readily explicable. (59 tetrads: Dony, 1967; 70 tetrads: 1950-1986)

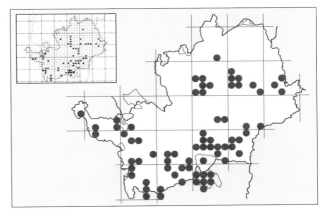

Map 739. *Carex leporina.*

Carex echinata Murray   Herts Rare
Star Sedge
Native
First record: 1838.
Tetrad occurrence: 3 (<1%).
Decreased? (-33%).

This has never been a common species in the County. It is found in more or less acidic, peaty places on permanently wet substrates, often associated with spring flushes. In the 19th century, it was known from about 15 localities, mostly in the south and west, but Dony (1967) only had recent records from four localities: near Moor Park (TQ09); Patmore Heath (42/M); Foulwells (30/I); and Rowley Green (= Arkley Manorial Lands) (29/D). It survived by the pond at Rowley Green, where it was last recorded in 1997 *T. J.* (Hb. HTN); and at Patmore Heath (42/M), where it was still found near the large pond in 1994 *S. Watson*, and in 2008 *S. W./T. J.* It was also found in a wet, heathy area in the valley bottom at Lockwell Wood (09/Q), 2002 *G. Salisbury*, which may be the heathy area at Batchworth Heath/Moor Park from which previous workers recorded it. It could still reappear at other sites, like Milwards Park, although some, such as Foulwells, have suffered from poor management.

Carex dioica L.   Herts Extinct
Dioecious Sedge
Native.
First record: 1839.

A plant of calcareous flushes, this was only ever known from Oughton Head Common and Walsworth Common at Hitchin, and was last seen at the former in 1878 by H. Groves (Dony, 1967).

[*Carex canescens* L.
White Sedge

There is a mention of this in Pryor (1887), based on a record by de Crespigny, but this was almost certainly an error.]

Carex hirta L.
Hairy Sedge
Native.
First record: 1838.
Tetrad occurrence: 275 (56%).
Stable (+3%).

Hairy Sedge is a common plant of damp, neutral or somewhat acidic clay soils, often found in ruderal, or waste places. It can appear in unlikely habitats, such as through tarmac or cracks in pavements, where it often does not flower. It has remained almost unchanged in occurrence since the 1960s (Dony, 1967), but has been found in some extra tetrads, probably through better recording.
(253 tetrads: Dony, 1967; 273 tetrads: 1950-1986)

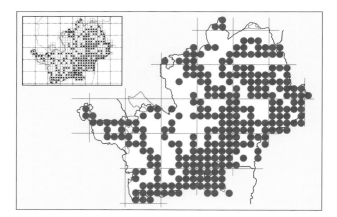

Map 740. *Carex hirta.*

Carex acutiformis Ehrh.
Lesser Pond-sedge
Native.
First record: 1838.
Tetrad occurrence: 184 (38%).
Increased (+70%).

Despite its name, this is one of the main sedges along river banks, where it tends to form stands landward of its cousin, *C. riparia.*

It also tends to prefer more calcarous substrates. However, it also forms dense stands in ponds, especially where these are spring-fed, or in marshy corners of river valley pastures. It has apparently increased since the 1960s, although some of this may be better recording.
(103 tetrads: Dony, 1967; 127 tetrads: 1950-1986)

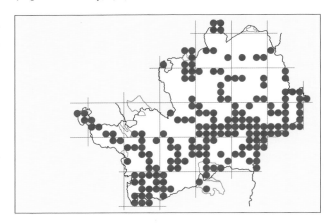

Map 741. *Carex acutiformis.*

[*Carex* × *subgracilis* Druce (*C. acutiformis* × *C. acuta*)

Burton (1992) reports this as having been found by G. Hounsome at a former sewage works site in VC20 [Greater London] at Friern Barnet (TQ29), 1991, but there is some doubt as to whether the site is in the vice-county or not. The record is omitted from Jermy *et al.* (2007) and may need confirmation.]

Carex riparia Curtis
Greater Pond-sedge
Native.
First record: *c*.1820.
Tetrad occurrence: 126 (25%).
Increased (+31%).

A plant of deeper water than *C. acutiformis*, and found often along the outer margin of vegetation by rivers, as well as sometimes in deeper ponds, and beside gravel pits. With the increase in flooded gravel pits in particular, this species has been able to take advantage of the expansion in habitat.
(92 tetrads: Dony, 1967; 110 tetrads: 1950-1986)

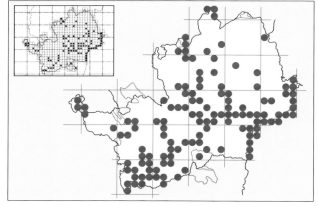

Map 742. *Carex riparia.*

[*Carex × csomadensis* Simonkai (*C. riparia × C. vesicaria*).

Druce was supposed to have identified this rare hybrid from specimens collected by J. Ansell at Franks Field near Brickendon (30/I), 1846 (Hb. OXF). Although he had not seen them, E. C. Wallace (in Stace, 1975) evidently considered this to be an error for *C. vesicaria*, which is what Ansell thought them to be in the first place. Without further study, this record must remain doubtful. The record is not mentioned in Jermy *et al.* (2007).]

Carex pseudocyperus L.
Cyperus Sedge
Native.
First record: 1838.
Tetrad occurrence: 35 (7%).
Increased? (+18%).

A rather local sedge of swamp by ponds on clay soils, and occasionally elsewhere, usually on less calcareous ground. It appears to have vanished from a few sites, especially in north Herts., but has been found in more localities than in the 1960s in the south.
(28 tetrads: Dony, 1967; 32 tetrads: 1950-1986)

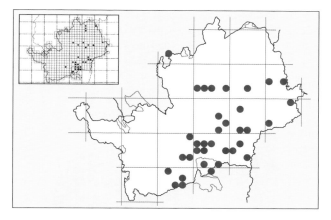

Map 743. *Carex pseudocyperus.*

Carex rostrata Stokes   Herts Rare
Bottle Sedge
Native.
First record: *c.*1835.
Tetrad occurrence: 4 (<1%).

First actually recorded from the County from Oughton Head Common (13/Q), *c.*1835 *J. D. Morell* through an annotation in his copy of Turner and Dillwyn's '*Botanist's Guide*' in North Herts. Museums. It was thought by Coleman and Pryor to be 'not uncommon' on peaty ground by marsh ditches, and by ponds on heathy ground. Some of the latter may have been errors for *C. vesicaria*, but many of the records are from the kind of spring-fed mires which would formerly have been much more frequent in the County's river valleys, and so its loss from most of these sites is perhaps explicable. Dony (1967) did not know it from the County, but it has since been found at 'Chadwell' spring in Purwell Meadow (12/Z, 22/E), 1968 *F. Bentley*, where it was found to have increased substantially in 2009 *T. J. et al.* It was also found in very small quantity by a spring-fed source adjoining the River Beane at Bengeo Mead (31/B), 1989 *T. J.* (Hb. HTN); and at Sopwell Mill Meadows (10/M), 2006 *G. J. White* (conf. T. J.) (Hb. HTN). This suggests it may well persist at some of its other old sites unnoticed.

Carex vesicaria L.
Bladder Sedge
Native.
First record: 1838.
Tetrad occurrence: 11 (2%).
Decreasing (-40%).

A scarce plant of sometimes shaded, often wooded pools on nutrient-poor, less calcareous substrates where the water table is high, this was formerly fairly frequent especially on the upland clays and gravels across southern and central Hertfordshire, but has decreased substantially over the last 30 years, probably mostly owing to eutrophication.
(17 tetrads: Dony, 1967; 24 tetrads: 1950-1986)

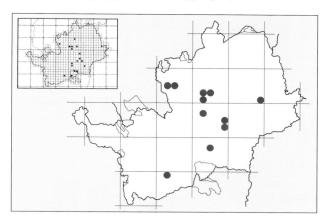

Map 744. *Carex vesicaria.*

Carex pendula Hudson
Pendulous Sedge
Native.
First record: 1805.
Tetrad occurrence: 202 (41%).
Increasing markedly (+115%).

This was almost exclusively a native plant of shady woodlands on more or less acidic clay soils in south and south-east Hertfordshire until very recently, where it occasionally formed dense stands. During the last 20 years, it has expanded rapidly, aided by its attractiveness as a garden plant, and by its introduction with building rubble to wet woodland paths and green lanes. No doubt, also, soils on the Boulder Clay and elsewhere have become more eutrophic, allowing this plant to gain a foothold, although increased deer browsing may also have allowed it to spread at the expense of more palatable fodder. It can now form dense stands in

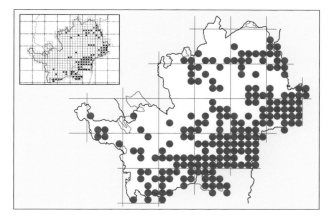

Map 745. *Carex pendula.*

some Boulder Clay woods, where it was absent only 30 years ago, and it is beginning to occur elsewhere as well.
(89 tetrads: Dony, 1967; 103 tetrads: 1950-1986)

Carex sylvatica Hudson
Wood Sedge
Native.
First record: 1838.
Tetrad occurrence: 307 (63%).
Increased (+16%).

This is predominantly a woodland plant, growing in damp ground on moderately calcareous soils especially, but also elsewhere. It can also colonise disturbed ground, especially on damp clays, and therefore turns up in shady margins of abandoned fields, and sometimes in damp areas of mineral workings. Very occasionally it will occur in shaded habitat on disturbed Chalk. It also has an interesting distribution, being strangely absent from some areas, such as around Hertford, Harpenden, and other areas in south Herts., as well as from most of the Chalk exposures in the north. The current survey shows that these absences generally remain the same as Dony (1967) recorded them.
(250 tetrads: Dony, 1967; 268 tetrads: 1950-1986)

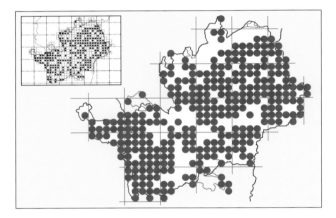

Map 746. *Carex sylvatica.*

Carex strigosa Hudson
Thin-spiked Wood Sedge
Native.
First record: 1838.
Tetrad occurrence: 14 (3%).
Possibly decreasing slightly (-9%).

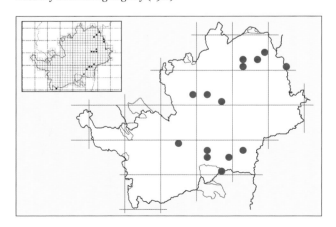

Map 747. *Carex strigosa.*

This is a plant of flushes on clay soils in woodland, and can be overlooked, especially when not flowering, as either robust *C. sylvatica*, or depauperate *C. otrubae*. Pryor (1887) thought it was quite rare, limited to Reading gravels and similar substrates, and Dony (1967) thought it had a similar distribution to *C. pendula*, although his map indicated it was found more on Boulder Clay. In 1978, the Hertfordshire Woodland Survey team found it more widely on wet clay soils across central and south-west Hertfordshire, although some records are unconfirmed. The current survey has broadly confirmed its distribution, and re-found it in many of Dony's and subsequent sites, but not all. The droughts during the 1990s may have affected it in some places.
(15 tetrads: Dony, 1967; 24 tetrads: 1950-1986)

Carex flacca Schreber
Glaucous Sedge
Native.
First record: 1838.
Tetrad occurrence: 233 (48%).
Probably stable (+5%).

Glaucous Sedge is a characteristic plant of damp, but not waterlogged calcareous ground in open habitats. It occurs widely in flushes on Boulder Clay, as well as in damp woodland rides, and in old chalky grassland where the soil is damp enough in winter. It colonises disturbed ground on calcareous clays and similar soils, being especially characteristic of nutrient-poor damp ground alongside newly-cut field drains or road verges that have been disturbed. Its distribution remains much as Dony found it, avoiding more acidic areas.
(211 tetrads: Dony, 1967; 235 tetrads: 1950-1986)

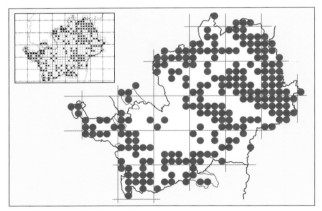

Map 748. *Carex flacca.*

Carex panicea L.
Carnation Sedge
Native.
First record: 1838.
Tetrad occurrence: 28 (6%).
Possibly increased slightly (+21%).

This is a plant of flushed peaty ground on calcareous substrates, in marshy pastures, and woodland rides, where it occurs with other sedges, including *C. flacca*, with which it can sometimes be confused. It is local, because its habitat is, but it still appears to be widespread, especially in flushes on the Boulder Clay, or where calcareous springs arise through more acidic soils elsewhere.
(22 tetrads: Dony, 1967; 34 tetrads: 1950-1986)

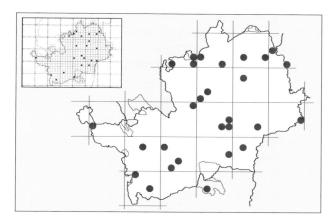

Map 749. *Carex panicea.*

[*Carex laevigata* Smith
Smooth Sedge
A record by A. E. Gibbs from Hedges Farm near St Albans of this plant of wet woodland on heavy clay soils was included in the Appendix to Pryor (1887). It was dismissed by Dony, and certainly seems unlikely at this locality.]

Carex binervis Smith
Green-ribbed Sedge
Native.
First record: 1846.
Tetrad occurrence: 8 (2%).
Stable?

Never a common plant in Hertfordshire, this characteristic moorland species nevertheless has a more secure foothold in the County than Dony (1967) recognised. It remains in the ride at Newton Wood (22/G) where he found it, being seen there in 1978 and again in 2003 *T. J.*; and it has increased at the Roundings, Hertford Heath (31/K), following scrub clearance on the remnant heathy areas. It has also been found again in some of Coleman's other localities, such as at Milwards Park (20/I, N), with several records up to 2003 *A. D. Marshall/T. J.*; in Bishop's and Lockwell Woods (09/Q, R), 1987, 2002, 2003 *I. D. Marshall* (Hb. HTN) *G. Salisbury, B. Harold*, not far from Batchworth Heath, where Coleman knew it; and at Brickground Wood near Bramfield (21/T), 1988 *A. D. Marshall* (Hb. HTN), which is near Bulls Green, also a Coleman locality. More surprisingly, it appeared on marshy ground adjoining tipped fly-ash at Amwell Quarry (31/R), 1990 *T. J.* (Hb. HTN), where it was found again in 1996. However, the fly-ash came from Rye House Power Station (30/Z), which was formerly Hoddesdon Marsh, again a locality where it was recorded by Coleman in the early 19th century. So it is tempting to think that it somehow survived the excavation of the old marshes here and was transferred to Amwell with the fly-ash!

Carex distans L.   Herts Rare
Distant Sedge
Native.
First record: 1838.
Tetrad occurrence: 4 (<1%).
Rare and decreasing (-27%).

Mostly a plant of coastal marshes on soils with a high mineral content, in Hertfordshire this has always been limited to mineral-rich flushed ground in long-standing habitats. Dony knew it at five localities. It was subsequently recorded at Moor Hall Meadow

(32/I), 1976 *T. J.* (Hb. HTN); Norton Common (23/B), 1976, 1978 *B. R. Sawford* (Hb. HTN); and by a spring seepage in old meadows at Cadwell, Ickleford (13/W), 1982 *M. Yeo*. A specimen collected at Claypits Meadow, Bayford (30/D), 1976 *T. J.* was referred tentatively to the species by R. W. David, but needs confirmation. The recent survey only managed to find it in four localities, three of which confirmed records given by Dony (1967): Ickleford Common (13/W), 1989 *T. J.* (Hb. HTN) (a new record); Blagrove Common (33/G), 1990, 1994, 2009 *T. J.* (Hb. HTN) (Dony's site at Green End); Rushy Meadow by Wilstone Reservoir (SP91/B), 1994 *M. Hicks/T. J.* (Hb. HTN); and Foulwells Spring by Wormley Wood (30/I), 1994 *A. M. Boucher/T. J.* (Hb. HTN). At none of its sites is it in any quantity, and at two of Dony's sites, it is almost certainly no longer present: Oughton Head and the former marsh below Easneye, which has since been ploughed. It has also not been re-found at most of its other more recent sites, despite searching.
(5 tetrads: Dony, 1967; 8 tetrads: 1950-1986)

Carex hostiana DC.   Herts Rare
Tawny Sedge
Native.
First record: 1839.
Tetrad occurrence: 2 (<1%).

A sedge of mineral-rich flushes, where it may occur with *C. distans* and other sedges. It was always very rare in Herts., and had apparently long been extinct in all the sites known to Coleman. Dony quotes one record from Burleigh Meadow (22/G), 1919 *A. W. Graveson* (Hb. HTN), and it was presumed extinct before a single plant was found at the much-disturbed Foulwells Spring (30/I), 1981 *T. J.* During the recent survey, it was re-found at Foulwells Spring, 1994 *A. M. Boucher/T. J.* (Hb. HTN). A small patch was also found by the Pix Brook at Norton Common (23/B), 1994 *T. J.* (Hb. HTN).

Carex viridula Michaux
Yellow Sedge
Native.
First record: 1838 (for the aggregate).

Coleman (1849) and Pryor (1887) both recorded the aggregate, but Dony (1967) separated two taxa as *C. lepidocarpa* and *C. demissa*, in line with then current thinking. More recently, these have been regarded as subspecies, the treatment followed here, but considered separately in order to compare directly with Dony's account.

Carex viridula ssp. *brachyrrhyncha* (Čelak.) B. Schmid
Long-stalked Yellow Sedge   Herts Rare
Native.
First record: 1841.
Tetrad occurrence: 3 (<1%).
Stable (or possibly increasing?).

This is a plant of base-rich marshy ground around seepages. It was always probably rare in the County, and Dony had only seen it at Rushy Meadow (91/B), 1958, confirming one of Coleman's sites. It was then discovered at Norton Common (23/B), 1981 *B. R. Sawford* (Hb. HTN). More recently, it has been found, unexpectedly, along seepages by recently created ditches in woodland rides at Bramfield Park Wood (21/X), 2000 *A. L. Bull/T. J.* (Hb. HTN); and in Cowheath Wood (30/I), 2003,

2006 *T. J.* (Hb. HTN), suggesting that some of Coleman's records from such sites could have been this subspecies. Most recently, it was confirmed from a specimen collected from a spring-fed mire adjoining Blagrove Common (33/G), 2005 *G. J. Wyatt* (det. T. J.) (Hb. HTN). This revised a previous record by F. Hall, 1998 from this locality, which had been identified previously as ssp. *oedocarpa*.

Carex viridula ssp. *oedocarpa* (Andersson) B. Schmid
Common Yellow Sedge
Native.
First record: 1838.
Tetrad occurrence: 9 (2%).
Stable, or now decreasing? (+6%).

This is a smaller plant than its relative, and is found in more acidic conditions, on heathy ground or peat associated with flushes. It has probably decreased over the last 100 years, as such habitats have been degraded and lost. However, the recent survey found it in nine widely-scattered localities, of which at least one, at Ponsfall Farm Meadows (20/X), 1992 *T. J.* is known to have been destroyed since through the creation of a golf course.
(8 tetrads: Dony, 1967; 10 tetrads: 1950-1986)

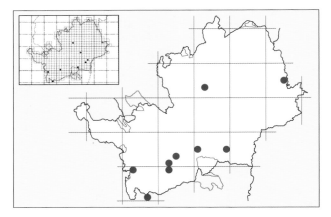

Map 750. *Carex viridula* ssp. *oedocarpa*.

Carex pallescens L.
Pale Sedge
Native.
First record: 1814.
Tetrad occurrence: 18 (4%).
Decreasing (-18%).

A woodland plant, on more or less acidic soils, usually found in

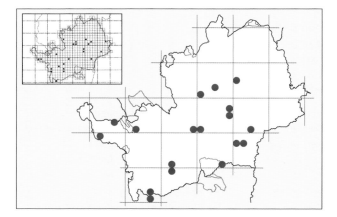

Map 751. *Carex pallescens*.

rides and glades, this appears to have always been rather local, and it now seems to be disappearing from some sites, possibly because of increased shade and the neglect of rides.
(21 tetrads: Dony, 1967; 28 tetrads: 1950-1986)

Carex caryophyllea Latourr.
Spring Sedge
Native.
First record: 1838.
Tetrad occurrence: 21 (4%).
Decreasing (-28%).

A conspicuous plant early in the season in short pasture on calcareous soils, but becoming hard to find later in the summer, which can mean it is under-recorded in some localities. Despite this, there does genuinely seem to be a decrease, particularly in calcareous pastures away from the Chalk, presumably owing to 'improvement' or eutrophication of grasslands.
(28 tetrads: Dony, 1967; 33 tetrads: 1950-1986)

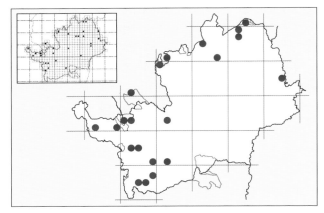

Map 752. *Carex caryophyllea*.

Carex pilulifera L.
Pill Sedge
Native.
First record: 1838.
Tetrad occurrence: 50 (10%).
Stable? (+5%).

A plant of heathy soils in woods or on old commons, this can often be rather inconspicuous, especially when not in flower, so that it may have been under-recorded in a few areas. It has also been found to be more widespread in others, such as the Ashridge complex, than Dony (1967) found it, which may also be down to

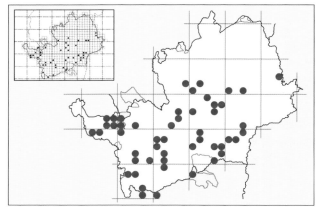

Map 753. *Carex pilulifera*.

previous under-recording.
(45 tetrads: Dony, 1967; 50 tetrads: 1950-1986)

Carex acuta L.
Slender Tufted Sedge
Native.
First record: 1838.
Tetrad occurrence: 12 (2%).
Stable?

Dony only knew of this from one locality: an upland site at Franks Field, near Ettridge Farm (30/I). He evidently did not recognise it in the field, because it has subsequently been found to occur fairly widely in two habitat types: in flood-plain marshes, and in spring-fed seepage wetlands in upland meadows on calcareous clay. It is uncommon, but where it does occur it can form extensive patches, often not flowering if water tables are low.

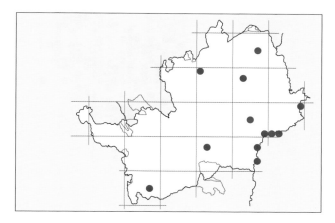

Map 754. *Carex acuta.*

Carex nigra (L.) Reichard
Common Sedge
Native.
First record: 1838.
Tetrad occurrence: 45 (9%).
Increasing? (+37%).

The English name for this is somewhat of a misnomer, in Herts. at least, as it is not particularly 'common' with us, occurring occasionally as stands or small tussocks in old wet pastures, marshes and sometimes by old gravel pits, and apparently tolerating a wide range of pH. It can go unrecorded when not in flower, which may account for some of its apparent increase.
(31 tetrads: Dony, 1967; 51 tetrads: 1950-1986)

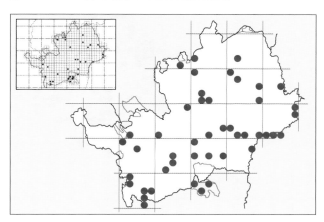

Map 755. *Carex nigra.*

Carex elata All.   Herts Rare
Tufted Sedge
Native.
First record: c.1840.

This was never a common species in the County, and is now very rare. Dony (1967) knew it from a meadow near Westmill (32/T), which has not been rediscovered. However, it was found to be a feature of a spring flush in Braughing Meads (32/X), 1985 *T. J.* (Hb. HTN). Although part of this site was later excavated to form a pond, the colony survived, last being formally recorded in 1992 *S. Watson*. It may well also survive at Westmill, and its former sites at Oughton Head and Gilston Park Lake are also still potentially suitable. In 2009, two tussocks were discovered in swamp at Purwell Meadow (12/Z) *T. J.* (Hb. HTN), a remarkable find at a well-studied locality.

Carex pulicaris L.   Herts Rare
Flea Sedge
Native.
First record: 1839.
Extinct?

Known formerly from flushes in grazed marshes in a number of places, this had apparently severely decreased by the time Dony was recording, and he knew it only in Rushy Meadow by Wilstone Reservoir (91/B), 1958, a site that has suffered severely from neglect, despite being a 'Site of Special Scientific Interest'. There have been no further records, although there was a report from Oxhey Wood (19/B), 1978 *S. and P. Blackmore*, which was not confirmed.

Poaceae (Grasses)

Genus: *Sasaella*

Sasaella ramosa (Makino) Makino
Hairy Bamboo
Introduced: neophyte.
First record: 1990.

This Asiatic grass is frequently planted for ornament in parks and large gardens, and can spread. It was first noted having spread in the grounds of Fanhams Hall (31/S), 1990 *C. G. Hanson*; and subsequently at Bayfordbury (31/A), 1994 *A. M. Boucher/C. G. H.*; as well as at Aldenham Park (19/T), 1998 *T. J./G. P. Smith* (Hb. HTN).

Genus: *Ehrharta*

Ehrharta erecta Lam.
Panic Veldt-grass
Introduced: casual.
First record: 1992.

The only records of this tropical grass as an escape were its 'spontaneous' appearance in a garden lawn at Ware (31/S), 1992, 1993 *C. G. Hanson*, having escaped from a greenhouse nearby (*BSBI News*, 62, p. 45).

Nardus stricta L.
Mat-grass
Native.
First record: 1838.
Tetrad occurrence: 8 (2%).
Rare and decreased (-27%).

This characteristic grass of ancient, often somewhat damp, heathy habitat has apparently never been very common in the County. It occurs here and there on acidic clay or gravelly soils, especially the London Clay and fluvial gravels, and can be very persistent. This was borne out by its having been re-found at Fisher's Green (22/I), 1977 *M. Hooper*, a site known to Pryor (1887), although it has not been seen again there since. David Marshall found it in several tetrads around Hatfield during the recent survey, but not at Colney Heath, one of its long-standing sites. It was newly found at Croxley Common Moor (09/X), 1990 *J. Colthup*, where it persists; and found to be locally abundant at Ashridge Park (91/W) (VC24 [Herts.]), 1995 *G. Salisbury/J. Saunders*, but appears to have succumbed to eutrophication and scrub growth at The Roundings, Hertford Heath (31/K), where it was last recorded in 1982 *J. Welsh*. It also persists at other long-known sites, such as Patmore Heath (42/M) and Rowley Green (29/D), but is often threatened by scrub encroachment. At Hadley Green (29/N) (VC21 [Herts., 1904-1965]), it was found in 2003 to be widespread and abundant *T. J./G. Salisbury/S. Hedley*. It has, however, been exterminated by weedkillers and fertilising at Easneye Park (31/R), where Dony knew it.
(10 tetrads: Dony, 1967; 11 tetrads: 1950-1986)

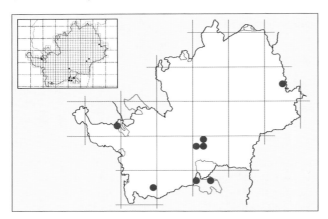

Map 756. *Nardus stricta.*

Stipa tenuissima Trin.
Introduced: casual.
First (only) record: 1999.

A rare adventive, usually introduced with wool waste, this had established itself in a garden at Ware (31/S), 1999 *C. G. Hanson* (conf. E. J. Clement) (Hb. HTN), but can scarcely be regarded as 'wild'.

Milium effusum L.
Wood Millet
Native.
First recorded: 1838.
Tetrad occurrence: 227 (46%).
Stable (+2%).

A frequent component of semi-natural woodland flora on free-draining, moderately acidic or neutral loam soils, tolerating shaded conditions well. As a result, its distribution remains very much as Dony recorded it.
(211 tetrads: Dony, 1967; 228 tetrads: 1950-1986)

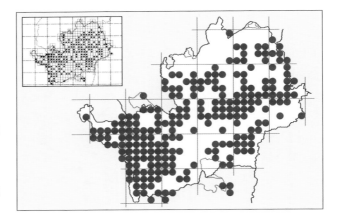

Map 757. *Milium effusum.*

The fescues comprise one of the more 'difficult' genera of grasses. The taxonomy of the fine-leaved fescues has been much examined since the 1960s, and both the broader *Festuca rubra* and *F. ovina* groups have been given much attention. They present difficulty studying them in the field, and the accounts, especially of the *F. ovina* group, have borne this in mind.

Festuca pratensis Hudson
Meadow Fescue
Native.
First record: 1748.
Tetrad occurrence: 195 (40%).
Decreased markedly (-36%).

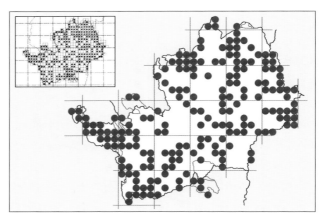

Map 758. *Festuca pratensis.*

A grass of old, semi-natural, unimproved or slightly improved grassland, in meadows, pastures, and long-established road verges, this was formerly a major component of such habitats, but is decreasing substantially owing to neglect or loss of old grasslands, the 'improvement' of other areas, and the eutrophication of road verges. As a result, it is showing marked losses across the County, especially on the Boulder Clay, where arable conversion of old grassland and road verge eutrophication are to blame; and on the London Clay, where acidification and neglect of road verges may be the cause.

(290 tetrads: Dony, 1967; 330 tetrads: 1950-1986)

Festuca arundinacea Schreber
Tall Fescue
Native.
First record: 1843.
Tetrad occurrence: 297 (61%).
Increased markedly (+39%).

Found in both old and more recent rough grassland, on road verges, *etc.* on moderately calcareous or neutral soils. Unlike its relative, it has apparently increased substantially, although even now it may be under-recorded, owing to observers not being familiar with its characteristic, tufted growth habit, and therefore overlooking it. This may be the reason for its apparent abundance on the Boulder Clay and in west Hertfordshire, and apparent scarcity in central Hertfordshire. It was formerly used for hay on poorer soils, but is now most often found as tough, persistent stands on road verges, where it can tolerate neglect.

(203 tetrads: Dony, 1967; 224 tetrads: 1950-1986)

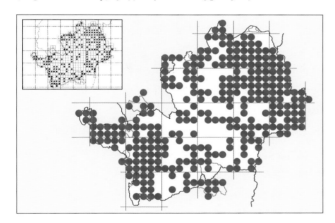

Map 759. *Festuca arundinacea.*

Festuca gigantea (L.) Villars
Giant Fescue
Native.
First record: 1824.
Tetrad occurrence: 360 (73%).
Decreased (-12%).

Despite its name, this can sometimes be quite an inconspicuous grass, growing in small quantity in damp roadside hedges and shady wood margins, in most places except open Chalk country and on very dry, gravelly soils elsewhere.

(389 tetrads: Dony, 1967; 403 tetrads: 1950-1986)

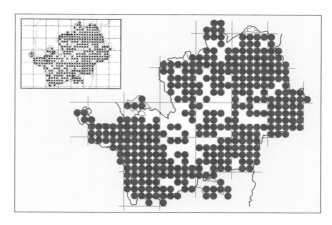

Map 760. *Festuca gigantea.*

Festuca heterophylla Lam.
Various-leaved Fescue
Introduced: casual.
First record: 1955.

Since Dony found this, presumably sown, at New England Woods (43/C), 1955 and at Plashes Wood (32/V), 1957 (Dony, 1967), the only confirmed records have been as casuals: from a building site at Hoddesdon (30/U), 1988 *A. M. Boucher* (Hb. HTN); beside a track at Clement's End (01/H) (VC20 [Beds.]), 1994 *C. R. Boon/T. J.* (Hb. HTN); and as probably sown near Graveley (22I), 2007 *T. J.* (Hb. HTN). A record reported from Hertford Heath in James (1985) may have been in error.

Festuca rubra L.
Red Fescue
Native.
First record: 1838.
Tetrad occurrence: 474 (97%).
Apparently stable (-1%).

The Red Fescue group remains one of the more difficult aggregates to study. The species as a whole is a major part of less eutrophic or rank grassland across the County. As a native, it is usually found in old pasture, undisturbed road verges, *etc.*, but it is also widely sown in new grasslands or for amenity. Although it is probably decreasing locally, owing to the loss of good quality old grassland, this is not yet evident at the scale of the tetrad, and it is still found throughout the County.

(455 tetrads: Dony, 1967; and from 1950-1986)

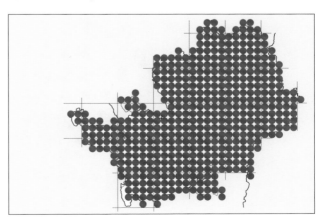

Map 761. *Festuca rubra.*

No concerted effort has been made to document the occurrence of the subspecies, although the widespread form is ssp. *rubra*. **Chewing's Fescue** (*F. rubra* ssp. *commutata* Gaudin) is frequent in short turf in chalk grassland and on old commons on somewhat acidic, dry soils, as well as on lawns, where it is frequently sown. Subspecies *juncea* (Hackel) K. Richter has been recorded a few times recently: roadside bank at Stapleford (31/D), 1990 *T. J.* (det. T. A. Cope) (Hb. HTN); on recently-created banks of A505, E. of Royston, possibly sown (34/Q) (VC29 [Herts.]), 1996 *T. J.* (Hb. HTN); and on Hertford North Station platform (31/B), 1997 *T. J.* (Hb. HTN). It probably occurs elsewhere in dry, calcareous habitats with thin, friable soil. Subspecies *megastachys* Gaudin has been identified from a specimen collected at Chadwell Bank, King's Meads (31/L), 1989 *T. J.* (det. T. A. Cope) (Hb. HTN). It is probably elsewhere, and is considered to be introduced.

Festuca ovina L.
Sheep's Fescue
Native.
First record: 1838.
Tetrad occurrence: 94 (19%).
Probably stable (+26%).

Sheep's Fescue is a plant of old grassland on poor, dry soils. It occurs on a range of soil types, from quite acidic heathy soils through to chalk, and therefore occurs widely across the County, wherever such habitats persist. It is a frequent component of good quality chalk grassland, especially where this is still grazed; but it is also a frequent feature of short grass on old commons, as well as some roadsides. It can persist by footpaths in otherwise unlikely places, and features like anthills can assist its survival. However, there are problems with recording it. It is one of a group of fine-leaved fescues with open leaf sheaths, which makes for difficulties. It also has three named subspecies, although the differences between these do not seem to be clear-cut. The map has attempted to ensure that other related taxa, notably *F. filiformis*, have been excluded. It is possible some records may, however, refer to *F. brevipila* or possibly *F. lemanii*. It may also have been overlooked in some sites, owing to mis-recording as *F. rubra* ssp. *commutata*. All these factors taken together probably mean that, although it was recorded more widely than in 1967, it is probably not really increasing at all. In fact, given the loss of old, well-grazed grassland on poor soils, it is quite likely to have decreased locally.
(71 tetrads: Dony, 1967; 104 tetrads: 1950-1986)

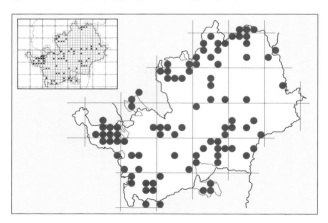

Map 762. *Festuca ovina.*

The only subspecies identified with any certainty in the County are ssp. *hirtula* (Hack. ex Travis) M. J. Wilk and ssp. *ophioliticola* (Kerg.) M. J. Wilk. The former grows on acidic soils, while the latter is the chalk grassland subspecies.

Festuca filiformis Pourret
Fine-leaved Sheep's Fescue
Native.
First record: 1909.
Tetrad occurrence: 23 (5%).

Once recognised, this is a distinctive grass of acidic, heathy ground, often under semi-shade, when its fine leaves and tufted growth are often very evident. J. E. Little was the first to recognise the distinction between this and *F. ovina* in the County, but Dony and his field workers evidently did not notice it in many sites. As a result, it has been seriously under-recorded in the past, and any measure of change in its status is unreliable. It occurs on old commons, occasionally on roadsides, across southern and central Hertfordshire, sometimes in association with *F. ovina*, and almost always in long-established habitat.
(7 tetrads: Dony, 1967; 19 tetrads: 1950-1986)

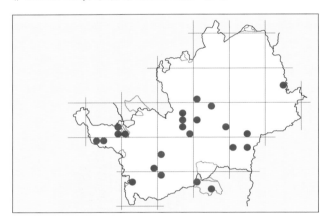

Map 763. *Festuca filiformis.*

[*Festuca lemanii* Bast.
Confused Fescue
Native.

Burton (1983) referred past records of '*F. longifolia*' to this species, and gave two recent tetrad records from 30/N and 31/K from Herts. However, neither of these has apparently been critically determined, and therefore these records cannot be accepted as distinct from *F. brevipila*. As *F. brevipila* and *F. lemanii* could both have been confused under the name '*F. longifolia*', it is possible that *F. lemanii* may be the species to which some past records should be referred, especially on calcareous soils.]

Festuca brevipila R. Tracey
Hard Fescue
Introduced: neophyte.
First confirmed record: 1959.

This species of the *ovina* group is reputed to have been introduced in the early 19th century (Stace, 1991; Preston *et al.*, 2002), used as a lawn seed, for amenity grasslands, and on roadsides. Coleman recorded '*F. duriuscula*', but appears to have confused *F. rubra* under this name, a mistake perpetuated by Pryor (1887), but including records that appear to reflect what later became known as '*F. longifolia*'. Dony (1967) listed '*F. longifolia*' as newly recorded, with a number of records from roadsides, railway banks and a golf course. These probably mostly refer to *F. brevipila*, having been introduced with seed-mixes. Herbarium specimens have not generally been examined critically, but there is one determined by C. E. Hubbard (as *F. longifolia* Thuill. var. *villosa* (Schred.) in Hb. LTN, which refers here, and a specimen from Hadham Mill (41/I), *c*.1960 *J. L. Fielding* that he named '*F. trachyphylla*' is also this. After 1970, it was recorded from the central reservation of the A505 at Slip End (23/Y), 1979 *T. J.* (Hb. HTN); Colney Heath (20/C), 1984 *B. Anderson* (det. T. J.) (Hb. HTN); and from a chalky bank at Ashwell Quarry (23/P), 1986 *T. J.* (Hb. HTN). A record from the motte at Berkhamsted Castle (90/Z), 1985 *P. Kingsbury* was not supported by a specimen. It has not been re-found at any of these localities during the recent survey, but may well be overlooked.

Hybrid Genus: ✕*Festulolium*

✕*Festulolium loliaceum* (Hudson) P. Fourn.
(*Festuca pratensis* × *Lolium perenne*)
Hybrid Fescue
Native.
First record: 1805.
Tetrad occurrence: 33 (7%).
Stable? (+43%).

A widespread hybrid, found in old grassland, usually on moist, clay soils, where *F. pratensis* is still frequent. It is still probably under-recorded.
(22 tetrads: Dony, 1967; 37 tetrads: 1950-1986)

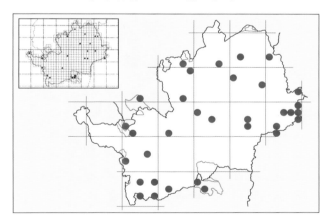

Map 764. ✕*Festulolium loliaceum*.

✕*Festulolium braunii* (K. Richt.) A. Camus
(*Festuca pratensis* × *Lolium multiflorum*)
Introduced.
First record: 2007.

This was found in a grass field edge near Graveley (22/I), probably introduced with a conservation seed-mix *T. J.* (Hb. HTN). It may occur more widely.

Festuca arundinacea × *Lolium multiflorum*
Native.
First record: 1989.

This uncommon hybrid was found at Pole Hole tip (41/L) *S. Watson* (det. T. A. Cope) (Hb. HTN).

Genus: *Lolium*

Lolium perenne L.
Perennial Rye-grass
Native (and introduced).
First record: 1748.
Tetrad occurrence: 481 (98%).
Stable (-1%).

An ubiquitous, hard-wearing grass of lawns, amenity grasslands and improved pasture, in which it is the major sown component. It is also native in neutral to mildly acidic grasslands elsewhere, in which the less robust wild form grows alongside other species. It is encouraged by nutrient enrichment, but eventually succumbs when nitrogen levels reach critical levels, being replaced by nettles and other rank herbs. Missed inexplicably in one tetrad.
(460 tetrads: Dony, 1967; and 1950-1986)

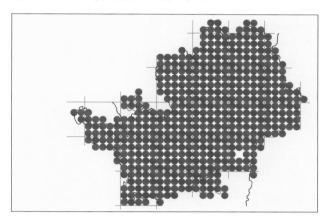

Map 765. *Lolium perenne*.

Lolium × *boucheanum* Kunth (*L. perenne* × *L. multiflorum*)
Native.
First record: 1975.

This is probably widespread, but was only first recorded from Ware tip (31/M), 1975 *C. G. Hanson* (det E. J. Clement). During the survey, it was firmly identified at Allens Green (41/N), 1992 *S. Watson* (det. T. A. Cope) (Hb. HTN); Brent Pelham (43/F), 1993 *S. W.* (det. T. A. Cope) (Hb. HTN); and near Studham (01/C), (VC20 [Beds.]), 1994, 1999 *C. R. Boon/T. J./G. Salisbury*.

Lolium multiflorum Lam.
Italian Rye-grass
Introduced: neophyte.
First record: 1849.
Tetrad occurrence: 223 (45%).
Decreased substantially (-44%).

Used especially for sown leys, persisting in field margins, waste places and as an arable weed, this grass appears to have declined significantly over the last 40 years, now only being abundant in parts of the Boulder Clay plateau, and on the Clay-with-Flints in west Herts.
(375 tetrads: Dony, 1967; 395 tetrads: 1950-1986)

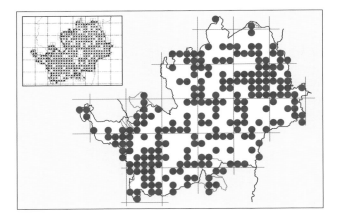

Map 766. *Lolium multiflorum.*

Lolium rigidum Gaudin
Mediterranean Rye-grass
Introduced: casual.
First (only) record: 1969.

The only record is from Park Street dump (10/L) *J. G. Dony* (Hb. HTN).

Lolium temulentum L.
Darnel
Introduced: archaeophyte, now casual.
First record: 1733.
Decreased, almost extinct.

Formerly a weed of agricultural land and waste places, this had become an occasional casual on waste tips only by the 1960s, and remained as such until the early 1980s, when waste tips began to be more closely managed and capped regularly. It was recorded from Moor Mill (10/L), Hitchin (13/V), Hatfield (20/D), Cole Green (21/Q), Waterford (31/C), Bulls Mill (31/D), Ware (31/M) and Rye Meads Sewage Works (31/V) between 1970 and 1986 *C. G. Hanson*. During the recent survey, it was only found once: at Tapp's Garden Centre, Baldock (23/L), 1995 *C. G. H.*

Lolium persicum Boiss. and Hohen. ex Boiss.
Introduced: casual.
First record: 1970.

This casual grain impurity was found at Cole Green tip (21/Q), 1970 and subsequently at Bulls Mill tip (31/D), 1977 *C. G. Hanson* (Hb. Hanson).

Genus: *Vulpia*

Vulpia bromoides (L.) Gray
Squirrel-tail Fescue
Native.
First record: 1838.
Tetrad occurrence: 65 (13%).
Decreased sharply (-44%).

A native species of dry, gravelly grassland on heathy commons, roadside banks and the like, especially on the riverine gravels of central and south-west Herts., this is also found on waste ground elsewhere. It was once a common plant along railway banks, but as these have become scrubbed up, this is no longer the case. Its present distribution is similar to that recorded by Dony, but it appears to have retreated from many semi-natural sites, as these

have become eutrophic, and it now occurs more often on waste ground.
(111 tetrads: Dony, 1967; 120 tetrads: 1950-1986)

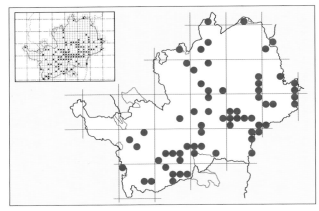

Map 767. *Vulpia bromoides.*

Vulpia myuros (L.) G. C. Gmelin
Rat's-tail Fescue
Introduced: archaeophyte.
First record: 1838.
Tetrad occurrence: 81 (17%).
Increased markedly (+267%).

This was always a weed of waste places, on poor, gravelly ground, sometimes occurring with its native relative. It has apparently extended its range in such habitats, especially along railways and by roads, and on bare sites in towns.
(21 tetrads: Dony, 1967; 32 tetrads: 1950-1986)

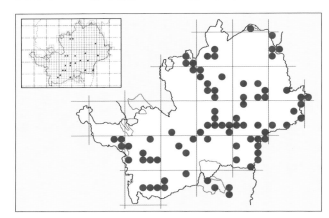

Map 768. *Vulpia myuros.*

Vulpia ciliata Dumort.   Herts Rare
Bearded Fescue
Native (or introduced?)
First record: 1998.

A mainly coastal grass of sandy ground, this also occurs on sandy ground inland, especially in East Anglia, and is apparently increasing. It was first found in Herts. at Holwell Pit (13/Q), 1998 *T. J.* (conf. T. A. Cope) (Hb. HTN). It has subsequently appeared on old concrete hard-standing of the former airfield at Scales Park (43/B), 2005 *A. L. Bull/T. J.* (Hb. HTN). It may well occur elsewhere, and should be looked for by salted roads.

The subspecies recorded in Herts. is ssp. *ambigua* (Le Gall) Stace and Auq., the native form in the U.K.

Genus: *Cynosurus*

Cynosurus cristatus L.
Crested Dog's-tail
Native.
First record: 1748.
Tetrad occurrence: 336 (68%).
Decreasing (-24%).

A characteristic and formerly abundant plant of long-established semi-natural pastures and hay-meadows on mildly acidic through neutral to mildly calcareous soils, this has steadily retreated as grassland has been 'improved' for agriculture. It has now been lost from almost a quarter of the County as a result, although it is now sometimes sown for amenity, or as 'conservation grassland' on former arable.
(419 tetrads: Dony, 1967; 427 tetrads: 1950-1986)

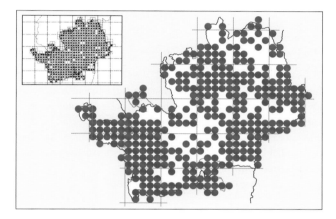

Map 769. *Cynosurus cristatus.*

Cynosurus echinatus L.
Rough Dog's-tail
Introduced: casual.
First record: 1913.

For a time a fairly frequent weed of waste places, sometimes introduced with seed, it was actually first found by H. C. Littlebury at West Mill, near Ickleford (13/Q), not at Rickmansworth, as given in Dony (1967). It was also found as late as 1949 at Brookmans Park (20/H) *P. Vernon*; and in 1951 and 1952 nearby at Hatfield (20/I), *R. A. Graham, S. C. Mortis* (Dony ms. index and *comm.*: Biological Records Centre: CEH Monks Wood). There have been no further records.

Genus: *Puccinellia*

Puccinellia distans (Jacq.) Parl.
Reflexed Saltmarsh-grass
Introduced [native in the U.K.].
First record: 1924.
Tetrad occurrence: 45 (9%).
Increasing steadily.

Dony (1967) only knew of the original record from Ware Park brickfield (TL31), 1924 *A. W. Graveson* (Hb. HTN), where no doubt the natural salts in clay used for the brick-making process enabled it to thrive. Subsequently, he found it by the A1 near the entrance to (appropriately!) Saltmore Farm, Caldecote (23/J), 1978 (Hb. LTN). It was then found in some quantity on dumped

fly-ash at the former Rye House Power Station (30/Z), 1982 *A. M. Boucher/T. J.* (Hb. HTN), no doubt supported by the unusual chemical constituents of the ash. It was not until the early 1990s that its full spread through Hertfordshire's main road network, encouraged by the enormous increase in road salting, was first noticed. It has now spread patchily throughout the major road network, and some minor roads, usually occurring for a few feet at most from the road margin, and being visible clearly as a grey-green strip down roadsides, after Danish Scurvy-grass has died down!

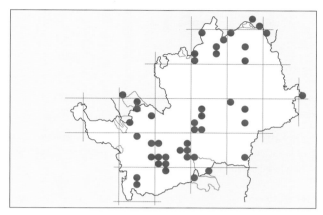

Map 770. *Puccinellia distans.*

Puccinellia fasciculata (Torey) E. Bickn.   [UK Vulnerable]
Borrer's Saltmarsh-grass
Introduced [native in the U.K.].
First record: 1986.

This was found to be abundant on introduced fly-ash deposited by Hollycross Lake, Amwell Quarry (31/R), 1986 *T. J.* (Hb. HTN). The fly-ash had been introduced to enable development of a colony of marsh orchids, and was reputed to have come from Brimsdown in Middx., although ash deposited there may have come originally from Barking. No doubt the seed came with it! The plant was still present in a limited area in 1997 *T. J.*

Genus: *Briza*

Briza media L.
Quaking Grass
Native.
First record: 1748.
Tetrad occurrence: 88 (18%)
Decreased substantially (-43%).
This beautiful grass is a charismatic plant of natural calcareous grasslands, occurring especially on the Chalk, but also on calcareous clays and gravels elsewhere. It was formerly a frequent component of hay meadows on the Boulder Clay, but these have all but disappeared. Away from its main sites, such as Therfield Heath, it is now frequently limited to relict patches of grassland, rarely as a result of 'conservation mix' seeding elsewhere.
(146 tetrads: Dony, 1967; 165 tetrads: 1950-1986)

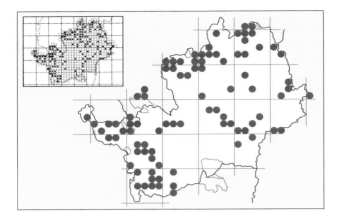

Map 771. *Briza media*.

[*Briza minor* L.
Lesser Quaking Grass

A record given in *Trans. H.N.H.S.*, 2 (1883), and repeated in Pryor (1887) was queried by both Pryor and Dony (1967). Without further details, it must remain doubtful.]

Briza maxima L.
Greater Quaking Grass
Introduced: casual.
First record: 1994.

This fine grass, often used for decorative purposes, was found as a casual in Bishop's Stortford (42/V), 1994 *J. Fielding*. A small colony on disturbed soil by a cleared pond in Balls Wood (31/K), 2007 *T. J.* (Hb. HTN) may represent a more permanent presence, although how it got there is a mystery.

Genus: *Poa*

Poa infirma Kunth
Early Meadow-grass
Introduced? [native in the U.K.].
First record: 2009.

This annual species of bare trodden ground, formerly only native in Britain in the extreme south-west, has slowly spread eastwards and north through the country recently, presumably through human agency. It was found at The Campus, Welwyn Garden City (21/G), on trodden mud under a tree, 2009 *T. J.* (conf. D. A. Pearman) (Hb. HTN).

Poa annua L.
Annual Meadow-grass
Native.
First record: *c*.1820.
Tetrad occurrence: 474 (97%).
Stable (-3%).
This weed of disturbed ground, trodden paths, arable margins and cultivated ground on most substrates is found throughout the County, and remains one of the most widespread species, only missed in some marginal tetrads.
(464 tetrads: Dony, 1967; and from 1950-1986)

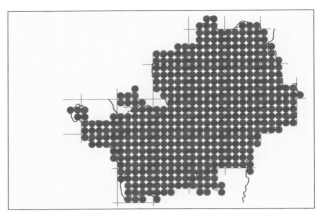

Map 772. *Poa annua*.

Poa trivialis L.
Rough Meadow-grass
Native.
First record: 1838.
Tetrad occurrence: 467 (95%).
Stable (-2%).

This grass forms a major part of most shaded, nutrient-enriched habitats, along with nettles and other rank herbs. It is abundant in semi-improved, damp pastures and roadside verges, and also occurs in early successional habitats on enriched ground. As such, it has probably increased, although it was missed unaccountably in a few tetrads during the survey.
(452 tetrads: Dony, 1967; and from 1950-1986)

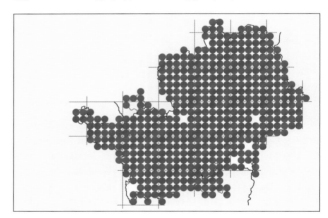

Map 773. *Poa trivialis*.

Poa humilis Ehrh. ex Hoffm.
Spreading Meadow-grass
Native.
First record: *c*.1970 (VC21 [Herts.]).
Tetrad occurrence: 24 (5%).

This is usually a grass of old damp pastures, where its stoloniferous growth and single stems tend to make it inconspicuous. It can also occur in other habitats, including waste ground and on old walls, where it has probably in the past been confused with *P. compressa*. Unfortunately it was not distinguished from *P. pratensis* by any of our earlier botanists, even as a subspecies. The first published record is from north of Little Heath, North Mymms (20/L), *c*.1970 *M. Kennedy* (Kent, 1975). Presumably the same record is given as a tetrad dot in Burton (1983), together with records from 10/P and 30/S, for which I have no details. It was found elsewhere before the current survey at Valley Farm Meadows, Kimpton (11/Z), 1986 *T. J.* (Hb. HTN); and at Woodhall Farm Meadows (21/F), 1986 *T. J.* (Hb. HTN). During the survey, not many field workers attempted to identify it, but it was found in 24 tetrads, by no means all in river valleys. It is almost certainly very under-recorded.

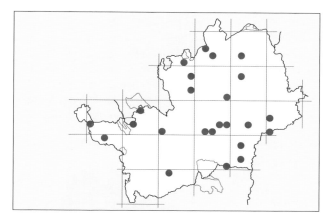

Map 774. *Poa humilis.*

Poa pratensis L.
Smooth Meadow-grass
Native.
First record: (1748, for the aggregate), 1838.
Tetrad occurrence: 424 (86%) (for the agg.).
Decreasing (-11%).

The strict species is a plant of dry, neutral or moderately calcareous soils, where its tufted growth can make it fairly conspicuous. As old pastures have disappeared, and road verges have become rank, it is likely to have declined quite substantially, although this is only just beginning to show at the tetrad level. While attempts were made to ensure accurate identification, it is not always clear from records submitted what was intended, and therefore all records of the aggregate are included in the map. The strict species was identified in 387 tetrads, while the aggregate was recorded from 425 tetrads.
(454 tetrads for the aggregate: Dony, 1967; 455 tetrads: 1950-1986)

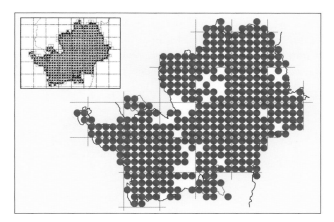

Map 775. *Poa pratensis.*

Poa angustifolia L.
Narrow-leaved Meadow-grass
Native.
First recorded: 1910.
Tetrad occurrence: 62 (13%).
Decreasing? (-22%).

Not recognised by 19th century botanists, this is a plant of open, dry, often calcareous habitats, such as chalky road banks, margins of gravel pits and similar places, where it can be mis-identified by casual observers as *Festuca rubra* when not in flower. Its habit of flowering early makes it sometimes quite conspicuous on roadsides, but it is still overlooked, and is almost certainly under-recorded, hence the different distribution from that shown by Dony, whose field workers also missed it in N.E. Herts. However, it was formerly a feature of open railway banks, where Dony (1967) thought it might have been planted (although on what evidence is unclear). The overgrowth of these and the loss of roadside verges to eutrophication might have caused a genuine decline.
(75 tetrads: Dony, 1967; 84 tetrads: 1950-1986)

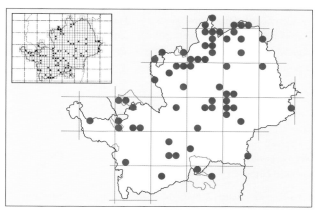

Map 776. *Poa angustifolia.*

Poa chaixii Villars
Broad-leaved Meadow-grass
Introduced: casual.
First record: 1955.

There have been no further confirmed records of this ornamental woodland grass since it was last found in Bramfield Park Wood (21/W), 1962 *J. G. Dony* (Hb. HTN). The record from near Langley given in James (1982) turned out to be an error.

Poa compressa L.
Flattened Meadow-grass
Native.
First record: 1819.
Tetrad occurrence: 59 (12%).
Stable? (-2%).

A rather local and enigmatic species of dry, bare ground on mainly calcareous substrates. It occurs in old chalk pits, on bare roadside banks, disturbed gravelly ground, old walls and similar places, and does not appear to tolerate competition. It can easily be overlooked, and has been confused with other *Poa* species, especially *P. humilis* on walls. Its current distribution may owe more to the areas where botanists felt able to identify it rather than its true distribution, as several areas in central Hertfordshire from which it was formerly recorded no longer appear to have it.
(57 tetrads: Dony, 1967; 74 tetrads: 1950-1986)

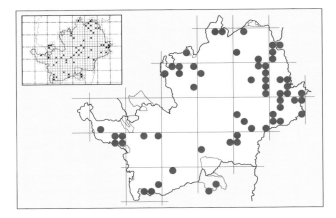

Map 777. *Poa compressa.*

Poa palustris L.
Swamp Meadow-grass
Introduced: casual.
First (only) record: 1966.

The only record of this European wetland grass, formerly grown for fodder, is from Park Street tip (10/L), 1966 *A. Brewis/A. M. Hugh-Smith* (Dony, 1969). It could be overlooked as *P. trivialis* in disturbed wetland areas.

Poa nemoralis L.
Wood Meadow-grass
Native.
First record: 1824.
Tetrad occurrence: 338 (69%).
Increased (+17%).

An ancient woodland plant on dry, neutral or mildly acidic soils, sometimes on Chalk, where this is overlain by a thin veneer of Clay-with-Flints. It has been much better recorded, especially in east Hertfordshire, than it was in 1967, although there does seem to be some spread, perhaps because of the increased shade of woodlands.
(272 tetrads: Dony, 1967; 285 tetrads: 1950-1986)

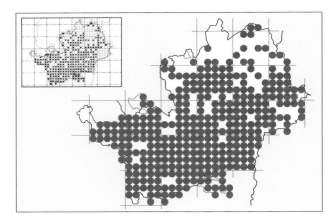

Map 778. *Poa nemoralis.*

Dactylis glomerata L.
Cock's-foot
Native.
First record: 1748.
Tetrad occurrence: 483 (98%).
Stable (-1%).

A common, tufted species of all more or less open grasslands, except the most acidic or wet, also occurring in ruderal habitats and waste ground, but not often as the dominant grass. It is occasionally sown alongside arable fields as 'beetle banks'. It shows no sign of having changed in occurrence significantly since 1967.
(465 tetrads: Dony, 1967; and from 1950-1986)

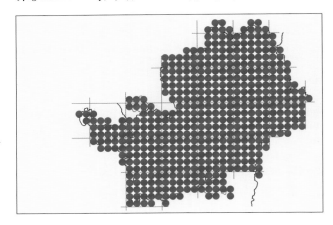

Map 779. *Dactylis glomerata.*

Catabrosa aquatica (L.) P. Beauv.
Water Whorl-grass
Native.
First record: 1838.
Tetrad occurrence: 22 (5%).
Decreasing markedly (-45%).

This rather delicate grass is characteristic of the muddy margins of ditches and rivers where they are adjacent to old cattle pastures. Not surprisingly, it has declined sharply since the 1960s as low-intensity cattle grazing has all but disappeared, and rivers have been fenced, supposedly for 'conservation' purposes! It appears to

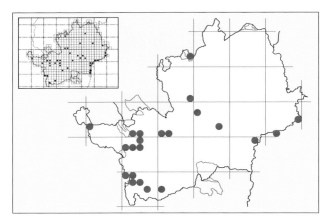

Map 780. *Catabrosa aquatica.*

be holding its own better in the Chess Valley than elsewhere, but in much of central and eastern Hertfordshire has now all but gone. (38 tetrads: Dony, 1967; 43 tetrads: 1950-1986)

Genus: *Catapodium*

Catapodium rigidum (L.) C. E. Hubbard
Fern Grass
Native.
First record: 1838.
Tetrad occurrence: 51 (10%).
Decreased (-35%).

This plant of bare chalky ground by fields, chalky banks, calcareous gravel pits and old walls or pavement cracks appears to have declined to some extent generally, although in some places it seems to be increasing, especially in villages in north Herts., where it may have benefited from increasing summer warmth, or has been introduced.
(75 tetrads: Dony, 1967; 85 tetrads: 1950-1986)

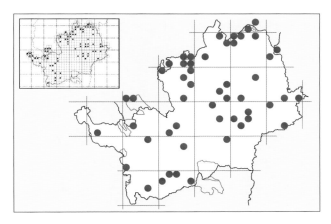

Map 781. *Catapodium rigidum.*

Genus: *Hainardia*

Hainardia cylindrica (Willd.) Greuter
One-glumed Hard-grass
Introduced: casual.
First record: 1965.

This Mediterranean weed is introduced with bird seed, and was first found at Cock Lane tip, Hoddesdon (30/U), 1965 *B. Wurzell* (Hb. HTN); and subsequently at Park Street tip (10/L), 1966 *J. G. Dony* (Hb. HTN). A record from tetrad 30/N, with no further details, is included in the Biological Records Centre database. There are no recent records.

Genus: *Glyceria*

Glyceria maxima (Hartmann) O. Holmb.
Reed Sweet-grass
Native.
First record: 1824.
Tetrad occurrence: 191 (39%).
Increased substantially (+31%).

A locally dominant plant of swamps, ditches, and river margins, colonising new water bodies where the water supply is eutrophic. Its increase has gone hand-in-hand with the neglect and fencing of water courses in many areas of pasture, and the increasing eutrophication of rivers.
(138 tetrads: Dony, 1967; 162 tetrads: 1950-1986)

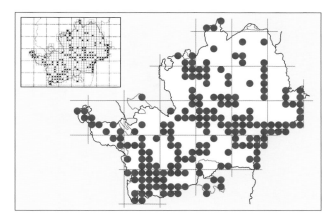

Map 782. *Glyceria maxima.*

Glyceria fluitans (L.) R. Br.
Floating Sweet-grass
Native.
First record: 1838.
Tetrad occurrence: 210 (43%).
Increased, now stable? (+15%).

Characteristic of semi-shaded, muddy ponds, pools in tracks and damp hollows in pasture, often dominant where it occurs, on a wide range of soil types, from quite acidic, through to moderately calcareous clays, especially if the habitat is eutrophic. It appears to have increased since the early 1960s, having been found in many more tetrads up to 1986. However, the recent survey may have shown that its increase has slackened.
(174 tetrads: Dony, 1967; 209 tetrads: 1950-1986)

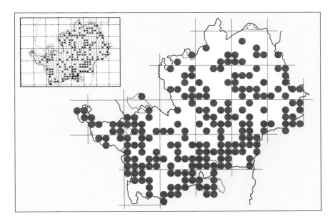

Map 783. *Glyceria fluitans.*

Glyceria × *pedicillata* F. Towns. (*G. fluitans* × *G. notata*)
Hybrid Sweet-grass
Native.
First record: 1875.
Tetrad occurrence: 18 (4%).
Decreased (-18%).

Found where its parents meet, and generally governed by the present or former occurrence of *G. notata*, therefore tending to occur in more calcareous habitats, beside ditches and ponds in old pastures. It can outlive its parents in such places, where it spreads vegetatively to form extensive patches. It appears to have declined, perhaps owing to the gradual loss of old meadows and the ponds in them.

(21 tetrads: Dony, 1967; 26 tetrads: 1950-1986)

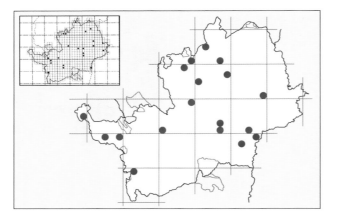

Map 784. *Glyceria × pedicillata.*

Glyceria declinata Bréb.
Small Sweet-grass
Native.
First record: 1905.
Tetrad occurrence: 41 (8%).
Increased? (+18%).

Local, found in similar places to *G. fluitans*, but often on rather more acidic clays in heathy areas. Its somewhat glaucous colour is often distinctive. The records given by Dony (1967) may include a few errors, as his ms. index includes a number of records from calcareous soils in north-east Herts., as well as elsewhere, that have been omitted from the map in his *Flora*. Evidently, he may have had doubts about these records, and given that others also occur in areas without acidic habitat, some of these may also be wrong. This makes it difficult to assess change in the occurrence of the species, although it appears to have increased.

(33 tetrads: Dony, 1967; 53 tetrads: 1950-1986)

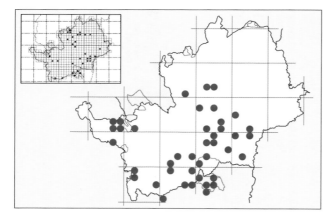

Map 785. *Glyceria declinata.*

Glyceria notata Chevall.
Plicate Sweet-grass
Native.
First record: 1849.
Tetrad occurrence: 107 (22%).
Increased? (or now decreased) (+3%).

This is the usual sweet-grass found in silted ponds and ditches in

pastures on the chalky Boulder Clay, as well as more calcareous silted waterbodies elsewhere. It appears to have increased following publication of the 1967 Flora, but may now have decreased again, as it has not been re-found in some areas where old pastures have been lost.

(99 tetrads: Dony, 1967; 123 tetrads: 1950-1986)

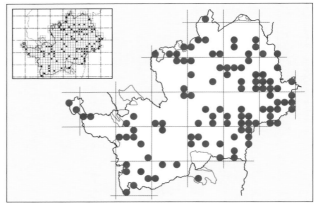

Map 786. *Glyceria notata.*

Genus: *Melica*

Melica uniflora Retz.
Wood Melick
Native.
First record: 1735.
Tetrad occurrence: 215 (44%).
Probably stable (-1%).

A beautiful woodland or woodland-edge grass, especially characteristic of the well-drained Clay-with-Flints soils, but also found on moderately acidic loams elsewhere in south-east and east Hertfordshire.

(206 tetrads: Dony, 1967; 224 tetrads: 1950-1986)

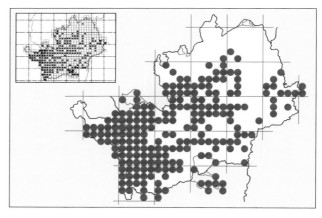

Map 787. *Melica uniflora.*

[*Melica nutans* L.
Mountain Melick

A record of this was reported by the Railway Survey team of the then Institute of Terrestrial Ecology from Bragbury End (22/Q), 1977. This must be considered an error without further evidence, although introduction with ballast is possible.]

Genus: *Helictotrichon*

Helictotrichon pubescens (Hudson) Pilger
Downy Oat-grass
Native.
First record: 1838.
Tetrad occurrence: 96 (20%).
Decreasing (-40%).

A plant of old grassland on calcareous soils, this is frequent on rough chalk downland, and occurs quite widely on road verges on dry, calcareous soils elsewhere. It is becoming very scarce in old Boulder Clay pastures. The recent survey showed a marked decrease in records from the 1960s. However, there are signs it may have been under-recorded in some areas, as it remains quite widespread on the Chalk, and on the dry, calcareous grasslands in west Herts. It may, therefore, not have decreased as much as the data suggest.
(153 tetrads: Dony, 1967; 164 tetrads: 1950-1986)

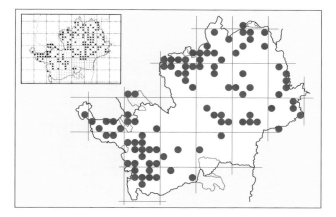

Map 788. *Helictotrichon pubescens.*

Helictotrichon pratense (L.) Besser
Meadow Oat-grass
Native.
First record: 1748.
Tetrad occurrence: 27 (6%).
Apparently increased (+224%).

A rather scarce, but by no means rare grass of dry, chalk grassland, usually growing in open, but neglected pasture. Its tough, glaucous leaf-rosettes with hooded leaf-tips can sometimes be quite conspicuous, and are unattractive to livestock. Dony

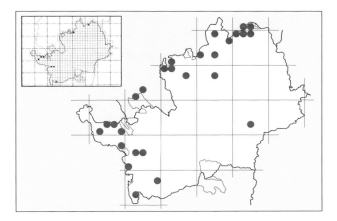

Map 789. *Helictotrichon pratense.*

(1967) thought it was rare, but it does not seem to be any rarer now than it was in the 19th century (Pryor, 1887), and may have increased in the sites where it occurs, possibly because it is now more evident in rough grassland. Its distribution clearly demarcates the Chalk outcrops across northern and western Hertfordshire, but old sites on the Chalk near Hertford may have been lost.
(8 tetrads: Dony, 1967; 15 tetrads: 1950-1986)

Genus: *Arrhenatherum*

Arrhenatherum elatius (L.) P. Beauv. ex J. S. Presl and C. Presl
False Oat-grass
Native.
First record: 1750.
Tetrad occurrence: 481 (98%).
Stable (-1%).

This is the principal grass of calcareous or neutral rough grassland, occurring abundantly on road verges, neglected pastures and waste ground throughout the County. It is only absent on very wet or very acidic soils. The lack of a record from one complete tetrad is an oversight.
(461 tetrads: Dony, 1967; and from 1950-1986)

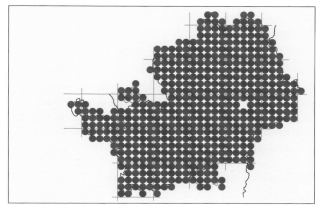

Map 790. *Arrhenatherum elatius.*

Genus: *Avena*

Avena strigosa Schreber
Bristle Oat
Introduced: casual
First record: 1841.

Dony (1967) appeared to suggest that there had only been one record, but it had in fact been first recorded as a grain contaminant from Hertford in 1841, and also occurred at Rye House and near Balls Wood in the 1840s (Pryor, 1887). Dony's ms. index also includes a reference to its occurrence at Hitchin tip (13/V), 1959 *C. C. Townsend*, which he was not aware of when writing the *Flora*.

Avena fatua L.
Wild Oat
Introduced: archaeophyte.
First record: 1733.
Tetrad occurrence: 340 (69%).
Increased substantially (+50%).

A virulent arable weed on especially calcareous clay soils, also occurring on waste ground. Its increase was obviously under way shortly after Dony's *Flora* was written, as it became widespread in several areas during the 1970s where before it had been scarce. Its present occurrence admirably demonstrates the ineffectiveness of weedkillers in the face of increased fertilisation in agriculture! (215 tetrads: Dony, 1967; 254 tetrads: 1950-1986)

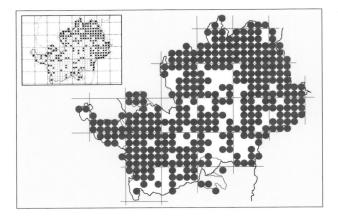

Map 791. *Avena fatua.*

Avena sterilis L.
Winter Wild Oat
Introduced: neophyte.
First record: 1945.
Tetrad occurrence: 59 (12%).
Increased? (+700%).

Like its relative, this is a weed of arable fields, usually on damper soils, and of waste places, tips, *etc.* It is still probably frequently overlooked, as it can grow with its commoner relative. As a result, the distribution map mostly indicates that some recorders were not looking out for it, although it does seem to favour more calcareous soils.
(7 tetrads: Dony, 1967; 10 tetrads: 1950-1986)

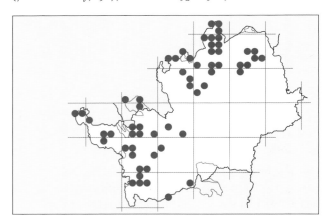

Map 792. *Avena sterilis.*

The Hertfordshire plants so far have appeared to be ssp. *ludoviciana* (Durieu) Gillet and Magne.

Avena sterilis L.
Oat
Introduced: casual.
First record: *c.*1950.
Tetrad occurrence: 40 (8%).

Cultivated Oat as an escape was not noted by most earlier botanists, being first reported at Bishop's Stortford by

D. McClintock (Dony, ms. index), although it must have occurred earlier as an escape. The current survey showed it can be quite widespread, sometimes possibly persistent, both as an arable weed, and as a casual in waste places. It was recorded mostly on the Boulder Clay and Chalk, parallel with its main areas of cultivation.

Genus: *Trisetum*

Trisetum flavescens (L.) P. Beauv.
Yellow Oat-grass
Native.
First record: 1838.
Tetrad occurrence: 333 (68%).
Decreasing (-21%).

An attractive grass of dry calcareous or neutral grasslands, found in old pastures, roadsides, and sometimes colonising waste ground. It occurs widely across the County in suitable habitats, but is steadily retreating from more eutrophic habitats, where it is out-competed by False Oat-grass.
(401 tetrads: Dony, 1967; 417 tetrads: 1950-1986)

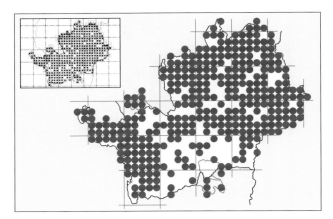

Map 793. *Trisetum flavescens.*

Genus: *Koeleria*

Koeleria macrantha (Ledeb.) Schultes
Crested Hair-grass
Native.
First record: 1838.
Tetrad occurrence: 35 (7%).
Decreasing (-37%).

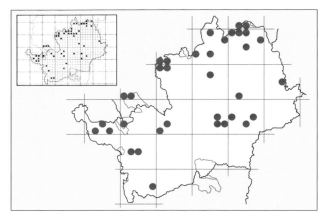

Map 794. *Koeleria macrantha.*

A characteristic plant of short, nutrient-poor grassland on Chalk or calcareous gravels and sands, found mainly now on chalk downland, but also rarely on dry knolls in flood-plain meadows, or on roadside banks. It has decreased markedly in its roadside sites, but remains in its main downland localities. The current survey demonstrated its disappearance from many areas, but it was found to be more widespread around Hertford than recorded by Dony (1967).

(52 tetrads: Dony, 1967; 60 tetrads: 1950-1986)

Genus: Deschampsia

Deschampsia cespitosa (L.) P. Beauv.
Tufted Hair-grass
Native.
First record: 1821.
Tetrad occurrence: 384 (78%).
Stable or slightly decreased (-7%).

An often abundant plant of damp pastures, roadside ditches, and woodland rides. Despite the loss of old grasslands, there does not seem to be a significant decrease in the occurrence of the species at the tetrad level. Unfortunately, there has been no attempt to distinguish between the plants of woodlands and those of wet grasslands, which are now considered to be separate subspecies. The former (ssp. *parviflora* (Thuill.) Dumort.), which was recorded first from the Bayfordbury estate (31/A) in the 1950s (Dony, ms. index), occurs widely in semi-natural coppices, especially on the Boulder Clay; while the nominate subspecies is the more robust plant of open grasslands, often forming dense stands in poorly maintained pasture.

(392 tetrads: Dony, 1967; 400 tetrads: 1950-1986)

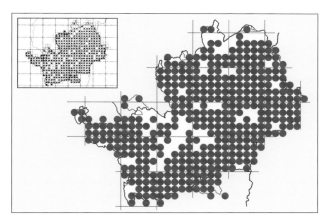

Map 795. *Deschampsia cespitosa.*

Deschampsia flexuosa (L.) Trin.
Wavy Hair-grass
Native.
First record: 1843.
Tetrad occurrence: 38 (8%).
Decreasing (-14%).

One of the characteristic plants of somewhat shaded, heathy ground on old commons and in woodlands on heathy soils, where it can be confused with *Festuca filiformis* when not flowering. It was regarded by Coleman and Pryor as rare in the County (Pryor, 1887), but is now occasional, being particularly characteristic of the Ashridge estate and adjoining commons. It was apparently under-recorded by Dony (1967), having been missed in most

of east Herts. Nevertheless it is now being lost owing to eutrophication and overgrowth of more open woodlands on acidic soils.

(42 tetrads: Dony, 1967; 49 tetrads: 1950-1986)

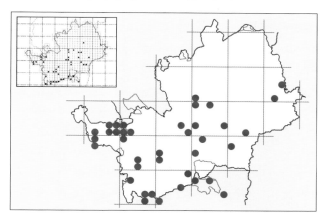

Map 796. *Deschampsia flexuosa.*

Genus: *Holcus*

Holcus lanatus L.
Yorkshire Fog
Native.
First record: 1824.
Tetrad occurrence: 469 (96%).
Stable or marginally decreased (-3%).

Occurring in semi-natural damp grasslands and woodland rides, as well as in ruderal habitats, damp roadsides and waste ground. It only becomes rare on the Chalk, and also on more acidic clay and gravels, where it is replaced by *H. mollis*.

(460 tetrads: Dony, 1967; 461 tetrads: 1950-1986)

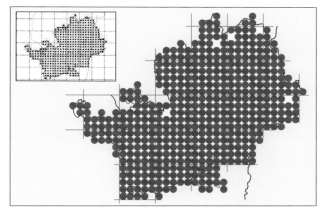

Map 797. *Holcus lanatus.*

Holcus × *hybridus* Wein (*H. lanatus* × *H. mollis*)
Native.
First record: 1997.

This hybrid, which looks more like *H. mollis* than it does *H. lanatus*, is probably widespread where the two plants meet, but the only actual record made was from a set-aside arable field at Jockey Farm, Caddington (01/P) (VC20 [Beds.]), 1997 *C. R. Boon/T. J./G. Salisbury.*

Holcus mollis L.
Creeping Soft-grass
Native.
First record: 1748.
Tetrad occurrence: 311 (63%).
Increased (+24%).

This is a specially characteristic grass of wood borders and semi-shaded grassland on acidic loams and clays in southern and western Hertfordshire, where it can form dominant stands, often in association with Bluebells and *Stellaria holostea*. It appears to be increasing on waste ground, and in shaded grasslands on more calcareous clay soils, possibly owing to nitrogen enrichment.
(238 tetrads: Dony, 1967; 259 tetrads: 1950-1986)

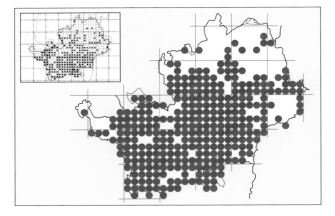

Map 798. *Holcus mollis.*

Genus: *Aira*

Aira caryophyllea L.   Herts Vulnerable
Silver Hair-grass
Native.
First record: 1838.
Tetrad occurrence: 13 (3%).
Severely decreased (-63%).

A beautiful, if unobtrusive grass of dry gravelly banks and grassland on moderately acidic, poor soils. It is a measure of the drastic decline in such habitats that this plant is rapidly disappearing, now mostly confined to a few sites in the south-west of the County, where it is often very limited in population size. Dony regarded it as characteristic of railway banks, but these have almost entirely been lost to scrub and eutrophication since the 1960s.
(34 tetrads: Dony, 1967; 46 tetrads: 1950-1986)

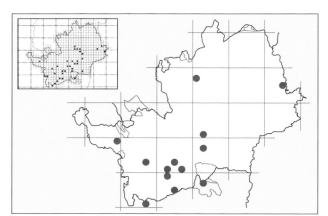

Map 799. *Aira caryophyllea.*

Aira praecox L.
Early Hair-grass
Native.
First record: 1838.
Tetrad occurrence: 44 (9%).
Decreased (-25%).

A local, but easily overlooked grass, flowering in the spring on dry gravelly ground, on commons, wood banks, *etc.* across the south of the County. It seems able to survive where its relative does not, possibly because its early flowering time and low growth allow it to set seed before it is mown off, such as on old golf courses. It appears to have disappeared from a number of localities in the Hertford area, but has been newly recorded elsewhere, especially in south-west Herts.
(56 tetrads: Dony, 1967; 64 tetrads: 1950-1986)

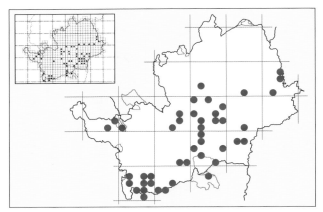

Map 800. *Aira praecox.*

Genus: *Anthoxanthum*

Anthoxanthum odoratum L.
Sweet Vernal-grass
Native.
First record: 1748.
Tetrad occurrence: 304 (62%).
Stable or somewhat decreasing (-8%).

A major constituent species of natural grasslands on freely-draining, neutral or moderately acidic loams, clays and gravels, occurring in pastures, hay fields, roadsides, old commons, woodland rides and the like. It is especially characteristic of old grasslands on the Clay-with-Flints, but also occurs on the London Clay, Reading gravels and Pleistocene gravels, *etc*. It is rare on

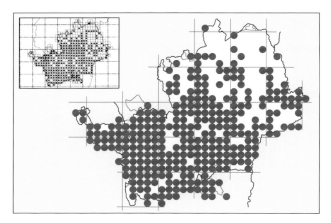

Map 801. *Anthoxanthum odoratum.*

Chalk, except where this is overlain by de-calcified glacial material. Where it occurs in north-east Herts., it is usually on patches of Clay-with-Flints soils that have been exposed through erosion of overlying calcareous Boulder Clay, which it avoids. (312 tetrads: Dony, 1967; 329 tetrads: 1950-1986)

Anthoxanthum aristatum Boiss.
Annual Vernal-grass
Introduced: neophyte or casual.
First record: 1913.

This appears to have persisted around West Wood, near Offley Holes (TL12) for a number of years, having first been found in 1913 *H. C. Littlebury*. It was last seen there in 1930 *R. Morse* (Hb. HTN). There have been no further records.

Genus: *Phalaris*

Phalaris arundinacea L.
Reed Canary-grass
Native.
First record: 1820.
Tetrad occurrence: 238 (49%).
Stable, or increased slightly (+4%).

Found frequently as large stands by rivers, lakes and ponds, often on less calcareous substrates. It has remained almost unchanged in distribution since the 1960s, although there may be some evidence that it has increased in the north of the County, as rivers have become more eutrophic.
(218 tetrads: Dony, 1967; 230 tetrads: 1950-1986)

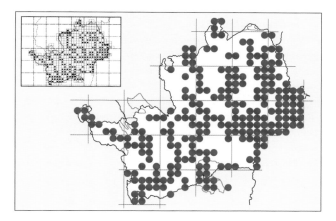

Map 802. *Phalaris arundinacea.*

Phalaris aquatica L.
Bulbous Canary-grass
Introduced: neophyte.
First record: 1990.

This was first noticed as a game crop relic at Kingswoodbury, Clothall (23/V), 1990 *T. J.* (Hb. HTN). During the survey, it has been noticed as an escape or relic in similar circumstances in nine tetrads, although it is almost certainly more widespread.

Phalaris canariensis L.
Canary-grass
Introduced: neophyte (or casual).
First record: 1821.
Tetrad occurrence: 42 (9%).
Decreased (-60%).

This has frequently been used as bird-feed, and has been present as an escape in consequence for a very long time. Dony (1967) thought it was increasing, but it now appears to be less widespread, other grains being favoured for this purpose.
(100 tetrads: Dony, 1967; 116 tetrads: 1950-1986)

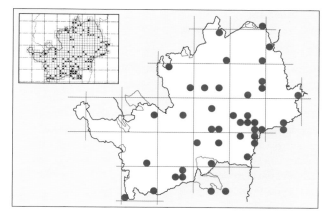

Map 803. *Phalaris canariensis.*

Phalaris brachystachys Link
Confused Canary-grass
Introduced: casual.
First record: 1961.

This has only ever been recorded from Hilfield Lane (19/M), 1961 (Dony, 1967), although, owing to its similarity to *P. canariensis* and other species, it could be overlooked.

Phalaris minor Retz.
Lesser Canary-grass
Introduced: casual.
First record: 1912.

Only ever a casual on waste tips, this was first seen at Purwell, Hitchin (22/E), 1912 *J. E. Little* (Hb. HTN). Dony (1967) gave two other records, and it was also seen at Welwyn (21/N), 1912 *J. E. Little* (Dony, ms. index). Recently, it appeared in a re-seeded grass field on former arable at Markham's Hill, Offley (12/J), 1999 *R. Keen/M. Hicks*; and as a bird-seed alien at Ashwell (23/U), 2002, 2003 *T. J.* (Hb. HTN). It is probably more widespread, and may have been misidentified as *P. canariensis*.

Phalaris paradoxa L.
Awned Canary-grass
Introduced: casual.
First record: 1912.

This was first found alongside *P. minor* at Purwell (22/E), 1912 *J. E. Little*. Dony (1967) also gave records from Ware and Hertford. There are no recent records, although it could be overlooked, as it is increasing nationally (Stace, 1997).

Phalaris angusta Nees ex Trin.
Introduced: casual.
First (only) record: 1923.

The only record of this north American cousin of *P. canariensis* was from Mead Lane, Hertford (31/G) *A. W. Graveson* (Hb. HTN).

Genus: *Agrostis*

Agrostis capillaris L.
Common Bent
Native.
First record: 1748.
Tetrad occurrence: 404 (82%).
Increased? (+23%).

A common, characteristic grass of agriculturally unimproved grassland on dry, more or less acidic soils, although it also can occur on neutral or even moderately calcareous soils as a minor component of the sward. As such, its apparent increase may be more down to better recording, because its principal habitat – unimproved acidic grassland – has certainly decreased in both quantity and quality since the 1960s. It only becomes rare on the Chalk and the most heavily agricultural areas of the Boulder Clay.
(311 tetrads: Dony, 1967; 321 tetrads: 1950-1986)

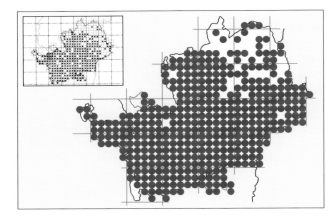

Map 804. *Agrostis capillaris.*

Agrostis × *murbeckii* Fouill. ex P. Fourn.
(*A. capillaris* × *A. stolonifera*)
Native.

This hybrid bent was not recorded until 1962 (Dony, 1967). During the survey, it was noticed in old acidic grassland at Dalmonds, by Elbow Lane, Goose Green (30/P) *T. J.* (det. T. A. Cope) (Hb. HTN); Hadham Hall (42/L), 1991 *M. J. Hicks* (det. T. A. Cope) (Hb. HTN); Hudnall Common (01/B) (VC24 [Herts.]), 1996 *T. J.* (Hb. HTN); Birklands, St Albans (10/S), 1997 *T. J./G. Salisbury* (Hb. HTN). It is probably widespread where the parent species overlap.

Agrostis × *sanionis* Asch. and Graebn.
(*A. capillaris* × *A. vinealis*)
Native.
First record: 1985.

This rare sterile hybrid was determined from a specimen collected from an old pasture at Barnet (29/M) (VC20 [Greater London]) *A. W. Vaughan* (det T. A. Cope, 2006) (Hb. HTN).

Agrostis gigantea Roth
Black Bent
Introduced: archaeophyte.
First record: 1927.
Tetrad occurrence: 202 (41%).
Decreasing (-12%).

This is a weed of arable fields and waste ground across much of the County, although there is some evidence it has decreased recently. It was under-recorded in the 1960s survey, and subsequent records found it to be more common than Dony reported in the south-east especially. Its decrease probably owes something to concerted efforts to eradicate it from arable land, but it remains common.
(219 tetrads: Dony, 1967; 256 tetrads: 1950-1986)

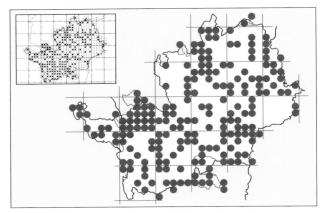

Map 805. *Agrostis gigantea.*

Agrostis castellana Boiss. and Reuter
Highland Bent
Introduced: neophyte.
First record: 1989.

This grass is apparently used in amenity mixes, and is probably sown widely on roadsides and other areas. However, there are few confirmed records from the County. It was first found in a recently partially re-seeded old grassland by Fiveacre Wood at Anstey (43/B), 1989 *T. J.* (Hb. HTN). It has subsequently turned up in a dry hay field at Queenswood Farm, North Mymms (20/S), 1990 *T. J.* (Hb. HTN); in a sown field by Hog Wood, Kimpton (11/Z), 1993 *T. J.* (Hb. HTN); at Purwell Meadows, Hitchin (12/Z), 1993 *C. R. Birkinshaw* (det. T. J.) (where it was probably sown after a pipeline was laid in the 1970s); and under birch trees in Watery Grove, Knebworth (22/G), 1996 *T. J.* (Hb. HTN) (an unlikely site, where its source is uncertain). It is almost certainly elsewhere, and can be mistaken for *A. capillaris*.

Agrostis stolonifera L.
Creeping Bent
Native.
First record: 1838.
Tetrad occurrence: 458 (93%).
Probably stable (-4%).

A very common species, found in rough grasslands, road verges, scrub, arable margins and waste ground throughout the County on most soils. It is only uncommon in intensively managed arable on dry soils, or on very acidic soils. It was apparently missed in a few tetrads around St Albans and elsewhere, but is almost certainly there.
(453 tetrads: Dony, 1967; and from 1950-1986)

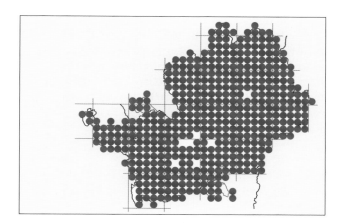

Map 806. *Agrostis stolonifera.*

Agrostis canina L.
Velvet Bent
Native.
First record: 1838.
Tetrad occurrence: 49 (10%).
Possibly stable (+92%).

Dony (1967) did not distinguish between this and *A. vinealis* (formerly regarded as ssp. *montana* (Hartm.) Hartm.). As a result, comparison between past and present records is more difficult. However, earlier botanists regarded it as an uncommon plant of damp, acidic soils, on heaths, wood margins and woodland rides., so past records are most likely to refer to the strict species. It is now recorded much more thoroughly, and was found during the survey in damp heathy grassland mainly in south and west Herts., especially at Ashridge; around Broxbourne Woods; the Cuffley and Barnet areas; Batchworth Heath and Bishop's Wood area; rides and clearings on Reading gravels in the Bramfield Woods complex; and in old woodland rides and grasslands associated with the Knebworth Woods.
(24 tetrads: Dony, 1967; 51 tetrads: 1950-1986)

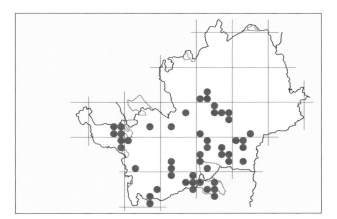

Map 807. *Agrostis canina.*

Agrostis vinealis Schreber
Brown Bent
Native.
First confirmed record: 1985.
Tetrad occurrence: 15 (3%).
Stable?

This was formerly subsumed under *A. canina*, and past botanists in the County did not distinguish it. It was not properly recorded

in the County (as *A. canina* ssp. *montana*) until 1985, when it was found at Berkhamsted (90/Z) *S. and P. Kingsbury*. However, it has probably always been rather rare, certainly since most of the large commons in S. and W. Herts. were lost to inclosure in the early 19th century or before. It is now especially characteristic of the Ashridge/Berkhamsted Common complex, where it is locally abundant in dry acidic grasslands in open areas, clearings, rides, and round the golf course. It is also found in other widely scattered dry heathy sites, mainly old commons, or former wood-pastures, such as Bricket Wood Common, Broxbourne Woods, Patmore Heath, Colney Heath, Nomansland Common and Chorleywood Common.

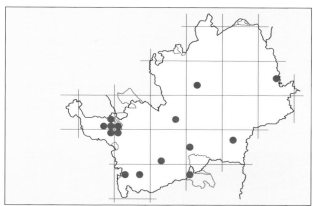

Map 808. *Agrostis vinealis.*

Genus: *Calamagrostis*

Calamagrostis epigejos (L.) Roth
Wood Small-reed
Native.
First record: 1838.
Tetrad occurrence: 58 (12%).
Increased (+141%).

This is mainly a species of scrubby grassland, woodland rides and clearings. It forms dense stands dominating often quite large areas, and has shown strong signs of increasing over the last 20 years or so. It now often appears on waste ground, and has spread out from its apparently preferred Boulder Clay areas, as shown by Dony (1967), now occurring patchily across most of the County, sometimes on roadside verges and railway banks, as well as young scrub on open land, or even in old damp grassland elsewhere. It may be encouraged by deer grazing in woods, and also perhaps by

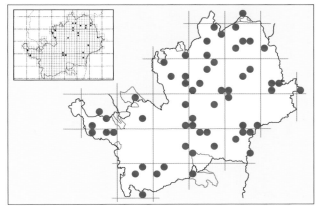

Map 809. *Calamagrostis epigejos.*

nutrient enrichment to some extent.
(23 tetrads: Dony, 1967; 40 tetrads: 1950-1986)

Calamagrostis canescens (Wigg.) Roth   Herts Rare
Purple Small-reed
Native.
First record: 1843.

Until recently, this was thought to be long-extinct in
Hertfordshire, being a plant of permanently wet fen or woodland.
Pryor (1887) repeats the three localities given by Webb and
Coleman (1849): 'Newlands Wood' near Rickmansworth (almost
certainly Newland's Spring, by Whippendell Wood) (09/T); Reed
Wood (33/S); and Balls Wood (31/K). In the latter, it was quoted
to occur in various parts of the wood in 'great plenty', and Dony
notes the existence of a specimen from Balls Wood in Hb. BM.
There is also a 19th century specimen from the locality at North
Herts. Museums (Hb. HTN). Attempts to re-find it at Balls Wood
have failed, it now appearing to have been replaced by *C. epigejos*.
However, a good stand of the species appeared unexpectedly by a
recently exposed pond at Watery Grove, Knebworth (22/G), 2008
T. J. (Hb. HTN).

Photo: Paula Shipway

Purple Small-reed Calamagrostis canescens *Watery Grove, Knebworth,*
2009.

Genus: *Gastridium*

Gastridium ventricosum (Gouan) Schinz and Thell.
Nit-grass
Probably introduced [native in the U.K.].
First record: 1831.
Apparently extinct.

This was a rare weed on disturbed, clay soils in the 19th century,
with scattered records from Rickmansworth, Bayford, near
Stevenage and near Hatfield. It was last seen 'near Cowheath
Wood, Bayford' (TL30) in 1946 *S. Phelp* (Kent and Lousley, 1957).
This was actually a different site from the Bayford site where
Coleman found it 'in plenty' in 1841 (Webb and Coleman, 1849;
Dony, 1967 and ms. index).

Genus: *Lagurus*

Lagurus ovatus L.
Hare's-tail
Introduced: casual [neophyte elsewhere in U.K.].
First record: 1977.

This Mediterranean grass of waste places and open habitats was
first recorded at Cuffley (30/B), 1977 *H. J. Killick* (James, 1982). It
occurred again at Berkhamsted (90/Z), 1985 *S. and P. Kingsbury*;
and in the recent survey it was also recorded from Hoddesdon
(30/U), 1987 *A. M. Boucher*; Hitchin (12/Z), 1988 *K. Robinson*
(Hb. HTN); and from Harpenden (11/H), 1994 *J. F. Southey*. All
records are likely to be from flower arrangement materials!

Genus: *Apera*

Apera spica-venti (L.) P. Beauv.   [UK Near Threatened]
Loose Silky-bent
Introduced: casual [archaeophyte in U.K.].
First record: 1805.

This is a plant of dry, sandy or gravelly ground, often as a cornfield
weed in other areas, and at one time also in Hertfordshire. As
Dony (1967) says, it had become a casual of waste ground by his
time, and its last confirmed records were as such from Bushey
(19/M), 1970 *C. R. Huxley et al.* (*comm.*: B. RC.: CEH Monks
Wood); Cassiobury Park (09/Y), 1973 *K. Preston-Mafham*
(*comm.*: St Albans Museum); and a single plant by Ware tip
(31/M), 1985 *C. G. Hanson* (Hb. HTN). There were a few reports
from the St Albans area during the survey, but none were
confirmed by a specimen. There was also a tetrad record from
29/W in Burton (1983), that may or may not have referred to
Hertfordshire.

Apera interrupta (L.) P. Beauv.
Dense Silky-bent
Introduced: casual? [neophyte in U.K.].
First (only) record: 1990.

This plant of open, sandy habitats, characteristic now of parts
of Breckland, was found on disturbed sandy ground around
Wymondley electricity grid station (22/D), 1990 *K. Robinson*
(det. T. J.) (Hb. HTN). How the seed got there is unknown, but
the disturbed soils in which it was growing derived from a former
gravel pit.

Genus: *Polypogon*

Polypogon monspeliensis (L.) Desf.
Annual Beard-grass
Introduced: casual [native in the U.K.].
First record: 1916.

Noted as a casual, probably from grain, at Ware and Hitchin by
earlier botanists, and at Abbots Langley in 1961 (Dony, 1967);
this was not found again until it turned up at Baldock (23/L),
1989 *K. Robinson* (det. T. J.) (Hb. HTN), and at Standon (32/W),
1994 *S. Watson* (Hb. HTN). Recently, it has also appeared in
considerabe quantity at Cooper's Green Gravel Pits (10/Z), 2009
W. Bishop (det. T. J.) (Hb. HTN).

Polypogon viridis (Gouan) Breistr.
Water Bent
Introduced: neophyte.
First record: 1988.
Increasing.

Potentially a plant that could be established on damp, disturbed
ground, pavements, *etc.*, this is usually currently a casual in
Hertfordshire, but is spreading. It was first found at an old

nursery at Turnford (30/S), 1988 *A. M. Boucher* (Hb. HTN), and subsequently has turned up at Hoddesdon (30/U), 1993 *A. M. B.*; near Borehamwood (19/Y), 1998 *T. J.* (Hb. HTN); Bishop's Stortford (42/W), 2003 *S. Watson*; and as a roadside weed at Baldock (23/L), 2007 *T. J.* The Borehamwood site was interesting, in that it was growing on a disturbed stream bank, away from habitation, much like its more natural habitats in Guernsey and elsewhere.

Genus: *Alopecurus*

Alopecurus pratensis L.
Meadow Foxtail
Native.
First record: 1838.
Tetrad occurrence: 438 (89%).
Decreased (-9%).

This characteristic and attractive grass of early summer, found in semi-natural grasslands throughout the County, was ubiquitous when Dony carried out his survey. It is most abundant on neutral, slightly damp soils, especially the Boulder Clay and London Clay, where it forms a major component of natural grasslands, and was also the result of having frequently been sown as hay-meadow or pasture mixes in the past. However, the recent survey showed a slight, but significant decrease, even at the tetrad level, and it was particularly scarce on the Chalk, where permanent grassland is limited, and where road verges have lost much of their interest through neglect, eutrophication and salt. It is quite an important grass for insects, which like to feed on its anthers, and its decrease may be a factor in the decline of some species of beetle.
(455 tetrads: Dony, 1967 and from 1950-1986)

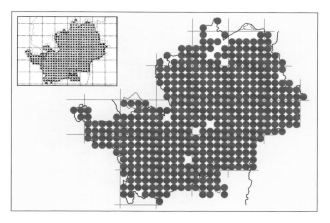

Map 810. *Alopecurus pratensis.*

Alopecurus geniculatus L.
Marsh Foxtail
Native.
First record: 1824.
Tetrad occurrence: 142 (29%).
Decreased (-13%).

This grass is more strictly limited to semi-natural grasslands, being characteristic of seasonally wet areas in old pastures, woodland rides and beside ponds, usually on clay soils. It can also colonise new habitats, in pools or vehicle ruts around old gravel pits, for example. It has also shown a significant decline in the last 40 years, owing to the general loss of old grasslands. It was evidently under-recorded in the 1960s, as it has been found widely in west Hertfordshire, and in different localities elsewhere. However, it has shown evident losses from many previously recorded areas.
(155 tetrads: Dony, 1967; 182 tetrads: 1950-1986)

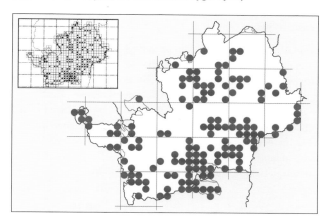

Map 811. *Alopecurus geniculatus.*

Alopecurus aequalis Sobol.   Herts Rare
Orange Foxtail
Native (and introduced).
First record: 1819.
Tetrad occurrence: 6 (1%).
Increased? (+100%).

As a native species, this is characteristic of the muddy margins of the drawdown zone around ponds, and sometimes beside sluggish streams. It has always been rather rare in Herts., with nine localities, scattered across the County, known to early botanists; while Dony (1967) only recorded it from three post-1950 localities: a pond at Hadham Hall, Aldenham Reservoir and Hilfield Park Reservoir. After publication of Dony's *Flora*, it was recorded from a pond at Coldharbour Farm, Tring (91/A), 1967 *E. J. Douglas* (conf. J. G. Dony); gravel pits at Cock Lane, Hoddesdon (30/N, T), 1978 *A. M. Boucher*; and again at Aldenham Reservoir (19/S), 1981 *O. Linford*. An unlocalised and undated tetrad record from 20/Z was also submitted to London Natural History Society (*comm.*: R. M. Burton), presumably from Water Hall Gravel Pits. During the Flora Survey, it has appeared at six localities, although two of these are ephemeral sites: a filled gravel pit at High Leigh, Hoddesdon (30/U), 1991 *A. M. Boucher* (Hb. HTN), near where it occurred in 1978; and as a weed among bog plants at Cole Green Nursery (21/Q), 1993 *A. M. B.* In addition, it has been recorded twice by a muddy inlet at Wilstone Reservoir (91/B), 1989, 1991 *T. J.*, *A. Showler* (Hb. HTN); by the source of the River Gade at Great Gaddesden (01/G), 1996 *G. Salisbury/J. Saunders* (Hb. HTN), as well as not far away at Water End Meadows (01/F), 2002 *A. Harris* (conf. T. J.) (Hb. HTN); and finally at Startop's End Reservoir, on exposed mud (91/G), 2002 *G. Salisbury* (Hb. HTN). The last of these is an historic site for the plant, where it was previously last seen in 1943 (Dony, 1967).
(3 tetrads: Dony, 1967; 8 tetrads: 1950-1986)

Alopecurus myosuroides Hudson
Black-grass
Introduced: archaeophyte.
First record: 1750.
Tetrad occurrence: 381 (78%).
Increased slightly (+6%).

An often abundant weed of cultivated land and waste ground, especially on more calcareous and drier soils. It is widespread across central and northern Hertfordshire, and to a lesser extent on the Clay-with-Flints in west Herts. It only becomes scarce on the more acidic, wet London Clay and in urban areas. Despite the best attempts of the farming community to exterminate it, it has in fact increased slightly since the 1960s, or at least it has been recorded more widely.

(340 tetrads: Dony, 1967; 362 tetrads: 1950-1986)

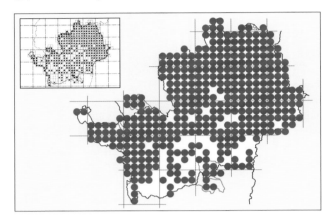

Map 812. *Alopecurus myosuroides.*

Genus: *Phleum*

Phleum pratense L.
Timothy
Native? (and introduced).
First record: (1748, for the agg.) 1910.
Tetrad occurrence: 386 (for the strict species (79%).
Decreased? (-9%).

The true Timothy grass is a usually rather tall species of pastures, hay-fields, grassy roadside verges and sometimes on waste land. In pastures, it was very often sown in the 19th century, being a better quality source of fodder than many more natural grasses; and it is now often sown as grass strips alongside agricultural headlands. As such, it is very difficult to tell whether it is, actually, a native plant at all! This is made worse by the fact that earlier botanists did not attempt to distinguish it from its smaller cousin, which definitely is native. This has been compounded until very recently by the fact that Clapham, Tutin and Warburg's '*Excursion flora*' (1981) persisted in the confusion! Therefore, even during the earlier part of the field work for the Flora Project, some botanists were not clear about the differences. However, an attempt has been made to sort the sheep from the goats, and the map presented here is, I hope, a good approximation to the truth. As such, it shows that it is frequent on damper clays, and even on the Chalk, but becomes a bit less common on the dry, more acidic Clay-with-Flints, much as Dony (1967) recorded. It is uncertain if the recorded decrease is real.

(402 tetrads: Dony, 1967; 420 tetrads: 1950-1986)

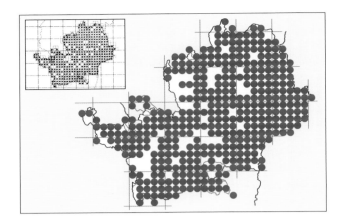

Map 813. *Phleum pratense.*

Phleum bertolonii DC.
Small Timothy
Native.
First record: *c.*1880 (for the segregate).
Tetrad occurrence: 404 (82%).
Decreased (-15%).

Small Timothy is an important constituent of semi-natural drier grasslands on most soils, only becoming scarce in more strongly acidic or wet habitats. The recent survey shows significant decreases, even at the tetrad level, from the ubiquitous distribution indicated in Dony (1967), especially on the Clay-with-Flints and the Chalk. In this case, the decrease is likely to be real. However, it is occasionally introduced with seed-mixes, and there are agricultural strains that can be difficult to identify (Preston *et al.*, 2002), so these factors need to be borne in mind.

(453 tetrads: Dony, 1967; 454 tetrads: 1950-1986)

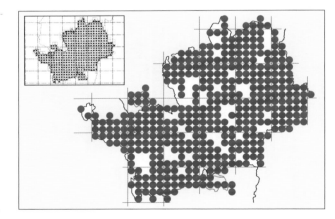

Map 814. *Phleum bertolonii.*

Phleum phleoides (L.) Karsten   Herts Rare
Purple-stem Cat's-tail
Native.
First record: 1839.

Purple-stem Cat's-tail is one of the most interesting plants in Hertfordshire, as Dony (1967) also acknowledged. It is an eastern plant in Europe generally, and is only at all frequent in Breckland in Britain, where it occurs in poor grasslands on calcareous sands and gravels. It typically grows on thin, friable soils in open vegetation, often associated with ants' nests, and is unable to compete with closed vegetation elsewhere. As such, its occurrence at Wilbury Hill, Letchworth (23/B), where it has for a long time

Purple-stem Cat's-tail Phleum phleoides *Wilbury Hill, 1996.*

been known to occur on both sides of the road (the western side being in VC30 [Herts.]), is a specially interesting feature. This thin deposit of glacial gravels, overlying Chalk, is typical of Breckland habitats, and is the most westerly surviving site for the plant in Europe. However, the scrap of good quality grassland adjoining the car park on the western side of the road has gradually become rank, possibly through eutrophication from the footpath, as well as scrub encroachment, so that the plant has not been seen here since 2001 *T. J.* It survives (2008) in small quantity by the old gravel pit on the eastern side of the road. Coleman (1849) also knew it from similar ground by the former Hertford Workhouse at Gallows Plain, Hertford (31/L), but, although apparently good habitat existed there until recently, it has not been found again. He also reported it from 'between Hatfield and Holwell [Hyde]', but the exact site for this is unknown.

Phleum paniculatum Hudson
Introduced: casual.
Only record: 1820.

There have been no records of this casual importation following its initial occurrence near Elstree (Dony, 1967).

Phleum exaratum Griseb.
Introduced: casual.
First record: 1916.

This appears to have been found more than once, as a casual grain import, being represented by a specimen in the Graveson Herbarium (Hb. HTN) from Ware, 1916; and also reported by

W. Graveson in 1920 from dredged mud by the Lee Navigation at Hertford (Dony, ms. index).

Genus: Bromus

Bromes, as a broad group, form quite a bewildering array of species, often of more or less open, disturbed habitats. The taxonomic treatment of these has also changed substantially over the years, so that it is sometimes difficult to be sure to what 'species' some earlier records belong. Identification of individual specimens can also be extremely problematic, and opinions have varied as to where real differences lie, and which characters may or may not be reliable. Apart from the most common species, identifications were largely carried out during the Flora Project using Wigginton and Graham (1981) to supplement Hubbard (1984) initially, and later with Rich *et al.* (1998), towards the end of the Project. Given that the treatments in these sources differ considerably, it is not surprising that, where specimens were not kept, some earlier identifications might now be suspect. I have tried to indicate where these problems might lie, and to remove obvious errors from the database. A number of specimens have recently been named by T. A. Cope, to whom I offer my thanks for his assistance.

Bromus arvensis L.
Field Brome
Introduced: neophyte.
First record: *c.*1880.
Extinct.

Although Webb and Coleman did not record it, Pryor (1887) gives quite a number of scattered records from various localities on gravels and Chalk especially, usually in cultivated fields; and J. E. Little also gives six records from the Hitchin and Pirton areas early in the 20th century. It was apparently quite often in Sainfoin crops. The last record appears to be from Haileybury (TL31), 1936 *A. G. Harrold* (Dony, ms. index).

Bromus commutatus Schrader
Meadow Brome
Native.
First record: 1843.
Tetrad occurrence: 79 (16%).
Increased markedly (+433%).

This was evidently quite a scarce grass when Dony was carrying out his survey, although he does remark that it occurs as often in

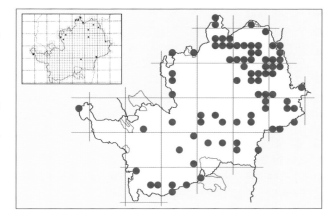

Map 815. *Bromus commutatus.*

443

arable fields as it does in grasslands. Pryor (1887) thought it was 'occasional', while most of his records appear to suggest the arable habitat also. In fact, there appears to be evidence that its increased occurrence in the margins of arable fields, particularly on the calcareous Boulder Clay, has been the major source of its recent increase. It is now frequent especially in the north-east, while its occurrence in old flood-plain grasslands has remained much as it was – rather rare, and therefore possibly as an adventive in such places, despite its common name. It is also now occasionally sown in grass leys on former arable, *e.g.* around Offley (TL12).
(14 tetrads: Dony, 1967; 20 tetrads: 1950-1986)

Bromus racemosus L.
Smooth Brome
Native.
First record: 1838.
Tetrad occurrence: 8 (2%).
Increased? (+167%).

This, rather than its relative, ought to be called Meadow Brome, because it is almost always found in old, damp, river valley pastures and hay meadows. It has a rather odd history of records in Hertfordshire, with scattered occurrences over a long period from Rickmansworth to Long Marston, and from Cheshunt to Ashwell and Reed. In a very few places, it has had records repeated over time, such as at Ickleford Common (13/W), where it was recorded by Pryor (1887), and was re-found in 1989 *T. J.* (Hb. HTN). It was also re-discovered at Long Marston (81/T), 1993 *M. Hicks* (det. T. J.) (Hb. HTN), near where Pryor recorded it. Dony (1967) recorded it from three locations only, one of which was Boxmoor (00/N), where it was re-discovered in 1999 by G. Salisbury, and again in 2005 *T. J.* (Hb. HTN). After Dony's survey, there was a record from near Roxford (31/A), 1974 *J. Killick*; but no subsequent records were received until the present survey began. Other localities for it recorded during the survey include: Hunsdon Mead (41/A, F), 1989, 1990 *S. Watson/T. J.* (Hb. HTN); meadow at The Wallbrooks, Totteridge (29/H), 1990 *A. W. Vaughan*; near Redhouse Farm, Puttenham (81/X), 1990 *V. Kempster* (det. T. J.) (Hb. HTN); and finally, atypically, on the margin of an arable field at Throcking (33/F), 1992 *T. J.* (Hb. HTN), although this may have been grassland not long before that time.
(3 tetrads: Dony, 1967; 4 tetrads: 1950-1986)

Bromus hordeaceus L.
Soft-brome
Native.
First record: 1824.
Tetrad occurrence: 431 (88%).
Marginally increased (+3%).

A weed of waste ground, roadside verges, arable fields, and poor, rough grassland throughout the County. It is almost ubiquitous, only becoming rather thinly recorded on the Chalk Marl, and some areas in central and eastern Hertfordshire on the Boulder Clay. Owing to the enormous variation in both stature and appearance, including forms with glabrous lemmas, or small forms with depauperate inflorescences, and large forms with widely branched inflorescences, this species has often been confused with other taxa. Attempts have been made to weed out these misidentifications, but it is possible that some remain.
(399 tetrads: Dony, 1967; 419 tetrads: 1950-1986)

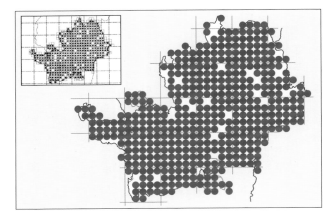

Map 816. *Bromus hordeaceus.*

The 'normal' form is ssp. *hordeaceus*. The alien subspecies *divaricatus* (Bonnier and Layens) Kerguelen was found as a wool shoddy casual in arable at Newnham (23/N), 1973 *C. G. Hanson* (det. E. J. Clement) (Hb. Hanson).

Bromus × pseudothominei P. M. Smith
(*Bromus hordeaceus* × *B. lepidus*)

This hybrid between the common Soft-brome and the introduced alien Slender Soft-brome has caused considerable difficulties. Until the publication of Wigginton and Graham (1981), its existence was not suspected by most botanists. Coupled with the misidentification of other subspecies of *B. hordeaceus* in the past, this has caused records of '*Bromus thominii*' [sic.] and '*Bromus lepidus*' in Dony (1967) to be unreliable. However, the principal characteristic of identification relied upon by Wigginton and Graham was the length of the lemma, and the intermediate nature of this between those of the two parents causes great difficulty in naming. Given that depauperate *B. hordeaceus*, according to Mr Cope, can approach the size of *B. lepidus* itself, the supposed range in the hybrid is likely to be an unreliable character altogether. The 'hybrid' was recorded from 18 tetrads during the survey, of which seven records were supported by specimens. However, none of these have yet been confirmed by experts, and therefore the current recorded occurrence of the taxon in Hertfordshire remains uncertain.

Bromus lepidus O. Holmb.
Slender Soft-brome
Introduced: neophyte.
First confirmed record: 1945.
Tetrad occurrence: 8? (2%).
Status uncertain.

A specimen in Hb. BM collected by J. E. Dandy from a field adjoining Tringford Reservoir (91/B), 1945 was referred to this species. Dony (ms. index) has 20 records from a range of places, at least two of which are indicated as having specimens in his herbarium. His *Flora*, however, gives records for no less than 59 tetrads. Following his survey, there were only four other records up to 1986, none supported by a specimen; and during the recent survey there were nine records attributed to this, although one of these has recently been re-identified by T. A. Cope from a specimen as *B. hordeaceus*. Most of the other records have no specimen to support them. Given the difficulties outlined above for the records of the supposed hybrid with *hordeaceus*, none of these records can be confirmed without further study. The true status (if any) of *B. lepidus* now in Hertfordshire therefore remains uncertain.

(59 tetrads: Dony, 1967; 63 tetrads: 1950-1986)

Bromus interruptus (Hackel) Druce

Interrupted Brome

Probably introduced: neophyte.

Only record: 1849.

Extinct in the wild?

Details of the finding of this plant at Odsey by Miss A. M. Barnard have been researched by G. Crompton and others, and it was likely to have been found in Sainfoin, just in Hertfordshire. It has not been seen since, and was last seen in the wild in Britain in 1972 (Preston *et al.*, 2002). No longer thought to have been a rare endemic to Britain, its native habitat and range, however, remain unknown.

Bromus secalinus L.

Rye Brome

Introduced: archaeophyte.

First record: 1736.

Tetrad occurrence: 11 (2%).

Rare, but increased (+266%).

Although this was quite frequent in the 19th century (Pryor (1887), Little (ms. notebooks, North Herts. Museums) only had seven records, while Dony (1967) only recorded it from three localities. Subsequently, until 1986, there was also only one other record: as an introduction with grass seed at Ware (31/S), 1973 *C. G. Hanson*. In 1990, plants identified as this by T. A. Cope were found in apparently ancient grassland at Dalmonds, Brickendon (30/P) *A. M. Boucher/T. J.* (Hb. HTN). Then, in 1991, it was also found at Broxbourne (30/T) *A. M. B.* (det. T. A. Cope) (Hb. HTN) and by Hook Copse, Northaw (20/V) *T. J.* (also det. T. A. Cope) (Hb. HTN). From this point, it has begun to turn up occasionally in a number of places, scattered across the County, usually in winter wheat, and sometimes in large quantity, alongside *B. commutatus*.

(3 tetrads: Dony, 1967; 4 tetrads: 1950-1986)

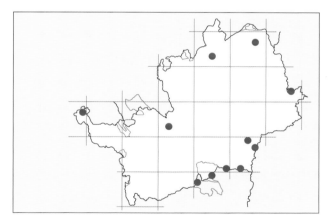

Map 817. *Bromus secalinus.*

Bromus lanceolatus Roth

Large-headed Brome

Introduced: casual.

First (only) record: 1912.

The only record remains that from Hitchin (det. *B. macrostachys* Desf.), reported in Dony (1967).

Bromus squarrosus L.

Introduced: casual.

First (only) record: 1927.

Again, the only record remains that from Mead Lane, Hertford (Dony, 1967).

Bromus briziformis Fisch. and C. A. Mey.

Introduced: casual.

First (only) record: 1974.

This was found, introduced with grass seed, on a new sports field at Ware (31/S) *C. G. Hanson.*

Genus: *Bromopsis*

Bromopsis ramosa (Hudson) Holub

Hairy-brome

Native.

First record: 1824.

Tetrad occurrence: 406 (83%).

Decreased (-12%).

A rather imposing grass of shaded places, in woodlands and shady roadsides or green lanes. It is a frequent species across the County wherever its habitat occurs, although it is most abundant in areas of old woodland and ancient hedgerows. There are distinct signs of a retreat in some areas, especially in drier, open agricultural country, and also around towns, where 'tidying' of scrubby habitats tends to occur.

(438 tetrads: Dony, 1967; and from 1950-1986)

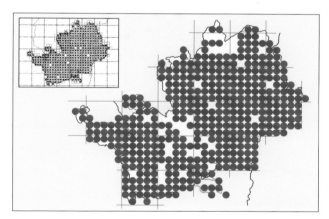

Map 818. *Bromopsis ramosa.*

Bromopsis benekenii (Lange) Holub   Herts Rare

Lesser Hairy-brome

Native.

First record: 1959.

Tetrad occurrence: 3 (<1%).

Sharply decreased (-65%).

This was only separated from *B. ramosa* fairly recently, and so its historic occurrence is unknown, although it has only ever been found in the shadier Chiltern Beech woods, which are its national stronghold. As the distinctions from its relative are rather obscure, it could possibly be overlooked. However, a concerted effort was made in the Chilterns to re-record it in its known sites, and many of these drew a blank, so its decline may be real. It was found during the survey only at Tom's Hill, Ashridge (91/Q), 1995 *G. Salisbury/J. Saunders* (det. T. J.) (Hb. HTN); Stubbings Wood (91/A), 1995 *G. S./J. S.* (Hb. HTN); Bottom Wood (09/G),

1999 *G. S./J. S.*; and Ladywalk Wood (09/G), 2002 *G. S.* It was
also found just in Herts. at Hockeridge Bottom (90/X), 1978
C. Blackbourn during the then Hertfordshire and Middlesex Trust
for Nature Conservation's 'Ancient Woodlands Survey'.
(8 tetrads: Dony, 1967; and from 1950-1986)

Bromopsis erecta (Hudson) Fourr.
Upright Brome
Native.
First record: 1843.
Tetrad occurrence: 89 (18%).
Decreased (-12%).

A very characteristic and often quite dominant plant of chalk
grassland, also occasionally found in open grassland on calcareous
soils elsewhere. Its recorded occurrences closely match those
recorded by Dony (1967), although some of its localities away
from the Chalk seem to be 'new' records, which might suggest
it is overlooked sometimes when it is not expected. However,
there do seem to be genuine losses, especially from marginal sites
in its core range, such as chalky road verges, where it was once
common, but is now often very limited. This parallels an earlier
decline on railway banks, such as those from Woolmer Green
to Knebworth and further north, where Pryor (1887) noted it as
'almost continuous', but where it is now rare.
(96 tetrads: Dony, 1967; 105 tetrads: 1950-1986)

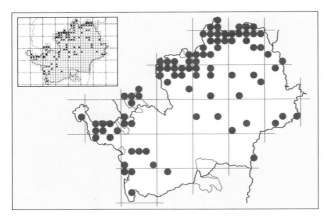

Map 819. *Bromopsis erecta.*

Bromopsis inermis (Leysser) Holub
Hungarian Brome
Introduced: neophyte.
First record: 1914.
Tetrad occurrence: 13 (3%).
Increased (+42%).

Originally introduced as a fodder grass (Preston *et al.*, 2002),
it now occurs mostly as a patch-forming escape, probably
introduced with grass seed. There are some signs, especially in the
Lea Valley, that it is spreading, but it can also disappear from sites
where it appeared to be established.
(9 tetrads: Dony, 1967; 13 tetrads: 1950-1986)

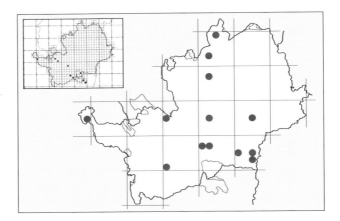

Map 820. *Bromopsis inermis.*

Genus: *Anisantha*

Anisantha diandra (Roth) Tutin ex Tzvelev
Great Brome
Introduced: neophyte.
First record: 1920.
Tetrad occurrence: 5 (1%).

Dony (1967) only reported one record, but it was found for a
second time at Ware in 1922 *G. C. Druce* (Dony, ms. index). It was
not recorded again until the current survey, when it appeared on
a roadside at Shingle Hall, High Wych (41/T), 1994 *J. L. Fielding*
(Hb. HTN). It was then found again on a road verge by Lamer
Park (11/S), 1997 *I. G. Denholm*, where it was well established,
alongside *Phalaris canariensis*, perhaps suggesting deliberate
introduction. In 1998, it was found on a field border at Long
Marston (81/Y) *G. Salisbury* (det. *T. J.*) (Hb. HTN); and in 2004
it was discovered at Barley Mo Farm, London Colney (10/R)
D. Bevan. After the survey was completed, it appeared in some
quantity on disturbed, chalky road works associated with the A505
Baldock bypass (23/L), 2007 *T. J.* (Hb. HTN), where it has the
potential to spread into chalky arable nearby. Given its similarity
to, and parallel habitat requirements with, *A. sterilis*, it could
already be under-recorded, and it could also take off, as it already
has in East Anglia.

Anisantha rigida (Roth) N. Hylander
Ripgut Brome
Introduced: neophyte.
Only record: 1920.

This close relative of *A. diandra*, which is sometimes considered
a subspecies, has only so far been found three times: at Ware tip
(31/M), 1920 *A. W. Graveson* (Dony, 1967); and at two separate
locations near Long Marston (81/Y), 1998 *T. J.* (Hb. HTN), source
unknown.

Anisantha sterilis (L.) Nevski
Barren Brome
Introduced: archaeophyte.
First record: 1824.
Tetrad occurrence: 476 (97%).
Stable (-1%).

An abundant and often very troublesome weed of arable fields,
waste places and roadsides throughout the County. Dony (1967)
recorded it as almost ubiquitous, and this remains the case, it

having only been missed in a very few marginal tetrads.
(455 tetrads: Dony, 1967; 456 tetrads: 1950-1986)

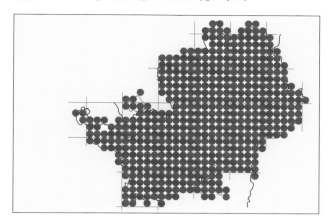

Map 821. *Anisantha sterilis.*

Anisantha tectorum (L.) Nevski
Drooping Brome
Introduced: neophyte.
First record: 1847.

A southern European weed of waste places and roadsides, this
was first found in Britain at 'New Mill' [= The Lynch], Hoddesdon
(30/U) by H. Williams. A detailed account of its finding was
given in Webb and Coleman (1849), with a description by
C. C. Babington. It was again found at Potters Bar (20/?K), 1912
J. E. Cooper (det. A. Melderis) (a record unknown to Dony);
and more recently appeared with other grass seed aliens at a
new sports field in Ware (31/S), 1973, 1974 *C. G. Hanson* (Hb.
Hanson).

Anisantha madritensis (L.) Nevski
Compact Brome
Introduced: casual.
First record: 1990.

The only record of this Mediterranean weed so far is from waste
ground near Cheshunt Station (30/R), 1990 *A. M. Boucher* (det.
R. M. Burton) (Hb. HTN).

Genus: *Ceratochloa*

These American bromes can be a difficult group to identify, and,
until recently, keys available in Britain were poor.

Ceratochloa carinata (Hook. and Arn.) Tutin
California Brome
Introduced: neophyte.
First record: 1966.
Tetrad occurrence: 5 (1%).
Increasing slowly.

The record assigned to this in Dony (1967) has been re-determined
as *C. marginatus* (see below). A record from tetrad 20/W in
Burton (1983) refers to a record from Northaw, 1966 *M. Kennedy*.
It was subsequently found at Standon (32/W), 1982 *A. M. Boucher*
(det. E. J. Clement) (Hb. Boucher), and again at Bayfordbury
(31/A), 1984 *C. G. Hanson*. The current survey found it in five
tetrads: at Standon again (32/W), 1988, 1991 *A. M. Boucher*,
S. Watson (Hb. HTN); Broxbourne Lido (30/T), 1989 *D. Bevan*;
Dobb's Weir (30/Z), 1991 *A. M. Boucher* (Hb. HTN); and by

allotments, Hertford (31/G), 2000, 2008 *T. J.* (Hb. HTN). Several
of these demonstrate that it can be very persistent.

Ceratochloa marginata (Nees ex Steud.) B. D. Jackson
Western Brome
Introduced: neophyte.
First record: 1961.

When Dony found this at Rickmansworth Aquadrome (09/M), it
was, according to Burton (1983), already well-established, which
is strange, given that it has not been reported since. At the time
it was misidentified as *C. carinata*, but was re-determined by
A. Melderis in 1967 (Melderis, 1968). There have been no other
records.

Ceratochloa cathartica (Vahl) Herter
Rescue Brome
Introduced: neophyte.
First record: c.1880.

A record of '*Bromus schraderi*' at Watford sewage works in Pryor
(1887) has been referred to this (Dony, 1967). He also reported a
record from Ware tip, 1920 *A. W. Graveson*, originally reported as
'*B. unioloides*'. It was also, apparently, found on waste ground at
Barnet (29/W), 1967 *D. E. G. Irvine* (Dony, ms index). There are
no other records.

Genus: *Brachypodium*

Brachypodium pinnatum (L.) P. Beauv.   Herts Rare
Heath False-brome
Native.
First record: 1843.

This is a local grass of nutrient-poor, dry soils, often on clay,
sometimes occurring in quantity in wood margins or glades.
Separation of the true *B. pinnatum* from *B. rupestre* was not
publicly proposed in Britain until 2001 (Chapman and Stace,
2001), although the two taxa had been recognised as separate in
vol. 5 of *Flora Europaea*. Hence all earlier records need critical
re-examination. As 'Tor-grass' was never common in the County,
this may be possible to some extent using herbarium specimens.
Confirmed records for the species to date are: moderately acidic
clay 'meadow' at Fir and Pond Woods Nature Reserve (20/Q)
(VC21 [Herts.]), 2006 *D. Gompertz* (det *T. J.*) (Hb. HTN);
calcareous clay bank by Radwell Meadows (23/H), 2007 *B. Harold*
(det. T. J.) (Hb. HTN); and hedge-bank near Pirton Grange (13/F),
2009 *T. J.* (Hb. HTN). The Radwell record is likely to be the same
locality as reported by W. H. Coleman (Webb and Coleman, 1849)
and by Pryor (1887), and also known by J. E. Little!

Brachypodium rupestre (Host) Roem. and Shult.   Herts Rare
Tor-grass
Native.
First record: (c.1845?) 1999.

This is the usual species of chalk grassland, where, in other parts
of Britain, it can be a menace. Old records of 'Tor-grass' from
chalk grassland in Herts. have included Therfield Heath, 'Slip
Inn' Hill near Ashwell, chalk pits near Hertford, Aldbury, and the
lost Sandon Heath. More recently, what was probably this was
reported from the downs by Tingley Wood (13/F), 1967 *H. Bowry*
and 1970 *F. Bentley* (Hb. HTN). The latter specimen has not
yet been re-examined. Dony (1967) reported it in small quantity

from 'the foot of Therfield Heath' (34/K) (although his ms. index gives tetrad 33/P), 1959. It was found in small quantity on Pen Hills, Therfield Heath (33/J), 1999 *T. J.* (Hb. HTN). The only other confirmed record is from a calcareous grassland clearing at Whippendell Wood (09/T), 1999 *G. Salisbury* (det. T. J.) (Hb. HTN). The latter might be thought unlikely, until we realise that open chalk grassland survived not that far away by the golf course until recently. Records given by Dony (1967) from Standon and Letchworth require confirmation, and are more likely to be *B. pinnatum*. A report from a road verge at Northchurch (90/U), 1975 may be an error.

Brachypodium sylvaticum (Huds.) P. Beauv.
Wood False-brome
Native.
First record: *c.*1820.
Tetrad occurrence: 444 (90%).
Decreased*?* (-7%).

This is the usual species of false-brome found in all but the most acidic semi-natural woodland, and old hedgerows. It can occasionally invade scrubby calcareous grassland, where it is very persistent, and can be mistaken for Tor-grass. The recent survey confirmed Dony's data, except that it was either missed or had disappeared from a few tetrads, mostly in central and southern Hertfordshire.
(451 tetrads: Dony, 1967; 453 tetrads: 1950-1986)

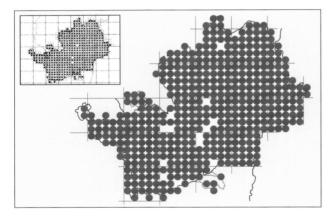

Map 822. *Brachypodium sylvaticum.*

Genus: *Elymus*

Elymus caninus (L.) L.
Bearded Couch
Native.
First record: 1838.
Tetrad occurrence: 269 (55%).
Increased substantially (+44%).

A characteristic and rather attractive grass of shaded woodland margins, old hedgerows and roadside banks across most of northern and central Hertfordshire, away from urban areas. It only becomes scarce on the more acidic London Clay and gravels, and on the driest and most open areas on the Chalk. Dony (1967) thought that it was characteristic of calcareous soils, but the current survey would suggest it is most frequent where soils are well-drained, mildly calcareous, but possibly quite nutrient-rich. Nutrient-enrichment may be the underlying reason for its apparent increase, although it is worth reflecting that it was

thought by Pryor (1887) to be frequent everywhere except on the acidic soils in south-east Herts., so it may have been somewhat under-recorded, for some reason, in the 1960s survey.
(178 tetrads: Dony, 1967; 209 tetrads: 1950-1986)

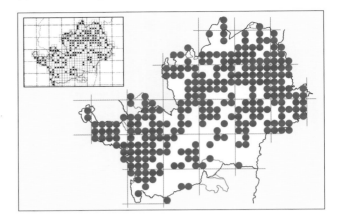

Map 823. *Elymus caninus.*

Genus: *Elytrigia*

Elytrigia repens (L.) Desv. ex Nevski
Common Couch
Native.
First record: 1824.
Tetrad occurrence: 458 (93%).
Decreased? (-5%).

This tough grass is a frequent, and sometimes abundant and unwelcome species of rough grassland, field borders and cultivated land across the County. Dony (1967) showed it to be ubiquitous, but there do appear to be signs that it has decreased to some extent, with apparent absences from a few tetrads, even where quite intensive survey has been carried out.
(460 tetrads: Dony, 1967; and from 1950-1986)

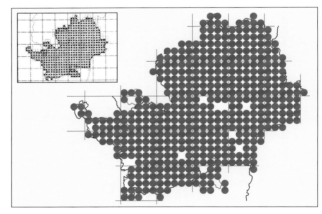

Map 824. *Elytrigia repens.*

Genus: *Hordelymus*

Hordelymus europaeus (L.) Jessen
Wood Barley
Native.
First record: 1787.
Tetrad occurrence: 13 (3%).
Increased? (+108%).

This is an interesting species. It occurs sparsely in old, shady woodlands, usually on Chalk in our area; and has a patchy, local distribution in the U.K. as a whole (Preston *et al.*, 2002). Dony (1967) implied that it was limited to the Chilterns, but historically this was not strictly true, as there is a record from Coleman (1849) from near Stevenage (22/M). Coleman also found it at Wain Wood (12/S), on the eastern-most fringes of the Chilterns. This record is interesting, because the current survey found it at an old plantation near Offley (12/N), not that far away. The apparent increase since the 1960s, therefore, may actually be a matter of better recording in the recent survey, and it could also survive elsewhere in other sites, unnoticed.

(6 tetrads: Dony, 1967; 9 tetrads: 1950-1986)

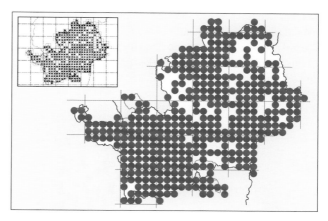

Map 826. *Hordelymus murinum.*

The usual subspecies is ssp. *murinum*. The alien subspecies *leporinum* (Link) Arcang. from southern Europe was found as a weed of wool shoddy waste at Newnham (23/N), 1973 *C. G. Hanson* (det. E. J. Clement) (Hb. Hanson).

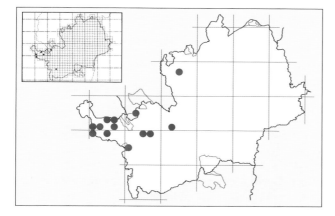

Map 825. *Hordelymus europaeus.*

Genus: *Hordeum*

Hordeum vulgare agg.
Barley
Introduced: casual.
First record (as escape): 1932.

Dony gives no details of records, and his ms. index only gives two early records by H. Phillips, the first, as *H. vulgare* L., from Letchworth. The recent survey recorded Barley from 31 tetrads, mostly in east Hertfordshire, where it was until recently a major crop, and is still frequent. Strictly speaking, the cultivated form is now usually *Hordeum distichon* L. (**Two-rowed Barley**), but records were not precise enough in identification to be sure. In the 1970s, both *H. vulgare s. str.* and *H. distichon* were recorded frequently from various tips.

Hordeum murinum L.
Wall Barley
Introduced: archaeophyte.
First record: *c.*1820.
Tetrad occurrence: 391 (80%).
Stable (-1%).

This is a very familiar grass of rough road verges, over-grazed horse-pastures and waste ground throughout the County. Dony (1967) suggested that it was absent from less inhabited areas, and the current survey found it to be very similarly absent from some parts of the County, particularly on the Boulder Clay in north-east Herts., but also on some areas of the Clay-with-Flints, and even on gravels in central Hertfordshire, almost as Dony found. Its persistent absence from some of these areas is difficult to explain, as they are not necessarily away from human habitation.

(375 tetrads: Dony, 1967; 390 tetrads: 1950-1986)

Hordeum jubatum L.
Foxtail Barley
Introduced: neophyte.
First record: 1920.
Tetrad occurrence: 4 (<1%).

This American species mainly used to occur as a casual escape, introduced either with grain, or with grass-seed. However, some of its records have suggested a tendency to persist, such as its occurrence at Oak Hill Park (29/S) (VC20 [Greater London]), 1995 *G. Hounsome*, not far from where it was recorded in 1964 by J. Mason (Dony, 1967). Dony gave four recent records; after which it was also found as a grass-seed alien at Ware (31/S), 1973 *C. G. Hanson*. Other records from the recent survey were from a new golf course, Essendon (20/U), 1992 *A. M. Boucher*; at Osidge (29/X) (VC20 [Greater London]), 1998 *T. J./G. P. Smith* (also not far from Oak Hill Park); and a central reservation on the A414, Hertford (31/G), 2000 *T. J.* The last of these records is the only one so far to suggest its occurrence by salted roads, a favoured habitat elsewhere in Britain.

Hordeum pubiflorum Hook *f.*
Antarctic Barley
Introduced: casual.
First (only) record: 1976.

This South American species was found as a wool shoddy alien at Newnham (23/N) *C. G. Hanson* (det. C. E. Hubbard) (Hb. Hanson).

Hordeum secalinum Schreber
Meadow Barley
Native.
First record: 1838.
Tetrad occurrence: 140 (29%).
Decreased slightly (-7%).

This is a grass that is especially characteristic of damp meadows and old rough grassland on clay soils. Dony (1967) thought it was found particularly on calcareous soils, and it certainly occurs especially frequently on Boulder Clay, wherever old grassland survives. However, it is also frequent on more well-drained old grassland on the London Clay, as well as on the Woburn Sands

and Chalk Marl in west and north Herts., where these damper soils still support old grassland. The recent survey showed a substantial decline since the 1960s, and the tetrad maps show that this is almost entirely down to a loss of old grasslands on the Boulder Clay, because it persists (and was better recorded) across the London Clay and elsewhere.
(143 tetrads: Dony, 1967; 163 tetrads: 1950-1986)

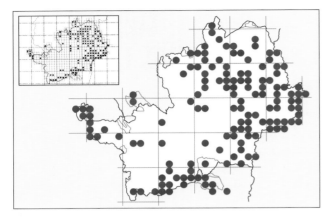

Map 827. *Hordelymus secalinum.*

Hordeum geniculatum All.
Mediterranean Barley
Introduced: casual.
First record: (1912?) 1973.

A record of '*Hordeum marinum*' from Purwell Field, Hitchin (12/Z?) by J. E. Little was referred to this species (as *H. hystrix* Roth.) by Dony (1967). It was also found among other wool shoddy aliens at Newnham (23/N), 1973 *C. G. Hanson* (det. E. J. Clement) (Hb. Hanson).

Genus: *Secale*

Secale cereale L.
Rye
Introduced: casual.
First record: 1875.

Pryor (1887) notes three records, including one from the manure sidings at Hatfield Station, where other introduced grasses were recorded in 1875. Dony (1967) also notes that it occurred occasionally as an escape, but there are no recent records, presumably because it is now much less frequently cultivated in the County.

Genus: *Triticum*

Triticum aestivum L.
Bread Wheat
Introduced: casual.
First record (as escape): 1970.

Only mentioned casually by Dony (1967), this turns up very frequently as a casual escape on road verges and by fields, and was recorded during the recent survey from 41 localities. It does not persist.

Triticum turgidum L.
Rivet Wheat
Introduced: casual.
First (only) record: 1974.

The only record is as a wool shoddy alien at Newnham (23/N) *C. G. Hanson* (det. E. J. Clement) (Hb. Hanson)

Triticum durum Desf.
Pasta Wheat
Introduced: casual.
First (only) record: 1992.

This was identified as an escape on a road verge at Shenley (10/V) *S. Hedley.*

Genus: *Aegilops*

Aegilops triuncialis L.
Introduced: casual.
First (only) record: 1912.

There is a specimen (labelled *Triticum triunciale*) in the Graveson Herbarium (HTN), collected by W. Graveson at Ware (TL31). Dony (ms. index) attributed this to '*A. ovata*', although he omitted reference to it in his *Flora*. However, it would appear to be this species, no doubt introduced with grain.

Genus: *Danthonia*

Danthonia decumbens (L.) DC.
Heath-grass
Native.
First record: 1838.
Tetrad occurrence: 23 (5%).
Decreased substantially (-43%).

Found in short grass on old commons, village greens, and in woodland glades where these woodlands have derived from former wood-pastures. As such, it is a very good indicator of old acidic grassland, and is not surprisingly much less common than it once was. It occurs mostly in southern and western Hertfordshire, on the acidic Reading gravels, London Clay and Clay-with-Flints formations, being especially a feature of Berkhamsted Common and Ashridge. One outlier in east Hertfordshire is at Patmore Heath (42/M). It seems to have gone from many of the localities known to Dony, including places like Hertford Heath and the Bramfield/ Tewin area, although the recent survey did find it at some new sites.
(38 tetrads: Dony, 1967; 43 tetrads: 1950-1986)

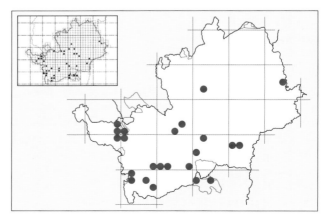

Map 828. *Danthonia decumbens.*

Cortaderia selloana (Schult. and Schult. *f.*) Asch. and Graebn.
Pampas-grass
Introduced: neophyte.
First record: 1999.

Long-known as a garden ornament, this was first found as an escape on the railway bank near Watford Junction station (19/D), 1999 *A. M. Boucher*. It has subsequently appeared by the railway at Fisher's Green (22/H), 2003 *T. J.*; and near Croxley Common Moor (09/X), *G. Hounsome*. As it has begun to be quite a feature of some railway banks around London, this is not entirely a surprising addition to the flora!

Cortaderia richardii (Endl.) Zotov
Early Pampas-grass
Introduced: casual/neophyte.
First (only) record: 2006.

A single plant in a derelict field near the underground railway at Croxley Hall (09/S) 2006 *T. J.* was identified as this species. It could be mistaken for its larger cousin.

Genus: *Molinia*

Molinia caerulea (L.) Moench
Purple Moor-grass
Native.
First record: 1838.
Tetrad occurrence: 14 (3%).
Increased, or stable? (+32%).

Purple Moor-grass is a rare grass with us, found in two quite distinct kinds of habitat: in wet, acidic conditions on old commons, or in woodland derived from former wood-pastures;

Photo: Brian Sawford

Purple Moor-grass Molinia caerulea *Patmore Heath, 1987.*

and in rare peat communities on calcareous spring-fed mires in fens or fen meadows. Neither habitat is common in the County, but the latter is rare and highly vulnerable to both dessication and to other problems, such as scrub-encroachment. Its occurrences in the more conventional, wet heath community are scattered across various sites in mostly southern and western Hertfordshire, such as Hertford Heath, Rowley Green, Bricket Wood Common, Berrygrove Wood and Patmore Heath, while its rare 'fen' occurrences are at Norton Common, Letchworth (23/B), Biggin Moor (33/W), Rushy Meadow by Wilstone Reservoir (91/B), Croxley Common Moor (09/S), Sawbridgeworth Marsh (41/X), and a marsh by Blagrove Common, Sandon (33/G). Owing to the fact that it is apparently limited to ancient semi-natural vegetation in our area, its apparent increase since the 1960s is likely to be due to better recording.
(10 tetrads: Dony, 1967; 14 tetrads: 1950-1986)

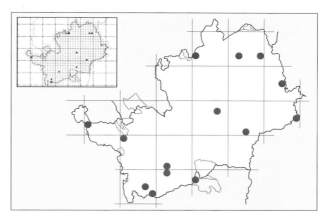

Map 829. *Molinia caerulea.*

Genus: *Phragmites*

Phragmites australis (Cav.) Trin. ex Steudel
Common Reed
Native.
First record: 1735.
Tetrad occurrence: 103 (21%).
Increased (+40%).

Common Reed is a naturally occurring plant of riverside fen, flood-plain ditches and spring-fed pools or seepages elsewhere, where these have calcareous sources. It was historically also likely to be a major constituent of flood-plain swamps along many of Hertfordshire's river valleys, but had become strongly limited in such places by the 19th century. Owing to the creation of gravel pits in these flood plains, and also the dereliction of their remaining wet grasslands, it has begun to re-assert its former position. This has also begun to be encouraged for bird conservation purposes, although the monoculture Reed-beds favoured for this are not entirely natural. There are a number of long-standing, large reed-beds in the County, such as at Maple Lodge (associated with a former sewage works), Wilstone and Marsworth Reservoirs (the result of impoundment of spring-sources), Tewinbury (former sewage works lagoons) and Stanborough Reed Marsh (the result of neglected drains under the railway, together with a spring source in flood-plain meadows). Others have now been developed at places like Amwell Quarry and Cheshunt Gravel Pits, or allowed to spread, as at Purwell Ninesprings, Hitchin. The overall result is that the Common Reed has increased dramatically since the 1960s, and even more since the 19th century, but sometimes at the expense of more delicate and more natural flood-plain wetlands.

(70 tetrads: Dony, 1967; 91 tetrads: 1950-1986)

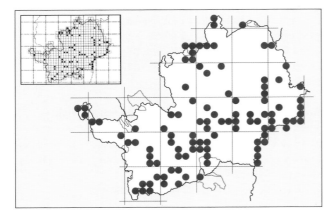

Map 830. *Phragmites australis.*

Genus: *Eragrostis*

Eragrostis cilianensis (All.) Vignolo ex Janch.
Stink-grass
Introduced: casual.
First record: 1995.

This was first found as a casual weed, probably from bird-seed, growing in cracks in the paving at St Mary's Square, Hitchin (12/Z), 1995 *T. J.* (Hb. HTN). It has subsequently turned up at Heron's Farm, Gustard Wood (11/S), 2003 *T. J.* (Hb. HTN), also probably a casual associated with grain.

Eragrostis tef (Zucc.) Trotter
Teff
Introduced: casual.
First (only) record: 1995.

Another import with bird seed, this was found at Tapp's Garden Centre, Baldock (23/L) *C. G. Hanson* (det. E. J. Clement) (Hb. Hanson).

Genus: *Eleusine*

Eleusine indica (L.) Gaertn.
Yard-grass
Introduced: casual.
First record: 1965.

Following Dony's record from Cock Lane Dump (30/U) (Dony, 1967), this was next found as a bird-seed alien at Hitchin Market Place (12/Z), 1994 *A. M. Boucher* (Hb. Boucher); and similarly in a garden at Ashwell (23/U), 2003 *T. J.* (Hb. HTN). Both these are of the nominate ssp. *indica*. Subspecies *africana* (Kenn. -O'Byrne) S. Phillips became a spontaneous garden weed at Ware (31/S), 1996 *C. G. Hanson* (Hb. HTN), having originally been introduced.

Genus: *Cynodon*

Cynodon incompletus Nees
African Bermuda-grass
Introduced: casual.
First (only) record: 1973.

The only record of this tropical weed is as a wool shoddy alien at Newnham (23/N) *C. G. Hanson* (Hb. Hanson) (Dony, 1975).

Genus: *Tragus*

Tragus australianus S. T. Blake
Australian Bur-grass
Introduced: casual.
First (only) record: 1973.

Also found as a wool shoddy alien at Newnham (23/N) *C. G. Hanson* (Hb. Hanson) (Dony, 1975).

Genus: *Panicum*

Panicum schinzii Hackel
Transvaal Millet
Introduced: casual.
First record: 1918.

This was recorded twice during the 1960s survey, it having first been found at Hertford (Dony, 1967). Burton (1983) gives three tetrad records (under the name *P. laevifolium*) from tips between 1965 and 1968, without details. Two of these are the records by Dony from his *Flora*, while the third (from 30/N) is not documented. This may also be Dony's. The species has not been seen again recently.

Panicum capillare L.
Witch-grass
Introduced: casual.
First record: 1875.

Dony had no records of this American grass subsequent to that from Hatfield by Pryor (1887), where it was apparently derived from manure. It was found at Rye Meads Sewage Works (31/V), 1982, 1983 *C. G. Hanson* (Hb. Hanson); and subsequently on waste ground by Ware Station (31/S), 1985 *C. G. H.* The current survey received three records: from Rye Meads again (31/V), 1994 *C. G. H.* (Hb. HTN); from a flower bed at Verulamium Park, St Albans (10/N), 1994 *A. M. Boucher* (Hb. Boucher); and finally from a bean field at Heron's Farm, Gustard Wood (11/S), 1999 *T. J./G. P. Smith* (Hb. HTN). Manure may remain a means of its being distributed.

Panicum miliaceum L.
Common Millet
Introduced: neophyte or casual.
First record: 1875.
Tetrad occurrence: 18 (4%).

Dony (1967) only notes this as 'common on rubbish dumps', without detailing records, but his ms. index shows nine post-1950 records; while earlier botanists had provided five records before 1940. Records were received after 1970 from 14 tetrads; while the recent survey continued to indicate an expansion, possibly as a result of deliberate sowing as bird food in field margins.

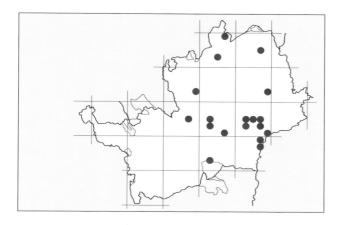

Map 831. *Panicum miliaceum.*

Panicum effusum R. Br.
Introduced: casual.
First (only) record: 1960.

This Australian millet was reported by Dony (1967) from Cock Lane tip (30/U), but there have been no other records.

Genus: *Echinochloa*

Echinochloa crus-galli (L.) P. Beauv.
Cockspur
Introduced: neophyte or casual.
First record: 1846.
Tetrad occurrence: 9 (2%).
Increasing?

Dony (1967) mentions two recent records, but his ms. index also gives two others. There were 10 tetrad records subsequently to 1986, almost all from tips. In the recent survey, there were 16 records from nine tetrads, several of which were as weeds in cultivated ground, or as escapes by roads. It has also been a persistent feature of sludge tips at Rye Meads Sewage Works (31/V).

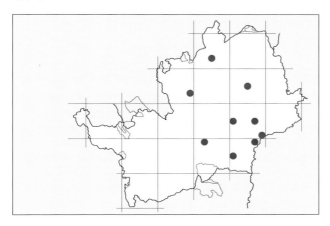

Map 832. *Echinochloa crus-galli.*

Echinochloa colona (L.) Link
Shama Millet
Introduced: casual.
First record: 1964.

Dony (1970) reported this as new to the County from Park Street dump (10/L) in 1969, but a specimen of his from Cock Lane tip (30/P), 1964 (Hb. HTN), named *E. crus-galli*, is in fact this

species, and is therefore the first documented record. It was also found at Ware tip (31/M), 1978 *C. G. Hanson*, and during the recent survey further occurrences were: roadside at Watton-at-Stone (21/Z), 1996 *T. J.* (Hb. HTN); by road near M1, Bedmond (10/B), 1997 *G. Salisbury* (det. T. J.) (Hb. HTN); and at Heron's Farm, Gustard Wood (11/S), 1999 *T. J./G. P. Smith* (Hb. HTN).

Echinochloa frumentacea Link
White Millet
Introduced: casual.
First certain record: 1970.

Unfortunately, early records of this are unreliable, owing to confusion with *E. esculenta*. The record from Cock Lane (given as 30/U, but in fact 30/P), 1959, in Dony (1967) has been re-determined as the latter, but his other records cannot be confirmed. Work by C. G. Hanson during the 1970s confirmed the presence of both species at some tips. The first of his records for the true *E. frumentacea* were from Moor Mill tip (10/L) and Pye Corner tip (41/L), 1970. It was recorded from eight tetrads between 1970 and 1986; while the recent survey found it at five localities: Rye Meads Sewage Works (31/V), 1993-1997, *C. G. H.*; garden, Broxbourne (30/T), 1995 *A. M. Boucher*; garden, Ware (31/S), 1997 *C. G. H.*; field edge, Watersplace Farm (31/X), 1997 *C. G. H.* (Hb. HTN); and yard, Heron's Farm, Gustard Wood (11/S), 2003 *T. J.* (Hb. HTN).

Echinochloa esculenta A. Braun (H. Scholz)
Japanese Millet
Introduced: casual.
First record: 1959.

The record of '*E. frumentacea*' from Cock Lane (30/U) (actually 30/P), 1959 *J. G. Dony* (Dony, 1967) is now identified as this species (Hb. HTN), and is the first documented record. A record of his from Pye Corner tip (41/L), 1970 is also referred to this. Subsequently, work by C. G. Hanson identified it from tips in eight further tetrads to 1986, and especially at Rye Meads Sewage Works (31/V), where it was present on a regular basis from 1975 to 1985. During the recent survey, it proved to be persistent at Rye Meads until at least 1995 (Hb. HTN), after which systems of sludge treatment changed. It was also found at two other localities: Hatchett Poultry Farm (32/K), 1993 *S. Watson*; and by Pymme's Brook, Osidge (29/W) (VC20 [Greater London]), 1998 *D. Furley* (det. T. J.) (Hb. HTN).

Genus: *Urochloa*

Urochloa panicoides P. Beauv.
Sharp-flowered Signal-grass
Introduced: casual.
First (only) record: 1969.

The only record of this tropical grass is from Park Street dump (10/L) *J. G. and C. M. Dony* (Hb. HTN) (Dony, 1970).

Genus: *Setaria*

Setaria parviflora (Poiret) Kerguelen
Knotroot Bristle-grass
Introduced: casual.
First (only) record: 1976.

The only record (named '*S. geniculata*') is from Van Hage's

Garden Centre, Amwell (31/R) *C. G. Hanson* (Hb. HTN).

Setaria pumila (Poiret) Roem. and Schult.
Yellow Bristle-grass
Introduced: casual.
First record: 1846.
Tetrad occurrence: 13 (3%).
Increased (+575%).

There were several 19th century records, after it was first found at
Hertford by Ansell (Pryor, 1887, as *S. glauca* Beauv.), but Dony
only gave two recent records (as *S. lutescens* (Weigel) Hubbard).
It was found quite widely on tips between 1970 and 1986, and in
the mid-1980s it started to appear in gardens and waste ground
elsewhere. During the recent survey, it was fairly widely reported,
often as a casual from bird seed in gardens. It is also occasionally
found with other bird-seed plants in game strips, no doubt part of
the seed mix.
(2 tetrads: Dony, 1967; 12 tetrads: 1950-1986)

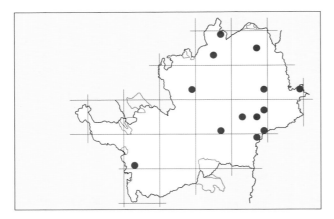

Map 833. *Setaria pumila.*

Setaria verticillata (L.) P. Beauv.
Rough Bristle-grass
Introduced: casual.
First record: 1846.

The first record was from 'near the gas works, Hertford' (31/G),
(Pryor, 1887). There were no further records until the current
survey, when var. *ambigua* (Guss.) Parl. was found on the site of
a derelict greenhouse at Bayfordbury (31/A), 1994 *C. G. Hanson*
(det. E. J. Clement) (Hb. HTN), where it persisted until at least
1999. The species was also found at Tapp's Garden Centre,
Baldock (23/L), 1995 *C. G. H.*; Rye Meads Sewage Works (31/V),
1995 *C. G. H.*; and re-appeared in Gordon Hanson's garden at
Ware (31/S), 1995 (Hb. HTN), having been grown there in 1976
from wool shoddy waste.

Setaria viridis (L.) P. Beauv.
Green Bristle-grass
Introduced: casual.
First record: 1843.
Tetrad occurrence: 16 (3%).
Increased?

The first record, by James Ansell, is quoted as 1843 in Pryor
(1887), not 1846 (Dony, 1967). It was evidently fairly widely
spread even by 1930. Dony (1967) does not specify its occurrence,
but his ms. index has eight post-1950 tetrad records. Between
1970 and 1986, it was recorded from tips in 13 tetrads, while

during the recent survey, it began to be found elsewhere, such
as waste ground or pavements, although still mostly near the
presumed original tip sources in the Hertford and Ware area.
Owing to the uncertainty about the completeness of Dony's
records, it has not been possible to judge if it has genuinely
increased or not.

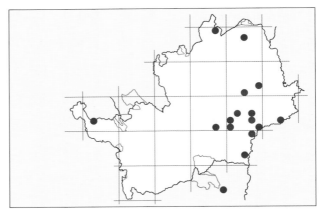

Map 834. *Setaria viridis.*

Setaria faberi Herrm.
Nodding Bristle-grass
Introduced: casual.
First record: 1976.

First found on a tip at Rickmansworth (09/L), 1976 *J. G. and
C. M. Dony* (Dony, 1977); this plant is usually associated with Soya
bean waste, which was probably its source here. It subsequently
appeared at Ware tip (31/M), 1983 *C. G. Hanson*; Rye Meads
Sewage Works (31/V), 1984 *A. M. Boucher* (Hb. Boucher); and
Waterford tip (31/C), 1984 *C. G. H.* (Hb. Hanson). The only record
during the survey period was from near the Carmelite Monastery
at Ware Park (31/H), 1994 *C. G. H.* This is actually not far from
the former Ware tip site, where it was in 1983.

Setaria italica (L.) P. Beauv.
Foxtail Bristle-grass
Introduced: casual.
First record: 1930.

The first record of this grass in the wild, more familiar as the
'millet' used for budgerigar food, was actually by A. W. Graveson,
from Hartham, Hertford (31/G), 1930 (Hb. HTN) (Dony, ms.
index), not 1950 (Dony, 1967). Dony also thought that it was
more common than *S. viridis*, but this is not the case now. It
was found on tips in 11 tetrads from 1970-1986 *C. G. Hanson*.
During the period of this survey, however, it was only found at two
places: Rye Meads Sewage Works (31/V), several dates 1989-1996
A. M. Boucher/C. G. H. (conf. T. A. Cope) (Hb. HTN); and Ware
tip (31/M), 1987 *C. G. H.*

Genus: *Digitaria*

Digitaria sanguinalis (L.) Scop.
Hairy Finger-grass
Introduced: casual.
First record: *c.*1840.
Tetrad occurrence: 8 (2%).

The first record was actually made at Rivers Nursery,
Sawbridgworth (41/S) by G. Wolsey, not Coleman (Dony, 1967),

although Coleman named the plant. Pryor (1887) also lists a record from Broxbournebury (30/N). There was only one subsequent record, from Park Street tip (10/L), 1964 (Dony, 1967), until the current survey. Since 1987, it has now been found in no less than eight tetrads: Rye Meads Sewage Works (31/V), 1989 *C. G. Hanson/A. M. Boucher* (Hb. Hanson; Hb. Boucher); waste ground, Ware (31/R, S), 1989 *C. G. H.*; pavement, Ware (31/M), 1992 *C. G. H.* (Hb. HTN); pavement, Hoddesdon (30/U), 1993 *A. M. Boucher* (Hb. Boucher); Tapp's Garden Centre, Baldock (23/L), 1995 *C. G. H.*; garden, Broxbourne (30/T), 1995 *A. M. B.*; and Bayfordbury (31/A), 1995 *A. M. B.* (Hb. HTN). Many of these recent records have been escapes from bird seed sources.

Digitaria ciliaris (Retz.) Koeler
Tropical Finger-grass
Introduced: casual.
First record: 1969.

This was first found at the former Hitchin tip in Grove Pit (13/V), 1969 *J. G. and C. M. Dony* (Hb. K) (Dony, 1970). This was rapidly followed by a record from the High Leigh tip, Hoddesdon (30/U), 1970 *C. G. Hanson* (det. E. J. Clement) (Hb. Hanson); and it was then also found at Bayfordbury, as a greenhouse weed (31/A), 1979 *C. G. H.* Its only more recent record has been as a pavement weed at St Mary's Square, Hitchin (12/Z), 1994 *A. M. Boucher* (Hb. HTN).

[*Digitaria ternata* (A. Rich.) Stapf
Introduced: casual.

This has been reported as a persistent weed in a garden at Ware (30/S), 1999 *C. G. Hanson* (Hb. HTN), but was originally introduced. It may appear elsewhere in the area in due course, but, until it does, cannot be admitted to the County list.]

Genus: *Sorghum*

Sorghum halepense (L.) Pers.
Johnson-grass
Introduced: casual.
First record: 1965.

This tropical plant was first found at Rickmansworth (09/M), 1965 (Dony, 1967). Subsequently, it turned up occasionally at other tips: at Grove Pit, Hitchin (13/V), 1969 *J. G. and C. M. Dony* (Hb. HTN), and again in 1973 *C. G. Hanson*; Bulls Mill tip (31/D), 1973 *C. G. H.*; Ware tip (31/M), 1976, 1984 *C. G. H.*; and at Rye Meads Sewage Works (31/V), 1981-1984 *A. M. Boucher/C. G. H.* It re-appeared during the recent survey at Rye Meads Sewage Works, 1994-1997 *C. G. Hanson/A. M. Boucher* (Hb. HTN), where it became 'naturalised' for a time on the former sludge dumps. It also appeared from scattered bird seed at Tapp's Garden Centre, Baldock (23/L), 1995 *C. G. H.*

Sorghum bicolor (L.) Moench
Great Millet
Introduced: casual.
First record: 1967.

This food plant appeared at Rye Meads Sewage Works (31/V), 1967 *J. G. and C. M. Dony* (Hb. HTN; Hb. K) (Dony, 1970). It was recorded there again in 1977 and 1997 *C. G. Hanson* (Hb. Hanson).

Genus: *Zea*

Zea mays L.
Maize
Introduced: casual.
First record: *c.*1880.

Two occurrences as escapes were reported by Pryor (1887), but Dony (1967) only briefly mentions it. From 1970-1986, it was reported by C. G. Hanson from six tetrads, mostly on tips; and during the survey it was recorded from a further five tetrads, including two records from roadsides: Sawbridgeworth (41/S), 1989 *S. Watson* and Hatfield (20/E), 1992 *A. D. Marshall.*

Sparganiaceae (Bur-reeds)

Sparganium erectum L.
Branched Bur-reed
Native.
First record: 1820.
Tetrad occurrence: 179 (37%).
Increased? (+6%).

This robust aquatic plant occurs in still or relatively sluggish flowing water in rivers, ditches, ponds and lake margins across much of the County. It seems to be favoured by moderate eutrophication, and is therefore often found in farm ponds and backwaters of rivers in arable farmland, sometimes almost to the exclusion of other plants. The distribution remains much as it was in Dony's time, although some pond sites have either been missed or it has disappeared from these. It seems to have expanded considerably along the Grand Union Canal/River Gade corridor in west Herts., and to have consolidated its occurrence around Hertford and Ware. Overall, therefore, its apparent 6% increase since the 1967 survey may be real.
(160 tetrads: Dony, 1967; 182 tetrads: 1950-1986)

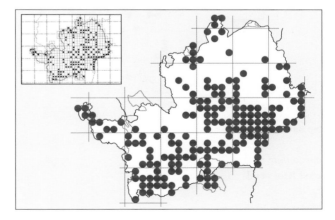

Map 835. *Sparganium erectum.*

The usual subspecies appears to be ssp. *erectum*, although no detailed study has been attempted recently. However, all three of the other U.K. subspecies appear to have been recorded:

Subspecies *neglectum* (Beeby) Schinz and Thell. was reported by Dony (1967) as having been found at a pond by Brickendon Lane (30/J), 1919 *A. W. Graveson* (Hb. HTN). There is also a specimen from 'Hitchin', 1929 (collector unknown) (det. C. D. K. Cook) (Hb. K); and another from near Langley (TL22), 1929 *A. W. Brunt*

(Hb. HTN). These could conceivably relate to the same locality. J. E. Little also reported it from Priory Park, Hitchin (12/Z) 1922, 1929; and from Purwell (22/E), 1925 (ms. notebooks, North Herts. Museums), although these were probably ssp. *microcarpum* (see below).

Subspecies *microcarpum* (Neuman) Domin is recorded from two specimens collected from 'Ippollitts Brook' and 'Priory Park, Hitchin' (12/Z), 1922 *J. E. Little* (Hb. CGE) (det. F. H. Perring) (*comm.*: B.R.C.: CEH Monks Wood). The latter may in fact have been collected in 1925 (see account for ssp. *neglectum* above).

Subspecies *oocarpum* (Čelak.) Domin has been identified from a specimen collected at Oughton Head (13/Q), 1921 *J. E. Little* (det. F. H. Perring) (Hb. CGE) (*comm.*: B.R.C.: CEH Monks Wood).

Sparganium emersum Rehmann
Unbranched Bur-reed
Native.
First record: 1838.
Tetrad occurrence: 77 (16%).
Increased (+50%).

Mostly found in rivers, although Dony also found it in ponds in south Herts., where it now tends to have been replaced by its relative. As it often does not flower, it can go unrecorded, especially in deeper waters. The increase may therefore be partly owing to better recording, although it does seem to have consolidated its occurrence in many areas, notably around Hertford. It has also appeared in the R. Hiz at Hitchin and Ickleford, where it has never previously been recorded.
(49 tetrads: Dony, 1967; 62 tetrads: 1950-1986)

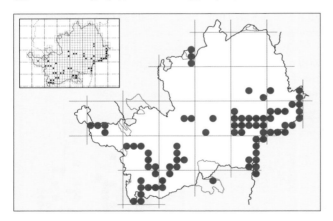

Map 836. *Sparganium emersum.*

Sparganium natans L.   Herts Extinct
Least Bur-reed
Native.
First record: 1843.

This was apparently found by Coleman (Webb and Coleman, 1849) in two ponds in central Hertfordshire: at Dalmond's Green (30/P) and near the lost Digswell Lodge Farm (21/L). The latter is supported by a specimen in Hb. BON. There have been no further records, although it is just possible it has been overlooked, as it could look like an impoverished specimen of *S. emersum.*

Typhaceae (Bulrushes or Reed Maces)

Typha latifolia L.
Bulrush *or* **Reed Mace**
Native.
First record: *c.*1810.
Tetrad occurrence: 260 (53%).
Increased (+77%).

A frequent plant of silted ponds, lakes, flooded gravel pits and ditches with more or less neutral and eutrophic water, where it forms floating mats that often overtake the entire water body. It was always common in southern Hertfordshire, but shows signs of having spread considerably in central and northern Hertfordshire, possibly in response to habitat enrichment and neglect of farm ponds.
(140 tetrads: Dony, 1967; 171 tetrads: 1950-1986)

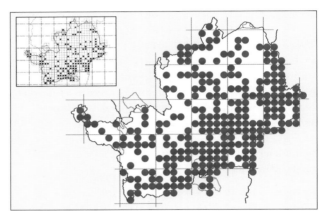

Map 837. *Typha latifolia.*

Typha angustifolia L.
Lesser Bulrush
Native and introduced.
First record: 1843.
Tetrad occurrence: 21 (4%).
Uncommon, but increased (+126%).

This is a plant of less eutrophic conditions than its relative, and also less often forms floating mats. Some populations may have derived from introductions, although there is no reason, as Dony (1967) suggested, to think that it is not actually native in at least some sites. It has increased substantially since the 1960s, having taken advantage of nutrient-poor conditions in flooded pits, or

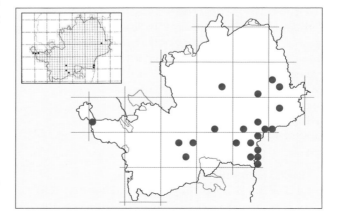

Map 838. *Typha angustifolia.*

new highway drainage ponds, especially in the south-east of the County.
(9 tetrads: Dony, 1967; 14 tetrads: 1950-1986)

Pontederiaceae (Pickerelweed family)

Genus: *Pontederia*

Pontederia cordata L.
Pickerelweed
Introduced: casual.
First (only) record: 1991.

This north American aquatic plant was found by a pond at Chorleywood Common (09/I), 1991 *P. J. Ellison*. It may have been planted.

Liliaceae (Lily family)

Genus: *Asphodelus*

Asphodelus fistulosus L.
Hollow-leaved Asphodel
Introduced: casual.
First record: 1916.

Dony (1967) mentions the first record of this Mediterranean plant, from Ware tip (TL31/M), 1916 *W. Graveson* (Hb. HTN); but there was also a record by Graveson from the station yard at Ware (31/S), 1926 (Hb. HTN).

Genus: *Kniphofia*

Kniphofia agg.
Red-hot-poker
Introduced: casual.
First record: 1976.

Red-hot-pokers have probably been escaping into the wild from gardens for a long time, but earlier botanists ignored them. The first record was from Blackbridge tip (11/X), 1976 *C. G. Hanson* (as *Kniphofia uvaria*). Unfortunately, garden Red-hot-pokers are probably complex hybrids that defy naming (Stace, 1997), and therefore identification of occurrences to species has been avoided. The recent survey noted escapes in three tetrads: Ware tip (31/M), 1991, 1997 *C. G. Hanson*; roadside by Christmas Wood, Kimpton (11/U), 1994 *T. J./A. R. Outen*; and near Hoddesdonbury (30/N), 2005 *T. J.*

Genus: *Colchicum*

Colchicum autumnale L.
Meadow Saffron
Introduced [native in the U.K.].
First record: (1826?), 2004.

Dony (1967) refers to a supposed record of this as having occurred near Hertford, the specimen being used to produce a plate in the *Botanical Magazine*. It is occasionally noted in the grounds of large houses, no doubt of planted origin. A more genuine 'escape' was noted at Sherrards Park Wood (21/G), 2004 *C. M. James*.

Genus: *Gagea*

Gagea lutea (L.) Ker Gawler   Herts Rare
Yellow Star-of-Bethlehem
Native.
First record: *c.*1871.
Extinct?

Probably a rare native plant of shady woodland stream banks in south-east Herts. However, its occurrences in Hertfordshire are poorly-documented. It was found at Easneye Park 'in a wood between the house and the River Ash' (31/R?), *c.*1871, probably by T. F. Buxton, although there seems to have been some confusion whether the finder may have been J. F. Duthie (Pryor, 1887). It was not then seen in the County until an un-named school girl brought back a specimen from 'Broxbourne Woods' (TL30), 1954 (Hb. HTN), but unfortunately could not remember exactly where it came from (Dony, 1967). It is likely that it would have occurred near the Spital Brook or one of its tributaries, although recent searches at the right time of year have failed to re-find it. It may yet re-appear.

Genus: *Tulipa*

Tulipa sylvestris L.
Wild Tulip
Introduced: neophyte.
First record: 1843.

This garden escape was naturalised in the wild at a number of sites in the 19th century: Bayford (30/E); near Thundridge Church (31/T); and Wyddial Hall (33/Q) (Pryor, 1887). It remained at Bayford until at least 1934; and at Wyddial until at least 1940 (Dony, 1967). It was also reported from Well Green, Brickendon (30/J) 1916 *D. M. Higgins*; and from a plantation near Sawbridgeworth (TL41), 1939 *F. Druce*, who noted that it 'rarely flowered' (Dony, ms. index). Its only recent record was as an introduced plant at Buncefield Depot, Hemel Hempstead (00/Z), 1992 (*comm.*: Industrial Enviroment Management consultants), where it was no doubt exterminated during the fire in 2004!

Tulipa gesneriana L.
Garden Tulip
Introduced: casual.
First documented record: 1996.

This scarcely merits a mention, except that it was noted growing on a road verge well away from any houses, and not obviously dumped, near Wallington Lodge (23/X), 1996 *T. J.*. It has probably been ignored at many other places.

Genus: *Fritillaria*

Fritillaria meleagris L.
Fritillary *or* **Snake's-head**
Probably introduced [native in the U.K.?].
First record: *c.*1815.
Tetrad occurrence: 7 (1%).

In the 19th century, Pryor (1887) gives quite a number of records of this from a range of damp meadow sites, some more 'wild' than others, mostly in central and southern Hertfordshire. One of the areas where it was widespread and locally abundant

Fritillary Fritillaria meleagris *Northaw, 1984.*

Fritillaria imperialis L.
Crown Imperial
Introduced: casual.
First (only) record: 1987.

Scarcely wild, this was found as a 'garden relic' in scrub by British Aerospace grounds, Hatfield (20/E), 1987 *P. Dyer*.

Genus: *Lilium*

Lilium martagon L.
Martagon Lily
Introduced: neophyte or casual.
First record: *c.*1850.

At one time a long-standing feature of Totteridge Park (TQ29) (Pryor, 1887), this was also recorded from a wood at Hertingfordbury (31/A) and at Moor Place, Much Hadham (41/J) by earlier botanists (Dony, 1967). During the recent survey, it was found in scrub by British Aerospace grounds (20/E), 1987 *P. Dyer*, with *Fritillaria imperialis*; as a garden relic near Hertford (31/G), 1994 *A. M. Boucher*; and by Kitwells Pond, Shenley (19/Z), 1996 *S. Murray*.

Genus: *Convallaria*

Convallaria majalis L.
Lily-of-the-valley
Native? (or introduced).
First record: 1597.
Tetrad occurrence: 6 (1%).

A plant of more or less acidic, shady woodland, this has always had a rather ambiguous record in Hertfordshire, because of its long cultivation in gardens. Even its first record by Gerard 'upon Bushey Heath' (Pryor, 1887) was not that far from human habitation. However, it has appeared in more probable habitat, especially in south-east Hertfordshire, for a very long time, where it could be native, at least in localities away from roads and houses! After 1970, the naturalised colony reported by Dony (1967) was found again at Thunderdell Wood (91/R), 1977, 1979 *J. C. Kerry*, and 1982 *R. M. Bateman*, when it was reckoned to hold at least 1000 plants, but has not been re-checked since. It appeared in both Wormley and Bencroft Woods (30/I), 1978 *T. Bell*, and in two separate places in Bencroft Wood, 1980 *A. Woods* and *C. M. James* (although one of these localities was uncomfortably near a car park!) (the Wormley Wood site is a long-standing locality, known to Coleman); on a roadside verge by Broxbourne Wood (30/I), 1980 *C. M. J.*; Oxhey Woods (19/B) (possibly an escape), 1978 *G. Harper*; Hoo Wood, Great Gaddesden (01/G), 1978 *T. Bell/A. Wadge* (also a site with ornamental plantings); and in Sherrards Park Wood (21/H), 1983 *R. M. Bateman*, where it remains, a large patch being recorded in April 2009 *N. Holmes-Smith*. The colony at Sherrards Park Wood has been thought to be an escape, but the plant was recorded in the wood in 1859 (Pryor, 1887), suggesting a long-standing locality, even if it did arrive with the nearby rhododendrons! During the recent survey, it was also re-found at Bencroft Wood (30/I) in two localities, 1999 *T. J.*; in Hoo Wood, Great Gaddesden again (01/G), 1996 *G. Salisbury/J. Saunders*; at Whippendell Wood (09/T) (also by the car park!), 1999 *A. L. Bull/T. J.*; and in more obviously non-native situations at Aldenham (19/J), Ashlyns (90/Y) and Totteridge (29/M).

was around Totteridge (TQ29) (VC20 [Greater London]), and Dony (1967) thought it might have been native here. It is still a feature of the Darlands Nature Reserve (29/L), although its occurrence alongside other ornamental plantings suggests original introduction. It is also still a feature of the Park Grass experimental plots at Rothamsted (11/G), where also it must originally have been introduced. In 1973, as a result of a radio appeal for records, it was reported to D. A. Wells of the Nature Conservancy by an inhabitant of Northaw to be growing near Northaw Place (20/R). Investigation in 1983 found that there were indeed 13 plants flowering in a rough paddock here (26 plants in 1984) *T. J.* Further investigation revealed that this is likely to be the same locality as reported to Joseph Sabine (Clutterbuck, 1815), the first County record! It was last properly recorded here in 1998 *G. White*, who counted 59 flowering plants. Elsewhere, it has turned up since 1970, more or less obviously as an escape, at Roxford (31/A), 1979 *R. Brown*; Danesbury Park (21/I), 1997 *K. Seaman*, and 1999 *P. Watt*; near Bayford School (30/E), 1992 *M. Grocock*; Brickendon Grange (30/I), 1992 *A. M. Boucher*; and, with cream flowers, in Sherrards Park Wood (21/H), 2004 *J. P. Widgery*.

Polygonatum multiflorum (L.) All.   Herts Rare
Solomon's Seal
Native.
First record: (1821?) *c*.1880.
Tetrad occurrence: 3 (<1%).

As a native, this is a rare plant of woodland on Chalk. Owing to the occurrence of escaped garden plants, which are almost always the hybrid between this and its northern relative *P. odoratum* (Whorled Solomon's Seal), its occurrence as a genuinely native plant in Hertfordshire was doubted by Dony (1967), when the hybrid's existence was not suspected. It was first recorded, as an almost certain native, at a wood near Tring, but this might have been in Buckinghamshire. It was then found at Howe Grove (00/P?), *c*.1880 by A. R. Pryor (Pryor, 1887), a quite probable native site; and at 'Foxcroft Wood' near Hemel Hempstead (TL00), *c*.1855 *A. Piffard* (Pryor, *op. cit.*), also likely to be native, although the site has probably been lost. After 1970, a number of records of '*P. multiflorum*' were received, but of these, only the following were probably of native colonies: Woodman's Wood, Belsize (00/F), 1985 *P. Alton*; near Potten End (00/E), 1986 *P. and S. Kingsbury*; The Hangings, Tom's Hill, Ashridge (91/Q), 1986 *T. J.* (just possibly the site first recorded in Pryor, 1887); and perhaps Whippendell Wood (09/T), 1979 *R. C. Hemming*. During the recent survey, the distinction between the native plant and the hybrid became clear, with the result that a better understanding of the distribution of native Solomon's Seal was gained, although none of the sites recorded up to 1986 was re-confirmed. Records overall have showed that it does, indeed, occur in a few woods on Chalk, mostly in west Herts., often among Bluebells and Dog's Mercury or with Wild Daffodils in native coppice communities. Recent confirmed records are from: Batch Wood (10/J), 1988 *J. Foster*; Greenlane Wood (01/R), 1996 *G. Salisbury* (Hb. HTN); and Kendal Wood (19/U), 2006 *B. Harold*.

Polygonatum × *hybridum* Bruegger
(*P. multiflorum* × *P. odoratum*)
Garden Solomon's Seal
Introduced: neophyte.
First documented record: 1982.
Tetrad occurrence: 28 (6%).

This has probably occurred for a long time, but only recently have records been clarified with its native parent. It was first properly recorded from Ivel Springs (23/M) B. R. Sawford and from Barnet

(29/M) *A. M. Boucher*, in the same year. Several other records were also made up to 1986. It has now been recorded widely on the Chalk and gravels of western and southern Hertfordshire, in scrub, woodlands, and roadsides, but appears not to occur much as an escape on the Boulder Clay, or in the drier north of the County.

Genus: *Paris*

Paris quadrifolia L.   Herts Vulnerable
Herb Paris
Native.
First record: 1838.
Tetrad occurrence: 8 (2%).
Decreased markedly (-69%).

This charismatic and rather enigmatic plant of ancient semi-natural woodland on damp, calcareous clay soils has shown a very marked decline since the 19th century, when it was reasonably widespread, not only on the Boulder Clay, where Dony (1967) mostly recorded it, but also on the Clay-with-Flints in west

Photo: June Crew

Herb Paris Paris quadrifolia *Balls Wood, 2009.*

Herts., and in various woods in southern Hertfordshire, where Boulder Clay overlies other deposits. It usually occurs in mosaic communities with Dog's Mercury and Tufted Hair-grass, and often where orchids occur, under coppiced Hazel, *etc*. The reason for its drastic decline are uncertain, although there has been a tendency for woods on the Boulder Clay to dry out during the 1990s droughts, and also Dog's Mercury has tended to become

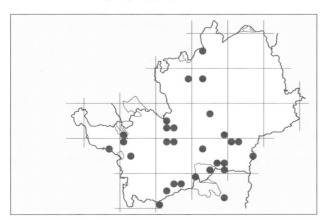

Map 839. *Polygonatum* × *hybridum*.

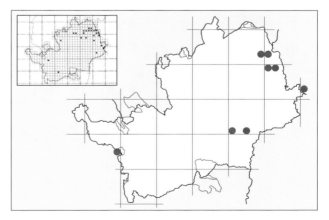

Map 840. *Paris quadrifolia*.

dominant, perhaps through pressure of deer browsing other species, although Herb Paris itself is poisonous and not apparently directly affected by grazing pressure (Jacquemyn *et al.*, 2008). The result is that Herb Paris may now have the status of 'Herts Rare', as several of the records during the survey were before the droughts took hold, and there have often not been any recent observations. However, signs of hope were its re-discovery during the survey period at Balls Wood (31/K), 1989 *N. Hall/A. M. Boucher* (with several records subsequently to the present), where it had not been seen since the 1930s; and also its occurrence beside a small copse at Hertingfordbury (31/A), 1993 *A. M. Boucher*, where there was no previous record. The records from west Herts. were from The Larches (90/X), 1988, 2007 *P. Casselden*, a site formerly in Bucks. (VC24 [Herts.]). Other recent localities for it have been: St Patrick's Wood (42/J), 1987 *T. J./B. R. Sawford* (where it was interestingly found in an area of old secondary woodland); Great Hormead Park Wood (42/E), 1987, 1988 *T. J./G. P. Smith*; Five-acre Wood, Anstey (43/B), 1988 *A. Marchant*; Northey Wood (33/W, 43/B), 1988, 1992 *B. R. Sawford/T. J.*; and Birchanger Wood (52/B), 2003 *S. Watson*. It may be that damper winters might encourage its re-appearance elsewhere.
(24 tetrads: Dony, 1967; 29 tetrads: 1950-1986)

Genus: *Ornithogalum*

Ornithogalum angustifolium Boreau
Star-of-Bethlehem
Introduced: neophyte.
First record: 1838.
Tetrad occurrence: 29 (6%).
Increased substantially (+293%).

Usually found singly or in small numbers in rough grassland on more or less gravelly soils. It was formerly called *O. umbellatum* L., but there seems to be some confusion amongst taxonomists as to which of these species (or both) actually occurs in Britain, or if they are subspecies of one plant. For now, all records have been ascribed to *O. angustifolium*. There is also dispute as to whether it is actually native or not, given its occurrence in semi-natural habitats well away from habitation. Sell and Murrell (1996) regard their 'ssp. *angustifolium*' as the native form. I have followed Preston *et al.* (2002) in regarding them all as one taxon, and as an old introduction. Whatever, the plant's increase does seem to be genuine over the last 40 years, and it may even have been under-recorded during the survey, around Hertford for example, where it was found in a number of places between 1967 and 1986. As a

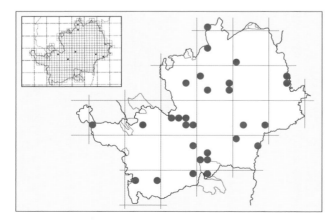

Map 841. *Ornithogalum angustifolium.*

plant of southern Europe, it may be responding to warmer climatic conditions. I would be interested in any records, and some idea as to whether they are likely to be the 'native' form.
(7 tetrads: Dony, 1967; 22 tetrads: 1950-1986)

Ornithogalum pyrenaicum L.   Herts Rare
Spiked Star-of-Bethlehem *or* **Bath Asparagus**
Native? (or introduced).
First record: 2004.

The appearance of this after sheep-grazing had been relaxed in an old orchard near elm hedgerows at Dunsley, Tring (91/F), 2004 *M. J. Hicks* (conf. T. J.) (Hb. HTN) was a complete surprise, both to Martin Hicks, and to others! There is no obvious suggestion it has been introduced, and the possibility that it is a very long-standing outlier of populations elsewhere must remain.

Spiked Star-of-Bethlehem Ornithogalum pyrenaicum *Dunsley Orchard, Tring, 2006.*

Ornithogalum nutans L.
Drooping Star-of-Bethlehem
Introduced: neophyte.
First record: 1862.

This species does not claim to be native, but is very long-persistent when it does occur. It remains in Dixies Meadow, Ashwell (23/U), still present in quantity 2009 *T. J.*, where it was first recorded (Pryor, 1887); a site that was formerly an orchard, now a casual piece of 'grass' used for occasional event car parking. It also survived the loss of a large part of an original colony at the roadside by the A120 near Little Hadham (42/G) in 1984, being reported in 1987 *S. Watson*, although I do not know if it still remains. A small colony was also found at Roughdown Common (00/M), 1979 *R. M. Bateman*, but has not been re-discovered recently.

Genus: *Scilla*

Scilla bifolia L.
Alpine Squill
Introduced: casual.
First record: 1988.

This garden escape was first found 'in the wild' on the edge of Stocking Wood (42/A), 1988 *S. Watson*. It was also found 'naturalised' in the grounds of Briggens (41/A), 1989 *S. W.*; and along a grassy roadside by the A505 at Letchworth (23/A), 1996 *T. J.*

Scilla messeniaca Boiss.
Greek Squill
Introduced: casual.
First record: 1992.

First found as an escape by the side of Jubilee Plantation, Walkern (22/X), 1992 *T. J. and C. M. James*; it also appeared in rough ground near Welwyn North Station (21/M), 1996 *A. D. Marshall*.

Scilla bythinica Boiss.
Turkish Squill
Introduced: casual.
First record: 1994.

For a time this was a fine feature of a long-derelict garden by the R. Lea at Ware (31/M), last recorded 2000 *C. G. Hanson/A. M. Boucher* (conf. E. J. Clement) (Hb. HTN). The site was re-developed shortly after.

Scilla siberica Haw.
Siberian Squill
Introduced: casual.
First (only) record: 1993.

A favourite garden plant, this has turned up in the wild on a bank by the road near Comb's Wood, Benington (32/A), 1993 *T. J.*, no doubt an outcast.

Genus: *Hyacinthoides*

Hyacinthoides non-scripta (L.) Chouard ex Rothm.
Bluebell
Native.
First record: 1653.
Tetrad occurrence: 404 (82%).
Increased? (+7%)

One of the spectacles of Hertfordshire's natural flora, this is especially characteristic of old woodlands on mildly acidic to moderately calcareous, free-draining loam soils, such as on the Clay-with-Flints, Reading gravels or glacial gravels. It occurs more thinly in damper semi-natural coppice woods on the calcareous Boulder Clay, and rather rarely, usually in valley bottoms, in woods on the London Clay or more acidic gravels of south-east Hertfordshire. It is almost absent on the Chalk itself, except where thin glacial caps occur, or Clay-with-Flints soils exist in pockets.

Outside ancient woodlands, it can often be found in assart wood-hedges throughout its native areas, as well as in sheltered rough grassland on old commons, although it does not tolerate open grassland in our part of Britain. This makes it a very good indicator of ancient plant communities in the County, although care needs to be taken in its identification from the escaped hybrid Bluebell. A few records might conceivably be the latter, but it does genuinely seem to have been recorded from more tetrads than in the 1960s. This may, however, be down to better recording where it is scarce.
(359 tetrads: Dony, 1967; 383 tetrads: 1950-1986)

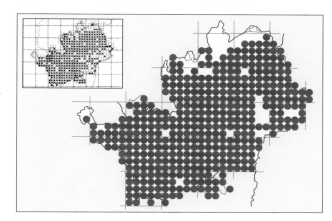

Map 842. *Hyacinthoides non-scripta.*

Hyacinthoides × *variabilis* P. D. Sell
(*H. non-scripta* × *H. hispanica*)
Garden Bluebell
Introduced: neophyte.
First record: 1989.
Tetrad occurrence: 65 (13%).
Increasing.

The occurrence of this vigorous hybrid 'in the wild' was not really considered before the late 1980s, although it must have been present long before that. It was first formally recorded independently in three different places in 1989: Carpenders Park (19/G), *J. K. Jackson*; Baas Hill (30/N), *A. M. Boucher*; and South Mimms (20/F) (VC21 [Herts.]), *T. C. G. Rich*. During the rest of the survey it was recorded very widely, although predominantly in the south-east and centre of the County. It remains local on the Boulder Clay in east Herts., and on the Clay-with-Flints in the Chilterns area. As the latter is a stronghold of native Bluebell, this might be a blessing, as the two taxa hybridise readily, producing

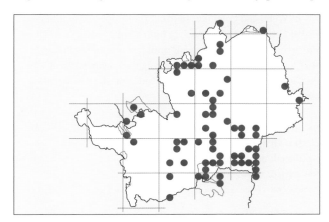

Map 843. *Hyacinthoides* × *variabilis.*

461

back-crossed hybrid swarms, sometimes to the final exclusion of the native species. It also tolerates a wider range of soil types than the native plant, even being found occasionally on Chalk.

Hyacinthoides hispanica (Miller) Rothm.
Spanish Bluebell
Introduced: neophyte or casual.
First record: 1916.
Tetrad occurrence: 48 (10%).

The real Spanish Bluebell, with its broad leaves and widely campanulate flowers with blue anthers, is sometimes confused with the hybrid. It tends to be rather scarce, but was probably overlooked by earlier botanists, as it is usually not persistent for long. Apart from the first record, and a second from Datchworth (TL21) in 1918, not reported by Dony (1967), there was only one other record before the current survey: at Berkhamsted (90/Z), 1985 *S. and P. Kingsbury*. However, with greater awareness of the threat of the hybrid, more attention was paid to these escapes during the survey, and it was found widely, with a concentration of records on the Chalk and associated soils in north Herts.

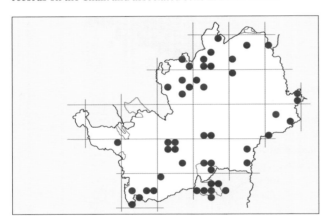

Map 844. *Hyacinthoides hispanica*.

Genus: *Muscari*

Muscari neglectum Guss. ex Ten.
Grape-hyacinth
Introduced [native in the U.K.?]
First record: *c.*1840.

A plant of short, open grassland on calcareous sandy or gravelly soils, thought by some to be a native of Breckland, the first record in Hertfordshire was from a field near Baldock (TL23), by Isaac Brown (Webb and Coleman, 1849). It then appeared as a nursery weed at Hitchin (12/Z), 1914 *J. E. Little* (Dony, ms. index). There were no other confirmed records until it was found at Potten End (00/E), 1986 *P. Kingsbury*; and during the recent survey it was found well-established in rough roadside grassland at Well End Green, Shenley (29/E), 1996 *T. J.*

Muscari armeniacum Leichtlin ex Baker
Garden Grape-hyacinth
Introduced: neophyte/casual.
First record: 1989.
Tetrad occurrence: 18 (4%).

A native of mountain pastures in the Balkans, *etc.*, this is the familiar bright blue grape-hyacinth of gardens, and turns up quite frequently on road verges, *etc.* from dumped garden refuse.

However, it also occurs occasionally away from such places, and its means of spread are uncertain.

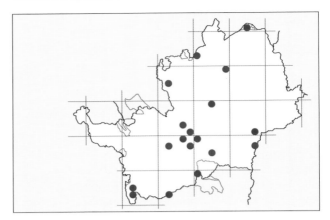

Map 845. *Muscari armeniacum*.

Muscari botryoides (L.) Mill.
Compact Grape-hyacinth
Introduced: casual.
First (only) record: 1990.

Also a garden outcast, this turned up on the tip at Pole Hole (41/L), 1990 *S. Watson*.

Genus: *Allium*

Allium schoenoprasum L.
Chives
Introduced: casual [native in the U.K.].
First record: 1994.

A scarce native in western Britain, this is only a casual outcast from gardens in our area, but can persist. It was first found in scrub near houses on the edge of Birchanger Wood (52/B), 1994 *T. J./A. R. Outen*. It has also been found by a roundabout at Tring (91/F), 1998 *R. Mabey*; by a footpath near Batford (11/M), 1999 *T. J.*; and by a farm track at Great Munden (32/M), 2001 *P. Millman*.

Allium cepa L.
Onion
Introduced: casual.
First documented record: 1933.

There are no mentions of the garden Onion as an escape in earlier Floras, but a specimen exists at Hb. E from 'Letchworth gravel pit' (TL23), 1933 *E. Macallister-Hall*. It was also reported from Pole Hole tip (41/L), 1990 *S. Watson*.

Allium roseum L.
Rosy Garlic
Introduced: casual.
First record: *c.*1970?

The only 'record' of this before the recent survey is a rather unsatisfactory undated one reported to John Dony as 'naturalised by a ditch by Aldenham Road' (19/T), *P. P. L. Maine*, from the files of London Natural History Society (and Burton, 1983). It was subsequently found by a road at Cottered (32/C), 2007 *K. Robinson* (Hb. HTN).

Allium subhirsutum L.
Hairy Garlic
Introduced: casual.
First (only) record: 2002.

This native of damp rocks in the Mediterranean area was found as an escape on a roadside near Aston pumping station (22/W), 2002 *K. Robinson* (det. T. J.) (Hb. HTN). How it got there is anyone's guess!

Allium triquetrum L.
Three-cornered Garlic
Introduced: neophyte.
First record: 1988.
Tetrad occurrence: 6 (1%).
Increasing.

This attractive, but potentially pernicious weed of hedge banks and waste ground was first found in a hedgerow at Marshmoor (20/I), 1988 *A. D. Marshall* (Hb. HTN). It has subsequently turned up in several places across south Hertfordshire: roadside bank, Broxbourne (30/T), 1990 *A. M. Boucher*; two localities near Berkhamsted (90/Y), 1995, 1996 *R. Mabey*; Roe Green, Hatfield (20/J), 1998 *P. Harvey*; Shepherd's Lane, Chorleywood (09/H), 2001 *J. Anders*; and Abbots Langley Churchyard (00/W), 2008 *B. Harold*.

Allium paradoxum (M. Bieb.) Don
Few-flowered Garlic
Introduced: neophyte.
First record: 1957.
Tetrad occurrence: 19 (4%).
Increasing (+550%).

A patch-forming weed of roadsides and waste ground, this has spread steadily, at least in central and western Hertfordshire, since it was first reported in Dony (1967). As it grows in similar places to, and somewhat resembles a feeble version of *Allium triquetrum*, botanists should be careful about recording either species.
(3 tetrads: Dony, 1967; 8 tetrads: 1950-1986)

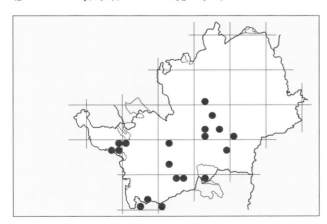

Map 846. *Allium paradoxum.*

Allium ursinum L.
Ramsons
Native.
First record: 1823.
Tetrad occurrence: 81 (17%).
Increased (+79%).

Forming large, spreading, showy patches that can be smelt in spring from a long distance, this has always been a feature of damp ground around streams in woodlands, especially in south and east Hertfordshire. It also occurs frequently in damp, shaded chalk pits or damp, wooded hedgebanks. It appears to have spread quite substantially, especially in the Chilterns dip-slope woods, perhaps owing to increased shade from overgrown woodlands.
(43 tetrads: Dony, 1967; 74 tetrads: 1950-1986)

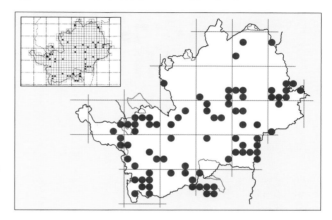

Map 847. *Allium ursinum.*

Allium oleraceum L.   UK Vulnerable
Field Garlic
Native.
First record: *c.*1820.

A native plant of dry grasslands, often in field borders, this has always been a rare plant in the County and of uncertain occurrence. It was first found in corn fields near Danesbury, Welwyn (TL21) (Pryor, 1887); and until recently its only other occurrences had been at Whempstead (TL32), 1919-1920 *A. W. Graveson* (Hb. HTN); and on a roadside north of Ashwell (TL24), 1950 *J. C. Gardiner* (det. S. M. Walters) (Hb. HTN). During the recent survey, a small colony was found by a corn field at Mill End, Rickmansworth (09/G), 1996 *J. Colthup* (Hb. HTN). It was still present in good numbers in at least 1998.

Allium vineale L.
Crow Garlic
Native.
First record: *c.*1730.
Tetrad occurrence: 194 (40%).
Increased substantially (+107%).

Usually now a plant of rough grassland along road verges and by corn fields, this has shown strong signs of increasing, having been described by Pryor (1887) as being 'rather rare'. Dony (1967) recorded it as 'frequent' on the Boulder Clay, but rare elsewhere. It is still most common on the Boulder Clay, where its slender shoots can be abundant along road verges in the spring, but it is also now common on the Chalk in north Hertfordshire, and widespread on the more calcareous areas of the Chilterns dip-slope in west Hertfordshire. In southern Hertfordshire, it is occasional in field margins, but not common. The reasons for its spread are not entirely clear, although dry seasons can encourage regeneration by opening up the sward. Preston *et al.* (2002) did not record any increase nationally, although the BSBI Local Change Project did show a relative change of +24% (Braithwaite, *et al.*, 2006). It tends to occur where road verge vegetation has been enriched by fertiliser run-off, and this may be a factor also. How it is able to spread so effectively is unknown.

(89 tetrads: Dony, 1967; 106 tetrads: 1950-1986)

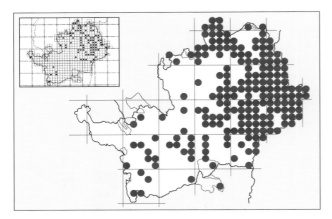

Map 848. *Allium vineale.*

Allium senescens L.
German Garlic
Introduced: casual.
First record: 1995.

A well-established clump of this escaped garden plant was found on a gravelly roadside at Welwyn Road, Hertford (31/B), 1995 *A. M. Boucher* (det. C. G. Hanson) (Hb. HTN). It was still present in 1999 *T. J.* (Hb. HTN).

Allium nigrum L.
Broad-leaved Leek
Introduced: casual.
First (only) record: 1993.

Another garden plant that has become fashionable recently, this was found on gravelly ground at Gallows Hill, Hertford (31/L), 1993 *A. M. Boucher* (Hb. HTN).

Genus: *Nectaroscordum*

Nectaroscordum siculum (Ucria) Lindley
Honey Garlic
Introduced: casual.
First (only) record: 1998.

Several flowering specimens of this escaped garden plant were found growing in a wooded clearing at Tring Park (91/F), 1998 *R. Mabey.*

Genus: *Tristagma*

Tristagma uniflorum (Lindl.) Traub
Spring Starflower
Introduced: neophyte.
First record: 1998.

Several specimens of this garden escape were found growing in the

edge of an old meadow near Baxter's Moat, Great Munden (32/M), 1998 *T. J.* This site is well away from houses, but interestingly it was also known in the 1930s as a site for the Snakeshead Fritillary (A. W. Graveson, ms diary: North Herts. Museums), and so may have been subject to some sort of gardening previously. It frequently seeds itself in gardens, and could be elsewhere as an escape.

Genus: *Leucojum*

Leucojum aestivum L.
Summer Snowflake
Introduced [native in the U.K.?].
First record: 1869.
Tetrad occurrence: 8 (2%).

The first record of this was made at Barnet (TQ29), 1869 *J. G. Farrar* (Hb. BM) (a record overlooked by Dony, 1967). It was not reported as an escape again until 1960, when it appeared near Cole Green (21/R) *P. Shearsby* (also omitted from Dony, 1967); as well as the record that Dony does give, from Totteridge Green (29/L) (VC20 [Greater London]), 1964 *D. J. Hinson*. Mr Hinson also reported it to Dony from Aldenham (19/J) subsequently (date not recorded). What was probably this was then recorded at Lower Plantation, Wymondley (22/E), 1981 *B. R. Sawford*, on the site of a long lost garden. During the recent survey, it was found in no less than eight localities, interestingly mostly in and around the ancient woodlands of south-east Hertfordshire.

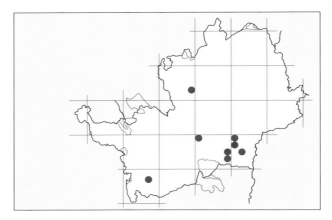

Map 849. *Leucojum aestivum*

The plant in Hertfordshire is probably ssp. *pulchellum* (Salisb.) Briq., but the only record identified to this subspecies was from Northaw (20/W), 1996 *A. D. Marshall.*

[*Leucojum vernum* L. **Spring Snowflake** has been reported a couple of times (*e.g.* see James, 1982), but probably in error for early-flowering specimens of its relative. Without confirmation, these records remain in doubt. It is a rare escape, long-established in the wild in some places in the U.K., and could conceivably have escaped from gardens in our area as well.]

Genus: *Galanthus*

Snowdrops are not a particularly easy group to identify, and the problems have been magnified because of the increased use of cultivated varieties of several species for 'wild planting', adding to the genuinely escaped colonies. They have also tended to be ignored by earlier botanists.

Galanthus nivalis L.
Snowdrop
Introduced: neophyte.
First record: *c.*1840.
Tetrad occurrence: 128 (26%).

As an escape, this sometimes forms almost convincingly wild-looking colonies in damp, wooded habitat. It is interesting to note that Coleman (Webb and Coleman, 1849) thought that it was quite rare in 'wild' situations; while Pryor (1887) was almost inclined to consider it as native, indicating perhaps that its desirability as a garden plant in Victorian times had allowed it to escape more widely. Dony (1967) scarcely acknowledged the plant. It is once again being favoured, this time for 'wild planting' in various places, which obscures its real occurrence as an escape. The map therefore tends to show where either people like to plant it out in the countryside, or where botanists have bothered to record it! However, its increased frequency around the river valleys in south-east Hertfordshire probably reflects its preference for wooded stream banks. Modern cultivars with larger flowers of different forms make recording difficult, and its hybrid with *Galanthus plicatus* also probably occurs, but has yet to be identified in the wild.

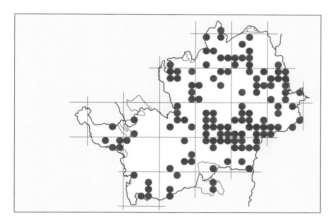

Map 850. *Galanthus nivalis.*

Galanthus plicatus M. Bieb.
Pleated Snowdrop
Introduced: neophyte.
First record: 1995.

This was first noticed by a track at Luffenhall (22/Z), 1995 *T. J.*; and again in a hedge bank near Sarratt Mill (09/J) the same year *T. J.*, only otherwise being found at Batford (11/N), 1999 *T. J.* It and its hybrid with *G. nivalis* are probably quite widespread and overlooked as ordinary Snowdrops elsewhere.

Galanthus elwesii J. D. Hook
Greater Snowdrop
Introduced: casual.
First (only) record: 1994.

This was found as an established introduction at Great Amwell Churchyard (31/R), 1994 *C. G. Hanson* (det. E. J. Clement), but has not been found in any more genuinely 'wild' situations.

[*Galanthus ikariae* Baker
Green Snowdrop

This was found by the pond at Bayfordbury (31/A), 1984 *C. G. Hanson* (det. E. J. Clement), but as there was no suggestion

it had spread from where it must have been planted, it cannot be regarded as 'wild'.]

Genus: *Narcissus*

The 'daffodils' of one sort or another are taxonomically challenging, even to specialists, and their occurrence as really 'wild' plants is also often very difficult to judge, owing to the propensity of landowners to beautify their grounds with spring cheer. It is therefore well-nigh impossible to sort the wheat from the chaff, as far as 'wild' plants are concerned, particularly the escaped species and hybrids. As a result, this *Flora* certainly has made no attempt to record planted daffodils, or even to record evident cultivated forms of daffodils in apparently 'wild' places on any systematic basis. Some obvious escapes have been included, but for the most part, only a brief notice is given of 'wild' occurrences of the main cultivated species and hybrids.

Narcissus tazetta L.
Bunch-flowered Daffodil
Introduced: casual.
First documented record: 1996.

The only record on file is a spontaneous occurrence on a building site at Royston (34/K) (VC29 [Herts.]), 1996 *T. J.*

Narcissus × medioluteus Miller (*Narcissus tazetta* × *N. poeticus*)
Primrose-peerless
Introduced: casual or neophyte.
First record: *c.*1840.

Both Webb and Coleman (1849) and Pryor (1887) list various records (as '*N. biflorus*'), and there is an old undated specimen in Hb. BM from Cumberlow Green (33/A) collected by A. W. Bennett (Dony, ms. notes) which is of interest, as it still occurs on the road verge there! The recent survey failed to give the plant much attention, but there is a record of it as an escape at Marshall's Heath (11/S), 1992 *J. Murray*. It probably occurs quite often.

Narcissus poeticus L.
Pheasant's-eye Daffodil
Introduced: casual or neophyte.
First record: *c.*1840.

This was noted briefly by Webb and Coleman (1849), but included under '*N. biflorus*'. There were no other records from 'wild' situations until the recent survey, when it was reported from eight locations. It no doubt occurs as an escape much more widely, but these are difficult to tell from planted specimens.

One record: from Darlands Lake (29/L) (VC20 [Greater London]), 2002 *R. M. Burton* was referred to ssp. *poeticus*, but no doubt most others were this also.

Narcissus × incomparabilis Miller
(*N. poeticus* × *N. pseudonarcissus*)
Nonesuch Daffodil
Introduced: casual.
First documented record: 1994.

There appear not to have been any records of this 'in the wild' before it was reported from Broxbourne (30/T), 1994 *A. M. Boucher*. The survey subsequently recorded it from seven tetrads, although it must be much more widespread than that.

Narcissus pseudonarcissus L.
Wild Daffodil
Native (and introduced).
First record: *c.*1730.
Tetrad occurrence: 33 (7%).
Increased? (+139%).

Wild Daffodils have been a feature of some areas of the County for a very long time. When Dony compiled his records, the species seems to have either been overlooked or to have become rare, and he attributed this to them having been dug up for gardens. However, records gathered after 1970 showed that it was widespread, especially in the south and centre of the County. During the recent survey, they were again recorded around Hatfield, the Ayot area, and across to Little Gaddesden, *etc.*, much as Pryor (1887) recorded, mostly in woodland sites, although a few grassland areas still support it, as well as some old churchyards. In some cases, its natural occurrence is doubtful, but as a native it often forms mixed communities with Bluebells and other characteristic ancient woodland plants, usually on a rather gravelly soil. A few localities have obviously had it for many centuries, as their names reflect its presence, notably Dilly Wood near Sacombe (31/P) and the Golden Parsonage at Gaddesden (01/L), whose name is supposed to have arisen because of the former show of Daffodils in its meadows, now sadly very much reduced. More recently, owing to the fashion for planting

'daffodils' into the wild, almost become a craze in some places, these are sometimes put in areas where the native form exists, with the result that the occurrence of the real thing gets obscured. Occasionally, also, true 'wild' Daffodils are also planted out, which are even more difficult to detect, except that human beings usually plant them in obvious clumps! While the survey tried to sort these records out, it appears to have been missed in some places in south Herts., for example, where it was recorded with reasonable certainty between 1970 and 1986, such as around Northaw. (13 tetrads: Dony, 1967; 30 tetrads: 1950-1986)

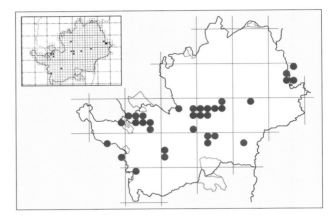

Map 851. *Narcissus pseudonarcissus* ssp. *pseudonarcissus.*

The native plant in the County is the rather dainty, slender ssp. *pseudonarcissus*, with its characteristic drooping flowers. The more gaudy ssp. *major* (Curtis) Baker **Spanish Daffodil**, with all its variants, is the normal cultivated form, and occurs widely as both planted bulbs, and as throw-outs. No real attempts were made to record it, and in any case it would most likely have been confused with other species and hybrids anyway.

Genus: *Asparagus*

Asparagus officinalis L.
Garden Asparagus
Introduced: neophyte.
First record: 1941.
Tetrad occurrence: 30 (6%).
Increasing?

The garden form of the plant is ssp. *officinalis*. There was a published record from 'Sawbridgeworth' (*i.e.* Allen's Green) by H. W. Pugsley in the *Journal of Botany*, 1941 (Dony, ms. index), but Dony kept no other records, and merely mentions it as an

Wild Daffodil Narcissus pseudonarcissus *Stocking Spring, Ayot St Lawrence, 2003.*

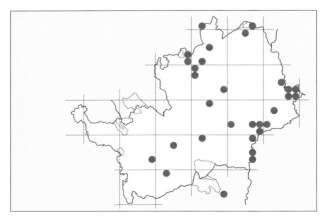

Map 852. *Asparagus officinalis.*

escape from cultivation. It is not mentioned by earlier botanists. It was recorded without details from nine scattered tetrads across southern Hertfordshire in Burton (1983), and the recent survey found it in no less than 30 tetrads across the County, perhaps showing some indications of a preference for damper, calcareous soils, with concentrations around Hitchin, and in the Lea and Stort valleys, although this may reflect where some botanists rather than others did their recording!

Genus: *Ruscus*

Ruscus aculeatus L.   Herts Rare? (as native)
Butcher's Broom
Native (and introduced).
First record: 1737.
Tetrad occurrence: 21 (4%).

As a native plant, this would have occurred in wood-pasture commons and open woodlands on acidic soils in the south of the County. Dony (1967) was doubtful about all the places he had seen it, because they occurred near country houses, old parks, *etc.* However, Pryor (1887) gives details of a range of sites with a long history as ancient woodlands, often derived from medieval common pasture, such as Milwards Park (20/I?); near Batchworth Heath (09/Q); Blackfan Wood (30/D); N. of Wormley Wood (30/I); Hook Wood (20/Q); and Broxbourne Wood (30/I). Of the sites where Dony saw it, Northaw Great Wood (20/S?) and Chase Wood near Potters Bar (29/U) are both sites with a history as wood pastures. Between 1970 and 1986, it was recorded from 11 tetrads, and of these, there were likely native records from Northaw Great Wood again (20/S, X); near Bayford Wood (20/Y); Nyn Park (20/R); Oak Hill Park area (29/S, X) (VC20 [Greater London]); and Cattlegate Wood, Northaw (20/V); as well as a possible native site at Park Wood, Tring (91/F), which was derived from the former Tring Heath. During the recent survey, several of these sites were re-examined without success, but there were likely native records from: hedge near Thunderfield Grove (30/M), 1996 *A. M. Boucher*; Chase Wood (29/U) (VC21 [Herts.], 1996, 1998 *N. Holmes-Smith/G. P. Smith*; Home Park, Hatfield (20/P), 1992 *A. D. Marshall*; and Fir and Pond Woods Nature Reserve (20/Q) (VC21 [Herts.]), 2004 *G. Salisbury*. It is still probably in some of the other native sites previously recorded, but is nowhere common. Elsewhere, it escapes readily from gardens, often in hedges.

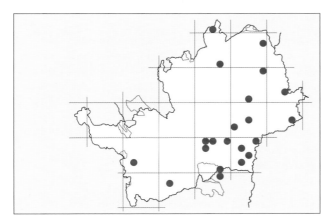

Map 853. *Ruscus aculeatus.*

Iridaceae (Iris family)

Genus: *Sisyrhinchium*

Sisyrinchium bermudiana L.
Blue-eyed-grass
Introduced: casual.
First record: 1923.

This was only recorded as an escape at Welwyn (TL21), 1923 *H. Phillips* and at Rickmansworth (TQ09), 1947 *O. M. Richards* (Dony, 1967; and ms. notes).

Sisyrinchium striatum Sm.
Pale Yellow-eyed-grass
Introduced: casual or neophyte.
First record: 2009.

First noted as an escape by the roadside at the A1(M)/A414 roundabout north of Hatfield (21/F), 2009 *T. J.*; this also appeared in some quantity by the A1(M)/A507 roundabout at Radwell (23/H) shortly afterwards *T. J.*

Genus: *Iris*

Iris germanica L.
Bearded Iris
Introduced: casual.
First record: *c.*1950.

A plant of complex garden origin, Dony (1967) does not mention it, but he had received one record, from Bishop's Stortford tip, undated (*c.*1950) from D. McClintock. It was subsequently recorded from Hitchin (12/Z), 1978 *J. M. Way*; Ware tip (31/M), 1986 *C. G. Hanson*; and from Waterford tip (31/C), 1986 *C. G. H.* The recent survey only received two records of it as an escape: Marshall's Heath (11/S), 1992 *J. Murray*; and Water End, North Mymms (20/G), 1996 *R. M. Burton*.

Iris sibirica L.
Siberian Iris
Introduced: casual.
First record: 1980.

An increasingly popular garden plant, this has had surprisingly few records as an escape: scrub on Harpenden Common (11/L), 1980 *R. M. Bateman*; and by a lagoon at Rye Meads Sewage Works (31/V), 1981-1982 *A. M. Boucher*.

Iris pseudacorus L.
Yellow Iris *or* **Yellow Flag**
Native (and introduced).
First record: 1820.
Tetrad occurrence: 286 (58%).
Increased (+119%).

As a native plant, this has always been widespread by ponds and in swampy areas by rivers across much of the County, only becoming scarce on the drier Clay-with-Flints and Chalk, or in more acidic areas in the south of the County. Unfortunately, with the fashion for water features, it has also become a favourite species for ornamental planting. This may well account for some of the quite substantial recorded increase, although it does seem to favour more highly eutrophic sites, and may have also increased

at the expense of other species in its more natural sites.
(124 tetrads: Dony, 1967; 173 tetrads: 1950-1986)

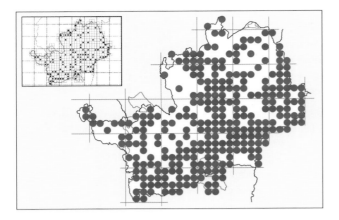

Map 854. *Iris pseudacorus.*

Iris laevigata Fischer in Fischer and C. A. Meyer
Japanese Water Iris
Introduced: casual.
First record: 1996.

This beautiful plant of swamps was first noted at a pond at
Haydon Hill open space, Bushey (19/H), 1996 *T. J.*, where it could
conceivably have been planted, but looked very established. It also
appeared by a wooded pond on Berkhamsted Common (00/E),
2004 *T. J./G. Salisbury*, where it certainly did not seem to have
been deliberately introduced.

Iris orientalis Mill.
Turkish Iris
Introduced: neophyte.
First record: 1989.

A rather rare escape from cultivation, this was first noted by the
A505 at Baldock (23/M), 1989 *R. Mabey*; and subsequently at
Water End, North Mymms (20/G), 1995 *A. D. Marshall* (det. T. J.)
(Hb. HTN); and as a spreading clump by Ashwell Quarry Springs
(23/P), 2004, *etc. T. J.*

Iris foetidissima L.
Stinking Iris *or* **Gladdon**
Native (and introduced).
First record: 1746.
Tetrad occurrence: 67 (14%).
Increased markedly (+300%).

A native plant of semi-natural woodlands on mainly calcareous
clay soils, this also increasingly turns up as an escape in
hedgerows and on waste ground across much of the County. Its
first record was by Blackstone from between Dunstable and St
Albans, 1746 (Pryor, 1887), not 1799 as given by Dony (1967). Both
Webb and Coleman (1849) and Pryor thought it was rare, although
they gave a fair number of records; and Dony also thought it was
rare. It is now quite frequent, with a slight preponderance of
records from woods and hedgerows on the Boulder Clay, although
it is fairly frequent also in west Herts. and on the Chalk in the
north.
(16 tetrads: Dony, 1967; 39 tetrads: 1950-1986)

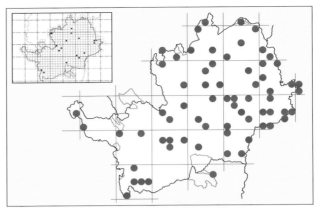

Map 855. *Iris foetidissima.*

Iris xyphium L.
Spanish Iris
Introduced: casual.
First (only) record: 1999.

This was noted as an escape near Bayford Station (30/E)
R. M. Burton.

Genus: *Crocus*

Crocus vernus (L.) Hill
Spring Crocus
Introduced: casual.
First record: *c.*1815.

This familiar flower, much planted in grass lawns across the
County, does also turn up as self-established. Its first record was
by J. Sabine (in Clutterbuck, 1815), not in 1835 (Dony, 1967).
Dony does not give any current records, and there were none
subsequently until it was noted as an escape at Broxbourne
(30/T), 1994 *A. M. Boucher*. It was then found by a path at
Waterend, Wheathampstead (21/B), 2000 *T. J.*; and by a field
path near Sarratt (09/J), 2005 *T. J.* Other occurrences tend to
have been ignored, because it is difficult to tell how 'natural' they
are!

Crocus tommasinianus Herbert
Early Crocus
Introduced: casual.
First record: 1988.

First found in a convincingly natural locality in scrub at Colney
Heath (20/C), 1988 *M. Nash* (det. T. J.); this has also been found
escaped at Bushey Heath (19/L), 1989 *J. K. Jackson*; on dumped
soil at Stanborough (21/F), 1994 *A. M. Boucher*; and similarly at
Hertford (31/B), 1996 *A. M. B.*

Crocus × stellaris Haw. (*C. angustifolius × C. flavus*)
Yellow Crocus
Introduced: casual.
First record: 1990.

This is the usual yellow crocus grown in gardens, and occasionally
escapes on dumped soil. It was initially mis-reported as '*C. flavus*'
itself, and was first found in a damp area at Sherrards Park Wood
(21/G), 1990 *A. M. Boucher*; who then also reported it from
Broxbourne (30/T) (with other garden escapes), 1991; and from a
roadside at Great Amwell (31/Q), 1996.

Crocus nudiflorus Smith
Autumn Crocus
Introduced: casual.
First record: 1967.

There have only been two reports of this as an escape: the first at Broxbourne (30/T), 1967 *J. Foreman*; and then from Whippendell Wood (09/T), 1979 *R. C. Hemming*. It probably occurs as such elsewhere, unnoticed.

Genus: *Gladiolus*

Gladiolus communis L.
Eastern Gladiolus
Introduced: casual.
First record: 1982.

This was found on a tip at Cock Lane (30/T), 1982 *C. G. Hanson*. It was also found in scrub near the Ayot Way (21/C), 2000 *L. J. Borg* (det. T. J. from a photograph).

Gladiolus × *hortulanus* Bailey
Garden Gladiolus
Introduced: casual.
First (only) record: 1982.

This garden outcast was also on a tip at Cock Lane (30/T) *C. G. Hanson*. It probably turns up occasionally elsewhere.

Genus: *Crocosmia*

Crocosmia × *crocosmiiflora* (Lemoine ex Burb. and Dean) N. E. Br. (*C. pottsii* × *C. aurea*)
Montbretia
Introduced: neophyte.
First record: 1970.
Tetrad occurrence: 11 (2%).
Increasing slowly.

This familiar garden plant, which can form locally dominant stands beside streams in western Britain, is now occasional as a persistent outcast in our County, but does not seem to spread. It was first reported from tips at Moor Mill (10/L) and Pye Corner (41/L), 1970 *C. G. Hanson*; and subsequently at eight other sites to 1986. The recent survey found it at 11 scattered localities, often in shaded scrub near houses or on tips.

Dioscoreaceae (Yam family)

Genus: *Tamus*

Tamus communis L.
Black Bryony
Native.
First record: c.1820.
Tetrad occurrence: 418 (85%).
Probably stable (-4%).

This is a familiar, but poisonous plant of scrub, and hedgerows on usually somewhat calcareous soils across much of the County, only becoming scarce or absent on strongly acidic or damp ground in river valleys, or in the driest, open Chalk country.
(415 tetrads: Dony, 1967; 422 tetrads: 1950-1986)

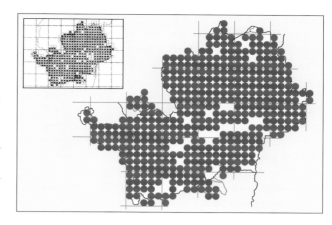

Map 856. *Tamus communis.*

Orchidaceae (Orchids)

The treatment followed here follows taxonomy and nomenclature proposed by R. M. Bateman (2001). It differs from that used by Stace (1997) in some areas, especially where some species have been considered to belong to different genera. In the late 1970s and early 1980s, we were fortunate enough to have the help of Richard Bateman, then at Rothamsted, who undertook a detailed re-examination of orchid localities across the County, using 19th century and other sources of information as a starting point (Bateman, 1981, 1982). The result was a much more detailed understanding of these enigmatic plants than was given in Dony (1967). However, his survey also coincided with a damper climatic period than was the case in the late 1950s, when much of Dony's survey was carried out. Similarly, during the recent survey, after 1988, the climate became much more dry, particularly during the winter, when orchids develop their rhizomes, with the result that some species may have suffered. Whether they have remained undetected at some sites is a matter for further study.

Genus: *Cephalanthera*

Cephalanthera damasonium (Miller) Druce
White Helleborine
Native.
First record: 1695.
Tetrad occurrence: 24 (5%).
Stable, or now decreasing? (+4%).

White Helleborine is a specially characteristic orchid of Beech

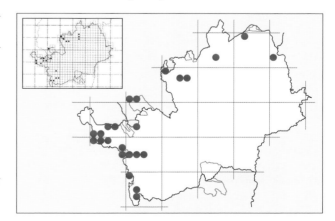

Map 857. *Cephalanthera damasonium.*

woodlands, where it forms root associations with the trees, although it can occur with other species. It prefers semi-shade, with little competing ground flora. As such, it has always been most frequent in the semi-natural woodlands of the Chilterns, but it can also appear wherever Beech trees exist, such as in relatively recent plantations. An example is the long-standing colony in the 19th century Beech plantation at Fox Covert, Therfield (33/J), which suffered from the opening up of the canopy by a storm in 1990. The recent survey did not find any significant change from Dony's, although with the damaging effects of storms and droughts on ageing Beech woodlands generally, its present position may have deteriorated since the current survey began, a picture perhaps re-inforced by the fact that many more sites were recorded during the 1980s.

(22 tetrads: Dony, 1967; 34 tetrads: 1950-1986)

[*Cephalanthera longifolia* (L.) Fritsch
Narrow-leaved Helleborine
Native.
Only record: *c.*1690.

There are two rather unsatisfactory mentions of this orchid from Hertfordshire. The first was a very brief mention in John Ray's 'Synopsis Britannicarum' (1690), based on information supplied by a Dr Eales of Welwyn, without locality details. The other is a mention in Gibson's edition of J. Camden's 'Britannia' (1722), reported by Pryor (1887), of details of Dr Eales' record: 'Handpost Farm, Hemel Hempstead... (= in the hanging meadow by the St Albans Lane from Hempstead; Hamilton. ms.)'. Bateman (1981) thought these were two separate records, but Pryor's note confirms that they probably refer to the same observation. Pryor also notes that there seemed to be some uncertainty about what Ray's idea of the species was. For this reason, Dony (1967) expressed doubt about the record. Without some further evidence, Dony's conclusion probably needs to be upheld, and its acceptance on the Hertfordshire list remains unsubstantiated.]

Genus: *Neottia*

This genus, formerly limited in Britain to the saprophytic Bird's-nest Orchid, has now been thought to include the twayblades as well.

Neottia ovata (L.) Bluff. and Fingerh.
Common Twayblade
Native.
First record: 1695.
Tetrad occurrence: 71 (15%).
Decreasing (-18%).

An orchid with fairly catholic tastes in habitat, this is found in calcareous, usually slightly damp ground, in semi-natural woodland, including fen carr; open rough grassland on calcareous soils, including chalk grassland where this is not too dry; and occasionally in disturbed habitats, such as calcareous silt-beds at old gravel pits or in old chalk pits. It is quite capable of colonising new sites, but does not tolerate nutrient enrichment, which may explain some of its decline, although droughts do also affect its appearances. As would be expected, it remains in several of the ancient woodlands on the Boulder Clay, where these have been less affected by nutrient enrichment, but was found to be much more widespread in the Chilterns dip-slope region than Dony (1967) recorded. Considering the extra tetrads in which it was

recorded during the 1980s, its decrease appears to have been even more substantial than a strict comparison with the 1960s survey would suggest.

(83 tetrads: Dony, 1967; 129 tetrads: 1950-1986)

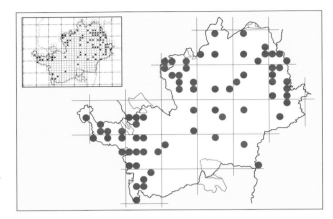

Map 858. *Neottia ovata.*

Neottia nidus-avis (L.) Rich.
Bird's-nest Orchid
Native.
First record: *c.*1700.
Tetrad occurrence: 4 (<1%).
Severely decreased (-81%).

This strange saprophytic orchid, usually thought of mostly as occurring in Beech woods, in the 19th century was known, sparsely, from a wide range of woods, from Rickmansworth to Royston, and from Northaw to Tring, on apparently even quite

Bird's-nest Orchid Neottia nidus-avis *Old Road Plantation, Offley, 1988.*

acidic soils of different kinds (Pryor, 1887). It was still quite widespread in the 1960s, when Dony recorded it from a good number of sites, scattered throughout its 19th century range. However, after 1970, it was only recorded from four tetrads: Bramfield Park Wood (21/X), c.1970 *J. Wheatcroft* (comm.: J. C. Doyle); Old Road Plantation, Offley (12/N), 1978, 1980 *R. M. Bateman*; 1979 *T. J./B. R. Sawford*; Aldbury Nowers (91/L), 1979, 1980 *R. M. Bateman*; and Marshland Wood (41/H), 1981 *E. F. Greenwood*. The recent survey also recorded it from just four places: Old Road Plantation, Offley again (12/N), where it survived to at least 1988, *T. J.*, possibly succumbing to the loss of shading mature Beeches in the storm of January 1990; Ridlins Wood, Stevenage (22/R), 1993 *M. Gurney*; Damsel's Spring (42/F), 1995 *S. Cuming*; and from secondary woodland near Furzeground Wood, Sacombe (31/P), 2003 *K. Robinson*. It is interesting that three of these sites were on neutral or even mildly acidic soils away from the Chalk, and that one was not ancient habitat. Its erratic behaviour means that it could yet be under-recorded in places it was previously known.

(20 tetrads: Dony, 1967; 21 tetrads: 1950-1986)

Genus: *Epipactis*

Epipactis palustris (L.) Crantz   Herts Rare
Marsh Helleborine
Native.
First record: *c.*1752.
Tetrad occurrence: 2 (<1%).

A plant of open, calcareous fen conditions, this has always been rare in the County. Early records show that it was known from at

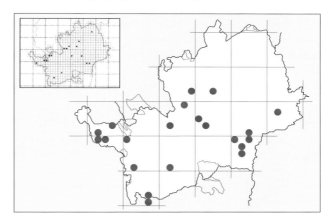

Photo: Brian Sawford

Marsh Helleborine Epipactis palustris *Near Moor Hall, Ardeley, 1987.*

least six sites, all on peaty ground derived from spring sources. By the 1960s, it had been reduced to two localities: Foulwells, near Wormley Wood (30/I), and a site near Moor Hall, Ardeley (32/I). Foulwells was severely damaged by the creation of a pond in 1963, and the species was considered lost from there (Dony, 1967). It remains at Ardeley, although the population has decreased steadily since the 1980s. It was re-introduced to the Foulwells locality in 1998, from stock salvaged at the time it was drained maintained in cultivation, and was still present in 2001 *J. C. Doyle*.

(2 tetrads: Dony, 1967; and from 1950-1986)

Epipactis purpurata Smith
Violet Helleborine
Native.
First record: 1843.
Tetrad occurrence: 21 (4%).
Increased? (+16%).

Violet Helleborine is an orchid that tends to appear in troupes from underground rhizomes that are associated often with Hornbeam, as well as with Beech, on damp clay loam soils derived from the Clay-with-Flints, and less calcareous Boulder Clay deposits. Its distribution remains more or less similar to that shown by Dony (1967), but Bateman (1981, 1982) showed that it was then much more widespread than his records indicated, especially in the Chilterns dip-slope woodlands. Given its unpredictable occurrence in dry years, it is likely to have been overlooked in the recent survey at some sites. It has, nevertheless, still been recorded more widely than in the 1960s, although it is doubtful if this is a genuine increase.

(17 tetrads: Dony, 1967; 40 tetrads: 1950-1986)

Map 859. *Epipactis purpurata.*

Epipactis helleborine (L.) Crantz
Broad-leaved Helleborine
Native.
First record: (1597 for the agg.), *c.*1840.
Tetrad occurrence: 17 (4%).
Decreased? (-5%).

Although Webb and Coleman (1849) considered this to be a separate species from Violet Helleborine, later 19th century records of these tend to be confused (Pryor, 1887), which makes assessment of change in its occurrence before 1950 difficult. As Dony (1967) found, it remains most frequent in the south-east of the County, although these sites are not necessarily actually on London Clay as he suggested. It occurs on damp, more-or-less calcareous or mildly acidic clay soils, often where these are irrigated with surface water during the winter, such as on shaded stream banks in woodland. Although it was recorded in a similar number of tetrads to Dony, there are some signs it may have decreased a little, at least since the 1980s, when Bateman and others found it especially abundantly in the Broxbourne Woods complex. Nevertheless, records from northern and western Hertfordshire, where Dony scarcely knew it, show that it can turn up in new localities. However, some plants have caused confusion, especially when growing in abnormal habitats. A particular case is the occurrence of rather depauperate, green-flowered forms in willow scrub on former silt-bed deposits at Waterford Gravel Pit (31/C), 1994 *T. J./T. C. G. Rich/G. P. Smith* (det A. J. Richards) (Hb. HTN). These were growing not far from normal forms in nearby woodland, and were very similar to *E. phyllanthes*, which has also been recorded from the same locality.

(17 tetrads: Dony, 1967; 43 tetrads: 1950-1986)

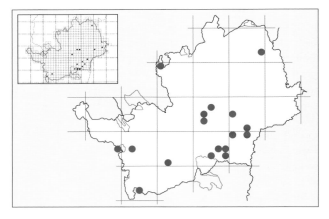

Map 860. *Epipactis helleborine.*

Epipactis leptochila (Godfery) Godfery   Herts Rare
Narrow-lipped Helleborine
Native.
First confirmed record: 1943.

Only ever known from woodlands on the Chalk scarp south of Tring, this was last seen at both Park Wood, Tring (91/F), and at Stubbings Wood (91/A, 90/E) in 1980 *R. M. Bateman* (Bateman, 1981, 1982). Repeated searches failed to find the plant in its known haunts, but a single specimen was located at Bishop's Wood, Tring (90/J), 2009 *G. Salisbury*. It is declining in the Chilterns generally, which is its major stronghold in Britain. Previous inclusion taxonomically with *E. dunensis* nationally (Preston *et al.*, 2002) has meant that it is not yet assessed as nationally vulnerable, although this is possibly its status (Cheffings and Farrell, 2007).

Epipactis phyllanthes G. E. Smith   Herts Rare
Green-flowered Helleborine
Native.
First record: 1959.
Tetrad occurrence: 4 (<1%).
Increased (+200%).

This is a peculiar plant, in our area being found largely in secondary habitats, often in otherwise species-poor scrub on damp loams or near streams, sometimes near willows or poplars. It also seems to be increasing, having only recently arrived in the County. Its variety *pendula* D. P. Young was first found in old willow scrub

Green-flowered Helleborine Epipactis phyllanthes *Millhoppers Pasture, Astrope, 1998.*

by Wilstone Reservoir (91/B), 1959, *J. G. Dony* (Dony, 1967), where it was re-discovered in 1979 *D. Turnbull* (Bateman, 1981), and in 1999 *T. J./G. Salisbury*. A record not attributed to variety was also made in 1959 at an orchard at Chorleywood *R. F. Turney* (Dony, *op. cit.*). Variety *vectensis* T. and T. A. Stephenson was then recorded at Little Frithsden Copse (00/E), 1980 *R. M. Bateman* (Bateman, 1982); and again in scrub on old chalk spoil heaps by Harmergreen Wood (21/N), 1982 *R. M. B.* More recently, plants appearing to be var. *vectensis* have been identified from the silt-bed scrub at the Waterford Gravel Pit site (31/C), 1995 *A. M. Boucher/C. G. Hanson*, where depauperate *E. helleborine* plants were also found in 1994. Identification of material from this site as *E. phyllanthes* was confirmed genetically by J. Squirrel (University of Glasgow), 1998. Finally, plants of var. *pendula* were discovered growing under blackthorn scrub near Black Poplars by a stream at Millhoppers Pasture, Astrope (81/X), 1998 *S. Hawkins* (conf. T. J.), not far from the Wilstone Reservoir location; and a plant of var. *vectensis* was found in scrub by the old railway at Sherrards Park Wood (21/G), 1999 *T. J.*

(2 tetrads: Dony, 1967; 4 tetrads: 1950-1986)

Hammarbya paludosa (L.) Kuntze — Herts Extinct
Bog Orchid
Native.
First (only) record: *c*.1640.

This was reported from 'wet grounds between St Albans and Bishop's Hatfield' in John Parkinson's '*Theatrum botanicum: or theatre of plants*' (1640). Its existence in this watershed area between the Colne and Lea Valleys gives a brief insight into the nature of the landscape around Colney Heath and Cooper's Green at the time.

Genus: *Spiranthes*

Spiranthes spiralis (L.) Chevall. — Herts Rare
Autumn Lady's-tresses
Native.
First record: 1811.
Possibly extinct.

Autumn Lady's-tresses is an inconspicuous plant, flowering in late summer, when many botanists might have given up field work. It requires nutrient-poor, very short vegetation on chalk, or on calcareous sands and gravels, often, as Pryor (1887) observed, with *Carex flacca*. It can also appear unexpectedly, such as on unfertilised lawns. Dony (1967) only gave one recent record: 'Alpine Meadow', near Berkhamsted (91/V) (now a nature reserve), 1956 *E. A. Glennie*. It in fact remained here until at least 1981 *P. J. Kingsbury*. Historically, it had also been recorded from a range of sites, such as Lilley Hoo, Hitch Wood Shrubs, Stevenage, Tingley Downs, North Mymms, Nomansland Common, Boxmoor, King's Langley Common, Totteridge Green, Bayford, Bedwell Park, Gustard Wood, Hatfield Park, *etc*. (Pryor, *op. cit.*). Two plants were found on Church Hill, Therfield Heath (33/J), 1968 *W. Darling*, and it also survived at this locality until at least 1979. A final record was from the lawns of St Mary and the Angels Convent, Hemel Hempstead (00/N), 1980, reported by the gardener to E. Evans and R. C. Hemming (Bateman, 1982). No records were received from the recent survey, but botanists need to examine carefully any barren chalky slope with short, abundant Glaucous Sedge in late summer!

Genus: *Herminium*

Herminium monorchis (L.) R. Br. — UK Vulnerable
Musk Orchid
Native.
First record: *c*.1700.
Tetrad occurrence: 2 (<1%).
Now extinct? (+100%).

This is also a rather inconspicuous, attractive orchid of bare habitat on Chalk, often occurring on exposed, sunny banks of old chalk pits and similar places, where there has previously been some disturbance. Again, such habitats are now rare, and it has always been a scarce plant in the County, but was at one time not restricted to the Chalk hills of north Hertfordshire, occurring as widely as Hatfield Park (TL20), Welwyn (TL21), a chalk pit by Wain Wood (long-since scrubbed over) (12/S), Tring (SP91), and Beechwood Park near Markyate (TL01). It has occurred on and off on the private chalk slopes below Tingley Wood (13/F), where it

numbered 65 spikes in 1981 (Bateman, 1982), but was last seen in 1987 *C. W. Burton*. One plant also appeared on sunny chalk banks near Markham's Hill, Offley (12/J), 1987 *T. J.* Repeated searches of both sites since have drawn a blank, not helped by the winter droughts of the 1990s. It has to be hoped that it is not now extinct in the County.
(1 tetrad: Dony, 1967; and from 1950-1986)

Genus: *Orchis*

This genus, which contains some of the most charismatic orchids native to Britain, has now been amended somewhat to accommodate the Man Orchid, previously in its own genus of *Aceras*, but has also 'lost' Burnt Orchid to *Neotinea*; and Green-winged Orchid to *Anacamptis*.

Orchis anthropophora (L.) All. — [UK Endangered]
Man Orchid — Herts Extinct
Native.
First record: 1815.

Never a common species in Hertfordshire, the locality of the first record was regarded as doubtfully in the County by Dony (1967), but it was, in fact, probably the chalk terraces below Ashridge Monument at Aldbury (91/R), now unfortunately almost scrubbed over. A report by E. G. Kellett that it occurred at Lockley's Warren, Digswell, *c*.1950 was probably rightly ignored by Dony (1967), but he did record its occurrence at chalk banks below Offley (12/N), where it was first seen by a Miss Mears, and reported by J. E. Little in 1931. Dony's ms. index also contains a reference to its occurrence in 1914 at Barley, but, again, he presumably dismissed the report as an error. It was last formally recorded at Offley in 1957, although the chalk banks remain, and have a reasonable chalk grassland flora, rather badly affected by horse-grazing.

Orchis militaris L. — [UK Vulnerable]
Military Orchid — Herts Extinct
Native.
First record: 1815.

At one time, earlier in the 19th century, this was evidently quite common on and around the chalky banks of Tring Park, south-west of Tring town (91/F) (Pryor, 1887), but had become rare by the time he was writing. It was also recorded from the chalk banks below Ashridge Monument (Moneybury Hill) (91/R) in 1841 *W. H. Coleman*, where it remained until at least 1878 (Bateman, 1981). Finally J. Benbow monitored a population on chalky banks by Garrett Wood, near Rickmansworth (09/L), between 1889 and 1902, its last record in the County. There are, unfortunately, all too many specimens, especially from Tring, in various herbaria around the country. Tring Park is being returned to good potential habitat for it, but its other sites have succumbed to pervasive scrub encroachment or heavy disturbance.

Orchis mascula (L.) L.
Early Purple Orchid
Native.
First record: 1820.
Tetrad occurrence: 52 (11%).
Increased? (+23%).

In our area, Early Purple Orchid is a species of neutral to moderately calcareous clay soils in semi-natural woodlands, being particularly frequent in old Hornbeam or Ash/Maple/Hazel coppices in central and eastern Hertfordshire. Its occurrence can be erratic, depending on the season, and on the state of the woodlands. Heavy deer grazing in many areas is now probably adversely affecting it, although the recent survey indicated a possible increase since the 1960s in some places, including west Hertfordshire, where it was found in more places than were known to Bateman (1981).

(40 tetrads: Dony, 1967; 85 tetrads: 1950-1986)

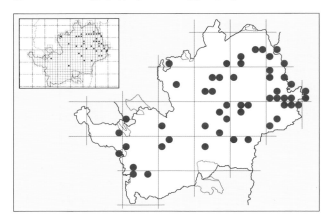

Map 861. *Orchis mascula.*

Genus: *Platanthera*

Platanthera chlorantha (Custer) Reichb.   UK Near Threatened
Greater Butterfly-orchid
Native.
First record: 1597.
Tetrad occurrence: 12 (2%).
Decreasing and now rare (-25%).

Mostly restricted to damp, calcareous soils in ancient woodlands on the Boulder Clay in east Hertfordshire, although it does occur associated with Beech woodland elsewhere. Dony (1967) only knew it from north-east Hertfordshire, but earlier botanists recorded it widely across the County, including more apparently acidic woodlands, such as Mimms Woods, Brickendonbury, Balls Wood, Hook Wood, *etc.* in southern Hertfordshire (Pryor, 1887). This suggests recent acidification of many of these woodlands, which is supported by other species declines. There was a record from Batch Wood (10/J), 1978 *R. Lord*; and others from Widow Bushes (31/D), 1983 *M. Crafer* and Bramfield Park Wood (21/X), 1984 *R. M. Bateman*, away from its core area. A plant also

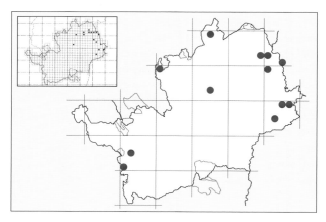

Map 862. *Platanthera chlorantha.*

appeared on a chalky road verge adjacent to Ashwell Quarry nature reserve (23/P), 1983 *T. J./C. M. James*, miles from any ancient woodland source, where it survived until 1991. In all, the recent survey found it in fewer sites than were known to Dony, and many fewer than were recorded even in the 1980s, although records from Telegraph Hill (12/E), 1987 *C. W. Burton*; and from Hanging Croft (00/A), 1988 and Hay Wood (00/H), 1993 *G. Salisbury/J. Saunders* show that it survives in a few localities in the west, unknown to Bateman (1981).

(15 tetrads: Dony, 1967; 24 tetrads: 1950-1986)

Platanthera bifolia (L.) Rich.   [UK Vulnerable]
Lesser Butterfly-orchid   Herts Extinct
Native.
First record: 1838.

There are very few reliable records of this plant of wet, more-or-less acidic, heathy habitats from Hertfordshire, owing to past identification difficulties. It was reported, probably reliably, from 'heathy ground' south of Tring (Pryor, 1887), on the lost Tring Heath and Wigginton Common by W. H. Coleman (Webb and Coleman, 1849). At least Wigginton Common is known to have been partly a heather heathland, with wet ground, before its inclosure in 1875 (and relict 'heath' still exists around woodlands locally). There are also reports in the *Transactions of the Hertfordshire Natural History Society* from 'a wood near Ashlyns' in 1882 and from Bricket Wood in 1883. The first of these was by Ada Selby, then County Recorder for plants, and the latter may also have been hers. The Ashlyns record is almost certainly an error for *P. chlorantha*. The record from Bricket Wood is more plausible, but calcareous ground also exists locally, and so the record remains uncertain. Brief notes in Dony's ms. index of reports from Hertford Heath (a potentially possible site) in 1951 by S. C. Mortis and from Blakesware Wood, undated, by J. Hoskins, as well as from Easneye and Box Wood, Hoddesdon – communicated by D. McClintock from others, are also unsubstantiated. Bateman (1981) was doubtful about all these records.

Genus: *Gymnadenia*

The treatment of the fragrant orchids has been re-assessed, so that the previous subspecies of 'Fragrant Orchid' are now considered to be separate species.

Gymnadenia conopsea (L.) R. Br.   Herts Rare
Downland Fragrant-orchid
Native.
First record: 1815.
Tetrad occurrence: 7 (1%).
Decreasing steadily (-18%).

This beautiful plant is strictly a chalk and limestone grassland species, occurring in high quality chalk grassland in our area. Pryor (1887) regarded it as rare, but listed records from around 20 localities, although a few of these might be doubtful records, and others probably refer to *G. densiflora*. Dony (1967) only gave eight localities for this plant (two others were of *G. densiflora*), but there were records from 13 tetrads between 1970 and 1986, indicating that he may have under-recorded it, owing to drought summers. The recent survey only found it in seven localities: Ashwell Quarry (23/P), many records to 2004, but not since *T. J./C. M. James*; private downs around Tingley Wood (both sides) (13/F), many records to 2003, various observers; chalk bank below Ashridge, Aldbury (91/R), 1987 *D. W. Soden*; Tring Park (91/F), 1987 *D. W. Soden*; Church Hill, Therfield Heath (33/J), 1992 *I. D. Alexander*; 'Alpine Meadow' Nature Reserve (91/V), 2002 *T. J.*; and Hexton Chalk Pit (12/E), 2009 *C. M. James/T. J.* Given the fact that several of these are now old records, and that it is disappearing at some sites despite intensive conservation management, it is almost certainly now threatened in the County, hence its 'Herts Rare' status.

(8 tetrads: Dony, 1967; 16 tetrads: 1950-1986)

Gymnadenia densiflora (Wahlenb.) A. Dietr.　　　Herts Rare
Marsh Fragrant-orchid
Native.
First record: *c.*1860?

Until recently regarded merely as a subspecies of the 'Fragrant Orchid', this has now been raised to specific status. It is specially characteristic of unimproved wet pastures on calcareous clay around spring sources and in seepages. Needless to say, it is now very rare in our area, and was probably always uncommon. Pryor (1887) gives one specific reference to it: from the lost Barkway Moor, undated, *W. W. Newbould*, with a specimen reputed to be in the Borrer Herbarium at Kew. However, Pryor also notes other occurrences of '*G. conopsea*' from wet habitats at Wilstone Reservoir (probably Rushy Meadow) (91/B); a marsh near Marford Bridge, by the R. Lea (11/X); and Pigeon's Wick, [Knebworth] (probably Burleigh Meadow) (22/G). Dony (1967)

Marsh Fragrant-orchid Gymnadenia densiflora, *Moor Hall, Ardeley, 1985.*

reported it from Foulwells (30/I), 1955; and from Bury Mead, Ardeley (32/I), 1959. Subsequently, Dony re-found it at Rushy Meadow (91/B), 1970 (Dony, 1971), although he had missed noticing the previous record from the area. It also re-appeared at Bury Mead (32/I), 1979 *B. R. Sawford*, and in a nearby meadow in 1985 *R. Crossley/T. J./B. R. S*, when at least 20 spikes were present. However, management of these sites has deteriorated since, and its survival may be in doubt. During the recent survey, it was only reported from Foulwells (30/I), where material that had been rescued from the site when it was damaged in 1963, and grown on in cultivation, was re-introduced. At least one plant was still present in 2001 *J. C. Doyle.*

Hybrid Genus: ✕*Dactylodenia*

✕*Dactylodenia st-quintinii* (Godfery) J. Duvign.
(*Gymnadenia conopsea* × *Dactylorhiza fuchsii*)
Native.
First record: 1979.

This scarce hybrid was found with both parents on chalk grassland by Tingley Wood (13/F), 1979 *T. J./B. R. Sawford* (conf. R. M. Bateman, 1980).

Genus: *Dactylorhiza*

The Dactylorchids have presented considerable taxonomic difficulties for a long time. The treatment used in this account differs somewhat from that used by Sell and Murrell (1996), as well as from the taxonomy in Stace (1997). There may well, also, be future changes. One change has been to include the Frog Orchid, previously in its own genus *Coeloglossum*. Hybrids in the genus produce particular problems, both of identification and taxonomy; while intraspecific variation in others can also result in problems of field identification. One characteristic of some species, however, is their ability to colonise new sites rapidly, and this has resulted in a steady shift of our perceptions of their rarity and occurrence over time.

Dactylorhiza incarnata (L.) Soó
Early Marsh-orchid
Native.
First record: (1840?) 1874.
Tetrad occurrence: 7(8) (1%).
Increased (+133%).

The Early Marsh-orchid is found in natural calcareous flushes and other marshes with strongly mineral-rich water supplies. Natural occurrences of this kind of habitat are rare in the County, but man-made substrates have recently proved to be able to support it, especially highly alkaline waste ash (PFA) from former coal-fired power stations (Shaw, 1994, 1998). As a species, it presented great identification difficulties to earlier botanists, with the result that the account in Pryor (1887) is very confused. Webb and Coleman (1849) did not recognise it as a separate species, and all of their records are lumped in Pryor under the name '*Orchis latifolia*'. However, Pryor had isolated some previous records as relating to '*O. incarnata*', although only a few of these are likely to be correct, such as the record from the lost Barkway Moor by W. H. Coleman, which he called 'var. *angustifolia*'; and a record from 'Wilstone Reservoir' (Rushy Meadow) (91/B) made by H. Harpur-Crewe. Other river valley records in his account need to be treated with caution. Subsequently, H. F. Hayllar made

Early Marsh Orchid Dactylorhiza incarnata *ssp.* incarnata *Moor Hall, Ardeley, 1998.*

somewhat; Moor Hall Meadows (32/I), 1998 *T. J./G. P. Smith*, although the site was damaged seriously in 2009; and from one new natural site: Sawbridgeworth Marsh (41/X), 2000 *J. L. Fielding*. Rushy Meadow is now derelict, and no longer supports it. The colony at Amwell Quarry: Hollycross Lake (31/R) has been monitored regularly, with 105 counted in 1998 *C. M. Shepperson.*; and the Cheshunt Gravel Pits colony was estimated at many hundreds in 1988 *A. M. Boucher*, although it has declined since. In 2005, S. Pilkington from Wiltshire was called in to count the colony that had survived at Rye House (30/Z), finding 60 plants. The possibility that one or both of the lower Lea Valley colonies had somehow derived from former populations at Broxbourne, not far away, is unproven, but intriguing.
(3 tetrads: Dony, 1967; 5 tetrads: 1950-1986)

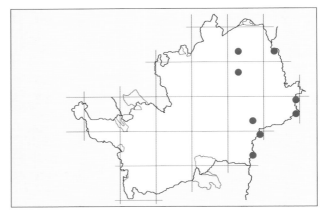

Map 863. *Dactylorhiza incarnata.*

an interesting observation of marsh orchids with 'flowers pink, leaves unspotted' in a marshy field near Broxbourne, 1909-1914 (Hayllar diary: North Herts. Museums). Dony thought this was Southern Marsh Orchid, but recent developments suggest it might have been *D. incarnata*. Dony (1967) presents a very sparse account of the species, with only three localities, all old wetlands derived from calcareous spring sources: Rushy Meadow (91/B), undated [1958] *J. G. D.*; Bury Mead, Ardeley (32/I), undated, *J. L. Fielding*; and Green End, Sandon (33/G) [= Blagrove Common], undated [1958] *J. G. D.* (Dony ms. index). After 1970, a further record was made at Moor Hall (32/I), 1976 *T. J.*; and the colony at Blagrove Common received ongoing study by many botanists. In 1979, attention was drawn to a colony of plants on calcareous PFA that had been dumped in an old gravel pit by Rye House Power Station (30/Z) *N. R. Campbell* (*comm.*: R. M. Bateman). This colony was monitored frequently, with at least 50 in 1982 *B. R. Sawford*. In 1982 also, another colony was discovered on similar dumped PFA in a thicket at Cheshunt Gravel Pits (30/R) *A. M. Boucher*; and these were counted at 1642 plants in 1985 *G. J. White*. At this point, the Rye House site seemed to be threatened with destruction, so some 50 plants were transferred to newly-dumped PFA at Amwell Quarry (31/R), 1985 *T. J./G. J. White*. These survived, although the colony is small. The recent survey received records from eight locations, although one of these: Meesden Green (43/G), 2001 *T. J.* is almost certainly also a recent introduction, and probably transitory, given the nature of the site. The other records included several from Blagrove Common (33/G), where the population appears to have declined

Early Marsh-orchid Dactylorhiza incarnata *ssp.* coccinea *Cheshunt Gravel Pits, 1990.*

The native form of the species seems to be ssp. *incarnata*, which is the one that occurs at all the natural sites. The fly-ash colonies are more variable, and both ssp. *coccinea* (Pugsley) Soó and ssp. *pulchella* (Druce) Soó have been recorded, in addition to ssp. *incarnata*. The Rye House Power Station site appears to have supported both *incarnata* and *pulchella* in 1982 *R. M. Bateman* (who counted *c*.300 plants of both subspecies), although Pilkington only saw *pulchella* there in 2005. The colonies at Cheshunt Gravel Pits (30/R) were even more diverse, with ssp. *coccinea* in some abundance alongside both other subspecies in 1982 *A. M. Boucher*, although no recent attempts appear to have been made to estimate the proportions of the different forms. The presence of ssp. *coccinea*, normally a dune-slack subspecies, might reflect the high sodium content of fly-ash. The small colony at Amwell Quarry (31/R) consists of all three subspecies, with a predominance of ssp. *pulchella*, 1998 *T. J.*, which seem to flower slightly earlier than ssp. *incarnata*.

Dactylorhiza × *wintoni* A. Camus
(*Dactylorhiza incarnata* × *D. praetermissa*)
Native.
First record: 1979.

This is a rather rare hybrid, partly because the parents tend not to overlap much in flowering times, but also because natural colonies of each tend to occur in different places. However, the hybrid was identified with some reservations at Blagrove Common (33/G), 1979 *R. M. Bateman* (Bateman, 1981); and again at Cheshunt Gravel Pits (30/R), 1998 *R. M. Burton*. It may be at all the sites where they occur together, but can be difficult to identify.

Dactylorhiza viridis (L.) Bateman, Pridgeon and Chase
Frog Orchid   UK Vulnerable
Native.
First record: 1650.
Tetrad occurrence: 2 (<1%).
Rare and declining.

This is a plant of short, unimproved calcareous pasture, often on somewhat damp soils, both on Chalk and clay. Its habitat is now very rare in the County, and so it is not surprising that it is on the verge of extinction. It was known to 19th century botanists from a wide range of sites, from Tring to Sandon in the north and south to Little Berkhamsted and the Broxbourne Woods area. However, it was evidently local by the 1920s, although fairly widespread, especially on the Boulder Clay. By the 1960s, it had declined dramatically, when Dony (1967) only recorded it from Sheethanger Common (00/H). There were about 100 plants there in 1980 (Bateman, 1981), but it has since decreased, owing to the loss of short, good quality chalk grassland adjacent to the golf course. Three plants were found there in 2000 *S. Oakes-Monger*, but other searches since have failed to find it. A small colony was also discovered at Moor Hall Meadow (32/I), 1985 *R. Crossley*; and a single plant was seen here in 1992 *M. Watson*, although its location has recently been severely damaged by drainage operations. It may yet be elsewhere.

Dactylorhiza × *mixta* (Asch. and Graebn.) Bateman, Pridgeon and Chase (*Dactylorhiza viridis* × *D. fuchsii*)
Native.
First record: 1972.

This rare hybrid was discovered with both parents at Sheethanger

Common (00/H) *N. R. Campbell* (conf. R. M. Bateman, 1980) (Bateman, 1981). It is not known how long this plant survived, but there are no further records.

Dactylorhiza fuchsii (Druce) Soó
Common Spotted-orchid
Native.
First record: (1820 for the aggregate), 1908.
Tetrad occurrence: 122 (25%).
Increased? (+16%).

Despite the loss of unimproved grasslands, the Common Spotted-orchid appears to be holding its own. It occurs on more or less calcareous soils in damp woodland rides, damper chalk grassland, old chalk pits, and on man-made substrates, such as abandoned gravel pits, motorway banks (*e.g.* the M25), and even on fly-ash deposits at old power station sites, among other places. The 1960s

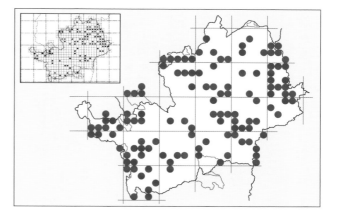

Map 864. *Dactylorhiza fuchsii.*

survey probably under-recorded it, owing to summer droughts in the late 1950s, as it was found very widely in the late 1970s and early 1980s, in many more tetrads. The recent survey found it in substantially more tetrads than Dony (1967), but fewer than in the 1980s, which might suggest a slight decline, although the 1990s droughts might also affected its occurrence in some sites during the survey. It is very variable in both flower colour and markings, as well as stature (see Bateman, 1981 for an account of some of these variants). Owing to earlier confusion between it and the Heath Spotted-orchid, 19th century records were all attributed to 'D. maculata', which is much less common in the County.
(100 tetrads: Dony, 1967; 161 tetrads: 1950-1986)

Dactylorhiza × *kernerorum* (Soó) Soó (*D. fuchsii* × *D. incarnata*)
Native.
First record: 1978.

A plant of this rather uncommon hybrid was first found at Blagrove Common, Sandon (33/G), 1978 *R. M. Bateman*. Several plants were found there in 1979 *T. J./B. R. Sawford*; and five were counted in 1980 *R. M. B.* Elsewhere, up to 30 robust plants were found on fly-ash at Rye House Power Station (30/Z), 1982 *A. M. Boucher/T. J./R. M. Bateman*. During the recent survey, one plant was found in the mixed orchid colonies on fly-ash at Cheshunt Gravel Pits (30/R), 1987 *D. Bevan*; eight plants were counted again at the Rye House site in 2005 *S. Pilkington*; and a single plant that appeared to be this was again found, alongside both parents, at Blagrove Common, 2009 *T. J./C. M. James*.

Dactylorhiza × *grandis* (Druce) P. Hunt
(*D. fuchsii* × *D. praetermissa*)
Hybrid Marsh-orchid
Native.
First record: 1923.
Tetrad occurrence: 9 (2%).

First recorded at Marsworth (SP91), 1923 *N. C. Rothschild* (*Rep. Bot. Exch. Club*: 214 (1924)) (a record overlooked in Dony, 1967), this rather spectacular, usually sterile hybrid occurs quite widely, usually with its parents, both in marshes, and also on damper chalk grassland. It was found at Grove Mill chalk pit (13/V) *G. L. Evans* (det. V. Summerhayes) (Hb. HTN); and after 1970 from seven other localities, mostly in old wetlands, but on the Chalk at Weston Hills (23/L) and Oddy Hill (91/F). During the recent survey, it occurred in nine scattered tetrads, especially in the north, sometimes away from either parent, as at Langley (22/B), 2008 *T. J.*

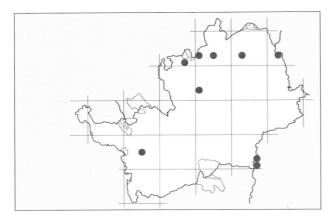

Map 865. *Dactylorhiza* × *grandis*.

Dactylorhiza maculata (L.) Soó   Herts Rare
Heath Spotted-orchid
Native.
First record: 1910 (for the segregate).
Tetrad occurrence: 4 (<1%).
Stable? (+50%).

Heath Spotted-orchid is a rare plant with us, as is its habitat, despite being a widespread and common orchid elsewhere in Britain. It was not until early in the 20th century that its distinction from Common Spotted-orchid was first recognised, hence its late first record, from Hertford Heath (31/B) *J. E. Little*. It was also recorded from Burleigh Meadow (22/G), 1924, 1926 *J. E. L.* Dony (1967) only gives records from Bricket Wood Common (10/F), 1956; and from a field adjoining Bayford Wood (30/E), 1955. After 1970, it was re-found at Burleigh Meadow, 1974 *M. Hooper*, where two plants were last seen in 1980; and a colony was also discovered in a scrubby paddock near Blackfan Wood (30/D), 1976 *T. J.*, with up to 15 plants in 1980 (conf. R. M. Bateman). The colony at Bricket Wood Common was estimated at *c.*100 plants in 1977 *R. M. Bateman*. During the recent survey, it has survived at Bricket Wood Common, although the colonies had become threatened by scrub encroachment by 2004 *J. P. Widgery*. New colonies, however, were discovered on a raised gravelly area at Frogmore Meadows SSSI, Sarratt (09/J), 1989 *G. Salisbury/J. Saunders*, where five plants were counted in 2007 *T. J.* Two plants turned up at the 'Furze Field', Colney Heath (20/C), 1987 *T. J.*, although they did not remain for long.

Finally, a plant that appeared to be this species appeared amongst Heather at Broxbourne Wood (30/I), 2005 *D. Holt*, although this needs confirmation. Unfortunately the site near Blackfan Wood suffered from severe disturbance in the early 1990s, and it has not re-appeared.
(2 tetrads: Dony, 1967; 4 tetrads: 1950-1986)

Dactylorhiza × *hallii* (Druce) Soó
(*Dactylorhiza maculata* × *D. praetermissa*)
Native.
First record: 2003.

Three plants of this rare and beautiful hybrid were found at Frogmore Meadows SSSI (09/J), 2003 *G. Salisbury* (det. I. Denholm), in close association with *D. praetermissa*, and with *D. maculata* not far away. Two plants were still present in 2007 *T. J.* (conf. R. M. Bateman).

Dactylorhiza praetermissa (Druce) Soó
Southern Marsh-orchid
Native.
First record: 1838.
Tetrad occurrence: 26 (5%).
Increased? (+104%).

This attractive orchid is especially found in long-established, calcareous river-valley wetlands, rich fen communities associated with spring sources, and occasionally in recently-established wetlands, where it can sometimes form large colonies. Early records were assigned to '*Orchis latifolia*' (Webb and Coleman 1849; Pryor, 1887), and it was not regarded as common, even in

Hybrid Southern Marsh × Heath Spotted-orchid Dactylorhiza × hallii *Frogmore Meadows, Sarratt, 2007.*

the 19th century. However, recorded sites were fairly widespread, especially in river valley sites. Dony (1967) regarded it as rare, but more widespread than *D. incarnata*. Records from the 1970s and 1980s seemed to indicate it was more widespread, especially

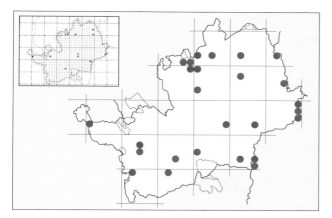

Map 865. *Dactylorhiza praetermissa.*

in east Herts., and the recent survey confirmed this impression, perhaps indicating an increase, although it is still local. A recent phenomenon, however, has also been its colonisation of fly-ash (PFA) deposits in old gravel pits at Cheshunt (30/R), and also its occasional occurrence on damper, sheltered chalk grassland, such as its regular occurrence at Weston Hills (23/L), and occasional records from elsewhere. It is also a rather variable plant. We have the normal form, with a broad lower lip and rather delicately marked pale pink petals, in many places, especially the fen habitats around Hitchin, but elsewhere, it appears with rather darker purplish flowers, often rather few in the spike, with lateral petals somewhat reflexed and a rather strongly toothed lower lip. These have sometimes been claimed as *D. traunsteinerioides* (Narrow-leaved Marsh-orchid), but genetic studies have confirmed them as a form of *D. praetermissa* (pers. comm.: R. M. Bateman) (see also Bateman, 1981).
(12 tetrads: Dony, 1967; 28 tetrads: 1950-1986)

[*Dactylorhiza elata* (Poir.) Soó
Robust Marsh-orchid
Introduced: casual.

This native of southern Europe and north Africa, sometimes grown in gardens, was introduced to a school nature reserve at Hadham Hall (42/L), 1975 *J. C. Doyle*, and was reported in 1979 to be 'slowly spreading by vegetative means'. It does not seem to have survived, and can scarcely be claimed as a 'wild' plant.]

Genus: *Neotinea*

As indicated earlier, the Burnt Orchid has now been included in this genus, alongside the Dense-flowered Orchid *Neotinea maculata* (Desf.) Stearn, which does not occur with us.

Neotinea ustulata (L.) Bateman, Pridgeon and Chase
Burnt Orchid   UK Endangered
Native.
First record: 1670.

This diminutive plant of short, high-quality chalk grassland was at one time found rarely, but widely, on chalk grassland sites across north Hertfordshire: Therfield Heath, Arbury Banks (23/U), High Down near Pirton (13/F), Bury Mead at Hitchin (13/V),

Burnt Orchid Neotinea ustulata *Therfield Heath, 1979.*

Photo: Brian Sawford

Ravensburgh Castle at Hexton (13/A), Kensworth (01/J), Aldbury (91/R) and near Tring (91/L) (Pryor, 1887), many of which have been severely degraded or lost entirely. Dony (1967) reported its survival at Therfield Heath (33/J), 1965 *W. Darling*. It survived here until at least 1994 *T. J.*, but has not been reported recently, and its last precise locality has now been subsumed into golf course mown grassland.

Genus: *Himantoglossum*

Himantoglossum hircinum (L.) Sprengel   UK Near Threatened
Lizard Orchid   Herts Extinct
Native.
First record: 1931.

This spectacular orchid of warm, sunny ground on chalk turned up unexpectedly at a site 'near Aston End, N. E. of Brook Hall', July 1931 *R. D. Wooster*. Received wisdom has equated this with Oxshott Hill, Benington (22/W) (Dony, 1967; Bateman, 1981), but it is not certain that this was the case. This was a period when it had appeared in similar circumstances elsewhere in Britain (Preston *et al.*, 2002). It unfortunately succumbed, however, to the craze for digging up interesting plants, and spent its last days in a garden!

The recent taxonomic revisions have brought Green-winged Orchid into this genus, alongside the Pyramidal Orchid.

Anacamptis morio (L.) Bateman, Prigeon and Chase UK Near
Green-winged Orchid Threatened
Native.
First record: 1823.
Tetrad occurrence: 7 (as native) (8) (1%).
Decreased (-46%).

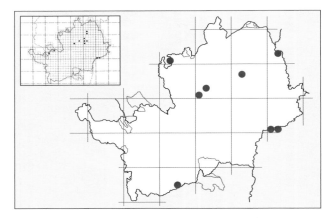

Map 867. *Anacamptis morio.*

A plant of somewhat damp, unimproved calcareous pastures, on Chalk, Boulder Clay or alluvial soils, this was at one time a widespread species, especially in east Hertfordshire (Pryor, 1887; Dony, ms. index). The progressive loss of these grasslands, or their severe degradation and mismanagement, resulted in its having become quite restricted by the 1960s (Dony, 1967). This steady attrition tends to have continued, despite some successes, such as the saving from ploughing of its most important colony at Langley (22/G) in the 1970s. However, it is capable of surprises, as it was found in recently regenerated grassland on an old meadow that had been ploughed near Rusling End (22/A), 2000 *T. J.*; and also turned up on a lawn at Bushey Heath (19/M), 2008 *S. Oakes-Monger*. It has had recent records from other long-standing sites at Hunsdon Mead (41/A, F); Langley Meadow (22/G); Moor Hall Meadow (32/I); and Tingley Downs (13/F). It was also introduced to Meesden Green (43/G), 1992 *J. Godfree*, where it was still present in 2000 *L. Mottram*.
(12 tetrads: Dony, 1967; 14 tetrads: 1950-1986)

Anacamptis pyramidalis (L.) Rich.
Pyramidal Orchid
Native.
First record: 1838.
Tetrad occurrence: 54 (11%).
Increased markedly (+134%).

Pyramidal Orchid is especially characteristic of calcareous grassland on previously disturbed ground. Dony (1967) thought it as a species restricted to Chalk, but both its historic records and its more recent ones indicate that it also occurs widely on calcareous gravelly or sandy ground, such as recently created roadside banks and old gravel pits. The recent survey strongly suggested that it has been able to take advantage of such sites, and has increased markedly. Some colonies can be very large, such as at Ashwell Quarry, where c.1400 spikes were counted in 2005 *T. J.*
(22 tetrads: Dony, 1967; 35 tetrads: 1950-1986)

Green-winged Orchid Anacamptis morio *Langley Meadow, 2008.*

Photo.: Brian Sawford

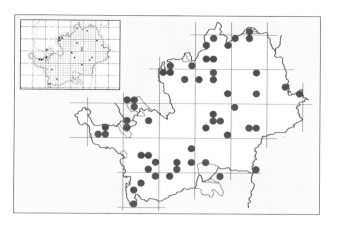

Map 868. *Anacamptis pyramidalis.*

Genus: *Ophrys*

Ophrys insectifera L.
Fly Orchid
Native.
First record: 1597.
Tetrad occurrence: 11 (2%).
Decreasing (-8%).

Almost restricted to the Chilterns, this is usually an orchid of shade, often associated with Beech, sometimes under Hazel coppice, rarely in more open, grassy habitats. It was alwaysconsidered to be rare in the County (Pryor, 1887), but has been known in some of its sites for over 100 years, such as a grove near Offley Holes (12/T), where it was known in the 1870s. Dony (1967) only knew it from the west of the County, but there were 19th century records from north-east Herts., and it was found in Great Hormead Park Wood (42/E), 1983 *K. Robinson*. The recent survey, however, found it only in its long-traditional area, where it appears to be declining, perhaps affected by droughts.
(11 tetrads: Dony, 1967; 22 tetrads: 1950-1986)

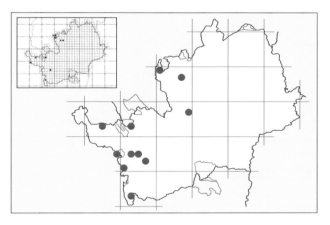

Map 869. *Ophrys insectifera.*

Ophrys sphegodes Miller   [Herts Rare]
Early Spider Orchid
Introduced [native in the U.K.].
First record: *c.*1972.

Two tubers from the Isle of Purbeck of this species of dry, open chalky habitats were deliberately introduced to a site near Little Hadham (42/G, L), 1972 *N. Stevens*. By 1978, these had increased to five plants *G. Crompton*; and to *c.*38 plants by 1982

B. R. Sawford. There were *c.*50 plants by 1993 *S. Oakes-Monger*, during the current survey, but by 2003 ownership of the site had changed and scrub was threatening the colony, so that only five plants were located *T. J.*

Ophrys apifera Hudson
Bee Orchid
Native.
First record: 1633.
Tetrad occurrence: 106 (22%).
Increased substantially (+204%).

Dony (1967) and earlier botanists thought this was mostly a plant of the Chalk, but the current survey has demonstrated that it is, now at least, more widespread on calcareous Boulder Clay and gravels than it is on the Chalk itself. It occurs erratically and unpredictably on bare, short, often recently-disturbed ground, lawns, road banks, gravel pits, *etc.* across much of the County, and invariably attracts attention. This might be the reason for its apparent large increase, although the increase in the number of disturbed road banks, gravel pits, *etc.* might also have helped.
(33 tetrads: Dony, 1967; 74 tetrads: 1950-1986)

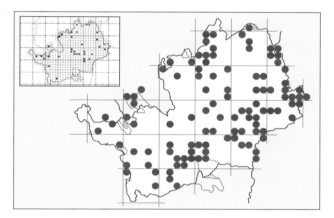

Map 870. *Ophrys apifera.*

The usual plant is var. *apifera*. However, a number of records have been attributed to var. *trollii* (Heg.) Druce ('**Wasp Orchid**'), which has a pointed *labellum* coloured paler yellowish, with brown markings. This was first reported at Marsworth (SP91), 1945 *J. E. Dandy* (Hb. BM) (Bateman, 1981); and has since occurred at Telegraph Hill (12/E), 1975 *T. J.*; and at Ashwell Quarry (23/P), 1986 *T. J./C. M. James*. During the survey, similar plants were also found at Tingley Downs (13/F), 1993 *T. J.*; and at Old Parkbury Gravel Pits (10/R), 2000 *S. Oakes-Monger*. In 1980, plants originally considered to be var. *trollii* were found by Hoo Wood, Great Gaddesden (01/G), 1980 *R. M. Bateman*. These were subsequently re-identified as a newly-described var. *belgarum* Turner Ettlinger, with a boldly patterned brown and yellow labellum. This has now also been reported from Hilfield Park Reservoir (19/M), 2008 *S. Murray/R. Cripps*; and on chalk banks at Chadwell, King's Meads (31/L), 2008 *A. Brown*, both confirmed by photographs.

Bee Orchid variety Ophrys apifera *var.* belgarum *at King's Meads, June 2008.*

Appendix 1. A Hertfordshire Plant Red Data List

The following list of native or archaeophyte species in Hertfordshire that have been found from the recent survey to be specially threatened or rare has been compiled as a stage towards producing a County Rare Plant Register.

The statuses of plants either derive from Cheffings and Farrell (2007), or at the local level are given as: 'Herts Rare' = five or fewer current localities; 'Herts Vulnerable' = species not otherwise Herts Rare or nationally under threat at any level, considered to

have declined 50% or more in the County since 1967, from the findings of the recent Hertfordshire Flora Survey. Plants that may merit 'Herts Rare' status, but whose current occurrence is uncertain, have also been listed. Plants thought to be extinct (having not been recorded since at least before 1950, or whose habitat is known to have been degraded) are given in bold. Other probably extinct species are also listed.

Species	Common name	Status	Localities 1987-2009	Herts Trend (1967-2009)
Lycopodium clavatum	**Stag's-horn Clubmoss**	Herts Extinct?	1	0
Equisetum sylvaticum	**Wood Horsetail**	Herts Rare	3	?
Osmunda regalis	**Royal Fern**	**Herts Extinct** (as native)	0	0
Pilularia globulifera	**Pillwort**	**Herts Extinct**	0	0
Oreopteris limbosperma	**Lemon-scented Fern**	Herts Rare	1	0?
Juniperus communis	**Juniper**	Herts Rare	5 native (some lost?)	0?
Ceratophyllum submersum	**Soft Hornwort**	Herts Extinct?	0	0
Pulsatilla vulgaris	**Pasque Flower**	UK Vulnerable	1 native	- 67%
Ranunculus parviflorus	**Small-flowered Buttercup**	Herts Rare	3	?
Ranunculus arvensis	**Corn Buttercup**	UK Critically Endangered	5 archaeophyte (9)	- 85%
Ranunculus fluitans	**River Water-crowfoot**	Herts Rare?	1	?
Adonis annua	**Pheasant's-eye**	UK Endangered Herts Extinct?	1	0
Myosurus minimus	**Mousetail**	UK Vulnerable	6	+ 33%
Thalictrum minus	**Lesser Meadow-rue**	Herts Rare	2 native	0
Papaver argemone	**Prickly Poppy**	UK Vulnerable	33 tetrads	- 46%
Fumaria parviflora	**Fine-leaved Fumitory**	UK Vulnerable	7 tetrads	+ 56%
Fumaria vaillantii	**Few-flowered Fumitory**	UK Vulnerable	15 tetrads	+ 29%
Chenopodium bonus-henricus	**Good King Henry**	UK Vulnerable	21 tetrads	- 26%
Chenopodium glaucum	**Oak-leaved Goosefoot**	UK Vulnerable	3	+ 20%
Chenopodium vulvaria	**Stinking Goosefoot**	UK Endangered Herts Extinct?	0	-100%
Chenopodium urbicum	**Upright Goosefoot**	UK Critically Endangered **Herts Extinct**	0	0
Chenopodium murale	**Nettle-leaved Goosefoot**	UK Vulnerable	4	+ 33%
Minuartia hybrida	**Fine-leaved Sandwort**	UK Endangered	3	+ 200%
Stellaria neglecta	**Greater Chickweed**	Herts Rare	3	?
Stellaria palustris	**Marsh Stitchwort**	UK Vulnerable **Herts Extinct**	0	0
Cerastium arvense	**Field Mouse-ear**	Herts Vulnerable	10 tetrads	- 51%
Moenchia erecta	**Upright Chickweed**	**Herts Extinct**	0	0
Sagina nodosa	**Knotted Pearlwort**	Herts Extinct?	0	- 100%
Scleranthus annuus	**Annual Knawel**	UK Endangered	11 tetrads	- 90%
Spergula arvensis	**Corn Spurrey**	UK Vulnerable	48 tetrads	- 61%
Agrostemma githago	**Corncockle**	UK Pending Red List	12 tetrads	?
Silene noctiflora	**Night-flowering Catchfly**	UK Vulnerable	8	- 87%
Dianthus deltoides	**Maiden Pink**	UK Near Threatened	3	+ 50%

Species	Common name	Status	Localities 1987-2009	Herts Trend (1967-2009)
Dianthus armeria	**Deptford Pink**	UK Endangered Herts Extinct?	0	-100%
Persicaria minor	**Small Water-pepper**	UK Vulnerable	1	0
Fallopia dumetorum	**Copse Bindweed**	UK Vulnerable **Herts Extinct**	0	0
Hypericum montanum	**Pale St John's-wort**	UK Near Threatened Herts Extinct?	0	0
Drosera rotundifolia	**Round-leaved Sundew**	**Herts Extinct**	0	0
Helianthemum nummularium	**Common Rock-rose**	Herts Vulnerable	50 tetrads	- 50%
Viola canina	**Heath Dog-violet**	UK Near Threatened	7	- 26%
Viola palustris	**Marsh Violet**	Herts Rare	1	?
Viola tricolor	**Wild Pansy**	UK Near Threatened	2?	?
Salix aurita	**Eared Willow**	Herts Rare Extinct as native?	1?	-87%
Salix repens	**Creeping Willow**	Herts Rare	3	+ 33%
Cardamine amara	**Large Bitter-cress**	Herts Rare	2	+ 100%
Cardamine impatiens	**Narrow-leaved Bitter-cress**	UK Near Threatened	1	?
Arabis glabra	**Tower Mustard**	UK Endangered Herts Extinct?	0	-100%
Arabis hirsuta	**Hairy Rock-cress**	Herts Rare	1	?
Erophila majuscula	**Hairy Whitlow-grass**	Herts Rare	2	?
Teesdalia nudicaulis	**Shepherd's Cress**	UK Near Threatened **Herts Extinct**	0	0
Iberis amara	**Wild Candytuft**	UK Vulnerable	5	- 9%
Erica tetralix	**Cross-leaved Heath**	Herts Extinct?	0	0
Erica cinerea	**Bell Heather**	Herts Rare	1	0
Vaccinium myrtillus	**Bilberry**	**Herts Extinct**	0	- 100%
Monotropa hypopitys	**Yellow Bird's-nest**	UK Endangered	4	- 47%
Primula elatior	**Oxlip**	UK Near Threatened	5?	?
Lysimachia vulgaris	**Yellow Loosestrife**	Herts Rare	4	- 33%
Anagallis tenella	**Bog Pimpernel**	**Herts Extinct**	0	- 100%
Anagallis minima	**Chaffweed**	UK Near Threatened **Herts Extinct**	0	0
Samolus valerandi	**Brookweed**	Herts Rare (Extinct?)	0	-100%
Sedum telephium	**Orpine**	Herts Vulnerable	30 tetrads	- 65%
Parnassia palustris	**Grass-of-Parnassus**	**Herts Extinct**	0	0
Rubus nessensis	**A bramble**	Herts Rare	1	?
Rubus plicatus	**A bramble**	**Herts Extinct**	0	0
Rubus scissus	**A bramble**	**Herts Extinct**	0	0
Rubus vigorosus	**A bramble**	Herts Rare	1	?
Rubus calvatus	**A bramble**	Herts Rare	2	?
Rubus errabundus	**A bramble**	Herts Rare	1	?
Rubus leptothyrsos	**A bramble**	Herts Rare	1	?
Rubus poliodes	**A bramble**	**Herts Extinct**	0	0
Rubus pyramidalis	**A bramble**	Herts Rare	2	?
Rubus robiae	**A bramble**	Herts Rare	1?	?
Rubus sciocharis	**A bramble**	Herts Rare	1	?
Rubus acclivitatum	**A bramble**	Herts Rare	1?	?
Rubus cissburiensis	**A bramble**	Herts Rare	3 native	?
Rubus nemoralis	**A bramble**	Herts Extinct?	0	0
Rubus rhombifolius	**A bramble**	Herts Rare	1	?
Rubus boraeanus	**A bramble**	Herts Rare	1	?
Rubus wirralensis	**A bramble**	Herts Rare	1	?
Rubus diversus	**A bramble**	Herts Rare	2	?
Rubus glareosus	**A bramble**	Herts Rare	2	?

Species	Common name	Status	Localities 1987-2009	Herts Trend (1967-2009)
Rubus leightonii	**A bramble**	Herts Rare	1?	?
Rubus lintonii	**A bramble**	Herts Rare	1	?
Rubus micans	**A bramble**	Herts Rare	1?	?
Rubus norvicensis	**A bramble**	Herts Rare	3	?
Rubus percrispus	**A bramble**	Herts Rare	1	?
Rubus raduloides	**A bramble**	Herts Rare	4	?
Rubus adamsii	**A bramble**	Herts Rare	1	?
Rubus anisacanthos	**A bramble**	Herts Rare	1	?
Rubus leyanus	**A bramble**	Herts Rare	3	?
Rubus bloxamianus	**A bramble**	Herts Rare	1	?
Rubus cantianus	**A bramble**	Herts Rare	3	?
Rubus fuscus	**A bramble**	Herts Rare	3	?
Rubus largificus	**A bramble**	Herts Rare	1	?
Rubus pannosus	**A bramble**	Herts Rare	1	?
Rubus atrebatum	**A bramble**	Herts Rare	1	?
Rubus hylocharis	**A bramble**	Herts Rare	3	?
Rubus iceniensis	**A bramble**	Herts Rare	1	?
Rubus murrayi	**A bramble**	Herts Rare	2?	?
Rubus newbridgensis	**A bramble**	Herts Rare	1	?
Rubus phaeocarpus	**A bramble**	Herts Rare	4	?
Rubus proiectus	**A bramble**	Herts Rare	3	?
Rubus angloserpens	**A bramble**	Herts Rare	4	?
Rubus hylonomus	**A bramble**	Herts Rare	2	?
Rubus leptadenes	**A bramble**	Herts Rare	2	?
Rubus pedemontanus	**A bramble**	Herts Rare	3	?
Rubus scaber	**A bramble**	Herts Rare	1?	?
Rubus nemorosus	**A bramble**	Herts Rare	2?	?
Potentilla palustris	**Marsh Cinquefoil**	**Herts Extinct**	0	0
Potentilla argentea	**Hoary Cinquefoil**	UK Near Threatened	9 tetrads	- 40%
Geum rivale	**Water Avens**	Herts Rare	3?	?
Agrimonia procera	**Fragrant Agrimony**	Herts Rare	1	?
Sanguisorba officinalis	**Great Burnet**	Herts Rare	4 native	0?
Alchemilla xanthochlora	**A lady's-mantle**	Herts Rare	1?	?
Alchemilla filicaulis	**Common Lady's-mantle**	Herts Vulnerable	15 tetrads	- 68%
Rosa stylosa	**Short-styled Field Rose**	Herts Rare	5	?
Rosa caesia	**Glaucous Dog-rose**	Herts Rare	1?	?
Rosa sherardii	**Sherard's Downy-rose**	**Herts Extinct**	0	0
Rosa agrestis	**Small-leaved Sweet-briar**	UK Near Threatened	1	?
[*Sorbus domestica*]	**Service-tree**	UK Critically Endangered (planted in Herts)	1	0
Astragalus danicus	**Purple Milk-vetch**	UK Endangered	4 (some lost?)	?
Astragalus glycyphyllos	**Wild Liquorice**	Herts Rare	4 native	- 38%
Onobrychis viciifolia	**Sainfoin**	UK Near Threatened	30 tetrads	- 47%
Lotus glaber	**Narrow-leaved Bird's-foot Trefoil**	Herts Rare?	4	?
Vicia sylvatica	**Wood Vetch**	Herts Rare	1	?
Vicia parviflora	**Slender Tare**	UK Vulnerable	2	?
Lathyrus linifolius	**Bitter-vetch**	Herts Rare?	6 (some lost?)	- 45%
Lathyrus sylvestris	**Narrow-leaved Everlasting-pea**	Herts Rare	1	?
[*Lathyrus aphaca*]	**Yellow Vetchling**	UK Vulnerable (but introduced in Herts)	4 recent	?
[*Medicago minima*]	**Bur Medick**	UK Vulnerable (but casual in Herts)	0	- 100%
Trifolium ornithopodioides	**Bird's-foot Clover**	**Herts Extinct**	0	0
Trifolium fragiferum	**Strawberry Clover**	Herts Vulnerable	11 tetrads	- 72%

Species	Common name	Status	Localities 1987-2009	Herts Trend (1967-2009)
Trifolium ochroleucon	**Sulphur Clover**	UK Near Threatened	10 tetrads	- 37%
Trifolium scabrum	**Rough Clover**	Herts Rare Extinct?	0	?
Trifolium subterraneum	**Subterranean Clover**	**Herts Extinct** (as native)	0	0
Genista tinctoria	**Dyer's Greenweed**	Herts Vulnerable (Herts Rare?)	7 (some lost?)	- 53%
Genista anglica	**Petty Whin**	UK Near Threatened	6	- 49%
Ulex gallii	**Western Gorse**	Herts Rare	1	?
Ulex minor	**Dwarf Gorse**	Herts Rare	3	0
Myriophyllum verticillatum	**Whorled Water-milfoil**	UK Vulnerable	13 tetrads	+ 80%
Myriophyllum alterniflorum	**Alternate Water-milfoil**	Herts Rare	3	?
Lythrum hyssopifolia	**Grass-poly**	UK Endangered **Herts Extinct**	0	0
Daphne mezereum	**Mezereon**	UK Vulnerable	1 (introduced?)	0
Epilobium palustre	**Marsh Willowherb**	Herts Rare	6 (some lost?)	+ 33%
Thesium humifusum	**Bastard-toadflax**	Herts Rare	1	0
Euphorbia platyphyllos	**Broad-leaved Spurge**	Herts Vulnerable (Herts Rare?)	8 (some lost?)	- 50%
Euphorbia exigua	**Dwarf Spurge**	UK Near Threatened	210 tetrads	- 27%
Frangula alnus	**Alder Buckthorn**	Herts Rare	4 native?	0?
Linum bienne	**Pale Flax**	Herts Rare	2	?
Linum perenne	**Perennial Flax**	Herts Rare	1	0
Radiola linoides	**Allseed**	UK Near Threatened **Herts Extinct**	0	0
Polygala serpyllifolia	**Heath Milkwort**	Herts Rare	2	- 83%
Geranium columbinum	**Long-stalked Crane's-bill**	Herts Vulnerable (Herts Rare?)	6 (some lost?)	- 54%
Scandix pecten-veneris	**Shepherd's-needle**	UK Critically Endangered	23 tetrads	- 71%
Bunium bulbocastanum	**Great Pignut**	Herts Vulnerable?	9 (some lost?)	- 44%
Sium latifolium	**Greater Water-parsnip**	UK Endangered	1	0
Seseli libanotis	**Moon-carrot**	UK Near Threatened **Herts Extinct**	0	- 100%
Oenanthe fistulosa	**Tubular Water-dropwort**	UK Vulnerable	6 tetrads	- 37%
Oenanthe pimpinelloides	**Corky-fruited Water-dropwort**	Herts Extinct?	0	- 100%
Oenanthe lachenalii	**Parsley Water-dropwort**	Herts Rare	1	0
Oenanthe aquatica	**Fine-leaved Water-dropwort**	Herts Rare	2	- 69%
Bupleurum rotundifolium	**Thorow-wax**	UK Critically Endangered **Herts Extinct**	0	0
Apium inundatum	**Lesser Marshwort**	Herts Rare	5	- 33%
Cicuta virosa	**Cowbane**	**Herts Extinct**	0	0
Torilis arvensis	**Spreading Hedge-parsley**	UK Endangered	8 tetrads (some lost?)	- 79%
Centaurium pulchellum	**Lesser Centaury**	**Herts Extinct**	0	0
Gentianella campestris	**Field Gentian**	UK Vulnerable **Herts Extinct**	0	0
Gentianella germanica	**Chiltern Gentian**	Herts Rare?	6 native (some lost?)	- 29%
Hyoscyamus niger	**Henbane**	UK Vulnerable	15 tetrads	- 28%
Cuscuta europaea	**Greater Dodder**	**Herts Extinct**	0	0
Cuscuta epithymum	**Common Dodder**	UK Vulnerable (Herts Extinct?)	0	- 100%
Lithospermum officinale	**Common Gromwell**	Herts Rare	3	0
Lithospermum arvense	**Field Gromwell**	UK Endangered	36 tetrads (some lost)	- 60%
Myosotis secunda	**Creeping Forget-me-not**	Herts Rare (Extinct as native?)	1	+ 100%
Cynoglossum officinale	**Hound's-tongue**	UK Near Threatened	7 tetrads	+ 27%
Cynoglossum germanicum	**Green Hound's-tongue**	UK Critically Endangered **Herts Extinct**	0	0
Stachys arvensis	**Field Woundwort**	UK Near Threatened	3	- 44%
Galeopsis angustifolia	**Red Hemp-nettle**	UK Critically Endangered	2 (1 lost?)	- 93%

Species	Common name	Status	Localities 1987-2009	Herts Trend (1967-2009)
Galeopsis speciosa	**Large-flowered Hemp-nettle**	UK Vulnerable (Herts Extinct?)	1?	- 80%
Scutellaria minor	**Lesser Skullcap**	Herts Rare	3	?
Ajuga chamaepitys	**Ground Pine**	UK Endangered (Herts Extinct?)	0	- 100%
Nepeta cataria	**Catmint**	UK Vulnerable	8 tetrads	- 57%
Clinopodium calamintha	**Lesser Calamint**	UK Vulnerable	1	0
Clinopodium acinos	**Basil Thyme**	UK Vulnerable	10 tetrads	- 65%
Mentha pulegium	**Pennyroyal**	UK Endangered **Herts Extinct** (as native)	0 (native)	0
Salvia pratensis	**Meadow Clary**	UK Near Threatened	3 (native?)	?
Salvia verbenaca	**Wild Clary**	Herts Rare	5	+ 11%
Littorella uniflora	**Shoreweed**	**Herts Extinct**	0	0
Limosella aquatica	**Mudwort**	Herts Rare	2	0
Misopates orontium	**Weasel's-snout**	UK Vulnerable (Herts Extinct?)	0	- 100%
[Veronica triphyllos]	**Fingered Speedwell**	UK Endangered	0 (Herts: casual)	0
Melampyrum cristatum	**Crested Cow-wheat**	UK Vulnerable	1	- 67%
Melampyrum arvense	**Field Cow-wheat**	UK Pending Red List **Herts Extinct**	0	0
[Euphrasia anglica]	**An eyebright**	UK Endangered [Herts extinct?]	0 (Herts status?)	0
Euphrasia arctica borealis	**Northern Eyebright**	**Herts Extinct**	0	0
Euphrasia pseudokerneri	**Chalk Eyebright**	UK Endangered	9 tetrads (some lost?)	+ 20%
Pedicularis palustris	**Marsh Lousewort**	**Herts Extinct**	0	- 100%
Pedicularis sylvatica	**Lousewort**	Herts Rare	3	- 70%
Orobanche purpurea	**Yarrow Broomrape**	UK Vulnerable **Herts Extinct**	0	0
Orobanche rapum-genistae	**Greater Broomrape**	UK Near Threatened	1	0
Pinguicula vulgaris	**Common Butterwort**	**Herts Extinct**	0	0
Utricularia vulgaris	**Greater Bladderwort**	Herts Rare	1	?
Utricularia australis	**Bladderwort**	Herts Rare	2	?
Campanula patula	**Spreading Bellflower**	UK Endangered (Herts status?)	0	0
Jasione montana	**Sheep's-bit**	**Herts Extinct**	0	0
Galium pumilum	**Slender Bedstraw**	UK Endangered (Herts Extinct?)	0	- 100%
Galium tricornutum	**Corn Cleavers**	UK Endangered	1	- 78%
Galium parisiense	**Wall Bedstraw**	UK Vulnerable (Herts status?)	0	?
Valerianella rimosa	**Broad-fruited Corn-salad**	UK Endangered (Herts Extinct?)	0	- 100%
Valerianella dentata	**Sharp-fruited Corn-salad**	UK Endangered	12 tetrads (some now lost)	- 66%
Cirsium dissectum	**Meadow Thistle**	**Herts Extinct**	0	- 100%
Serratula tinctoria	**Saw-wort**	Herts Rare	5 (some lost)	?
[Centaurea calcitrapa]	**Red Star-thistle**	UK Endangered	Casual in Herts	0
Arnoseris minima	**Lamb's Succory**	**UK Extinct**	0	0
[Hypochaeris glabra]	**Smooth Cat's-ear**	UK Vulnerable	Casual in Herts	0
Hypochaeris maculata	**Spotted Cat's-ear**	UK Threatened	1? (may be lost)	0
Taraxacum acutum	**A dandelion**	UK Rare; Endemic	1	0
Taraxacum palustre	**A dandelion**	Herts Rare (Extinct?)	?	?
Taraxacum richardsianum	**A dandelion**	Herts Rare Endemic	1	?
Taraxacum tamesense	**A dandelion**	Herts Rare?	1	?
Hieracium virgultorum	**Long-leaved Hawkweed**	Herts Rare	2	?

Species	Common name	Status	Localities 1987-2009	Herts Trend (1967-2009)
Hieracium umbellatum	**Umbellate Hawkweed**	Herts Rare	2	?
Hieracium trichocaulon	**Hairy-stemmed Hawkweed**	Herts Rare	1?	?
Hieracium calcaricola	**Toothed Hawkweed**	Herts Rare	2	?
Hieracium vulgatum	**Common Hawkweed**	Herts Rare	2?	?
Hieracium nemophilum	**Grassland Hawkweed**	Herts Rare	2	?
Filago lutescens	**Red-tipped Cudweed**	UK Endangered **Herts Extinct**	0	0
Filago pyramidata	**Broad-leaved Cudweed**	UK Endangered	2	+ 50%?
Filago minima	**Small Cudweed**	Herts Rare	3	- 45%
Filago gallica	**Narrow-leaved Cudweed**	**UK Extinct**	0	0
Antennaria dioica	**Mountain Everlasting**	**Herts Extinct**	0	0
Gnaphalium sylvaticum	**Heath Cudweed**	UK Endangered Herts Extinct?	0?	- 100%
Pulicaria vulgaris	**Small Fleabane**	UK Vulnerable **Herts Extinct**	0	0
Solidago virgaurea	**Golden-rod**	Herts Rare	2	?
Chamaemelum nobile	**Chamomile**	UK Vulnerable	1 native	- 50%
Anthemis arvensis	**Corn Chamomile**	UK Endangered	1 native?	- 50%
Anthemis cotula	**Stinking Chamomile**	UK Vulnerable	40 tetrads	- 59%
Xanthophthalmum segetum	**Corn Marigold**	UK Vulnerable	13 tetrads	- 27%
[Senecio paludosus]	**Fen Ragwort**	UK Critically Endangered	Herts status doubtful	0
Tephroseris integrifolia	**Field Fleawort**	UK Endangered	2 (1 lost?)	0?
Baldellia ranunculoides	**Lesser Water-plantain**	**Herts Extinct**	0	0
Damasonium alisma	**Star-fruit**	UK Critically Endangered **Herts Extinct**	0	0
Hydrocharis morsus-ranae	**Frogbit**	UK Vulnerable	2 (native?)	?
Stratiotes aloides	**Water-soldier**	UK Near Threatened	10 tetrads (all introduced?)	?
Potamogeton polygonifolius	**Bog Pondweed**	Herts Rare	4	+ 33%
Potamogeton coloratus	**Fen Pondweed**	**Herts Extinct**	0	0
Potamogeton lucens	**Shining Pondweed**	Herts Rare?	9 tetrads (some lost?)	- 47%
Potamogeton alpinus	**Red Pondweed**	Herts Extinct?	0	- 100%
Potamogeton perfoliatus	**Perfoliate Pondweed**	Herts Rare?	12 tetrads (some lost?)	- 29%
Potamogeton friesii	**Flat-stalked Pondweed**	UK Near Threatened	2	- 67%
Potamogeton pusillus	**Lesser Pondweed**	Herts Rare	5	+ 67%
Potamogeton obtusifolius	**Blunt-leaved Pondweed**	Herts Rare	3 (4?)	?
Potamogeton compressus	**Grass-wrack Pondweed**	UK Endangered **Herts Extinct**	0	0
Potamogeton acutifolius	**Sharp-leaved Pondweed**	UK Critically Endangered **Herts Extinct**	0	0
Juncus squarrosus	**Heath Rush**	Herts Rare	4	?
Juncus compressus	**Round-fruited Rush**	UK Near Threatened	2	?
Juncus foliosus	**Leafy Rush**	Herts Rare	1	?
Eriophorum angustifolium	**Common Cottongrass**	Herts Rare	1	?
Eriophorum latifolium	**Broad-leaved Cottongrass**	**Herts Extinct**	0	0
Scirpus sylvaticus	**Wood Club-rush**	Herts Rare	2	- 50%
Eleocharis multicaulis	**Many-stalked Spike-rush**	**Herts Extinct**	0	0
Eleocharis acicularis	**Needle Spike-rush**	Herts Extinct?	0	- 100%
Eleocharis quinqueflora	**Few-flowered Spike-rush**	Herts Rare	2	0
Isolepis fluitans	**Floating Club-rush**	Herts Rare	2	0
[Cyperus longus]	**Galingale**	UK Near Threatened	Introduced in Herts	+ 675%
Blysmus compressus	**Flat Sedge**	Herts Rare	1	- 50%
Schoenus nigricans	**Black Bog-rush**	**Herts Extinct**	0	0
Carex appropinquata	**Fibrous Tussock-sedge**	UK Vulnerable **Herts Extinct**	0	0

Species	Common name	Status	Localities 1987-2009	Herts Trend (1967-2009)
Carex diandra	**Lesser Tussock-sedge**	UK Near Threatened **Herts Extinct**	0	0
Carex echinata	**Star Sedge**	Herts Rare	3 (1 lost?)	- 33%
Carex dioica	**Dioecious Sedge**	**Herts Extinct**	0	0
Carex rostrata	**Bottle Sedge**	Herts Rare	3	?
Carex distans	**Distant Sedge**	Herts Rare	4	- 27%
Carex hostiana	**Tawny Sedge**	Herts Rare	2	?
Carex viridula brachyrrhyncha	**Long-stalked Yellow-sedge**	Herts Rare	3	?
Carex elata	**Tufted Sedge**	Herts Rare	2	+ 100%
Carex pulicaris	**Flea Sedge**	Herts Rare (Extinct?)	0	- 100%
Vulpia ciliata	**Bearded Fescue**	Herts Rare	2 (1 lost?)	?
[Puccinellia fasciculata]	**Borrer's Saltmarsh-grass**	UK Vulnerable	1 (introduced)	0
Aira caryophyllea	**Silver Hair-grass**	Herts Vulnerable	13 tetrads	- 63%
Calamagrostis canescens	**Purple Small-reed**	Herts Rare	1	?
[Apera spica-venti]	**Loose Silky-bent**	UK Near Threatened	Casual in Herts	0
Alopecurus aequalis	**Orange Foxtail**	Herts Rare	6 (some lost?)	+ 100%
Phleum phleoides	**Purple-stem Cat's-tail**	Herts Rare	1	0
Bromopsis benekenii	**Lesser Hairy-brome**	Herts Rare	4	- 65%
Brachypodium pinnatum	**Heath False-brome**	Herts Rare	3	?
Brachypodium rupestre	**Tor-grass**	Herts Rare	2	?
Sparganium natans	**Least Bur-reed**	**Herts Extinct**	0	0
Gagea lutea	**Yellow Star-of-Bethlehem**	Herts Rare (Extinct?)	0	- 100%
Polygonatum multiflorum	**Solomon's Seal**	Herts Rare	3	?
Paris quadrifolia	**Herb Paris**	Herts Vulnerable	8 tetrads (some lost?)	- 69%
Ornithogalum pyrenaicum	**Spiked Star-of-Bethlehem**	Herts Rare	1	?
Allium oleraceum	**Field Garlic**	UK Vulnerable	1	0
Ruscus aculeatus	**Butcher's Broom**	Herts Rare (as native)	4 native?	?
Neottia nidus-avis	**Bird's-nest Orchid**	UK Near Threatened	4	- 81%
Epipactis palustris	**Marsh Helleborine**	Herts Rare	2	0
Epipactis leptochila	**Narrow-lipped Helleborine**	UK Data-deficient Herts Rare	1	?
Epipactis phyllanthes	**Green-flowered Helleborine**	Herts Rare	4	+ 200%
Hammarbya paludosa	**Bog Orchid**	**Herts Extinct**	0	0
Spiranthes spiralis	**Autumn Lady's-tresses**	Herts Rare (Extinct?)	0	- 100%
Herminium monorchis	**Musk Orchid**	UK Vulnerable (Herts Extinct?)	2 (lost?)	?
Orchis anthropophora	**Man Orchid**	UK Endangered **Herts Extinct**	0	- 100%
Orchis militaris	**Military Orchid**	UK Vulnerable **Herts Extinct**	0	0
Platanthera chlorantha	**Greater Butterfly-orchid**	UK Near Threatened	12 tetrads	- 25%
Platanthera bifolia	**Lesser Butterfly-orchid**	UK Vulnerable **Herts Extinct**	0	0
Gymnadenia conopsea	**Downland Fragrant-orchid**	Herts Rare	6 (some lost)	- 18%
Gymnadenia densiflora	**Marsh Fragrant-orchid**	Herts Rare	2? (may be lost)	?
Dactylorhiza viridis	**Frog Orchid**	UK Vulnerable	2 (now lost?)	?
Neotinea ustulata	**Burnt Orchid**	UK Endangered Herts Extinct?	1 (lost?)	?
Himantoglossum hircinum	**Lizard Orchid**	UK Near Threatened **Herts Extinct**	0	0
Anacamptis morio	**Green-winged Orchid**	UK Near Threatened	7 tetrads (native)	- 46%
[Ophrys sphegodes]	**Early Spider-orchid**	[Herts Rare]	1 (introduced)	0

Appendix 2. Plant sites in Hertfordshire – localities of interest accessible to the public

Listed is a selection of sites accessible to the public, which have some less common plant species of special interest for visiting botanists, alongside a brief description of their plant habitats, from a broad perspective. It is not a complete list. Many other nature reserves or public open spaces will have a range of species of local interest, while many of the most important sites botanically have no public access. The list does not include privately owned sites unless they have footpaths with general access at least at times; nor does it include nature reserves with access limited by permit.

When visiting please observe any local restrictions and be aware that access may be limited by owners or public authorities at any time. Visitors to these sites do so at their own risk, neither the author nor the Hertfordshire Natural History Society can accept any responsibility. Public access does not necessarily mean that there is any permission to collect specimens. Details of the existence of public transport or parking availability are a guide only and may change.

The indication of a 'nature reserve' means either that it is a statutorily designated 'Local Nature Reserve' under the National Parks and Access to the Countryside Act 1949, or a nature reserve operated by the Hertfordshire and Middlesex Wildlife Trust or other conservation organisation, from whom further information may be available. Grid references are generally given for the most useful point of access.

Aldbury Common (National Trust: Ashridge) SP978128

Common land, former wood-pasture, with dry acid grassland, bracken heath scrub, oak/birch and beech woodland, ponds. Car park (donations solicited).

Aldbury Nowers (Nature Reserve) SP950128

Chalk grassland and scrub, beech woodland. Limited parking by road. Tring Station nearby.

Aldenham Reservoir (Country Park) TQ168961

Old reservoir with marginal wetlands, grasslands, woodland. Car park (pay).

'Alpine Meadow', Berkhamsted (Nature Reserve) SP990102

Small chalk grassland site adjoining beech woodland/plantation. Accessible by footpath only from Berkhamsted.

Amwell Nature Reserve (Amwell Quarry) TL374125; TL375134

Former gravel pit, with mixed wetlands, reed beds, fen woodland. Access limited to walkways except by permission. Limited parking by roads.

Archer's Green Meadows, Tewin (Access land) TL278133

Calcareous and neutral damp pasture, riverside fen, alder woodland, scrub. Limited parking by road.

Balls Wood, Hertford Heath (Nature Reserve) TL348105

Damp oak/hornbeam, partially re-planted mixed woodland, ponds, rides. Limited parking by road. Bus services nearby.

Batch Wood, St Albans TL141091

Mixed beech and oak/hornbeam woodland on chalk and gravel. Limited parking by road.

Batchworth Heath, Rickmansworth (Nature Reserve) TQ077925

Acid grassland, pond, scrub. Some parking.

Bencroft Wood, Wormley (National Nature Reserve – part) TL326065

Acid oak/hornbeam woodland, with rides, calcareous seepages. Two small car parks.

Berkhamsted Common (part: National Trust: Ashridge) SP978116; TL010092

Open common land, with remnant heather and bracken heath, oak/birch and beech woodland, ponds. Golf course in part. Some parking by roads.

Berrygrove Wood, Aldenham TQ134983

Damp oak/hazel clay woodland, partially re-planted mixed, acid and neutral grassland, pond, rides. Access by footpaths from Aldenham.

Bishop's Wood, Rickmansworth TQ069915

Mixed acid oak/birch, beech and hornbeam woodland, partially re-planted. Rides, streams, seepages, remnant heath areas. Car park.

Blagrove Common, Sandon (Nature Reserve) TL328336

Calcareous clay fen meadow, seepages, streams, scrub. Access from Green End Green, limited parking.

Blows Down, Dunstable (Open Space) TL030215

Chalk grassland, scrub. Access from adjoining road. Limited parking.

Boxmoor, Hemel Hempstead TL049061

Neutral/calcareous valley meadows and pasture on gravel/chalk, river, seepages. Limited parking by roads. Bus/train services nearby.

Bramfield Park Wood TL290156

Oak/hornbeam woodland, partially re-planted mixed, rides. Certain rides open only (shooting reserved). Access on foot from Bramfield village.

Bramfield Woods TL280166

Heavily re-planted oak/hornbeam woodland on gravels and clay, open rides, ponds. Limited parking by roads, access by footpath from Bramfield.

Bricket Wood Common (Nature Reserve) TL133006

Wet acid heath, scrub and oak/hornbeam woodland on clay. Rich flora. Limited parking by road. Station nearby.

Broxbourne Wood (National Nature Reserve – part) TL324071

Former oak/hornbeam woodland with mixed plantation, largely now mixed oak/birch scrub and heathy clearings, calcareous seepages, streams, rides. Two small car parks.

Cassiobury (**Park**), Watford TQ093967

Neutral grassland, swamp, alder carr, river, springs, ancient trees, some calcareous grassland. Part golf course. Parking, and bus/underground services nearby.

Cheshunt Gravel Pits (Lee Valley Park) TL367023

Former gravel pits with fen woodland, scrub, some damp grassland, river, canal, calcareous fen on fly-ash tips. Car parking. Station nearby.

Chipperfield Common TL044016

Acid oak/hornbeam and birch scrub on open common, remnant heath, ponds, some grassland. Small car park.

Chorleywood Common (Nature Reserve) TQ033967

Acid grassland, heath, oak/birch scrub woodland, rides, ponds, some calcareous grassland. Golf course in part. Car park. Bus services nearby.

Chorleywood Dell (Nature Reserve) TQ036970

Calcareous grassland, scrub and beech woodland. Access by footpath from Chorleywood House. Car parking at Chorleywood Common. Bus services nearby.

Church Hill, Therfield Heath (Nature Reserve) TL332396

Chalk grassland, some scrub, with rare flora. Car park nearby. Royston Station 2 miles. Bus services nearby.

Colney Heath (Nature Reserve) TL205056

Acid and damp neutral grassland, remnant heath, scrub, river. Limited car parking. Bus services nearby.

Commons Wood Nature Reserve, Welwyn Garden City TL258113

Calcareous fen, scrub, neutral and calcareous grassland, arable weed areas. Limited parking by road. Bus services nearby.

Croxley Common Moor (Nature Reserve) TQ082951

Rich alluvial flood-plain fen, heath, neutral grassland, swamp, river. Access on foot from Croxley Green. Station and bus services nearby.

Danesbury Park, Welwyn (Nature Reserve) TL234168

Neutral grassland, scrub, old parkland trees, pond. Limited car parking by road. Bus services nearby. Welwyn North Station 2 miles.

Darlands, Totteridge (Nature Reserve) TQ246941

Mixed old ornamental oak woodland, scrub, lake, remnant acid and neutral grassland. Access on foot from Totteridge. Bus services nearby.

Fir and Pond Woods, Potters Bar (Nature Reserve) TL277012

Acid oak/hornbeam woodland, scrub, acid grassland, lake, swamp, streams. Limited parking by road.

Frogmore Meadows, Sarratt (Nature Reserve – part) TQ021989

Calcareous and neutral grassland, fen swamp, scrub, riverside. Access on foot from Chenies or Sarratt Bottom.

Gobions Wood, Brookman's Park (Nature Reserve) TL248034

Damp oak/hornbeam and alder woodland, scrub, streams, ponds. Access on foot from car park at Gobions Park.

Grove Wood, Tring SP917096
Beech woodland, scrub. Access on foot from Hastoe Hill. Limited parking.

Gustard Wood Common, Wheathampstead TL173163

Acid grassland, remnant heath, scrub, oak/birch woodland. Part golf course. Limited parking.

Hadley Green, Barnet TQ248974

Acid grassland, ponds, scrub. Limited car parking by roads. Bus services and underground nearby.

Harebreaks Wood, Watford (Nature Reserve) TQ101992

Acid oak/birch woodland. Limited parking by roads.

Harpenden Common TL140132

Acid and neutral grassland, remnant heath, scrub woodland, ponds. Part golf course. Small car park. Bus services nearby. Station 1 mile.

Harrocks Wood, Watford (Woodland Trust) TQ070978

Beech woodland. Access on foot from Rousebarn Lane. Car park at Whippendell Wood nearby.

Haydon Hill, Bushey (Open Space) TQ128951

Neutral grassland, scrub, ponds. Limited parking by road. Bus services nearby.

Hertford Heath (Roundings and Goldingtons) (Nature Reserve) TL352109

Remnant heath, ponds, oak/birch scrub woodland, acid and neutral grassland. Limited car parking by road. Bus services nearby.

Hexton Chalk Pit (Nature Reserve) TL106300
Chalk grassland, scrub. Access on foot from Hexton village. Limited parking by road.

Hoddesdon Park Wood (National Nature Reserve) (Woodland Trust) TL349088

Acid oak/hornbeam woodland, rides, streams, seepages. Limited parking by road.

Hoo Bit, Lilley (Nature Reserve) TL117289

Calcareous grassland, scrub, beech plantation. Access on foot only from Pegsdon (limited parking) or Lilley Road (Icknield Way).

Hudnall Common, Little Gaddesden TL005131

Acid and neutral grassland, some calcareous grassland, scrub. Limited parking by road.

Hunsdon Mead (Nature Reserve) TL422113

Flood plain neutral meadow, swamp, river, scrub. Access on foot from Hunsdon Mill or Roydon. Very limited parking. Roydon Station 1 mile.

Ivel Springs, Baldock TL243344

Calcareous spring sources, swamp, rough grassland, willow fen, scrub. Access on foot from Baldock. Station and bus services nearby.

King George's Fields, Barnet TQ246971

Neutral rough grassland, scrub, streams. Limited parking by roads. Bus services nearby.

King's Meads, Hertford (Nature Reserve) TL350136; TL338133

Alluvial flood plain, neutral and calcareous grassland, chalk grass banks, swamp, flood meadows, ditches, river. Limited parking by roads. Ware and Hertford East Stations 1 mile, bus services nearby.

Knebworth Park (part) TL239209

Acid and neutral rough grassland, seepages, scrub, old park trees. Access on foot from Codicote Road or Old Knebworth. Access limited to rights of way.

Mardley Heath, Welwyn (Nature Reserve) TL248183

Acid oak/birch and hornbeam woodland, scrub, secondary acidic and calcareous grassland, remnant heath, ponds, seepages. Small car park. Bus services nearby.

Meesden Green TL429324

Calcareous rough grassland, scrub, ponds. 'Wildflower Meadow' with some introduced and native flora. Limited car parking by road.

Merryhills Farm, Bushey (Open Space) TQ129948; TQ127936

Mostly secondary neutral rough grassland on former arable, some old neutral pasture, scrub, ponds. Limited parking by roads. Bus services nearby.

Millhoppers Pasture, Astrope (Nature Reserve) SP899148

Damp calcareous rough pasture, scrub, stream, old black poplars. Limited parking by road, or access on foot from Wilstone village.

Monken Hadley Common, Barnet TQ254975

Remnant acid grassland, neutral grassland, scrub and oak woodland, lake, seepages. Limited parking by roads. Bus services nearby. High Barnet Underground 1 mile.

Nomansland Common TL171124

Acid grassland, remnant heath, scrub, oak woodland. Car park. Bus services (limited) nearby.

Northaw Great Wood (Country Park and Nature Reserve) TL282038

Acid oak/hornbeam/birch woodland, acid grassland rides, bracken heath, streams, ponds. Car park (pay).

Northchurch Common, Wheathampstead (National Trust: Ashridge) SP979094

Acid and calcareous grassland, bracken heath, scrub and oak/birch woodland. Limited car parking. Bus services 1 mile.

Norton Common, Letchworth TL218331

Damp oak/ash secondary woodland, fen mire, streams, calcareous grassland, scrub. Limited car parking by roads. Bus services and Letchworth Station nearby.

Oak Hill Park (Wood), East Barnet (Open Space) TQ281946

Acid oak/hornbeam woodland, rough neutral grassland, stream. Limited car parking. Station and bus services nearby.

Oddy Hill, Tring (Woodland Trust) SP934107

Chalk grassland, scrub on old pit. Very limited parking by road, or access on foot from Tring Park or Wigginton village.

Oughton Head/Oughton Head Common, Hitchin (Nature Reserve) TL171307

Calcareous fen meadow, swamp, springs, alder/willow fen woodland, scrub, pond, river. Access on foot from Hitchin or West Mill, Ickleford (limited parking). Bus services nearby. Hitchin Station 2 miles.

Oxhey Woods (Nature Reserve) TQ103932

Acid oak/birch woodland, remnant acid grassland rides, scrub, seepages. Limited parking by roads.

Oxley's Wood, Hatfield (Nature Reserve) TL227073

Small calcareous fen woodland site, spring-fed pond, swamp. Limited parking by road.

Patmore Heath, Albury (Nature Reserve) TL443258

Acid grassland, acid mire, ponds, scrub, secondary oak woodland. Limited parking by road.

Purwell Meadows, Hitchin (Nature Reserve) TL200299

Calcareous fen meadow, swamp, springs, river, scrub. Limited parking by road. Hitchin Station ½ mile. Bus services nearby.

Purwell Ninesprings Nature Reserve, Hitchin TL207293

Calcareous fen swamp, alder woodland, scrub. Access on foot from Purwell Lane. Limited parking by road. Bus services ½ mile. Hitchin Station 1 mile.

Roughdown Common, Hemel Hempstead TL046057

Chalk grassland, neutral grassland, scrub. Access on foot from Boxmoor. Station and bus services nearby.

Rowley Green (Nature Reserve) TQ217960

Acid grassland, remnant heath, acid oak/birch woodland, ponds. Limited parking by road.

Sawbridgeworth Marsh (Nature Reserve) TL494160

Calcareous fen swamp, neutral grassland, alder/willow fen woodland, scrub. Very limited parking by road, or access on foot from Sawbridgeworth. Station ½ mile.

Sheethanger Common, Hemel Hempstead TL035053

Remnant chalk grassland, secondary scrub woodland. Part golf course. Limited parking. Limited bus services nearby.

Sherrards Park Wood, Welwyn Garden City TL228141

Acid and calcareous oak/hornbeam woodland, scrub, rides, old railway, seepages. Small car park or access on foot from Welwyn Garden City. Bus services nearby. Welwyn Garden City Station 1 mile.

Silvermead, Broxbourne (Lee Valley Park) TL372067

Alluvial fen meadow, ditches, willow carr, riverside. Access on foot from Broxbourne. Station ½ mile.

Stockers Lake, Rickmansworth (Nature Reserve) TQ052934

Former gravel pit, alder/willow fen woodland, swamp, river, rough neutral grassland, scrub. Access on foot from Stockers Farm or Rickmansworth only.

Stubbings Wood, Tring SP920106

Calcareous beech woodland, scrub. Access on foot from Tring or Hastoe Hill only.

Telegraph Hill, Lilley (Nature Reserve) TL116287

Chalk grassland, scrub, neutral rough grassland, arable margins, pond. Access on foot from Pegsdon or Lilley Road (Icknield Way) only.

Therfield Heath (Nature Reserve) TL337399; TL348405

Chalk grassland, scrub, secondary beech woodland. Car parks. Bus services nearby. Royston Station 1 mile.

Thunderfield Grove, Wormley (Woodland Trust) TL341054

Oak/hornbeam/birch woodland, rides, seepages. Car park.

Totteridge Fields (Open Space) TQ222938

Damp neutral grassland, old hedges, scrub. Access on foot from Totteridge Common.

Tring Park (Woodland Trust) SP926108

Chalk grassland, neutral grassland, scrub, acid and calcareous beech woodland. Limited parking by road. Bus services nearby.

Tring Reservoirs (Nature Reserve) SP904135; SP919141

Spring-fed reservoirs, fen swamp, willow carr, scrub. Car parks (some pay). Bus services nearby.

Water End Meadows, Great Gaddesden TL032102; TL030113

Calcareous fen meadows, springs, river, scrub. Access on foot from Water End or Great Gaddesden. Limited parking by road.

Waterford Gravel Pits ('Waterford Heath') (Nature Reserve) TL314169

Rough secondary calcareous and acid grassland on former pits, scrub, calcareous willow fen, ponds. Small car park. Bus service nearby. Hertford North Station 2 miles.

Waterford Marsh (Meadows) TL313151

Alluvial neutral grass pasture, riverside, ditches, scrub. Limited car parking by road. Bus service nearby. Hertford North Station 2 miles.

Weston Church Meadows TL264301

Neutral/calcareous pasture, calcareous hay meadow, pond, scrub. Access on foot from Weston village or Weston Church only. Limited parking.

Weston Hills, Baldock (Open Space) TL247323

Chalk grassland, beech and sycamore woodland, scrub. Small car park. Bus services nearby. Baldock Station 1 mile.

Whippendell Wood, Watford TQ078983; TQ073976

Calcareous and acid beech/oak woodland, scrub, calcareous grassland, rides. Two small car parks. Bus services and Underground 1 mile.

Wilbury Hill, Letchworth TL201326

Small calcareous rough grassland site on old gravel pit(s), scrub. Small car park. Bus services nearby. Letchworth Station 1 mile.

Wormley Wood (National Nature Reserve) (Woodland Trust) TL326063

Acid oak/hornbeam woodland, rides, streams, seepages. Car park at Bencroft Wood nearby, or access on foot from Hammond Street/Darnicle Hill. Bus services at Hammond Street.

Select bibliography of published works relevant to the Hertfordshire flora, and sources cited in the text

Allen-Williams, L. , Hall, A., Shepperson, D. and Shepperson, C. M. (2002). 'Mistletoe (*Viscum album* L.) in Hertfordshire: a survey carried out by the University of Hertfordshire, 1997-2000' *The Hertfordshire Naturalist: Trans. Herts. N.H.S.*, 34 (1): 126-137.

Babington, C. C. (1897). *Memoirs, journal and botanical correspondence of Charles Cardale Babington*. Cambridge.

Bangerter, E. B. (1967). 'A survey of *Calystegia* in the London area: fifth and final report' *London Naturalist*, 46: 15-22.

Bateman, R. M. (1981). 'The Hertfordshire *Orchidaceae*' *Trans. Herts. N.H.S.*, 28 (4): 56-79.

Bateman, R. M. (1982). 'The Hertfordshire *Orchidaceae* – further records' *Trans. Herts. N.H.S.*, 28 (6): 13-15.

Bateman, R. M. (2001). 'Evolution and classification of European orchids: insights from molecular and morphological characters'. *Jour. Eur. Orch.*, 33 (1): 33-119.

Blackstone, J. (1746). *Specimen botanicum, quo plantarum plurium rariorum Angliae indigenarum loci natales illustrantur*. London: G. Faden.

Braithwaite, M. E., Ellis, R. W. and Preston, C. D. (2006). *Change in the British flora 1987-2004*. London: Botanical Society of the British Isles.

Briggs, J. (2000). *Kissing goodbye to mistletoe?* Peterborough: Botanical Society of the British Isles and Plantlife.

Bull, A. L. (1998). 'Four new species of *Rubus* L. (Rosaceae) from eastern England' *Watsonia*, 22: 97-104.

Burton, R. M. (1978). 'Botanical records for 1977' *London Naturalist*, 57: 70-80.

Burton, R. M. (1979a). '*Bidens* in Britain' *London Naturalist*, 58: 9-14.

Burton, R. M. (1979b). 'Botanical records for 1978' *London Naturalist*, 58: 62-68.

Burton, R. M. (1980). 'Botanical records for 1979' *London Naturalist*, 59: 76-83.

Burton, R. M. (1981). 'Botanical records for 1980' *London Naturalist*, 60: 87-93.

Burton, R. M. (1982). 'Botanical records for 1981' *London Naturalist*, 61: 100-107.

Burton, R. M. (1983a). *Flora of the London area*. London: London Natural History Society.

Burton, R. M. (1983b). 'Botanical records for 1982' *London Naturalist*, 62: 105-110.

Burton, R. M. (1984). 'Botanical records for 1983' *London Naturalist*, 63: 141-147.

Burton, R. M. (1985). 'Botanical records for 1984' *London Naturalist*, 64: 113-124.

Burton, R. M. (1986). 'Botanical records for 1985' *London Naturalist*, 65: 193-198.

Burton, R. M. (1987). 'Botanical records for 1986' *London Naturalist*, 66: 185-189.

Burton, R. M. (1988). 'Botanical records for 1987' *London Naturalist*, 67: 171-176.

Burton, R. M. (1989). 'Botanical records for 1988' *London Naturalist*, 68: 147-184.

Burton, R. M. (1990). 'Botanical records for 1989' *London Naturalist*, 69: 139-144.

Burton, R. M. (1991). 'Botanical records for 1990' *London Naturalist*, 70: 153-162.

Burton, R. M. (1992). 'Botanical records for 1991, with some notes on common species' *London Naturalist*, 71: 177-187.

Burton, R. M. (1993). 'Botanical records for 1992' *London Naturalist*, 72: 113-121.

Burton, R. M. (1994). 'Botanical records for 1993' *London Naturalist*, 73: 191-198.

Burton, R. M. (1995a). 'Botanical records for 1994' *London Naturalist*, 76: 171-178.

Burton, R. M. (1995b). 'The present distribution of Guernsey fleabane *Conyza sumatrensis* in the London Area' *London Naturalist*, 76: 169-170.

Burton, R. M. (1996a). 'Botanical records for 1995, with a note on computerization' *London Naturalist*, 75: 137-146.

Burton, R. M. (1996b). 'Danish scurvy-grass *Cochlearia danica* in the London Area' *London Naturalist*, 77: 133-135.

Burton, R. M. (1997). 'Botanical records for 1996' *London Naturalist*, 76: 193-201.

Chapman, M. A. and Stace, C. A. (2001). 'Tor-grass is not *Brachypodium pinnatum*!' *BSBI News*, 87: 74.

Cheffings, C. M. and Farrell, L. (eds.) (2007). *Species status no. 7: the vascular plant red data list for Great Britain*. Peterborough: JNCC. Published on-line.

Clapham, A. R., Tutin, T. G. and Warburg, E. F. (1981). *Excursion flora of the British Isles*. 3rd ed. Cambridge: Cambridge University Press.

Clement, E. J. and Foster, M. C. (1994). *Alien plants of the British Isles*. London: Botanical Society of the British Isles.

Clutterbuck, R. (1815). *The history and antiquities of the County of Hertford*. Vol. 1. London.

Coleman, M., Hollingsworth, M. L. and Hollingsworth, P. M. (2000). 'Application of RAPDs to the critical taxonomy of the English endemic elm *Ulmus plotii* Druce' *Botanical Journal of the Linnaean Society*, 133: 241-262.

Cronquist, A. (1981). *An integrated system of classification of flowering plants*. New York: Columbia University Press.

Cuming, S. (1997). *The habitat survey of Hertfordshire*. Unpublished District and summary reports. Hertford: Hertfordshire Biological Records Centre, and St Albans: Hertfordshire and Middlesex Wildlife Trust.

Davis, B. N. K. *et al.* (1992) *The soil*. London: Harper Collins. The New Naturalist Series.

Dony, J. G. (1953). *Flora of Bedfordshire*. Luton: Luton Museum and Art Gallery.

Dony, J. G. (1961). 'The Oxlip in Hertfordshire' *Proc. Bot. Soc. Brit. Isles*, 4: 149-150.

Dony, J. G. (1963). 'Botanists in Hertfordshire' *Hertfordshire, Past & Present*, 3: 39-44.

Dony, J. G. (1967). *Flora of Hertfordshire*. Hitchin: Hitchin Museum.

Dony, J. G. (1969). 'Notes on the flora of Hertfordshire'. *Trans. Herts. N.H.S.*, 27 (1): 23-24.

Dony, J. G. (1970). 'Plant notes for 1969' *Trans. Herts. N.H.S.*, 27 (2): 83.

Dony, J. G. (1971). 'Plant notes for 1970' *Trans. Herts. N.H.S.*, 27 (3): 119-120.

Dony, J. G. (1974). 'Changes in the flora of Hertfordshire'. *Trans. Herts. N.H.S.*, 27(6): 255-264.

Dony, J. G. (1975). 'Plant notes 1971-1974'. *Trans. Herts. N.H.S.*, 27 (7): 323-324.

Dony, J. G. (1977). 'Plant notes 1975-1976'. *Trans. Herts. N.H.S.*, 28 (1): 26-27.

Dudman, A. A. and Richards, A. J. (1997). *Dandelions of Great Britain and Ireland.* Botanical Society of the British Isles.

Edees, E. S. and Newton, A. (1988). *Brambles of the British Isles.* London: The Ray Society.

Edgington, J. (2007). 'The flora of Bricket Wood Common'. *The Hertfordshire Naturalist: Trans. Herts. N.H.S.*, 39 (2): 156-176.

English, R. D. S. (1955). 'Botanical observations on Bricket Wood'. *Trans. Herts. N.H.S.*, 24 (4): 146-156.

Geltman, D. V. (1992). '*Urtica galeopsifolia* Wierzb. ex Opiz (Urticaceae) in Wicken Fen (E. England)'. *Watsonia*, 19: 127-129.

Gil, L., Fuentes-Utrilla, P., Soto, A., Cervera, M. T. and Collada, C. (2004). 'English elm is a 2000-year-old Roman clone'. *Nature*, 431: 1053.

Godwin, H. G. (1975). *The history of the British flora: a factual basis for phytogeography.* 2nd ed. Cambridge: Cambridge University Press.

Graveson, W. (1917). *British wild flowers: their haunts and associations.* London: Headley Brothers.

Harley, J. L. and Lewis, D. H. (eds.) (1985). *The flora and vegetation of Britain: origins and changes – the facts and their interpretation.* London: Academic Press. (Reprint from *The New Phytologist*, 98 (1) (1984)).

Harper, G. (1981). 'Wild Service in Hertfordshire and Middlesex'. *Trans. Herts. N.H.S.*, 28 (4): 17-26.

Hill, M. O., Preston, C. D. and Roy, D. B. (2004). *PLANTATT: attributes of British and Irish plants – status, size, life history, geography and habitats.* Monks Wood, Huntingdon: NERC, Biological Records Centre.

Hine, R. L. (ed.) (1934). *The Natural History of the Hitchin Region.* Hitchin: Hitchin & District Regional Survey Association.

Hubbard, C. E. (1984). *Grasses: a guide to their structure, identification, uses and distribution in the British Isles.* 3rd ed. Harmondsworth: Penguin Books.

Jacquemyn, H., Brys, R. and Hutchings, M. J. (2008). 'Biological Flora of the British Isles: *Paris quadrifolia* L.'. *Journal of Ecology*, 96: 833-844.

James, T. J. (1980a). 'The flora of Oughton Head, Hitchin'. *Trans. Herts. N.H.S.*, 28 (3): 79-90.

James, T. J. (1980b). 'The Spotted Catsear *Hypochoeris maculata* at Therfield Heath'. *Trans. Herts. N.H.S.*, 28 (3): 91.

James, T. J. (1982). 'Higher plant records in Hertfordshire, 1977-1981'. *Trans. Herts. N.H.S.*, 28 (6): 6-12.

James, T. J. (1985). 'Higher plant records in Hertfordshire, 1981-1984' *Trans. Herts. N.H.S.*, 29 (5): 181-187.

James, T. J. (1989). 'Higher plant records in Hertfordshire, 1984-1986' *Trans. Herts. N.H.S.*, 30 (3): 251-256.

James, T. J. (1990a). 'The flora and vegetation of a gravel pit: Amwell Quarry'. *Trans. Herts. N.H.S.*, 30 (5): 371-404.

James, T. J. (1990b). 'The flora of Amwell Quarry' *in: Amwell Quarry 6th report: restoration and wildlife, 1983-1989.* Cheshunt: St Albans Sand & Gravel Co. Ltd. pp. 38-49.

James, T. J. (1997). 'The changing flora of Hertfordshire'. *Trans. Herts. N.H.S.*, 33 (1): 62-84.

James, T. J. and Goldsmith, F.B. (1993). 'The decline and extinction of Common Cotton-grass (*Eriophorum angustifolium* Honckeny) in Hertfordshire'. *Trans. Herts. N.H.S.*, 31 (5): 353-363.

Jermy, C., Simpson, D, Foley, M and Porter, M. (2007). *Sedges of the British Isles.* 3rd revised ed. London: Botanical Society of the British Isles. BSBI Handbook, no. 1.

Kent, D. H. (1975). *The historical flora of Middlesex: an account of the wild plants found in the Watsonian vice-county 21 from 1548 to the present time.* London: Ray Society.

Kent, D. H. (2000). *Flora of Middlesex: a supplement to the historical flora of Middlesex.* London: Ray Society.

Kent, D. H. and Lousley, J. E. (1951-1957). 'A hand list of the plants of the London area: flowering plants, ferns and stoneworts'. Parts 1-7. *London Naturalist*, 30-36. Issued as separate reprints: nos. 70, 73, 77, 83, 90, 100, 104.

Lansdown, R. V. (2006). 'Notes on the water-starworts (*Callitriche*) recorded in Europe'. *Watsonia*, 26: 105-120.

Lansdown, R. V. (2008). *Water-starworts (Callitriche) of Europe.* London: Botanical Society of the British Isles. BSBI Handbook no. 11.

Leslie, A. C. and Walters, S.M. (1983). 'The occurrence of *Lemna minuscula* Herter in the British Isles'. *Watsonia*, 14: 243-248.

Leslie, A. C. (2007). 'Vascular plant records'. *Nature in Cambridgeshire*, 49: 89-95.

Little, J. E. (1916). 'Hertfordshire poplars'. *Jour. of Bot.*, 54: 233-236.

Little, J. E. (1922). 'Notes on north Herts. willows' *Jour. of Bot.*, 60: 78-80.

Lousley, J. E. (1970). 'Botanical records for 1969', *London Naturalist*, 49: 17-19.

Melderis, A. (1968). '*Bromus* (section *Ceratochloa*) in Britain'. *Proc. Bot. Soc. Brit. Isles*, 7: 392-393.

Meyer, D. and H. (1951). 'The distribution of *Primula elatior* (L.) Hill' *in*: Lousley, J. E. (ed.) *The study of the distribution of British plants.* Arbroath: T. Buncle.

Muir, R. (2006). *Ancient trees, living landscapes.* 2nd ed. Stroud: Tempus Publishing Ltd.

Munby, L. M. (1977). *The Hertfordshire landscape.* London: Hodder and Stoughton.

Newton, A. and Randall, R.D. (2004). *Atlas of British and Irish brambles.* London: Botanical Society of the British Isles.

Pennington, W. (1969). *The history of British vegetation.* London: The English Universities Press Ltd.

Peterken, G. (1993). *Woodland conservation and management.* 2nd ed. London: Chapman and Hall.

Preston, C. D., Pearman, D. A. and Dines, T. D. (2002). *New atlas of the British and Irish flora.* Oxford: Oxford University Press.

Preston, C. D. and Croft, J. M. (1997). *Aquatic plants in Britain and Ireland.* Colchester: Harley Books.

Preston, C. D. and Sell, P. D. (1989). 'The Aizoaceae naturalized in the British Isles'. *Watsonia*, 17: 217-245.

Preston, C. D., Sheail, J., Armitage, P. and Davy-Bowker, J. (2003). 'The long-term impact of urbanisation on aquatic plants: Cambridge and the River Cam'. *Science Direct*, doi:10.1016/S0048-9697(03)00097-4 (web publication).

Pryor, A. R. (1875). 'Additions to the flora of Hertfordshire'. *Jour. of Bot.*, 13: 212.

Pryor, A. R. (1887). *A Flora of Hertfordshire*, ed. B. D. Jackson.

London: Gurney and Jackson; and Hertford: Stephen Austin.

Rackham, O. (1980). *Ancient woodland: its history, vegetation and uses in England*. London: Edward Arnold.

Rich, T. C. G. (1999). 'Conservation of Britain's biodiversity: *Filago lutescens* Jordan (Asteraceae), Red-tipped Cudweed'. *Watsonia*, 22: 251-260.

Rich, T. C. G, Jermy. A. C. and Carey, J. L. (1998). *Plant crib 1998*. London : Botanical Society of the British Isles.

Rich, T. C. G. and Woodruff, E. R. (1990). *The BSBI Monitoring Scheme 1987-1988: report to the Nature Conservancy Council*. [Huntingdon: Institute of Terrestrial Ecology].

Richens, R. H. (1959). 'Studies on *Ulmus* III: the village elms of Hertfordshire'. *Forestry*, 32.

Rodwell, J. (ed.) (1991). *British plant communities*. Vol. 1: *Woodlands and scrub*. Cambridge: Cambridge University Press.

Rodwell, J. (ed.) (1991). *British plant communities*. Vol. 2: *Mires and heaths*. Cambridge: Cambridge University Press.

Rodwell, J. (ed.) (1992). *British plant communities*. Vol. 3: *Grasslands and montane communities*. Cambridge: Cambridge University Press.

Rodwell, J. (ed.) (1995). *British plant communities*. Vol. 4: *Aquatic communities, swamps and tall-herb fens*. Cambridge: Cambridge University Press.

Rodwell, J. (ed.) (2000). *British plant communities*. Vol. 5: *Maritime communities and vegetation of open habitats*. Cambridge: Cambridge University Press.

Rostański, N. (1982). 'The species of *Oenothera* L. in Britain'. *Watsonia*, 14: 1-34.

Rowe, A. (2009). *Medieval parks of Hertfordshire*. Hatfield: Hertfordshire Publications (University of Hertfordshire).

Ryves, T. B., Clement, E. J. and Foster, M. C. (1996). *Alien grasses of the British Isles*. London: Botanical Society of the British Isles.

Salisbury, E. J. (1912). 'Botanical observations in Hertfordshire during the year 1910'. *Trans. Herts. N.H.S.*, 14 (4): 301-302.

Salisbury, E. J. (1914). 'Botanical observations in Hertfordshire during the years 1911 and 1912'. *Trans. Herts. N.H.S.*, 15 (3): 172.

Salisbury, E. J. (1916). 'Botanical observations in Hertfordshire during the year 1914, with notes on *Silene dichotoma* and *Gentiana praecox*'. *Trans. Herts. N.H.S.*, 16 (2): 75-78.

Salisbury, E. J. (1917). 'Report on botanical observations in Hertfordshire during the year 1915'. *Trans. Herts. N.H.S.*, 16 (3): 157-160.

Salisbury, E. J. (1918). 'The ecology of scrub in Hertfordshire: a study in colonisation'. *Trans. Herts. N.H.S.*, 17: 53-64.

Salisbury, E. J. (1924a). 'The effects of coppicing as illustrated by the woods of Hertfordshire'. *Trans. Herts. N.H.S.*, 18 (1): 1-21.

Salisbury, E. J. (1924b). 'Changes in the Hertfordshire flora: a consideration of the influence of man'. *Trans. Herts. N.H.S.*, 18 (1): 51-68.

Saunders, J. (1911). *Field flowers of Bedfordshire*. London: Eyre and Spottiswood.

Sawford, B. R. (1974). 'Lesser Meadow Rue in north Hertfordshire'. *Trans. Herts. N.H.S.* 27 (6): 293-294.

Sawford, B. R. (1989). *Wild flower habitats of Hertfordshire: past, present, and future?* Ware: Castlemead Pubs.

Selby, A. (1884). 'List of flowering plants observed in Hertfordshire during the year 1883'. *Trans. Herts. N.H.S.*, 3 (3): 101-102.

Sell, P. (1991) .'The cherries and plums of Cambridgeshire' *Nature in Cambridgeshire*, 33: 29-39.

Sell, P. (2007). 'Introduced 'look-alikes' and other difficult introduced plants in our Cambridgeshire flora'. *BSBI News*, 105: 24-30.

Sell, P. and Murrell, G. (1996). *Flora of Great Britain and Ireland* Vol. 5: *Butomaceae – Orchidaceae*. Cambridge: Cambridge University Press.

Sell, P. and Murrell, G. (2006). *Flora of Great Britain and Ireland* Vol. 4: *Campanulaceae – Asteraceae*. Cambridge: Cambridge University Press.

Sell, P. and Murrell, G. (2009). *Flora of Great Britain and Ireland* Vol. 3: *Mimosaceae – Lentibulariaceae*. Cambridge: Cambridge University Press.

Shaw, P. J. A. (1994). 'Orchid woods and floating islands – the ecology of fly ash'. *British Wildlife*, 5: 149-157.

Shaw, P. J. A. (1998). 'Morphometric analyses of mixed *Dactylorhiza* colonies (Orchidaceae) on industrial waste sites in England'. *Bot. Jour. Linn. Soc.*, 128: 385-401.

Simpson, D. A. (1984). 'A short history of the introduction and spread of *Elodea* Michx in the British Isles'. *Watsonia*, 15: 1-9.

Showler, A. J. and Rich, T. C. G. (1993). '*Cardamine bulbifera* (L.) Crantz (Cruciferae) in the British Isles'. *Watsonia*, 19: 231-245.

Smith, K. W. *et al.* (eds.) (1993). *The breeding birds of Hertfordshire*. Hertforshire Natural History Society.

Stace, C. A. (ed.) (1975). *Hybridisation and the flora of the British Isles*. London: Academic Press.

Stace, C. A. (1991). 'A new taxonomic treatment of the *Festuca ovina* L. aggregate (Poaceae) in the British Isles'. *Biol. Jour. Linn. Soc.*, 106: 347-397.

Stace, C. A. (1997). *New Flora of the British Isles*. 2nd ed. Cambridge: Cambridge University Press.

Stace, C. A. *et. al.* (2003). *Vice-county census catalogue of the vascular plants of Great Britain, the Isle of Man and the Channel Islands*. London: Botanical Society of the British Isles.

Trevis, E. (2005). 'An investigation of changes in the flora of a re-seeded chalk grassland over 30 years and comparisons with nearby ancient chalk grassland at Therfield Heath'. *The Hertfordshire Naturalist: Trans. Herts. N.H.S.*, 37 (2): 195-206.

Vera, F. W. M. (2000). *Grazing ecology and forest history*. Wallingford (Oxfordshire): CABI Publishing.

Walker, K. J., Preston, C. D. and Boon, C. R. (2009). 'Fifty years of change in an area of intensive agriculture: plant trait responses to habitat modification and conservation, Bedfordshire, England'. *Biodivers. Conserv.*, DOI 10.1007/s10531-009-9662-y (web publication).

Webb, R. H. (1859). 'Additional supplement to the *Flora Hertfordiensis, 1851-1857*'. *Phytologist* (New Series), 2: 156-163.

Webb, R. H. and Coleman, W. H. (1849). *Flora Hertfordiensis: or a catalogue of plants found in the County of Hertford, with the stations of rarer species*. London: William Pamplin and Hertford: Stephen Austin.

Webb, R. H and Coleman, W. H. (1851). *Flora Hertfordiensis* Supplement 1, 1848-1849. London: William Pamplin.

Whiteman, R. J. (1936). *Hexton: a parish survey*. Hexton: privately printed.

Wigginton, M. J. and Graham, G. G. (1981). *Guide to the identification of some of the more difficult vascular plant species*. England Field Unit Occasional Paper no. 1. Banbury: Nature Conservancy Council.

Williamson, T. (2000). *The origins of Hertfordshire*. Manchester and New York: Manchester University Press.

Young, C. and Warrington, S. (2003). 'The status and distribution of the wild service tree in Hertfordshire'. *The Hertfordshire Naturalist: Trans. Herts. N.H.S.*, 35 (1): 72-86.

Archives and biological research collections sourced for information on the Hertfordshire flora

Manuscript sources:

Below are the more important unpublished sources for the Hertfordshire flora, but other miscellaneous material has also been examined where possible.

Barnard, A. M. (diaries) (Hunnybun mss., Cambridge Botanic Garden).
Coleman, W. H. (ms. notes for the *Flora Hertfordiensis*) (Hitchin: North Herts. Museums).
Dony mss. (including: annotated card index of the Herts. Flora; record cards compiled for the *Flora of Hertfordshire* (1967); miscellaneous correspondence and research notes) (Hitchin: North Herts. Museums).
Graveson, A. W. (diaries) (Hitchin: North Herts. Museums).
Hayllar, H. F. (diary) (Hitchin: North Herts. Museums).
Little, J. E. (diaries and ms. notebooks) (Hitchin: North Herts. Museums).
Morell, J. D. (annotated copy of Turner and Dillwyn's *Botanist's Guide*) (Hitchin: North Herts. Museums).
Newbould, W.W. (annotated copy of Webb and Coleman's *Flora Hertfordiensis*) (Hitchin: North Herts. Museums, formerly at Luton Museum).
Ransom, J. (diary, 1814) (Hitchin: North Herts. Museums).

Herbaria (public):

Some indication is given of the principal collectors whose material is present in each, but the lists are not exhaustive. Standard herbarium abbreviations follow those proposed in D. H. Kent and D. E. Allen (1984) *British and Irish herbaria,* London: Botanical Society of the British Isles.

BIRA: Birmingham Museum and Art Gallery (miscellaneous specimens).
BM: Natural History Museum, London (Hb. H. Brown *etc.*).
BON: Bolton Museum (Hb. W.H.Coleman (part)).
CGE: Cambridge Botanic Garden: Herbarium (Hb. J. E. Little).
E: Edinburgh Botanic Garden: Herbarium (Hb. E. McAllister-Hall (part)).

HTN: North Hertfordshire Museums Service, Hitchin – containing: A. W. Graveson, H. F. Hayllar, Hitchin Museum (incl. A. M. Boucher (some), W. H. Coleman (some), J. G. Dony (part), G. L. Evans, C. G. Hanson (some), A. G. Harrold, T. J. James, B. R. Sawford, *etc.*), Letchworth Museum (incl. A. G. Brunt, T.A.Dymes and D. Meyer, *etc.*), J. C. Littlebury (part), L. Manser, H. Phillips/E. MacAllister-Hall (part), J. Pollard).
K: Royal Botanic Gardens, Kew: Herbarium (miscellaneous specimens).
LIV: World Museum, Liverpool (miscellaneous specimens).
LTN: Luton Museum and Art Gallery (Hb. J.G.Dony (part), J. Saunders *etc.*).
LTR: Leicester Museum and Art Gallery (Hb. Bishop's Stortford College, Hb. Haileybury College (major part)).
NMW: National Museum of Wales, Cardiff (Hb. W. C. R.Watson).
OXF: University of Oxford Botany School: Herbarium (various specimens in Hb. Druce).

Herbaria (private):

Hb. Boucher: Mrs A. M. Boucher, formerly of Hoddesdon, now Kendal, Cumbria.
Hb. Bull: Mr A. L. Bull of East Tuddenham, Norfolk.
Hb. Ellison: Mr P. J. Ellison, formerly of Ruislip, Middx., now New Milton, Hampshire.
Hb. Hanson: Mr C. G. Hanson of Ware.
Hb. Killick: Mr H. J. Killick, formerly of Cuffley, now Abingdon, Oxfordshire.
Hb. Marshall: Mr A. D. Marshall of Hatfield.
Hb. Southey: Mr J. F. Southey, formerly of Harpenden, now Exeter, Devon.
Hb. Vaughan: Mr A. W. Vaughan, formerly of Wigginton, now Builth Wells, Powys.

Plant specimens and other supporting material collected by or received by the author as voucher material for the Hertfordshire Flora Survey are intended to be deposited in the County Herbarium at North Hertfordshire Museums Service, Hitchin (HTN), together with all original correspondence and survey cards, alongside similar material collected for the 1967 Survey.

Index of sites

The following is an index of all the specific locations mentioned in the main account of the Flora where particular plants have been recorded. It omits private grounds of houses, general town/village names, or the names of long, linear features such as main roads or rivers, unless there is a well-defined site associated with them. It also does not index any mentions of these sites in the introductory chapters or appendices.

Synonyms of taxon names

The following list of synonyms covers all significant name changes from Dony (1967) and subsequent U.K. Floras, and is intended to enable users of this book to more easily trace information on particular plants. The list should be used in conjunction with the Index of plant names.

Aceras anthropophorum (L.) W. T. Aiton see: *Orchis anthropophora* (L.) All.

Acinos arvensis Mill. see: *Clinopodium acinos* (L.) Kuntze

Agrimonia odorata (*auct.*) see: *Agrimonia procera* Wallr.

Agropyron caninum (L.) P. Beauv. see: *Elymus caninus* (L.) L.

Agropyron repens (L.) P. Beauv. see: *Elytrigia repens* (L.) Desv. ex Nevski

Agrostis canina ssp. *montana* (Hartm.) Hartm. see: *Agrostis vinealis* Schreber

Agrostis semiverticillata (Forssk.) C.Chr. see: *Polypogon viridis* (Gouan) Breistr.

Agrostis tenuis Sibth. see: *Agrostis capillaris* L.

Alchemilla vestita (Buser) Raunk. see: *Alchemilla filicaulis* ssp. *vestita* (Buser) M. E. Bradshaw

Amaranthus lividus L. see: *Amaranthus blitum* L.

Amsinckia angustifolia Lehm. see: *Amsinckia calycina* (Moris) Chater

Amsinckia intermedia Fisch. and Mey. see: *Amsinckia micrantha* Suksd.

Anthoxanthum puellii Lecoq and Lamotte see: *Anthoxanthum aristatum* Boiss.

Aphanes inexspectata W. Lippert see: *Aphanes australis* Rydb.

Aphanes microcarpa (*auct.*) see: *Aphanes australis* Rydb.

Arctium pubens Bab. see: *Arctium minus* (Hill) Bernh.

Arenaria leptoclados (Rchb.) Guss. see: *Arenaria serpyllifolia* ssp. *leptoclados* (Rchb.) Nyman

Arenaria tenuifolia L. see: *Minuartia hybrida* (Vill.) Schischk.

Atriplex hastata (*auct.*) see: *Atriplex prostrata* Boucher ex DC.

Avena ludoviciana Durieu see: *Avena sterilis* ssp. *ludoviciana* (Durieu) Gillet and Magne

Avenula pratensis (L.) Holub see: *Helictotrichon pratense* (L.) Besser

Avenula pubescens (Huds.) Dumort. see: *Helictotrichon pubescens* (Hudson) Pilger

Betonica officinalis L. see: *Stachys officinalis* (L.) Trev. St Léon

Bromus benekenii (Lange) Trimen see: *Bromopsis benekenii* (Lange) Holub

Bromus carinatus Hook. and Arn. see: *Ceratochloa carinata* (Hook. and Arn.) Tutin

Bromus catharticus Vahl see: *Ceratochloa cathartica* (Vahl) Herter

Bromus diandrus Roth see: *Anisantha diandra* (Roth) Tutin ex Tzvelev

Bromus erectus Hudson see: *Bromopsis erecta* (Hudson) Fourr.

Bromus inermis Leyss. see: *Bromopsis inermis* (Leysser) Holub

Bromus macrostachys Desf. see: *Bromus lanceolatus* Roth

Bromus madritensis L. see: *Anisantha madritensis* (L.) Nevski

Bromus marginatus Nees ex Steud. see: *Ceratochloa marginata* (Nees ex Steud.) B. D. Jackson

Bromus mollis L. see: *Bromus hordeaceus* L.

Bromus ramosus Hudson see: *Bromopsis ramosa* (Hudson) Holub

Bromus rigidus Roth see: *Anisantha rigida* (Roth) N.Hylander

Bromus sterilis L. see: *Anisantha sterilis* (L. Nevski

Bromus tectorum L. see: *Anisantha tectorum* (L.) Nevski

Bromus thominei (*auct.*) see: *Bromus* × *pseudothominei* P. M. Sm.

Bromus unioloides Kunth see: *Ceratochloa cathartica* (Vahl) Herter

Buglossoides purpureocaerulea (L.) I. M. Johnst. see: *Lithospermum purpureocaeruleum* L.

Bupleurum lancifolium (*auct.*) see: *Bupleurum subovatum* Link ex Sprengel

Calamintha ascendens Jordan see: *Clinopodium ascendens* (Jordan) Samp.

Calamintha nepeta (L.) Savi see: *Clinopodium calamintha* (L.) Stace

Callitriche hamulata Kütz. ex Koch see: *Callitriche brutia* var. *hamulata* Kütz. ex Koch

Callitriche intermedia Hoffm. see: *Callitriche brutia* Petagna

Calystegia dahurica (*auct.*) see: *Calystegia pulchra* Brummitt and Heyw.

Cardaria draba (L.) Desv. see: *Lepidium draba* L.

Carduus acanthoides (*auct.*) see: *Carduus crispus* L.

Carex curta Gooden. see: *Carex canescens* L.

Carex demissa Hornem. see: *Carex viridula* ssp. *oedocarpa* (Andersson) B. Schmid

Carex lepidocarpa Tausch see: *Carex viridula* ssp. *brachyrrhyncha* (Čelak.) B. Schmid

Carex ovalis Gooden. see: *Carex leporina* L.

Centromadia fitchii (*auct.*) see: *Hemizonia pungens* Torrey and A. Gray

Cerastium holosteoides Fr. see: *Cerastium fontanum* Baumg.

Chaerophyllum temulentum L. see: *Chaerophyllum temulum* L.

Chamaenerion angustifolium (L.) Scop. See: *Chamerion angustifolium* (L.) Holub

Cheiranthus cheiri L. see: *Erysimum cheiri* (L.) Crantz

Chenopodium pratericola Rydb. see: *Chenopodium desiccatum* A.Nelson

Chrysanthemum coronarium L. see: *Xanthophthalmum coronarium* L.

Chrysanthemum leucanthemum L. see: *Leucanthemum vulgare* Lam.

Chrysanthemum maximum (*auct.*) see: *Leucanthemum lacustre* (Brot.) Samp.

Chrysanthemum parthenium (L.) Bernh. see: *Tanacetum parthenium* (L.) Schultz Bip.

Chrysanthemum segetum L. see: *Xanthophthalmum segetum* L.

Chrysanthemum serotinum L. see: *Leucanthemella serotina* (L.) Tzvelev

Chrysanthemum vulgare (L.) Bernh. see: *Tanacetum vulgare* L.

Cirsium acaulon (mis-spelling) see: *Cirsium acaule* L.

Coeloglossum viride (L.) Hartm. see: *Dactylorhiza viridis* (L.) Bateman, Pridgeon and Chase

Consolida ambigua (*auct.*) see: *Consolida ajacis* (L.) Schur

Cornus alba L. see: *Swida alba* (L.) Holub

Cornus sanguinea L. see: *Swida sanguinea* (L.) Opiz

Cornus sericea L. see: *Swida sericea* (L.) Holub

Coronilla varia L. see: *Securigera varia* (L.) Lassen

Corydalis bulbosa (L.) DC. see: *Corydalis cava* (L.) Schweigg. and Körte

Corydalis lutea (L.) DC. see: *Pseudofumaria lutea* (L.) Borkh.

Corydalis ochroleuca Koch see: *Corydalis cava* (L.) Schweigg. and Körte

Crataegus oxyacanthoides Thuill. see: *Crataegus laevigata* (Poir.) DC.

Crocus purpureus Weston see: *Crocus vernus* (L.) Hill

Dentaria bulbifera L. see: *Cardamine bulbifera* (L.) Crantz

Desmazeria rigida (L.) Tutin see: *Catapodium rigidum* (L.) C.E.Hubbard

Dryopteris borreri (Newman) Newman ex Oberh. and Tavel see: *Dryopteris affinis* ssp. *borreri* (Newman) Fraser-Jenkins

Echinochloa utilis Ohwi and Yabuno see: *Echinochloa esculenta* (A.Braun) H.Scholz

Eleocharis palustris ssp. *microcarpa* Walters see: *Eleocharis palustris* ssp. *palustris*

Eleogiton fluitans (L.) Link see: *Isolepis fluitans* (L.) R. Br.

Endymion hispanicus (Mill.) Chouard see: *Hyacinthoides hispanica* (Miller) Rothm.

Endymion non-scriptus (L.) Garcke see: *Hyacinthoides non-scripta* (L.) Chouard ex Rothm.

Epilobium adenocaulon Hausskn. see: *Epilobium ciliatum* Rafin.

Epilobium angustifolium L. see: *Chamerion angustifolium* (L.) Holub

Epilobium nerteroides (*auct.*) see: *Epilobium brunnescens* (Cock.) Raven and Engel.

Erodium obtusiplicatum (Maire, Weill. and Wilcz.) Howell see: *Erodium brachycarpum* (Godr.) Thell.

Erophila spathulata Ling. see: *Erophila verna* (L.) DC.

Euphorbia esula (*auct.*) see: *Euphorbia* × *pseudovirgata* (Schur) Soó

Euphorbia uralensis (*auct.*) see: *Euphorbia* × *pseudovirgata* (Schur) Soó

Euphrasia borealis (F.Towns.) Wettst. see: *Euphrasia arctica* ssp. *borealis* (F.Towns.) Yeo

Festuca longifolia (*auct.*). see: *Festuca brevipila* R. Tracey (and *F. lemanii* Bast.)

Festuca tenuifolia Sibth. see: *Festuca filiformis* Pourret

Filago apiculata G. E. Sm. ex Borbás see: *Filago lutescens* Jordan

Filago germanica L. see: *Filago vulgaris* Lam.

Filago spathulata (*auct.*) see: *Filago pyramidata* L.

Galeobdolon luteum Huds. see: *Lamiastrum galeobdolon* (L.) Ehrend. and Polatschek

Galinsoga ciliata (Raf.) S. F. Blake see: *Galinsoga quadriradiata* Ruiz, Lopez and Pavón

Galium album Mill. see: *Galium mollugo* ssp. *erectum* Syme

Galium cruciata (L.) Scop. see: *Cruciata laevipes* Opiz

Glyceria plicata (Fr.) Fr. see: *Glyceria notata* Chevall.

Gymnadenia conopsea ssp. *densiflora* (Wahlenb.) E. G. Camus, Berg. and A. Camus see: *Gymnadenia densiflora* (Wahlenb.) A. Dietr.

Helianthus decapetalus (*auct.*) see: *Helianthus × multiflorus* L.

Helianthus rigidus (*auct.*) see: *Helianthus × laetiflorus* Pers.

Helxine soleirolii Req. see: *Soleirolia soleirolii* (Req.) Dandy

Hieracium brunneocroceum Pugsley see: *Pilosella aurantiaca* (L.) F. W. Schultz and Sch. Bip.

Hieracium maculatum (*sensu* Dony, 1967) see: *Hieracium naevuliferum* Jordan

Hieracium murorum L. *sensu lato* see: Genus *Hieracium*

Hieracium perpropinquum (Zahn) Druce see: *Hieracium sabaudum* L.

Hieracium pilosella L. see: *Pilosella officinarum* F. W. Schultz and Sch. Bip.

Hieracium praealtum Vill. ex Gochnat see: *Pilosella praealta* (Villars ex Gochnat) F. W. Schultz and Sch. Bip.

Hieracium spraguei Pugsley see: *Pilosella praealta* ssp. *thaumasia* (Peter) P. D. Sell

Hieracium strumosum (*auct.*) see: *Hieracium* Section *Vulgata*

Hordeum hystrix Roth see: *Hordeum geniculatum* All.

Hordeum marinum (*sensu* Dony, 1967) see: *Hordeum geniculatum* All.

Inula conyza DC. see: *Inula conyzae* (Griess) Meikle

Juncus subuliflorus Drej. see: *Juncus conglomeratus* L.

Koeleria cristata (*auct.*) see: *Koeleria macrantha* (Ledeb.) Schultes

Lathyrus montanus Bernh. see: *Lathyrus linifolius* (Reichard) Bässler

Lavatera olbia (*auct.*) see: *Lavatera thuringiaca* (L.)

Lemna minuscula Herter see: *Lemna minuta* Kunth

Lemna polyrihiza L. see: *Spirodela polyrhiza* (L.) Schleiden

Leontodon autumnalis L. see: *Scorzoneroides autumnalis* L.

Leontodon taraxacoides (Vill.) Mérat) see: *Leontodon saxatilis* Lam.

Lepidium densiflorum Schrad. see: *Lepidium virginicum* L.

Lepidium neglectum Thell. see: *Lepidium virginicum* L.

Leucanthemum × superbum (Berg. ex J. W. Ingram) Kent see: *Leucanthemum lacustre* (Brot.) Samp.

Linum anglicum Mill. see: *Linum perenne* L.

Listera ovata (L.) R. Br. see: *Neottia ovata* (L.) Bluff. and Fingerh.

Lotus tenuis Waldst. and Kit. ex Willd. see: *Lotus glaber* Miller

Lotus uliginosus Schkuhr see: *Lotus pedunculatus* Cav.

Lycium halimifolium Mill. see: *Lycium barbarum* L. (and *Lycium chinense* Mill.)

Lycopsis arvensis L. see: *Anchusa arvensis* (L.) M.Bieb.

Malus pumila P.Miller see: *Malus domestica* Borkh.

Matricaria matricarioides (Less.) Porter see: *Matricaria discoidea* DC.

Matricaria suaveolens (Pursh) Buch. see: *Matricaria discoidea* DC.

Medicago falcata L. see: *Medicago sativa* ssp. *falcata* (L.) Arcang.

Mentha × gentilis (*auct.*) see: *Mentha × gracilis* Sole

Mentha rotundifolia (*auct.*) see: *Mentha suaveolens* Ehrh.

Monerma cylindrica (Willd.) Coss. and Dur. see: *Hainardia cylindrica* (Willd.) Greuter

Montia perfoliata (Donn ex Willd.) Howell see: *Claytonia perfoliata* Donn ex Willd.

Montia sibirica (L.) Howell see: *Claytonia sibirica* L.

Muscari atlanticum Boiss. and Reut. see: *Muscari neglectum* Guss. ex Ten.

Myosotis caespitosa Schultz see: *Myosotis laxa* Lehm.

Nasturtium microphyllum (Boenn.) Rchb. see: *Rorippa microphylla* (Boenn.) N. Hylander ex A. Löve and D. Löve

Nasturtium officinale W. T. Aiton see: *Rorippa nasturtium-aquaticum* (L.) Hayek

Oenothera erythrosepala Borbás see: *Oenothera glazioviana* P. Mich. ex C. Martius

Ononis salzmanniana Boiss. and Reuter see: *Ononis baetica* Clemente

Orchis morio L. see: *Anacamptis morio* (L.) Bateman, Prigeon and Chase

Orchis ustulata L. see: *Neotinea ustulata* (L.) Bateman, Prigeon and Chase

Ornithogalum umbellatum L. see: *Ornithogalum angustifolium* Boreau

Oxalis corymbosa DC. see: *Oxalis debilis* Kunth

Oxalis europaea Jord. see: *Oxalis stricta* L.

Panicum laevifolium Hackel see: *Panicum schinzii* Hackel

Papaver lecoquii Lamotte see: *Papaver dubium* ssp. *lecoquii* (Lamotte) Syme

Parietaria diffusa Mert. and W.D.J.Koch see: *Parietaria judaica* L.

Peplis portula L. see: *Lythrum portula* (L.) D. A. Webb

Phegopteris calcarea (Sm.) Fée see: *Gymnocarpium robertianum* (Hoffm.) Newman

Phleum pratense ssp. *bertolonii* (DC.) Bornm. see: *Phleum bertolonii* DC.

Phragmites communis Trin. see: *Phragmites australis* (Cav.) Trin. ex Steudel

Phytolacca americana (*auct.*) see: *Phytolacca acinosa* Roxb.

Plantago indica L. see: *Plantago arenaria* Waldst. and Kit.

Poa subcaerulea Sm. see: *Poa humilis* Ehrh. ex Hoffm.

Polygonum aequale Lindm. see: *Polygonum arenastrum* Boreau

Polygonum amphibium L. see: *Persicaria amphibia* (L.) Gray

Polygonum baldschuanicum Regel see: *Fallopia baldschuanica* (Regel) Holub

Polygonum bistorta L. see: *Persicaria bistorta* (L.) Samp.

Polygonum convolvulus L. see: *Fallopia convolvulus* (L.) À. Löve

Polygonum cuspidatum Siebold and Zucc. see: *Fallopia japonica* (Houtt.) Ronse Decraene

Polygonum dumetorum L. see: *Fallopia dumetorum* (L.) Holub

Polygonum hydropiper L. see: *Persicaria hydropiper* (L.) Spach

Polygonum lapathifolium L. see: *Persicaria lapathifolia* (L.) Gray

Polygonum minus Hudson see: *Persicaria minor* (Hudson) Opiz

Polygonum mite Schrank see: *Persicaria mitis* (Schrank) Opiz ex Assenov

Polygonum persicaria L. see: *Persicaria maculosa* Gray

Polygonum polystachyum Wall. ex Meisn. see: *Persicaria wallichii* Greuter and Burdet

Polygonum sachalinense F. Schmidt ex Maxim. see: *Fallopia sachalinense* (F. Schmidt ex Maxim.) Ronse Decraene

Populus candicans (*auct.*) see: *Populus × jackii* Sarg.

Populus tacamahacca (*auct.*) see: *Populus × jackii* Sarg.

Poterium sanguisorba L. see: *Sanguisorba minor* Scop.

Reynoutria japonica Houtt. see: *Fallopia japonica* (Houtt.) Ronse Decraene

Reynoutria sachalinensis (F. Schmidt ex Maxim.) Nakai see: *Fallopia sachalinense* (F. Schmidt ex Maxim.) Ronse Decraene

Rhinanthus major Ehrh. see: *Rhinanthus angustifolius* C. Gmelin

Rhus hirta (L.) Sudw. see: *Rhus typhina* L.

Rorippa islandica (*auct.*) see: *Rorippa palustris* (L.) Besser

Rosa afzeliana Fr. see: *Rosa caesia* Sm.

Rosa glauca Pourr. non Vill. ex Loisel. see: *Rosa caesia* Sm.

Rosa pimpinellifolia L. see: *Rosa spinosissima* L.

Rubus procerus (*auct.*) see: *Rubus armeniacus* Focke

Rumex triangulivalvis (Danser) Rech. *f.* see: *Rumex salicifolius* Weinm.

Salvia bertolonii Vis. see: *Salvia pratensis* L.

Salvia horminoides Pourr. see: *Salvia verbenaca* L.

Salvia horminum L. see: *Salvia viridis* L.

Sarothamnus scoparius (L.) W. D. J. Koch see: *Cytisus scoparius* (L.) Link

Scirpus fluitans L. see: *Isolepis fluitans* (L.) R. Br.

Scirpus lacustris L. see: *Schoenoplectus lacustris* (L.) Palla

Scirpus maritimus L. see: *Bolboschoenus maritimus* (L.) Palla

Scorpiurus subvillosus L. see: *Scorpiurus muricatus* L.

Scorpiurus sulcatus L. see: *Scorpiurus muricatus* L.

Scrophularia aquatica (*auct.*) see: *Scrophularia auriculata* L.

Sedum reflexum L. see: *Sedum rupestre* L.

Senecio × londinensis Lousley see: *Senecio × subnebrodensis* Simonkai

Senecio cineraria DC. see: *Senecio ambiguus* (Biv.) DC.

Senecio integrifolius (L.) Clairv. see: *Tephroseris integrifolia* (L.) Holub

Setaria lutescens F. T. Hubb. see: *Setaria pumila* (Poir.) Roem. and Schult.

Sieglingia decumbens (L.) Bernh. see: *Danthonia decumbens* (L.) DC.

Silene alba (Mill.) E. H. L. Krause see: *Silene latifolia* Poiret

Silene cucubalus Wibel see: *Silene vulgaris* Garcke

Silene rubella L. see: *Silene diversifolia* Otth in DC.

Sparganium minimum Wallr. see: *Sparganium natans* L.

Stellaria alsine Grimm see: *Stellaria uliginosa* Murray

Symphoricarpos rivularis Suksd. see: *Symphoricarpos albus* (L.) S. F. Blake

Taraxacum laevigatum (Willd.) DC. see: *Taraxacum* Section *Erythrosperma*

Taraxacum spectabile Dahlst. see: *Taraxacum faeroense* (Dahlst.) Dahlst.

Thelypteris dryopteris (L.) Sloss see: *Gymnocarpium dryopteris* (L.) Newman

Thelypteris limbosperma (Bellardi ex All.) H. P. Fuchs see: *Oreopteris limbosperma* (Bellardi ex All.) Bech.

Thymus drucei Ronniger see: *Thymus polytrichus* A. Kerner ex Borbás

Thymus praecox (*auct.*) see: *Thymus polytrichus* A. Kerner ex Borbás

Tilia × vulgaris Hayne see: *Tilia × europaea* K.Koch

Tripleurospermum maritimum ssp. *inodorum* Hyland ex Var. see: *Tripleurospermum inodorum* (L.) Schultz Bip.

Ulmus carpinifolia Gled. see: *Ulmus minor* Miller

Ulmus coritana Melville see: *Ulmus minor* Miller

Vaccaria pyramidata Medik. see: *Vaccaria hispanica* (Miller) Rauschert

Vicia dasycarpa (*auct.*) see: *Vicia villosa* Roth

Vicia sativa ssp. *angustifolia* (L.) Gaudin see: *Vicia sativa* ssp. *nigra* (L.) Ehrh.

Vicia tenuissima (*auct.*) see: *Vicia parviflora* Cav.

Vulpia ambigua (Le Gall) More see: *Vulpia ciliata* ssp. *ambigua* (Le Gall) Stace and Auq.

Index of plant names